ESSENTIALS OF
anatomy &
physiology

FIFTH EDITION

Frederic H. Martini, Ph.D.

Edwin F. Bartholomew, M.S.

WITH

William C. Ober, M.D.
ART COORDINATOR AND ILLUSTRATOR

Claire W. Garrison, R.N.
ILLUSTRATOR

Kathleen Welch, M.D.
CLINICAL CONSULTANT

Ralph T. Hutchings
BIOMEDICAL PHOTOGRAPHER

Benjamin Cummings

San Francisco Boston New York
Cape Town Hong Kong London Madrid Mexico City
Montreal Munich Paris Singapore Sydney Tokyo Toronto

Executive Editor: *Leslie Berriman*

Project Editor: *Katy German*

Development Manager: *Barbara Yien*

Art Development Manager: *Mark Ong*

Assistant Editor: *Kelly Reed*

Director, Media Development: *Lauren Fogel*

Media Producers: *Sarah Young-Dualan, Suzanne Rasmussen*

Managing Editor: *Deborah Cogan*

Production Supervisor: *Caroline Ayres*

Copyeditor: *Alan Titche*

Proofreader: *Marie Zartman*

Production Management and Compositor: *S4Carlisle Publishing Services*

Interior Designer: *Marilyn Perry*

Cover Designer: *Yvo Riezebos*

Director, Image Resource Center: *Melinda Patelli*

Image Rights and Permissions Manager: *Zina Arabia*

Senior Manufacturing Buyer: *Stacey Weinberger*

Text printer: *Courier Kendallville*

Cover printer: *PhoenixColor*

Cover Photo Credit: *Donal Miralle/Allsport Concepts/Getty Images, Inc.*

Library of Congress Cataloging-in-Publication data

Martini, Frederic.
    Essentials of anatomy & physiology/Frederic H. Martini, Edwin F. Bartholomew; with William C. Ober, art coordinator and illustrator; Claire W. Garrison, illustrator; Kathleen Welch, clinical consultant; Ralph T. Hutchings, biomedical photographer.—5th ed.
        p. cm.
    Includes bibliographical references and index.
    ISBN 0-13-136216-X, 978-0-13-136216-1 High School Binding
    ISBN 978-0-321-57653-8 College Edition
    1. Human physiology. 2. Human anatomy. I. Bartholomew, Edwin F. II. Title. III. Title: Essentials of anatomy and physiology.

QP36.M42 2010   2008045416
612—dc22

3 4 5 6 7 8 9 10—RRDW—13 12 11

Benjamin Cummings
is an imprint of

www.pearsonhighered.com

ISBN 10: 0-13-136216-X (High School Binding)
ISBN 13: 978-0131-36216-1 (High School Binding)

Text and Illustration Team

FREDERIC (RIC) MARTINI, PH.D. (author) received his Ph.D. from Cornell University in comparative and functional anatomy for work on the pathophysiology of stress. His publications include journal articles and contributed chapters, technical reports, and magazine articles. He is the lead author of six other undergraduate texts on anatomy and physiology or anatomy, and has a feature column, "Back to Basics," in *Physician License and Practice Today,* a quarterly publication for medical students and residents. He is currently affiliated faculty of the University of Hawaii at Manoa and remains connected with the Shoals Marine Laboratory, a joint venture between Cornell University and the University of New Hampshire. Dr. Martini has been active in the Human Anatomy and Physiology Society (HAPS) for 18 years and was a member of the committee that established the course curriculum guidelines for A&P. He is now a President Emeritus of HAPS after serving as President-Elect, President, and Past-President during 2004–2007. He is also a member of the American Physiological Society, the American Association of Anatomists, the Society for Integrative and Comparative Biology, the Australia/New Zealand Association of Clinical Anatomists, the Hawaii Academy of Science, the American Association for the Advancement of Science, and the International Society of Vertebrate Morphologists.

EDWIN F. BARTHOLOMEW (author) received his undergraduate degree from Bowling Green State University in Ohio and his M.S. from the University of Hawaii. His interests range widely, from human anatomy and physiology to the marine environment and the "backyard" aquaculture of escargots and ornamental fish. During the last three decades, Mr. Bartholomew has taught human anatomy and physiology at both the secondary and undergraduate levels. In addition, he has taught a wide variety of other science courses (from botany to zoology) at Maui Community College. He is presently teaching at historic Lahainaluna High School, the oldest high school west of the Rockies, where he assisted in establishing a Health Occupations Students of America (HOSA) chapter. He has written journal articles, a weekly newspaper column, and many magazine articles. Working with Dr. Martini, he coauthored *Structure and Function of the Human Body* (Benjamin Cummings) and *The Human Body in Health and Disease* (Benjamin Cummings). Mr. Bartholomew is a member of the Human Anatomy and Physiology Society, the National Association of Biology Teachers, the National Science Teachers Association, and the American Association for the Advancement of Science.

KATHLEEN WELCH, M.D. (clinical consultant) received her M.D. from the University of Washington in Seattle and did her residency at the University of North Carolina in Chapel Hill. For two years, she served as Director of Maternal and Child Health at the LBJ Tropical Medical Center in American Samoa and subsequently was a member of the Department of Family Practice at the Kaiser Permanente Clinic in Lahaina, Hawaii. She has been in private practice since 1987. Dr. Welch is a Fellow of the American Academy of Family Practice and a member of the Hawaii Medical Association, the American Medical Association, and the Human Anatomy and Physiology Society.

WILLIAM C. OBER, M.D. (art coordinator and illustrator) received his undergraduate degree from Washington and Lee University and his M.D. from the University of Virginia. While in medical school, he also studied in the Department of Art as Applied to Medicine at Johns Hopkins University. After graduation, Dr. Ober completed a residency in Family Practice and later was on the faculty at the University of Virginia in the Department of Family Medicine. He is currently an Instructor in the Division of Sports Medicine at UVA and is part of the Core Faculty at Shoals Marine Laboratory, where he teaches Biological Illustration every summer. The textbooks illustrated by his company Medical & Scientific Illustration have won numerous design and illustration awards.

CLAIRE W. GARRISON, R.N. (illustrator) practiced pediatric and obstetric nursing before turning to medical illustration as a full-time career. She returned to school at Mary Baldwin College, where she received her degree with distinction in studio art. Following a five-year apprenticeship, she has worked as Dr. Ober's partner in Medical and Scientific Illustration since 1986. She is on the Core Faculty at Shoals Marine Laboratory and co-teaches the Biological Illustration course.

RALPH T. HUTCHINGS (biomedical photographer) was associated with the Royal College of Surgeons for 20 years. An engineer by training, he has focused for years on photographing the structure of the human body. The result has been a series of color atlases, including the *Color Atlas of Human Anatomy,* the *Color Atlas of Surface Anatomy,* and *The Human Skeleton* (all published by Mosby-Yearbook Publishing). For his anatomical portrayal of the human body, the International Photographers Association has chosen Mr. Hutchings as the best photographer of humans in the twentieth century. He lives in North London, where he tries to balance the demands of his photographic assignments with his hobbies of early motorcars and airplanes.

DEDICATION

To Kitty, P.K., Ivy, Kate, and Awley:
We couldn't have done this without you.
Thank you for your encouragement, patience, and understanding.

Preface

Welcome to the Fifth Edition of *Essentials of Anatomy & Physiology*! This textbook is designed to introduce the specialized terms, basic concepts, and principles important to an understanding of the human body. It has two primary goals:

1. **To build a foundation of essential knowledge in human anatomy and physiology.** Constructing this knowledge requires answers to questions such as: What structure is that? How does it work? What happens when it does not work normally?

2. **To provide a framework for interpreting and applying information for problem solving.** This framework is built around the themes and patterns that appear repeatedly in the study of anatomy and physiology. These themes and patterns provide the hooks on which to organize and hang the information in this text. Interpreting and applying information to problems involves asking questions such as: How does a change in one body system affect the others? How does aging affect various body systems?

Essentials of Anatomy & Physiology, Fifth Edition is designed to help students place information in a meaningful context and develop their problem-solving skills. Anyone embarking on a career in a medical or allied health field must master the same skills needed to succeed in this course. Developing an extensive technical vocabulary and retaining a large volume of detailed information is not enough. A person needs to know how to learn—how to organize new information, how to connect it to what is already known, and how then to apply it as needed.

This text uses a learning system that simplifies the processes involved in teaching and learning anatomy and physiology. The visual introduction (which begins on page x) outlines the pieces that make up our specific teaching framework and shows the many learning aids that are built into this textbook. These features were developed through feedback from students and teachers on a variety of campuses. Many students have told us—in person, by phone, or by email—that this system really works for them, whereas others have not.

What's Different About the Fifth Edition?

Each new edition provides an opportunity for revising and updating. Our first step in planning for the Fifth Edition was to integrate the feedback and queries from teachers and students with our own experiences in the classroom. We identified key areas in which students were having trouble following the text narrative or grasping important concepts and then revised the text accordingly. We targeted sections in which students struggled to match the text narrative with the figures and worked with the illustration team to improve the art program. The Fifth Edition also provides students and teachers with updated media that will benefit their learning and teaching.

Improvements to the Text

New features, revised features, and other key revisions in this Fifth Edition include the following:

- **Learning Outcomes** are chapter-opening numbered lists that indicate what students should be able to do after studying the chapter. A&P educators have begun to shift from general "objectives" (which focus on what students "need to know") to these more concrete "learning outcomes" (which focus on what students "need to be able to do").

- **Full-sentence chapter headings** do more than introduce new topics; they state the core fact or concept that will be presented in the section. These numbered chapter headings are directly correlated with the numbered Learning Outcomes on the chapter-opening page. Together, the two elements help students readily grasp and learn the chapter's core content.

- **Checkpoint** is the new name of what was called "Concept Check" in previous editions. Each Checkpoint checks not only students' understanding of concepts but also of facts— according to what they most need at a precise point in a chapter. By appearing consistently throughout each chapter, the Checkpoints reinforce the Learning Outcomes so that they are systematically integrated over the course of the chapter. The Checkpoint questions are numbered sequentially throughout each chapter so that students can easily access the answers located in the blue Answers tab at the back of the book.

- **The Big Picture** was called "Key Note" in the Fourth Edition. Strategically placed throughout each chapter, The Big Picture presents the core facts and concepts necessary to an understanding of the basics of anatomy and physiology—the "nuggets" that students should remember five years after taking their A&P course, regardless of their chosen profession.

- **Clinical Notes**—a favorite feature among students—have been updated with the latest available clinical information and statistics. Definitions and descriptions of pathological processes have been revised as needed.

- **The Review Questions** at the end of the chapter include new questions based on modified chapter figures to ensure student understanding of key illustrations. Many other Review Questions are new or revised. A reference to the companion website is placed at the beginning of the Review Questions to remind students of additional study and assessment materials that can be found there.

- **Eponymous terms** have, in most cases, been replaced with the preferred terms in *Terminologia Anatomica: International Anatomical Terminology (TA)*, the standard reference book of anatomical terminology created jointly by the Federative Committee on Anatomical Terminology (FCAT) and the International Federation of Associations of Anatomists (IFAA). Because terms other than those in the *TA* are still in common usage, we present those other terms parenthetically where appropriate. Furthermore, following the recommendations in the American Medical Association's *Manual of Style,* we use the non-possessive forms of eponyms in most instances; when the term appeared too foreign to us without the apostrophe "s," however, we let past convention rule.

- **Concept Links,** signaled by blue chain link icons, have been retained from previous editions and alert students to material that is related to, or builds upon, previous discussions. Each link contains a page number so that students can quickly review relevant material from an earlier chapter.

Chapter-by-Chapter Changes

Chapter 1 An Introduction to Anatomy and Physiology

1. Figure 1-4 was revised to clarify negative feedback regulation in thermoregulation.

2. A new **Clinical Note** entitled "Homeostasis and Disease" was added.

3. For clarification, an explanation of the conventional orientation of cross-sectional views was added to the text (p. 19) and to the caption for Figure 1-10. (By convention, transverse or cross-sectional views and radiological images are always presented as seen when standing at the feet looking toward the head.)

Chapter 2 The Chemical Level of Organization

1. Figure 2-6 was revised to clarify hydrogen bonding between water molecules.

2. Figure 2-7 was revised for clarity.

3. Figure 2-18 was revised to clarify an enzyme's active site.

4. Figure 2-19 was revised to show the proper helical orientation of DNA.

Chapter 3 Cell Structure and Function

1. Figure 3-2 was revised to illustrate that (1) cells may have microvilli or cilia, but not both structures, and (2) *plasma membrane* is the primary term for the membrane surrounding a cell, thus distinguishing it from other internal cell membranes.

2. Table 3-1 was reorganized for clarity.

3. Figure 3-14 was enhanced by illustrating the three dimensions of the ER and Golgi apparatus.

4. Figure 3-22 was revised to clarify the different stages of mitosis.

Chapter 4 The Tissue Level of Organization

1. Terminology related to intercellular connections in Figure 4-2 was revised.

2. The discussion of stratified epithelia was revised to include both stratified cuboidal and stratified columnar epithelia.

3. The text description of transitional epithelium, and the art depicting it (Figure 4-5), were revised to clearly indicate that it is a stratified epithelium.

4. The discussion of connective tissue proper cell types was revised to include fibrocytes and their functions.

Chapter 5 The Integumentary System

1. The **System in Perspective** was revised to more clearly delineate the functional relationships between different body systems.

Chapter 6 The Skeletal System

1. Terminology related to some cranial bones was revised (for example, "external acoustic canal" was changed to "external acoustic meatus").

2. The **System in Perspective** was revised to more clearly delineate the functional relationships between different body systems.

Chapter 7 The Muscular System

1. Terminology related to some sarcomere features was revised (for example, "H zone" was changed to "H band").

2. Figure 7-4 was revised to include a Step 5 (return to initial state).

3. The **System in Perspective** was revised to more clearly delineate the functional relationships between different body systems.

Chapter 8 The Nervous System

1. Figure 8-1 was revised to clarify the effectors receiving inputs from both divisions of the autonomic nervous systems.

2. Figure 8-4 features updated art of the axons in white matter and astrocyte connections.

3. Figure 8-8 was revised to correct the x-axis time scale.

4. Figure 8-14 contains updated art.

5. Terminology related to the ventricles of the brain was revised (for example, "mesencephalic aqueduct" was changed to "aqueduct of midbrain").

6. Labeling of cranial nerves VII and VIII was corrected in Figure 8-24.

7. The **System in Perspective** was revised to more clearly delineate the functional relationships between different body systems.

Chapter 9 The General and Special Senses

1. Figure 9-28 was revised to illustrate that axons of the cochlear branch of N VIII enter both the left and right cochlear nuclei of the medulla oblongata.

Chapter 10 The Endocrine System

1. The abbreviation for oxytocin, OXT, was introduced in the text discussion and also appears in Figure 10-8.

2. Figure 10-12 and related text were revised to reflect the designation of *suprarenal gland* as the primary term and *adrenal gland* as a secondary term.

3. The discussion of resistin in the adipose tissue section was deleted because it hasn't been scientifically substantiated for human physiology.

4. The **System in Perspective** was revised to more clearly delineate the functional relationships between different body systems.

Chapter 11 The Cardiovascular System: Blood

1. Figure 11-6 was enhanced for clarity with an updated design.

2. Figure 11-10 was enhanced for clarity.

Chapter 12 The Cardiovascular System: The Heart

1. Terminology was revised (from "voltage-regulated channels" to "voltage-gated channels") in the text and Figure 12-8.

Chapter 13 The Cardiovascular System: Blood Vessels and Circulation

1. Terminology was revised (from "tunica interna" to "tunica intima") in the text and Figure 13-2.

2. Figure 13-9 was enhanced for clarity.

3. Text within Figure 13-10 was changed from plural to singular (for example, "vasomotor centers" to "vasomotor center").

4. The **System in Perspective** was revised to more clearly delineate the functional relationships between different body systems.

Chapter 14 The Lymphoid System and Immunity

1. This chapter has been retitled using "Lymphoid" instead of "Lymphatic" to reflect internationally accepted terminology for the system.

2. Figure 14-6 now includes labels indicating the distributions of B cells and T cells within a lymph node.

3. The **System in Perspective** was revised to more clearly delineate the functional relationships between different body systems.

Chapter 15 The Respiratory System

1. The **System in Perspective** was revised to delineate more clearly the functional relationships between different body systems.

Chapter 16 The Digestive System

1. The singular form for the term given to the transverse folds of the digestive tract lining was corrected to "plica circulares."

2. The presence of microvilli on the intestinal epithelium of villi was clarified with a revised label in Figure 16-11.

3. The **System in Perspective** was revised to more clearly delineate the functional relationships between different body systems.

Chapter 17 Nutrition and Metabolism

1. Figures 17-1, 17-2, 17-3, 17-4, 17-5 (note that the label "Hydrogen ion channel" has been changed to "ATP synthase"), 17-6, 17-7, 17-8, and 17-9 were revised for clarity.

2. Figure 17-10 (The MyPyramid Plan) was replaced to reduce repetition of USDA Food Pyramid information given in Table 17-1.

3. Corrections were made to the "Recommended Daily Intake" values in Tables 17-2 and 17-3.

Chapter 18 The Urinary System

1. The text and art were revised to reflect the designation of *nephron loop* as the primary term and *loop of Henle* as a secondary term (see Figure 18-4).

2. Terminology for some of the arteries and veins within the kidneys has been updated (for example, "interlobular arteries" was changed to "cortical radiate arteries"; see Figure 18-4).

3. Missing description of Step 7 from Figure 18-8 was added to the text.

4. Corrections were made to the values in Table 18-2.

5. The **System in Perspective** was revised to more clearly delineate the functional relationships between different body systems.

Chapter 19 The Reproductive System

1. The text and art of the male reproductive system were revised to reflect the designations of *seminal gland(s)* as the primary term and *seminal vesicle(s)* as a secondary term, and *nurse cell* as the primary term and *sustentacular cell* as a secondary term.

2. Figure 19-13 was revised to indicate the distinction between the lobes of a mammary gland and the many lobules that make up each lobe.

3. Figure 19-14 (Hormonal Regulation of Ovarian Activity) now precedes Figure 19-15 (Hormonal Regulation of the Female Reproductive Cycle).

4. The **System in Perspective** was revised to more clearly delineate the functional relationships between different body systems.

Chapter 20 Development and Inheritance

1. Terminology was corrected in Table 20-1.

2. "The Human Genome Project and Beyond" section was revised with updated information.

Enhancements to the Art and Design

The art program builds on illustrations described as the most "teachable" and "learnable" of any illustrations in any anatomy and physiology textbook. We worked closely with our medical illustrators, William Ober, M.D. and Claire Garrison, R.N., to assess the illustrations and make improvements throughout the text. With their input, we revised, replaced, or added figures to enhance the visual presentation. The labels and leaders of virtually every anatomical figure in the book were reoriented and placed to make them visually cleaner and easier to follow. Increased color contrast and increased dimensionality help students see, understand, and appreciate the close relationship between structures and functions.

Features retained and revised from the previous edition include the following:

- Art-photo pairings that give students more than one way to see structures.
- Step-by-step diagrams with clearer headings and arrows to make sequences easier to follow.
- Illustrations combined with photographs to help students see the "real thing" in context.

For the Fifth Edition, we also worked with our editors and designers to create a fresh, contemporary, and welcoming look for the book. The new design highlights the pedagogical features more prominently and calls them out for easier navigation and use.

Media Ancillaries

Included with each new copy of the text is the Interactive Physiology® 10-System Suite (IP-10) CD-ROM, an award-winning student tutorial featuring animations and quizzes. Practice Anatomy Lab (PAL™) 2.0, for purchase only, is a virtual anatomy practice tool that gives students 24/7 access to the most widely used lab specimens, including human cadaver, anatomical models, histology, cat, and fetal pig. See the supplements listing on page xvi for more about IP-10 and PAL 2.0.

The Anatomy & Physiology Place open-access companion website is available, complete with chapter-correlated vocabulary practice, quizzes, and animations. The **Instructor's Resource DVDs/CD-ROM** organizes all instructor media resources by chapter and includes all of the art and photos from the book, in multiple customizable formats, as well as PowerPoint® lecture outlines and the brand-new 3D movie-quality A&P Flix animations.

Acknowledgments

Every textbook represents a group effort. Foremost on the list are the faculty and reviewers whose advice, comments, and collective wisdom helped shape this edition. Their interest in the subject, their concern for the accuracy and method of presentation, and their experience with students of widely varying abilities and backgrounds made the review process an educational experience. To these individuals, who carefully recorded their comments, opinions, and sources, we express our sincere thanks and best wishes.

We would also like to acknowledge the many users, survey respondents, and focus group members whose advice, comments, and collective wisdom helped shape this text into its final form. Their passion for the subject, their concern for accuracy and method of presentation, and their experience with students of widely varying abilities and backgrounds have made the review process much more fruitful.

The following individuals devoted large amounts of time reviewing drafts of *Essentials of Anatomy & Physiology*:

High School Reviewers

Adam Bergeron, *Parkway Central High School*
Lisa Bhoopat, *Anaheim High School*
Laura McCreery, *North High School*
Megan Morrissey, *Oxford Academy*
Karen Reta, *Western High School*
Steve Saladino, *Davenport West High School*
Caryn Stankewich, *Pacifica High School*
Laurie Turner, *Freemont High School*
Christina Valentine, *Firebaugh High School*

Reviewers for the Fifth Edition

Diane Berger, *Kankakee Community College*
Meg Flemming, *Austin Community College—Rio Grande*
Ann Geller, *San Diego Mesa College*
Michael Guthrie, *City College of San Francisco*
Georgia Householder, *Southwest Virginia Community College*
Sue Caley Opsal, *Illinois Valley Community College*
Diane Pelletier, *Green River Community College*
Penny Revelle, *City College Baltimore County—Essex*
Deborah Temperly, *Delta College*
Larry Walker, *Trident Tech College*
Bert Wartski, *Duke University*
Thomas White, *State University College at Buffalo*

Reviewers for the Fourth Edition

William Armstrong, *Eastern Michigan University*
Lynn Atkins, *University of Maine*
Sheri Boyce, *Messiah College*
Barbara Engebretsen, *Wayne State College*
Demetrio Fajardo, *Las Vegas College*
Joseph Gar, *Paducah Community College*
Lauren Gollahon, *Texas Technical University*
Mary Hall, *Rhodes/Western Business College*
Donna Hazelwood, *Dakota State University*
John Hertner, *University of Nebraska, Kearney*
Julie Huggins, *Arkansas State University*
Gary Hunt, *Tulsa Community College*
Nancy Klepper-Kilgore, *Mount Ida College*

Laura Mastrangelo, *Hudson Valley Community College*
Melissa Presch, *California State University, Fullerton*
Marcy Waldie, *Las Vegas College*

Student Reviewers for the Fourth Edition

Karla Bushmaker, *Bellevue Community College*
Courtney O'Neill, *Howard Community College*
Jay Prosser, *Wallace State College*
Mick Seeley, *Bergen Community College*
Stephen Wagner, *University of Washington*

Technical Reviewers for the Fourth Edition

Nathan Collie, *Texas Technical University*
Christine Eckel, *Salt Lake Community College*
Lauren Gollahon, *Texas Technical University*
Cynthia Herbrandson, *Kellogg Community College*

Our gratitude is also extended to the many faculty and students at campuses across the United States (and out of the country) who made suggestions and comments that helped us improve this edition of *Essentials of Anatomy & Physiology.*

A textbook has two components: narrative and visual. In preparing the narrative, we were ably assisted yet again by our keen-eyed copyeditor Alan Titche, who played a vital role in shaping this text by helping us keep the text organization, general tone, and level of presentation consistent throughout.

Virtually without exception, reviewers stressed the importance of accurate, integrated, and visually attractive illustrations in helping students understand essential material. The creative talents brought to this project by our artist team, William Ober, M.D., and Claire Garrison, R.N., are inspiring and very much appreciated. Bill and Claire worked intimately and tirelessly with us, imparting a unity of vision to the book as a whole while making it both clear and beautiful. The superb art program is also greatly enhanced by the incomparable bone and cadaver photographs of Ralph T. Hutchings, formerly of The College of Surgeons in England.

We are deeply indebted to the Benjamin Cummings production staff and S4Carlisle, whose efforts were so vital to the creation of this edition. Special thanks are due to Caroline Ayres and Norine Strang for their skillful management of the project through the entire production process. We appreciate the excellent design contributions of Mark Ong, Design Manager, and Marilyn Perry, interior text designer and cover designer. We must also express our appreciation to Kelly Reed, Assistant Editor, for her work on the numerous print supplements, and to Suzanne Rasmussen for her work on the media supplements that accompany this title.

Thanks also to Christy Lawrence, Director of Marketing, and the entire Pearson Science sales team for keeping their fingers on the pulse of the market and helping us meet the needs of our users.

Above all, thanks to our editor, Katy German, for her patience in nurturing this project and her efforts to coordinate the various components of the package, and to Leslie Berriman, Executive Editor, for her dedication to the success of this book.

Finally, we would like to thank our families for their love and support during the revision process.

No two people could expect to produce a flawless textbook of this scope and complexity. Any errors or oversights are strictly our own rather than those of the reviewers, artists, or editors. In an effort to improve future editions, we ask that readers with pertinent information, suggestions, or comments concerning the organization or content of this textbook send their remarks to us by email. Any and all comments and suggestions will be deeply appreciated and carefully considered in the preparation of the next edition.

Frederic H. Martini
Haiku, Hawaii
martini@maui.net

Edwin F. Bartholomew
Lahaina, Hawaii
edbarth@maui.net

ART THAT TEACHES

Macro-to-Micro Figures help students bridge the gap between familiar and unfamiliar body structures by **sequencing anatomical views** from whole organs or other structures to their smaller body parts.

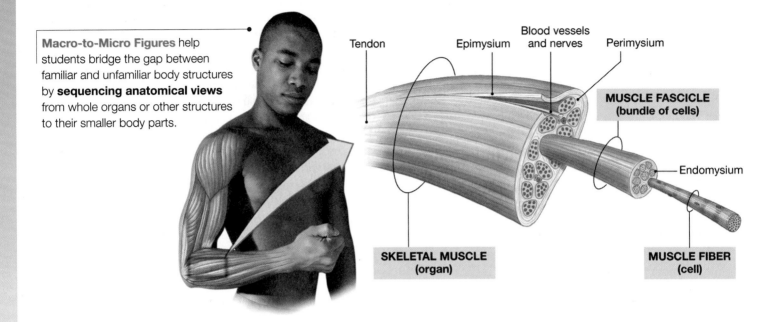

Tendon

Epimysium

Blood vessels and nerves

Perimysium

MUSCLE FASCICLE (bundle of cells)

Endomysium

SKELETAL MUSCLE (organ)

MUSCLE FIBER (cell)

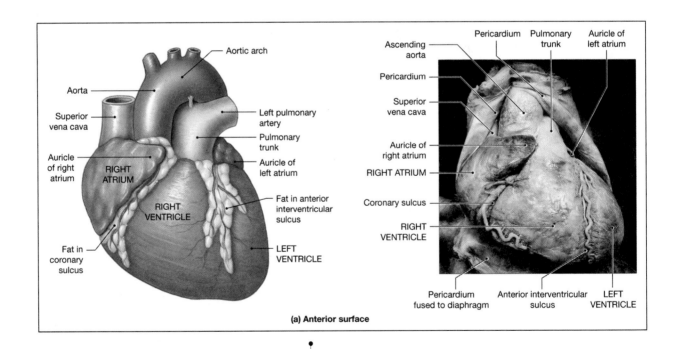

Aortic arch

Aorta

Superior vena cava

Auricle of right atrium

RIGHT ATRIUM

RIGHT VENTRICLE

Fat in coronary sulcus

Left pulmonary artery

Pulmonary trunk

Auricle of left atrium

Fat in anterior interventricular sulcus

LEFT VENTRICLE

Pericardium

Ascending aorta

Pericardium

Superior vena cava

Auricle of right atrium

RIGHT ATRIUM

Coronary sulcus

RIGHT VENTRICLE

Pulmonary trunk

Auricle of left atrium

Pericardium fused to diaphragm

Anterior interventricular sulcus

LEFT VENTRICLE

(a) Anterior surface

Side-by-Side Figures provide students with **multiple views** of the **same structure,** allowing them to compare an illustrator's rendering with a photo of the actual structure as it may be seen in a lab or clinical setting.

Ascending aorta
Superior vena cava
Right lung
Right pulmonary arteries
Right pulmonary veins
Inferior vena cava
Descending aorta

Aortic arch
Pulmonary trunk
Left lung
Left pulmonary arteries
Left pulmonary veins
Alveolus
Capillary
O_2
CO_2

Illustration-over-Photo Figures, in addition to being visually dramatic with their 3D effects, teach **realistic body proportions and structure placement.**

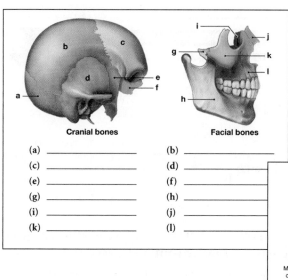

Cranial bones

Facial bones

(a) _____
(b) _____
(c) _____
(d) _____
(e) _____
(f) _____
(g) _____
(h) _____
(i) _____
(j) _____
(k) _____
(l) _____

NEW! Visually-Based Questions have been added to the Review Questions at the end of each chapter to give students **visual practice** with what they are learning.

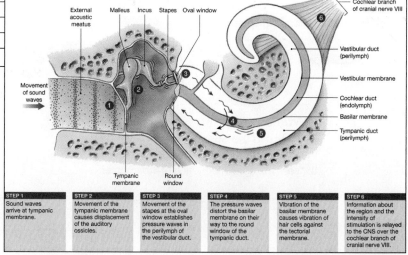

External acoustic meatus
Malleus Incus Stapes Oval window
Cochlear branch of cranial nerve VIII
Vestibular duct (perilymph)
Vestibular membrane
Cochlear duct (endolymph)
Basilar membrane
Tympanic duct (perilymph)
Movement of sound waves
Tympanic membrane
Round window

STEP 1	STEP 2	STEP 3	STEP 4	STEP 5	STEP 6
Sound waves arrive at tympanic membrane.	Movement of the tympanic membrane causes displacement of the auditory ossicles.	Movement of the stapes at the oval window establishes pressure waves in the perilymph of the vestibular duct.	The pressure waves distort the basilar membrane on their way to the round window of the tympanic duct.	Vibration of the basilar membrane causes vibration of hair cells against the tectorial membrane.	Information about the region and the intensity of stimulation is relayed to the CNS over the cochlear branch of cranial nerve VIII.

Step-by-Step Figures break down **multifaceted processes** into numbered step-by-step illustrations that coordinate with the authors' narrative descriptions.

AN ORGANIZATION THAT IS EASY TO USE AND TIED TO ASSESSMENT

*The **Fifth Edition** has been revised for ease of use and ease of assessment—starting with the new **Learning Outcomes**.*

NEW! Learning Outcomes, based on the Learning Outcomes developed and recommended by the Human Anatomy and Physiology Society (HAPS), are chapter-opening numbered lists that indicate what students should be able to do after studying the chapter.

> **11-4** Discuss the factors that determine a person's blood type, and explain why blood types are important.

NEW! Full-sentence numbered chapter headings are directly correlated to the numbered Learning Outcomes. The two elements, working together, help students "see," navigate through, and learn the chapter content. Additionally, as full sentences, the chapter headings do more than introduce new topics—they state the core fact or concept presented in the chapter section.

> **11-4** The ABO blood types and Rh system are based on antigen-antibody responses

Checkpoint questions map to the chapter's Learning Outcomes, further integrating the assessment-based Learning Outcomes into the chapter structure.

> **CHECKPOINT**
>
> **10.** Which blood type(s) can be safely transfused into a person with Type AB blood?
>
> **11.** Why can't a person with Type A blood safely receive blood from a person with Type B blood?
>
> *See the blue Answers tab at the back of the book.*

Assessment is easy! Just like the text, the **Test Bank** and the **website tests and quizzes** are organized by the Learning Outcomes.

NEW! Repetition of the full-sentence chapter headings in the Summary Outline at the end of the chapter provides students with another opportunity to "see" the core information of the chapter.

> **11-4** The ABO blood types and Rh system are based on antigen-antibody responses
>
> 12. **Blood type** is determined by the presence or absence of three specific **surface antigens** (*agglutinogens*) in the cell membranes of RBCs: antigens A, B, and Rh. Antibodies (*agglutinins*) in the plasma of individuals of some blood types can react with surface antigens on the RBCs of different blood types. Anti-Rh antibodies are synthesized only after an Rh-negative individual becomes sensitized to the Rh surface antigen. (*Figure 11-7; Table 11-2*)

FEATURES THAT PREPARE STUDENTS FOR FUTURE CAREERS

SKELETAL

The Skeletal System in Perspective

Functional Relationships Between the Skeletal System and Other Systems

The Integumentary System
- The Integumentary System synthesizes vitamin D_3, essential for calcium and phosphorus absorption (bone maintenance and growth)
- The Skeletal System provides structural support

The Muscular System
- The Muscular System stabilizes bone positions; tension in tendons stimulates bone growth and maintenance
- The Skeletal System provides calcium needed for normal muscle contraction; bones act as levers to produce body movements

The Nervous System
- The Nervous System regulates bone position by controlling muscle contractions
- The Skeletal System provides calcium for neural function; protects brain, spinal cord; receptors at joints provide information about body position

The Endocrine System
- The Endocrine System regulates skeletal growth with growth hormone, thyroid hormones, and sex hormones; calcium mobilization regulated by parathyroid hormone and calcitonin
- The Skeletal System protects endocrine organs, especially in brain, chest, and pelvic cavity

The Cardiovascular System
- The Cardiovascular System provides oxygen, nutrients, hormones, blood cells; removes waste products and carbon dioxide
- The Skeletal System provides calcium needed for cardiac muscle contraction; blood cells produced in bone marrow; axial skeleton protects heart and great vessels

The Lymphoid System
- The Lymphoid System's lymphocytes assist in the defense and repair of bone following injuries
- The Skeletal System's bone marrow produces and stores lymphocytes and other cells of the immune response

The Respiratory System
- The Respiratory System provides oxygen and eliminates carbon dioxide
- The Skeletal System surrounds and protects lungs; movement of ribs important in breathing

The Digestive System
- The Digestive System provides nutrients, calcium, and phosphate
- The Skeletal System protects portions of liver, stomach, and intestines

The Urinary System
- The Urinary System conserves calcium and phosphate needed for skeletal system growth; disposes of waste products
- The Skeletal System provides protection for kidneys and ureters; pelvis protects urinary bladder and proximal urethra

The Reproductive System
- The Reproductive System's sex hormones stimulate growth and maintenance of bones; surge of hormones at puberty causes acceleration of growth and closure of skeletal system (pelvis)
- The Skeletal System (pelvis) appendicular skeleton protects reproductive organs of females, protects portion of ductus deferens and accessory glands in males

For All Systems
The Skeletal System provides mechanical support; stores energy reserves; stores calcium and phosphate reserves

---

System in Perspective summaries appear at the end of each body system to help students quickly review that body system's structures, functions, and associated organs **in relationship to all other body systems.**

Professional Profile

SPORTS TRAINER
Andy Walshe

❝ **Anatomy and physiology is essential. It teaches you the parts of the engine you're trying to improve, and it's the foundation on which all sports disciplines are based.** ❞

Andy Walshe is the high-performance manager for the athletic program of the U.S. Ski and Snowboard Association. He works closely with over 150 athletes training to become Olympic champions. Andy supervises a staff of physiologists, nutritionists, dieticians, biomechanicists, and sports psychologists.

For trainers at this level, there is no such thing as a typical day. "This profession is full of variety. One day you may be running training camps, and the next you may be on the snow in South America shooting high-speed video for movement analysis."

ELITE TRAINING

In addition to supervising the training team, Andy develops elite sports performance models—frameworks that allow a trainer to analyze athletes in relation to their sport to determine their strengths and weaknesses. His expertise is in biomechanical physiological analysis. "You need to understand and analyze movement patterns, and you can't do that without a good understanding of muscles and bones. And you need to understand energy systems as well, so the physiology element is very important."

In fact, says Andy, for all of his staff, "Anatomy and physiology is essential. It teaches you the parts of the engine you're trying to improve, and it's the foundation on which all sports disciplines are based."

Andy is one of a small group of elite-level trainers working with the best athletes in the world. Elite trainers bring to the job a combination of advanced academic work and practical experience. A master's degree is required for this type of job.

Andy worked first as a volunteer assistant physiologist, traveling with teams in an unpaid position, and worked his way up to his current job, which he's had for seven years. "I was always interested in sports and performance. At the elite level, most entry-level jobs are unpaid internships, opportunities to learn while showing the trainers what you can do. Andy suggests, "Find out what organizations are associated with sports that interest you. The U.S. Olympic Committee has internship programs, and there are many organizations to investigate for each sport."

Andy loves his job working in the world of elite sports, even though the pace is intense. "You live this job. You are on call all the time, doing anything and everything that involves preparing elite athletes. In a job like this, you're a jack-of-all-trades. It's important to be flexible and be willing to put parts of your life on hold. I travel over 200 days a year and I work 24/7."

However, the rewards are great. "The athletes and the coaches are the best part of this job. It's great being a part of the team that helps athletes chase their dreams. Along the way, you make great friends."

And there's a larger goal as well. "Our number one goal is to get more kids into the sport. Of course, we're here to get our athletes medals, but the impact of those medals is that we get more kids involved in the sport."

Professional Profiles give students insight into health-related careers that require an understanding of A&P. These enlightening interview-based vignettes appear at the end of each body system.

Clinical Note

Hip Fractures

Hip fractures most often occur in individuals over the age of 60, when osteoporosis has weakened the thighbones. These injuries may be accompanied by dislocation of the hip or by pelvic fractures. For individuals with osteoporosis, healing of such fractures proceeds very slowly. In addition, the powerful muscles that surround the joint can easily prevent proper alignment of the bone fragments. Trochanteric fractures usually heal well if the joint can be stabilized; steel frames, pins, screws, or some combination of these devices may be required to preserve alignment and permit normal healing.

Clinical Notes present engaging information on diseases and disorders to prepare students for future workplace situations.

The Big Picture

The autonomic nervous system operates largely outside of our conscious awareness. It has two divisions: a sympathetic division concerned with increasing alertness, metabolic rate, and muscular abilities, and a parasympathetic division concerned with reducing metabolic rate and promoting visceral activities such as digestion.

NEW! The Big Picture boxes succinctly organize core concepts at salient points in a chapter. They include the information all students should remember five years after their A&P course, regardless of their chosen career.

THE ANATOMY & PHYSIOLOGY PLACE WEBSITE

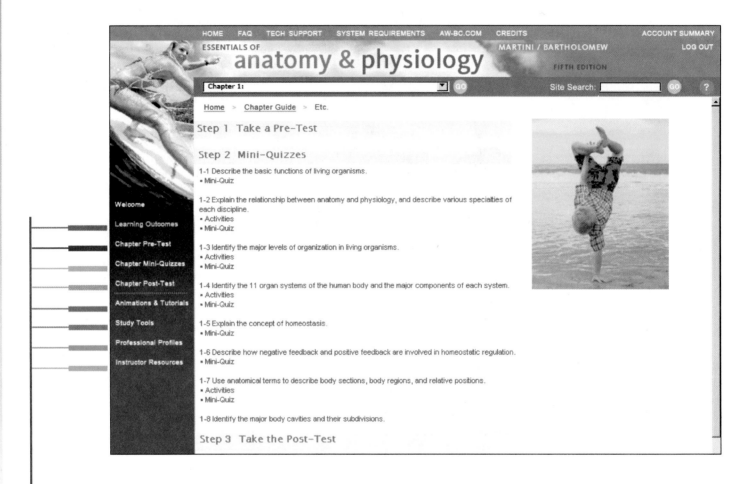

The Anatomy & Physiology Place (**www.anatomyandphysiology.com**) is an open-access website with resources for both students and teachers. Chapter content is organized around each chapter's Learning Outcomes to keep students within an outcomes-based learning and assessment environment.

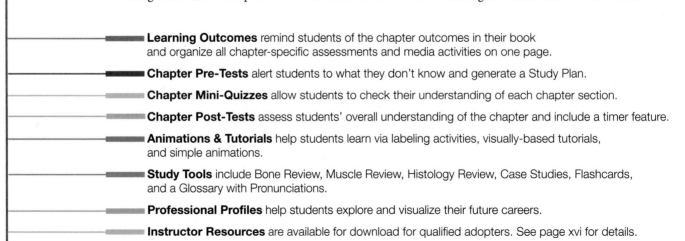

Learning Outcomes remind students of the chapter outcomes in their book and organize all chapter-specific assessments and media activities on one page.

Chapter Pre-Tests alert students to what they don't know and generate a Study Plan.

Chapter Mini-Quizzes allow students to check their understanding of each chapter section.

Chapter Post-Tests assess students' overall understanding of the chapter and include a timer feature.

Animations & Tutorials help students learn via labeling activities, visually-based tutorials, and simple animations.

Study Tools include Bone Review, Muscle Review, Histology Review, Case Studies, Flashcards, and a Glossary with Pronunciations.

Professional Profiles help students explore and visualize their future careers.

Instructor Resources are available for download for qualified adopters. See page xvi for details.

INSTRUCTOR'S RESOURCE DVDs/CD-ROM

The Instructor's Resource DVDs/CD-ROM organizes all instructor media resources **by chapter** into one convenient and easy-to-use package. **DVD 1** includes **chapter-specific material. DVD 2** includes **Additional Resources.** A **CD-ROM** includes the **Computerized Test Bank** (on the TestGen® platform) for all chapters. A **fold-out Quick Reference Guide** displays all media assets by chapter. Included on the disks:

DVD 1: Chapter-Specific Material

- **All illustrations and photos from the textbook in labeled and unlabeled versions in JPEG format;** in many cases, the images from the textbook are followed by detailed breakout figures

- **All illustrations and photos from the textbook in customizable PowerPoint® format with the Label Edit function;** in many cases, the images from the textbook are followed by detailed breakout figures

- **All tables from the textbook**

- **The brand-new 3D movie-quality A&P Flix animations** organized by chapter. See detailed description under DVD 2: Additional Resources

- **Customizable PowerPoint lecture slides** that combine lecture notes, illustrations, photos, tables, and links to animations

- **Active Lecture Questions** (in PRS-enabled Clicker Question format) that stimulate effective classroom discussions and check comprehension

- **"Quiz Show" Chapter Review Questions** (in PRS-enabled Clicker Question format) that encourage student interaction

- **Lecture Outlines** in Microsoft® Word format

- **Test Bank** in Microsoft Word format

DVD 2: Additional Resources

- **The brand-new 3D movie-quality A&P Flix animations** accompanied by Quizzes in PRS-enabled Clicker Question format:
  - 3D physiology animations that focus on the toughest topics in physiology—including the cross-bridge cycle, excitation-contraction coupling of skeletal muscle, and generation of an action potential
  - 65+ 3D anatomy animations of origins, insertions, actions, and innervations of individual muscles
  - 50+ 3D anatomy animations of joint movements and actions of group muscles

- **More than 550 images from the Practice Anatomy Lab (PAL™) 2.0** media program

- *Interactive Physiology®* (IP) Worksheets

- All images from *Martini's Atlas of the Human Body*

- All images from Martini's *A&P Applications Manual*

- MRI/CT scans, histology slides, and muscle origins and insertions images

CD-ROM: The Computerized Test Bank

Images from the **new** A&P Flix

SUPPLEMENTS

The following supplements are avilable to qualified adopters:

Teacher Supplements

Most of the teacher supplements and resources for this book are available electronically on the Instructor Resource Center. Upon adoption or to preview, please go to PearsonSchool.com/Advanced and click "Online Teacher Supplements." You will be required to complete a one-time registration subject to verification before being emailed access information to download materials.

Instructor's Resource DVDs/CD-ROM
978-0-321-57652-1 | 0-321-57652-7

This media tool organizes all instructor media resources by chapter into one convenient and easy-to-use package:

- A DVD of all chapter-specific material
- A DVD of Additional Resources
- A CD-ROM of the Computerized Test Bank (on the TestGen® platform) for all chapters
- A fold-out Quick Reference Guide that displays all media assets by chapter

Instructor's Manual
978-0-321-56977-6 | 0-321-56977-6

This guide makes it easy to **see content at a glance** in detailed lecture outlines for each chapter. **Unique analogies** and **useful teaching techniques** help teachers engage students and promote lively classroom discussion.

Printed Test Bank
978-0-321-57412-1 | 0-321-57412-5

The Test Bank has been **reorganized by Learning Outcomes** to correspond to the new chapter organization and to tie the Learning Outcomes into assessments. Each question has also been tagged with a **skill and difficulty rating.** Also available in Exam*View®* format. 978-0-13-136418-9 | 0-13-136418-9

Transparency Acetates
978-0-321-57651-4 | 0-321-57651-9

More than 400 images from the text make up this outstanding transparency set. Figures and labels are enlarged for easy visibility. Complex figures are broken out for enlarged projected display.

Website and Course Management Programs

The Anatomy & Physiology Place Website
www.anatomyandphysiology.com

CourseCompass™
www.coursecompass.com
This premium course management system contains all of the website content plus premium media, such as Interactive Physiology® (IP) and the A&P Flix. In order to utilize this material, a teacher must already have CourseCompass.

WebCT
www.pearsonhighered.com/webct
In order to utilize this material, a teacher must already have WebCT.

Blackboard
www.pearsonhighered.com/blackboard

These open-access course management systems contain preloaded content such as testing and assessment question pools. In order to utilize this material, a teacher must already have Blackboard.

Student Supplements

The following supplements are available for purchase:

***Interactive Physiology*® 10-System Suite (IP-10)** with the **new Immune System** module comes packaged as a CD-ROM with the book. References to it appear in the Summary Outline in each chapter. A replacement CD is also available by using ISBN 978-0-13-136275-8 | 0-13-136275-5.

Practice Anatomy Lab (PAL™) 2.0 is an indispensable virtual anatomy practice tool that gives students 24/7 access to the most widely used lab specimens including **human cadaver, anatomical models, histology, cat, and fetal pig.**
978-0-321-54725-5 | 0-321-54725-X

***Get Ready for A&P,* Second Edition**
by Lori K. Garrett

This workbook saves classroom time and frustration by helping students quickly prepare for their A&P course. The hands-on workbook gets students up to speed with basic study skills, math skills, anatomical terminology, basic chemistry, cell biology, and other basics of the human body. Each topic area includes a pre-test, guided explanation, interactive quizzes and exercises, and end-of-chapter cumulative tests.

Martini Study Card: Body System Overview
978-0-321-53601-3 | 0-321-53601-0

The updated Study Card is a six-panel laminated card showing all body systems and their organs and functions.

Study Guide for Essentials of Anatomy & Physiology
by Charles M. Seiger
978-0-321-56980-6 | 0-321-56980-6

Designed to help students master the topics and concepts covered in the textbook, the Study Guide includes a variety of review questions, including labeling, multiple choice, concept mapping, and crossword puzzles. It is keyed to each chapter's Learning Outcomes and the three-level learning system in the textbook.

Contents in Brief

Contents

7 The Muscular System *194*

An Introduction to Muscle Tissue *195*

13 The Cardiovascular System: Blood Vessels and Circulation *428*

14 The Lymphoid System and Immunity *470*

17 Nutrition and Metabolism *574*

18 The Urinary System *600*

1 An Introduction to Anatomy and Physiology

Every day we perform a balancing act of sorts. This complex performance goes on continuously, and every part of our physical being is involved, from individual atoms to the largest organs and organ systems. Injury, disease, and other stresses, whether they occur inside us or outside, threaten this delicate balance. Adjusting to these changes is crucial, for if the body loses its balance, it may plunge out of control into dysfunction and illness—even death.

VOCABULARY DEVELOPMENT

bios life; *biology*
cardium heart; *pericardium*
dorsum back; *dorsal*
homeo- unchanging; *homeostasis*
-logy study of; *biology*

medianus situated in the middle; *median*
paries wall; *parietal*
pathos disease; *pathology*
peri- around; *perimeter*

pronus inclined forward; *prone*
-stasis standing; *homeostasis*
supinus lying on the back; *supine*
venter belly or abdomen; *ventral*

1-1 The common functions of all living things include responsiveness, growth, reproduction, movement, and metabolism

The world around us contains an enormous diversity of living organisms that vary widely in appearance and lifestyle. One aim of **biology**—the study of life—is to discover the common patterns that underlie this diversity. Such discoveries show that all living things perform the following basic functions:

- *Responsiveness.* Organisms respond to changes in their immediate environment; this property is also called *irritability.* You move your hand away from a hot stove, your dog barks at approaching strangers, fish are alarmed by loud noises, and tiny amoebas glide toward potential prey. Organisms also make longer-term changes as they adjust to their environments. For example, an animal may grow a heavier coat of fur as winter approaches, or it may migrate to a warmer climate. The capacity to make such adjustments is termed *adaptability.*

- *Growth.* Over a lifetime, organisms increase in size through the growth of *cells,* the simplest units of life. Single-celled creatures grow by getting larger, whereas more complex organisms grow primarily by increasing the number of cells. Familiar organisms, such as dogs, cats, and humans, are composed of trillions of cells. In such multicellular organisms, individual cells become specialized to perform particular functions. This specialization is called *differentiation.*

- *Reproduction.* Organisms reproduce, creating subsequent generations of similar organisms.

- *Movement.* Organisms are capable of producing movement, which may be internal (transporting food, blood, or other materials within the body) or external (moving through the environment).

- *Metabolism.* Organisms rely on complex chemical reactions to provide the energy required for responsiveness, growth, reproduction, and movement. They must also synthesize complex chemicals, such as proteins. *Metabolism* refers to all of the chemical operations under way in the body. Normal metabolic operations require the absorption of materials from the environment. To generate energy efficiently, most cells require various nutrients obtained in food, as well as oxygen, a gas. *Respiration* refers to the absorption, transport, and use of oxygen by cells. Metabolic operations often generate unneeded or potentially harmful waste products that must be eliminated through the process of *excretion.*

For very small organisms, absorption, respiration, and excretion involve the movement of materials across exposed surfaces. But creatures larger than a few millimeters across seldom absorb nutrients directly from their environment. For example, humans cannot absorb steaks, apples, or ice cream without processing them first. That processing, called *digestion,* occurs in specialized structures in which complex foods are broken down into simpler components that can be transported and absorbed easily. Respiration and excretion are also more complicated for large organisms. Humans have specialized structures responsible for gas exchange (lungs) and excretion (kidneys). Although digestion, respiration, and excretion occur in different parts of the body, the cells of the body cannot travel to one place for nutrients, another for oxygen, and a third to get rid of waste products. Instead, individual cells remain where they are but communicate with other areas of the body through an internal transport system—the circulation. For example, the blood absorbs the waste products released by each of your cells and carries those wastes to the kidneys for excretion.

Biology includes many subspecialties. This text considers two biological subjects: **anatomy** (ah-NAT-o-mē) and **physiology** (fiz-ē-OL-o-jē). Over the course of 20 chapters, you will become familiar with the basic anatomy and physiology of the human body.

1-2 Anatomy is structure, and physiology is function

The word *anatomy* has Greek origins, as do many other anatomical terms and phrases. **Anatomy,** which means "a cutting open," is the study of internal and external structure and the physical relationships between body parts. **Physiology,** another word derived from Greek, is the study of how living organisms perform their vital functions. The two subjects are interrelated. Anatomical information provides clues about probable functions, and physiological mechanisms can be explained only in terms of their underlying anatomy.

The link between structure and function is always present but not always understood. For example, the anatomy of the heart was clearly described in the fifteenth century, but almost 200 years passed before anyone realized that it pumped blood. This text will familiarize you with basic anatomy and give you an appreciation of the physiological processes that make human life possible. The information will enable you to understand many kinds of disease processes and will help you make informed decisions about your own health.

ANATOMY

Anatomy can be divided into gross (macroscopic) anatomy or microscopic anatomy on the basis of the degree of structural detail under consideration. Other anatomical specialties focus on specific processes, such as respiration, or medical applications, such as developing artificial limbs.

Gross Anatomy

Gross anatomy, or *macroscopic anatomy,* considers features visible with the unaided eye. There are many ways to approach gross anatomy. **Surface anatomy** refers to the study of general form and superficial markings. **Regional anatomy** considers all of the superficial and internal features in a specific region of the body, such as the head, neck, or trunk. **Systemic anatomy** considers the structure of major *organ systems,* which are groups of organs that function together in a coordinated manner. For example, the heart, blood, and blood vessels form the *cardiovascular system,* which circulates oxygen and nutrients throughout the body.

Microscopic Anatomy

Microscopic anatomy concerns structures that cannot be seen without magnification. The boundaries of microscopic anatomy are established by the limits of the equipment used. A light microscope reveals basic details about cell structure, whereas an electron microscope can visualize individual molecules only a few nanometers (nm, 1 millionth of a millimeter) across. As we proceed through the text, we will be considering details at all levels, from macroscopic to microscopic. (Readers unfamiliar with the terms used to describe measurements and weights should consult the reference tables in Appendix 2.)

Microscopic anatomy can be subdivided into specialties that consider features within a characteristic range of sizes. **Cytology** (sī-TOL-o-jē) analyzes the internal structure of individual **cells.** The trillions of living cells in our bodies are composed of chemical substances in various combinations, and our lives depend on the chemical processes occurring in those cells. For this reason we will consider basic chemistry (Chapter 2) before examining cell structure (Chapter 3).

Histology (his-TOL-o-jē) takes a broader perspective and examines **tissues,** groups of specialized cells and cell products that work together to perform specific functions (Chapter 4). Tissues combine to form **organs,** such as the heart, kidney, liver, and brain. Many organs can be examined without a microscope, so at the organ level we cross the boundary into gross anatomy.

PHYSIOLOGY

Physiology is the study of the function of anatomical structures. **Human physiology** is the study of the functions of the human body. These functions are complex and much more difficult to examine than most anatomical structures. As a result, the science of physiology includes even more specialties than does the science of anatomy.

The cornerstone of human physiology is **cell physiology,** the study of the functions of living cells. Cell physiology includes events at the chemical or molecular levels—both chemical processes within cells and between cells. **Special physiology** is the study of the physiology of specific organs. Examples include renal physiology (kidney function) and cardiac physiology (heart function). **Systemic physiology** considers all aspects of the function of specific organ systems. Respiratory

The Big Picture

All physiological functions are performed by anatomical structures. These functions follow the same physical and mechanical principles that can be seen in the world at large.

physiology and reproductive physiology are examples. **Pathological physiology,** or **pathology** (pah-THOL-o-jē), is the study of the effects of diseases on organ or system functions. (The Greek word *pathos* means "disease.") Modern medicine depends on an understanding of both normal and pathological physiology, of understanding not only what has gone wrong but also how to correct it.

Special topics in physiology address specific functions of the human body as a whole. These specialties focus on physiological interactions among multiple-organ systems. Exercise physiology, for example, studies the physiological adjustments to exercise.

CHECKPOINT

2. Describe how anatomy and physiology are closely related.

3. Would a histologist more likely be considered a specialist in microscopic anatomy or in gross anatomy? Why?

See the blue Answers tab at the back of the book.

1-3 Levels of organization progress from molecules to a complete organism

To understand the human body, we must examine its organization at several different levels, from the submicroscopic to the macroscopic. Figure 1-1 presents the relationships among the various levels of organization, using the cardiovascular system as an example.

- *Chemical (or molecular) level. Atoms,* the smallest stable units of matter, combine to form *molecules* with complex shapes. Even at this simplest level, a molecule's specialized shape determines its function. This is the chemical, or molecular, level of organization.

- *Cellular level.* Different molecules can interact to form larger structures, each type of which has a specific func-

tion in a cell. For example, different types of protein filaments interact to produce the contractions of muscle cells in the heart. *Cells,* the smallest living units in the body, make up the cellular level of organization.

- *Tissue level.* A *tissue* is composed of similar cells working together to perform a specific function. Heart muscle cells form *cardiac muscle tissue,* an example of the tissue level of organization.

- *Organ level.* An *organ* consists of two or more different tissues working together to perform specific functions. An example of the organ level of organization is the *heart,* a hollow, three-dimensional organ with walls composed of layers of cardiac muscle and other tissues.

- *Organ system level.* Organs interact in *organ systems.* Each time it contracts, the heart pushes blood into a network of blood vessels. Together, the heart, blood, and blood vessels form the *cardiovascular system,* an example of the organ system level of organization.

- *Organism level.* All of the organ systems of the body work together to maintain life and health. This brings us to the highest level of organization, that of the *organism*—in this case, a human being.

The organization at each level determines both the structural characteristics and the functions of higher levels. For example, the arrangement of atoms and molecules at the chemical level creates the protein filaments that, at the cellular level, give cardiac muscle cells the ability to contract powerfully. At the tissue level, these cells are linked, forming cardiac muscle tissue. The structure of the tissue ensures that the contractions are coordinated, producing a heartbeat. When that beat occurs, the internal anatomy of the heart, an organ, enables it to function as a pump. The heart is filled with blood and connected to the blood vessels, and the pumping action circulates blood through the vessels of the cardiovascular system. Through interactions with the respiratory, digestive, urinary, and other systems, the cardiovascular system performs a variety of functions essential to the survival of the organism.

Something that affects a system will ultimately affect each of the system's components. For example, the heart cannot pump blood effectively after massive blood loss. If the heart cannot pump and blood cannot flow, oxygen and nutrients cannot be distributed. Very soon, the cardiac muscle tissue begins to break down as individual muscle cells die from oxygen and nutrient starvation. These changes will not be restricted to the cardiovascular system; cells, tissues, and organs throughout the body will be damaged.

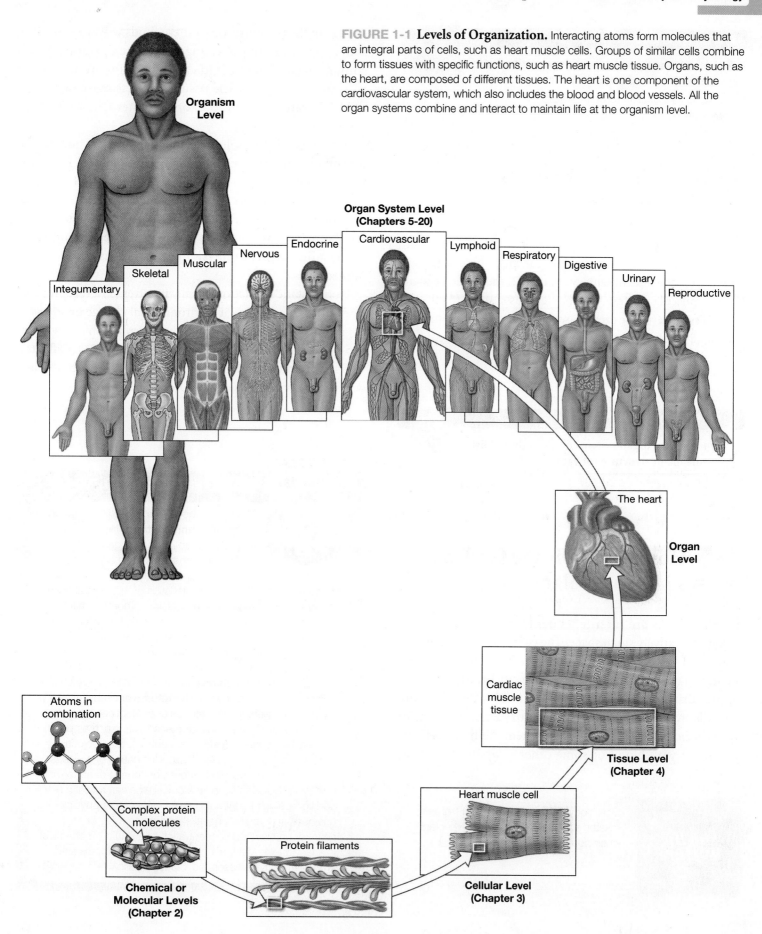

FIGURE 1-1 Levels of Organization. Interacting atoms form molecules that are integral parts of cells, such as heart muscle cells. Groups of similar cells combine to form tissues with specific functions, such as heart muscle tissue. Organs, such as the heart, are composed of different tissues. The heart is one component of the cardiovascular system, which also includes the blood and blood vessels. All the organ systems combine and interact to maintain life at the organism level.

Organism Level

Organ System Level
(Chapters 5-20)

Integumentary

Skeletal

Muscular

Nervous

Endocrine

Cardiovascular

Lymphoid

Respiratory

Digestive

Urinary

Reproductive

The heart

Organ Level

Cardiac muscle tissue

Tissue Level (Chapter 4)

Heart muscle cell

Atoms in combination

Complex protein molecules

Protein filaments

Cellular Level (Chapter 3)

Chemical or Molecular Levels (Chapter 2)

CHECKPOINT

4. Identify the major levels of organization from the simplest to the most complex.

See the blue Answers tab at the back of the book.

1-4 The human body consists of 11 organ systems

Figure 1-2 introduces the 11 organ systems in the human body, and their major functions and components. These organ systems are (1) the integumentary system, (2) the skeletal system, (3) the muscular system, (4) the nervous system, (5) the endocrine system, (6) the cardiovascular system, (7) the lymphoid system, (8) the respiratory system, (9) the digestive system, (10) the urinary system, and (11) the reproductive system.

CHECKPOINT

5. Identify the organ systems of the body and list some major structures of each.

See the blue Answers tab at the back of the book.

1-5 Homeostasis is the tendency toward internal balance

Organ systems are interdependent, interconnected, and occupy a relatively small space. The cells, tissues, organs, and systems of the body function together in a shared environment. Just as the inhabitants of a large city breathe the same air and drink water provided by the local water company, the cells in the human body absorb oxygen and nutrients from the body fluids that surround them. All living cells are in contact with blood or some other body fluid, and any

change in the composition of these fluids will affect them in some way. For example, changes in the temperature or salt content of the blood could cause anything from a minor adjustment (heart muscle tissue contracts more often, and the heart rate goes up) to a total disaster (the heart stops beating altogether).

A variety of physiological mechanisms act to prevent potentially dangerous changes in the environment inside the body. **Homeostasis** (hō-mē-ō-STĀ-sis; *homeo,* unchanging + *stasis,* standing) refers to the existence of a stable internal environment. To survive, every living organism must maintain homeo-stasis. The term **homeostatic regulation** refers to the adjustments in physiological systems that preserve homeostasis.

Homeostatic regulation usually involves (1) a **receptor** that is sensitive to a particular environmental change or *stimulus;* (2) a **control center,** or *integration center,* which receives and processes information from the receptor; and (3) an **effector,** which responds to the commands of the control center and whose activity opposes or reinforces the stimulus.

The Big Picture

The body can be divided into 11 organ systems, but they all work together, and their boundaries are not absolute.

Clinical Note

Homeostasis and Disease

The human body is amazingly effective in maintaining **homeostasis.** Nevertheless, an infection, an injury, or a genetic abnormality can sometimes have effects so severe that homeostatic mechanisms can't fully compensate for them. One or more characteristics of the internal environment may then be pushed outside of normal limits. When this happens, organ systems begin to malfunction, producing a state known as illness or **disease.**

An understanding of normal homeostatic mechanisms usually enables one to draw conclusions about what might be responsible for the signs and symptoms that are characteristic of many diseases. **Symptoms** are subjective—things that a person experiences and describes but that aren't otherwise detectable or measurable, such as pain, nausea, and anxiety. A **sign,** by contrast, is an objectively observable or measurable physical indication of a disease, such as a rash, a swelling, a fever, or sounds of abnormal breathing. Nowadays, technological aids can reveal many additional signs that would not be evident to a physician's unaided senses: an unusual shape on an x-ray or MRI scan, or an elevated concentration of a particular chemical in a blood test. Many aspects of human health, disease, and treatment are described in this textbook.

FIGURE 1-2 The Organ Systems of the Human Body.

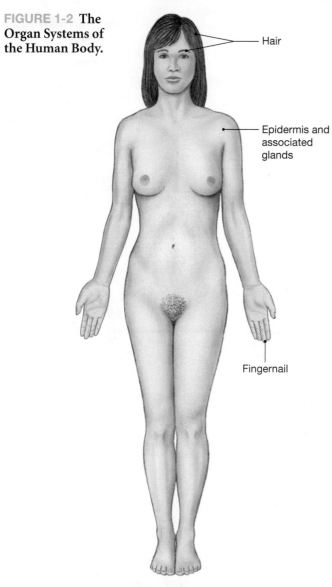

- Hair
- Epidermis and associated glands
- Fingernail

(a) THE INTEGUMENTARY SYSTEM

Protects against environmental hazards;
helps control body temperature

ORGAN/COMPONENT	PRIMARY FUNCTIONS
CUTANEOUS MEMBRANE **Epidermis** **Dermis**	Covers surface; protects deeper tissues Nourishes epidermis; provides strength; contains glands
HAIR FOLLICLES **Hairs** **Sebaceous Glands**	Produce hair Provide some protection for head Secrete oil that lubricates hair shaft and epidermis
SWEAT GLANDS	Produce perspiration for evaporative cooling
NAILS	Protect and stiffen distal tips of digits
SENSORY RECEPTORS	Provide sensations of touch, pressure, temperature, pain
SUBCUTANEOUS LAYER	Stores fat; attaches skin to deeper structures

AXIAL SKELETON

APPENDICULAR SKELETON

- Skull
- Sternum
- Ribs
- Vertebrae
- Sacrum
- Supporting bones (scapula and clavicle)
- Upper limb bones
- Pelvis (supporting bones plus sacrum)
- Lower limb bones

(b) THE SKELETAL SYSTEM

Provides support; protects tissues;
stores minerals; forms blood

ORGAN/COMPONENT	PRIMARY FUNCTIONS
BONES, CARTILAGES, AND JOINTS **Axial Skeleton** (skull, vertebrae, ribs, sternum, sacrum, cartilages, and ligaments)	Support, protect soft tissues; bones store minerals Protects brain, spinal cord, sense organs, and soft tissues of thoracic cavity; supports the body weight over the lower limbs
Appendicular Skeleton (limbs and supporting bones and ligaments)	Provides internal support and positioning of the limbs; supports and moves axial skeleton
BONE MARROW	Acts as primary site of red blood cell and white blood cell production

FIGURE 1-2
Continued.

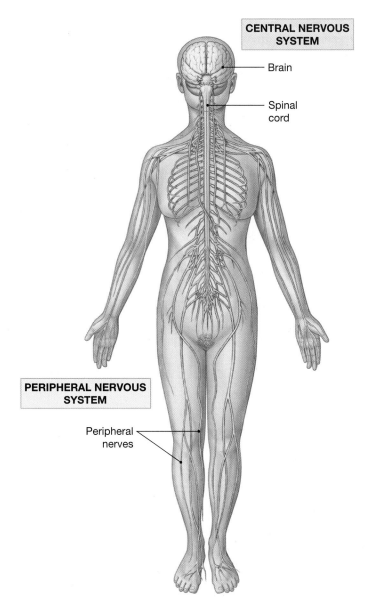

Axial muscles

Appendicular muscles

Tendons

CENTRAL NERVOUS SYSTEM

Brain

Spinal cord

PERIPHERAL NERVOUS SYSTEM

Peripheral nerves

(c) THE MUSCULAR SYSTEM

Produces movement and locomotion; provides support; generates heat

ORGAN/COMPONENT	PRIMARY FUNCTIONS
SKELETAL MUSCLES (700)	Provide skeletal movement; control entrances and exits of digestive tract; produce heat; support skeletal position; protect soft tissues
Axial Muscles	Support and position axial skeleton
Appendicular Muscles	Support, move, and brace limbs
TENDONS	Harness forces of contraction to perform specific tasks

(d) THE NERVOUS SYSTEM

Directs immediate response to stimuli, usually by coordinating the activities of other organ systems

ORGAN/COMPONENT	PRIMARY FUNCTIONS
CENTRAL NERVOUS SYSTEM (CNS)	Acts as control center for nervous system; processes information; provides short-term control over activities of other systems
Brain	Performs complex integrative functions; controls both voluntary and autonomic activities
Spinal Cord	Relays information to and from brain; performs less complex integrative functions; directs many simple involuntary activities
PERIPHERAL NERVOUS SYSTEM (PNS)	Links CNS with other systems and with sense organs

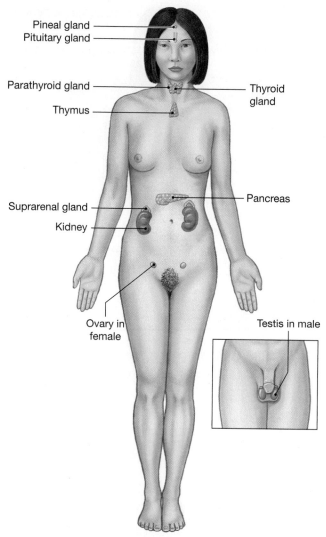

(e) THE ENDOCRINE SYSTEM

Directs long-term changes in other organ systems

ORGAN/COMPONENT	PRIMARY FUNCTIONS
PINEAL GLAND	May control timing of reproduction and set day-night rhythms
PITUITARY GLAND	Controls other endocrine glands; regulates growth and fluid balance
THYROID GLAND	Controls tissue metabolic rate; regulates calcium levels
PARATHYROID GLANDS	Regulate calcium levels (with thyroid)
THYMUS	Controls maturation of lymphocytes
ADRENAL GLANDS	Adjust water balance, tissue metabolism, cardiovascular and respiratory activity
KIDNEYS	Control red blood cell production and assist in calcium regulation
PANCREAS	Regulates blood glucose levels
GONADS **Testes**	Support male sexual characteristics and reproductive functions (*part k*)
Ovaries	Support female sexual characteristics and reproductive functions (*part l*)

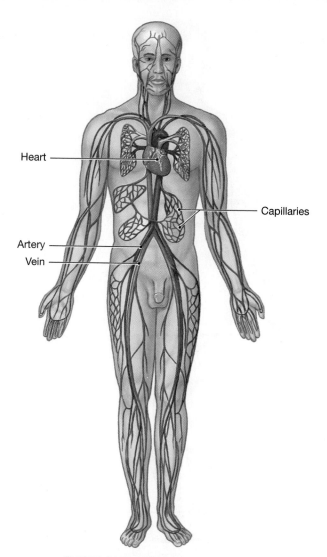

(f) THE CARDIOVASCULAR SYSTEM

Transports cells and dissolved materials, including nutrients, wastes, and gases

ORGAN/COMPONENT	PRIMARY FUNCTIONS
HEART	Propels blood; maintains blood pressure
BLOOD VESSELS **Arteries** **Capillaries** **Veins**	Distribute blood throughout the body Carry blood from heart to capillaries Permit diffusion between blood and interstitial fluids Return blood from capillaries to the heart
BLOOD	Transports oxygen, carbon dioxide, and blood cells; delivers nutrients and hormones; removes waste products; assists in temperature regulation and defense against disease

FIGURE 1-2
Continued.

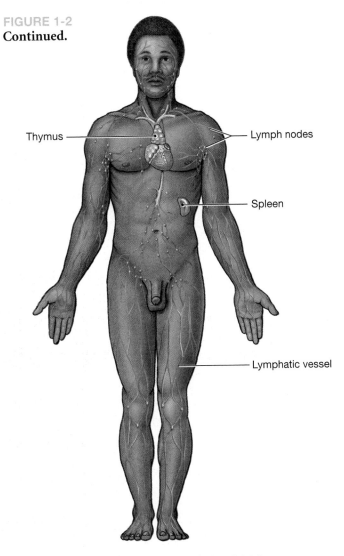

Thymus

Lymph nodes

Spleen

Lymphatic vessel

(g) THE LYMPHOID SYSTEM

Defends against infection and disease;
returns tissue fluid to the bloodstream

ORGAN/COMPONENT	PRIMARY FUNCTIONS
LYMPHATIC VESSELS	Carry lymph (water and proteins) and lymphocytes from peripheral tissues to veins of the cardiovascular system
LYMPH NODES	Monitor the composition of lymph; contain cells that engulf pathogens and stimulate immune response
SPLEEN	Monitors circulating blood; contains cells that engulf pathogens and stimulate immune response
THYMUS	Controls development and maintenance of one class of lymphocytes (T cells)

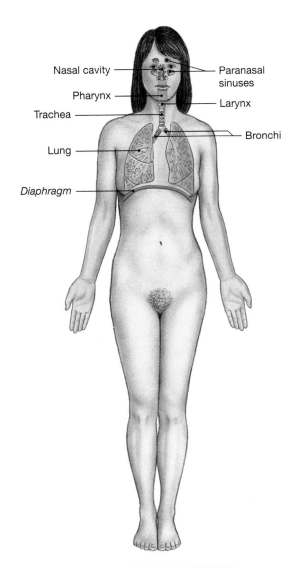

Nasal cavity

Paranasal sinuses

Pharynx

Larynx

Trachea

Bronchi

Lung

Diaphragm

(h) THE RESPIRATORY SYSTEM

Delivers air to sites where gas exchange can
occur between the air and circulating blood

ORGAN/COMPONENT	PRIMARY FUNCTIONS
NASAL CAVITIES, PARANASAL SINUSES	Filter, warm, humidify air; detect smells
PHARYNX	Conducts air to larynx; the pharnyx is a chamber shared with the digestive tract *(part i)*
LARYNX	Protects opening to trachea and contains vocal cords
TRACHEA	Filters air, traps particles in mucus; cartilages keep airway open
BRONCHI	(Same functions as trachea)
LUNGS	Responsible for air movement through volume changes resulting from movements of ribs and diaphragm; include airways and alveoli
Alveoli	Sites of gas exchange between air and blood

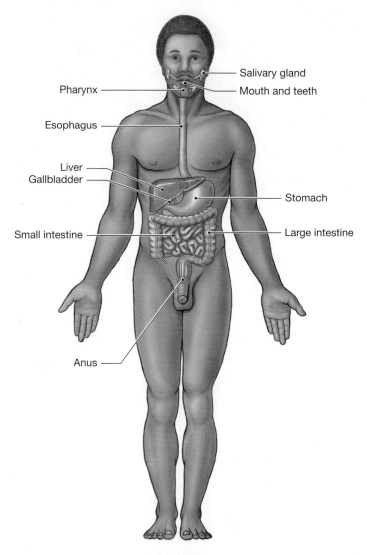

(i) THE DIGESTIVE SYSTEM

Processes food; absorbs nutrients; eliminates waste products

ORGAN/COMPONENT	PRIMARY FUNCTIONS
SALIVARY GLANDS	Provide buffers and lubrication; produce enzymes that begin digestion
PHARYNX	Conducts solid food and liquids to esophagus; is a chamber shared with respiratory tract *(part h)*
ESOPHAGUS	Delivers food to stomach
STOMACH	Secretes acids and enzymes
SMALL INTESTINE	Secretes digestive enzymes, buffers, and hormones; absorbs nutrients
LIVER	Secretes bile; regulates nutrient composition of blood
GALLBLADDER	Stores bile for release into small intestine
PANCREAS	Secretes digestive enzymes and buffers; secretes hormones *(part e)*
LARGE INTESTINE	Removes water from fecal material; stores wastes

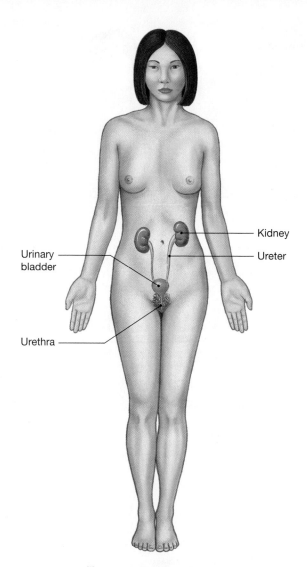

(j) THE URINARY SYSTEM

Eliminates excess water, salts, and waste products

ORGAN/COMPONENT	PRIMARY FUNCTIONS
KIDNEYS	Form and concentrate urine; regulate blood pH and ion concentrations; perform endocrine functions *(part e)*
URETERS	Conduct urine from kidneys to urinary bladder
URINARY BLADDER	Stores urine for eventual elimination
URETHRA	Conducts urine to exterior

FIGURE 1-2
Continued.

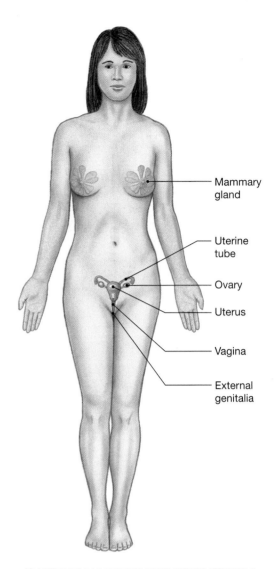

Prostate gland

Seminal gland

Ductus deferens

Urethra

Epididymis

Testis

Penis

Scrotum

Mammary gland

Uterine tube

Ovary

Uterus

Vagina

External genitalia

(k) THE MALE REPRODUCTIVE SYSTEM

Produces sex cells and hormones

ORGAN/COMPONENT	PRIMARY FUNCTIONS
TESTES	Produce sperm and hormones *(part e)*
ACCESSORY ORGANS **Epididymis (pl., Epididymides)**	Acts as site of sperm maturation
Ductus Deferens (Sperm Duct)	Conducts sperm between epididymis and prostate gland
Seminal Glands	Secrete fluid that makes up much of the volume of semen
Prostate Gland	Secretes fluid and enzymes
Urethra	Conducts semen to exterior
EXTERNAL GENITALIA **Penis**	Contains erectile tissue; deposits sperm in vagina of female; produces pleasurable sensations during sexual activities
Scrotum	Surrounds the testes and controls their temperature

(l) THE FEMALE REPRODUCTIVE SYSTEM

Produces sex cells and hormones

ORGAN/COMPONENT	PRIMARY FUNCTIONS
OVARIES	Produce oocytes and hormones *(part e)*
UTERINE TUBES	Deliver oocyte or embryo to uterus; normal site of fertilization
UTERUS	Site of embryonic development and exchange between maternal and embryonic bloodstreams
VAGINA	Site of sperm deposition; acts as birth canal at delivery; provides passageway for fluids during menstruation
EXTERNAL GENITALIA **Clitoris**	Contains erectile tissue; produces pleasurable sensations during sexual activities
Labia	Contain glands that lubricate entrance to vagina
MAMMARY GLANDS	Produce milk that nourishes newborn infant

You are probably already familiar with several examples of homeostatic regulation, although not in those terms. As an example, consider the operation of the thermostat in a house or apartment (Figure 1-3).

The thermostat is a control center that monitors room temperature. The gauge on the thermostat establishes the set point, the "ideal" room temperature—in this example, 22°C (about 72°F). The function of the thermostat is to keep room temperature within acceptable limits, usually within a degree or so of the set point. The thermostat receives information from a receptor, a thermometer exposed to air in the room, and it controls one of two effectors: a heater or an air conditioner. In the summer, for example, a rise in temperature above the set point causes the thermostat to turn on the air conditioner, which then cools the room (Figure 1-3); when the temperature at the thermometer returns to the set point, the thermostat turns off the air conditioner. The essential feature of temperature control by a thermostat can be summarized very simply: A variation outside the desired range triggers an automatic response that corrects the situation. This method of homeostatic regulation is called *negative feedback*, because an effector activated by the control center opposes, or *negates*, the original stimulus.

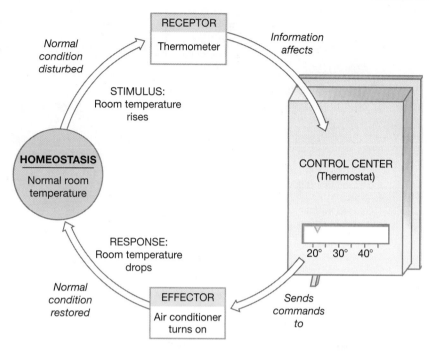

FIGURE 1-3 **The Control of Room Temperature.** In response to input from a receptor (a thermometer), a thermostat (the control center) triggers a response from an effector (in this case, an air conditioner) that restores normal temperature. When room temperature rises above the set point, the thermostat turns on the air conditioner, and the temperature returns to normal.

CHECKPOINT

6. Why is homeostatic regulation important to an organism?

See the blue Answers tab at the back of the book.

1-6 Negative feedback opposes variations from normal, whereas positive feedback exaggerates them

Homeostatic regulation controls aspects of the internal environment that affect every cell in the body. Most commonly, such regulation is provided by negative feedback; positive feedback is less frequent because it tends to produce extreme responses.

NEGATIVE FEEDBACK

The essential feature of **negative feedback** is this: Regardless of whether the stimulus (such as temperature) rises or falls at the receptor, *a variation outside normal limits triggers an automatic response that corrects the situation.*

Most homeostatic mechanisms in the body involve negative feedback. For example, consider the control of body temperature, a process called *thermoregulation* (Figure 1-4). Thermoregulation involves altering the relationship between heat loss, which occurs primarily at the body surface, and heat production, which occurs in all active tissues. In the human body, skeletal muscles are the most important generators of body heat.

The cells of the thermoregulatory control center are located in the brain. Temperature receptors are located in the skin and in cells in the control center. The thermoregulatory center has a normal set point near 37°C (98.6°F). If body temperature rises above 37.2°C (99°F), activity in the control center targets two effectors: (1) smooth muscles in the walls of blood vessels supplying the skin and (2) sweat glands. The muscle tissue relaxes and the blood vessels widen, or dilate, increasing blood flow at the body surface, and the sweat glands accelerate their secretion. The skin then acts like a radiator, losing heat to the environment, and the evaporation of sweat speeds the process. When body temperature returns to normal, the control center becomes inactive, and superficial blood flow and sweat gland activity decrease to normal resting levels.

If temperature at the control center falls below 36.7°C (98°F), the control center targets the same two effectors and skeletal

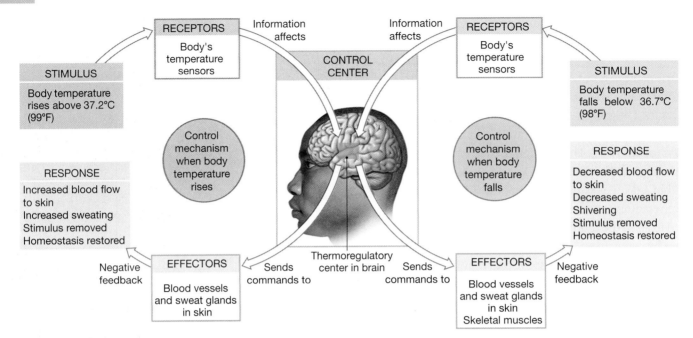

FIGURE 1-4 Negative Feedback in Thermoregulation. In negative feedback, a stimulus produces a response that opposes the original stimulus. Body temperature is regulated by a control center in the brain that functions as a thermostat with a set point of 37°C. If body temperature climbs above 37.2°C (99°F), heat loss is increased through enhanced blood flow to the skin and increased sweating. If body temperature falls below 36.7°C (98°F), heat loss is decreased through decreases in blood flow to the skin and sweating, and heat is produced by shivering.

muscles. This time, blood flow to the skin declines, and sweat gland activity decreases. This combination reduces the rate of heat loss to the environment. Because heat production by skeletal muscles continues, body temperature gradually rises; once the set point has been reached, the thermoregulatory center turns itself "off," and both blood flow and sweat gland activity in the skin increase to normal resting levels. Additional heat may be generated by shivering, which is caused by random contractions of skeletal muscles.

Homeostatic mechanisms using negative feedback usually ignore minor variations, and they maintain a normal range rather than a fixed value. In the previous example, body temperature oscillates around the ideal set-point temperature. Thus, for any single individual, any measured value (such as body temperature) can vary from moment to moment or day to day. The variability among individuals is even greater, for each person has slightly different homeostatic set points. It is, therefore, impractical to define "normal" homeostatic conditions very precisely. By convention, physiological values are reported either as average values obtained by sampling a large number of individuals or as a range that includes 95 percent or more of the sample population. However, 5 percent of normal adults have a body temperature outside the "normal" range (below 36.7°C or above 37.2°C). Still, these temperatures are

perfectly normal for them, and the variations have no clinical significance.

POSITIVE FEEDBACK

In **positive feedback,** *the initial stimulus produces a response that reinforces that stimulus.* For example, suppose a thermostat was wired so that when the temperature rose, the thermostat would turn on the heater rather than the air conditioner. In that case, the initial stimulus (rising room temperature) would cause a response (heater turns on) that strengthens the stimulus. Room temperature would continue to rise until someone switched off the thermostat, unplugged the heater, or intervened in some other way before the house caught fire and burned down. This kind of escalating cycle is called a *positive feedback loop.*

In the body, positive feedback loops are involved in the regulation of a potentially dangerous or stressful process that must be completed quickly (Figure 1-5). For example, the immediate danger from a severe cut is blood loss, which can lower blood pressure and reduce the pumping efficiency of the heart. Damage to cells in the cut blood vessel wall releases chemicals that begin the multistep process of blood clotting. As clotting gets under way, each step releases chemicals that accelerate the

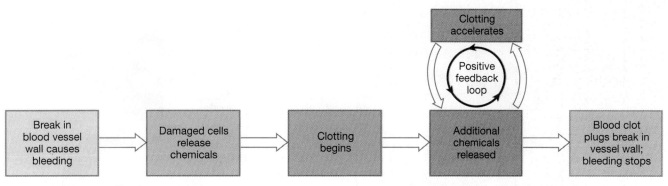

FIGURE 1-5 **Positive Feedback.** In positive feedback, a stimulus produces a response that reinforces the original stimulus. Positive feedback is important in accelerating processes that must proceed to completion rapidly. In this example, positive feedback accelerates blood clotting until bleeding stops.

process. This escalating process is a positive feedback loop that ends with the formation of a blood clot, which patches the vessel wall and stops the bleeding. Blood clotting will be examined more closely in Chapter 11. Labor and delivery, another example of positive feedback in action, will be discussed in Chapter 20.

The human body is amazingly effective in maintaining homeostasis. Nevertheless, an infection, an injury, or a genetic abnormality can sometimes have effects so severe that homeostatic mechanisms can't fully compensate for them. When homeostatic regulation fails, organ systems begin to malfunction, producing a state known as illness, or **disease.**

The Big Picture

Physiological systems work together to maintain a stable internal environment, the foundations of homeostasis. In doing so they monitor and adjust the volume and composition of body fluids, and keep body temperature within normal limits. If they cannot do so, internal conditions become increasingly abnormal and survival becomes uncertain.

CHECKPOINT

7. Explain the function of negative feedback systems.

8. Why is positive feedback helpful in blood clotting but unsuitable for the regulation of body temperature?

9. What happens to the body when homeostasis breaks down?

See the blue Answers tab at the back of the book.

1-7 Anatomical terms describe body regions, anatomical positions and directions, and body sections

Early anatomists faced serious communication problems. For example, stating that a bump is "on the back" does not give very precise information about its location. So anatomists created maps of the human body. Prominent anatomical structures serve as landmarks, distances are measured (in centimeters or inches), and specialized directional terms are used. In effect, anatomy uses a language of its own that must be learned almost at the start of your study.

A familiarity with Latin and Greek word roots and their combinations makes anatomical terms more understandable. As new terms are introduced in the text, notes on their pronunciation and the relevant word roots will be provided. Additional information on foreign word roots, prefixes, suffixes, and combining forms can be found inside the back cover.

Latin and Greek terms are not the only foreign words imported into the anatomical vocabulary over the centuries, and the vocabulary continues to expand. Many anatomical structures and clinical conditions were initially named after either the discoverer or, in the case of diseases, the most famous victim. Although most such commemorative names, or *eponyms*, have been replaced by more precise terms, many are still in use.

SURFACE ANATOMY

With the exception of the skin, none of the organ systems can be seen from the body surface. Therefore, you must create your own mental maps and extract information from the terms given in Figures 1-6 and 1-7. Learning these terms now will make subsequent chapters more understandable.

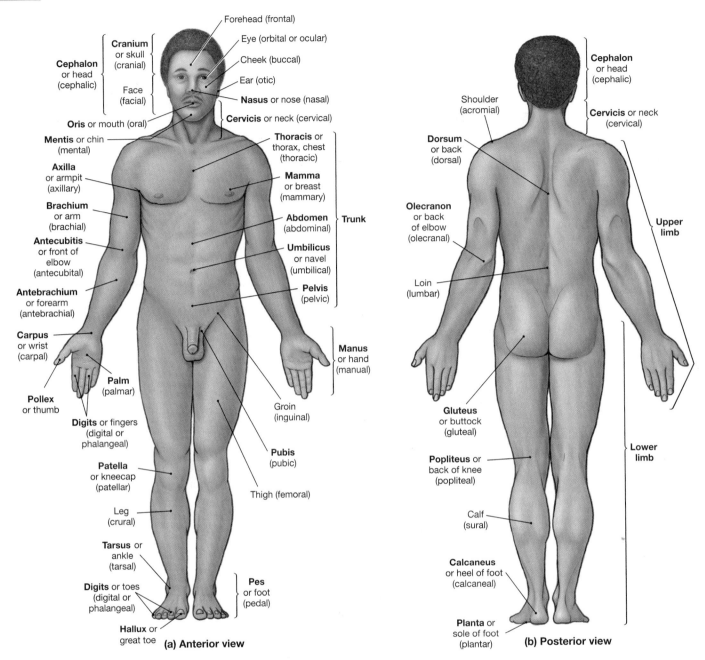

FIGURE 1-6 Anatomical Landmarks. In this figure showing the body in the anatomical position, anatomical terms are in boldface type, common names are in plain type, and anatomical adjectives are in parentheses.

Anatomical Landmarks

Standard anatomical illustrations show the human form in the **anatomical position,** with the hands at the sides with the palms facing forward, and the feet together (**Figure 1-6**). A person lying down in the anatomical position is said to be **supine** (soo-PĪN) when face up and **prone** when face down.

Important anatomical landmarks are also presented in **Figure 1-6**. The anatomical terms are in boldface, the common names in plain type, and the anatomical adjectives in parentheses. Understanding these terms and their origins can help you remember both the location of a particular structure and its name. For example, the term *brachium* refers to the arm, and later chapters will discuss the brachial artery, brachial nerve, and so forth. You might remember this term more easily if you know that the Latin word *brachium* is also the source of Old English and French words meaning "to embrace."

Anatomical Regions

Major regions of the body are listed in Table 1-1 and shown in Figure 1-6. Anatomists and clinicians often need to use regional terms as well as specific landmarks to describe a general area of interest or injury. Two methods are used to map the surface of the abdomen and pelvis. Clinicians refer to four **abdominopelvic quadrants** formed by a pair of imaginary perpendicular lines that intersect at the *umbilicus* (navel). This simple method, shown in Figure 1-7a, is useful for describing the location of aches, pains, and injuries, which can help a doctor determine the possible cause. For example, tenderness in the right lower quadrant (RLQ) is a symptom of appendicitis, whereas tenderness in the right upper quadrant (RUQ) may indicate gallbladder or liver problems.

Anatomists like to use more precise regional distinctions to describe the location and orientation of internal organs. They recognize nine **abdominopelvic regions** (Figure 1-7b). Figure 1-7c shows the relationships among quadrants, regions, and internal organs.

TABLE 1-1 **Regions of the Human Body**
(see Figure 1-6)

STRUCTURE	REGION
Cephalon (head)	Cephalic region
Cervicis (neck)	Cervical region
Thoracis (thorax or chest)	Thoracic region
Abdomen	Abdominal region
Pelvis	Pelvic region
Loin (lower back)	Lumbar region
Buttock	Gluteal region
Pubis (anterior pelvis)	Pubic region
Groin	Inguinal region
Axilla (armpit)	Axillary region
Brachium (arm)	Brachial region
Antebrachium (forearm)	Antebrachial region
Manus (hand)	Manual region
Thigh	Femoral region
Leg (anterior)	Crural region
Calf	Sural region
Pes (foot)	Pedal region
Planta (sole)	Plantar region

(a) Abdominopelvic quadrants

(b) Abdominopelvic regions

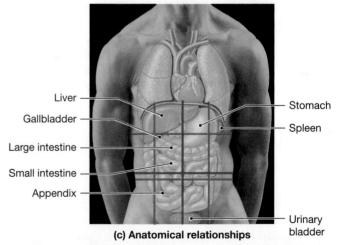

(c) Anatomical relationships

FIGURE 1-7 Abdominopelvic Quadrants and Regions. (a) Two imaginary perpendicular lines divide the area into four abdominopelvic quadrants. These quadrants, or their abbreviations, are most often used in clinical discussions. **(b)** More precise regional descriptions are provided by referring to one of nine abdominopelvic regions. **(c)** The usefulness of quadrants or regions results from the known relationships between superficial anatomical landmarks and underlying organs.

Anatomical Directions

Figure 1-8 and Table 1-2 present the principal directional terms and some examples of their use. There are many different terms, and some can be used interchangeably. For example, *anterior* refers to the front of the body, when viewed in the anatomical position; in humans, this term is equivalent to *ventral*, which refers to the belly. Likewise, the terms *posterior* and *dorsal* refer to the back of the human body. Terms that appear frequently in later chapters have been emphasized. Remember that *left* and *right* always refer to the left and right sides of the *subject*, not of the observer.

SECTIONAL ANATOMY

Sometimes the only way to understand the relationships among the parts of a three-dimensional object is to slice through it and look at the internal organization. An understanding of sectional views has become increasingly important since the development of electronic imaging techniques that enable us to see inside the living body without resorting to surgery (Figure 1-12 shows representative views).

> **The Big Picture**
>
> Anatomical descriptions refer to an individual in the anatomical position: standing, with the hands at the sides, palms facing forward, and feet together.

FIGURE 1-8 Directional References. Important directional terms used in this text are indicated by arrows; definitions and descriptions are included in Table 1-2.

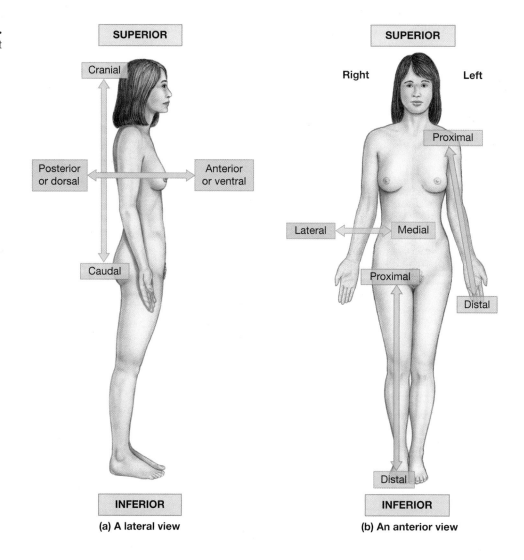

(a) A lateral view

(b) An anterior view

TABLE 1-2 **Directional Terms** (see Figure 1-8)

TERM	REGION OR REFERENCE	EXAMPLE
Anterior	The front; before	The navel is on the *anterior (ventral)* surface of the trunk.
Ventral	The belly side (equivalent to anterior when referring to the human body)	
Posterior	The back; behind	The shoulder blade is located *posterior (dorsal)* to the rib cage.
Dorsal	The back (equivalent to posterior when referring to the human body)	
Cranial or Cephalic	The head	The *cranial,* or *cephalic,* border of the pelvis is superior to the thigh.
Superior	Above; at a higher level (in the human body, toward the head)	The nose is *superior* to the chin.
Caudal	The tail (coccyx in humans)	The hips are *caudal* to the waist.
Inferior	Below; at a lower level	The knees are *inferior* to the hips.
Medial	Toward the body's longitudinal axis	The *medial* surfaces of the thighs may be in contact; moving medially from the arm across the chest surface brings you to the sternum.
Lateral	Away from the body's longitudinal axis	The thigh articulates with the *lateral* surface of the pelvis; moving laterally from the nose brings you to the eyes.
Proximal	Toward an attached base	The thigh is *proximal* to the foot; moving proximally from the wrist brings you to the elbow.
Distal	Away from an attached base	The fingers are *distal* to the wrist; moving distally from the elbow brings you to the wrist.
Superficial	At, near, or relatively close to the body surface	The scalp is *superficial* to the skull.
Deep	Farther from the body surface	The bone of the thigh is *deep* to the surrounding skeletal muscles.

Any slice through a three-dimensional object can be described with reference to three primary **sectional planes,** indicated in Figure 1-9 and Table 1-3:

1. *Transverse plane.* The **transverse plane** lies at right angles to the long (head-to-foot) axis of the body, dividing the body into **superior** and **inferior** portions. A cut in this plane is called a **transverse section,** or *cross section.* (Unless otherwise noted, all anatomical diagrams of cross sectional views of the body are oriented as though the subject were supine, with the observer looking toward the subject's head.)

2. *Frontal plane.* The **frontal plane,** or *coronal plane,* runs along the long axis of the body. The frontal plane extends laterally (side to side), dividing the body into **anterior** and **posterior** portions.

3. *Sagittal plane.* The **sagittal plane** also runs along the long axis of the body, but it extends anteriorly and posteriorly (front to back). A sagittal plane divides the body into *left* and *right* portions. A cut that passes along the body's midline and divides the body into left and right halves is a **midsagittal section.** (Note that a midsagittal section does not cut through the legs.)

CHECKPOINT

10. What is the purpose of anatomical terms?

11. Describe an anterior view and a posterior view in the anatomical position.

12. What type of section would separate the two eyes?

See the blue Answers tab at the back of the book.

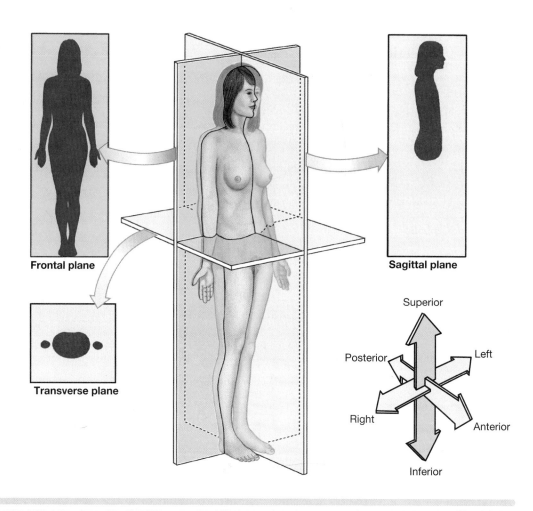

FIGURE 1-9 **Planes of Section.** The three primary planes of section are indicated here. Table 1-3 defines and describes them.

Frontal plane

Transverse plane

Sagittal plane

Superior

Posterior

Left

Right

Anterior

Inferior

TABLE 1-3 **Terms That Indicate Planes of Section** (see Figure 1-9)

ORIENTATION OF PLANE	ADJECTIVE	DIRECTIONAL REFERENCE	DESCRIPTION
Parallel to Long Axis	Sagittal	Sagittally	A *sagittal section* separates right and left portions. You examine a sagittal section, but you section sagittally.
	Midsagittal		In a *midsagittal section*, the plane passes through the midline, dividing the body in half and separating right and left sides.
	Frontal or coronal	Frontally or coronally	A *frontal*, or *coronal*, *section* separates anterior and posterior portions of the body; *coronal* usually refers to sections passing through the skull.
Perpendicular to Long Axis	Transverse or horizontal	Transversely or horizontally	A *transverse*, or *horizontal*, *section* separates superior and inferior portions of the body.

1-8 Body cavities protect internal organs and allow them to change shape

Viewed in sections, the human body is not a solid object, like a rock, in which all of the parts are fused together. Many vital organs are suspended in internal chambers called *body cavities*. These cav-ities have two essential functions: (1) They protect delicate organs from accidental shocks and cushion them from the jolting that oc-curs when we walk, jump, or run; and (2) they permit significant changes in the size and shape of internal organs. For example, be-cause they are inside body cavities, the lungs, heart, stomach, in-testines, urinary bladder, and many other organs can expand and contract without distorting surrounding tissues or disrupting the activities of nearby organs.

The **ventral body cavity,** or *coelom* (SĒ-lōm; *koila*, cavity), appears early in embryonic development. It contains organs of the respiratory, cardiovascular, digestive, urinary, and reproductive systems. As these internal organs develop, their relative positions change, and the ventral body cavity is gradually subdivided. The **diaphragm** (DĪ-uh-fram), a flat muscular sheet, divides the ventral body cavity into a superior **thoracic cavity,** bounded by the chest wall, and an inferior **abdominopelvic cavity,** enclosed by the abdominal wall and by the bones and muscles of the pelvis. The boundaries between the divisions of the ventral body cavity are shown in Figure 1-10.

Many of the organs in these cavities change size and shape as they perform their functions. For example, the lungs inflate and deflate as you breathe, and your stomach swells during each meal and shrinks between meals. These organs are surrounded by moist internal spaces that permit expansion and limited movement while preventing friction. The internal organs within the thoracic and abdominopelvic cavities are called **viscera** (VIS-e-ruh). A delicate layer called a *serous membrane* lines the walls of these internal cavities and covers the surfaces of the enclosed viscera. Serous membranes are moistened by a watery fluid that coats the opposing surfaces and reduces

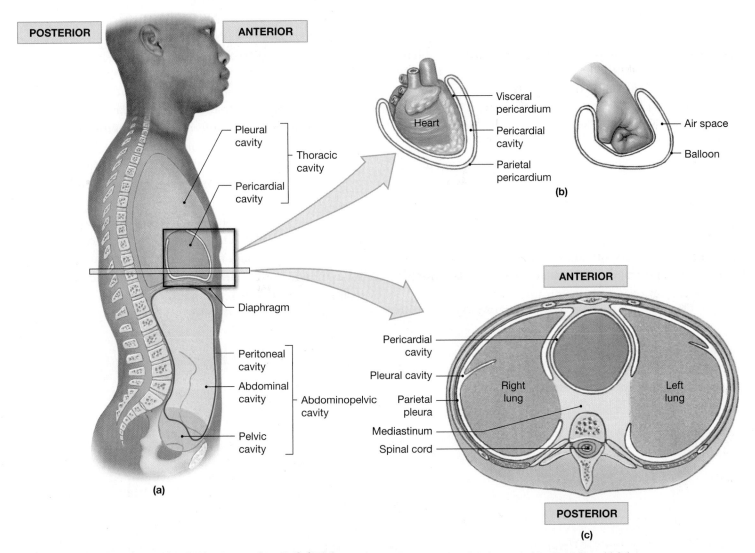

FIGURE 1-10 **The Ventral Body Cavity and Its Subdivisions. (a)** A lateral view showing the ventral body cavity, which is divided by the muscular diaphragm into a superior thoracic (chest) cavity and an inferior abdominopelvic cavity. **(b)** The heart is suspended within the pericardial cavity like a fist pushed into a balloon. The attachment site, corresponding to the wrist of the hand, lies at the connection between the heart and major blood vessels. **(c)** A transverse section through the ventral body cavity, showing the central location of the pericardial cavity within the thoracic cavity. Notice how the mediastinum divides the thoracic cavity into two pleural cavities. Note that this transverse or cross sectional view is oriented as though the observer were standing at the subject's feet and looking toward the subject's head.

friction. The portion of a serous membrane that covers a visceral organ is called the *visceral* layer; the opposing layer that lines the inner surface of the body wall or chamber is called the *parietal* layer.

THE THORACIC CAVITY

The thoracic cavity contains three internal chambers: a single *pericardial cavity* and a pair of *pleural cavities* (Figure 1-10a,c). Each of these cavities is lined by shiny, slippery serous membranes. The heart projects into a space known as the **pericardial cavity.** The relationship between the heart and the pericardial cavity resembles that of a fist pushing into a balloon (Figure 1-10b). The wrist corresponds to the *base* (attached portion) of the heart, and the balloon corresponds to the serous membrane lining the pericardial cavity. The serous membrane is called the **pericardium** (*peri-*, around + *cardium*, heart). The layer covering the heart is the **visceral pericardium,** and the opposing surface is the **parietal pericardium.**

The pericardium lies within the **mediastinum** (mē-dē-as-TĪ-num or mē-dē-AS-ti-num) (Figure 1-10c). The connective tissue of the mediastinum surrounds the pericardial cavity and heart, the large arteries and veins attached to the heart, and the thymus, trachea, and esophagus.

Each **pleural cavity** surrounds a lung. The serous membrane lining a pleural cavity is called a **pleura** (PLOOR-ah). The *visceral pleura* covers the outer surfaces of a lung, whereas the *parietal pleura* covers the opposing surface of the mediastinum and the inner body wall.

THE ABDOMINOPELVIC CAVITY

The abdominopelvic cavity extends from the diaphragm to the pelvis. It is subdivided into a superior **abdominal cavity** and an inferior **pelvic cavity** (Figure 1-10a). The abdominopelvic cavity contains the **peritoneal** (per-i-tō-NĒ-al) **cavity,** a chamber lined by a serous membrane known as the **peritoneum** (per-i-tō-NĒ-um). The *parietal peritoneum* lines the inner surface of the body wall. A narrow space containing a small amount of fluid separates the parietal peritoneum from the *visceral peritoneum*, which covers the enclosed organs.

The **abdominal cavity** extends from the inferior surface of the diaphragm to the level of the superior margins of the pelvis. This cavity contains the liver, stomach, spleen, small intestine, and most of the large intestine. The **pelvic cavity** is the portion of the ventral body cavity inferior to the abdominal cavity. The pelvic cavity contains the distal portion of the large intestine, the urinary bladder, and various reproductive organs.

This chapter provided an overview of the locations and functions of the major components of each organ system. It also introduced the anatomical vocabulary you need to follow more detailed anatomical descriptions in later chapters. In addition, some modern methods of visualizing anatomical structures in living individuals are described in "Clinical Note: Sectional Anatomy and Clinical Technology."

Clinical Note

Sectional Anatomy and Clinical Technology

The term **radiological procedures** includes not only those scanning techniques that involve radioisotopes but also methods that employ radiation sources outside the body. Physicians who specialize in the performance and analysis of these procedures are called radiologists. Radiological procedures can provide detailed information about internal systems in a living individual. **Figures 1–11** and **1–12** present the views provided by several different techniques. These figures include examples of x-rays, CT scans, MRI scans, and ultrasound images. Other examples of clinical technology can be found in later chapters.

CHECKPOINT

13. Describe two essential functions of body cavities.

14. Identify the subdivisions of the ventral body cavity.

15. If a surgeon makes an incision just inferior to the diaphragm, what body cavity will be opened?

See the blue Answers tab at the back of the book.

(a)

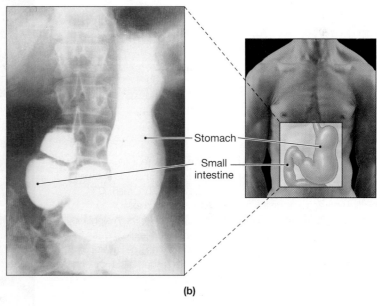

Stomach

Small intestine

(b)

FIGURE 1-11 X-rays. (a) An x-ray of the skull, taken from the left side. **X-rays** are a form of high-energy radiation that can penetrate living tissues. In the most familiar procedure, a beam of x-rays travels through the body before striking a photographic plate. Not all of the projected x-rays arrive at the film; some are absorbed or deflected as they pass through the body. Resistance to x-ray penetration is called **radiodensity.** In the human body, air has the lowest radiodensity; fat, liver, blood, muscle, and bone are increasingly radiodense. The result is an image in which radiodense tissues, such as bone, appear white, and less dense tissues are in shades of gray to black. The picture is a two-dimensional image of a three-dimensional object; in this image it is difficult to decide whether a particular feature is on the left side (toward the viewer) or on the right side (away from the viewer). **(b)** A **barium-contrast x-ray** of the upper digestive tract. The presence of the very radiodense barium solution causes the contours of the gastric and intestinal lining to appear white.

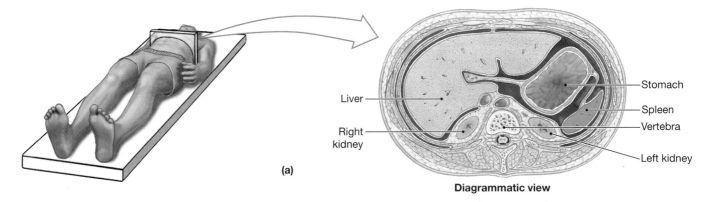

(a)

Liver — Stomach
Right kidney — Spleen
— Vertebra
— Left kidney

Diagrammatic view

Liver   Stomach   Spleen

Right kidney   Vertebra   **(b)**   Left kidney

Liver   Stomach

Liver   Vertebra   **(c)**   Kidney

FIGURE 1-12 Common Scanning Techniques. (a) Diagrammatic views showing the relative position and orientation of the scans shown in parts (b) and (c). **(b)** A color-enhanced CT scan of the abdomen. **CT** (computed tomography), formerly called **CAT** (computed axial tomography), uses computers to reconstruct sectional views. A single x-ray source rotates around the body, and the x-ray beam strikes a sensor monitored by the computer. The x-ray source completes one revolution around the body every few seconds; it then moves a short distance and repeats the process. The result is usually displayed as a sectional view in black and white, but it can be colorized for visual effect. CT scans show three-dimensional relationships and soft tissue structures more clearly than do standard x-rays. **(c)** A color-enhanced **MRI** scan of the same region. Magnetic resonance imaging surrounds part or all of the body with a magnetic field about 3000 times as strong as that of the earth. This field causes particles within atoms throughout the body to line up in a uniform direction. Energy from pulses of radio waves are absorbed and released by the different atoms in body tissues. The released energy is used to create an image. Details of soft tissue structure are usually much clearer than in CT scans. Note the differences in detail between this image and the CT scan. **(d)** In **ultrasound** procedures, a small transmitter contacting the skin broadcasts a brief, narrow burst of high-frequency sound and then detects the echoes. The sound waves are reflected by internal structures, and a picture, or **echogram,** is assembled from the pattern of echoes. These images lack the clarity of other procedures, but no adverse effects have been reported, and fetal development can be monitored without a significant risk of birth defects. Special methods of transmission and processing permit analysis of the beating heart without the complications that can accompany dye injections.

(d)

RELATED CLINICAL TERMS

abdominopelvic quadrant: One of four divisions of the anterior abdominal surface.

abdominopelvic region: One of nine divisions of the anterior abdominal surface.

auscultation (aws-kul-TĀ-shun): Listening to a patient's body sounds using a stethoscope.

CT, CAT (computerized [axial] tomography): An imaging technique that uses X-rays to reconstruct the body's three-dimensional structure.

disease: A malfunction of organs or organ systems resulting from a failure in homeostatic regulation.

echogram: An image created by ultrasound.

histology (his-TOL-o-jē): The study of tissues.

MRI (magnetic resonance imaging): An imaging technique that employs a magnetic field and radio waves to make subtle structural differences visible.

PET (positron emission tomography) scan: An imaging technique that shows the chemical functioning, as well as the structure of an organ.

radiologist: A physician who specializes in performing and analyzing radiological procedures.

radiology (rā-dē-OL-o-jē): The study of radioactive energy and radioactive substances and their use in the diagnosis and treatment of disease.

sign: The physical evidence of a disease that can be measured and observed through sight, hearing, or touch.

symptom: A patient's perception of a change in normal body function.

ultrasound: An imaging technique that uses brief bursts of high-frequency sound waves reflected by internal structures.

x-rays: High-energy radiation that can penetrate living tissues.

Chapter **1** Review

KEY TERMS

SUMMARY OUTLINE

1-1 The common functions of all living things include responsiveness, growth, reproduction, movement, and metabolism   *p. 2*

1. **Biology** is the study of life; one of its goals is to discover the unity and patterns that underlie the diversity of living organisms.

2. All living things, from single *cells* to large multicellular organisms, perform the same basic functions: They respond to changes in their environment; they grow and reproduce to create future generations; they are capable of producing movement; and they absorb materials from the environment. Organisms absorb and consume oxygen during respiration, and they discharge waste products during excretion. Digestion occurs in specialized body structures that break down complex foods. The circulation forms an internal transportation system between areas of the body.

1-2 Anatomy is structure, and physiology is function   *p. 3*

3. **Anatomy** is the study of internal and external structure and the physical relationships among body parts. **Physiology** is the study of how living organisms perform vital functions. All specific functions are performed by specific structures.

4. **Gross (macroscopic) anatomy** considers features visible without a microscope. It includes *surface anatomy* (general form and superficial markings), *regional anatomy* (superficial and internal features in a specific area of the body), and *systemic anatomy* (structure of major organ systems).

5. The boundaries of **microscopic anatomy** are established by the equipment used. **Cytology** analyzes the internal structure of individual **cells. Histology** examines **tissues** (groups of cells that have specific functional roles). Tissues combine to form organs, anatomical units with specific functions.

6. **Human physiology** is the study of the functions of the human body. It is based on **cell physiology,** the study of the functions of living cells. *Special physiology* studies the physiology of specific organs. *System physiology* considers all aspects of the function of specific organ systems. *Pathological physiology* (**pathology**) studies the effects of diseases on organ or system functions.

1-3 Levels of organization progress from molecules to a complete organism   *p. 4*

7. Anatomical structures and physiological mechanisms are arranged in a series of interacting levels of organization. (*Figure 1-1*)

1-4 The human body consists of 11 organ systems   *p. 6*

8. The major organs of the human body are arranged into 11 organ systems. The organ systems of the human body are the *integumentary, skeletal, muscular, nervous, endocrine, cardiovascular, lymphoid, respiratory, digestive, urinary,* and *reproductive systems. (Figure 1-2)*

1-5 Homeostasis is the tendency toward internal balance   *p. 6*

9. **Homeostasis** is the tendency for physiological systems to stabilize internal conditions; through **homeostatic regulation** these systems adjust to preserve homeostasis.

10. Homeostatic regulation usually involves a **receptor** sensitive to a particular stimulus; a **control center,** which receives and processes the information from the receptor, and then sends out commands; and an **effector** whose activity either opposes or enhances the stimulus. *(Figure 1-3).*

1-6 Negative feedback opposes variations from normal, whereas positive feedback exaggerates them   *p. 13*

11. **Negative feedback** is a corrective mechanism involving an action that directly opposes a variation from normal limits. *(Figure 1-3)*

12. In **positive feedback** the initial stimulus produces a response that reinforces the stimulus. *(Figure 1-5)*

13. Symptoms of **disease** appear when failure of homeostatic regulation causes organ systems to malfunction.

1-7 Anatomical terms describe body regions, anatomical positions and directions, and body sections   *p. 15*

14. Standard anatomical illustrations show the body in the **anatomical position.** If the figure is shown lying down, it can be either **supine** (face up) or **prone** (face down). *(Figure 1-6; Table 1-1)*

15. **Abdominopelvic quadrants** and **abdominopelvic regions** represent two different approaches to describing anatomical regions of the body. *(Figure 1-7)*

16. The use of special directional terms provides clarity when describing anatomical structures. *(Figure 1-8; Table 1-2)*

17. The three **sectional planes** (**frontal** or **coronal plane, sagittal plane,** and **transverse plane**) describe relationships between the parts of the three-dimensional human body. *(Figure 1-9; Table 1-3)*

1-8 Body cavities protect internal organs and allow them to change shape   *p. 20*

18. **Body cavities** protect delicate organs and permit changes in the size and shape of visceral organs. The **ventral body cavity** surrounds developing respiratory, cardiovascular, digestive, urinary, and reproductive organs. *(Figure 1-10)*

19. The **diaphragm** divides the ventral body cavity into the superior **thoracic** and inferior **abdominopelvic cavities.** The thoracic cavity contains two **pleural cavities** (each containing a lung) and a **pericardial cavity** (which surrounds the heart). The abdominopelvic cavity consists of the **abdominal cavity** and the **pelvic cavity.** It contains the *peritoneal cavity,* an internal chamber lined by *peritoneum, a serous membrane. (Figure 1-10)*

20. Important **radiological procedures** (which can provide detailed information about internal systems) include **x-rays, CT scans, MRI,** and **ultrasound.** Each of these noninvasive techniques has advantages and disadvantages. *(Figures 1-11, 1-12)*

REVIEW QUESTIONS

WWW Access more review material online at The Anatomy & Physiology Place
(**www.anatomyandphysiology.com**). There, you'll find Chapter Guides, Chapter Quizzes,
Chapter Practice Tests, Interactive Flashcards, a Glossary with Pronunciations, and more to help
you succeed in the course.

Level 1 • Reviewing Facts and Terms

*Match each item in column A with the most closely related item in column B. Place letters for
answers in the spaces provided.*

COLUMN A

_____ 1. cytology
_____ 2. physiology
_____ 3. histology
_____ 4. metabolism
_____ 5. homeostasis
_____ 6. muscle
_____ 7. heart
_____ 8. endocrine
_____ 9. temperature regulation
_____ 10. blood clot formation
_____ 11. supine
_____ 12. prone
_____ 13. ventral body cavity
_____ 14. thoracic body cavity
_____ 15. pericardium

COLUMN B

a. study of tissues
b. constant internal environment
c. face up
d. study of functions
e. positive feedback
f. organ system
g. study of cells
h. negative feedback
i. heart and lungs
j. all chemical activity in body
k. thoracic and abdominopelvic
l. tissue
m. serous membrane
n. organ
o. face down

16. Label the directional terms in the figures below.

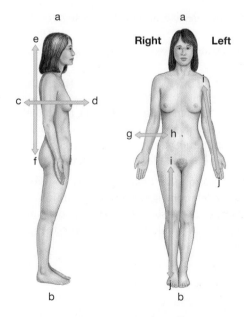

(a) _____   (b) _____
(c) _____   (d) _____
(e) _____   (f) _____
(g) _____   (h) _____
(i) _____   (j) _____

17. Label the three sectional planes in the figure below.

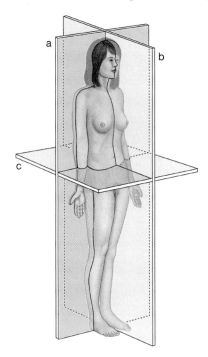

(a) _____ (b) _____
(c) _____

18. The process by which an organism increases the size and/or number of its cells is called
    (a) reproduction.
    (b) adaptation.
    (c) growth.
    (d) metabolism.

19. When a variation outside normal limits triggers a response that restores the normal condition, the regulatory mechanism involves
    (a) negative feedback.
    (b) positive feedback.
    (c) compensation.
    (d) adaptation.

20. The terms that apply to the front of the body in the anatomical position are
    (a) posterior, dorsal.
    (b) back, front.
    (c) medial, lateral.
    (d) anterior, ventral.

21. A cut through the body that passes perpendicular to the long axis of the body and divides the body into superior and inferior portions is known as a
    (a) sagittal section.
    (b) transverse section.
    (c) coronal section.
    (d) frontal section.

22. The diaphragm, a flat muscular sheet, divides the ventral body cavity into a superior _____ cavity and an inferior _____ cavity.
    (a) pleural, pericardial
    (b) abdominal, pelvic
    (c) thoracic, abdominopelvic
    (d) cranial, thoracic

23. The mediastinum is the region between the
    (a) lungs and heart.
    (b) two pleural cavities.
    (c) thorax and abdomen.
    (d) heart and pericardium.

Level 2 • Reviewing Concepts

24. What basic functions are performed by all living things?

25. Beginning at the molecular level, list in correct sequence the levels of organization, from the simplest level to the most complex.

26. Define homeostatic regulation in a way that states its physiological importance.

27. How does negative feedback differ from positive feedback?

28. Describe the position of the body when it is in the anatomical position.

29. As a surgeon, you perform an invasive procedure that necessitates cutting through the peritoneum. Are you more likely to be operating on the heart or on the stomach?

30. In which body cavity would each of the following organs or systems be found?
    (a) cardiovascular, digestive, and urinary systems
    (b) heart, lungs
    (c) stomach, intestines

Level 3 • Critical Thinking and Clinical Applications

31. A hormone called *calcitonin*, produced by the thyroid gland, is released in response to increased levels of calcium ions in the blood. If this hormone acts through negative feedback, what effect will its release have on blood calcium levels?

32. An anatomist wishes to make detailed comparisons of medial surfaces of the left and right sides of the brain. This work requires sections that show the entire medial surface. Which kind of sections should be ordered from the lab for this investigation?

2 The Chemical Level of Organization

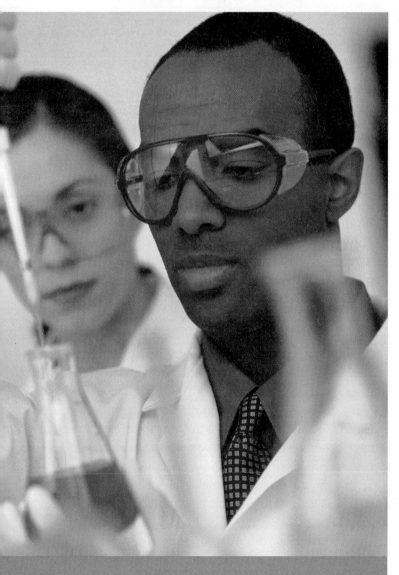

The chemistry of life is intimately connected with water and the substances which dissolve in it. Water's structure is the key to understanding its many unusual properties. In this chapter you will learn how atoms are bound together to form molecules small and large. The larger molecules form the structural framework of the body's cells and tissues. Understanding how the interaction of molecules enables our cells to grow, divide, and perform the many functions that make life possible is the focus of activity in the field of molecular biology.

LEARNING OUTCOMES

After completing this chapter, you should be able to do the following:

2-1 Describe an atom and how its structure affects interactions between atoms.

2-2 Compare the ways in which atoms combine to form molecules and compounds.

2-3 Use chemical notation to symbolize chemical reactions, and distinguish among the three major types of chemical reactions that are important for studying physiology.

2-4 Describe the crucial role of enzymes in metabolism.

2-5 Distinguish between organic and inorganic compounds.

2-6 Explain how the chemical properties of water make life possible.

2-7 Describe the pH scale and the role of buffers in body fluids.

2-8 Describe the physiological roles of inorganic compounds.

2-9 Discuss the structures and functions of carbohydrates.

2-10 Discuss the structures and functions of lipids.

2-11 Discuss the structures and functions of proteins.

2-12 Discuss the structures and functions of nucleic acids.

2-13 Discuss the structures and functions of high-energy compounds.

2-14 Explain the relationship between chemicals and cells.

An Introduction to the Chemical Level of Organization

Our study of the human body begins at the most basic level of organization, that of individual atoms and molecules. The characteristics of all living and nonliving things—people, elephants, oranges, oceans, rocks, and air—result from the types of atoms involved and the ways those atoms combine and interact. **Chemistry** is the science that investigates *matter* and its interactions. A familiarity with basic chemistry helps us understand how the properties of atoms can affect the anatomy and physiology of the cells, tissues, organs, and organ systems that make up the human body.

2-1 Atoms are the basic particles of matter

Matter is anything that takes up space and has mass. *Mass* is a physical property that determines the weight of an object in Earth's gravitational field. On our planet, the weight of an object is essentially the same as its mass. However, the two are not always the same: In orbit you would be weightless, but your mass would remain unchanged. Matter occurs in one of three familiar states: solid (such as a rock), liquid (such as water), or gas (such as the atmosphere).

All matter is composed of substances called **elements.** Elements cannot be changed or broken down into simpler substances, whether by chemical processes, heating, or other ordinary physical means. The smallest, stable unit of matter is an **atom.** Atoms are so small that atomic measurements are most conveniently reported in billionths of a meter or *nanometers* (NA-nō-mē-terz) (nm). The very largest atoms approach half of one-billionth of a meter (0.5 nm) in diameter. One million atoms placed side-by-side would span a period on this page, but the line would be far too thin to be visible with anything but the most powerful of microscopes.

ATOMIC STRUCTURE

Atoms contain three major types of subatomic particles: protons, neutrons, and electrons. Protons and neutrons are similar in size and mass, but **protons** (p^+) have a positive electrical charge, whereas **neutrons** (n^0) are neutral—that is, uncharged. **Electrons** (e^-) are much lighter—only 1/1836 as massive as protons—and have a negative electrical charge. Figure 2-1 is a diagram of a simple atom: the element *helium*. This atom contains two protons, two neutrons, and two electrons.

All atoms contain protons and electrons, normally in equal numbers. The number of protons in an atom is known as its **atomic number.** A chemical element is a substance that consists entirely of atoms with the same atomic number. For example, all atoms of the element helium contain two protons.

Table 2-1 lists the 13 most abundant elements in the human body. Each element is universally known by its own abbreviation, or chemical symbol. Most of the symbols are easily connected with the English names of the elements, but a few, such as Na for sodium, are abbreviations of their original Latin names—in this case, *natrium*. (Appendix 2, the *periodic table*, gives the chemical symbols and atomic numbers of each element.)

Hydrogen, the simplest element, has an atomic number of 1 because its atom contains one proton (Figure 2-2). The proton is located in the center of the atom and forms the **nucleus.** Hydrogen atoms seldom contain neutrons, but whenever neutrons are present in any type of atom, they are also located

Helium (He)

FIGURE 2-1 **A Diagram of Atomic Structure.** The atom shown here—helium—contains two of each type of subatomic particle: two protons, two neutrons, and two electrons.

TABLE 2-1 The Principal Elements in the Human Body

ELEMENT (% OF BODY WEIGHT)	SIGNIFICANCE
Oxygen, O (65)	A component of water and other compounds; oxygen gas is essential for respiration
Carbon, C (18.6)	Found in all organic molecules
Hydrogen, H (9.7)	A component of water and most other compounds in the body
Nitrogen, N (3.2)	Found in proteins, nucleic acids, and other organic compounds
Calcium, Ca (1.8)	Found in bones and teeth; important for membrane function, nerve impulses, muscle contraction, and blood clotting
Phosphorus, P (1)	Found in bones and teeth, nucleic acids, and high-energy compounds
Potassium, K (0.4)	Important for proper membrane function, nerve impulses, and muscle contraction
Sodium, Na (0.2)	Important for membrane function, nerve impulses, and muscle contraction
Chlorine, Cl (0.2)	Important for membrane function and water absorption
Magnesium, Mg (0.06)	Required for activation of several enzymes
Sulfur, S (0.04)	Found in many proteins
Iron, Fe (0.007)	Essential for oxygen transport and energy capture
Iodine, I (0.0002)	A component of hormones of the thyroid gland

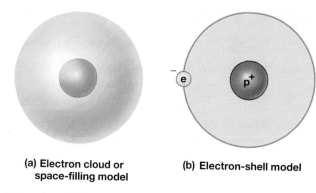

(a) Electron cloud or space-filling model   **(b)** Electron-shell model

FIGURE 2-2 **Hydrogen Atoms.** A typical hydrogen atom consists of a nucleus containing one proton and no neutrons, around which a single electron orbits. **(a)** This space-filling model of a hydrogen atom depicts the three-dimensional electron cloud formed by the single orbiting electron. **(b)** In a two-dimensional electron-shell model, it is easier to visualize the atom's components.

ally has no effect on the chemical properties of an atom of a particular element. As a result, isotopes can be distinguished from one another only by their **mass number**—the total number of protons and neutrons in the nucleus. The nuclei of some isotopes may be unstable. Unstable isotopes are radioactive; that is, they spontaneously emit subatomic particles or radiation in measurable amounts. These *radioisotopes* are sometimes used in diagnostic procedures.

ATOMIC WEIGHT

Atomic mass numbers are useful because they tell us the number of protons and neutrons in the nuclei of different atoms. However, they do not tell us the *actual* mass of an atom, because they do not take into account the masses of electrons and the slight difference between the masses of a proton and neutron. They also don't tell us the mass of a "typical" atom, since any element consists of a mixture of isotopes. It is, therefore, useful to know the *average mass* of an element's atoms, and this value is that element's **atomic weight**. Atomic weight takes into account the mass of the subatomic particles and the relative proportions of any isotopes. For example, even though the atomic number of hydrogen is 1, the atomic weight of hydrogen is 1.0079. In this case, the atomic number and atomic weight differ primarily because a few hydrogen atoms have a mass number of 2 (one proton plus one neutron), and an even smaller number have a mass number of 3 (one proton plus two neutrons). The atomic weights of the elements are included in Appendix 2.

in the nucleus. In a hydrogen atom, a single electron orbits the nucleus at high speed, forming an **electron cloud** (**Figure 2-2a**). To simplify matters, this cloud is usually represented as a spherical **electron shell** (**Figure 2-2b**).

ISOTOPES

The atoms of a given element can differ in terms of the number of neutrons in the nucleus. Such atoms of an element are called **isotopes**. The presence or absence of neutrons gener-

ELECTRON SHELLS

Atoms are electrically neutral; every positively charged proton is balanced by a negatively charged electron. Thus, each increase in the atomic number is accompanied by a comparable increase in the number of electrons. These electrons occupy an orderly series of electron shells around the nucleus, and only the electrons in the outer shell can interact with other atoms. *The number of electrons in an atom's outer electron shell determines the chemical properties of that element.*

Atoms with an unfilled outer electron shell are unstable—that is, they will react with other atoms, usually in ways that give them full outer electron shells. An atom with a filled outer shell is stable and will not interact with other atoms. The first electron shell (the one closest to the nucleus) is filled when it contains two electrons. A hydrogen atom has one electron in this electron shell (Figure 2-2b), and thus hydrogen atoms can react with many other atoms. A helium atom has two electrons in this electron shell (Figure 2-1). Because its outer electron shell is full, a helium atom is stable. Helium is called an inert gas because its atoms will neither react with one another nor combine with atoms of other elements.

The second electron shell can contain up to eight electrons. Carbon, with an atomic number of 6, has six electrons. In a carbon atom, the first shell is filled (two electrons), and the second shell contains four electrons (Figure 2-3a). In a neon atom (atomic number 10), the second shell is filled (Figure 2-3b); neon is another inert gas.

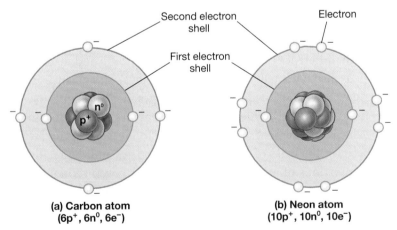

Second electron shell

First electron shell

Electron

(a) Carbon atom $(6p^+, 6n^0, 6e^-)$

(b) Neon atom $(10p^+, 10n^0, 10e^-)$

FIGURE 2-3 The Electron Shells of Two Atoms. The first electron shell of any atom can hold only two electrons; the second shell can hold up to eight electrons. **(a)** In a carbon atom, which has six protons and six electrons, the first shell is full, but the second shell contains only four electrons. **(b)** In a neon atom, which has 10 protons and 10 electrons, both the first and second electron shells are filled. Notice that the nuclei of carbon and neon contain neutrons as well as protons.

The Big Picture

All matter is composed of atoms in various combinations. The chemical rules governing the interactions among atoms alone and in combination establish the foundations of physiology at the cellular level.

CHECKPOINT

1. Define atom.

2. How is it possible for two samples of hydrogen to contain the same number of atoms but have different weights?

See the blue Answers tab at the back of the book.

2-2 Chemical bonds are forces formed by atom interactions

An atom with a full outer electron shell is very stable and not reactive. The atoms that are most important to biological systems are *un*stable because those atoms can interact to form larger structures (see Table 2-1). Atoms with unfilled outer electron shells can achieve stability by sharing, gaining, or losing electrons through chemical reactions with other atoms. This often involves the formation of **chemical bonds,** which hold the participating atoms together once the reaction has ended.

Chemical bonding produces *molecules* and *compounds.* **Molecules** are chemical structures that contain more than one atom bonded together by shared electrons. A **compound** is any chemical substance made up of atoms of two or more elements, regardless of the type of bond joining them. A compound is a new chemical substance with properties that can be quite different from those of its component elements. For example, a mixture of hydrogen and oxygen gases is highly flammable, but chemically combining hydrogen and oxygen atoms produces a compound—water—that can put out a fire's flames.

IONIC BONDS

Atoms are electrically neutral because the number of protons (each with a +1 charge) equals the number of electrons (each with a −1 charge). If an atom loses an electron, it then exhibits a charge of +1 because there is one proton without a corresponding electron; losing a second electron would leave the atom with a charge of +2. Similarly, adding one or two extra electrons to the atom gives it a charge of −1 or −2, respectively. Atoms or molecules that have an electric charge are called **ions.** Ions with a positive charge (+) are **cations** (KAT-ī-onz); those with a negative charge (−) are **anions** (AN-ī-onz). Table 2-2 lists several important ions in body fluids.

Ionic (ī-ON-ik) **bonds** are chemical bonds created by the electrical attraction between anions and cations. Ionic bonds are formed in a process called *ionic bonding,* as shown in Figure 2-4a. In the example shown, a sodium atom donates an electron to a chlorine atom. This loss of an electron creates a

sodium ion with a +1 charge and a *chloride ion* with a −1 charge. The two ions do not move apart after the electron transfer because the positively charged sodium ion is attracted to the negatively charged chloride ion. In this case, the combination of oppositely charged ions forms the *ionic compound* **sodium chloride,** the chemical name for the crystals we know as table salt (Figure 2-4b).

COVALENT BONDS

Another way atoms can fill their outer electron shells is by sharing electrons with other atoms. The result is a molecule held together by **covalent** (kō-VA-lent) **bonds** (Figure 2-5).

As an example, consider hydrogen. Individual hydrogen atoms, as diagrammed in Figure 2-2, are not found in nature. Instead, we find hydrogen molecules (Figure 2-5a). In chemical shorthand, molecular hydrogen is indicated by H_2, where H is the chemical symbol for hydrogen, and the subscript 2 indicates the number of atoms. Molecular hydrogen is a gas present in the atmosphere in very small quantities. The two hydrogen atoms share their electrons, with each electron

TABLE 2-2 The Most Common Ions in Body Fluids

CATIONS	ANIONS
Na^+ (sodium)	Cl^- (chloride)
K^+ (potassium)	HCO_3^- (bicarbonate)
Ca^{2+} (calcium)	HPO_4^{2-} (biphosphate)
Mg^{2+} (magnesium)	SO_4^{2-} (sulfate)

(a) Formation of an ionic bond

FIGURE 2-4 Ionic Bonding. (a) Step 1: A sodium atom loses an electron, which is accepted by a chlorine atom. **Step 2:** Because the sodium (Na^+) and chloride (Cl^-) ions have opposite charges, they are attracted to one another. **Step 3:** The association of sodium and chloride ions forms the ionic compound sodium chloride. **(b)** Large numbers of sodium and chloride ions form a crystal of sodium chloride (table salt).

	ELECTRON-SHELL MODEL AND STRUCTURAL FORMULA	SPACE-FILLING MODEL
(a) Hydrogen (H_2)	H–H	
(b) Oxygen (O_2)	O=O	
(c) Carbon dioxide (CO_2)	O=C=O	

FIGURE 2-5 Covalent Bonds. (a) In a molecule of hydrogen, two hydrogen atoms share their electrons such that each has a filled outer electron shell. This sharing creates a single covalent bond. **(b)** A molecule of oxygen consists of two oxygen atoms that share two pairs of electrons. The result is a double covalent bond. **(c)** In a molecule of carbon dioxide, a central carbon atom forms double covalent bonds with a pair of oxygen atoms.

whirling around both nuclei. The sharing of one pair of electrons creates a **single covalent bond.**

Oxygen, with an atomic number of 8, has two electrons in its first electron shell and six in the second. Oxygen atoms (**Figure 2-5b**) reach stability by sharing two pairs of electrons, forming a **double covalent bond.** Molecular oxygen (O_2) is an atmospheric gas that is very important to living organisms; our cells would die without a constant supply of oxygen.

In our bodies, the chemical processes that consume oxygen also produce carbon dioxide (CO_2) as a waste product. The oxygen atoms in a carbon dioxide molecule form double covalent bonds with the carbon atom, as shown in **Figure 2-5c.**

Covalent bonds are very strong because the shared electrons tie the atoms together. In most covalent bonds the atoms remain electrically neutral because the electrons are shared equally. Such bonds are called **nonpolar covalent bonds.** Nonpolar covalent bonds between carbon atoms create the stable framework of the large molecules that make up most of the structural components of the human body.

Elements differ in how strongly they hold or attract shared electrons. An unequal sharing between atoms of different elements creates a **polar covalent bond.** Such bonding often forms a *polar molecule* because one end, or pole, has a slight negative charge and the other a slight positive charge. For example, in a molecule of water, an oxygen atom forms covalent bonds with two hydrogen atoms. However, the oxygen atom has a much stronger attraction for the shared electrons than do the hydrogen atoms, so those electrons spend most of their time with the oxygen atom. Because of the two extra electrons, the oxygen atom develops a slight negative charge (**Figure 2-6a**). At the same time, the hydrogen atoms develop a slight positive charge because their electrons are away part of the time.

Hydrogen bonding

KEY
● Hydrogen   ● Oxygen   - - - - Hydrogen bond

(a)

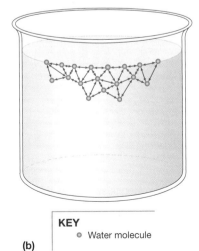

KEY
○ Water molecule

(b)

FIGURE 2-6 Hydrogen Bonds.
(a) The unequal sharing of electrons in a water molecule causes each of its two hydrogen atoms to have a slight positive charge and its oxygen atom to have a slight negative charge. Attraction between a hydrogen atom of one water molecule and the oxygen atom of another is a hydrogen bond (indicated by dashed lines). **(b)** Hydrogen bonding between water molecules at a free surface creates surface tension and restricts evaporation.

HYDROGEN BONDS

In addition to ionic and covalent bonds, weaker attractive forces act between adjacent molecules and between atoms within a large molecule. The most important of these weak attractive forces is the **hydrogen bond.** A hydrogen bond is the attraction between a slight positive charge on the hydrogen atom of one polar covalent bond and a weak negative charge on an oxygen or nitrogen atom of another polar covalent bond. The polar covalent bond containing the oxygen or nitrogen atom can be in a different molecule from, or in the same molecule as, the hydrogen atom. For example, water molecules are attracted to each other through hydrogen bonding (Figure 2-6a).

Hydrogen bonds are too weak to create molecules, but they can alter molecular shapes or pull molecules together. For example, the attraction between water molecules at a free surface slows the rate of evaporation and creates the phenomenon known as **surface tension** (Figure 2-6b). Surface tension acts as a barrier that keeps small objects from entering the water; it is the reason that insects can walk across the surface of a pond or puddle. Similarly, a layer of watery tears keeps small dust particles from touching the surface of the eye.

CHECKPOINT

3. Define chemical bond, and identify several types of chemical bonds.

4. Oxygen and neon are both gases at room temperature. Why does oxygen combine readily with other elements, but neon does not?

5. Which kind of bond holds atoms in a water molecule together? What attracts water molecules to each other?

See the blue Answers tab at the back of the book.

2-3 Decomposition, synthesis, and exchange reactions are important chemical reactions in physiology

Cells remain alive by controlling chemical reactions. In a **chemical reaction,** new chemical bonds form between atoms or existing bonds between atoms are broken. These changes occur as atoms in the reacting substances, or **reactants,** are rearranged to form different substances, or **products.**

In effect, each cell is a chemical factory. For example, growth, maintenance and repair, secretion, and muscle contraction all involve complex chemical reactions. Cells use chemical reactions to provide the energy required to maintain homeostasis and to perform essential functions. **Metabolism** (me-TAB-ō-lizm; *metabole,* change) refers to all of the chemical reactions in the body.

Complex chemical compounds and reactions are most easily described using a simple form of "chemical shorthand" known as **chemical notation.** The rules of chemical notation are summarized in Table 2-3.

TABLE 2-3 **Rules of Chemical Notation**

1. The abbreviation of an element indicates one atom of that element:

    H = an atom of hydrogen; O = an atom of oxygen

2. A number preceding the abbreviation of an element indicates more than one atom:

    2H = two individual atoms of hydrogen

    2O = two individual atoms of oxygen

3. A subscript following the abbreviation of an element indicates a molecule with that number of atoms:

    H_2 = a hydrogen molecule composed of two hydrogen atoms

    O_2 = an oxygen molecule composed of two oxygen atoms

4. In a description of a chemical reaction, the interacting participants are called **reactants,** and the reaction generates one or more **products.** An arrow indicates the direction of the reaction, from reactants (usually on the left) to products (usually on the right). In the following reaction, two atoms of hydrogen combine with one atom of oxygen to produce a single molecule of water.

    $$2H + O \longrightarrow H_2O$$

5. A superscript plus or minus sign following the abbreviation for an element indicates an ion. A single plus sign indicates an ion with a charge of +1 (loss of one electron). A single minus sign indicates an ion with a charge of −1 (gain of one electron). If more than one electron has been lost or gained, the charge on the ion is indicated by a number preceding the plus or minus.

    Na^+ = one sodium ion (has lost 1 electron)

    Cl^- = one chloride ion (has gained 1 electron)

    Ca^{2+} = one calcium ion (has lost 2 electrons)

6. Chemical reactions neither create nor destroy atoms—they merely rearrange them into new combinations. Therefore, the numbers of atoms of each element must always be the same on both sides of the equation. When this is the case, the equation is balanced.

    Unbalanced: $H_2 + O_2 \longrightarrow H_2O$

    Balanced: $2H_2 + O_2 \longrightarrow 2H_2O$

BASIC ENERGY CONCEPTS

Knowledge of some basic relationships between matter and energy is essential for understanding any discussion of chemical reactions. **Work** is movement or a change in the physical structure of matter. In your body, work includes movements like walking or running and also the synthesis of organic molecules and the conversion of liquid water to water vapor (evaporation). **Energy** is the capacity to perform work. There are two major types of energy: *kinetic energy* and *potential energy.*

Kinetic energy is the energy of motion. When you fall off a ladder, it is kinetic energy that does the damage. **Potential energy** is stored energy. It may result from an object's position (you standing on a ladder) or from its physical or chemical structure (a stretched spring or a charged battery). Kinetic energy must be used in climbing the ladder, in stretching the spring, or in charging the battery. The potential energy is converted back into kinetic energy when you fall, the spring recoils, or the battery discharges. The kinetic energy can then be used to perform work.

Energy cannot be destroyed; it can only be converted from one form to another. A conversion between potential energy and kinetic energy is not 100 percent efficient. Each time an energy exchange occurs, some of the energy is released as heat. *Heat* is an increase in random molecular motion. The temperature of an object is directly related to the average kinetic energy of its molecules. Heat can never be completely converted to work or to any other form of energy, and cells cannot capture it or use it to perform work.

Living cells perform work in many forms, and the cells' energy exchanges produce heat. For example, when skeletal muscle cells contract, they perform work; potential energy (the positions of protein filaments and the covalent bonds between molecules inside the cells) is converted into kinetic energy, and heat is released. The amount of heat is related to the amount of work done. As a result, when you exercise, your body temperature rises.

The Big Picture

When energy is exchanged, heat is produced. Heat raises local temperatures, but cells cannot capture it or use it to perform work.

TYPES OF REACTIONS

Three types of chemical reactions are important to the study of physiology: *decomposition reactions, synthesis reactions,* and *exchange reactions.*

Decomposition Reactions

A **decomposition reaction** breaks a molecule into smaller fragments. Such reactions occur during digestion, when food molecules are broken into smaller pieces. You could diagram a typical decomposition reaction as:

$$AB \longrightarrow A + B$$

Decomposition reactions involving water are important in the breakdown of complex molecules in the body. In **hydrolysis** (hī-DROL-i-sis; *hydro-*, water + *lysis*, a loosening), one of the bonds in a complex molecule is broken, and the components of a water molecule (H and OH) are added to the resulting fragments:

$$A - B - C - D - E + H_2O \longrightarrow$$
$$A - B - C - H + HO - D - E$$

Catabolism (kah-TAB-o-lizm; *katabole*, a throwing down) refers to the decomposition reactions of complex molecules within cells. When a covalent bond—a form of potential energy—is broken, it releases kinetic energy that can perform work. Cells can harness some of that energy to power essential functions such as growth, movement, and reproduction.

Synthesis Reactions

Synthesis (SIN-the-sis) is the opposite of decomposition. A synthesis reaction assembles larger molecules from smaller components. These relatively simple reactions could be diagrammed as:

$$A + B \longrightarrow AB$$

A and B could be individual atoms that combine to form a molecule, or they could be individual molecules combining to form even larger products. Synthesis always involves the formation of new chemical bonds, whether the reactants are atoms or molecules.

Dehydration synthesis, or *condensation*, is the formation of a complex molecule by the removal of water:

$$A - B - C - H + HO - D - E \longrightarrow$$
$$A - B - C - D - E + H_2O$$

Dehydration synthesis is, therefore, the opposite of hydrolysis. We will encounter examples of both reactions in later sections.

Anabolism (a-NAB-ō-lizm; *anabole*, a building up) is the synthesis of new compounds in the body. Because it takes energy to create a chemical bond, anabolism is usually an "uphill" process. Living cells are constantly balancing their chemical activities, with catabolism providing the energy needed to support anabolism as well as other vital functions.

Exchange Reactions

In an **exchange reaction,** parts of the reacting molecules are shuffled, as follows:

$$AB + CD \longrightarrow AD + CB$$

Although the reactants and products contain the same components (A, B, C, and D), the components are present in different combinations. In an exchange reaction, the reactant molecules AB and CD break apart (a decomposition), and then the resulting components interact to form AD and CB (a synthesis).

REVERSIBLE REACTIONS

Many important biological reactions are freely reversible. Such reactions can be diagrammed as:

$$A + B \rightleftharpoons AB$$

This equation indicates that two reactions are occurring simultaneously, one a synthesis (A + B $\longrightarrow$ AB) and the other a decomposition (AB $\longrightarrow$ A + B). At **equilibrium** (ē-kwi-LIB-rē-um), the rates of the two reactions are in balance. As fast as a molecule of AB forms, another degrades into A + B. As a result, the numbers of A, B, and AB molecules present at any given moment do not change. Altering the concentrations of one or more of these molecules will temporarily upset the equilibrium. For example, adding additional molecules of A and B will accelerate the synthesis reaction (A + B $\longrightarrow$ AB). As the concentration of AB rises, however, so does the rate of the decomposition reaction (AB $\longrightarrow$ A + B), until a new equilibrium is established.

The Big Picture Things tend to even out, unless something prevents this from happening. Most reversible reactions quickly reach equilibrium, a point where opposing reaction rates are balanced. If reactants are added or removed, reaction rates change until a new equilibrium is established.

2-4 Enzymes catalyze specific biochemical reactions by lowering a reaction's activation energy

Most chemical reactions do not occur spontaneously, or they occur so slowly that they would be of little value to cells. Before a reaction can proceed, enough energy must be provided to activate the reactants. The amount of energy required to start a reaction is called the **activation energy.** Although many reactions can be activated by changes in temperature or pH, such changes are deadly to cells. For example, to break down a complex sugar in the laboratory, you must boil it in an acid solution. Cells, however, avoid such harsh requirements by using special molecules called **enzymes** to speed up the reactions that support life. Enzymes belong to a class of substances called **catalysts** (KAT-uh-lists; *katalysis*, dissolution), compounds that accelerate chemical reactions without themselves being permanently changed. Cells make an enzyme molecule to promote each specific reaction.

Enzymes promote chemical reactions by lowering the activation energy requirements (**Figure 2-7**). Lowering the activation energy affects only the rate of a reaction, not the direction of the

CHECKPOINT

6. Using the rules for chemical notation, write the molecular formula for glucose, a compound composed of six carbons, 12 hydrogen atoms, and six oxygen atoms.

7. Identify and describe three types of chemical reactions important to human physiology.

8. In living cells, glucose, a six-carbon molecule, is converted into two three-carbon molecules. What type of chemical reaction is this?

9. If the product of a reversible reaction is continuously removed, what will be the effect on the equilibrium?

See the blue Answers tab at the back of the book.

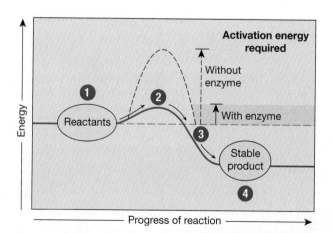

FIGURE 2-7 The Effect of Enzymes on Activation Energy.
Enzymes lower the activation energy required for a reaction to proceed readily (in order, from 1 to 4) under conditions in the body.

The Big Picture

Most of the chemical reactions that sustain life cannot occur under homeostatic conditions unless appropriate enzymes are present.

reaction or the products that are formed. An enzyme cannot bring about a reaction that would otherwise be impossible.

It takes activation energy to start a chemical reaction, but once it has begun, the reaction as a whole may absorb or release energy, generally in the form of heat, as it proceeds to completion. If the amount of energy released is greater than the activation energy needed to start the reaction, there will be a net release of energy. Reactions that release energy are said to be **exergonic** (*exo-*, outside). If more energy is required to begin the reaction than is released as it proceeds, the reaction as a whole will absorb energy. Such reactions are called **endergonic** (*endo-*, inside). Exergonic reactions are relatively common in the body; they are responsible for generating the heat that maintains your body temperature.

CHECKPOINT

10. What is an enzyme?

11. Why are enzymes needed in our cells?

See the blue Answers tab at the back of the book.

2-5 Inorganic compounds usually lack carbon, and organic compounds always contain carbon

The rest of this chapter focuses on nutrients and metabolites. **Nutrients** are the essential elements and molecules obtained from the diet. **Metabolites** (me-TAB-ō-līts) include all of the molecules (including nutrients) synthesized or broken down by chemical reactions inside our bodies. Like all chemical substances, nutrients and metabolites can be broadly categorized as inorganic or organic. **Inorganic compounds** are small molecules that generally do not contain carbon and hydrogen atoms. **Organic compounds** are primarily composed of carbon and hydrogen atoms, and they can be much larger and more complex than inorganic compounds.

The most important inorganic substances in the human body are water, carbon dioxide, oxygen, inorganic acids and

bases, and salts. Most of the inorganic molecules and compounds in the human body exist in association with water, the primary component of our body fluids and an essential compound for many chemical reactions. Carbon dioxide and oxygen are important gases dissolved in body fluids.

Carbon dioxide (CO_2) is produced by cells through normal metabolic activity. It is transported in the blood and released into the air in the lungs. Oxygen (O_2), an atmospheric gas, is absorbed at the lungs, transported in the blood, and consumed by cells throughout the body. The chemical structures of these compounds were introduced earlier in the chapter. ∞ p. 34

CHECKPOINT

12. Distinguish between inorganic compounds and organic compounds.

See the blue Answers tab at the back of the book.

2-6 Physiological systems depend on water

Water (H_2O) is the single most important constituent of the body, accounting for almost two-thirds of total body weight. A change in body water content can have fatal consequences because virtually all physiological systems will be affected.

Three general properties of water are particularly important to our discussion of the human body:

- *Water is an essential reactant in the chemical reactions of living systems.* Chemical reactions in our bodies occur in water, and water molecules are also participants in some reactions. During the dehydration synthesis of large molecules, water molecules are released; during hydrolysis, complex molecules are broken down by the addition of water molecules. ∞ p. 36

- *Water has a very high heat capacity.* *Heat capacity* is the ability to absorb and retain heat. It takes a lot of energy to change the temperature of a quantity of water because of the linking of water molecules by hydrogen bonds. Once the water has reached a particular temperature, it will change temperature only slowly. As a result, body temperature is stabilized, and the water in our cells remains a liquid over a wide range of environmental temperatures. Hydrogen bonding also explains why a large amount of energy is required to change liquid water to a gas, or ice to liquid. When water finally changes from a liquid to a gas, it carries a great deal of heat away with it. This feature accounts for the cooling effect of perspiration on the skin.

- *Water is an excellent solvent.* Water dissolves a remarkable variety of inorganic and organic molecules, creating a *solution.* As the molecules dissolve, they break apart, releasing ions or smaller molecules that become uniformly dispersed throughout the solution. The chemical reactions within living cells occur in solution, and the watery component of blood, called plasma, carries dissolved nutrients and waste products throughout the body.

Most chemical reactions in the body occur in **solutions,** which consist of a uniform mixture of a fluid *solvent* and dissolved *solutes.* Within organisms the solvent is usually water, forming an *aqueous solution,* and the solutes may be inorganic or organic. Inorganic compounds held together by ionic bonds undergo **ionization** (ī-on-i-ZĀ-shun), or *dissociation* (dis-sō-sē-Ā-shun), in solution. In this process, ionic bonds are broken apart as individual ions interact with the positive or negative ends of polar water molecules (Figure 2-8a). As shown in Figure 2-8b, the result is a mixture of cations and anions surrounded by so many water molecules that they are unable to re-form their original bonds.

An aqueous solution containing anions and cations can also conduct an electrical current. Electrical forces across cell membranes affect the functioning of all cells, and small electrical

The Big Picture	Water accounts for most of your body weight. Proteins, the key structural and functional components of cells, and nucleic acids, which control cell structure and function, work only in solution.

currents carried by ions are essential to muscle contraction and nerve function. Chapters 7 and 8 discuss these processes in more detail.

CHECKPOINT

13. List the chemical properties of water that make life possible.

14. Why does water resist changes in temperature?

See the blue Answers tab at the back of the book.

2-7 Body fluid pH is vital for homeostasis

A hydrogen atom involved in a chemical bond or participating in a chemical reaction can easily lose its electron, to become a hydrogen ion, H^+. The concentration of hydrogen ions in blood or other body fluids is important because hydrogen ions are extremely reactive. In excessive numbers, they will break chemical bonds, change the shapes of complex molecules, and disrupt cell and tissue functions. The concentration of hydrogen ions must, therefore, be precisely regulated.

The concentration of hydrogen ions is usually reported as the **pH** of the solution. The pH value is a number between 0 and 14. Pure water has a pH of 7. A solution with a pH of 7 is called *neutral* because it contains equal numbers of hydrogen ions and hydroxide ions. A solution with a pH below 7 is *acidic* (a-SI-dik) because there are more hydrogen ions than hydroxide ions. A pH above 7 is called *basic,* or *alkaline* (AL-kahlin), because hydroxide ions outnumber hydrogen ions.

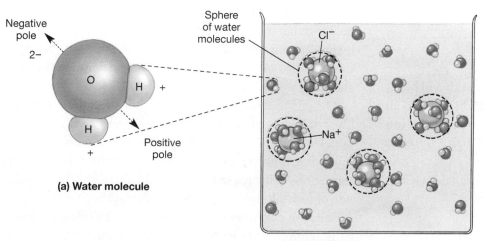

(a) Water molecule

(b) Sodium chloride in solution

FIGURE 2-8 **The Role of Water Molecules in Solutions. (a)** In a water molecule, oxygen forms polar covalent bonds with two hydrogen atoms. Because the hydrogen atoms are located near one end of the molecule, the molecule has an uneven distribution of charges, creating positive and negative poles. **(b)** Ionic compounds dissociate in water as the polar water molecules disrupt the ionic bonds. The ions remain in solution because the sphere of water molecules surrounding them prevents the ionic bonds from re-forming.

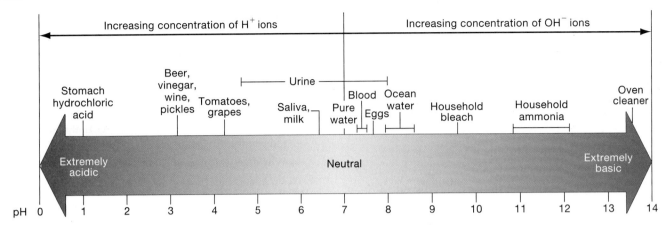

FIGURE 2-9 **pH and Hydrogen Ion Concentration.** An increase or decrease of one unit corresponds to a tenfold change in H^+ concentration.

The pH values of some common liquids are indicated in Figure 2-9. The pH of blood and most body fluids normally ranges from 7.35 to 7.45. Variations in pH outside this range can damage cells and disrupt normal cellular functions. For example, a blood pH below 7 can produce coma, and a blood pH higher than 7.8 usually causes uncontrollable, sustained muscular contractions.

CHECKPOINT

15. Define pH, and explain how the pH scale relates to acidity and alkalinity.

16. Why is an extreme change in pH of body fluids undesirable?

See the blue Answers tab at the back of the book.

2-8 Acids, bases, and salts are inorganic compounds with important physiological roles

The body contains both inorganic and organic acids and bases. An **acid** is any substance that breaks apart (dissociates) in solution to *release* hydrogen ions. (Because a hydrogen ion consists solely of a proton, hydrogen ions are often referred to simply as protons, and acids as "proton donors.") A *strong acid* dissociates completely in solution. Hydrochloric acid (HCl) is an excellent example:

$$HCl \longrightarrow H^+ + Cl^-$$

The stomach produces this powerful acid to assist in the breakdown of food.

A **base** is a substance that removes hydrogen ions from a solution. Many common bases are compounds that dissociate in solution to liberate a hydroxide ion (OH^-). Hydroxide ions have a strong affinity for hydrogen ions and quickly react with them to form water molecules. A *strong base* dissociates completely in solution. For example, sodium hydroxide (NaOH) dissociates in solution as follows:

$$NaOH \longrightarrow Na^+ + OH^-$$

Strong bases have a variety of industrial and household uses; drain openers and lye are two familiar examples.

Weak acids and *weak bases* do not dissociate completely in solution. The human body contains weak bases that are important in counteracting acids produced during cellular metabolism.

SALTS

A **salt** is an ionic compound consisting of any cation except a hydrogen ion and any anion except a hydroxide ion. Salts are held together by ionic bonds, and in water they dissociate, releasing cations and anions. For example, table salt (NaCl) in solution dissociates into Na^+ and Cl^- ions; these are the most abundant ions in body fluids.

The dissociation of table salt does not affect the concentrations of hydrogen ions or hydroxide ions, so NaCl, like many salts, is a "neutral" solute. Through their interactions with water molecules, however, other salts may indirectly affect the concentrations of hydrogen ions and hydroxide ions. The dissociation of such salts makes a solution slightly acidic or slightly basic.

Salts are examples of **electrolytes** (e-LEK-trō-līts), inorganic compounds whose ions can conduct an electrical current in solution. For example, sodium ions (Na^+), potassium ions (K^+), calcium ions (Ca^{2+}), and chloride ions (Cl^-)

are released by the dissociation of electrolytes in blood and other body fluids. Alterations in the concentrations of these ions in body fluids will disturb almost every vital function. For example, declining potassium levels will lead to general muscular paralysis, and rising concentrations will cause weak and irregular heartbeats.

BUFFERS AND pH

Buffers are compounds that stabilize pH by either removing or replacing hydrogen ions. Antacids such as Alka-Seltzer, Rolaids, and Tums are buffers that tie up excess hydrogen ions in the stomach. A variety of buffers, including sodium bicarbonate (also known as baking soda), are responsible for keeping the pH of most body fluids between 7.35 and 7.45. We will consider the role of buffers and pH control in Chapter 18.

2-9 Carbohydrates contain carbon, hydrogen, and oxygen in a 1:2:1 ratio

Carbohydrates are one of the four major classes of organic compounds. Organic compounds always contain the elements carbon and hydrogen, and generally oxygen as well. Many organic molecules are made up of long chains of carbon atoms linked by covalent bonds. These carbon atoms often form additional covalent bonds with hydrogen or oxygen atoms, and less often with nitrogen, phosphorus, sulfur, iron, or other elements.

Many organic molecules are soluble in water. Although the previous discussion focused on inorganic acids and bases, there are also important organic acids and bases. For example, active muscle tissues generate *lactic acid*, an organic acid that must be neutralized to prevent potentially dangerous pH changes in body fluids.

A **carbohydrate** (kar-bō-HĪ-drāt) is an organic molecule that contains carbon, hydrogen, and oxygen in a ratio near 1:2:1. Familiar carbohydrates include the sugars and starches

that make up roughly half of the typical U.S. diet. Our tissues can break down most carbohydrates, and although they sometimes have other functions, carbohydrates are most important as sources of energy. Despite their importance as an energy source, however, carbohydrates account for about 1 percent of total body weight. The three major types of carbohydrates are *monosaccharides*, *disaccharides*, and *polysaccharides*.

MONOSACCHARIDES

A **simple sugar**, or **monosaccharide** (mon-ō-SAK-uh-rīd; *mono-*, single + *sakcharon*, sugar), is a carbohydrate containing from three to seven carbon atoms. Included within this group is **glucose** (GLOO-kōs), ($C_6H_{12}O_6$), the most important metabolic "fuel" in the body (Figure 2-10). Glucose and other monosaccharides dissolve readily in water and are rapidly distributed throughout the body by blood and other body fluids.

DISACCHARIDES AND POLYSACCHARIDES

Carbohydrates other than simple sugars are complex molecules composed of monosaccharide building blocks. Two monosaccharides joined together form a **disaccharide** (dī-SAK-uh-rīd; *di-*, two). Disaccharides such as *sucrose* (table sugar) have a sweet taste and, like monosaccharides, are quite soluble in water. The formation of sucrose (Figure 2-11a) involves dehydration synthesis, a process introduced earlier in the chapter. ∞ p. 36 Dehydration synthesis, or condensation, links molecules together by the removal of a water molecule. The breakdown of sucrose into simple sugars is an example of hydrolysis, the functional opposite of dehydration synthesis (Figure 2-11b).

(a) **(b)** **(c)**

FIGURE 2-10 Glucose. (a) The straight-chain structural formula. **(b)** The ring form that is most common in nature. **(c)** An abbreviated diagram of the ring form of glucose. In such carbon-ring diagrams, atoms attached to the ring are omitted, and only the symbols for elements other than carbon are shown.

CH₂OH

(a) During dehydration synthesis, two molecules are joined by the removal of a water molecule.

DEHYDRATION SYNTHESIS

Glucose + Fructose → Sucrose + H_2O

(b) Hydrolysis reverses the steps of dehydration synthesis; a complex molecule is broken down by the addition of a water molecule.

HYDROLYSIS

Sucrose + H_2O → Glucose + Fructose

Glucose molecules

(c) Glycogen, a branching chain of glucose molecules, is stored in muscle cells and liver cells.

FIGURE 2-11 **The Structure, Formation, and Breakdown of Complex Sugars. (a, b)** The formation and breakdown of complex sugars (such as disaccharides) are functionally opposite reactions. **(c)** The structure of glycogen, a polysaccharide.

ars are stored as fat). Many such people use artificial sweeteners in their foods and beverages. These compounds have a very sweet taste but either cannot be broken down in the body or are used in such small amounts that their breakdown does not contribute to the overall energy balance of the body.

Larger carbohydrate molecules are called **polysaccharides** (pol-ē-SAK-uh-rīdz; *poly-*, many). They result when repeated dehydration synthesis reactions add additional monosaccharides or disaccharides. *Starches* are glucose-based polysaccharides important in our diets. Most starches are manufactured by plants. Your digestive tract can break these molecules into simple sugars. Starches found in potatoes and grains are important energy sources. In contrast, *cellulose*, a component of the cell walls of plants, is a polysaccharide that our bodies cannot digest. The cellulose of foods such as celery contributes to the bulk of digestive wastes but is useless as an energy source.

Glycogen (GLĪ-kō-jen), or *animal starch*, is a polysaccharide composed of interconnected glucose molecules (**Figure 2-11c**). Like most other large polysaccharides, glycogen will not dissolve in water or other body fluids. Liver and muscle tissues make and store glycogen. When these tissues have a high demand for energy, glycogen molecules are broken down into glucose; when demands are low, the tissues absorb glucose from the bloodstream and rebuild glycogen reserves. Table 2-4 summarizes information about the carbohydrates in the body.

Many foods contain disaccharides, but all carbohydrates except monosaccharides must be disassembled through hydrolysis before they can provide useful energy. Most sweet junk foods, such as candy and soft drinks, abound in simple sugars (commonly fructose) and disaccharides (generally sucrose). Some people cannot tolerate sugar for medical reasons; others avoid it because they do not want to gain weight (excess sug-

TABLE 2-4 Carbohydrates in the Body

STRUCTURE	EXAMPLES	PRIMARY FUNCTIONS	REMARKS
Monosaccharides (Simple Sugars)	Glucose, fructose	Energy source	Manufactured in the body and obtained from food; found in body fluids
Disaccharides	Sucrose, lactose, maltose	Energy source	Sucrose is table sugar, lactose is present in milk; all must be broken down to monosaccharides before absorption
Polysaccharides	Glycogen	Storage of glucose molecules	Glycogen is in animal cells; other polysaccharides (starches and cellulose) are in plant cells

CHECKPOINT

19. A food contains organic molecules with the elements C, H, and O in a ratio of 1:2:1. What class of compounds do these molecules represent, and what are their major functions in the body?

20. When two monosaccharides undergo a dehydration synthesis reaction, which type of molecule is formed?

See the blue Answers tab at the back of the book.

2-10 Lipids contain a carbon-to-hydrogen ratio of 1:2

Lipids (*lipos*, fat) also contain carbon, hydrogen, and oxygen, but because they have relatively less oxygen than do carbohydrates, the ratios do not approximate 1:2:1. In addition, lipids may contain small quantities of other elements, including phosphorus, nitrogen, or sulfur. Familiar lipids include *fats*, *oils*, and *waxes*. Most lipids are insoluble in water, but special transport mechanisms carry them in the circulating blood.

Lipids form essential structural components of all cells. In addition, lipid deposits are important as energy reserves. Based on equal weights, lipids provide roughly twice as much energy as carbohydrates when broken down in the body. When the supply of lipids exceeds the demand for energy, the excess is stored in fat deposits. For this reason there has been great interest in developing *fat substitutes* that provide less energy but have the same taste and texture as lipids.

Lipids normally account for 12–18 percent of total body weight of adult men, and 18–24 percent of that of adult women. There are many kinds of lipids in the body. The major types are *fatty acids*, *fats*, *steroids*, and *phospholipids* (Table 2-5).

FATTY ACIDS

Fatty acids are long chains of carbon atoms with attached hydrogen atoms that end in a *carboxylic* (kar-bok-SIL-ik) *acid group* (— COOH). The name *carboxyl* should help you remember that a carbon and a hydroxyl (— OH) group are the important structural features of fatty acids. When a fatty acid

TABLE 2-5 Representative Lipids and Their Functions in the Body

LIPID TYPE	EXAMPLES	PRIMARY FUNCTIONS	REMARKS
Fatty Acids	Lauric acid	Energy sources	Absorbed from food or synthesized in cells; transported in the blood for use in many tissues
Fats	Monoglycerides, diglycerides, triglycerides	Energy source, energy storage, insulation, and physical protection	Stored in fat deposits; must be broken down to fatty acids and glycerol before they can be used as an energy source
Steroids	Cholesterol	Structural component of cell membranes, hormones, digestive secretions in bile	All have the same carbon-ring framework
Phospholipids	Lecithin	Structural components of cell membranes	Composed of fatty acids and nonlipid molecules

is in solution, only the carboxyl end dissolves in water. The carbon chain, known as the hydrocarbon *tail* of the fatty acid, is relatively insoluble. Figure 2-12a shows a representative fatty acid, *lauric acid*.

In a **saturated** fatty acid, such as lauric acid, the four single covalent bonds of each carbon atom permit each neighboring carbon to link to each other and to two hydrogen atoms. If any of the carbon-to-carbon bonds are double covalent bonds, then fewer hydrogen atoms are present and the fatty acid is **unsaturated.** The structures of saturated and unsaturated fatty acids are shown in Figure 2-12b. A *monounsaturated* fatty acid has a lone double bond in the hydrocarbon tail. A *polyunsaturated* fatty acid contains multiple double bonds.

Both saturated and unsaturated fatty acids can be broken down for energy, but a diet containing large amounts of saturated fatty acids increases the risk of heart disease and other circulatory problems. Butter, fatty meat, and ice cream are popular dietary sources of saturated fatty acids. Vegetable oils such as olive oil or corn oil contain a mixture of unsaturated fatty acids.

FATS

Unlike simple sugars, individual fatty acids cannot be strung together in a chain by dehydration synthesis. But they can be attached to another compound, **glycerol** (GLIS-er-ol), to make a **fat** through a similar reaction. In a **triglyceride** (trī-GLI-se-rīd), a glycerol molecule is attached to three fatty acids (Figure 2-13). Triglycerides are the most common fats in the body.

In addition to serving as an energy reserve, fat deposits under the skin serve as insulation, and a mass of fat around a delicate organ, such as a kidney, provides a protective cushion. *Saturated fats*—triglycerides containing saturated fatty acids—are usually solid at room temperature. *Unsaturated fats*, which are triglycerides containing unsaturated fatty acids, are usually liquid at room temperature. Such liquid fats are oils.

(a) Lauric acid ($C_{12}H_{24}O_2$)

Saturated

Unsaturated

(b)

FIGURE 2-12 **Fatty Acids.** (a) Lauric acid has the basic structure of a fatty acid: a long chain of carbon atoms and a carboxylic acid group (—COOH). (b) A fatty acid is either saturated or unsaturated. Unsaturated fatty acids have double covalent bonds that cause sharp bends in the molecule.

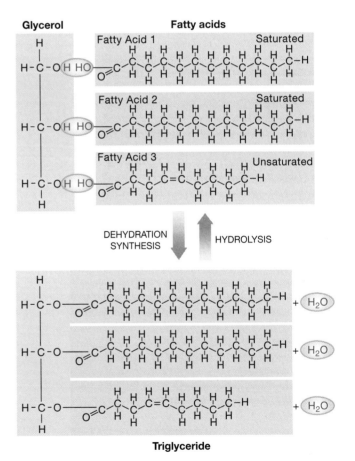

FIGURE 2-13 **Triglyceride Formation.** The formation of a triglyceride involves the attachment of three fatty acids to the carbons of a glycerol molecule. This example shows the attachment of one unsaturated and two saturated fatty acids to a glycerol molecule.

STEROIDS

Steroids are large lipid molecules composed of four connected rings of carbon atoms. They differ in the carbon chains that are attached to this basic structure. **Cholesterol** (ko-LES-ter-ol; *chole-*, bile + *stereos*, solid) is probably the best-known steroid (Figure 2-14). All of our cells are surrounded by *cell membranes*, or *plasma membranes*, that contain cholesterol, and some chemical messengers, or *hormones*, are derived from cholesterol. Examples include the sex hormones testosterone and estrogen.

The cholesterol needed to maintain cell membranes and manufacture steroid hormones comes from two sources. One source is the diet; animal products such as meat, cream, and egg yolks are especially rich in cholesterol. The second is the body itself, for the liver can synthesize large amounts of cholesterol. The body's ability to synthesize this steroid can make it difficult to control blood cholesterol levels by dietary restriction alone. This difficulty can have serious repercussions because a strong link exists between high blood cholesterol levels and heart disease. Current nutritional advice suggests limiting cholesterol intake to under 300 mg per day; this amount represents a 40 percent reduction for the average adult in the United States. The connection between blood cholesterol levels and heart disease will be examined more closely in Chapters 11 and 12.

FIGURE 2-14 A Cholesterol Molecule. Cholesterol, like all steroids, contains a complex four-ring structure.

PHOSPHOLIPIDS

Phospholipids (FOS-fō-lip-idz) consist of a glycerol and two fatty acids (a diglyceride) linked to a nonlipid group by a phosphate group (PO_4^{3-}) (Figure 2-15). The nonlipid portion of a phospholipid is soluble in water, whereas the fatty acid portion is relatively insoluble. Phospholipids are the most abundant lipid components of cell membranes.

FIGURE 2-15 A Phospholipid Molecule. In a phospholipid, a glycerol with two fatty acids (a diglyceride) is linked to a nonlipid molecule by a phosphate group. This phospholipid is lecithin.

The Big Picture

Proteins are the most abundant organic components of the body, and they are the key to both anatomical structure and physiological function. Proteins determine cell shape and tissue properties, and almost all cell functions are performed by proteins and by interactions between proteins and their immediate environment.

2-11 Proteins are formed from amino acids and contain carbon, hydrogen, oxygen, and nitrogen

Proteins are the most abundant organic components of the human body and in many ways the most important. The human body contains many different proteins, and they account for about 20 percent of total body weight. All proteins contain carbon, hydrogen, oxygen, and nitrogen; smaller quantities of sulfur and phosphorus may also be present.

PROTEIN FUNCTION

Proteins perform a variety of functions, which can be grouped into seven major categories:

1. *Support.* **Structural proteins** create a three-dimensional framework for the body, providing strength, organization, and support for cells, tissues, and organs.

2. *Movement.* **Contractile proteins** are responsible for muscular contraction; related proteins are responsible for the movement of individual cells.

3. *Transport.* Insoluble lipids, respiratory gases, minerals such as iron, and several hormones are carried in the blood attached to **transport proteins.** Other specialized proteins transport materials between different parts of a cell.

4. *Buffering.* Proteins provide a considerable buffering action, helping to prevent potentially dangerous changes in pH in cells and tissues.

5. *Metabolic regulation.* Enzymes speed up chemical reactions in living cells. The sensitivity of enzymes to environmental factors is extremely important in controlling the pace and direction of metabolic operations.

6. *Coordination and control.* Protein **hormones** can influence the metabolic activities of every cell in the body or affect the function of specific organs or organ systems.

7. *Defense.* The tough, waterproof proteins of the skin, hair, and nails protect the body from environmental hazards. In addition, proteins known as **antibodies** protect us from disease, and special **clotting proteins** restrict bleeding following an injury to the cardiovascular system.

PROTEIN STRUCTURE

Proteins are long chains of organic molecules called **amino acids.** The human body contains significant quantities of the 20 different amino acids that are the building blocks of proteins. Each amino acid consists of a central carbon atom bonded to a hydrogen atom, an amino group ($-NH_2$), a carboxylic acid group ($-COOH$), and a variable R group or side chain (Figure 2-16a). The R group may be a straight chain or a ring of atoms. The name *amino acid* refers to the presence of the *amino* group and the carboxylic *acid* group, which all amino acids have in common. The different R groups distinguish one amino acid from another, giving each its own chemical properties.

A typical protein contains 1000 amino acids, but the largest protein complexes may have 100,000 or more. The individual amino acids are strung together like beads on a string, with the carboxylic acid group of one amino acid attached to the amino group of another. This connection is called a **peptide bond** (Figure 2-16b). **Peptides** are molecules made up of amino acids held together by peptide bonds. If a molecule consists of two amino acids, it is called a *dipeptide.* Tripeptides and larger chains of amino acids are called *polypeptides.* Polypeptides containing more than 100 amino acids are usually called proteins.

At its most basic level, the *structure* of a protein is established by the sequence of its amino acids (Figure 2-17a). The *characteristics* of a particular protein are determined in part by the R groups on its amino acids. But the properties of a protein are more than just the sum of the properties of its parts, for

(a) Structure of an amino acid

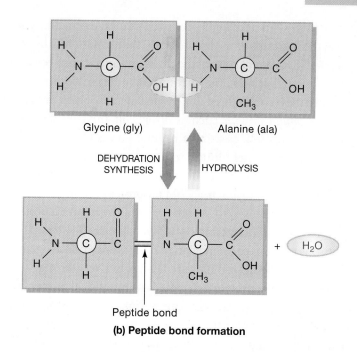

FIGURE 2-16 **Amino Acids and the Formation of Peptide Bonds.** **(a)** Each amino acid consists of a central carbon atom to which four different groups are attached: a hydrogen atom, an amino group (—NH$_2$), a carboxylic acid group (—COOH), and a variable group generally designated R. **(b)** Peptides form when a dehydration synthesis reaction creates a peptide bond between the carboxyl group of one amino acid and the amino group of another. In this example, glycine and alanine are linked to form a dipeptide.

(b) Peptide bond formation

(a) Polypeptide chain

Globular protein subunit

(c) Hemoglobin

(b) Myoglobin

(d) Keratin fiber

FIGURE 2-17 **Protein Structure.** **(a)** Protein structure is established by the amino acid sequence in a polypeptide chain. **(b)** Attraction between R groups plays a large role in forming globular proteins such as myoglobin, a protein involved in the storage of oxygen in muscle tissue. **(c)** A single hemoglobin molecule contains four globular subunits, each structurally similar to myoglobin. Hemoglobin transports oxygen in the blood. **(d)** In keratin, a structural protein in skin and hair, three fibrous subunits intertwine like the strands of a rope.

polypeptides can have highly complex shapes. Interactions between the R groups of the amino acids, the formation of hydrogen bonds at different parts of the chain, and interactions between the polypeptide chain and surrounding water molecules contribute to the complex three-dimensional shapes of large proteins.

In a *globular protein,* such as *myoglobin,* the peptide chain folds back on itself, creating a rounded mass (Figure 2-17b). Myoglobin is a protein found in muscle cells.

Complex proteins may consist of several protein subunits. An example is *hemoglobin,* a globular protein found inside red blood cells (Figure 2-17c). Another protein with several protein subunits is keratin, an example of a *fibrous protein* (Figure 2-17d). In fibrous proteins the polypeptide strands are wound together as in a rope. Fibrous proteins are flexible but very strong.

The shape of a protein determines its functional properties. The 20 common amino acids can be linked in an astonishing number of combinations, creating proteins of enormously varied shape and function. Small differences can have large effects; changing one amino acid in a protein containing 10,000 or more amino acids may make it incapable of performing its normal function. For example, several cancers and *sickle cell anemia,* a blood disorder, result from single changes in the amino acid sequences of complex proteins.

The shape of a protein—and thus its function—can also be altered by small changes in the ionic composition, temperature, or pH of its surroundings. For example, very high body temperatures (over 43°C, or 110°F) cause death because at these temperatures proteins undergo **denaturation,** a change in their three-dimensional shape. Denatured proteins are nonfunctional, and the loss of structural proteins and enzymes causes irreparable damage to organs and organ systems. You see denaturation in progress each time you fry an egg. As the temperature rises, the structure of the abundant proteins dissolved in the clear egg white changes, and eventually the egg proteins form an insoluble white mass.

ENZYME FUNCTION

Among the most important of all the body's proteins are enzymes. ∞ p. 37 These molecules catalyze the reactions that sustain life: Almost everything that happens inside the human body does so because a specific enzyme makes it possible.

Figure 2-18 shows a simple model of enzyme function. The reactants in an enzymatic reaction, called **substrates,** interact to form a specific **product.** Before an enzyme can function as a catalyst—to accelerate a chemical reaction without itself being permanently changed or consumed—the substrates must bind to a special region of the enzyme called the **active site.** This binding depends on the complementary shapes of the two molecules, much as a key fits into a lock. The shape of the active site is determined by the three-dimensional shape of the enzyme molecule. Once the reaction is completed and the products are released, the enzyme is free to catalyze another reaction. Enzymes work quickly; an enzyme providing energy during a

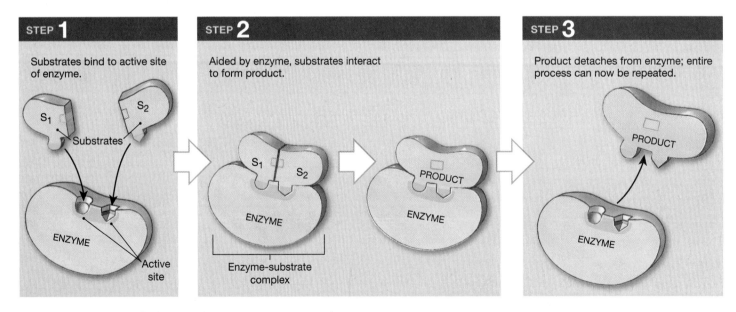

FIGURE 2-18 A Simplified View of Enzyme Structure and Function. Each enzyme contains a specific active site on its exposed surface. Because the structure of the enzyme has not been affected, the entire process can be repeated.

muscular contraction performs its reaction sequence 100 times per second.

Each enzyme works best at an optimal temperature and pH. As temperatures rise or pH shifts outside normal limits, proteins change shape and enzyme function deteriorates.

Each enzyme catalyzes only one type of reaction. This *specificity* is determined by the ability of its active sites to bind only to substrates with particular shapes and charges. The complex reactions that support life proceed in a series of interlocking steps, each step controlled by a different enzyme. Such a reaction sequence is called a *pathway*. We will consider important pathways in later chapters.

CHECKPOINT

24. Describe a protein.

25. How does boiling a protein affect its structural and functional properties?

See the blue Answers tab at the back of the book.

2-12 DNA and RNA are nucleic acids

Nucleic (noo-KLĀ-ik) **acids** are large organic molecules composed of carbon, hydrogen, oxygen, nitrogen, and phosphorus. Nucleic acids store and process information at the molecular level inside cells. The two classes of nucleic acid molecules are **deoxyribonucleic** (dē-oks-ē-rī-bō-noo-KLĀ-ik) **acid,** or **DNA,** and **ribonucleic** (rī-bō-noo-KLĀ-ik) **acid,** or **RNA.**

The DNA in our cells determines our inherited characteristics, including eye color, hair color, and blood type. DNA affects all aspects of body structure and function because DNA molecules encode the information needed to build proteins. By directing the synthesis of structural proteins, DNA controls the shape and physical characteristics of our bodies. By controlling the manufacture of enzymes, DNA regulates not only protein synthesis, but all aspects of cellular metabolism, including the creation and destruction of lipids, carbohydrates, and other vital molecules.

Several forms of RNA cooperate to manufacture specific proteins using the information provided by DNA. The functional relationships between DNA and RNA will be detailed in Chapter 3.

STRUCTURE OF NUCLEIC ACIDS

A nucleic acid (Figure 2-19) is made up of subunits called **nucleotides.** Each single nucleotide has three basic components: a *sugar,* a *phosphate group* (PO_4^{3-}), and a *nitrogenous (nitrogen-containing) base* (Figure 2-19a). The sugar is always a five-carbon sugar, either **ribose** (in RNA) or **deoxyribose** (in DNA). There are five nitrogenous bases: **adenine (A), guanine (G), cytosine (C), thymine (T),** and **uracil (U).** Both RNA and DNA contain adenine, guanine, and cytosine. Uracil is found only in RNA, and thymine only in DNA (Figure 2-19b).

Important structural differences between RNA and DNA are listed in Table 2-6. A molecule of RNA consists of a single chain of nucleotides (Figure 2-19c). A DNA molecule consists of two nucleotide chains held together by weak

TABLE 2-6 **A Comparison of RNA and DNA**

CHARACTERISTIC	RNA	DNA
Sugar	Ribose	Deoxyribose
Nitrogenous Bases	Adenine Guanine Cytosine Uracil	Adenine Guanine Cytosine Thymine
Number of Nucleotides in a Typical Molecule	Varies from fewer than 100 nucleotides to about 50,000	Always more than 45 million nucleotides
Shape of Molecule	Single strand	Paired strands coiled in a double helix
Function	Performs protein synthesis as directed by DNA	Stores genetic information that controls protein synthesis

(a) Nucleotide structure

Sugar

Phosphate group

Nitrogenous base

(b) Nitrogenous bases in nucleic acids

A — Adenine

G — Guanine

C — Cytosine

T — Thymine (DNA only)

U — Uracil (RNA only)

(c) RNA molecule

Phosphate group

Deoxyribose

Adenine Thymine

Hydrogen bond

DNA strand 1

DNA strand 2

Cytosine Guanine

(d) DNA molecule

FIGURE 2-19 **The Structure of Nucleic Acids.** Nucleic acids are long chains of nucleotides. **(a)** A nucleotide is composed of a five-carbon sugar attached to both a phosphate group and a nitrogenous base. **(b)** Shown here are the structures of the five nitrogenous bases. **(c)** An RNA molecule consists of a single nucleotide chain. Its shape is determined by the sequence of nucleotides and the interactions between them. **(d)** A DNA molecule consists of a pair of nucleotide chains linked by hydrogen bonding between complementary base pairs.

hydrogen bonds between the opposing nitrogenous bases (**Figure 2-19d**). Because of their shapes, adenine can bond only with thymine, and cytosine only with guanine. As a result, adenine-thymine and cytosine-guanine are known as **complementary base pairs.**

The two strands of DNA twist around one another in a **double helix** that resembles a spiral staircase, with the stair steps corresponding to the nitrogenous base pairs.

CHECKPOINT

26. Describe a nucleic acid.

27. A large organic molecule composed of the sugar ribose, nitrogenous bases, and phosphate groups is which kind of nucleic acid?

See the blue Answers tab at the back of the book.

2-13 ATP is a high-energy compound used by cells

The energy that powers a cell is obtained by the breakdown (catabolism) of organic molecules such as glucose. To be useful, that energy must be transferred from molecule to molecule or from one part of the cell to another.

The usual method of energy transfer involves the creation of **high-energy bonds** by enzymes within cells. A high-energy bond is a covalent bond that stores an unusually large amount of energy (as does a tightly wound rubber band attached to the pro-

peller of a model airplane). When that bond is later broken, the energy is released under controlled conditions (as when the propeller is turned by the unwinding rubber band). In our cells, a high-energy bond usually connects a phosphate group (PO_4^{3-}) to an organic molecule, resulting in a **high-energy compound.** Most high-energy compounds are derived from nucleotides, the building blocks of nucleic acids. The most important high-energy compound in the body is **adenosine triphosphate,** or **ATP.** ATP is composed of the nucleotide *adenosine monophosphate (AMP)* and two phosphate groups (Figure 2-20). The addition of the two phosphate groups requires a significant amount of energy.

In ATP, a high-energy bond connects a phosphate group to **adenosine diphosphate (ADP).** Within our cells, the conversion of ADP to ATP represents the primary method of energy storage, and the reverse reaction provides a means for the release of energy. The arrangement can be summarized as:

$$ADP + phosphate\ group + energy \rightleftharpoons ATP + H_2O$$

Throughout life, our cells continuously generate ATP from ADP and use the energy provided by that ATP to perform vital functions, such as the synthesis of protein molecules or the contraction of muscles. Figure 2-21 shows the relationship between energy flow and the recycling of ADP and ATP within cells.

FIGURE 2-20 **The Structure of ATP.** An ATP molecule is formed by the linkage of two phosphate groups to the nucleotide adenosine monophosphate (AMP). (The adenosine portion is made up of adenine and the five-carbon sugar ribose.) The two phosphate groups are connected to AMP by high-energy bonds. Cells most often store energy by attaching a third phosphate group to ADP. Removing the phosphate group releases the energy for cellular work, including the synthesis of other molecules.

FIGURE 2-21 **Energy Flow and the Recycling of ATP within Cells.**

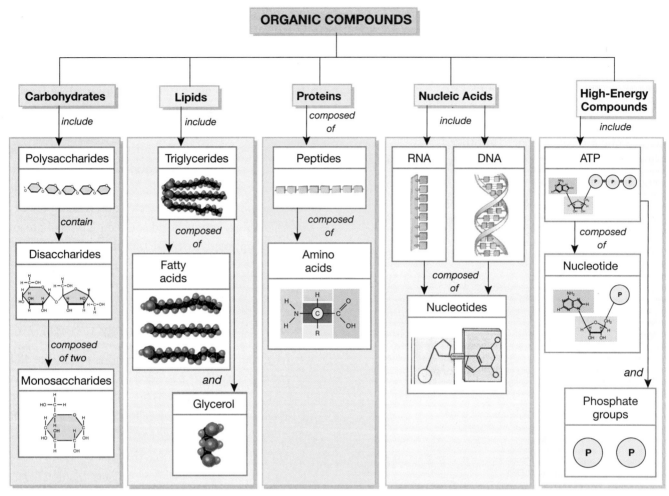

FIGURE 2-22 **An Overview of the Structures of Organic Compounds in the Body.** Each of the classes of organic compounds is composed of simple structural subunits. Specific compounds within each class are depicted above the basic subunits. Fatty acids are the main subunits of all lipids except steroids, such as cholesterol; only one type of lipid, the triglyceride, is represented here.

Figure 2-22 and Table 2-7 review the major chemical compounds we have discussed in this chapter.

CHECKPOINT

28. Describe ATP.

29. What are the products of the hydrolysis of ATP?

See the blue Answers tab at the back of the book.

2-14 Chemicals form functional units called cells

The human body is more than a random collection of chemicals. The biochemical building blocks discussed in this chapter are the components of *cells.* ∞ p. 4 Each cell behaves like a miniature organism, responding to internal and external stimuli. A lipid membrane separates the cell from its environment, and internal membranes create compartments with specific functions. Proteins form an internal supporting framework and act as enzymes to accelerate and control the chemical reactions that maintain homeostasis. Nucleic acids direct the synthesis of all cellular proteins, including the enzymes that enable the cell to synthesize a wide variety of other substances. Carbohydrates provide energy for vital activities and form part of specialized compounds in combination with proteins or lipids. The next chapter considers the combination of these compounds within a living, functional cell.

CHECKPOINT

30. Identify the biochemical building blocks that are the components of cells.

See the blue Answers tab at the back of the book.

TABLE 2-7 The Structure and Function of Biologically Important Compounds

CLASS	BUILDING BLOCKS	SOURCES	FUNCTIONS
INORGANIC			
Water	Hydrogen and oxygen atoms	Absorbed as liquid water or generated by metabolism	Solvent; transport medium for dissolved materials and heat; cooling through evaporation; medium for chemical reactions; reactant in hydrolysis
Acids, bases, salts	H^+, OH^-, various anions and cations	Obtained from the diet or generated by metabolism	Structural components; buffers; sources of ions
Dissolved gases	Oxygen, carbon, nitrogen, and other atoms	Atmosphere	O_2: required for normal cellular metabolism CO_2: generated by cells as a waste product
ORGANIC			
Carbohydrates	C, H, and O; CHO in a 1:2:1 ratio	Obtained from the diet or manufactured in the body	Energy source; some structural role when attached to lipids or proteins; energy storage
Lipids	C, H, O, sometimes N or P; CHO not in 1:2:1 ratio	Obtained from the diet or manufactured in the body	Energy source; energy storage; insulation; structural components; chemical messengers; protection
Proteins	C, H, O, N, often S	20 common amino acids; roughly half can be manufactured in the body, others must be obtained from the diet	Catalysts for metabolic reactions; structural components; movement; transport; buffers; defense; control and coordination of activities
Nucleic acids	C, H, O, N, and P; nucleotides composed of phosphates, sugars, and nitrogenous bases	Obtained from the diet or manufactured in the body	Storage and processing of genetic information
High-energy compounds	Nucleotides joined to phosphates by high-energy bonds	Synthesized by all cells	Storage or transfer of energy

RELATED CLINICAL TERMS

cholesterol: A steroid and an important component of cellular membranes; in high concentrations it increases the risk of heart disease.

familial hypercholesterolemia: A genetic disorder resulting in high cholesterol levels in blood and cholesterol buildup in body tissues, especially the walls of blood vessels.

galactosemia: A metabolic disorder resulting from the lack of an enzyme that converts galactose, a monosaccharide in milk, to glucose within cells. Affected individuals have elevated galactose levels in the blood and urine. High levels of galactose during childhood can cause abnormalities in nervous system development and liver function, and cataracts.

nuclear imaging: A procedure in which an image is created on a photographic plate or video screen by the radiation emitted by injected radioisotopes.

omega-3 fatty acids: Fatty acids, abundant in fish flesh and fish oils, that have a double bond three carbon atoms away from the end of the hydrocarbon chain. Their presence in the diet has been linked to reduced risks of heart disease and other conditions.

radioisotopes: Isotopes with unstable nuclei, which spontaneously emit subatomic particles or radiation in measurable amounts.

phenylketonuria (PKU): A metabolic disorder resulting from a defect in the enzyme that normally converts the amino acid phenylalanine to tyrosine, another amino acid. If the resulting elevated phenylalanine levels are not detected in infancy, mental retardation can result from damage to the developing nervous system.

radiopharmaceuticals: Drugs that incorporate radioactive atoms; administered to expose specific target tissues to radiation.

tracer: A radioisotope-labeled compound that can be tracked in the body by the radiation it releases.

Chapter 2 Review

KEY TERMS

atom *30*	ion *33*
buffer *41*	isotope *31*
carbohydrate *41*	lipid *43*
covalent bond *33*	metabolism *35*
decomposition reaction *36*	molecule *32*
electrolytes *40*	neutron *30*
electron *30*	nucleic acid *49*
element *30*	protein *46*
enzyme *37*	proton *30*

SUMMARY OUTLINE

An Introduction to the Chemical Level of Organization   *p. 30*

1. Chemicals combine to form complex structures.

2-1 Atoms are the basic particles of matter   *p. 30*

2. **Atoms** are the smallest units of matter; they consist of **protons, neutrons,** and **electrons**. *(Figure 2-1)*

3. An **element** consists entirely of atoms with the same number of protons (**atomic number**). Within an atom, an **electron cloud** surrounds the nucleus. *(Figure 2-2; Table 2-1)*

4. The atomic mass of an atom is equal to the total number of protons and neutrons in its nucleus. **Isotopes** are atoms of the same element whose nuclei contain different numbers of neutrons. The **atomic weight** of an element takes into account the abundance of its various isotopes.

5. Electrons occupy a series of **electron shells** around the nucleus. The number of electrons in the outermost electron shell determines an atom's chemical properties. *(Figure 2-3)*

2-2 Chemical bonds are forces formed by atom interactions   *p. 32*

6. Atoms can combine through chemical reactions that create **chemical bonds**. A **molecule** is any chemical structure consisting of atoms held together by shared electrons. A **compound** is any chemical substance made up of atoms of two or more elements.

7. An **ionic bond** results from the attraction between **ions**—atoms that have gained or lost electrons. **Cations** are positively charged, and **anions** are negatively charged. *(Figure 2-4; Table 2-2)*

8. Sharing one pair of electrons creates a single **covalent bond;** sharing two pairs forms a **double covalent bond**. An unequal sharing of electrons creates a **polar covalent bond**. *(Figure 2-5)*

9. A **hydrogen bond** is the attraction between a hydrogen atom with a slight positive charge and a negatively charged atom in another molecule or within the same molecule. Hydrogen bonds can affect the shapes and properties of molecules. *(Figure 2-6)*

2-3 Decomposition, synthesis, and exchange reactions are important chemical reactions in physiology   *p. 35*

10. **Metabolism** refers to all the **chemical reactions** in the body. Our cells capture, store, and use energy to maintain homeostasis and support essential functions.

11. Chemical notation allows us to describe chemical reactions between reactants that generate one or more products. *(Table 2-3)*

12. **Work** involves movement of an object or a change in its physical structure, and **energy** is the capacity to perform work. There are two major types of energy: kinetic and potential.

13. **Kinetic energy** is the energy of motion. **Potential energy** is stored energy that results from the position or structure of an object. Conversions from potential to kinetic energy are not 100 percent efficient; every energy exchange produces **heat.**

14. A chemical reaction may be classified as a **decomposition, synthesis,** or **exchange reaction.**

15. Cells gain energy to power their functions through **catabolism,** the breakdown of complex molecules. Much of this energy supports **anabolism,** the synthesis of new organic molecules.

16. Reversible reactions consist of simultaneous synthesis and decomposition reactions. At **equilibrium** the rates of these two opposing reactions are in balance.

2-4 Enzymes catalyze specific biochemical reactions by lowering a reaction's activation energy   *p. 37*

17. **Activation energy** is the amount of energy required to start a reaction. Molecules called **enzymes** control many chemical reactions within our bodies. Enzymes are **catalysts** that participate in reactions without themselves being permanently changed. *(Figure 2-7)*

18. **Exergonic** reactions release heat; **endergonic** reactions absorb heat.

2-5 Inorganic compounds usually lack carbon, and organic compounds always contain carbon   *p. 38*

19. **Nutrients** and **metabolites** can be broadly classified as **organic** or **inorganic compounds.**

20. Living cells in the body consume oxygen and generate carbon dioxide.

2-6 Physiological systems depend on water   *p. 38*

21. Water is the most important inorganic component of the body.

22. Water is an excellent solvent, has a high heat capacity, and participates in the metabolic reactions of the body.

23. Many inorganic compounds undergo **ionization,** or dissociation, in water to form ions. *(Figure 2-8)*

2-7 Body fluid pH is vital for homeostasis   *p. 39*

24. The **pH** of a solution indicates the concentration of hydrogen ions it contains. Solutions can be classified as neutral (pH = 7), acidic (pH < 7), or basic (alkaline) (pH > 7) on the basis of pH. *(Figure 2-9)*

25. **Buffers** maintain pH within normal limits (7.35–7.45 in most body fluids) by releasing or absorbing hydrogen ions.

2-8 Acids, bases, and salts are inorganic compounds with important physiological roles   *p. 40*

26. An **acid** releases hydrogen ions into a solution, and a **base** removes hydrogen ions from a solution.

27. A **salt** is an ionic compound whose cation is not H^+ and whose anion is not OH^-. Salts are **electrolytes,** compounds that dissociate in water and conduct an electrical current.

2-9 Carbohydrates contain carbon, hydrogen, and oxygen in a 1:2:1 ratio   *p. 41*

28. Organic compounds contain carbon and hydrogen and usually oxygen as well.

29. **Carbohydrates** are most important as an energy source for metabolic processes. The three major types are **monosaccharides** (simple sugars), **disaccharides,** and **polysaccharides.** *(Figures 2-10, 2-11; Table 2-4)*

2-10 Lipids contain a carbon-to-hydrogen ratio of 1:2   *p. 43*

30. **Lipids** are water-insoluble molecules that include fats, oils, and waxes. There are four important classes of lipids: **fatty acids, fats, steroids,** and **phospholipids.** *(Table 2-5)*

31. **Triglycerides (fats)** consist of three fatty acid molecules attached to a molecule of **glycerol.** *(Figures 2-12, 2-13)*

32. Cholesterol is a precursor of steroid hormones and is a component of cell membranes. *(Figure 2-14)*

33. Phospholipids are the most abundant components of cell membranes. *(Figure 2-15)*

2-11 Proteins are formed from amino acids and contain carbon, hydrogen, oxygen, and nitrogen   *p. 46*

34. Proteins perform a great variety of functions in the body. Important types of proteins include **structural proteins, contractile proteins, transport proteins, enzymes, hormones,** and **antibodies.**

35. Proteins are chains of **amino acids** linked by **peptide bonds.** The sequence of amino acids and the interactions of their R groups influence the final shape of a protein molecule. *(Figures 2-16, 2-17)*

36. The shape of a protein determines its function. Each protein works best at an optimal combination of temperature and pH.

37. The reactants in an enzymatic reaction, called **substrates,** interact to form a **product** by binding to the enzyme at the **active site.** *(Figure 2-18)*

2-12 DNA and RNA are nucleic acids   *p. 49*

38. **Nucleic acids** store and process information at the molecular level. There are two kinds of nucleic acids: **deoxyribonucleic acid (DNA)** and **ribonucleic acid (RNA).** *(Figure 2-19; Table 2-6)*

39. Nucleic acids are chains of nucleotides. Each nucleotide contains a sugar, a **phosphate group,** and a **nitrogenous base.** The sugar is always **ribose** or **deoxyribose.** The nitrogenous bases found in DNA are **adenine, guanine, cytosine,** and **thymine.** In RNA, **uracil** replaces thymine.

2-13 ATP is a high-energy compound used by cells   *p. 51*

40. Cells store energy in **high-energy compounds.** The most important high-energy compound is **ATP (adenosine triphosphate).** When energy is available, cells make ATP by adding a phosphate group to ADP. When energy is needed, ATP is broken down to ADP and phosphate. *(Figures 2-20, 2-21)*

41. Biologically important compounds are composed of simple structural subunits. *(Figure 2-22; Table 2-7)*

2-14 Chemicals form functional units called cells   *p. 52*

42. Biochemical building blocks form *cells.*

REVIEW QUESTIONS

 Access more review material online at The Anatomy & Physiology Place (**www.anatomyandphysiology.com**). There, you'll find Chapter Guides, Chapter Quizzes, Chapter Practice Tests, Interactive Flashcards, a Glossary with Pronunciations, and more to help you succeed in the course.

Level 1 • Reviewing Facts and Terms

Match each item in column A with the most closely related item in column B. Place the letters for answers in the spaces provided.

COLUMN A	COLUMN B
_____ 1. atomic number	**a.** synthesis
_____ 2. covalent bond	**b.** catalyst
_____ 3. ionic bond	**c.** sharing of electrons
_____ 4. catabolism	**d.** A + B $\rightleftharpoons$ AB
_____ 5. anabolism	**e.** stabilize pH
_____ 6. exchange reaction	**f.** number of protons
_____ 7. reversible reaction	**g.** decomposition
_____ 8. acid	**h.** carbohydrates, lipids, proteins
_____ 9. enzyme	**i.** loss or gain of electrons
_____ 10. buffer	**j.** water, salts
_____ 11. organic compounds	**k.** H^+ donor
_____ 12. inorganic compounds	**l.** AB + CD $\longrightarrow$ AD + CB

13. An oxygen atom has eight protons. (a) In the following diagram, sketch in the arrangement of electrons around the nucleus of the oxygen atom. (b) How many more electrons will it take to fill the outermost electron shell?

Oxygen atom

(**b**) _____

14. In atoms, protons and neutrons are found
    (**a**) only in the nucleus.
    (**b**) outside the nucleus.
    (**c**) inside and outside the nucleus.
    (**d**) in the electron cloud.

15. The number and arrangement of electrons in an atom's outer electron shell determine its
    (**a**) atomic weight.   (**b**) atomic number.
    (**c**) electrical properties.   (**d**) chemical properties.

16. The bond between sodium and chlorine in the compound sodium chloride (NaCl) is
    (**a**) an ionic bond.
    (**b**) a single covalent bond.
    (**c**) a nonpolar covalent bond.
    (**d**) a double covalent bond.

17. Explain how enzymes function in chemical reactions.

18. List the six most abundant elements in the body.

19. What four major classes of organic compounds are found in the body?

20. List seven major functions performed by proteins.

21. Identify the components of an amino acid in the following diagram.

(**a**) _____   (**b**) _____
(**c**) _____   (**d**) _____

Level 2 • Reviewing Concepts

22. Oxygen has 8 protons, 8 neutrons, and 8 electrons. What is its atomic mass?
    (**a**) 8   (**b**) 16
    (**c**) 24   (**d**) 32

23. Which of the following groups contains only inorganic compounds?
(a) water, electrolytes, oxygen, carbon dioxide
(b) oxygen, carbon dioxide, water, sugars
(c) water, electrolytes, salts, nucleic acids
(d) carbohydrates, lipids, proteins, vitamins

24. Glucose and fructose are examples of
(a) monosaccharides (simple sugars).
(b) isotopes.
(c) lipids.
(d) a, b, and c are all correct.

25. Explain the differences among nonpolar covalent bonds, polar covalent bonds, and ionic bonds.

26. What does it mean to say a solution has a neutral pH?

27. A biologist analyzes a sample that contains an organic molecule and finds the following constituents: carbon, hydrogen, oxygen, nitrogen, and phosphorus. On the basis of this information, is the molecule a carbohydrate, a lipid, a protein, or a nucleic acid?

Level 3 • Critical Thinking and Clinical Applications

28. The element sulfur has an atomic number of 16 and an atomic mass of 32. How many neutrons are in the nucleus of a sulfur atom? Assuming that sulfur forms covalent bonds with hydrogen, how many hydrogen atoms could bond to one sulfur atom?

29. An important buffer system in the human body involves carbon dioxide (CO_2) and bicarbonate ions (HCO_3^-) as shown:

$$CO_2 + H_2O \rightleftharpoons H_2CO_3 \rightleftharpoons H^+ + HCO_3^-$$

If a person becomes excited and exhales large amounts of CO_2, how will his or her body's pH be affected?

3 Cell Structure and Function

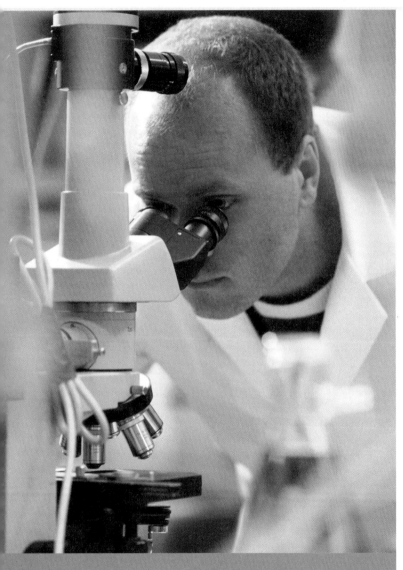

Many familiar structures, from pyramids to patchwork quilts, are made of numerous small, similar components. A microscope reveals that the human body is built on the same principle, for it consists of several trillion tiny units known as cells. Cells are the smallest entities that can perform all basic life functions. In this chapter, we will explore the internal structure and specific functions of cells.

VOCABULARY DEVELOPMENT

aero- air; *aerobic*
ana- apart; *anaphase*
chondrion granule; *mitochondrion*
chroma color; *chromosome*
cyto- cell; *cytoplasm*
endo- inside; *endocytosis*
exo- outside; *exocytosis*
hemo- blood; *hemolysis*
hyper- above; *hypertonic*
hypo- below; *hypotonic*

inter- between; *interphase*
interstitium something standing between; *interstitial fluid*
iso- equal; *isotonic*
kinesis motion; *cytokinesis*
meta- after; *metaphase*
micro- small; *microtubules*
mitos thread; *mitosis*
osmos thrust; *osmosis*
phagein to eat; *phagocyte*

pinein to drink; *pinocytosis*
podon foot; *pseudopod*
pro- before; *prophase*
pseudo- false; *pseudopod*
ptosis a falling away; *apoptosis*
reticulum network; *endoplasmic reticulum*
soma body; *lysosome*
telos end; *telophase*
tonos tension; *isotonic*

3-1 The study of cells provides the foundation for understanding human physiology

Just as atoms are the building blocks of molecules, **cells** are the building blocks of the human body. Over the years, biologists have developed the **cell theory,** which includes the following four basic concepts:

1. Cells are the building blocks of all plants and animals.

2. Cells are the smallest functioning units of life.

3. Cells are produced through the division of preexisting cells.

4. Each cell maintains homeostasis.

An individual organism maintains homeostasis only through the combined and coordinated actions of many different types of cells. Figure 3-1 shows some of the variety of cell shapes and sizes in the human body.

Numbering in the trillions, human body cells form and maintain anatomical structures, and they perform physiological functions as different as running and thinking. Thus an understanding of how the human body functions requires a familiarity with the nature of cells.

THE STUDY OF CELLS

The study of the structure and function of cells is called **cytology** (sī-TOL-ō-jē; *cyto-,* cell + *-logy,* the study of). What we have learned since the 1950s has provided new insights into the physiology of cells and their means of homeostatic control. This knowledge resulted from improved equipment for viewing cells and new experimental techniques, not only from biology but also from chemistry and physics.

The two most common methods used to study cell and tissue structure are light microscopy and electron microscopy. Before the 1950s, cells were viewed through light microscopes. Using a series of glass lenses, *light microscopy* can magnify cellular structures about 1000 times. Light microscopy typically involves looking at thin sections sliced from a larger piece of tissue. A photograph taken through a light microscope is called a *light micrograph* (*LM*).

Many fine details of intracellular structure are too small to be seen with a light microscope. These details remained a mystery until cell biologists began using *electron microscopy,* a technique that replaced light with a focused beam of electrons. *Transmission electron micrographs* (*TEMs*) are photographs of very thin sections, and they can reveal fine details of cell membranes and intracellular structures. *Scanning electron micrographs* (*SEMs*) provide less magnification but reveal the three-dimensional nature of cell structures. An SEM provides a surface view of a cell, a portion of a cell, or extracellular structures rather than a detailed sectional view.

You will see examples of light micrographs and both kinds of electron micrographs in figures throughout this text. The abbreviations LM, TEM, and SEM are followed by a number that indicates the total magnification of the image. For example, "LM × 160" indicates that the structures shown in a light micrograph have been magnified 160 times. (See Appendix 3 for the size ranges and scales included in the study of anatomy and physiology.)

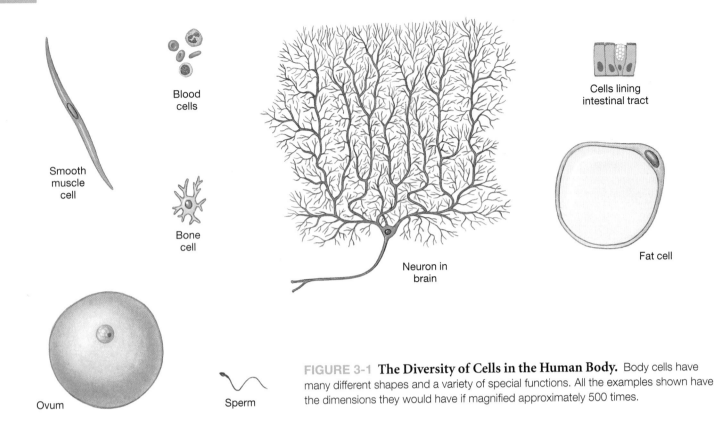

Smooth muscle cell

Blood cells

Bone cell

Neuron in brain

Cells lining intestinal tract

Fat cell

Ovum

Sperm

FIGURE 3-1 The Diversity of Cells in the Human Body. Body cells have many different shapes and a variety of special functions. All the examples shown have the dimensions they would have if magnified approximately 500 times.

AN OVERVIEW OF CELL ANATOMY

The "typical" cell is like the "average" person; any such description masks enormous individual variations. Our model (or representative) cell shares features with most cells of the body without being identical to any specific one (Figure 3-2). Table 3-1 summarizes the structures and functions of a cell's parts.

Our model body cell is surrounded by a watery medium known as the **extracellular fluid.** The extracellular fluid in most tissues is called **interstitial** (in-ter-STISH-ul) **fluid** (*interstitium*, something standing between). A **plasma membrane,** or **cell membrane,** separates the cell contents, or **cytoplasm,** from the extracellular fluid. The cytoplasm surrounds the **nucleus**—the control center for cellular operations.

The cytoplasm can be subdivided into a liquid—the *cytosol*—and intracellular structures collectively known as *organelles*. Our discussion of the cell begins at its boundary with the external environment—the plasma membrane. It then proceeds to the cytosol and the individual organelles and concludes with the nucleus.

CHECKPOINT

1. The cell theory was developed over many years. What are its four basic concepts?

2. The study of cells is called _____.

See the blue Answers tab at the back of the book.

3-2 The plasma membrane separates the cell from its surrounding environment and performs various functions

As noted, the outer boundary of the cell is formed by a plasma membrane. Its general functions include:

- *Physical isolation.* The plasma membrane is a physical barrier that separates the inside of the cell from the surrounding extracellular fluid. Conditions

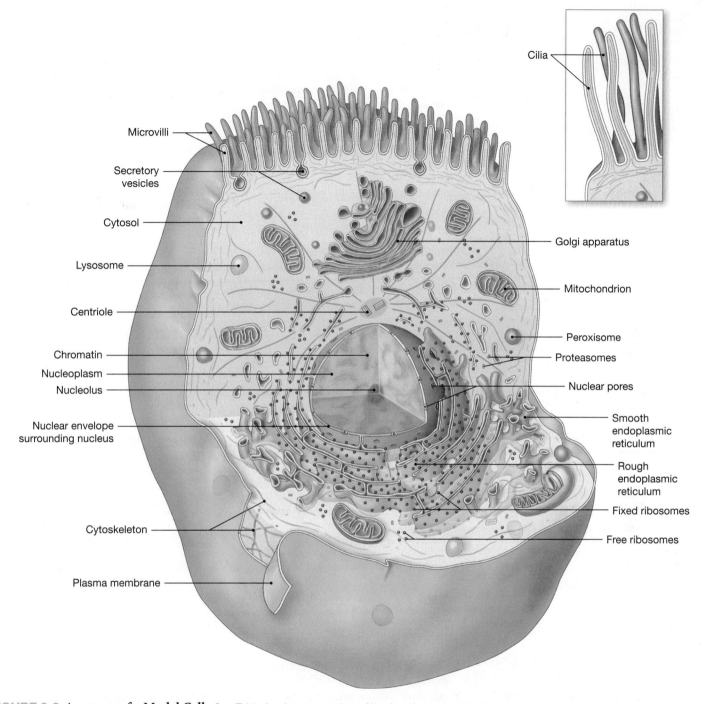

Cilia

Microvilli

Secretory vesicles

Cytosol

Lysosome

Centriole

Chromatin

Nucleoplasm

Nucleolus

Nuclear envelope surrounding nucleus

Cytoskeleton

Plasma membrane

Golgi apparatus

Mitochondrion

Peroxisome

Proteasomes

Nuclear pores

Smooth endoplasmic reticulum

Rough endoplasmic reticulum

Fixed ribosomes

Free ribosomes

FIGURE 3-2 Anatomy of a Model Cell. See Table 3-1 for an overview of the functions associated with the various structures shown.

inside and outside the cell are very different, and those differences must be maintained to preserve homeostasis.

- *Regulation of exchange with the environment.* The plasma membrane controls the entry of ions and nutri-

ents, the elimination of wastes, and the release of secretions.

- *Sensitivity to the environment.* The plasma membrane is the first part of the cell affected by changes in the extracellular fluid. It also contains a variety of receptors

TABLE 3-1 Components of a Model Cell

APPEARANCE	STRUCTURE	COMPOSITION	FUNCTION
	Plasma membrane	Lipid bilayer, containing phospholipids, steroids, proteins, and carbohydrates	Provides isolation, protection, sensitivity, and support; controls entrance/exit of material
	Cytosol	Fluid component of cytoplasm	Distributes materials by diffusion
	NONMEMBRANOUS ORGANELLES Cytoskeleton: Microtubule Microfilament	Proteins organized in fine filaments or slender tubes	Provide strength and support; enable movement of cellular structures and materials
	Microvilli	Membrane extensions containing microfilaments	Increase surface area to facilitate absorption of extracellular materials
	Cilia	Membrane extensions containing microtubules	Move materials over cell surface
	Centrioles	Two centrioles, at right angles; each composed of microtubules	Essential for movement of chromosomes during cell division
	Ribosomes	RNA + proteins; fixed ribosomes bound to endoplasmic reticulum, free ribosomes scattered in cytoplasm	Synthesize proteins
	Proteasomes	Hollow cylinders of proteolytic (protein-breaking) enzymes	Break down and recycle damaged or abnormal intracellular proteins
	MEMBRANOUS ORGANELLES Endoplasmic reticulum (ER):	Network of membranous channels extending throughout the cytoplasm	Synthesizes secretory products; provides intracellular storage and transport
	Rough ER	Has ribosomes attached to membranes	Packages newly synthesized proteins
	Smooth ER	Lacks attached ribosomes	Synthesizes lipids and carbohydrates
	Golgi apparatus	Stacks of flattened membranes containing chambers	Stores, alters, and packages secretory products; forms lysosomes
	Lysosome	Vesicles containing powerful digestive enzymes	Remove damaged organelles or pathogens within cells
	Peroxisome	Vesicles containing degradative enzymes	Catabolize fats and other organic compounds; neutralize toxic compounds generated in the process
	Mitochondria	Double membrane, with inner folds (cristae) enclosing important metabolic enzymes	Produce 95% of the ATP required by the cell
	Nucleus	Nucleoplasm containing DNA, nucleotides, enzymes, and proteins; surrounded by double membrane (nuclear envelope)	Controls metabolism; stores and processes genetic information; controls protein synthesis
	Nucleolus	Dense region in nucleoplasm containing DNA and RNA	Synthesizes RNA and assembles ribosomal subunits

that enable the cell to recognize and respond to specific molecules in its environment.

- *Structural support.* Specialized connections between plasma membranes, or between membranes and extracellular materials, give tissues a stable structure.

The plasma membrane is extremely thin and delicate, ranging from 6 nm to 10 nm in thickness. This membrane contains lipids, proteins, and carbohydrates (Figure 3-3).

MEMBRANE LIPIDS

Phospholipids are a major component of plasma membranes. ∞ p. 45 In a phospholipid, a phosphate group (PO_4^{3-}) serves as a link between a diglyceride (a glycerol molecule bonded to two fatty acid "tails") and a nonlipid "head." The phospholipids in a plasma membrane lie in two distinct layers, with the **hydrophilic** (hī-drō-FI-lik; *hydro-*, water + *philos*, loving) (soluble in water) heads on the outside, and the **hydrophobic** (hī-drō-FŌB-ik; *hydro-*, + *phobos*, fear) (insoluble in water) tails on the inside. For

this reason, the plasma membrane is often called a **phospholipid bilayer** (Figure 3-3). Mixed in with the fatty acid tails are cholesterol molecules and small quantities of other lipids.

The hydrophobic lipid tails will not associate with water or charged molecules, and this characteristic enables the plasma membrane to act as a selective physical barrier. Lipid-soluble molecules and compounds such as oxygen and carbon dioxide are able to cross the lipid portion of a plasma membrane, but ions and water-soluble compounds cannot. Consequently, the plasma membrane isolates the cytoplasm from the surrounding extracellular fluid.

MEMBRANE PROTEINS

Several types of proteins are associated with the plasma membrane. The most common of these membrane proteins span the width of the membrane one or more times and are known as *transmembrane proteins*. Other membrane proteins are either partially embedded in the membrane's phospholipid bilayer or loosely bound to its inner or outer surface. Membrane

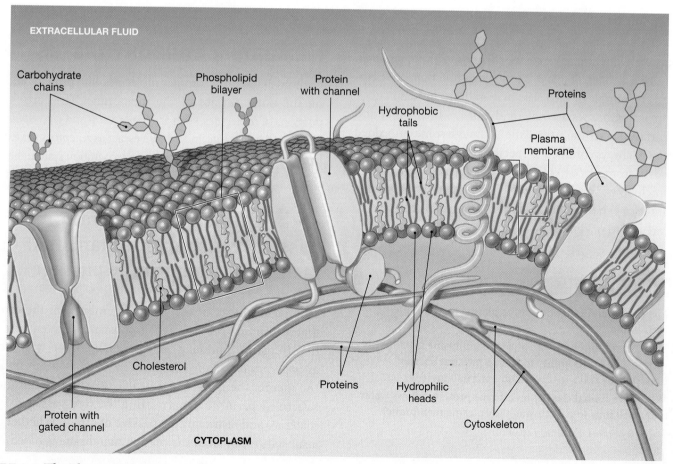

FIGURE 3-3 **The Plasma Membrane.**

TABLE 3-2 **Types of Membrane Proteins**

CLASS	FUNCTION	EXAMPLE
Receptor Proteins	Sensitive to specific extracellular materials that bind to them and trigger a change in a cell's activity.	Binding of the hormone insulin to membrane receptors increases the rate of glucose absorption by the cell.
Channel Proteins	Central pore, or channel, permits water, ions, and other solutes to bypass lipid portion of plasma membrane.	Calcium ion movement through channels is crucial to muscle contraction and the conduction of nerve impulses.
Carrier Proteins	Bind and transport solutes across the plasma membrane. This process may or may not require energy.	Carrier proteins bring glucose into the cytoplasm and also transport sodium, potassium, and calcium ions into and out of the cell.
Enzymes	Catalyze reactions in the extracellular fluid or within the cell.	Dipeptides are broken down into amino acids by enzymes on the exposed membranes of cells lining the intestinal tract.
Anchoring Proteins	Attach the plasma membrane to other structures and stabilize its position.	Inside the cell, anchor proteins bind to the cytoskeleton (network of supporting filaments). Outside the cell, anchor proteins attach the cell to extracellular protein fibers or to another cell.
Recognition (Identifier) Proteins	Identify a cell as self or nonself, normal or abnormal, to the immune system.	One group of such recognition proteins is the major histocompatibility complex (MHC) discussed in Chapter 14.

proteins may function as *receptors, channels, carriers, enzymes, anchors,* or *identifiers.* Table 3-2 provides a functional description and an example of each class of membrane protein.

Plasma membranes are not rigid, nor are their inner and outer surfaces structurally the same. Although some embedded proteins are always confined to specific areas of the membrane, others drift from place to place along its surface like ice cubes in a punch bowl. In addition, the composition of the plasma membrane can change over time, as components of the membrane are added or removed.

CHECKPOINT

3. List the general functions of the plasma membrane.

4. Which component of the plasma membrane is primarily responsible for its ability to form a physical barrier between the cell's internal and external environments?

5. Which functional class of membrane proteins allows water and small ions to pass through the plasma membrane?

See the blue Answers tab at the back of the book.

MEMBRANE CARBOHYDRATES

Carbohydrates form complex molecules with proteins and lipids on the outer surface of the membrane. The carbohydrate portions of molecules, such as *glycoproteins* and *glycolipids,* function as cell lubricants and adhesives, act as receptors for extracellular compounds, and form part of a recognition system that keeps the immune system from attacking the body's own cells and tissues.

3-3 Diffusion and filtration are passive transport mechanisms facilitating membrane passage

The **permeability** of the plasma membrane is the property that determines precisely which substances can enter or leave the cytoplasm. If nothing can cross a membrane, it is described as *impermeable.* If any substance can cross without difficulty, the membrane is *freely permeable.* Plasma membranes are *selectively permeable,* permitting the free passage of some materials and restricting the passage of others. Whether or not a substance can cross the plasma membrane is based on the substance's size, electrical charge, molecular shape, lipid solubility, or some combination of these factors.

Movement across the membrane may be passive or active. **Passive processes** move ions or molecules across the plasma membrane without any energy expenditure by the cell. **Active processes** require that the cell expend energy, usually in the form of adenosine triphosphate (ATP).

In this section we consider two types of passive processes: (1) *diffusion,* including a special type of diffusion called *osmosis,* and (2) *filtration.* In the next section we will examine some types of *carrier-mediated transport,* which includes both active and passive processes. We will consider *facilitated diffusion,* a passive carrier-mediated process, and *active transport,* an active carrier-mediated process. Finally, we will examine two active processes involving *vesicular transport:* endocytosis and exocytosis.

DIFFUSION

Ions and molecules are in constant motion, colliding and bouncing off one another and off obstacles in their paths. **Diffusion** is the net movement of molecules from an area of relatively high concentration (of many collisions) to an area of relatively low concentration (of fewer collisions). The difference between the high and low concentrations represents a **concentration gradient,** and diffusion is often described as proceeding "down a concentration gradient" or "downhill." As a result of the process of diffusion, molecules eventually become uniformly distributed, and concentration gradients are eliminated.

Diffusion in air and water is slow, and it is important over very small distances. However, an everyday example can give you a mental image of how diffusion works. Consider a colored sugar cube dropped into a beaker of water (Figure 3-4). As the cube dissolves, its sugar and dye molecules establish a steep concentration gradient with the surrounding clear water. Eventually, dissolved molecules of both types spread through the water until they are distributed evenly.

Diffusion is important in body fluids because it tends to eliminate local concentration gradients. For example, every cell in your body generates carbon dioxide, and its intracellular (within the cell) concentration is relatively high. Carbon dioxide concentrations are lower in the surrounding extracellular fluid, and lower still in the circulating blood. Because plasma membranes are freely permeable to carbon dioxide, it can diffuse down its concentration gradient—dispersing from the cell's interior into the extracellular fluid, and from the extracellular fluid into the bloodstream, for delivery to and elimination from the lungs.

Diffusion Across Plasma Membranes

In extracellular fluids of the body, water and dissolved solutes diffuse freely. A plasma membrane, however, acts as a barrier that selectively restricts diffusion. Some substances can pass through easily, whereas others cannot penetrate the membrane at all. An ion or molecule can independently diffuse across a plasma membrane in one of two ways: (1) by moving across the lipid portion of the membrane or (2) by passing through a channel protein in the membrane. Therefore, the primary factors

FIGURE 3-4 **Diffusion.** When a colored sugar cube dissolves in a beaker of water, both sugar and dye molecules diffuse from where they are highly concentrated to where they are absent or in a lower concentration. Eventually, the molecules are distributed evenly, and their concentrations are the same everywhere.

EXTRACELLULAR FLUID

Lipid-soluble molecules diffuse through the plasma membrane.

Plasma membrane

Channel protein

Large molecules that cannot diffuse through lipids cannot cross the plasma membrane unless they are transported by a carrier mechanism.

Small water-soluble molecules and ions diffuse through membrane channels.

CYTOPLASM

FIGURE 3-5 **Diffusion Across Plasma Membranes.** The path a substance takes in crossing a plasma membrane depends on the substance's size and lipid solubility.

determining whether a substance can diffuse across a plasma membrane are its lipid solubility and its size relative to the sizes of membrane channels (Figure 3-5).

Alcohol, fatty acids, and steroids can enter cells easily because they can diffuse through the lipid portions of the membrane. Dissolved gases such as oxygen and carbon dioxide also enter and leave cells by diffusing through the phospholipid bilayer.

Ions and most water-soluble compounds are not lipid soluble, so they must pass through membrane channels to enter the cytoplasm. These channels are very small, about 0.8 nm in diameter. Water molecules can enter or exit freely, as can ions such as sodium and potassium, but even a small organic molecule, such as glucose, is too big to fit through the channels.

Osmosis: A Special Case of Diffusion

The diffusion of water across a membrane is called **osmosis** (oz-MŌ-sis; *osmos,* thrust). Both intracellular and extracellular fluids are solutions that contain a variety of dissolved materials, or **solutes.** Each solute tends to diffuse as if it were the only substance in solution. Thus, changes in the concentration of potassium ions, for example, have no effect on the rate or direction of sodium ion diffusion. Some ions and molecules (solutes) diffuse into the cytoplasm, others diffuse out, and a few, such as proteins, are unable to diffuse across a plasma

membrane. But if we ignore the individual identities and simply count ions and molecules, we find that the total concentration of ions and molecules on the inside of the plasma membrane equals the total on the outside.

This state of solute equilibrium persists because *the plasma membrane is freely permeable to water.* Whenever a solute concentration gradient exists across a plasma membrane, a concentration gradient for water exists also. Because the dissolved solute molecules occupy space that would otherwise be taken up by water molecules, the higher the solute concentration, the lower the water concentration. As a result, *water molecules tend to flow across a membrane toward the solution containing the higher solute concentration,* because this movement is down the concentration gradient for water molecules. Water movement continues until water concentrations—and, thus, total solute concentrations—are the same on either side of the membrane.

Three characteristics of osmosis are important to remember:

1. Osmosis is the diffusion of water molecules across a membrane.

2. Osmosis occurs across a selectively permeable membrane that is freely permeable to water but is not freely permeable to solutes.

3. In osmosis, water flows across a membrane toward the solution that has the higher concentration of solutes, because that is where the concentration of water is lower.

OSMOSIS AND OSMOTIC PRESSURE. Figure 3-6 diagrams the process of osmosis. Step 1 shows two solutions (A and B), with different solute concentrations, separated by a selectively permeable membrane. As osmosis occurs, water molecules cross the membrane until the solute concentrations in the two solutions are identical (Step 2). Thus, the volume of solution B increases at the expense of that of solution A. The greater the initial difference in solute concentrations, the stronger is the osmotic flow. The **osmotic pressure** of a solution is an indication of the force of water movement *into that solution* as a result of solute concentration. As the solute concentration of a solution increases, so does its osmotic pressure. Osmotic pressure can

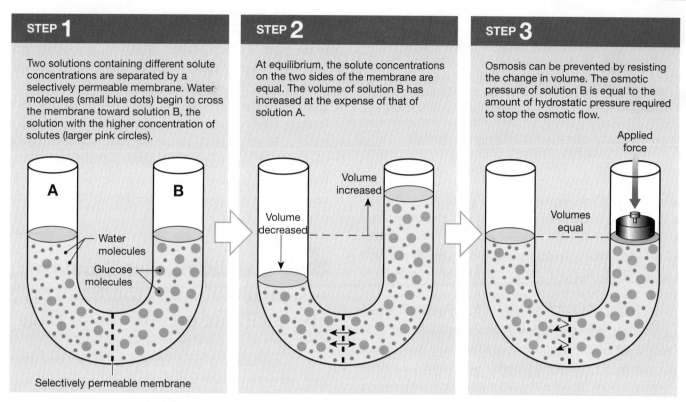

STEP 1

Two solutions containing different solute concentrations are separated by a selectively permeable membrane. Water molecules (small blue dots) begin to cross the membrane toward solution B, the solution with the higher concentration of solutes (larger pink circles).

A   B

Water molecules

Glucose molecules

Selectively permeable membrane

STEP 2

At equilibrium, the solute concentrations on the two sides of the membrane are equal. The volume of solution B has increased at the expense of that of solution A.

Volume increased

Volume decreased

STEP 3

Osmosis can be prevented by resisting the change in volume. The osmotic pressure of solution B is equal to the amount of hydrostatic pressure required to stop the osmotic flow.

Applied force

Volumes equal

FIGURE 3-6 Osmosis. The osmotic flow of water can create osmotic pressure across a membrane. The osmotic pressure of solution B is equal to the amount of hydrostatic pressure required to stop the osmotic flow.

Water molecules   Solute molecules

(a) Isotonic   **(b) Hypotonic**   **(c) Hypertonic**

SEMs × 833

be measured in several ways. For example, a strong enough opposing pressure can prevent the entry of water molecules. Pushing against a fluid generates *hydrostatic pressure*. In Step 3, hydrostatic pressure opposes the osmotic pressure of solution B, so no net osmotic flow occurs.

Solutions of various solute concentrations are described as *isotonic, hypotonic,* or *hypertonic* with regard to their effects on the shape or tension of the plasma membrane of living cells. Although the effects of various osmotic solutions are difficult to see in most tissues, they are readily observable in red blood cells (**Figure 3-7**).

FIGURE 3-7 Effects of Osmosis Across Plasma Membranes. Blue arrows indicate the direction of net osmotic water movement. **(a)** Because these red blood cells are immersed in an isotonic saline solution, no osmotic flow occurs and the cells have their normal appearance. **(b)** Immersion in a hypotonic saline solution results in the osmotic flow of water into the cells. The swelling may continue until the plasma membrane ruptures. **(c)** Exposure to a hypertonic solution results in the movement of water out of the cells. The red blood cells shrivel and become crenated.

The Big Picture

Things tend to even out, unless something—like a plasma membrane—prevents this from happening. In the absence of a plasma membrane, or across a freely permeable membrane, diffusion will quickly eliminate concentration gradients. Osmosis tends to eliminate concentration gradients across membranes that are permeable to water but impermeable to the solutes involved.

In an **isotonic** (*iso-*, equal + *tonos*, tension) solution—one that does not cause a net movement of water into or out of the cell—red blood cells retain their normal appearance (Figure 3-7a). In this case, an equilibrium exists, and as one water molecule moves out of the cell, another moves in to replace it.

When a red blood cell is placed in a **hypotonic** (*hypo-*, below) solution, water will flow into the cell, causing it to swell up like a balloon (Figure 3-7b). Eventually the cell may burst, or *lyse*. In the case of red blood cells, this event is known as **hemolysis** (*hemo-*, blood + *lysis*, a loosening). Red blood cells in a **hypertonic** (*hyper-*, above) solution will lose water by osmosis. As they do, they shrivel and dehydrate. The shrinking of red blood cells is called **crenation** (Figure 3-7c).

It is often necessary to give patients large volumes of fluid after severe blood loss or dehydration. One commonly administered fluid is a 0.9 percent (0.9 g/dl) solution of sodium chloride (NaCl). This solution, which approximates the normal *osmotic concentration* (total solute concentration) of extracellular fluids, is called *normal saline*. It is used because sodium and chloride are the most abundant ions in the body's extracellular fluid. Because little net movement of either type of ion occurs across plasma membranes, normal saline is essentially isotonic with respect to body cells.

CHECKPOINT

6. What is meant by "selectively permeable," when referring to a membrane?

7. Define diffusion.

8. How would a decrease in the concentration of oxygen in the lungs affect the diffusion of oxygen into the blood?

9. Define osmosis.

10. Relative to a surrounding hypertonic solution, the contents of a red blood cell is _____.

See the blue Answers tab at the back of the book.

FILTRATION

In the passive process called **filtration,** hydrostatic pressure forces water across a membrane. If solute molecules are small enough to fit through membrane pores, they will be carried along with the water. In the body, the heart pushes blood through the circulatory system and generates hydrostatic pressure, or *blood pressure*. Filtration occurs across the walls of small blood vessels, pushing water and dissolved nutrients into the tissues of the body. Filtration across specialized blood vessels in the kidneys is an essential step in the production of urine.

3-4 Carrier-mediated and vesicular transport mechanisms also facilitate membrane passage

Carrier-mediated transport requires the presence of specialized membrane proteins. It can be passive or active, depending on the substance transported and the nature of the transport mechanism. *Vesicular transport* involves the movement of materials within small membranous sacs, or *vesicles*. Vesicular transport is always an active process.

CARRIER-MEDIATED TRANSPORT

In **carrier-mediated transport,** membrane proteins bind specific ions or organic substrates and carry them across the plasma membrane. These proteins share several characteristics with enzymes. They may be used repeatedly and they can only bind to specific substrates; the carrier protein that transports glucose, for example, will not carry other simple sugars.

Carrier-mediated transport can be passive (no ATP required) or active (ATP dependent). In *passive transport*, solutes are typically carried from an area of high concentration to an area of low concentration. *Active transport* mechanisms may follow or oppose an existing concentration gradient.

Many carrier proteins transport one ion or molecule at a time, but some move two solutes simultaneously. In *cotransport*, the carrier transports the two substances in the same direction, either into or out of the cell. In *countertransport*, one substance is moved into the cell while the other is moved out. Two major examples of carrier-mediated transport—*facilitated diffusion* and *active transport*—are discussed next.

Facilitated Diffusion

Many essential nutrients, including glucose and amino acids, are insoluble in lipids and too large to fit through membrane channels. However, these compounds can be passively transported across the membrane by carrier proteins in a process called **facilitated diffusion** (Figure 3-8). First, the molecule to be transported binds to a **receptor site** on the carrier protein. Then the shape of the protein changes, moving the molecule to the inside of the plasma membrane, where it is released into the cytoplasm.

As in the case of simple diffusion, no ATP is expended in facilitated diffusion, and the molecules move from an area of higher concentration to one of lower concentration. Facilitated diffusion differs from simple diffusion, however, in that the rate of transport cannot increase indefinitely; only a limited number of carrier proteins are available in the membrane. Once all of them are operating, any further increase in the solute concentration in the extracellular fluid will have no effect on the rate of movement into the cell.

Active Transport

In **active transport,** the high-energy bond in ATP provides the energy needed to move ions or molecules across the membrane. Despite the energy cost, active transport offers one great advantage: It is not dependent on a concentration gradient. This means that the cell can import or export specific materials *regardless of their intracellular or extracellular concentrations.*

All cells contain carrier proteins called **ion pumps** that actively transport the cations sodium (Na^+), potassium (K^+), calcium (Ca^{2+}), and magnesium (Mg^{2+}) across plasma membranes. Specialized cells can transport other ions, including iodide (I^-), chloride (Cl^-), and iron (Fe^{2+}). Many of these carrier proteins move a specific cation or anion in one direction only, either into or out of the cell. In a few cases, one carrier protein can move more than one ion at a time. If one kind of ion moves in one direction and the other moves in the opposite direction (countertransport), the carrier protein is called an **exchange pump.**

A major function of exchange pumps is to maintain cell homeostasis. Sodium and potassium ions are the principal cations in body fluids. Sodium ion concentrations are high in the extracellular fluids but low in the cytoplasm. The distribution of potassium in the body is just the opposite—low in the extracellular fluids and high in the cytoplasm. Because of the presence of channel proteins in the membrane that are always open (so-called *leak channels*), sodium ions slowly diffuse into the cell, and potassium ions diffuse out.

Homeostasis within the cell depends on maintaining sodium and potassium ion concentration gradients with the extracellular fluid. The **sodium–potassium exchange pump** maintains these gradients by ejecting sodium ions and recapturing lost potassium ions. For each ATP molecule consumed, three sodium ions are ejected and two potassium ions are reclaimed by the cell (Figure 3-9). The energy demands are impressive: The sodium–potassium exchange pump may use up to 40 percent of the ATP produced by a resting cell.

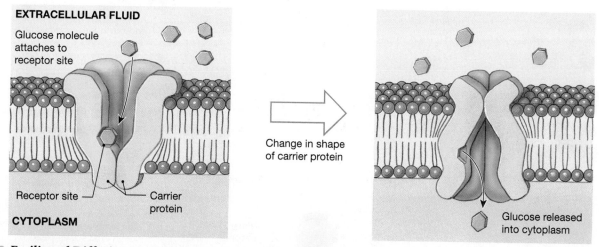

EXTRACELLULAR FLUID

Glucose molecule attaches to receptor site

Receptor site — Carrier protein

CYTOPLASM

Change in shape of carrier protein

Glucose released into cytoplasm

FIGURE 3-8 **Facilitated Diffusion.** In this process, an extracellular molecule, such as glucose, binds to a receptor site on a carrier protein. The binding alters the shape of the protein, which then releases the molecule to diffuse into the cytoplasm.

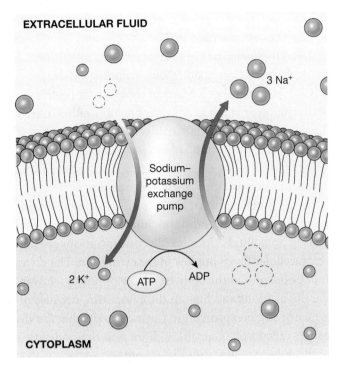

FIGURE 3-9 The Sodium–Potassium Exchange Pump. The operation of the sodium–potassium exchange pump is an example of active transport because its operation requires the release of energy through the conversion of ATP to ADP.

VESICULAR TRANSPORT

In **vesicular transport,** materials move into or out of the cell in vesicles, small membranous sacs that form at, or fuse with, the plasma membrane. The two major categories of vesicular transport are *endocytosis* and *exocytosis.*

Endocytosis

The process called **endocytosis** (EN-dō-sī-TŌ-sis; *endo-*, inside + *cyte*, cell) is the packaging of extracellular materials in a vesicle at the cell surface for import *into* the cell. Relatively large volumes of extracellular material may be involved. There are three major types of endocytosis: *receptor-mediated endocytosis, pinocytosis,* and *phagocytosis.* All three are active processes that require ATP or other sources of energy.

● **Receptor-mediated endocytosis** involves the formation of small vesicles at the membrane surface to import selected substances into the cell. This process produces vesicles that contain a specific target molecule in high concentrations. Receptor-mediated endocytosis begins when molecules in the extracellular fluid bind to receptors on the membrane surface (Figure 3-10). The receptors bind to specific target

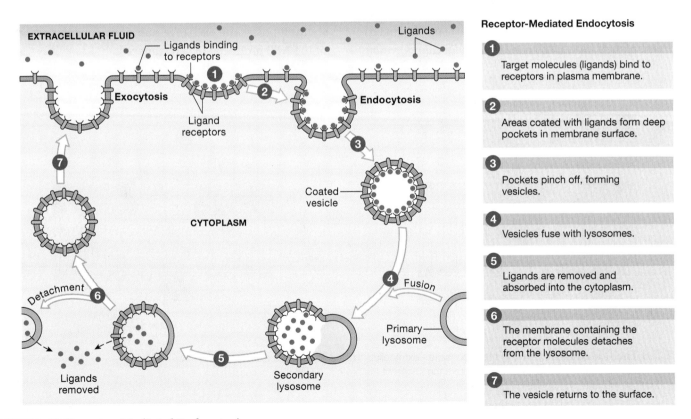

Receptor-Mediated Endocytosis

1. Target molecules (ligands) bind to receptors in plasma membrane.

2. Areas coated with ligands form deep pockets in membrane surface.

3. Pockets pinch off, forming vesicles.

4. Vesicles fuse with lysosomes.

5. Ligands are removed and absorbed into the cytoplasm.

6. The membrane containing the receptor molecules detaches from the lysosome.

7. The vesicle returns to the surface.

FIGURE 3-10 Receptor-Mediated Endocytosis.

molecules, called *ligands* (LĪ-gandz), such as a transport protein or hormone, and then cluster together on the membrane. The area of the membrane with the bound receptors forms a groove or pocket that pinches off to form a vesicle. Many important substances, such as cholesterol and iron ions (Fe^{2+}), are carried throughout the body attached to special transport proteins. These transport proteins are too large to pass through membrane channels but can enter cells through receptor-mediated endocytosis.

- **Pinocytosis** (pi-nō-sī-TŌ-sis; *pinein,* to drink), or "cell drinking," is the formation of small vesicles filled with extracellular fluid. In this process, common to all cells, a deep groove or pocket forms in the plasma membrane and then pinches off. Because no receptor proteins are involved, pinocytosis is not as selective a process as receptor-mediated endocytosis.

- **Phagocytosis** (FAG-ō-sī-TŌ-sis; *phagein,* to eat), or "cell eating," produces vesicles containing solid objects that may be as large as the cell itself (**Figure 3-11**). Cytoplasmic extensions called **pseudopodia** (soo-dō-PŌ-dē-ah;

pseudo-, false + *podon,* foot) surround the object, and their membranes fuse to form a vesicle. This vesicle then fuses with many *lysosomes,* and the vesicle contents are broken down by the lysosomes' digestive enzymes.

Most cells display pinocytosis, but phagocytosis is performed only by specialized cells that protect tissues by engulfing bacteria, cell debris, and other abnormal materials. Phagocytic cells will be considered in chapters dealing with blood cells (Chapter 11) and the immune response (Chapter 14).

Exocytosis

The process called **exocytosis** (ek-sō-sī-TŌ-sis; *exo-,* outside) is the functional reverse of endocytosis. In exocytosis, a vesicle created inside the cell fuses with the plasma membrane and discharges its contents into the extracellular environment. The ejected material may be a secretion such as a *hormone* (a compound that circulates in the blood and affects cells in other parts of the body), mucus, or waste products remaining from the recycling of damaged organelles (**Figure 3-11**).

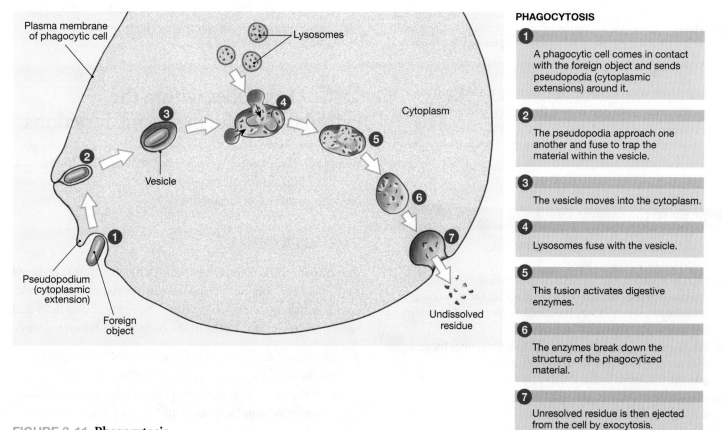

PHAGOCYTOSIS

1 A phagocytic cell comes in contact with the foreign object and sends pseudopodia (cytoplasmic extensions) around it.

2 The pseudopodia approach one another and fuse to trap the material within the vesicle.

3 The vesicle moves into the cytoplasm.

4 Lysosomes fuse with the vesicle.

5 This fusion activates digestive enzymes.

6 The enzymes break down the structure of the phagocytized material.

7 Unresolved residue is then ejected from the cell by exocytosis.

FIGURE 3-11 **Phagocytosis.**

TABLE 3-3 **A Summary of the Mechanisms Involved in Movement Across Plasma Membranes**

MECHANISM	PROCESS	FACTORS AFFECTING RATE OF MOVEMENT	SUBSTANCES INVOLVED
DIFFUSION	Molecular movement of solutes; direction determined by relative concentrations	Steepness of gradient, molecular size, electric charge, lipid solubility, temperature	Small inorganic ions, lipid-soluble materials (all cells)
Osmosis	Movement of water molecules toward solution containing relatively higher solute concentration; requires selectively permeable membrane	Concentration gradient, opposing osmotic or hydrostatic pressure	Water only (all cells)
FILTRATION	Movement of water, usually with solute, by hydrostatic pressure; requires filtration membrane	Amount of pressure, size of pores in filtration membrane	Water and small ions (blood vessels)
CARRIER-MEDIATED TRANSPORT			
Facilitated diffusion	Carrier proteins passively transport solutes down a concentration gradient	Steepness of gradient, temperature, and availability of carrier proteins	Glucose and amino acids (all cells)
Active transport	Carrier proteins actively transport solutes regardless of any concentration gradients	Availability of carrier proteins, substrate, and ATP	Na^+, K^+, Ca^{2+}, Mg^{2+} (all cells); other solutes by specialized cells
VESICULAR TRANSPORT			
Endocytosis	Creation of membranous vesicles containing fluid or solid material	Mechanism depends on substance being moved into cell; requires ATP	Fluids, nutrients (all cells); debris, pathogens (specialized cells)
Exocytosis	Fusion of vesicles containing fluids and/or solids with the plasma membrane	Mechanism depends on substance being carried; requires ATP	Fluids, debris (all cells)

At any given moment, various transport mechanisms are moving materials into and out of the cell. These mechanisms are summarized in Table 3-3.

CHECKPOINT

11. What is the difference between active and passive transport processes?

12. During digestion, the concentration of hydrogen ions (H^+) in the stomach rises to many times that within the cells lining the stomach, where H^+ are produced. Is the type of transport process involved passive or active?

13. When certain types of white blood cells encounter bacteria, they are able to engulf them and bring them into the cell. What is this process called?

See the blue Answers tab at the back of the book.

3-5 Organelles within the cytoplasm perform specific functions

Cytoplasm is a general term for the material inside the cell, from the plasma membrane to the nucleus. The cytoplasm contains cytosol and organelles.

THE CYTOSOL

The **cytosol** is the *intracellular fluid,* which contains dissolved nutrients, ions, soluble and insoluble proteins, and waste products. It differs in composition from the extracellular fluid that surrounds most of the cells in the body in the following ways:

● The cytosol contains a higher concentration of potassium ions and a lower sodium-ion concentration, whereas extracellular fluid contains a higher concentration of sodium ions and a lower potassium-ion concentration.

- The cytosol contains a high concentration of dissolved proteins, many of them enzymes that regulate metabolic operations. These proteins give the cytosol a consistency that varies between that of thin maple syrup and almost-set gelatin.

- The cytosol usually contains small quantities of carbohydrates and large reserves of amino acids and lipids. The carbohydrates are broken down to provide energy, and the amino acids are used to manufacture proteins. The lipids are used primarily as an energy source when carbohydrates are unavailable.

The cytosol may also contain insoluble materials known as **inclusions.** Examples include stored nutrients (such as glycogen granules in muscle and liver cells) and lipid droplets (in fat cells).

THE ORGANELLES

Organelles (or-gan-ELZ; "little organs") are internal structures that perform specific functions essential to normal cell structure, maintenance, and metabolism (see Table 3-1). Membrane-enclosed organelles include the *nucleus, mitochondria, endoplasmic reticulum, Golgi apparatus, lysosomes,* and *peroxisomes.* The membrane isolates the organelle from the cytosol, so that the organelle can manufacture or store secretions, enzymes, or toxins that might otherwise damage the cell. The *cytoskeleton, microvilli, centrioles, cilia, flagella, ribosomes,* and *proteasomes* are nonmembranous organelles. Because they are not surrounded by membranes, their parts are in direct contact with the cytosol.

The Cytoskeleton

The **cytoskeleton** is an internal protein framework of various threadlike filaments and hollow tubules that gives the cytoplasm strength and flexibility (Figure 3-12). In most cells, the most important cytoskeletal elements are microfilaments, intermediate filaments, and microtubules. Thick filaments are found only in muscle cells.

MICROFILAMENTS. The thinnest strands of the cytoskeleton are **microfilaments,** which are usually composed of the protein **actin.** In most cells, they form a dense layer just inside the plasma membrane. Microfilaments attach the plasma membrane to the underlying cytoplasm by forming connections with proteins of the plasma membrane. In muscle cells, actin microfilaments interact with **thick filaments,** made of the protein **myosin,** to produce powerful contractions.

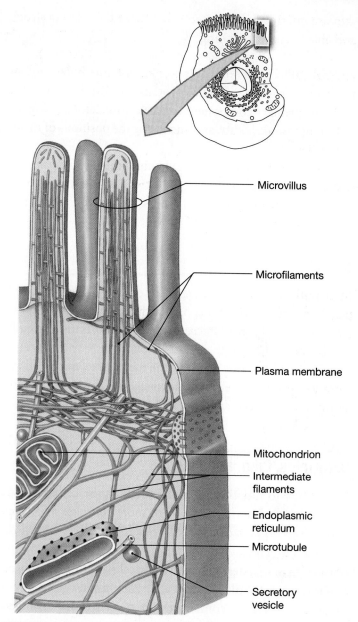

- Microvillus
- Microfilaments
- Plasma membrane
- Mitochondrion
- Intermediate filaments
- Endoplasmic reticulum
- Microtubule
- Secretory vesicle

FIGURE 3-12 **The Cytoskeleton.** The cytoskeleton provides strength and structural support for the cell and its organelles. Interactions between cytoskeletal components are also important in moving organelles and changing the shape of the cell.

INTERMEDIATE FILAMENTS. These cytoskeletal filaments are intermediate in size between microfilaments and the thick filaments of muscle cells. Their protein composition varies among cell types. Intermediate filaments strengthen the cell and stabilize its position with respect to surrounding cells through specialized attachments to the plasma membrane. Many cells contain specialized intermediate filaments with unique functions. For example, keratin fibers in the superficial layers of the skin are intermediate filaments that make these layers strong and able to resist stretching.

MICROTUBULES. All body cells contain **microtubules,** hollow tubes built from the globular protein **tubulin.** Microtubules form the primary components of the cytoskeleton, giving the cell strength and rigidity, and anchoring the positions of major organelles.

During cell division, microtubules form the *spindle apparatus,* which distributes the duplicated chromosomes to opposite ends of the dividing cell. This process will be considered in a later section.

Microvilli

Microvilli are small, finger-shaped projections of the plasma membrane on the exposed surfaces of many cells (Figure 3-2). An internal core of microfilaments supports the microvilli and connects them to the cytoskeleton (Figure 3-12). Because they increase the surface area of the membrane, microvilli are common features of cells actively engaged in absorbing materials from the extracellular fluid, such as the cells of the digestive tract and kidneys.

Centrioles, Cilia, and Flagella

In addition to functioning individually in the cytoskeleton, microtubules also interact to form more complex structures known as *centrioles, cilia,* and *flagella.*

CENTRIOLES. A **centriole** is a cylindrical structure composed of short microtubules (Figure 3-2). All animal cells that are capable of dividing contain a pair of centrioles arranged perpendicular to each other. The centrioles produce the spindle fibers that move DNA strands during cell division. Mature red blood cells, skeletal muscle cells, cardiac muscle cells, and typical neurons lack centrioles; as a result, these cells cannot divide.

CILIA. Structures called **cilia** (SIL-ē-uh; singular *cilium*) are relatively long, slender extensions of the plasma membrane (Figure 3-2). They are supported internally by a cylindrical array of microtubules. Cilia undergo active movements that require energy from ATP. Their coordinated actions move fluids or secretions across the cell surface. For example, cilia lining the respiratory passageways beat in a synchronized manner to move sticky mucus and trapped dust particles toward the throat and away from delicate respiratory surfaces. If these cilia are damaged or immobilized by heavy smoking or a metabolic problem, the cleansing action is lost, and the irritants will no longer be removed. As a result, a chronic cough and respiratory infections develop.

FLAGELLA. Organelles called **flagella** (fla-JEL-uh; singular *flagellum,* whip) resemble cilia but are much longer. Flagella move a cell through the surrounding fluid, rather than moving the fluid past a stationary cell. Sperm cells are the only human cells that have a flagellum. If the flagella of sperm are paralyzed or otherwise abnormal, the individual will be sterile, because immobile sperm cannot perform fertilization.

Ribosomes

Ribosomes are organelles that manufacture proteins, using information provided by the DNA of the nucleus. Each ribosome consists of a small and large subunit composed of ribosomal RNA and protein. Ribosomes are found in all cells, but their number varies depending on the type of cell and its activities. For example, liver cells, which manufacture blood proteins, have many more ribosomes than do fat cells, which synthesize triglycerides.

There are two major types of ribosomes: free ribosomes and fixed ribosomes. **Free ribosomes** are scattered throughout the cytoplasm, and the proteins they manufacture enter the cytosol. **Fixed ribosomes** are attached to the *endoplasmic reticulum* (ER), a membranous organelle. Proteins manufactured by fixed ribosomes enter the endoplasmic reticulum, where they are modified and packaged for export.

Proteasomes

Whereas free ribosomes produce proteins within the cytoplasm, proteasomes remove them. **Proteasomes** are hollow, cylindrical organelles that contain an assortment of protein-breaking proteolytic enzymes, or *proteases.* Proteasomes are responsible for removing and recycling damaged or denatured proteins and for breaking down abnormal proteins such as those produced within cells infected by viruses.

The Endoplasmic Reticulum

The **endoplasmic reticulum** (en-dō-PLAZ-mik re-TIK-ū-lum; *reticulum,* a network), or **ER,** is a network of intracellular membranes connected to the membranous *nuclear envelope* surrounding the nucleus (Figure 3-2). The ER has four major functions:

1. *Synthesis.* Specialized regions of the ER manufacture proteins, carbohydrates, and lipids.

Ribosomes

Rough endoplasmic reticulum with fixed (attached) ribosomes

Smooth endoplasmic reticulum

2. *Storage.* The ER can store synthesized molecules or materials absorbed from the cytosol without affecting other cellular operations.

3. *Transport.* Materials can be moved from place to place in the ER.

4. *Detoxification.* Drugs or toxins can be absorbed by the ER and neutralized by enzymes within it.

There are two types of endoplasmic reticulum, **smooth endoplasmic reticulum (SER)** and **rough endoplasmic reticulum (RER)** (Figure 3-13). The term *smooth* refers to the fact that no ribosomes are associated with the SER. The SER is the site where lipids and carbohydrates are produced. The membranes of the RER contain fixed ribosomes, giving the RER a beaded or rough appearance. The ribosomes participate in protein synthesis.

SER functions include (1) the synthesis of the phospholipids and cholesterol needed for maintenance and growth of the plasma membrane, ER, nuclear membrane, and Golgi apparatus in all cells; (2) the synthesis of steroid hormones, such as *testosterone* and *estrogen* (sex hormones) in cells of the reproductive organs; (3) the synthesis and storage of glycerides, especially triglycerides, in liver cells and fat cells; and (4) the synthesis and storage of glycogen in skeletal muscle and liver cells.

The rough endoplasmic reticulum (RER) functions as a combination workshop and shipping depot. The fixed ribosomes on its outer surface release newly synthesized proteins into chamber-like spaces of the RER. Some proteins will remain in the RER and function as enzymes. Others are chemically modified and packaged into small membranous sacs that pinch off from the tips of the ER. The sacs, called *transport vesicles,* deliver the proteins to the Golgi apparatus, another membranous organelle, where they are processed further.

The amount of endoplasmic reticulum and the ratio of RER to SER vary with the type of cell and its activities. For example, pancreatic cells that manufacture digestive enzymes contain an extensive RER, and the SER is relatively small. The proportion is just the reverse in reproductive system cells that synthesize steroid hormones.

The Golgi Apparatus

The **Golgi** (GŌL-jē) **apparatus** consists of a set of five or six flattened membranous discs. A single cell may contain several sets, each resembling a stack of dinner plates (Figure 3-2). The major functions of the Golgi apparatus are (1) the modification and packaging of secretions, such as hormones and enzymes; (2) the renewal or modification of the plasma membrane; and (3) the packaging of special enzymes for use in the cytosol.

The various packaging roles of the Golgi apparatus are diagrammed in Figure 3-14a. The synthesis of proteins and other substances occurs in the RER, and then transport vesicles move these products to the Golgi apparatus. Enzymes in the Golgi apparatus modify the newly arrived molecules as other vesicles move them closer to the cell surface through succeeding membranes. Ultimately, the modified materials are repackaged in vesicles that leave the Golgi apparatus.

The Golgi apparatus creates three types of vesicles, each with a different fate. One type of vesicle, called *lysosomes,* contains digestive enzymes. These vesicles remain in the cytoplasm. A second type, **secretory vesicles,** contains secretions that will

FIGURE 3-14 The Golgi Apparatus. (a) Transport vesicles carry molecules manufactured in the endoplasmic reticulum to the Golgi apparatus, where these molecules are modified and transported through succeeding membranes toward the cell surface. At the membrane closest to the cell surface, three types of vesicles develop. Enzyme-filled lysosomes remain in the cytoplasm, secretory vesicles carry secretions from the Golgi apparatus to the cell surface, and membrane renewal vesicles add additional phospholipids and proteins to the plasma membrane. **(b)** Exocytosis of secretions at the cell surface.

be discharged from the cell. Secretion occurs through exocytosis at the cell surface (Figure 3-14b). A third type of vesicle, **membrane renewal vesicles,** fuses with the surface of the cell to add new lipids and proteins to the plasma membrane. At the same time, other areas of the plasma membrane are being removed and recycled. Through such activities, the Golgi apparatus can change the properties of the plasma membrane over time. For example, receptors can be added or removed, making the cell more or less sensitive to a particular stimulus.

Lysosomes

As just noted, **lysosomes** (LĪ-sō-sōmz; *lyso-*, a loosening + *soma,* body) are vesicles filled with digestive enzymes. Lysosomes perform cleanup and recycling functions within the cell. Their enzymes are activated when they fuse with the membranes of damaged organelles, such as mitochondria or fragments of the endoplasmic reticulum. Then the enzymes break down the lysosomal contents. Nutrients reenter the cytosol through passive or active transport processes, and the remaining material is eliminated by exocytosis.

Lysosomes also function in defense against disease. Through endocytosis, immune system cells may engulf bacteria, fluids, and organic debris in their surroundings and isolate them within vesicles. ∞ p. 70 Lysosomes fuse with vesicles created in this way, and the digestive enzymes then break down the contents and release usable substances such as sugars or amino acids.

Lysosomes perform essential recycling functions inside the cell. For example, when muscle cells are inactive, lysosomes

gradually break down their contractile proteins; if the cells become active once again, this destruction ends. However, in damaged or dead cells, lysosome membranes disintegrate, releasing active enzymes into the cytosol. These enzymes rapidly destroy the proteins and organelles of the cell, a process called **autolysis** (aw-TOL-i-sis; *auto-*, self). Because the breakdown of lysosomal membranes can destroy a cell, lysosomes have been called cellular "suicide packets." We do not know how lysosomal activities are controlled or why the enclosed enzymes do not digest the lysosomal membranes unless the cell is damaged.

Peroxisomes

Peroxisomes are smaller than lysosomes and carry a different group of enzymes. In contrast to lysosomes, which are produced at the Golgi apparatus, new peroxisomes arise from the growth and subdivision of existing peroxisomes. Peroxisomes absorb and break down fatty acids and other organic compounds. As they do so, they generate hydrogen peroxide (H_2O_2), a potentially dangerous *free radical.* **Free radicals** are ions or molecules that contain unpaired electrons. They are highly reactive and enter additional reactions that can be destructive to vital compounds such as proteins. Other enzymes in peroxisomes break down hydrogen peroxide into oxygen and water, thus protecting the cell from the damaging effects of free radicals produced during catabolism. Found in all cells, peroxisomes are most abundant in metabolically active cells, such as liver cells.

Cells are the basic structural and functional units of life that respond directly to the environment to help maintain homeostasis. Over time, they are capable of changing their internal structure and physiological functions.

Mitochondria

Mitochondria (mī-tō-KON-drē-uh; singular *mitochondrion; mitos,* thread + *chondrion,* granule) are small organelles that provide energy for the cell. The number of mitochondria in a particular cell varies with the cell's energy demands. Red blood cells, for example, have no mitochondria, whereas these organelles may account for 20 percent of the volume of an active liver cell.

Mitochondria are made up of an unusual double membrane. The outer membrane surrounds the entire organelle; the inner membrane contains numerous folds called *cristae* (**Figure 3-15**). Cristae increase the surface area exposed to the fluid contents, or *matrix,* of the mitochondria. Metabolic enzymes in the matrix catalyze energy-producing reactions.

Most of the chemical reactions that release energy occur in the mitochondria, but most of the cellular activities that require energy occur in the surrounding cytoplasm. Cells must, therefore, store energy in a form that can be moved from place to place. Energy is stored and transferred in the high-energy bond of ATP, as discussed in Chapter 2. ∞ p. 51 Living cells break the high-energy phosphate bond under controlled conditions, reconverting ATP to ADP and releasing energy for the cell's use.

MITOCHONDRIAL ENERGY PRODUCTION. Most cells generate ATP and other high-energy compounds through the breakdown of carbohydrates, especially glucose. Although most of the actual energy production occurs inside mitochondria, the first steps take place in the cytosol. In this reaction sequence, called *glycolysis,* six-carbon glucose molecules are broken down into three-carbon *pyruvic acid* molecules. These molecules are then absorbed by the mitochondria. If glucose or other carbohydrates are not available, mitochondria can absorb and utilize small carbon chains produced by the breakdown of proteins or lipids. So long as oxygen is present, these molecules will be broken down to carbon dioxide, which diffuses out of the cell, and hydrogen atoms, which participate in a series of energy-releasing steps resulting in the enzymatic conversion of ADP to ATP. ∞ p. 51

Because the key reactions involved in mitochondrial activity consume oxygen, the process of mitochondrial energy production is known as **aerobic** (*aero-,* air + *bios,* life) **metabolism,** or *cellular respiration.* Aerobic metabolism in mitochondria produces about 95 percent of the energy a cell needs to stay alive. Aerobic metabolism is discussed in more detail in Chapters 7 and 17.

Several inheritable disorders result from abnormal mitochondrial activity. The mitochondria involved have defective enzymes, reducing their ability to generate ATP. Cells throughout the body

Mitochondria provide most of the energy needed to keep your cells (and you) alive. They require oxygen and organic substrates, and they generate carbon dioxide and ATP.

FIGURE 3-15 Mitochondria. Shown here are the three-dimensional organization of a typical mitochondrion and a color-enhanced TEM of a mitochondrion in section. Mitochondria absorb short carbon chains and oxygen and generate carbon dioxide and ATP.

TEM × 46,332

may be affected, but symptoms involving muscle cells, nerve cells, and the light receptor cells in the eye are most common, because these cells have especially high energy demands.

CHECKPOINT

14. Describe the difference between the cytoplasm and the cytosol.

15. Identify the membranous organelles, and list their functions.

16. Cells lining the small intestine have numerous fingerlike projections on their free surface. What are these structures, and what is their function?

17. How does the absence of centrioles affect a cell?

18. Why do certain cells in the ovaries and testes contain large amounts of smooth endoplasmic reticulum (SER)?

19. What does the presence of many mitochondria imply about a cell's energy requirements?

See the blue Answers tab at the back of the book.

3-6 The nucleus contains DNA and enzymes essential for controlling cellular activities

The **nucleus** is usually the largest and most conspicuous structure in a cell. It is the control center for cellular operations. A single nucleus stores all the information needed to control the synthesis of the more than 100,000 different proteins in the human body. The nucleus determines both the structure of the cell and the functions it can perform by controlling which proteins are synthesized, under what circumstances, and in what amounts.

NUCLEAR STRUCTURE AND CONTENTS

Most cells contain a single nucleus, but there are exceptions: Skeletal muscle cells have many nuclei, and mature red blood cells have none. Figure 3-16 shows the structure of a typical nucleus. A **nuclear envelope** consisting of a double membrane surrounds the nucleus and separates its fluid contents—the *nucleoplasm*—from the cytosol. The nucleoplasm contains ions, enzymes, RNA and DNA nucleotides, proteins, small amounts of RNA, and DNA.

Chemical communication between the nucleus and the cytosol occurs through **nuclear pores.** These pores are large enough to permit the movement of ions and small molecules yet small enough to regulate the transport of proteins and RNA.

Most nuclei contain several **nucleoli** (noo-KLĒ-ō-lī; singular *nucleolus*). Nucleoli are organelles that synthesize **ribosomal RNA (rRNA)** and assemble the ribosomal subunits into functional ribosomes. For this reason, they are most prominent in cells that manufacture large amounts of proteins, such as muscle and liver cells.

It is the DNA in the nucleus that stores instructions for protein synthesis, and this DNA is contained in **chromosomes** (*chroma,* color). The nuclei of human body cells contain 23 pairs of chromosomes. One member of each pair is derived from the mother and one from the father. The structure of a typical chromosome is shown in Figure 3-17.

Each chromosome contains DNA strands wrapped around special proteins called *histones.* The tightness of DNA coiling determines whether the chromosome is long and thin or short and fat. Chromosomes in a dividing cell are very tightly coiled, and they can be seen clearly as separate structures in light or electron micrographs. In cells that are not dividing, the DNA is loosely coiled, forming a tangle of fine filaments known as **chromatin.**

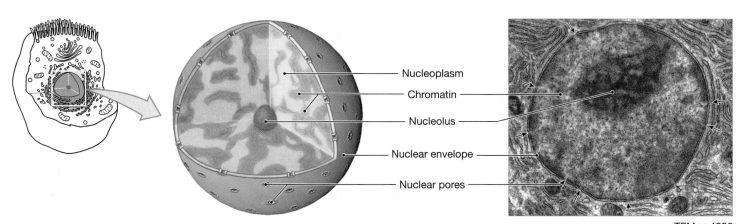

Nucleoplasm

Chromatin

Nucleolus

Nuclear envelope

Nuclear pores

TEM × 4828

FIGURE 3-16 The Nucleus. The electron micrograph and diagrammatic view show important nuclear structures. The arrows indicate the locations of nuclear pores.

FIGURE 3-17 Chromosome Structure. DNA strands wound around histone proteins (at bottom) form coils that may be very tight or rather loose. In cells that are not dividing, the DNA is loosely coiled, forming a tangled network known as chromatin. When the coiling becomes tighter, as it does in preparation for cell division, the DNA becomes visible as distinct structures called chromosomes.

The Big Picture

The nucleus contains the genetic instructions needed to synthesize the proteins that determine cell structure and function. This information is stored in chromosomes, which consist of DNA and various proteins involved in controlling and accessing the genetic information.

INFORMATION STORAGE IN THE NUCLEUS

Each protein molecule consists of a unique sequence of amino acids. ∞ p. 46 Any instructions for constructing a protein, therefore, must include information concerning the amino acid sequence. This information is stored in the chemical structure of the DNA strands in the nucleus. The chemical "language" the cell uses is known as the **genetic code.** An understanding of the genetic code has enabled us to determine how cells build proteins and how various structural and functional traits, such as

hair color or blood type, are inherited from generation to generation.

The basic structure of nucleic acids was described in Chapter 2. ∞ p. 49 A single DNA molecule consists of a pair of DNA strands held together by hydrogen bonding between complementary nitrogenous bases. Information is stored in the sequence of nitrogenous bases (adenine, A; thymine, T; cytosine, C; and guanine, G) along the length of the DNA strands.

The genetic code is called a *triplet code* because a sequence of three nitrogenous bases specifies the identity of a single amino acid. The DNA triplet adenine–cytosine–adenine (ACA), for example, codes for the amino acid cysteine.

A **gene** is the functional unit of heredity, and each gene consists of all the triplets needed to produce a specific protein. The number of triplets varies from gene to gene, depending on the size of the protein that will be produced. Each gene also contains special segments responsible for regulating its own activity. In effect these triplets say, "Do (or do not) read this message," "Message starts here," or "Message ends here." The "read me," "don't read me," and "start" signals form a special region of the DNA called the *promoter,* or *control segment,* at the start of each gene. Each gene ends with a "stop" signal. Not all genes code for proteins. Some contain instructions for the synthesis of transfer RNA or ribosomal RNA, some regulate other genes, and others have no apparent function.

Clinical Note

DNA Fingerprinting

Every nucleated cell in the body carries a set of 46 chromosomes identical to the set formed at fertilization. Not all the DNA of these chromosomes codes for proteins, however, and long stretches of DNA have no known function. Some of the "useless" segments contain the same nucleotide sequence repeated over and over. The number of segments and the number of repetitions per segment vary from individual to individual. The chance that any two individuals, other than identical twins, will have the same pattern is less than one in 9 billion. The identification of individuals can, therefore, be made on the basis of DNA pattern analysis, just as it can on the basis of a fingerprint. Skin scrapings, blood, semen, hair, or other tissues can be used as a sample source. Information from **DNA fingerprinting** has been used to convict (and to acquit) people accused of committing violent crimes, such as rape or murder. The science of molecular biology has thus become a useful addition to the crime-fighting toolbox.

20. Describe the contents and structure of the nucleus.

21. What is a gene?

See the blue Answers tab at the back of the book.

3-7 DNA controls protein synthesis, cell structure, and cell function

Each DNA molecule contains thousands of genes and, therefore, holds the information needed to synthesize thousands of proteins. These genes are normally tightly coiled and bound to histones, which prevent their activation and, in doing so, prevent the synthesis of proteins. Before a specific gene can be activated, enzymes must temporarily break the weak bonds between its ni-

trogenous bases and remove the histone that guards the promoter at the start of each gene. Although the process of gene activation is only partially understood, more is known about protein synthesis. The process of **protein synthesis** is divided into *transcription*, the production of RNA from a single strand of DNA, and *translation*, the assembling of a protein by ribosomes, using the information carried by the RNA molecule. Transcription takes place within the nucleus, and translation occurs in the cytoplasm.

TRANSCRIPTION

Ribosomes, the organelles of protein synthesis, are located in the cytoplasm, whereas the genes are confined to the nucleus. This separation between the protein manufacturing site and the DNA's protein blueprint is overcome by the movement of a molecular messenger, a single strand of RNA known as **messenger RNA (mRNA)**. The process of mRNA formation is called **transcription** (Figure 3-18). Transcription, which is the process of transcribing or "copying," is an appropriate term

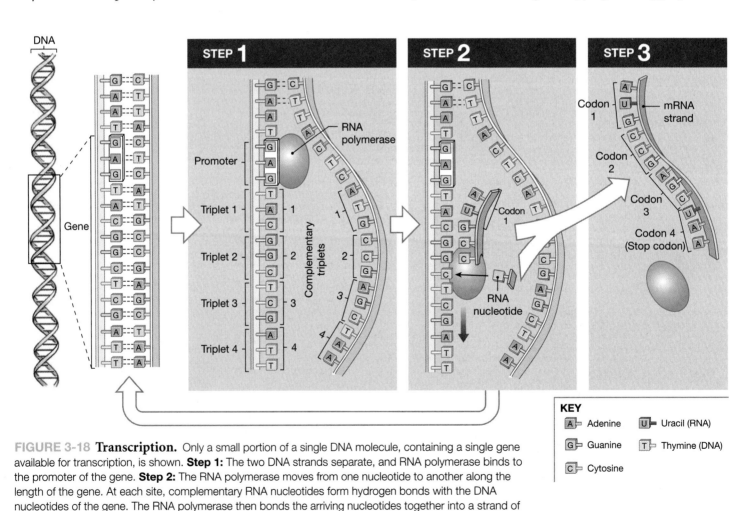

FIGURE 3-18 Transcription. Only a small portion of a single DNA molecule, containing a single gene available for transcription, is shown. **Step 1:** The two DNA strands separate, and RNA polymerase binds to the promoter of the gene. **Step 2:** The RNA polymerase moves from one nucleotide to another along the length of the gene. At each site, complementary RNA nucleotides form hydrogen bonds with the DNA nucleotides of the gene. The RNA polymerase then bonds the arriving nucleotides together into a strand of mRNA. **Step 3:** On reaching the stop codon at the end of the gene, the RNA polymerase and the mRNA strand detach, and the two DNA strands reattach.

because the newly formed mRNA is a transcript (a copy) of the information contained in the gene.

Each DNA strand contains thousands of genes. Transcription begins when an enzyme, *RNA polymerase,* binds to the promoter of a gene (Step 1 in Figure 3-18). This enzyme promotes the synthesis of an mRNA strand, using nucleotides complementary to those in the gene (Step 2). The nucleotides involved are those characteristic of RNA, not those of DNA; RNA polymerase may attach adenine, guanine, cytosine, or uracil (U), but never thymine. Thus, wherever an A occurs in the DNA strand, RNA polymerase will attach a U rather than a T. The mRNA strand, thus, contains a sequence of nitrogenous bases that are complementary to those of the gene. A sequence of three nitrogenous bases along the new mRNA strand represents a **codon** (KŌ-don) that is complementary to the corresponding triplet along the gene (Step 3). At the DNA "stop" signal, the enzyme and the mRNA strand detach, and the complementary DNA strands reassociate.

The mRNA formed in this way may be altered before it leaves the nucleus. For example, some regions (called *introns*) may be removed and the remaining segments (called *exons*) spliced together. This modification creates a shorter, functional mRNA strand that enters the cytoplasm through a nuclear pore. We now know that by removing different introns, a single gene can produce mRNAs that code for several different proteins. How such alterations are regulated remains a mystery.

TRANSLATION

Translation is the synthesis of a protein using the information provided by the sequence of codons along the mRNA strand. Every amino acid has at least one unique and specific codon;

Table 3-4 includes several examples. During translation, the sequence of codons determines the sequence of amino acids in the protein.

Translation begins when the newly synthesized mRNA leaves the nucleus and binds with a ribosome in the cytoplasm. Molecules of **transfer RNA (tRNA)** then deliver amino acids that will be used by the ribosome to assemble a protein. There are more than 20 different types of transfer RNA, at least one for each amino acid used in protein synthesis. Each tRNA molecule contains a complementary triplet of nitrogenous bases, known as an **anticodon,** that will bind to a specific codon on the mRNA.

TABLE 3-4 Examples of the Triplet Code

DNA TRIPLET	mRNA CODON	tRNA ANTICODON	AMINO ACID (AND/OR INSTRUCTION)
AAA	UUU	AAA	Phenylalanine
AAT	UUA	AAU	Leucine
ACA	UGU	ACA	Cysteine
CAA	GUU	CAA	Valine
GGG	CCC	GGG	Proline
CGA	GCU	CGA	Alanine
TAC	AUG	UAC	Methionine; start codon
ATT	UAA	[none]	Stop codon

Clinical Note

Mutations

Mutations are permanent changes in a cell's DNA that affect the nucleotide sequence of one or more genes. The simplest is called a *point mutation,* a change in a single nucleotide that affects one codon. With roughly 3 billion pairs of nucleotides in the DNA of a human cell, a single mistake might seem relatively unimportant. Several hundred inherited disorders have been traced to abnormalities in enzyme or protein structure that reflect single changes in nucleotide sequence. A single change in the amino acid sequence of a structural protein or enzyme can prove fatal. For example, several cancers and two potentially lethal blood disorders, *thalassemia* and *sickle-cell anemia,* result from variations in a single nucleotide. More elaborate mutations resulting from the addition or deletion of nucleotides can affect multiple codons in one gene, in several adjacent genes, or in the structure of one or more chromosomes.

Most mutations occur during DNA replication, when cells are duplicating their DNA in preparation for cell division. A single cell or group of daughter cells may be affected. If the mutations occur early in development, however, every cell in the body may be affected. For example, a mutation affecting the DNA of an individual's sex cells will be inherited by that individual's children. Our increasing understanding of genetic structure is opening the possibility for diagnosing and correcting some of these problems.

FIGURE 3-19 **Translation.** Once transcription has been completed, the mRNA diffuses into the cytoplasm and interacts with the ribosome.

The translation process is illustrated in Figure 3-19:

Step 1 Translation begins at the "start" codon of the mRNA strand, with its binding to the small ribosomal subunit and the arrival of the first tRNA. That tRNA carries a specific amino acid. The first codon of the mRNA strand always has the base sequence AUG, which codes for methionine. (This initial methionine will be removed from the finished protein.)

Step 2 The small and large ribosomal units join together and enclose the mRNA.

Step 3 A second tRNA then arrives, carrying a different amino acid, and its anticodon binds to the second codon of the mRNA strand.

Step 4 Ribosomal enzymes now remove amino acid 1 from the first tRNA and attach it to amino acid 2 with a peptide bond. ∞ p. 46 The first tRNA then detaches from the ribosome and reenters the cytosol, where it can pick up another amino acid molecule and repeat the process. The ribosome now moves one codon farther along the length of the mRNA strand, and a third tRNA arrives, bearing amino acid 3.

Step 5 Amino acids will continue to be added to the growing protein in this way until the ribosome reaches the "stop" codon. The ribosomal subunits then detach, leaving an intact strand of mRNA and a completed polypeptide.

As you may recall from Chapter 2, a protein is a polypeptide containing 100 or more amino acids. ∞ p. 46 Translation proceeds swiftly, producing a typical protein (about 1000 amino acids) in around 20 seconds. The protein begins as a simple linear strand, but a more complex structure develops as it grows longer.

The Big Picture

Genes are the functional units of DNA that contain the instructions for making one or more proteins. The creation of specific proteins involves multiple enzymes and three types of RNA.

CHECKPOINT

22. How does the nucleus control the cell's activities?

23. What process would be affected by the lack of the enzyme RNA polymerase?

24. During the process of transcription, a nucleotide was deleted from an mRNA sequence that coded for a protein. What effect would this deletion have on the amino acid sequence of the protein?

See the blue Answers tab at the back of the book.

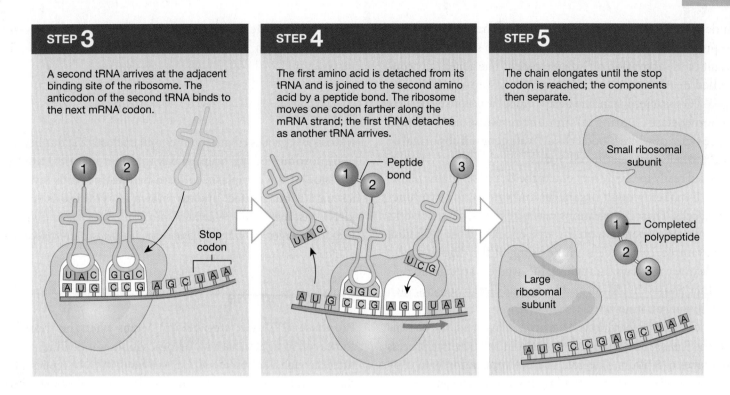

STEP 3

A second tRNA arrives at the adjacent binding site of the ribosome. The anticodon of the second tRNA binds to the next mRNA codon.

STEP 4

The first amino acid is detached from its tRNA and is joined to the second amino acid by a peptide bond. The ribosome moves one codon farther along the mRNA strand; the first tRNA detaches as another tRNA arrives.

STEP 5

The chain elongates until the stop codon is reached; the components then separate.

3-8 Stages of a cell's life cycle include interphase, mitosis, and cytokinesis

During the time between fertilization and physical maturity, the number of cells making up an individual increases from a single cell to roughly 75 trillion cells. This amazing increase in numbers occurs through a form of cellular reproduction called **cell division.** Even when development has been completed, cell division continues to be essential to survival because it replaces old and damaged cells.

For cell division to be successful, the genetic material in the nucleus must be duplicated accurately, and a complete copy must be distributed to each daughter cell. The duplication of the cell's genetic material is called *DNA replication,* and nuclear division is called **mitosis** (mī-TŌ-sis). Mitosis occurs during the division of **somatic** (*soma,* body) **cells,** which include the vast majority of the cells in the body. The production of sex cells—sperm and ova (eggs)—involves a different process, called **meiosis** (mī-Ō-sis), described in Chapter 19.

Figure 3-20 represents the life cycle of a typical cell. Most cells spend only a small part of their life cycle engaged in cell division. For most of their lives, cells are in **interphase,** an interval of time between cell divisions when they perform normal functions.

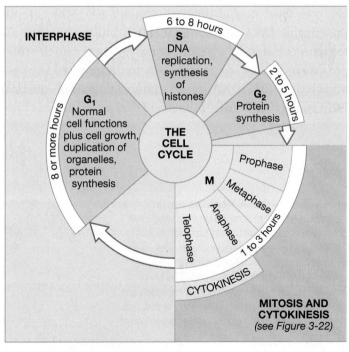

FIGURE 3-20 The Cell Life Cycle.

INTERPHASE

Somatic cells differ in the length of time spent in interphase and their frequency of cell division. For example, *stem cells* divide repeatedly with very brief interphase periods. In contrast, mature skeletal muscle cells and most nerve cells never undergo mitosis or cell division. Certain other cells appear to be programmed not to divide but instead to self-destruct as a result of the activation of "suicide genes." The genetically controlled death of cells is called **apoptosis** (ap-op-TŌ-sis or ap-ō-TŌ-sis; *ptosis,* a falling away). Apoptosis is a key process in homeostasis. During an immune response, for example, some types of white blood cells activate genes in abnormal or infected cells that tell the cell to die.

A cell ready to divide first enters the G_1 phase. In this phase, the cell makes enough organelles and cytosol for two functional cells. These preparations may take hours, days, or weeks to complete, depending on the type of cell and the situation. For example, certain cells in the lining of the digestive tract divide every few days throughout life, whereas specialized cells in other tissues divide only under special circumstances, such as following an injury.

Once these preparations have been completed, the cell enters the S phase and replicates the DNA in its nucleus, a process that takes 6–8 hours. The goal of **DNA replication** is to copy the genetic information in the nucleus so that one set of chromosomes can be given to each of the two cells produced.

DNA replication starts when the complementary strands begin to separate and unwind (**Figure 3-21**). Molecules of the enzyme *DNA polymerase* then bind to the exposed nitrogenous bases. As a result, complementary nucleotides present in the nucleoplasm attach to the exposed nitrogenous bases of the DNA strand and form a pair of identical DNA molecules. Shortly following DNA replication is a brief

G_2 phase for protein synthesis and for the completion of centriole replication. The cell then enters the M phase, and mitosis begins.

MITOSIS

Mitosis is a process that separates and encloses the duplicated chromosomes of the original cell into two identical nuclei. Division of the cytoplasm to form two distinct cells involves a separate, but related, process known as **cytokinesis** (sī-tō-ki-NĒ-sis; *cyto-,* cell + *kinesis,* motion). Mitosis is divided into four stages: *prophase, metaphase, anaphase,* and *telophase* (**Figure 3-22**).

Stage 1: Prophase

Prophase (PRŌ-fāz; *pro-,* before) begins when the chromosomes coil so tightly that they become visible as individual structures through a light microscope. As a result of DNA replication, there are now two copies of each chromosome. Each copy, called a **chromatid** (KRŌ-ma-tid), is connected to its duplicate copy at a single point, the **centromere** (SEN-trō-mēr).

As the chromosomes appear, the nucleoli disappear and the two pairs of centrioles move toward opposite poles of the nucleus. An array of microtubules, called **spindle fibers,** extends between the centriole pairs. Late in prophase, the nuclear envelope disappears and the chromatids become attached to the spindle fibers.

FIGURE 3-21 DNA Replication. In replication, the DNA strands unwind, and DNA polymerase begins attaching complementary DNA nucleotides along each strand. The complementary copy of one original strand is produced as a continuous strand. The other copy is produced as short segments, which are then spliced together. The end result is that two identical copies of the original DNA molecule are produced.

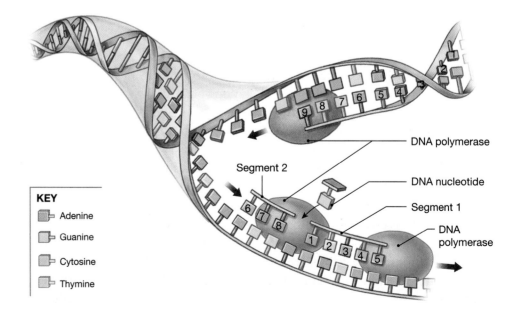

KEY
Adenine
Guanine
Cytosine
Thymine

FIGURE 3-22 **Interphase, Mitosis, and Cytokinesis.**

Stage 2: Metaphase

Metaphase (MET-a-fāz; *meta-*, after) begins as the chromatids move to a narrow central zone called the **metaphase plate.** Metaphase ends when all of the chromatids are aligned in the plane of the metaphase plate.

Stage 3: Anaphase

Anaphase (AN-a-fāz; *ana-*, apart) begins when the centromere of each chromatid pair splits and the chromatids separate. The two resulting **daughter chromosomes** are now pulled toward opposite ends of the cell. Anaphase ends when the daughter chromosomes arrive near the centrioles at opposite ends of the cell.

Stage 4: Telophase

During **telophase** (TĒL-ō-fāz; *telos,* end), the cell prepares to return to interphase. The nuclear membranes form, the nuclei enlarge, and the chromosomes gradually uncoil. Once the

Cell division includes mitosis, the separation and packaging or duplicated chromosomes into two nuclei, and cytokinesis, the division of cyctoplasm into two daughter cells.

chromosomes have relaxed and the fine filaments of chromatin become visible, nucleoli reappear and the nuclei resemble those of interphase cells.

CYTOKINESIS

Telophase marks the end of mitosis proper, but the daughter cells have yet to complete their physical separation. **Cytokinesis,** the cytoplasmic division that forms two daughter cells, usually begins in late anaphase (Figure 3-20). As the daughter chromosomes near the ends of the spindle fibers, the cytoplasm constricts along the plane of the metaphase plate, forming a *cleavage* *furrow.* This process continues throughout telophase and is usually completed after a nuclear membrane has re-formed around each daughter nucleus. The completion of cytokinesis marks the end of cell division.

CHECKPOINT

25. Give the biological terms for (a) cellular reproduction and (b) cell death.

26. Describe interphase, and identify its stages.

27. Define mitosis, and list its four stages.

28. What would happen if spindle fibers failed to form in a cell during mitosis?

See the blue Answers tab at the back of the book.

3-9 Tumors and cancers are characterized by abnormal cell growth and division

When the rates of cell division and growth exceed the rate of cell death, a tissue begins to enlarge. A **tumor,** or *neoplasm,* is a mass or swelling produced by abnormal cell growth and division. In a **benign tumor,** the abnormal cells are confined within a connective-tissue capsule. Such a tumor is seldom life threatening and can usually be surgically removed if its size or position disturbs tissue function.

Cells in a **malignant tumor** no longer respond to normal control mechanisms. These cells do not remain within a connective-tissue capsule but spread into surrounding tissues. The tumor of origin is called the *primary tumor* (or *primary neoplasm*), and the spreading process is called **invasion.** Malignant cells may also travel to distant tissues and organs and produce *secondary tumors.* This migration, called **metastasis** (me-TAS-ta-sis), is difficult to control.

Cancer is an illness resulting from the effects of malignant cells. Such cancer cells lose their resemblance to normal cells. The secondary tumors they form are extremely active metabolically, and their presence stimulates the growth of blood vessels into the area. The increased blood supply provides additional nutrients to the cancer cells, further accelerating tumor growth and metastasis.

As malignant tumors grow, organ function begins to deteriorate. The malignant cells may no longer perform their original functions, or they may perform normal functions in an abnormal way. Cancer cells do not use energy very efficiently, and they grow and multiply at the expense of healthy tissues, competing for space and nutrients with normal cells. This competition accounts for the starved appearance of many patients in the late stages of cancer. Death may occur as a result of the compression of vital organs when nonfunctional cancer cells have killed or replaced the healthy cells in those organs, or when the cancer cells have starved normal tissues of essential nutrients.

The Big Picture Cancer results from mutations that disrupt the control mechanism that regulates cell growth and division. Cancers most often begin where cells are dividing rapidly, because the more times chromosomes are copied, the greater the chances of error.

CHECKPOINT

29. An illness characterized by mutations that disrupt normal control mechanisms and produce potentially malignant cells is termed _____.

30. Define metastasis.

See the blue Answers tab at the back of the book.

3-10 Differentiation is cellular specialization as a result of gene activation or repression

All the somatic cells that make up an individual have the same chromosomes and genes, yet liver cells, fat cells, and nerve cells are quite different from each other in appearance and function. These differences exist because, in each case, a different set of genes has been turned *off.* In other words, these cells differ because liver cells have one set of genes accessible for transcription, and fat cells another. When a gene is deactivated, the cell loses the ability to make a particular protein, and thus cannot perform any functions involving that protein. As more genes are switched off, the cell's functions become more restricted or specialized. This specialization process is called **differentiation.**

Fertilization produces a single cell with all its genetic potential intact. A period of repeated cell divisions follows, and differentiation begins as the number of cells increases. Differentiation produces specialized cells with limited capabilities.

These cells form organized collections known as *tissues*, each with different functional roles. The next chapter examines the structure and function of tissues, and the role of tissue interactions in the maintenance of homeostasis.

RELATED CLINICAL TERMS

benign tumor: A mass or swelling in which the cells usually remain within a connective-tissue capsule; rarely life threatening.

cancer: An illness characterized by gene mutations leading to the formation of malignant tumors and metastasis.

carcinogen (kar-SIN-ō-jen): An environmental factor that stimulates the conversion of a normal cell to a cancer cell.

DNA fingerprinting: A technique for identifying an individual on the basis of repeating nucleotide sequences in his or her DNA.

genetic engineering: The research on and techniques for changing the genetic makeup (DNA) of an organism.

malignant tumor: A mass or swelling in which the cells no longer respond to normal control mechanisms but divide rapidly and spread.

metastasis (me-TAS-ta-sis): The spread of malignant cells into distant tissues and organs, where secondary tumors subsequently develop.

normal saline: A solution that approximates the normal osmotic concentration of extracellular fluids.

primary tumor (*primary neoplasm*): An abnormal mass where cancer cells first developed and the source of secondary tumors.

recombinant DNA: DNA created by inserting (splicing) a specific gene from one organism into the DNA strand of another organism.

secondary tumor: A colony of cancerous cells resulting from metastasis.

Chapter **3** Review

KEY TERMS

active transport 69

cells 59

chromosomes 78

cytoplasm 60

cytosol 72

diffusion 65

endocytosis 70

endoplasmic reticulum 74

exocytosis 71

gene 79

Golgi apparatus 75

mitochondria 77

mitosis 83

nucleus 60

organelles 73

osmosis 66

phagocytosis 71

protein synthesis 80

ribosome 74

translation 81

transcription 80

tumor 86

SUMMARY OUTLINE

3-1 The study of cells provides the foundation for understanding human physiology *p. 59*

1. Modern **cell theory** incorporates several basic concepts: (1) **Cells** are the building blocks of all plants and animals; (2) cells are the smallest functioning units of life; (3) cells are produced by the division of preexisting cells; and (4) each cell maintains homeostasis. (*Figure 3-1*)

2. Light and electron microscopes are important tools used in **cytology,** the study of the structure and function of cells.

3. A cell is surrounded by **extracellular fluid.** The cell's outer boundary, the **plasma membrane,** separates the **cytoplasm,** or cell contents, from the extracellular fluid. (*Figure 3-2; Table 3-1*)

3-2 The plasma membrane separates the cell from its surrounding environment and performs various functions *p. 60*

4. The functions of the plasma membrane include (1) physical isolation, (2) control of the exchange of materials with the cell's surroundings, (3) sensitivity, and (4) structural support.

5. The plasma membrane, or cell membrane, contains lipids, proteins, and carbohydrates. Its major components, lipid molecules, form a **phospholipid bilayer.** (*Figure 3-3*)

6. Membrane proteins may function as receptors, channels, carriers, enzymes, anchors, or identifiers. (*Table 3-2*)

3-3 Diffusion and filtration are passive transport mechanisms facilitating membrane passage *p. 64*

7. Plasma membranes are **selectively permeable.**

8. **Diffusion** is the net movement of material from an area where its concentration is relatively high to an area where its concentration is lower. Diffusion occurs until the **concentration gradient** is eliminated. *(Figures 3-4, 3-5)*

9. **Osmosis** is the diffusion of water across a membrane in response to differences in concentration. The force of movement is **osmotic pressure.** *(Figures 3-6, 3-7)*

10. In **filtration,** hydrostatic pressure forces water across a membrane. If membrane pores are large enough, molecules of solute will be carried along with the water.

3-4 Carrier-mediated and vesicular transport mechanisms also facilitate membrane passage   *p. 68*

11. **Facilitated diffusion** is a type of **carrier-mediated transport** and requires the presence of carrier proteins in the membrane. *(Figure 3-8)*

12. **Active transport** mechanisms consume ATP and are independent of concentration gradients. Some **ion pumps** are **exchange pumps.** *(Figure 3-9)*

13. In **vesicular transport,** material moves into or out of a cell in membranous sacs. Movement into the cell occurs through **endocytosis,** an active process that includes **receptor-mediated endocytosis, pinocytosis** ("cell-drinking"), and **phagocytosis** ("cell-eating"). Movement out of the cell occurs through **exocytosis.** *(Figures 3-10, 3-11; Table 3-3)*

3-5 Organelles within the cytoplasm perform specific functions   *p. 72*

14. The cytoplasm surrounds the nucleus and contains a fluid **cytosol** and intracellular structures called *organelles*.

15. The **cytosol** (*intracellular fluid*) differs in composition from the extracellular fluid that surrounds most cells of the body.

16. Membrane-enclosed **organelles** are surrounded by lipid membranes that isolate them from the cytosol. Membranous organelles include the endoplasmic reticulum, the nucleus, the Golgi apparatus, lysosomes, and mitochondria. *(Table 3-1)*

17. Nonmembranous organelles are always in contact with the cytosol. They include the cytoskeleton, microvilli, centrioles, cilia, flagella, proteasomes, and ribosomes. *(Table 3-1)*

18. The **cytoskeleton** gives the cytoplasm strength and flexibility. Its main components are **microfilaments, intermediate filaments,** and **microtubules.** *(Figure 3-12)*

19. **Microvilli** are small projections of the plasma membrane that increase the surface area exposed to the extracellular environment. *(Figure 3-12)*

20. **Centrioles** direct the movement of chromosomes during cell division.

21. **Cilia** beat rhythmically to move fluids or secretions across the cell surface.

22. **Flagella** move a cell through surrounding fluid rather than moving fluid past a stationary cell.

23. A **ribosome** is an intracellular factory that manufactures proteins. **Free ribosomes** are in the cytoplasm, and **fixed ribosomes** are attached to the endoplasmic reticulum.

24. **Proteasomes** remove and break down damaged or abnormal proteins.

25. The **endoplasmic reticulum (ER)** is a network of intracellular membranes. **Rough endoplasmic reticulum (RER)** contains ribosomes and is involved in protein synthesis. **Smooth endoplasmic reticulum (SER)** does not contain ribosomes; it is involved in lipid and carbohydrate synthesis. *(Figure 3-13)*

26. The **Golgi apparatus** forms **secretory vesicles** and new membrane components, and it packages *lysosomes*. Secretions are discharged from the cell by exocytosis. *(Figure 3-14)*

27. **Lysosomes** are vesicles filled with digestive enzymes. Their functions include ridding the cell of bacteria and debris.

28. **Mitochondria** are responsible for 95 percent of the ATP production within a typical cell. The **matrix,** or fluid contents of a mitochondrion, lies inside **cristae,** or folds of an inner mitochondrial membrane. *(Figure 3-15)*

3-6 The nucleus contains DNA and enzymes essential for controlling cellular activities   *p. 78*

29. The **nucleus** is the control center for cellular operations. It is surrounded by a **nuclear envelope,** through which it communicates with the cytosol by way of **nuclear pores.** *(Figure 3-16)*

30. The nucleus controls the cell by directing the synthesis of specific proteins using information stored in the DNA of **chromosomes.** *(Figure 3-17)*

31. The cell's information storage system, the **genetic code,** is called a *triplet code* because a sequence of three nitrogenous bases identifies a single amino acid. Each **gene** consists of all the triplets needed to produce a specific protein. *(Table 3-4)*

3-7 DNA controls protein synthesis, cell structure, and cell function   *p. 80*

32. **Protein synthesis** includes both *transcription,* which occurs in the nucleus, and *translation,* which occurs in the cytoplasm.

33. During **transcription,** a strand of **messenger RNA (mRNA)** is formed and carries protein-making instructions from the nucleus to the cytoplasm. *(Figure 3-18)*

34. During **translation,** a functional protein is constructed from the information contained in an mRNA strand. Each triplet of nitrogenous bases along the mRNA strand is a **codon;** the sequence of codons determines the sequence of amino acids in the protein. *(Figure 3-19)*

35. Molecules of **transfer RNA (tRNA)** bring amino acids to the ribosomes involved in translation. *(Figure 3-19)*

3-8 Stages of a cell's life cycle include interphase, mitosis, and cytokinesis *p. 83*

36. **Cell division** is the reproduction of cells. **Apoptosis** is the genetically controlled death of cells. **Mitosis** is the nuclear division of **somatic cells.**

37. Most somatic cells are in **interphase** most of the time. Cells preparing for mitosis undergo **DNA replication** in this phase. *(Figures 3-20, 3-21)*

38. Mitosis proceeds in four stages: **prophase, metaphase, anaphase,** and **telophase.** *(Figure 3-22)*

39. During **cytokinesis,** the cytoplasm divides, producing two identical daughter cells.

3-9 Tumors and cancers are characterized by abnormal cell growth and division *p. 86*

40. Abnormal cell growth and division forms **tumors** that are either **benign** (encapsulated) or **malignant** (able to invade other tissues). **Cancer** is a disease characterized by the presence of malignant tumors; over time, cancer cells tend to spread to new areas of the body.

3-10 Differentiation is cellular specialization as a result of gene activation or repression *p. 86*

41. **Differentiation** is the specialization that produces cells with limited capabilities. These specialized cells form organized collections called *tissues,* each of which has specific functional roles.

REVIEW QUESTIONS

WWW Access more review material online at The Anatomy & Physiology Place (**www.anatomyandphysiology.com**). There, you'll find Chapter Guides, Chapter Quizzes, Chapter Practice Tests, Interactive Flashcards, a Glossary with Pronunciations, and more to help you succeed in the course.

Level 1 • Reviewing Facts and Terms

Match each item in column A with the most closely related item in column B. Place letters for answers in the spaces provided.

COLUMN A
_____ 1. filtration
_____ 2. osmosis
_____ 3. hypotonic solution
_____ 4. hypertonic solution
_____ 5. isotonic solution
_____ 6. facilitated diffusion
_____ 7. carrier proteins
_____ 8. vesicular transport
_____ 9. cytosol
_____ 10. cytoskeleton
_____ 11. microvilli
_____ 12. ribosomes
_____ 13. mitochondria
_____ 14. lysosomes
_____ 15. nucleus
_____ 16. chromosomes
_____ 17. nucleoli

COLUMN B
a. water out of cell
b. passive carrier-mediated transport
c. endocytosis, exocytosis
d. movement of water
e. hydrostatic pressure
f. normal saline
g. ion pump
h. water into cell
i. manufacture proteins
j. digestive enzymes
k. internal protein framework
l. control center for cellular operations
m. intracellular fluid
n. DNA strands
o. cristae
p. synthesize components of ribosomes
q. increase cell surface area

18. The study of the structure and function of cells is called
   (a) histology.
   (b) cytology.
   (c) physiology.
   (d) biology.

19. The proteins in the plasma membranes may function as
    (a) receptors and channels.
    (b) carriers and enzymes.
    (c) anchors and identifiers.
    (d) a, b, and c are correct.

20. In the following diagram, identify the type of solution (hypertonic, hypotonic, or isotonic) in which the red blood cells are immersed.
    (a) _____
    (b) _____
    (c) _____

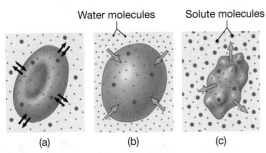

    Water molecules   Solute molecules

    (a)   (b)   (c)

21. All of the following membrane transport mechanisms are passive processes *except*
    (a) diffusion.
    (b) facilitated diffusion.
    (c) vesicular transport.
    (d) filtration.

22. _____ ion concentrations are high in the extracellular fluids, and _____ ion concentrations are high in the cytoplasm.
    (a) Calcium, magnesium
    (b) Chloride, sodium
    (c) Potassium, sodium
    (d) Sodium, potassium

23. Structures that perform specific functions within the cell are
    (a) organs.
    (b) organisms.
    (c) organelles.
    (d) chromosomes.

24. The construction of a functional protein using the information provided by an mRNA strand is
    (a) translation.
    (b) transcription.
    (c) replication.
    (d) gene activation.

25. Label the blanks in the following cell life cycle diagram using the following terms: S, G_1, G_2, M, prophase, anaphase, telophase, metaphase.

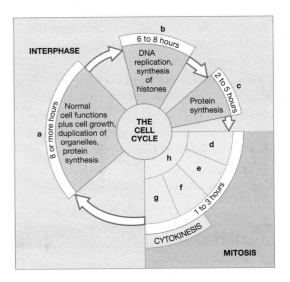

    (a) _____
    (b) _____
    (c) _____
    (d) _____
    (e) _____
    (f) _____
    (g) _____
    (h) _____

26. The term *differentiation* refers to
    (a) the loss of genes from cells.
    (b) the acquisition of new functional capabilities by cells.
    (c) the production of functionally specialized cells.
    (d) the division of genes among different types of cells.

27. What are the four general functions of the plasma membrane?

28. By what four major transport mechanisms do substances get into and out of cells?

29. What are the four major functions of the endoplasmic reticulum?

Level 2 • Reviewing Concepts

30. Diffusion is important in body fluids because this process tends to
    (a) increase local concentration gradients.
    (b) eliminate local concentration gradients.
    (c) move substances against their concentration gradients.
    (d) create concentration gradients.

31. When placed in a _____ solution, a cell will lose water through osmosis. The process results in the _____ of red blood cells.
    (a) hypotonic, crenation
    (b) hypertonic, crenation
    (c) isotonic, hemolysis
    (d) hypotonic, hemolysis

32. Suppose that a DNA segment has the following nucleotide sequence: CTC ATA CGA TTC AAG TTA. Which of the following nucleotide sequences would be found in a complementary mRNA strand?
    (a) GAG UAU GAU AAC UUG AAU
    (b) GAG TAT GCT AAG TTC AAT
    (c) GAG UAU GCU AAG UUC AAU
    (d) GUG UAU GGA UUG AAC GGU

33. How many amino acids are coded in the DNA segment in the previous question?
    (a) 18   (b) 9
    (c) 6   (d) 3

34. Construct a simple table indicating the similarities of and differences between facilitated diffusion and active transport.

35. How does the cytosol, or intracellular fluid, differ in composition from the extracellular fluid?

36. Differentiate between transcription and translation.

37. List the stages of mitosis, and briefly describe the events that occur in each.

38. What is cytokinesis, and what role does it play in the cell cycle?

Level 3 • Critical Thinking and Clinical Applications

39. Experimental evidence shows that the transport of a certain molecule exhibits the following characteristics: (1) The molecule moves down its concentration gradient; (2) at concentrations above a given level, there is no increase in the rate of transport; and (3) cellular energy is not required for transport to occur. Which type of transport process is at work?

40. Two solutions, A and B, are separated by a selectively permeable barrier. Over a period of time, the level of fluid on side A increases. Which solution initially had the higher concentration of solute?

4 The Tissue Level of Organization

This researcher is viewing a thin section of the cerebellum, a region of the brain which helps maintain body posture and control complex movements. The stain that has been applied aids the study of the cell organization in this part of the brain. Groups of similar cells specialized to perform a particular set of functions are called tissues. Each of your body's tissues has its own distinctive structure and its own role to play in maintaining homeostasis. We will meet them all in this chapter.

LEARNING OUTCOMES

After completing this chapter, you should be able to do the following:

4-1 Identify the body's four basic tissue types and describe their roles.

4-2 Discuss the types and functions of epithelial cells.

4-3 Describe the relationship between form and function for each type of epithelium.

4-4 Compare the structures and functions of the various types of connective tissues.

4-5 Explain how epithelial and connective tissues combine to form four types of membranes, and specify the functions of each.

4-6 Describe the three types of muscle tissue and the distinctive structural features of each.

4-7 Discuss the basic structure and role of neural tissue.

4-8 Explain how injuries affect the tissues of the body.

4-9 Describe how aging affects the tissues of the body.

VOCABULARY DEVELOPMENT

a- without; *avascular*	**holos** entire; *holocrine*	**peri-** around; *perichondrium*
apo- from; *apocrine*	**hyalos** glass; *hyaline cartilage*	**phagein** to eat; *macrophage*
cardium heart; *pericardium*	**inter-** between; *interstitial*	**pleura** rib; *pleural membrane*
chondros cartilage; *perichondrium*	**krinein** to separate; *exocrine*	**pseudes** false; *pseudostratified*
dendron tree; *dendrites*	**lacus** lake; *lacunae*	**sistere** to set; *interstitial*
desmos ligament; *desmosome*	**meros** part; *merocrine*	**soma** body; *desmosome*
glia glue; *neuroglia*	**neuro** nerve; *neuron*	**squama** plate or scale; *squamous*
histos tissue; *histology*	**os** bone; *osseous tissue*	**vas** vessel; *vascular*

4-1 The four tissue types are epithelial, connective, muscle, and neural

No single cell is able to perform the many functions of the human body. Instead, through differentiation, each cell specializes to perform a relatively restricted range of functions. Although there are trillions of individual cells in the human body, there are only about 200 different types of cells. These cell types combine to form **tissues,** collections of specialized cells and cell products that perform a limited number of functions. **Histology** (*histos*, tissue) is the study of tissues. Four basic *tissue types* exist: *epithelial tissue, connective tissue, muscle tissue,* and *neural tissue* (Figure 4-1).

The Big Picture

Tissues are collections of cells and extracellular material that perform a specific but limited range of functions. All of the structures of the human body are formed from various combinations of four basic tissue types: epithelial, connective, muscle, and neural.

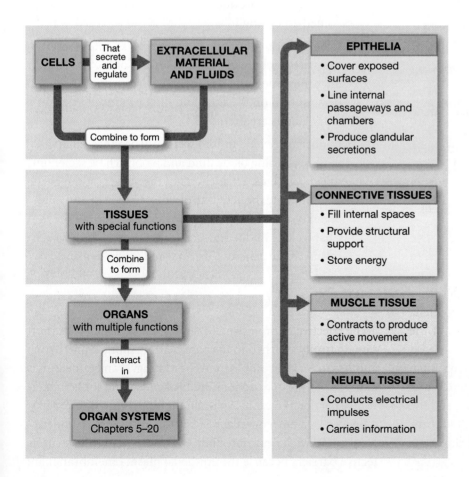

FIGURE 4-1 An Orientation to the Tissues of the Body.

CHECKPOINT

1. Define histology.

2. List the four basic types of tissues in the body.

See the blue Answers tab at the back of the book.

4-2 Epithelial tissue covers body surfaces, lines cavities and tubular structures, and serves essential functions

Epithelial tissue includes epithelia and *glands*. **Epithelia** (ep-i-THĒ-lē-a; singular, *epithelium*) are layers of cells that cover internal or external surfaces. **Glands** are composed of secreting cells derived from epithelia. Epithelia have the following important characteristics:

- Cells that are bound closely together. In other tissue types, the cells are often widely separated by extracellular materials.

- A free (apical) surface exposed to the environment or to some internal chamber or passageway.

- Attachment to underlying connective tissue by a *basement membrane*.

- The absence of blood vessels. Because of this **avascular** (ā-VAS-kū-lar; *a-*, without + *vas*, vessel) condition, epithelial cells must obtain nutrients across their attached surface from deeper tissues or across their exposed surfaces.

- Continual replacement or regeneration of epithelial cells that are damaged or lost at the exposed surface.

Epithelia cover both external and internal body surfaces. In addition to covering the skin, epithelia line internal passageways that communicate with the outside world, such as the digestive, respiratory, reproductive, and urinary tracts. These epithelia form selective barriers that separate the deep tissues of the body from the external environment.

Epithelia also line internal cavities and passageways, such as the chest cavity; the fluid-filled chambers in the brain, eye, and inner ear; and the inner surfaces of blood vessels and the heart. These epithelia prevent friction, regulate the fluid composition of internal cavities, and restrict communication between the blood and tissue fluids.

FUNCTIONS OF EPITHELIA

Epithelia perform four essential functions:

1. *Provide physical protection.* Epithelia protect exposed and internal surfaces from abrasion, dehydration, and destruction by chemical or biological agents. For example, as long as it remains intact, the epithelium of your skin resists impacts and scrapes, restricts water loss, and prevents invasion of underlying structures by bacteria.

2. *Control permeability.* Any substance that enters or leaves the body must cross an epithelium. Some epithelia are relatively impermeable; others are easily crossed by compounds as large as proteins.

3. *Provide sensation.* Specialized epithelial cells can detect changes in the environment and relay information about such changes to the nervous system. For example, touch receptors in the deepest layers of the epithelium of the skin respond by stimulating neighboring sensory nerves.

4. *Produce specialized secretions.* Epithelial cells that produce secretions are called **gland cells.** Individual gland cells are typically scattered among other cell types in an epithelium. In a **glandular epithelium,** most or all of the cells actively produce secretions. These secretions are classified according to where they are discharged:

   - **Exocrine** (*exo-*, outside + *krinein*, to secrete) secretions are discharged onto the surface of the epithelium. Enzymes entering the digestive tract, perspiration on the skin, and milk produced by mammary glands are examples.

   - **Endocrine** (*endo-*, inside) secretions are released into the surrounding tissue fluid and blood. These secretions, called *hormones*, act as chemical messengers and regulate or coordinate the activities of other tissues, organs, and organ systems. (Hormones are discussed further in Chapter 10.) Endocrine secretions are produced in such organs as the pancreas, thyroid, and pituitary gland.

INTERCELLULAR CONNECTIONS

To be effective in protecting other tissues, epithelial cells must remain firmly attached to the basement membrane and to one another to form a complete cover or lining. If an epithelium is damaged or the connections are broken, it is no longer an effective barrier. For example, when the epithelium of the skin is damaged by a burn or an abrasion, bacteria can enter underlying tissues and cause an infection. Undamaged epithelia form effective barriers because the epithelial plasma membranes are held together by specialized transmembrane proteins called *cell adhesion molecules (CAMs)* and by a thin layer of *intercellular cement* (composed of a protein–polysaccharide mixture). The CAMs bind to cytoskeletal filaments, to each other, and to extracellular materials, and form specialized attachment sites known as *cell junctions*. Three common intercellular connections are *tight junctions, gap junctions*, and *desmosomes* (Figure 4-2).

At a **tight junction,** or *occluding junction*, the lipid layers of adjacent plasma membranes are tightly bound together by interlocking membrane proteins (Figure 4-2a, b). Inferior to the tight junction is a continuous *adhesion belt* that encircles cells and binds them to their neighbors. The bands are connected to a network of actin filaments in the cytoskeleton. Tight junctions prevent the passage of water and solutes between cells. These junctions are

(a)

(b) Tight junction and adhesion belt

(c) Gap junction

(d) Spot desmosome

(e) Hemidesmosome

FIGURE 4-2 Intercellular Connections. (a) A diagrammatic view of an epithelial cell, showing the major types of intercellular connections. **(b)** A tight junction is formed by the fusion of the outer layers of two plasma membranes. A continuous adhesion belt deep to the tight junction connects to microfilaments of the cytoskeleton. **(c)** Gap junctions permit the free diffusion of ions and small molecules between two cells. **(d)** A spot desmosome attaches one cell to another. **(e)** Hemidesmosomes attach a cell to extracellular structures, such as the protein fibers in the basement membrane.

common between epithelial cells exposed to harsh chemicals or powerful enzymes. Tight junctions between epithelial cells lining the digestive tract, for example, keep digestive enzymes, stomach acids, or waste products from damaging underlying tissues.

Some epithelial functions require rapid intercellular communication. At a **gap junction,** two cells are held together by embedded membrane protein groups called *connexons* (Figure 4-2c). The connexons contain a narrow passageway that lets small molecules and ions pass from cell to cell. Gap junctions interconnect cells in ciliated epithelia, but they are most abundant in cardiac muscle and smooth muscle tissue, where they are essential to the coordination of muscle contractions.

Most epithelial cells are subject to mechanical stresses—stretching, bending, twisting, or compression—so they must have durable interconnections. At a **desmosome** (DEZ-mō-sōm; *desmos*, ligament + *soma*, body), the plasma membranes of two cells are locked together by intercellular cement and by membrane proteins connected to a network of intermediate filaments (Figure 4-2d). Desmosomes that form a small disc are called *spot desmosomes. Hemidesmosomes* resemble half of a spot desmosome and attach a cell to the basement membrane (Figure 4-2e). Desmosomes are abundant between cells in the superficial layers of the skin. As a result, damaged skin cells are usually lost in sheets rather than as individual cells. (That is why your skin peels rather than comes off as a powder after a sunburn.)

THE EPITHELIAL SURFACE

The *apical surface* of epithelial cells often have specialized structures that distinguish them from other body cells (Figure 4-3). Many epithelia that line internal passageways have microvilli on their exposed surfaces. ∞ p. 74 Microvilli may vary in number from just a few to so many that they carpet the entire surface. They are especially abundant on epithelial surfaces where absorption and secretion take place, such as along portions of the digestive and urinary tracts. These epithelial cells specialize in the active and passive transport of materials across their plasma membranes. ∞ p. 65 A cell with microvilli has at least 20 times the surface area of a cell without them; the greater the surface area of the plasma membrane, the more transport proteins are exposed to the extracellular environment. Some epithelia contain cilia on their exposed surfaces. ∞ p. 74 A typical cell within a *ciliated epithelium* has roughly 250 cilia that beat in a coordinated fashion to move materials across the epithelial surface. For example, the ciliated epithelium that lines the respiratory tract (Figure 4-3b) moves mucus-trapped irritants away from the lungs and toward the throat.

Cilia

Microvilli

Golgi apparatus

Nucleus

Basement membrane

Mitochondria

(a)

(b)   SEM × 13,469

FIGURE 4-3 **The Surfaces of Epithelial Cells.** The surfaces of most epithelia are specialized for specific functions. **(a)** In this diagram of a generalized epithelium, the free (apical) surface bears microvilli and cilia. Mitochondria are shown concentrated near the basal surface of the cells, where they likely provide energy for the cell's transport activities. **(b)** This SEM shows the surface of a ciliated epithelium that lines most of the respiratory tract. The small, bristly areas are microvilli on the exposed surfaces of mucus-producing cells that are scattered among the ciliated epithelial cells. Prof. P. Motta, Dept. of Anatomy, University La Sapienza.

THE BASEMENT MEMBRANE

Epithelial cells must not only adhere to one another but also must remain firmly connected to the rest of the body. This function is performed by the **basement membrane,** which lies between the epithelium and underlying connective tissues (Figure 4-3a). There are no cells within the basement membrane, which consists of a network of protein fibers. The epithelial cells adjacent to the basement membrane are firmly attached to these protein fibers by hemidesmosomes. In addition to providing strength and resisting distortion, the basement membrane also provides a barrier that restricts the movement of proteins and other large molecules from the underlying connective tissue into the epithelium.

EPITHELIAL RENEWAL AND REPAIR

An epithelium must continually repair and renew itself. Epithelial cells may survive for just a day or two, because they are lost or destroyed by exposure to disruptive enzymes, toxic chemicals, pathogenic microorganisms, or mechanical abrasion. The only way the epithelium can maintain its structure over time is through the continuous division of unspecialized cells known as **stem cells,** or *germinative cells.* These cells are found in the deepest layers of the epithelium, near the basement membrane.

CHECKPOINT

3. List five important characteristics of epithelial tissue.

4. Identify four essential functions of epithelial tissue.

5. Identify the three main types of epithelial intercellular connections.

6. What physiological functions are enhanced by the presence of microvilli or cilia on epithelial cells?

See the blue Answers tab at the back of the book.

4-3 Cell shape and number of layers determine the classification of epithelia

There are many different specialized types of epithelia. Yet they can easily be classified according to the number of cell layers and the shape of the exposed cells. This classification scheme recognizes two types of layering—*simple* and *stratified*—and three cell shapes—*squamous, cuboidal,* and *columnar* (Table 4-1).

CELL LAYERS

A **simple epithelium** consists of a single layer of cells covering the basement membrane. Simple epithelia are thin. A single layer of cells is fragile and cannot provide much mechanical protection, so simple epithelia are found only in protected areas inside the body. They line internal compartments and passageways, including the ventral body cavities, the heart chambers, and blood vessels.

Simple epithelia are characteristic of regions where secretion or absorption occurs, such as the lining of the digestive and urinary tracts, and the gas-exchange surfaces of the lungs. In such places, thinness is an advantage, for it reduces the diffusion time for materials crossing the epithelial barrier.

A **stratified epithelium** provides a greater degree of protection because it has several layers of cells above the basement membrane. Stratified epithelia are usually found in areas subject to mechanical or chemical stresses, such as the surface of the skin and the linings of the mouth and anus.

CELL SHAPES

In sectional view (perpendicular to the exposed surface and basement membrane), cells at the surface of the epithelium usually have one of three basic shapes.

1. *Squamous.* In a **squamous epithelium** (SKWĀ-mus; *squama,* a plate or scale), the cells are thin and flat, and the nucleus occupies the thickest portion of each cell. Viewed from the surface, the cells look like fried eggs laid side by side.

2. *Cuboidal.* The cells of a **cuboidal epithelium** resemble little hexagonal boxes when seen in three dimensions, but in typical sectional view, they appear square. The nuclei lie near the center of each cell, and they form a neat row.

3. *Columnar.* In a **columnar epithelium** the cells are also hexagonal but taller and more slender, resembling rectangles in sectional view. The nuclei are crowded into a narrow band close to the basement membrane, and the height of the epithelium is several times the distance between two nuclei.

The two basic epithelial arrangements (simple and stratified) and the three possible cell shapes (squamous, cuboidal, and columnar) enable one to describe almost every epithelium in the body. We will focus here on only a few major types of epithelia; additional examples will be encountered in later chapters.

TABLE 4-1 **Classifying Epithelia**

	SQUAMOUS	CUBOIDAL	COLUMNAR
Simple	Simple squamous epithelium	Simple cuboidal epithelium	Simple columnar epithelium
Stratified	Stratified squamous epithelium	Stratified cuboidal epithelium	Stratified columnar epithelium

CLASSIFICATION OF EPITHELIA

Simple Squamous Epithelia

A **simple squamous epithelium** is found in protected regions where absorption takes place or where a slippery surface reduces friction (Figure 4-4a). Examples are portions of the kidney tubules, the exchange surfaces of the lungs, the lining of ventral body cavities, and the linings of blood vessels and the inner surfaces of the heart.

Simple Cuboidal Epithelia

A **simple cuboidal epithelium** provides limited protection and occurs where secretion or absorption takes place (Figure 4-4b). These functions are enhanced by larger cells, which have more room for the necessary organelles. Simple cuboidal epithelia secrete enzymes and buffers in the pancreas and salivary glands and line the ducts that discharge these secretions. Simple cuboidal epithelia also line portions of the kidney tubules involved in the production of urine.

Simple Columnar Epithelia

A **simple columnar epithelium** provides some protection and may also occur in areas of absorption or secretion (Figure 4-4c). This type of epithelium lines the stomach, the intestinal tract, and many excretory ducts.

Stratified Squamous Epithelia

A **stratified squamous epithelium** is found where mechanical stresses are severe. The surface of the skin and the lining of the mouth, tongue, esophagus, and anus are good examples (Figure 4-5a).

SIMPLE SQUAMOUS EPITHELIUM

LOCATIONS: Epithelia lining ventral body cavities; lining heart and blood vessels; portions of kidney tubules (thin sections of nephron loops); inner lining of cornea; alveoli (air sacs) of lungs

FUNCTIONS: Reduces friction; controls vessel permeability; performs absorption and secretion

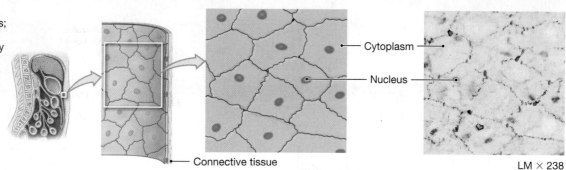

Cytoplasm

Nucleus

Connective tissue

LM × 238

(a) Lining of peritoneal cavity

SIMPLE CUBOIDAL EPITHELIUM

LOCATIONS: Glands; ducts; portions of kidney tubules; thyroid gland

FUNCTIONS: Limited protection, secretion, absorption

Connective tissue

Nucleus

Cuboidal cells

Basement membrane

LM × 1426

(b) Kidney tubule

SIMPLE COLUMNAR EPITHELIUM

LOCATIONS: Lining of stomach, intestine, gallbladder, uterine tubes, and collecting ducts of kidneys

FUNCTIONS: Protection, secretion, absorption

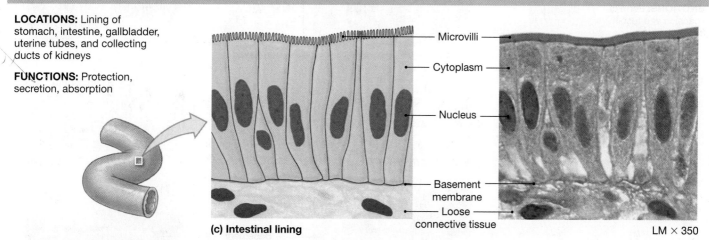

Microvilli

Cytoplasm

Nucleus

Basement membrane

Loose connective tissue

LM × 350

(c) Intestinal lining

FIGURE 4-4 **Simple Epithelia.** **(a)** A simple squamous epithelium lines the peritoneal cavity. The three-dimensional drawing shows the epithelium in superficial and sectional views. **(b)** A simple cuboidal epithelium lines the kidney tubules. The diagrammatic view emphasizes the pertinent structural details for classifying this epithelium as cuboidal. **(c)** A simple columnar epithelium lines portions of the intestinal tract. In the diagrammatic view, note the relationships between the height and width of each cell; the relative size, shape, and location of nuclei; and the distance between adjacent nuclei. Compare with Figure 4-4b.

STRATIFIED SQUAMOUS EPITHELIUM

LOCATIONS: Surface of skin; lining of mouth, throat, esophagus, rectum, anus, and vagina

FUNCTIONS: Provides physical protection against abrasion, pathogens, and chemical attack

Squamous superficial cells

Stem cells

Basement membrane

Connective tissue

(a) Surface of tongue

LM × 310

PSEUDOSTRATIFIED CILIATED COLUMNAR EPITHELIUM

LOCATIONS: Lining of nasal cavity, trachea, and bronchi; portions of male reproductive tract

FUNCTIONS: Protection, secretion

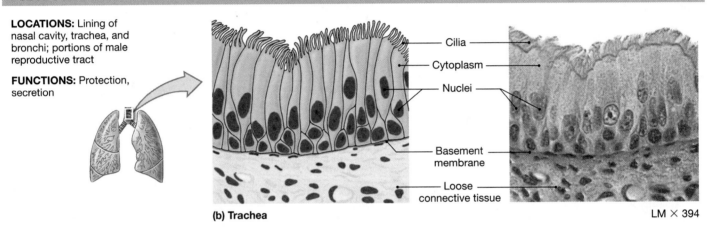

Cilia

Cytoplasm

Nuclei

Basement membrane

Loose connective tissue

(b) Trachea

LM × 394

TRANSITIONAL EPITHELIUM

LOCATIONS: Urinary bladder; renal pelvis of kidneys; ureters

FUNCTIONS: Permits expansion and recoil after stretching

Epithelium (relaxed)

Basement membrane

Connective tissue and smooth muscle layers

EMPTY BLADDER

LM × 394

Epithelium (stretched)

Basement membrane

Connective tissue and smooth muscle layers

FULL BLADDER

LM × 454

(c) Urinary bladder

FIGURE 4-5 **Stratified Epithelia. (a)** A stratified squamous epithelium covers the tongue. **(b)** A pseudo-stratified ciliated columnar epithelium lines portions of the respiratory tract. Note that despite the uneven layering of the nuclei, all the cells contact the basement membrane. **(c)** A transitional epithelium lines the urinary bladder. At left is the relaxed epithelium in an empty bladder; in a full bladder (at right) the epithelium is stretched.

Stratified Cuboidal Epithelia

Stratified cuboidal epithelium is relatively rare; it is located along the ducts of sweat glands and in the larger ducts of the mammary glands.

Stratified Columnar Epithelia

Stratified columnar epithelium is also relatively rare. It is found along portions of the pharynx, epiglottis, anus, urethra, and a few, large excretory ducts.

Pseudostratified Epithelia

Portions of the respiratory tract contain a columnar epithelium that includes a mixture of cell types. The distances between the cell nuclei and the exposed surface vary, so the epithelium appears stratified. It is not truly stratified, though, because all of the cells contact the basement membrane. Because it looks stratified but is not, it is known as a **pseudostratified columnar epithelium** (Figure 4-5b). Epithelial cells of this tissue typically possess cilia. A ciliated pseudostratified columnar epithelium lines most of the nasal cavity, the trachea (windpipe) and bronchi, and portions of the male reproductive tract.

Transitional Epithelia

A **transitional epithelium** is a stratified epithelium that tolerates repeated stretching. It is called transitional because the appearance of the epithelium changes from the unstretched to stretched state. It lines the ureters and urinary bladder, where large changes in volume occur (Figure 4-5c). In an empty urinary bladder, the epithelium is layered with the outermost cells appearing plump and cuboidal. In a full urinary bladder, when the volume of urine has stretched the lining to its limits, the epithelium appears flattened, and more like a stratified squamous epithelium.

GLANDULAR EPITHELIA

Many epithelia contain gland cells that produce exocrine or endocrine secretions. Exocrine secretions are produced by exocrine glands, which discharge their products through a *duct*, or tube, onto some external or internal surface. Endocrine secretions (*hormones*) are produced by ductless glands and released into blood or tissue fluids.

Based on their structure, exocrine glands can be categorized as unicellular glands (called *mucous* or *goblet cells*) or as multicellular glands. The simplest multicellular exocrine gland is a *secretory sheet*, such as the epithelium of mucin-secreting cells that lines the stomach and protects it from its own acids and enzymes. Multicellular glands are further classified according to the branching pattern of the duct and the shape and branching pattern of the secretory portion of the gland. Additionally, exocrine glands can be classified according to *mechanism of secretion* or *type of secretion*.

Mechanism of Secretion

Each glandular epithelial cell releases its secretions by one of three mechanisms: (1) *merocrine secretion,* (2) *apocrine secretion,* or (3) *holocrine secretion* (Figure 4-6).

In the most common mechanism of secretion, the product is released from secretory vesicles by exocytosis. ∞ p. 71 This mechanism, called **merocrine secretion** (MER-u-krin; *meros,* part + *krinein,* to secrete), is depicted in Figure 4-6a. One type of merocrine secretion, *mucin,* mixes with water to form **mucus,** an effective lubricant, a protective barrier, and a sticky trap for foreign particles and microorganisms. **Apocrine secretion** (AP-ō-krin; *apo-,* off) involves the loss of both cytoplasm and the secretory product (Figure 4-6b). The outermost portion of the cytoplasm becomes packed with secretory vesicles before it is shed. Milk production in the mammary glands involves both

Clinical Note

Exfoliative Cytology

Exfoliative cytology (eks-FŌ-lē-a-tiv; *ex-,* from + *folium,* leaf) is the study of cells shed or collected from epithelial surfaces. The cells are examined for a variety of reasons—for example, to check for cellular changes that indicate cancer or for genetic screening of a fetus. The cells are collected by sampling the fluids that cover the epithelia lining the respiratory, digestive, urinary, or reproductive tracts; by removing fluid from one of the ventral body cavities; or by removing cells from an epithelial surface.

A common example of exfoliative cytology is a *Pap test,* named after Dr. George Papanicolaou, who pioneered its use. The most familiar Pap test is that for cervical cancer, which involves scraping a small number of cells from the tip of the *cervix,* the portion of the uterus that projects into the vagina.

Amniocentesis is another important test involving exfoliative cytology. In this procedure, exfoliated epithelial cells are collected from a sample of *amniotic fluid,* the fluid that surrounds and protects a developing fetus. Examination of these cells can determine whether the fetus has a genetic abnormality, such as *Down syndrome,* that affects the number or structure of chromosomes.

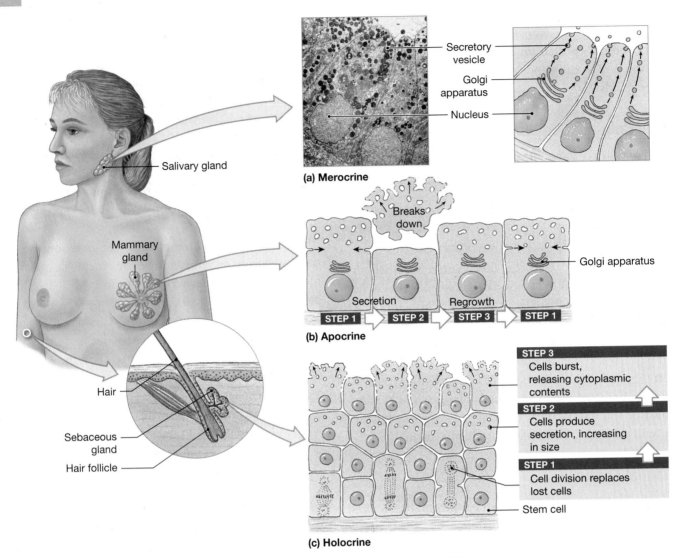

FIGURE 4-6 Mechanisms of Glandular Secretion. (a) In merocrine secretion, secretory vesicles are discharged at the free surface of the gland cell through exocytosis. **(b)** Apocrine secretion involves the loss of cytoplasm. Inclusions, secretory vesicles, and other cytoplasmic components are shed in the process. The gland cell then undergoes a period of growth and repair before releasing additional secretions. **(c)** Holocrine secretion occurs as superficial gland cells burst. Continued secretion involves the replacement of these cells through the mitotic divisions of underlying stem cells.

merocrine and apocrine secretions. Whereas the processes of merocrine and apocrine secretion leave the cell intact and able to continue secreting, **holocrine secretion** (HOL-ō-krin; *holos*, entire) does not. Instead, the entire cell becomes packed with secretions and then bursts apart and dies (Figure 4-6c). Sebaceous glands, associated with hair follicles, produce an oily hair coating by means of holocrine secretion.

Type of Secretion

There are many kinds of exocrine secretions, all performing a variety of functions. Examples are enzymes entering the digestive tract, perspiration on the skin, and the milk produced by mammary glands.

Based on the type or types of secretions produced, exocrine glands can also be categorized as serous, mucous, or mixed. The secretions can have a variety of functions. *Serous glands* secrete a watery solution containing enzymes. *Mucous glands* secrete mucins that form a thick, slippery mucus. *Mixed glands* contain more than one type of gland cell and may produce two different exocrine secretions, one serous and the other mucous.

Table 4-2 summarizes the classification of exocrine glands according to their mechanism of secretion and type of secretion.

TABLE 4-2 A Classification of Exocrine Glands

FEATURE	DESCRIPTION	EXAMPLES
SECRETION MECHANISM		
Merocrine	Secretion occurs through exocytosis.	Saliva from salivary glands; mucus in digestive and respiratory tracts; perspiration on the skin; milk in breasts
Apocrine	Secretion occurs through loss of cytoplasm containing secretory product.	Milk in breasts; viscous underarm perspiration
Holocrine	Secretion occurs through loss of entire cell containing secretory product.	Skin oils and waxy coating of hair (produced by sebaceous glands of the skin)
SECRETION TYPE		
Serous	Watery solution containing enzymes	Secretions of parotid salivary gland
Mucous	Thick, slippery mucus	Secretions of sublingual salivary gland
Mixed	Contains more than one type of secretion	Secretions of submandibular salivary gland (serous and mucous)

CHECKPOINT

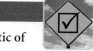

7. Identify the three cell shapes characteristic of epithelial cells.

8. Using a light microscope, you examine a tissue and see a simple squamous epithelium on the outer surface. Can this be a sample of the skin surface?

9. Name the two primary types of glandular epithelia.

10. The secretory cells of sebaceous glands fill with secretions and then rupture, releasing their contents. Which mechanism of secretion occurs in sebaceous glands?

11. A gland has no ducts to carry the glandular secretions, and the gland's secretions are released directly into the extracellular fluid. Which type of gland is this?

See the blue Answers tab at the back of the book.

4-4 Connective tissue provides a protective structural framework for other tissue types

Connective tissues are the most diverse tissues of the body. Bone, blood, and fat are familiar connective tissues that have very different functions and properties. All connective tissues have three basic components: (1) specialized cells, (2) protein fibers, and (3) a fluid known as **ground substance**. The extracellular protein fibers and ground substance form the **matrix** that surrounds the cells. Whereas epithelial tissue consists almost entirely of cells, the extracellular matrix accounts for most of the volume of connective tissues.

Connective tissues are distributed throughout the body but are never exposed to the outside environment. Many connective tissues are highly vascular (that is, they have many blood vessels) and contain receptors that provide pain, pressure, temperature, and other sensations. Connective tissue functions include the following:

- *Support and protection.* The minerals and fibers produced by connective tissue cells establish a bony structural framework for the body, protect delicate organs, and surround and interconnect other tissue types.

- *Transportation of materials.* Fluid connective tissues provide an efficient means of moving dissolved materials from one region of the body to another.

- *Storage of energy reserves.* Fats are stored in connective tissue cells called *adipose cells* until needed.

- *Defense of the body.* Specialized connective tissue cells respond to invasions by microorganisms through cell-to-cell interactions and the production of *antibodies.*

Based on the physical properties of their matrix, connective tissues are classified into three major types (Figure 4-7):

1. **Connective tissue proper** consists of many types of cells and fibers within a matrix containing a syrupy ground substance. Examples are the tissue that underlies the skin, fatty tissue, and *tendons* and *ligaments.*

2. **Fluid connective tissues** have a distinctive population of cells suspended in a matrix of watery ground substance containing dissolved proteins. The two fluid connective tissues are *blood* and *lymph.*

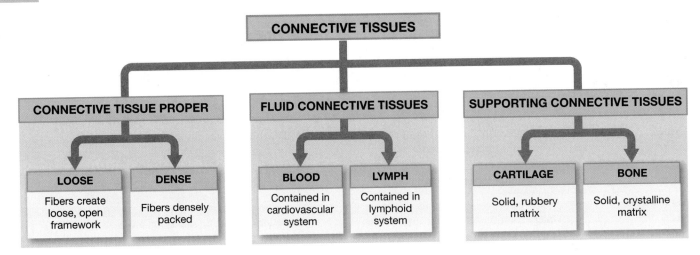

FIGURE 4-7 **Major Types of Connective Tissue.**

3. **Supporting connective tissues** have a less diverse cell population than connective tissue proper, and a matrix of dense ground substance and closely packed fibers. The body contains two supporting connective tissues: *cartilage* and *bone.* The fibrous matrix of bone is said to be calcified because it contains mineral deposits (primarily calcium salts) that give the bone strength and rigidity.

CONNECTIVE TISSUE PROPER

Connective tissue proper contains a varied cell population, extracellular fibers, and a syrupy ground substance (**Figure 4-8**). Some cells of connective tissue proper are "permanent residents"; others are not always present because they leave to defend and repair areas of injured tissue.

Cells of Connective Tissue Proper

Connective tissue proper includes the following major cell types:

- **Fibroblasts** (FĪ-brō-blasts) are the most abundant cells in connective tissue proper. These permanent residents are responsible for producing connective tissue fibers and ground substance. **Fibrocytes** (FĪ-brō-sīts) are next in abundance and differentiate from fibroblasts. Fibrocytes maintain the connective tissue fibers of connective tissue proper.

- **Macrophages** (MAK-rō-fā-jez; *phagein,* to eat) are scattered throughout the matrix. These "big eater" cells engulf, or *phagocytize,* damaged cells or pathogens that enter the tissue; they also release chemicals that mobilize the immune system, attracting additional macrophages and other cells involved in tissue defense. ∞ p. 71 Macrophages that spend long periods of time in connective tissue are known

as *fixed macrophages.* When an infection occurs, migrating macrophages (called *free macrophages*) are drawn to the affected area.

- **Fat cells**—also known as adipose cells, or **adipocytes** (AD-i-pō-sīts)—are permanent residents. A typical adipocyte contains such a large droplet of lipid that the nucleus and other organelles are squeezed to one side of the cell. The number of fat cells varies from one connective tissue to another, from one region of the body to another, and among individuals.

- **Mast cells** are small, mobile connective tissue cells often found near blood vessels. The cytoplasm of a mast cell is packed with vesicles filled with chemicals that are released to begin the body's defensive activities after an injury or infection (as discussed later in the chapter).

In addition to mast cells and free macrophages, both phagocytic and antibody-producing white blood cells may move through connective tissue proper. Their numbers increase markedly if the tissue is damaged, as does the production of **antibodies,** proteins that destroy invading microorganisms or foreign substances. *Stem cells* also respond to local injury by dividing to produce daughter cells that differentiate into fibroblasts, macrophages, or other connective tissue cells.

Connective Tissue Fibers

The three basic types of fibers—*collagen, elastic,* and *reticular*—are formed from protein subunits secreted by fibroblasts (**Figure 4-8**):

1. **Collagen fibers** are long, straight, and unbranched. These strong but flexible fibers are the most common fibers in connective tissue proper.

2. **Elastic fibers** contain the protein *elastin*. They are branched and wavy and after stretching will return to their original length.

3. **Reticular fibers** (*reticulum*, a network), the least common of the three, are thinner than collagen fibers and commonly form a branching, interwoven framework in various organs.

Ground Substance

Ground substance fills the spaces between cells and surrounds the connective tissue fibers (Figure 4-8). In normal connective tissue proper, it is clear, colorless, and similar in consistency to maple syrup. This dense consistency slows the movement of bacteria and other pathogens, making them easier prey for phagocytes.

TYPES OF CONNECTIVE TISSUE PROPER

Connective tissue proper is categorized as either *loose connective tissues* or *dense connective tissues* on the basis of the relative proportions of cells, fibers, and ground substance. Loose connective tissues are the packing material of the body. These tissues fill spaces between organs, provide cushioning, and support epithelia. They also anchor blood vessels and nerves, store

Marfan Syndrome

Marfan syndrome is an inherited condition caused by the production of an abnormal form of *fibrillin*, a carbohydrate–protein complex important to normal connective tissue strength and elasticity. Because most organs contain connective tissues, the effects of this defect are widespread. The most visible sign of Marfan syndrome involves the skeleton; individuals with Marfan syndrome are tall and have abnormally long arms, legs, and fingers. The most serious consequences involve the cardiovascular system. Roughly 90 percent of individuals with Marfan syndrome have structural abnormalities in their cardiovascular systems. The most dangerous potential result is that the weakened connective tissues in the walls of major arteries, such as the aorta, may burst, causing a sudden, fatal loss of blood.

lipids, and provide a route for the diffusion of materials. Dense connective tissues are tough, strong, and durable. They resist tension and distortion and interconnect bones and muscles. Dense connective tissue also forms a thick fibrous layer, called a *capsule*, that surrounds internal organs (such as the liver, kidneys, and spleen) and encloses joint cavities.

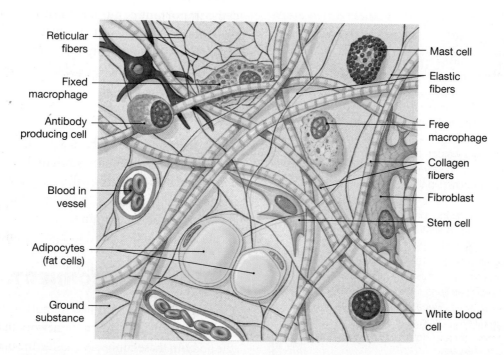

FIGURE 4-8 Cells and Fibers of Connective Tissue Proper. This diagrammatic view shows the common cell types and fibers of connective tissue proper.

Loose Connective Tissue

Loose connective tissue, or *areolar tissue* (*areola*, little space), is the least specialized connective tissue in the adult body (**Figure 4-9a**). It contains all of the cells and fibers found in any connective tissue proper, in addition to an extensive blood supply.

Loose connective tissue forms a layer that separates the skin from underlying muscles, providing both padding and a considerable amount of independent movement. Pinching the skin of the arm, for example, does not distort the underlying muscle. The ample blood supply in this tissue carries wandering cells to and from the tissue and provides for the metabolic needs (oxygen and nutrients) of nearby epithelial tissue.

Adipose tissue, or fat, is a loose connective tissue containing large numbers of fat cells, or adipocytes (**Figure 4-9b**). The difference between loose connective tissue and adipose tissue is one of degree; a loose connective tissue is called adipose tissue when it becomes dominated by fat cells. Adipose tissue provides another source of padding and shock absorption for the body. It also provides insulation that slows heat loss through the skin, and it functions in energy storage.

Adipose tissue is common under the skin of the sides, buttocks, and breasts. It fills the bony sockets behind the eyes, surrounds the kidneys, and dominates extensive areas of loose connective tissue in the pericardial and peritoneal (abdominal) cavities.

Clinical Note
Adipose Tissue and Weight Control

Adipocytes are metabolically active cells; their lipids are continually being broken down and replaced. When nutrients are scarce, adipocytes deflate like collapsing balloons. This deflation occurs during a weight-loss program. Because the cells are not killed but merely reduced in size, the lost weight can easily be regained in the same areas of the body.

In adults, adipocytes cannot divide. However, an excess of circulating lipids can stimulate the division of connective tissue stem cells, which then differentiate into additional fat cells. As a result, areas of loose connective tissue can become adipose tissue after chronic overeating. In the procedure known as *liposuction,* unwanted adipose tissue is surgically removed. Because adipose tissue can regenerate through differentiation of stem cells, liposuction provides only a temporary and potentially risky solution to the problem of excess weight.

Dense Connective Tissues

Dense connective tissues consist mostly of collagen fibers; they may also be called *fibrous,* or *collagenous* (ko-LAJ-e-nus), tissues. The body has two types of dense connective tissues. In *dense regular connective tissue,* the collagen fibers are parallel to each other, packed tightly, and aligned with the forces applied to the tissue. **Tendons** are cords of dense regular connective tissue that attach skeletal muscles to bones (**Figure 4-9c**). Their collagen fibers run along the length of the tendon and transfer the pull of the contracting muscle to the bone. **Ligaments** (LIG-a-ments) resemble tendons but connect one bone to another. Ligaments often contain elastic fibers as well as collagen fibers and thus can tolerate a modest amount of stretching. *Dense irregular connective tissue* (not shown) contains an interwoven meshwork of collagen fibers. This structural pattern provides support to areas subjected to stresses from many directions and is what gives skin its strength.

FLUID CONNECTIVE TISSUES

Blood and **lymph** are connective tissues that contain distinctive collections of cells in a fluid matrix. Under normal conditions, the proteins dissolved in this watery matrix do not form large insoluble fibers. In blood, the watery matrix is called **plasma.**

A single cell type, the **red blood cell,** accounts for almost half the volume of blood. Red blood cells transport oxygen in the blood. Blood also contains small numbers of **white blood cells,** important components of the immune system, and **platelets,** cell fragments that function in blood clotting.

Together, plasma, lymph, and interstitial fluid constitute most of the extracellular fluid of the body. Plasma, confined to the blood vessels of the cardiovascular system, is kept in constant motion by contractions of the heart. When blood reaches tissues within thin-walled vessels called capillaries, filtration moves water and small solutes out of the capillaries and into the *interstitial fluid,* which surrounds the body's cells. Lymph forms as interstitial fluid enters small passageways, or *lymphatic vessels,* that eventually return it to the cardiovascular system. Along the way, cells of the immune system monitor the composition of the lymph and respond to signs of injury and infection.

SUPPORTING CONNECTIVE TISSUES

Cartilage and bone are called supporting connective tissues because they provide a strong framework that supports the rest of the body. In these connective tissues the matrix contains numerous fibers and, in some cases, deposits of insoluble calcium salts.

LOOSE CONNECTIVE TISSUE

LOCATIONS: Beneath dermis of skin, digestive tract, respiratory and urinary tracts; between muscles; around blood vessels, nerves, and around joints

FUNCTIONS: Cushions organs; provides support but permits independent movement; phagocytic cells provide defense against pathogens

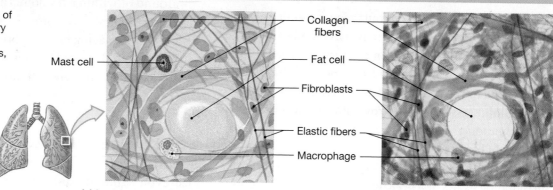

Mast cell

Collagen fibers

Fat cell

Fibroblasts

Elastic fibers

Macrophage

(a) Loose connective tissue

LM × 400

ADIPOSE TISSUE

LOCATIONS: Deep to the skin, especially at sides, buttocks, breasts; padding around eyes and kidneys

FUNCTIONS: Provides padding and cushions shocks; insulates (reduces heat loss); stores energy reserves

Adipocytes

(b) Adipose tissue

LM × 133

DENSE CONNECTIVE TISSUES

LOCATIONS: Between skeletal muscles and skeleton (tendons); between bones (ligaments); covering skeletal muscles; capsules of internal organs

FUNCTIONS: Provides firm attachment; conducts pull of muscles; reduces friction between muscles; stabilizes relative positions of bones; helps prevent overexpansion of organs (such as the urinary bladder)

Collagen fibers

Fibroblast nuclei

(c) Tendon

LM × 440

FIGURE 4-9 Connective Tissue Proper: Loose and Dense Connective Tissues. (a) All of the cells of connective tissue proper are found in loose connective tissue. **(b)** Adipose tissue is loose connective tissue dominated by adipocytes. In standard histological preparations, the tissue looks empty because the lipids in the fat cells dissolve in the alcohol used during tissue processing. **(c)** The dense regular connective tissue in a tendon largely consists of densely packed, parallel bundles of collagen fibers. The fibroblast nuclei are flattened between the bundles.

Cartilage

The matrix of **cartilage** is a firm gel containing embedded fibers. **Chondrocytes** (KON-drō-sīts), the only cells found within the matrix, live in small pockets known as *lacunae* (la-KOO-nē; *lacus*, pool). Because cartilage is avascular, chondrocytes must obtain nutrients and eliminate waste products by diffusion through the matrix. Blood vessels do not grow into cartilage because chondrocytes produce a chemical that discourages their formation. This lack of blood supply also limits the repair capabilities of cartilage. Structures of cartilage are covered and set apart from surrounding tissues by a **perichondrium** (per-i-KON-drē-um; *peri-*, around + *chondros*, cartilage), which contains an inner cellular layer and an outer fibrous layer.

The three major types of cartilage are *hyaline cartilage, elastic cartilage,* and *fibrous cartilage* (**Figure 4-10**):

1. **Hyaline cartilage** (HĪ-uh-lin; *hyalos*, glass) is the most common type of cartilage (**Figure 4-10a**). The matrix contains closely packed collagen fibers, making hyaline cartilage tough but somewhat flexible. This type of cartilage connects the ribs to the sternum (breastbone), supports the conducting passageways of the respiratory tract, and covers opposing bone surfaces within joints.

2. **Elastic cartilage** contains numerous elastic fibers that make it extremely resilient and flexible (**Figure 4-10b**). Elastic cartilage forms the external flap (the *auricle,* or *pinna*) of the outer ear, the epiglottis, and an airway to the middle ear (the *auditory tube*).

3. **Fibrous cartilage**, or **fibrocartilage,** has little ground substance, and its matrix is dominated by collagen fibers (**Figure 4-10c**). These fibers are densely interwoven, making this tissue extremely durable and tough. Pads of fibrous cartilage lie between the vertebrae of the spinal column, between the pubic bones of the pelvis, and around or within a few joints and tendons. In these positions they resist compression, absorb shocks, and prevent damaging bone-to-bone contact. Cartilages heal poorly, and damaged fibrous cartilage in joints such as the knee can interfere with normal movements.

Bone

Because the detailed histology of **bone,** or *osseous tissue* (OS-ē-us; *os*, bone), will be considered in Chapter 6, this discussion focuses on significant differences between cartilage and bone. The volume of ground substance in bone is very small. The matrix of bone consists mainly of hard calcium compounds and flexible collagen fibers. This combination gives bone truly remarkable properties, making it both strong and resistant to shattering. In its overall properties, bone can compete with the best steel-reinforced concrete.

The general organization of bone is shown in **Figure 4-11.** Lacunae within the matrix contain bone cells, or **osteocytes** (OS-tē-ō-sīts; *os*, bone + *cyte*, cell). The lacunae surround the blood vessels that branch through the bony matrix. Although diffusion cannot occur through the bony matrix, osteocytes obtain nutrients through cytoplasmic extensions that reach blood vessels and other osteocytes. These extensions run through a branching network within the bony matrix called **canaliculi** (kan-a-LIK-ū-lē; little canals).

Except in joint cavities, where opposing surfaces are covered by hyaline cartilage, each bone is surrounded by a **periosteum** (per-ē-OS-tē-um), a covering made up of fibrous (outer) and cellular (inner) layers. Unlike cartilage, bone is constantly being remodeled throughout life, and complete repairs can be made even after severe damage has occurred. Table 4-3 compares cartilage and bone.

Clinical Note

Cartilages and Joint Injuries

Several complex joints, including the knee, contain both hyaline cartilage and fibrous cartilage. The hyaline cartilage covers bony surfaces, and fibrous cartilage pads in the joint prevent bone-to-bone contact when movements are underway. Injuries to these joints can produce tears in the fibrous cartilage pads that do not heal. This loss of cushioning places more strain on the cartilages within joints and leads to further joint damage. Eventually, joint mobility is severely reduced. Cartilages heal poorly because they are avascular. Joint cartilages heal even more slowly than other cartilages. Surgery usually results in only a temporary or incomplete repair.

CHECKPOINT

12. Identify several functions of connective tissues.

13. List the three types of connective tissues.

14. Which type of connective tissue contains primarily triglycerides?

15. Lack of vitamin C in the diet interferes with the ability of fibrocytes to produce collagen. What effect might this interference have on connective tissue?

16. Which two types of connective tissue have a fluid matrix?

17. Identify the two types of supporting connective tissue.

18. Why does cartilage heal so slowly?

See the blue Answers tab at the back of the book.

HYALINE CARTILAGE

LOCATIONS: Between tips of ribs and bones of sternum; covering bone surfaces at synovial joints; supporting larynx (voice box), trachea, and bronchi; forming part of nasal septum

FUNCTIONS: Provides stiff but somewhat flexible support; reduces friction between bony surfaces

Chondrocytes in lacunae

Matrix

(a) Hyaline cartilage

LM × 500

ELASTIC CARTILAGE

LOCATIONS: Auricle of external ear; epiglottis; auditory tube; cuneiform cartilages of larynx

FUNCTIONS: Provides support, but tolerates distortion without damage and returns to original shape

Chondrocyte in lacuna

Elastic fibers in matrix

(b) Elastic cartilage

LM × 358

FIBROUS CARTILAGE

LOCATIONS: Pads within knee joint; between pubic bones of pelvis; intervertebral discs

FUNCTIONS: Resists compression; prevents bone-to-bone contact; limits relative movement

Collagen fibers in matrix

Chondrocyte in lacuna

(c) Fibrous cartilage

LM × 1000

FIGURE 4-10 Types of Cartilage. (a) Hyaline cartilage has a translucent matrix and lacks prominent fibers. **(b)** In elastic cartilage, the closely packed elastic fibers are visible between the chondrocytes. **(c)** In fibrous cartilage, the collagen fibers are extremely dense, and the chondrocytes are relatively far apart.

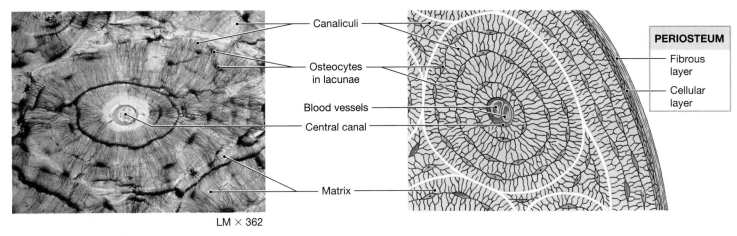

FIGURE 4-11 Bone. The osteocytes in bone are usually organized in groups around a central space that contains blood vessels. In preparation for making the micrograph, a sample of bone was ground thin enough to become transparent. Bone dust filled the lacunae and the central canal, making them appear dark.

LM × 362

TABLE 4-3 A Comparison of Cartilage and Bone

CHARACTERISTIC	CARTILAGE	BONE
STRUCTURAL FEATURES		
Cells	Chondrocytes in lacunae	Osteocytes in lacunae
Ground substance	Protein–polysaccharide gel and water	A small volume of liquid surrounding insoluble crystals of calcium salts (calcium phosphate and calcium carbonate)
Fibers	Collagen, elastic, reticular fibers (proportions vary)	Collagen fibers predominate
Vascularity	None	Extensive
Covering	Perichondrium	Periosteum
Strength	Limited: bends easily but difficult to break	Strong: resists distortion until breaking point is reached
METABOLIC FEATURES		
Oxygen demands	Low	High
Nutrient delivery	By diffusion through matrix	By diffusion through cytoplasm and fluid in canaliculi
Repair capabilities	Limited	Extensive

4-5 Membranes are physical barriers of four types: mucous, serous, cutaneous, and synovial

Some anatomical terms have more than one meaning, depending on the context. One such term is *membrane*. For example, at the cellular level, plasma membranes are lipid bilayers that restrict the passage of ions and other solutes. ⇨ p. 60 At the tissue level, membranes also form a barrier, such as the basement membranes that separate epithelia from connective tissues. At still another level, epithelia and connective tissues combine to form membranes that cover and protect other structures and tissues. The body has four such membranes: *mucous membranes, serous membranes, the cutaneous membrane, and synovial membranes* (Figure 4-12).

MUCOUS MEMBRANES

Mucous membranes, or **mucosae** (mū-KŌ-sē), line cavities that communicate with the exterior, including the digestive, respiratory, reproductive, and urinary tracts (Figure 4-12a). The epithelial surfaces are kept moist at all times, typically by mucous secretions or by exposure to fluids such as urine or semen. The connective tissue portion of a mucous membrane is called the *lamina propria* (PRŌ-prē-uh).

Many mucous membranes are lined by simple epithelia that perform absorptive or secretory functions, such as the simple

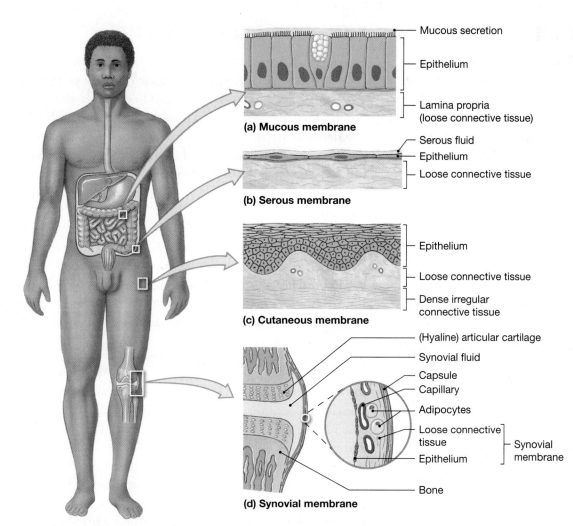

FIGURE 4-12 **Membranes.**
(a) Mucous membranes are coated with the secretions of mucous glands. These membranes line the digestive, respiratory, urinary, and reproductive tracts. **(b)** Serous membranes line the ventral body cavities (the peritoneal, pleural, and pericardial cavities). **(c)** The cutaneous membrane, or skin, covers the outer surface of the body. **(d)** Synovial membranes line joint cavities and produce the fluid within the joint.

(a) Mucous membrane
- Mucous secretion
- Epithelium
- Lamina propria (loose connective tissue)

(b) Serous membrane
- Serous fluid
- Epithelium
- Loose connective tissue

(c) Cutaneous membrane
- Epithelium
- Loose connective tissue
- Dense irregular connective tissue

(d) Synovial membrane
- (Hyaline) articular cartilage
- Synovial fluid
- Capsule
- Capillary
- Adipocytes
- Loose connective tissue
- Epithelium
- Synovial membrane
- Bone

columnar epithelium of the digestive tract. However, other types of epithelia may be involved. For example, a stratified squamous epithelium is part of the mucous membrane of the mouth, and the mucous membrane along most of the urinary tract has a transitional epithelium.

SEROUS MEMBRANES

Serous membranes line the sealed, internal subdivisions of the ventral body cavity. There are three serous membranes, each consisting of a simple epithelium supported by loose connective tissue (Figure 4-12b). The **pleura** (PLOO-ra; *pleura,* rib) lines the pleural cavities and covers the lungs. The **peritoneum** (per-i-tō-NĒ-um; *peri,* around + *teinein,* to stretch) lines the peritoneal (abdominal) cavity and covers the surfaces of enclosed organs such as the liver and stomach. The **pericardium** (per-i-KAR-dē-um) lines the pericardial cavity and covers the heart.

A serous membrane has *parietal* and *visceral* portions that are in close contact at all times. p. 22 The parietal por-

tion lines the inner surface of the cavity, and the visceral portion covers the outer surface of organs within the body cavity. For example, the visceral pericardium covers the heart, and the parietal pericardium lines the inner surfaces of the pericardial sac that surrounds the pericardial cavity. The primary function of any serous membrane is to minimize friction between the opposing parietal and visceral surfaces when an organ moves or changes shape. Friction is reduced by a watery, *serous fluid* formed by fluids diffusing from underlying tissues.

THE CUTANEOUS MEMBRANE

The **cutaneous membrane,** or skin, covers the surface of the body (Figure 4-12c). It consists of a stratified squamous epithelium and the underlying dense connective tissues. In contrast to serous or mucous membranes, the cutaneous membrane is thick, relatively waterproof, and usually dry. The skin is discussed in detail in Chapter 5.

SYNOVIAL MEMBRANES

Bones contact one another at joints, or **articulations** (ar-tik-ū-LĀ-shuns). Joints that allow free movement are surrounded by a fibrous capsule and contain a joint cavity lined by a **synovial** (si-NO-vē-ul) **membrane** (Figure 4-12d). Unlike the other three membranes, the synovial membrane consists primarily of loose connective tissue and an incomplete layer of epithelial tissue. In freely movable joints, the bony surfaces do not come into direct contact with one another. If they did, impacts and abrasion would damage the opposing surfaces, and smooth movement would become almost impossible. Instead, the ends of the bones are covered with hyaline cartilage and separated by a viscous *synovial fluid* produced by fibroblasts in the connective tissue of the synovial membrane. The synovial fluid helps lubricate the joint and permits smooth movement.

CHECKPOINT

19. Identify the four types of membranes found in the body.

20. How does a plasma (cell) membrane differ from a tissue-level membrane?

21. What is the function of fluids produced by serous membranes?

22. The lining of the nasal cavity is normally moist, contains numerous goblet cells, and rests on a layer of loose connective tissue. Which type of membrane is this?

See the blue Answers tab at the back of the book.

4-6 The three types of muscle tissue are skeletal, cardiac, and smooth

Muscle tissue is specialized for contraction. Muscle cell contraction involves interaction between filaments of *myosin* and *actin*, proteins found in the cytoskeletons of many cells. ∞ p. 73 In muscle cells, however, the filaments are more numerous and arranged so that their interaction produces a contraction of the entire cell.

There are three types of muscle tissue in the body—*skeletal, cardiac,* and *smooth muscle tissues* (Figure 4-13). The contraction mechanism is the same in all of them, but the organization of their actin and myosin filaments differs. Because each type will be examined in later chapters, notably Chapter 7, this discussion will focus on general characteristics rather than specific details.

SKELETAL MUSCLE TISSUE

Skeletal muscle tissue contains very large, multinucleated cells (Figure 4-13a). A large skeletal muscle cell may be 100 micrometers (μm; 1 μm = 1/25,000 in.) in diameter and 25 cm (10 in.) long. Because skeletal muscle cells are relatively long and slender, they are usually called *muscle fibers.* Skeletal muscle fibers are incapable of dividing, but new muscle fibers are produced through the divisions of stem cells in adult skeletal muscle tissue. As a result, at least partial repairs can occur after an injury.

Because the actin and myosin filaments are arranged in an organized pattern, skeletal muscle fibers appear to be marked by a series of bands known as *striations.* Skeletal muscle fibers will not usually contract unless stimulated by nerves. Because the nervous system provides voluntary control over its activities, skeletal muscle is described as *striated voluntary muscle.*

CARDIAC MUSCLE TISSUE

Cardiac muscle tissue is found only in the heart. Like skeletal muscle tissue, cardiac muscle tissue is striated, but each cardiac muscle cell is much smaller than a skeletal muscle fiber and usually has only a single nucleus (Figure 4-13b). Cardiac muscle cells are interconnected at **intercalated** (in-TER-ka-lā-ted) **discs,** specialized attachment sites containing gap junctions and desmosomes. Cardiac muscle cells branch, forming a network that efficiently conducts the force and stimulus for contraction from one area of the heart to another. Cardiac muscle tissue has a very limited ability to repair itself. Stem cells are lacking, and although some cardiac muscle cells do divide after an injury to the heart, the repairs are incomplete.

Cardiac muscle cells do not rely on nerve activity to start a contraction. Instead, specialized cells, called *pacemaker cells,* establish a regular rate of contraction. Although the nervous system can alter the rate of pacemaker activity, it does not provide voluntary control over individual cardiac muscle cells. Therefore, cardiac muscle is called *striated involuntary muscle.*

SMOOTH MUSCLE TISSUE

Smooth muscle tissue is found in the walls of blood vessels; around hollow organs such as the urinary bladder; and in layers around the respiratory, circulatory, digestive, and reproductive tracts.

A smooth muscle cell is small and slender, tapering to a point at each end; each smooth muscle cell has one nucleus (Figure 4-13c). Unlike skeletal and cardiac muscle, the actin and myosin filaments in smooth muscle cells are scattered throughout the

SKELETAL MUSCLE TISSUE

Cells are long, cylindrical, striated, and multinucleate.

LOCATIONS: Combined with connective tissues and neural tissue in skeletal muscles

FUNCTIONS: Moves or stabilizes the position of the skeleton; guards entrances and exits to the digestive, respiratory, and urinary tracts; generates heat; protects internal organs

Nuclei

Muscle fiber

Striations

(a) Skeletal muscle

LM × 180

CARDIAC MUSCLE TISSUE

Cells are short, branched, and striated, usually with a single nucleus; cells are interconnected by intercalated discs.

LOCATION: Heart

FUNCTIONS: Circulates blood; maintains blood (hydrostatic) pressure

Nucleus

Cardiac muscle cells

Intercalated discs

Striations

(b) Cardiac muscle

LM × 450

SMOOTH MUSCLE TISSUE

Cells are short, spindle-shaped, and nonstriated, with a single, central nucleus

LOCATIONS: Found in the walls of blood vessels and in digestive, respiratory, urinary, and reproductive organs

FUNCTIONS: Moves food, urine, and reproductive tract secretions; controls diameter of respiratory passageways; regulates diameter of blood vessels

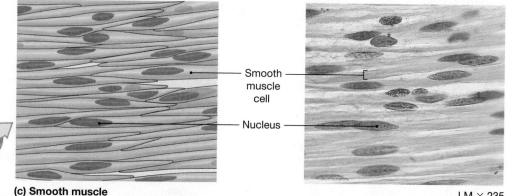

Smooth muscle cell

Nucleus

(c) Smooth muscle

LM × 235

FIGURE 4-13 Muscle Tissue. (a) Skeletal muscle fibers are large and have prominent striations (banding), multiple nuclei, and an unbranched arrangement. **(b)** Cardiac muscle cells differ from skeletal muscle fibers in three major ways: They are smaller, they branch, and they typically have a single centrally placed nucleus. Like skeletal muscle fibers, cardiac muscle cells have striations. **(c)** Smooth muscle cells are small and spindle-shaped, have a central nucleus, and lack branches and striations.

cytoplasm, so there are no striations. Smooth muscle cells can divide, so smooth muscle tissue can regenerate after injury.

Smooth muscle cells may contract on their own, or their contractions may be triggered by neural activity. The nervous system usually does not provide voluntary control over smooth muscle contractions, so smooth muscle is known as *nonstriated involuntary muscle*.

CHECKPOINT

23. Identify the three types of muscle tissue in the body.

24. Voluntary control is restricted to which type of muscle tissue?

25. Which type of muscle tissue has small, tapering cells with single nuclei and no obvious striations?

See the blue Answers tab at the back of the book.

4-7 Neural tissue responds to stimuli and conducts electrical impulses throughout the body

Neural tissue, which is also known as *nervous tissue* or *nerve tissue*, is specialized for the conduction of electrical impulses from one region of the body to another. Most neural tissue (98 percent) is concentrated in the brain and spinal cord, the control centers for the nervous system.

Neural tissue contains two basic types of cells: **neurons** (NOOR-onz; *neuro-*, nerve) and several different kinds of supporting cells, or **neuroglia** (noo-ROG-lē-uh or noo-rō-GLE-uh; *glia*, glue). Our conscious and unconscious thought processes reflect communication among neurons. Neurons communicate through electrical events that affect their plasma membranes. The neuroglia provide physical support for neural tissue, maintain the chemical composition of the tissue fluids, supply nutrients to neurons, and defend the tissue from infection.

The longest cells in your body are neurons, reaching up to a meter (39 in.) long. Most neurons cannot divide under normal circumstances, so they have a very limited ability to repair themselves after injury. A typical neuron has three main parts: (1) a **cell body** containing a large nucleus, (2) numerous branching projections called **dendrites** (DEN-drīts; *dendron*, tree), and (3) one **axon** (Figure 4-14). Dendrites receive information, typically from other neurons, and axons carry that information to other cells. Because axons tend to be very long and slender, they are also called *nerve fibers*. Each axon ends at *synaptic terminals*, where the neuron communicates with other cells. Chapter 8 considers the properties of neural tissue.

CHECKPOINT

26. A tissue contains irregularly shaped cells with many fibrous projections, some several centimeters long. These are probably which type of cell?

27. Why are both skeletal muscle cells and axons also called fibers?

See the blue Answers tab at the back of the book.

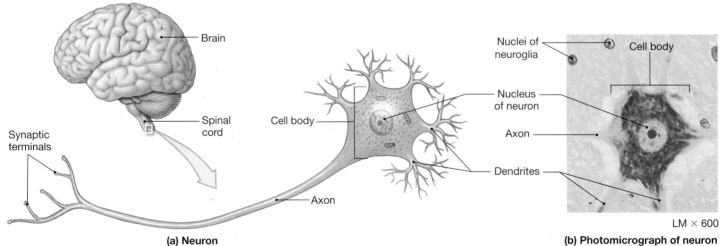

(a) Neuron

(b) **Photomicrograph of neuron cell body**

LM × 600

FIGURE 4-14 **Neural Tissue.**

4-8 The response to tissue injury involves inflammation and regeneration

Tissues in the body are not isolated; they combine to form organs with diverse functions. Any injury affects several tissue types simultaneously, and these tissues must respond in a coordinated manner to restore homeostasis.

The restoration of homeostasis following a tissue injury involves two related processes: inflammation and regeneration. First, the area is isolated from neighboring healthy tissue while damaged cells, tissue components, and any dangerous microorganisms are cleaned up. This phase, which coordinates the activities of several different tissues, is called **inflammation,** or the *inflammatory response.* It produces several familiar signs and symptoms, including swelling, warmth, redness, and pain. Inflammation can also result from an *infection*, the presence of pathogens (such as harmful bacteria) in tissues.

Inflammation can result from many other stimuli, including impact, abrasion, chemical irritation, and extreme temperatures (hot or cold). When any of these stimuli either kill cells, damage fibers, or injure tissues, they trigger the inflammatory response by stimulating connective tissue cells called mast cells. ⬯ p. 104. The mast cells release chemicals (*histamine* and *heparin*) that cause local blood vessels to *dilate* (enlarge in diameter) and become more permeable. The increased blood flow to the injured region makes it red and warm to the touch, and the diffusion of blood plasma causes the injured area to swell. The abnormal tissue conditions and the chemicals released by the mast cells also stimulate sensory nerve endings that produce sensations of pain. These local circulatory changes increase the delivery of nutrients, oxygen, phagocytic white blood cells, and blood-clotting proteins, and they speed up the removal of waste products and toxins. Over a period of hours to days, this coordinated response generally succeeds in eliminating the inflammatory stimulus.

In the second phase following injury, damaged tissues are replaced or repaired to restore normal function. This repair process is called **regeneration.** During regeneration, fibroblasts produce a dense network of collagen fibers known as *scar tissue* or *fibrous tissue.* Over time, scar tissue is usually remodeled and gradually assumes a more normal appearance.

Regeneration is more successful in some tissues than others: Epithelia, connective tissues (except cartilage), and smooth muscle tissue usually regenerate well; other muscle tissues and neural tissue regenerate relatively poorly if at all. Because of different patterns of tissue organization, each organ has a different ability to regenerate after injury. Your skin, which is made up mostly of epithelia and connective tissues, regenerates rapidly. In contrast, damage to the heart is more serious, because, although its connective tissue can be repaired, most of the damaged cardiac muscle cells are replaced only by fibrous connective tissue. Such permanent replacement of normal tissues is called **fibrosis** (fī-BRŌ-sis). Fibrosis may occur in muscle and other tissues in response to injury, disease, or aging.

Inflammation and regeneration are controlled at the tissue level. The two phases overlap; isolation of the area of damaged tissue establishes a framework that guides the cells responsible for reconstruction, and repairs are under way well before cleanup operations have ended. Later chapters will examine inflammation (Chapter 14) and regeneration (Chapter 5) in more detail.

CHECKPOINT

28. Identify the two phases in the response to tissue injury.

29. What signs and symptoms are associated with inflammation?

30. What is fibrosis?

See the blue Answers tab at the back of the book.

4-9 With advancing age, tissue repair declines and cancer rates increase

This section considers two important effects of aging on tissues: the body's decreasing ability to repair tissue damage, and an increase in the occurrence of cancer.

AGING AND TISSUE STRUCTURE

Tissues change with age, and the speed and effectiveness of tissue repairs decrease. Repair and maintenance activities throughout the body slow down, and energy consumption generally declines. These changes reflect a combination of hormonal alterations and changes in lifestyle that affect the structure and chemical composition of many tissues. Epithelia get thinner and connective tissues more fragile. Individuals bruise more easily and bones become brittle; joint pain and broken bones are common in the elderly. Cardiac muscle fibers and neurons cannot be replaced, and cumulative losses from even relatively minor damage can contribute to major health problems, such as cardiovascular disease or deterioration in mental function.

In later chapters we will consider the effects of aging on specific organs and systems. Some of these effects are genetically programmed. For example, as people age, their chondrocytes produce a slightly different form of the gelatinous compound making up the cartilage matrix. This difference in composition probably accounts for the thinner and less resilient cartilage of older people.

Other age-related changes in tissue structure have multiple causes. The age-related reduction in bone strength in women, a condition called *osteoporosis*, is often caused by a combination of inactivity, low dietary calcium intake, and a reduction in circulating estrogens (sex hormones). A program of exercise, calcium supplements, and medication can generally maintain normal bone structure for many years.

AGING AND CANCER INCIDENCE

Cancer rates increase with age, and roughly 25 percent of all Americans develop cancer at some point in their lives. It has been estimated that 70–80 percent of cancer cases result from chemical exposure, environmental factors, or some combination of the two, and 40 percent of these cancers are caused by cigarette smoke. Each year in the United States, over 500,000 individuals die of cancer, making it second only to heart disease as a cause of death. Cancer development was discussed in Chapter 3. p. 86

CHECKPOINT

31. Identify some age-related factors that affect tissue repair and structure.

See the blue Answers tab at the back of the book.

RELATED CLINICAL TERMS

adhesions: Restrictive fibrous connections that can result from surgery, infection, or other injuries to serous membranes.

anaplasia (a-nuh-PLĀ-zē-uh)**:** An irreversible change in the size and shape of tissue cells.

chemotherapy: The administration of drugs that either kill cancerous tissues or prevent mitotic divisions.

dysplasia (dis-PLĀ-zē-uh)**:** A change in the normal shape, size, and organization of tissue cells.

exfoliative cytology: The study of cells shed or collected from epithelial surfaces.

liposuction: A surgical procedure to remove unwanted adipose tissue by sucking it out through a tube.

metaplasia (me-tuh-PLĀ-zē-uh)**:** A structural change in cells that alters the character of a tissue.

necrosis (ne-KRŌ-sis)**:** Tissue destruction that occurs after cells have been injured or killed.

oncologists (on-KOL-o-jists)**:** Physicians who specialize in identifying and treating cancers.

pathologists (pa-THOL-o-jists)**:** Physicians who specialize in the study of disease processes.

pericarditis: An inflammation of the pericardial lining that may lead to the accumulation of pericardial fluid (*pericardial effusion*).

peritonitis: An inflammation of the peritoneum after infection or injury.

pleural effusion: The accumulation of fluid within the pleural cavities as a result of chronic infection or inflammation of the pleura.

pleuritis *(pleurisy)***:** An inflammation of the pleural cavities.

regeneration: The repair of injured tissues following inflammation.

remission: A stage in which a tumor stops growing or becomes smaller; a major goal of cancer treatment.

Chapter 4 Review

KEY TERMS

basement membrane	*97*	inflammation	*115*
blood	*106*	lymph	*106*
bone	*108*	macrophage	*104*
cartilage	*108*	mucous membrane	*110*
connective tissue	*103*	muscle tissue	*112*
epithelium	*94*	neural tissue	*114*
fibroblasts	*104*	neuron	*114*
gap junction	*96*	serous membrane	*111*
gland cells	*94*	stem cells	*97*
histology	*93*	tissue	*93*

SUMMARY OUTLINE

4-1 The four tissue types are epithelial, connective, muscle, and neural *p. 93*

1. **Tissues** are collections of specialized cells and cell products that are organized to perform a relatively limited number of functions. The four **tissue types** are *epithelial tissue, connective tissues, muscle tissue,* and *neural tissue.* **Histology** is the study of tissues. *(Figure 4-1)*

4-2 Epithelial tissue covers body surfaces, lines cavities and tubular structures, and serves essential functions *p. 94*

2. An **epithelium** is an **avascular** layer of cells that forms a barrier that covers internal or external surfaces. **Glands** are secretory structures derived from epithelia.

3. Epithelia provide physical protection, control permeability, provide sensations, and produce specialized secretions.

4. **Gland cells** are epithelial cells that produce secretions. **Exocrine** secretions are released onto body surfaces; **endocrine** secretions, known as hormones, are released by gland cells into the surrounding tissues.

5. The individual cells that make up tissues connect to one another or to extracellular protein fibers by means of *cell adhesion molecules (CAMs)* and intercellular cement to make specialized attachment sites called cell junctions. The three types are **tight junctions, gap junctions,** and **desmosomes.** *(Figure 4-2)*

6. Many epithelial cells have microvilli. The coordinated beating of the cilia on a ciliated epithelium moves materials across the epithelial surface. *(Figure 4-3)*

7. The basal surface of each epithelium is connected to a noncellular **basement membrane.**

8. Divisions by **stem cells,** or *germinative cells,* continually replace the short-lived epithelial cells.

4-3 Cell shape and number of layers determine the classification of epithelia *p. 97*

9. Epithelia are classified based on the number of cell layers and the shape of the exposed cells. *(Table 4-1)*

10. A **simple epithelium** has a single layer of cells covering the basement membrane; a **stratified epithelium** has several layers. In a **squamous epithelium** the cells are thin and flat. Cells in a **cuboidal epithelium** resemble little boxes; those in a **columnar epithelium** are taller and more slender. *(Figures 4-4, 4-5)*

11. A glandular epithelial cell may release its secretions through *merocrine, apocrine,* or *holocrine mechanisms. (Figure 4-6)*

12. In **merocrine secretion** (the most common method of secretion), the product is released through exocytosis. **Apocrine secretion** involves the loss of both secretory product and cytoplasm. Unlike the first two methods, **holocrine secretion** destroys the cell, which becomes packed with secretions before it finally bursts.

13. Exocrine secretions may be serous (watery, usually containing enzymes), mucous (thick and slippery), or mixed (containing enzymes and lubricants). *(Table 4-2)*

4-4 Connective tissue provides a protective structural framework for other tissue types *p. 103*

14. All **connective** tissues have specialized cells and a **matrix,** composed of extracellular protein fibers and a **ground substance.**

15. Connective tissues are internal tissues with many important functions: establishing a structural framework; transporting fluids and dissolved materials; protecting delicate organs; supporting, surrounding, and interconnecting tissues; storing energy reserves; and defending the body from microorganisms.

16. **Connective tissue proper** refers to connective tissues that contain varied cell populations and fiber types surrounded by a syrupy ground substance. *(Figure 4-7)*

17. **Fluid connective tissues** have a distinctive population of cells suspended in a watery ground substance containing dissolved proteins. The two types are *blood* and *lymph.* *(Figure 4-7)*

18. **Supporting connective tissues** have a less diverse cell population than connective tissue proper and a dense matrix that contains closely packed fibers. The two types of supporting connective tissues are cartilage and bone. *(Figure 4-7)*

19. Connective tissue proper contains fibers, a viscous ground substance, and a varied cell population, including **fibroblasts, fibrocytes, macrophages, fat cells, mast cells,** and various white blood cells. *(Figure 4-8)*

20. There are three types of fibers in connective tissue: **collagen fibers, elastic fibers,** and **reticular fibers.**

21. Connective tissue proper is classified as **loose** or **dense connective tissues.** Loose connective tissues include loose connective tissue (or *areolar tissue*) and **adipose tissue.** *(Figure 4-9a, b)*

22. Most of the volume in dense connective tissue consists of fibers. *Dense regular connective tissues* form **tendons** and **ligaments.** *(Figure 4-9c)*

23. **Blood** and **lymph** are connective tissues that contain distinctive collections of cells in a fluid matrix.

24. Blood contains **red blood cells, white blood cells,** and **platelets;** the watery ground substance is called **plasma.**

25. Lymph forms as *interstitial fluid* enters the *lymphatic vessels,* which return lymph to the cardiovascular system.

26. Cartilage and bone are called supporting connective tissues because they support the rest of the body.

27. The matrix of **cartilage** consists of a firm gel and cells called **chondrocytes.** A fibrous **perichondrium** separates cartilage from surrounding tissues. The three types of cartilage are **hyaline cartilage, elastic cartilage,** and **fibrous cartilage.** *(Figure 4-10)*

28. Chondrocytes rely on diffusion through the avascular matrix to obtain nutrients.

29. **Bone,** or *osseous tissue,* has a matrix primarily consisting of collagen fibers and calcium salts, which give it unique properties. *(Figure 4-11; Table 4-3)*

30. **Osteocytes** depend on diffusion through **canaliculi** for nutrient intake.

31. Each bone is surrounded by a **periosteum.**

4-5 Membranes are physical barriers of four types: mucous, serous, cutaneous, and synovial

p. 110

32. Membranes form a barrier or an interface. Epithelia and connective tissues combine to form membranes that cover and protect other structures and tissues. There are four types of membranes: *mucous, serous, cutaneous,* and *synovial.* (*Figure 4-12*)

33. **Mucous membranes** line cavities that communicate with the exterior. Their surfaces are normally moistened by mucous secretions.

34. **Serous membranes** line internal cavities and are delicate, moist, and very permeable.

35. The **cutaneous membrane** covers the body surface. Unlike serous and mucous membranes, it is relatively thick, waterproof, and usually dry.

36. **Synovial membranes,** located at joints (articulations), produce *synovial fluid* in joint cavities. Synovial fluid helps lubricate the joint and promotes smooth movement.

4-6 The three types of muscle tissue are skeletal, cardiac, and smooth *p. 112*

37. **Muscle tissue** is specialized for contraction. The three types of muscle tissue are *skeletal muscle, cardiac muscle,* and *smooth muscle.* (Figure 4-13)

38. **Skeletal muscle tissue** contains large cells, or *muscle fibers,* tied together by collagen and elastic fibers. Skeletal muscle fibers are multinucleated and have a striped appearance because of the organization of contractile proteins. Because we can control the contraction of skeletal muscle fibers through the nervous system, skeletal muscle is considered *striated voluntary muscle.*

39. **Cardiac muscle tissue** is found only in the heart. The nervous system does not provide voluntary control over cardiac muscle cells. Thus, cardiac muscle is *striated involuntary muscle.*

40. **Smooth muscle tissue** is found in the walls of blood vessels, around hollow organs, and in layers around various tracts. It is classified as *nonstriated involuntary muscle.*

4-7 Neural tissue responds to stimuli and conducts electrical impulses throughout the body

p. 114

41. **Neural tissue** is specialized to conduct electrical impulses that convey information from one area of the body to another.

42. Cells in neural tissue are either neurons or neuroglia. **Neurons** transmit information as electrical impulses in their plasma membranes. Several kinds of **neuroglia** serve both supporting and defense functions. (*Figure 4-14*)

43. A typical neuron has a **cell body, dendrites,** and an **axon,** which ends at *synaptic terminals.*

4-8 The response to tissue injury involves inflammation and regeneration *p. 115*

44. Any injury affects several tissue types simultaneously, and they respond in a coordinated manner. Homeostasis is restored through two processes: *inflammation* and *regeneration.*

45. **Inflammation,** or the *inflammatory response,* isolates the injured area while damaged cells, tissue components, and any dangerous microorganisms are cleaned up.

46. **Regeneration** is the repair process that restores normal function.

4-9 With advancing age, tissue repair declines and cancer rates increase *p. 115*

47. Tissues change with age. Repair and maintenance grow less efficient, and the structure and chemical composition of many tissues are altered.

48. Cancer incidence increases with age; roughly three-quarters of all cases are caused by exposure to chemicals or environmental factors.

REVIEW QUESTIONS

WWW Access more review material online at The Anatomy & Physiology Place (**www.anatomyandphysiology.com**). There, you'll find Chapter Guides, Chapter Quizzes, Chapter Practice Tests, Interactive Flashcards, a Glossary with Pronunciations, and more to help you succeed in the course.

Level 1 • Reviewing Facts and Terms

Match each item in column A with the most closely related item in column B. Place letters for answers in the spaces provided.

COLUMN A

_____ 1. histology
_____ 2. microvilli
_____ 3. gap junction
_____ 4. tight junction
_____ 5. germinative cells
_____ 6. destroys gland cell
_____ 7. hormones
_____ 8. adipocytes
_____ 9. bone-to-bone attachment
_____ 10. muscle-to-bone attachment
_____ 11. skeletal muscle
_____ 12. cardiac muscle

COLUMN B

a. repair and renewal
b. ligament
c. endocrine secretion
d. absorption and secretion
e. fat cells
f. holocrine secretion
g. study of tissues
h. tendon
i. intercellular connection
j. interlocking of membrane proteins
k. intercalated discs
l. striated, voluntary

13. Identify the six categories of epithelial tissue shown in the drawing below.

(a) _____ (b) _____
(c) _____ (d) _____
(e) _____ (f) _____

14. The four basic tissue types found in the body are
   (a) epithelia, connective, muscle, neural.
   (b) simple, cuboidal, squamous, stratified.
   (c) fibroblasts, adipocytes, melanocytes, mesenchymal.
   (d) lymphocytes, macrophages, microphages, adipocytes.

15. The most abundant connections between cells in the superficial layers of the skin are
   (a) intermediate junctions.   (b) gap junctions.
   (c) desmosomes.   (d) tight junctions.

16. The three cell shapes making up epithelial tissue are
   (a) simple, stratified, transitional.
   (b) simple, stratified, pseudostratified.
   (c) hexagonal, cuboidal, spherical.
   (d) cuboidal, squamous, columnar.

17. Mucous secretions that coat the passageways of the digestive and respiratory tracts result from _____ secretion.
   (a) apocrine   (b) merocrine
   (c) holocrine   (d) endocrine

18. The tissue that contains a fluid ground substance is
   (a) epithelial.   (b) neural.
   (c) muscle.   (d) connective.

19. The three major types of cartilage in the body are
   (a) collagen, reticular, elastic.
   (b) areolar, adipose, reticular.
   (c) hyaline, elastic, fibrous.
   (d) keratin, reticular, elastic.

20. The primary function of serous membranes in the body is
   (a) to minimize friction between opposing surfaces.
   (b) to line cavities that communicate with the exterior.
   (c) to perform absorptive and secretory functions.
   (d) to cover the surface of the body.

21. Large muscle fibers that are multinucleated, striated, and voluntary are found in
    (a) cardiac muscle tissue.   **(b)** skeletal muscle tissue.
    (c) smooth muscle tissue.   **(d)** a, b, and c are correct.

22. Intercalated discs and pacemaker cells are characteristic of
    (a) smooth muscle tissue.   **(b)** cardiac muscle tissue.
    (c) skeletal muscle tissue.   **(d)** a, b, and c are correct.

23. Dendrites, an axon, and a cell body are characteristics of cells found in
    (a) neural tissue.   **(b)** muscle tissue.
    (c) connective tissue.   **(d)** epithelial tissue.

24. Identify the four kinds of membranes shown in the drawing below.

(a) _____

(b) _____

(c) _____

(d) _____

25. What two types of layering make epithelial tissue recognizable?

26. What three basic components are found in connective tissues?

27. Which fluid connective tissues and supporting connective tissues are found in the human body?

28. What two cell populations make up neural tissue? What is the function of each?

Level 2 • Reviewing Concepts

29. In body surfaces where mechanical stresses are severe, the dominant epithelium is
    (a) stratified squamous epithelium.
    (b) simple cuboidal epithelium.
    (c) simple columnar epithelium.
    (d) stratified cuboidal epithelium.

30. Why does holocrine secretion require continuous cell division?

31. What is the difference between an exocrine secretion and an endocrine secretion?

32. A significant structural feature in the digestive system is the presence of tight junctions located near the exposed surfaces of cells lining the digestive tract. Why are these junctions so important?

33. Why are infections always a serious threat after a severe burn or an abrasion?

34. What characteristics make the cutaneous membrane different from serous and mucous membranes?

Level 3 • Critical Thinking and Clinical Applications

35. Your lab partner in a biology class loses the labels of two prepared slides—one of an animal's intestine, the other an animal's esophagus. How could you help her tell which slide is which?

36. You are asked to develop a scheme that can be used to identify the three types of muscle tissue in just two steps. What would the two steps be?

5 The Integumentary System

Eager for a day of fun at the pool, this young boy patiently waits as his mother applies sunblock to protect his exposed skin from a painful sunburn. The skin is a remarkable structure that absorbs ultraviolet radiation, prevents dehydration, preserves normal body temperature, and tolerates chafing and abrasion. Although few people think of it in these terms, the skin is actually an organ—the largest organ of the body. In this chapter we will examine its varied functions.

LEARNING OUTCOMES

After completing this chapter, you should be able to do the following:

5-1 Describe the main structural features of the epidermis, and explain their functional significance.

5-2 Explain what accounts for individual differences in skin color, and discuss the response of melanocytes to sunlight exposure.

5-3 Describe the interaction between sunlight and vitamin D_3 production.

5-4 Describe the structure and functions of the dermis.

5-5 Describe the structure and functions of the hypodermis.

5-6 Describe the mechanisms that produce hair and the structural basis for hair texture and color.

5-7 Discuss the various kinds of glands in the skin, and list the secretions of those glands.

5-8 Describe the anatomical structure of nails, and explain how they are formed.

5-9 Explain how the skin responds to injury and repairs itself.

5-10 Summarize the effects of aging on the skin.

5-11 Give examples of interactions between the integumentary system and each of the other organ systems.

VOCABULARY DEVELOPMENT

cornu horn; *stratum corneum*
cutis skin; *cutaneous*
derma skin; *dermis*
epi- above or over; *epidermis*
facere to make; *cornified*

germinare to start growing; *stratum germinativum*
keros horn; *keratin*
kyanos blue; *cyanosis*
luna moon; *lunula*

melas black; *melanin*
onyx nail; *eponychium*
papilla a nipple-shaped mound; *dermal papillae*

An Introduction to the Integumentary System

The integumentary system consists of the skin, hair, nails, and various glands. As the most visible organ system of the body, we devote a lot of time to improving its appearance. Washing your face and hands, brushing or trimming your hair, clipping your nails, showering, and applying deodorant are activities that modify the appearance or properties of the skin. And when something goes wrong with your skin, the effects are immediately apparent. You may notice a minor skin condition or blemish at once, whereas you may ignore more serious problems in other organ systems. Physicians also pay attention to the skin because changes in its color, flexibility, or sensitivity may provide important clues about a disorder in another body system.

The **integumentary system,** or simply the **integument** (in-TEG-ū-ment), has two major components: the cutaneous membrane and accessory structures. The **cutaneous membrane,** or *skin,* is an organ composed of the superficial epithelium, or **epidermis** (*epi-,* above), and the underlying connective tissues of the **dermis.** The **accessory structures** include hair, nails, and a variety of exocrine glands.

The general structure of the integument is shown in Figure 5-1. Beneath the dermis, the loose connective tissue of

Epidermis

Dermis

Subcutaneous layer (hypodermis)

Hair shaft
Pore of sweat gland duct
Epidermal ridge
Dermal papilla
Sebaceous gland
Arrector pili muscle
Sweat gland duct
Touch and pressure receptors
Hair follicle
Artery
Vein
Sweat gland
Nerve fibers
Fat

FIGURE 5-1 The General Structure of the Integumentary System. This diagrammatic section of skin shows the relationships among the major components of the integumentary system (with the exception of nails, shown in Figure 5-8).

the **subcutaneous layer,** or **hypodermis,** attaches the integument to deeper structures, such as muscles or bones. Although often not considered to be part of the integumentary system, we will include it here because its connective tissue fibers are interwoven with those of the dermis.

As we will see, the five major functions of the integument are:

1. *Protection.* The skin covers and protects underlying tissues and organs from impacts, chemicals, and infections, and it prevents the loss of body fluids.

2. *Temperature maintenance.* The skin maintains normal body temperature by regulating heat exchange with the environment.

3. *Synthesis and storage of nutrients.* The epidermis synthesizes vitamin D_3, a steroid building block for a hormone that aids calcium uptake. The dermis stores large reserves of lipids in adipose tissue.

4. *Sensory reception.* Receptors in the integument detect touch, pressure, pain, and temperature stimuli and relay that information to the nervous system.

5. *Excretion and secretion.* Integumentary glands excrete salts, water, and organic wastes. Additionally, specialized integumentary glands of the breasts secrete milk.

Each of these functions will be explored more fully as we discuss the individual components of the integument, beginning with the superficial layer of the skin: the epidermis.

CHECKPOINT

1. List the general functions of the integumentary system.

See the blue Answers tab at the back of the book.

5-1 The epidermis is composed of strata (layers) with various functions

The epidermis consists of a stratified squamous epithelium of several different cell layers. ∞ p. 98 **Thick skin,** found on the palms of the hands and soles of the feet, contains five layers. Only four layers make up **thin skin,** which covers the rest of the body. Thin skin is about as thick as the wall of a plastic sandwich bag (about 0.08 mm thick), whereas thick skin is about as thick as a paper towel (0.5 mm). The words *thin* and *thick* refer to the relative thickness of the epidermis only, not to that of the integument as a whole.

Figure 5-2 shows the cell layers, or **strata** (singular *stratum*), in a section of thick skin. In order, from the basement membrane toward the free surface, are the *stratum germinativum,* three intermediate layers (the *stratum spinosum,* the *stratum granulosum,* and the *stratum lucidum*), and the *stratum corneum.* We consider these strata next.

LM × 150

Surface

Stratum corneum

Stratum lucidum
Stratum granulosum
Stratum spinosum
Stratum germinativum
Basement membrane

Epidermis

Dermis

FIGURE 5-2 **The Structure of the Epidermis.** This section of the epidermis in thick skin shows all five epidermal layers.

STRATUM GERMINATIVUM

The deepest epidermal layer is called the **stratum germinativum** (STRA-tum jer-mi-na-TĒ-vum; *stratum*, layer + *germinare*, to start growing), or *stratum basale* (ba-SAY-lē; *basis*, base). The cells of this layer are firmly attached to the basement membrane by hemidesmosomes. ∞ p. 96 The basement membrane separates the epidermis from the loose connective tissue of the adjacent dermis. The stratum germinativum forms **epidermal ridges,** which extend into the dermis, increasing the area of contact between the two regions (**Figure 5-1**). Dermal projections called *dermal papillae* (singular *papilla;* a nipple-shaped mound) extend upward between adjacent ridges. Because there are no blood vessels in the epidermis, epidermal cells must obtain nutrients delivered by dermal blood vessels. The combination of ridges and papillae increases the surface area for diffusion between the dermis and epidermis.

The contours of the skin surface follow the ridge patterns, which vary from small conical pegs (in thin skin) to the complex whorls on the thick skin of the palms and soles. The superficial ridges on the palms and soles (which overlie the dermal papillae) increase the surface area of the skin and increase friction, ensuring a secure grip. Ridge contours are genetically determined; those of each person are unique and do not change over the course of a lifetime. Fingerprints are ridge patterns on the tips of the fingers; they have been used to identify individuals in criminal investigations for over a century.

Large stem cells, or *germinative cells,* dominate the stratum germinativum, making it the layer where new cells are generated and begin to grow. The divisions of these cells replace cells that are lost or shed at the epithelial surface. The stratum germinativum also contains *melanocytes,* cells whose cytoplasmic processes extend between epithelial cells in this layer, and receptors that provide information about objects touching the skin. Melanocytes synthesize *melanin,* a brown, yellow-brown, or black pigment that colors the epidermis.

INTERMEDIATE STRATA

The cells in these three layers are progressively displaced from the basal layer as they become specialized to form the outer protective barrier of the skin. Each time a stem cell divides, one of the resulting daughter cells enters the next layer, the **stratum spinosum** (spiny layer), where it may continue to divide and add to the thickness of the epithelium. The **stratum granulosum** (grainy layer) consists of cells displaced from the stratum spinosum. The cells in this grainy layer have stopped dividing and begin making large amounts of the protein **keratin** (KER-a-tin; *keros,* horn). ∞ p. 48 Keratin is extremely durable and water-resistant. In hu-

mans, keratin not only coats the surface of the skin but also forms the basic structure of hair, calluses, and nails. In various other animals, it forms structures such as horns and hooves, feathers, and baleen plates (in the mouths of whales). In the thick skin of the palms and soles, a glassy **stratum lucidum** (clear layer) covers the stratum granulosum. The cells in this layer are flattened, densely packed, and filled with keratin.

STRATUM CORNEUM

The most superficial layer of the epidermis, the **stratum corneum** (KOR-nē-um; *cornu,* horn), consists of 15–30 layers of flattened and dead epithelial cells that have accumulated large amounts of keratin. Such cells are said to be **keratinized** (ker-A-tin-īzed), or **cornified** (KOR-ni-fīd; *cornu,* horn + *facere,* to make). The dead cells in each layer of the stratum corneum remain tightly connected by desmosomes. ∞ p. 96 As a result, the keratinized cells of the stratum corneum are generally shed in large groups or sheets rather than individually.

Clinical Note — Drug Administration Through the Skin

Drugs dissolved in oils or other lipid-soluble solvents can be carried across the cell membranes of the epidermis. The movement is slow, particularly through the stratum corneum, but once a drug reaches the underlying tissues, it will be absorbed into the circulation.

A useful technique for long-term drug administration involves affixing a sticky, drug-containing patch over an area of thin skin. To overcome the slow rate of diffusion, the patch must contain an extremely high concentration of the drug. This procedure, called *transdermal administration,* has the advantage that a single patch may work for several days, making daily pills unnecessary. Among the several drugs now routinely administered transdermally are:

- Scopolamine, which can control the nausea associated with motion sickness by affecting the nervous system.
- Estrogens, which are administered to women to reduce symptoms of menopause or are combined with progesterone for birth control.
- Nicotine, the addictive compound in tobacco, for suppressing the craving for a cigarette. The transdermal dosage of nicotine can gradually be reduced in small controlled steps.

Another procedure involves administering a brief pulse of electricity to the skin. The electrical pulse temporarily changes the positions of the cells in the stratum corneum, creating channels that allow the drug to penetrate.

It takes 2–4 weeks for a cell to move from the stratum germinativum to the stratum corneum. During this time, the cell is displaced from its oxygen and nutrient supply, becomes packed with keratin, and finally dies. The dead cells usually remain in the stratum corneum for an additional 2 weeks before they are shed or washed away. As superficial layers are lost, new layers arrive from the underlying strata. Thus, the deeper layers of the epithelium and underlying tissues remain protected by a barrier of dead, durable, and expendable cells. Normally, the surface of the stratum corneum is relatively dry, so it is unsuitable for the growth of many microorganisms.

CHECKPOINT

2. Identify the five layers of the epidermis.

3. Dandruff is caused by excessive shedding of cells from the outer layer of skin in the scalp. Thus, dandruff is composed of cells from which epidermal layer?

4. Some criminals sand their fingertips to avoid leaving recognizable fingerprints. Would this practice permanently remove fingerprints? Why or why not?

See the blue Answers tab at the back of the book.

5-2 Factors influencing skin color are epidermal pigmentation and dermal circulation

The color of your skin is caused by the interaction between the pigments in the epidermis and blood flow in the dermis.

THE ROLE OF PIGMENTATION

The epidermis contains variable amounts of two pigments, carotene and melanin. **Carotene** (KAR-uh-tēn) is an orange-yellow pigment that normally accumulates in epidermal cells. Carotene pigments are present in a variety of orange-colored vegetables, including carrots and squashes. Eating large amounts of carrots can actually cause the skin of light-skinned individuals to turn orange. The color change is less striking in the skin of darker individuals. Carotene can be converted to vitamin A, which is required for the normal maintenance of epithelial tissues and the synthesis of photoreceptor pigments in the eye. As noted earlier, **melanin** is a brown, yellow-brown, or black pigment produced by melanocytes.

Melanocytes (me-LAN-ō-sīts) manufacture and store melanin within intracellular vesicles (**Figure 5-3**). These vesicles are transferred to the epithelial cells of the stratum ger-

FIGURE 5-3 Melanocytes. These views show the location and orientation of melanocytes in the deepest layer of the epidermis (stratum germinativum) of a dark-skinned person.

minativum, coloring the entire epidermis. Melanocyte activity slowly increases in response to sunlight exposure, peaking around 10 days after the initial exposure. *Freckles* are small pigmented spots that appear on the skin of pale-skinned individuals. Freckles represent areas of greater-than-average melanin production. They tend to be most abundant on surfaces exposed to the sun, such as the face.

Sunlight contains significant amounts of **ultraviolet (UV) radiation.** A small amount of UV radiation is beneficial because it stimulates the synthesis of vitamin D_3 in the epidermis; this process is discussed in a later section. Too much ultraviolet radiation, however, produces immediate effects of mild or even serious burns. Melanin helps prevent skin damage by absorbing UV radiation before it reaches the deep layers of the epidermis and dermis. Within epidermal cells, melanin concentrates around the nuclear envelope and absorbs the UV radiation before it can damage nuclear DNA.

Despite the presence of melanin, long-term damage can result from repeated exposure to sunlight, even in darkly pigmented individuals. For example, alterations in the underlying connective tissues lead to premature wrinkling, and skin cancers can result from chromosomal damage in stem cells of the stratum germinativum or in melanocytes. One of the likely major consequences of the global depletion of the ozone layer in the upper atmosphere is a sharp increase in the rate of skin cancers, such as *malignant melanoma.* For this reason, limiting UV exposure through a combination of protective clothing and a sunblock with a sun protection factor (SPF) of at least 15 is recommended during outdoor activities. Individuals with fair skin are better off with an SPF of 20 to 30.

The ratio of melanocytes to stem cells ranges between 1:4 and 1:20, depending on the region of the body surveyed. The observed differences in skin color among individuals do not reflect the numbers of melanocytes but instead reflect the levels of melanin production. For example, in the inherited condition *albinism,* melanin is not produced by the melanocytes, even though these cells are of normal abundance and distribution. Individuals with this condition, known as *albinos,* have light-colored skin and hair.

THE ROLE OF DERMAL CIRCULATION

Blood with abundant oxygen is bright red, so blood vessels in the dermis normally give the skin a reddish tint that is most apparent in lightly pigmented individuals. If those vessels are dilated, the red tones become much more pronounced. For example, skin becomes flushed and red when body temperature rises because the superficial blood vessels widen so that the skin can act like a radiator and lose heat. ∞ p. 13 When the vessels are temporarily constricted, as when you are frightened, the skin becomes relatively pale. During a sustained reduction in circulatory supply, the blood in the skin loses oxygen and takes on a darker red tone. The skin then takes on a bluish coloration called **cyanosis** (sī-uh-NŌ-sis; *kyanos,* blue). In individuals of any skin color, cyanosis is most apparent in areas of thin skin, such as the lips, ears, or beneath the nails. It can be a response to extreme cold or a result of circulatory or respiratory disorders, such as heart failure or severe asthma.

CHECKPOINT

5. Name the two pigments in the epidermis.

6. Why does exposure to sunlight or sunlamps darken skin?

7. Why does the skin of a fair-skinned person appear red during exercise in hot weather?

See the blue Answers tab at the back of the book.

5-3 Sunlight has detrimental and beneficial effects on the skin

In this section we briefly consider how interactions between sunlight and skin cells regularly produce an important vitamin, and can sometimes result in skin cancers.

THE EPIDERMIS AND VITAMIN D₃

Although strong sunlight can damage epithelial cells and deeper tissues, limited exposure to sunlight is very beneficial. When exposed to UV radiation, epidermal cells in the stratum spinosum and stratum germinativum convert a cholesterol-related steroid into **vitamin D_3**. This product is absorbed, modified, and released by the liver and then converted by the kidneys into *calcitriol,* a hormone essential for the absorption of calcium and phosphorus by the small intestine. An inadequate supply of vitamin D_3 can lead to abnormally weak and flexible bones.

SKIN CANCERS

Skin cancers are the most common form of cancer. The most common *skin* cancer is **basal cell carcinoma** (Figure 5-4a), which originates in the stratum germinativum (basal) layer. Less common are **squamous cell carcinomas,** which involve more superficial layers of epidermal cells. Metastasis seldom occurs in either cancer, and most people survive these cancers. The usual treatment involves surgical removal of the tumor.

Compared with these common and seldom life-threatening cancers, **malignant melanomas** (mel-a-NŌ-maz) (Figure 5-4b) are extremely dangerous. A melanoma usually begins from a mole but may appear anywhere in the body. In this condition, cancerous melanocytes grow rapidly and metastasize through the lymphoid system. The outlook for long-term survival de-

(a) Basal cell carcinoma   (b) Melanoma

FIGURE 5-4 **Two Important Types of Skin Cancer.**

The Big Picture

The epidermis is a multilayered, flexible, self-repairing barrier that prevents fluid loss, provides protection from UV radiation, produces vitamin D$_3$, and resists damage from abrasion, chemicals, and pathogens.

pends on when the condition is detected and treated. Avoiding exposure to UV radiation in sunlight (especially during the middle of the day) and using a sunblock (not a tanning oil) would largely prevent all three forms of cancer.

CHECKPOINT

8. Explain the relationship between sunlight exposure and vitamin D$_3$ synthesis.

9. What is the most common skin cancer?

See the blue Answers tab at the back of the book.

5-4 The dermis is the tissue layer that supports the epidermis

The dermis lies beneath the epidermis. It has two major components: a superficial *papillary layer* and a deeper *reticular layer.*

The **papillary layer,** named after the dermal papillae, consists of loose connective tissue that supports and nourishes the epidermis. This region contains the capillaries and nerves supplying the surface of the skin. The deeper **reticular layer** consists of an interwoven meshwork of dense, irregular connective tissue. Both *elastic fibers* and *collagen fibers* are present. The elastic fibers provide flexibility, and the collagen fibers limit that flexibility to prevent damage to the tissue. Bundles of collagen fibers blend into those of the papillary layer above, blurring the boundary between these layers. Collagen fibers also extend into the subcutaneous layer below.

In addition to protein-based elastic and collagen fibers, the dermis contains the mixed cell populations of connective tissue proper. ∞ p. 104 Epidermal accessory organs, such as hair follicles and sweat glands, extend into the dermis (**Figure 5-1**).

The Big Picture

The dermis provides mechanical strength, flexibility, and protection for underlying tissues. It is highly vascular and contains a variety of sensory receptors that provide information about the external environment.

Other organ systems communicate with the skin through their connections to the dermis. For example, both dermal layers contain a network of blood vessels (cardiovascular system), lymphatic vessels (lymphoid system), and nerve fibers (nervous system).

Blood vessels provide nutrients and oxygen and remove carbon dioxide and waste products. Both the blood vessels and the lymphatic vessels help local tissues defend and repair themselves after injury or infection. The nerve fibers control blood flow, adjust gland secretion rates, and monitor sensory receptors in the dermis and the deeper layers of the epidermis. These receptors, which provide sensations of touch, pain, pressure, and temperature, will be described in Chapter 9.

CHECKPOINT

10. Describe the location of the dermis.

11. Where are the capillaries that supply the epidermis located?

See the blue Answers tab at the back of the book.

5-5 The hypodermis is tissue that connects the dermis to underlying tissues

An extensive network of connective tissue fibers attaches the dermis to the subcutaneous layer, or **hypodermis.** The boundary between the two is indistinct, and although the hypodermis is not actually a part of the integument, it is important in stabilizing the position of the skin relative to underlying tissues, such as skeletal muscles or other organs, while permitting independent movement.

The hypodermis consists of loose connective tissue with many fat cells. These adipose cells provide infants and small children with a layer of "baby fat," which helps them reduce heat loss. Subcutaneous fat also serves as an energy reserve and a shock absorber for the rough-and-tumble activities of our early years.

As we grow and mature, the distribution of subcutaneous fat changes. Beginning at puberty, men accumulate subcutaneous fat at the neck, upper arms, along the lower back, and over the buttocks; women do so in the breasts, buttocks, hips, and thighs. Both women and men, however, may accumulate distressing amounts of adipose tissue in the abdominal region, producing a prominent "potbelly."

The hypodermis is quite elastic. Below its superficial region with its large blood vessels, the hypodermis contains no vital organs and few capillaries. The lack of vital organs makes *subcutaneous injection* a useful method for administering drugs using a *hypodermic needle.*

CHECKPOINT

12. List the two terms for the tissue that connects the dermis to underlying tissues.

13. Describe the hypodermis.

See the blue Answers tab at the back of the book.

5-6 Hair is composed of keratinized dead cells that have been pushed to the surface

Hair and several other structures—hair follicles, sebaceous and sweat glands, and nails—are considered accessory structures of the integument.

Hairs project above the surface of the skin almost everywhere except the sides and soles of the feet, the palms of the hands, the sides of the fingers and toes, the lips, and portions of the external genital organs. Hairs are nonliving structures produced in organs called **hair follicles** (Figure 5-5).

THE STRUCTURE OF HAIR AND HAIR FOLLICLES

Hair follicles project deep into the dermis and often extend into the underlying subcutaneous layer (Figure 5-5a). The walls of each follicle contain all the cell layers found in the epidermis. The epithelium at the base of a follicle forms a cap over the **hair papilla,** a peg of connective tissue containing capillaries and nerves. Hair is formed by the repeated divisions of epithelial stem cells surrounding the hair papilla. As the daughter cells are pushed toward the surface, the hair lengthens, and the cells undergo keratinization and die. The point at which this occurs is about halfway to the skin surface and marks the boundary between the **hair root** (the portion that anchors the hair into the skin) and the **hair shaft** (the part we see on the surface) (Figure 5-5b). Each hair shaft consists of three layers of dead, keratinized cells (Figure 5-5c). The surface layer, or **cuticle,** is made up of an overlapping shingle-like layer of cells. The underlying layer is called the **cortex,** and the **medulla** makes up

the core of the hair. The medulla contains a flexible *soft keratin;* the cortex and cuticle contain thick layers of *hard keratin,* which give the hair its stiffness.

Hairs grow and are shed according to a *hair growth cycle* based on the activity level of hair follicles. In general, a hair in the scalp grows for 2–5 years, at a rate of about 0.3 mm per day, and then its follicle may become inactive for a comparable period of time. When another growth cycle begins, the follicle produces a new hair, and the old hair gets pushed toward the surface to be shed. Variations in growth rate and in the length of the hair growth cycle account for individual differences in the length of uncut hair. Other differences in hair appearance result from the size of the follicles and the shapes of the hairs. For example, straight hairs are round in cross section, whereas curly ones are rather flattened.

FUNCTIONS OF HAIR

The 2.5 million hairs on the human body have important functions. The roughly 500,000 hairs on the head protect the scalp from UV light, help cushion a light blow to the head, and provide insulating benefits for the skull. The hairs guarding the entrances to the nostrils and external ear canals help prevent the entry of foreign particles, and eyelashes perform a similar function for the surface of the eye. A sensory nerve fiber is associated with the base of each hair follicle. As a result, you can feel the movement of the shaft of even a single hair. This sensitivity provides an early-warning system that may help prevent injury. For example, you may be able to swat a mosquito before it reaches the skin surface.

Clinical Note

Hair Loss

Many people experience anxiety attacks when they find hairs clinging to their hairbrush instead of to their heads. On the average, about 50 hairs are lost from the head each day, but several factors may affect this rate. Sustained losses of over 100 hairs per day generally indicate a net loss of hair. Temporary increases in hair loss can result from drugs, dietary factors, radiation, high fever, stress, or hormonal factors related to pregnancy. In males, changes in the level of circulating sex hormones can affect the scalp, causing a shift in production from normal hair to fine "peach fuzz" hairs, beginning at the temples and the crown of the head. This alteration is called *male pattern baldness.* Some cases of male pattern baldness respond to drug therapies, such as topical application of *minoxidil (Rogaine).*

FIGURE 5-5 **Hair Follicles and Hairs.** **(a)** A In this section of skin of the scalp, notice that the many hair follicles extend into the dermis and subcutaneous layer. **(b)** This drawing shows a longitudinal section of a single hair follicle and hair. **(c)** This cross section through a hair follicle was taken at the boundary between the shaft and the root.

A bundle of smooth muscle cells forms the **arrector pili** (a-REK-tor PI-lē) muscle, which extends from the papillary dermis to the connective tissue sheath that surrounds each hair follicle (Figure 5-5b). When stimulated, the arrector pili pulls on the follicle, forcing the hair to stand up. Contraction may be caused by emotional states (such as fear or rage) or a response to cold, producing "goose bumps."

HAIR COLOR

Hair color reflects differences in the type and amount of pigment produced by melanocytes at the hair papilla. Different forms of melanin produce hair colors that can range from black to red. These pigment differences are genetically determined, but hormonal and environmental factors also influence the condition of your hair. As pigment production decreases with age, hair color lightens. White hair results from both a lack of pigment and the presence of air bubbles within the hair shaft. As the proportion of white hairs increases, the individual's hair color is described as gray. Because each hair is dead and inert, changes in coloration are gradual. Unless bleach is used, it is not possible for hair to "turn white overnight," as some horror stories would have us believe.

14. Describe a typical strand of hair.

15. What happens when the arrector pili muscle contracts?

16. Once a burn on the forearm that destroys the epidermis and the deep dermis heals, will hair grow again in the affected area?

See the blue Answers tab at the back of the book.

5-7 Sebaceous glands and sweat glands are exocrine glands found in the skin

The integument contains two types of exocrine glands: *sebaceous glands* and *sweat glands.*

SEBACEOUS (OIL) GLANDS

Sebaceous (se-BĀ-shus) **glands,** or *oil glands,* are holocrine glands that discharge an oily lipid secretion into hair follicles or, in some cases, onto the skin (Figure 5-6). The gland cells produce large quantities of lipids as they mature. The lipid is released through holocrine secretion, a process that involves the rupture and death of the cells. ∞ p. 102 The contraction of the arrector pili muscle that elevates the hair squeezes the sebaceous gland, forcing the oily secretions into the hair follicle and onto the surrounding skin. This secretion, called **sebum** (SĒ-bum), lubricates the hair and skin and inhibits the growth of bacteria. *Sebaceous follicles* are large sebaceous glands that discharge sebum directly onto the skin. They are located on the face, back, chest, nipples, and external genitalia.

Sebaceous glands are sensitive to changes in the concentrations of sex hormones, and their secretions accelerate at puberty. For this reason, individuals with large sebaceous glands may be especially prone to develop **acne** during adolescence. In acne, sebaceous ducts become blocked and secretions accumulate, causing inflammation and a raised "pimple." The trapped secretions provide a fertile environment for bacterial infection.

SWEAT GLANDS

The skin contains two types of sweat glands, or *sudoriferous glands: apocrine sweat glands* and *merocrine sweat glands* (Figure 5-7). The names refer to their mechanism of secretion, as discussed in Chapter 4 (see Table 4-2, p. 103).

Apocrine Sweat Glands

The sweat glands that secrete their products into hair follicles in the armpits, around the nipples, and in the groin are called **apocrine sweat glands.** The name *apocrine* was originally chosen because it was thought these gland cells use an apocrine method of secretion. Even though we now know that they rely on merocrine secretion, the name has not changed. At puberty, these glands begin discharging a sticky, cloudy, and potentially odorous secretion. This sweat becomes odorous when bacteria break it down as a food source. In other mammals, this odor is an important form of communication; in our culture, whatever function it might have is masked by products such as

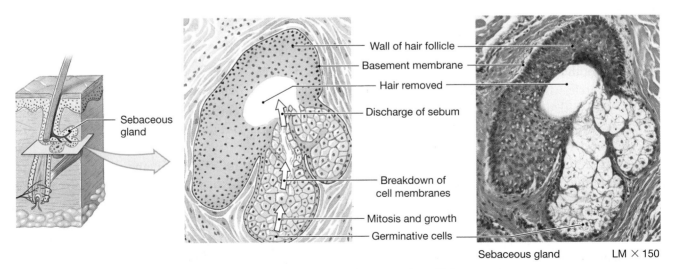

Sebaceous gland

Wall of hair follicle
Basement membrane
Hair removed
Discharge of sebum
Breakdown of cell membranes
Mitosis and growth
Germinative cells

Sebaceous gland   LM × 150

FIGURE 5-6 **The Structure of Sebaceous Glands and Their Relationship to Hair Follicles.**

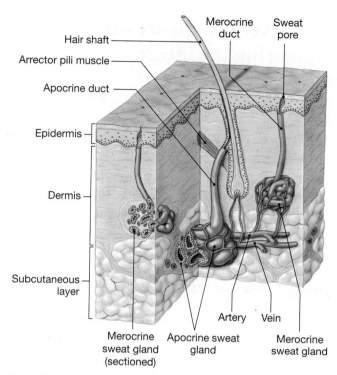

Hair shaft
Arrector pili muscle
Apocrine duct
Epidermis
Dermis
Subcutaneous layer
Merocrine duct
Sweat pore
Merocrine sweat gland (sectioned)
Apocrine sweat gland
Artery
Vein
Merocrine sweat gland

FIGURE 5-7 Sweat Glands. Merocrine sweat glands secrete directly onto the skin, whereas apocrine sweat glands secrete into hair follicles.

deodorants. Other products, such as antiperspirants, contain astringent compounds that contract the skin and its sweat gland openings, thereby decreasing the quantity of both apocrine and merocrine secretions.

Merocrine Sweat Glands

Coiled tubular glands that discharge their secretions directly onto the surface of the skin are **merocrine sweat glands,** or *eccrine* (EK-rin) *sweat glands.* They are far more numerous and widely distributed than apocrine glands. The skin of an adult contains 2–5 million eccrine glands. Palms and soles have the highest numbers; it has been estimated that the palm of the hand has about 500 glands per square centimeter (3000 per square inch).

The perspiration, or sweat, produced by merocrine glands is 99 percent water, but it also contains a mixture of electrolytes (chiefly sodium chloride), organic nutrients, and waste products such as urea. Sodium chloride gives sweat its salty taste. The primary function of merocrine gland activity and perspiration is to cool the surface of the skin and lower body temperature. When a person is sweating in the hot sun, all the merocrine glands are working together. The blood vessels beneath the epidermis are dilated and flushed with blood, the skin reddens in light-colored individuals, and the skin sur-

face becomes warm and wet. As the moisture evaporates, the skin cools. If body temperature then falls below normal, perspiration ceases, blood flow to the skin is reduced, and the skin surface cools and dries, releasing little heat into the environment. The roles of the skin and negative feedback mechanisms in thermoregulation (temperature control) were considered in Chapter 1 (see p. 13); Chapter 17 will examine this process in greater detail.

Perspiration results in the excretion of water and electrolytes from the body. As a result, excessive perspiration to maintain normal body temperature can lead to problems. For example, when all of the merocrine sweat glands are working at maximum, perspiration may exceed a gallon (about 4 liters) per hour, and dangerous fluid and electrolyte losses can occur. For this reason, marathoners and other endurance athletes must drink fluids at regular intervals.

Sweat also provides protection from environmental hazards. Sweat dilutes harmful chemicals in contact with the skin and flushes microorganisms from its surface. The presence of dermicidin, a small peptide molecule with antibiotic properties, provides additional protection from microorganisms.

The skin also contains other types of modified sweat glands with specialized secretions. For example, the mammary glands of the breasts are structurally related to apocrine sweat glands and secrete milk. Another example are the *ceruminous glands* in the passageway of the external ear. Their secretions combine with those of nearby sebaceous glands to form earwax.

> ### CHECKPOINT
>
> **17.** Identify two types of exocrine glands found in the skin.
> **18.** What are the functions of sebaceous secretions?
> **19.** Deodorants are used to mask the effects of secretions from which type of skin gland?
>
> *See the blue Answers tab at the back of the book.*

5-8 Nails are keratinized epidermal cells that protect the tips of fingers and toes

Nails form on the dorsal surfaces of the fingers and toes, where they protect the exposed tips and help limit their distortion when they are subjected to mechanical stress—for example, when you run or grasp objects. The structure of a nail is shown in Figure 5-8. The visible **nail body** consists of a dense mass of

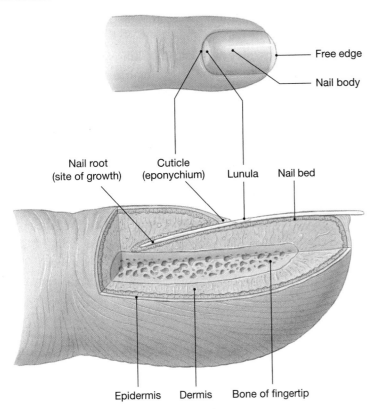

FIGURE 5-8 **The Structure of a Nail.**

dead, keratinized cells. The nail body is recessed beneath the level of the surrounding epithelium. The body of the nail covers an area of epidermis called the **nail bed.** Nail production occurs at the **nail root,** an epithelial fold not visible from the surface. A portion of the stratum corneum of the fold extends over the exposed nail nearest the root, forming the **cuticle,** or *eponychium* (ep-ō-NIK-ē-um; *epi-*, over + *onyx*, nail). Underlying blood vessels give the nail its pink color, but near the root these vessels may be obscured, leaving a pale crescent known as the **lunula** (LOO-nū-la; *luna*, moon).

The skin plays a major role in controlling body temperature by acting like a radiator. Heat delivered by the dermal circulation is removed from the body primarily by the evaporation of sweat (perspiration).

CHECKPOINT

20. Describe a typical fingernail.

21. Where does nail growth occur?

See the blue Answers tab at the back of the book.

5-9 Several steps are involved in repairing the integument following an injury

The integumentary system can respond directly and independently to many local influences or stimuli. For example, when the skin is subjected to mechanical stresses, stem cells in the stratum germinativum divide more rapidly, and the thickness of the epithelium increases. That is why calluses form on your palms when you perform manual labor. A more dramatic example of a local response can be seen after an injury to the skin.

REPAIR OF SKIN INJURIES

The skin can regenerate effectively even after considerable damage because stem cells are present in both its epithelial and connective tissue components. Divisions by these stem cells replace lost epidermal and dermal cells, respectively. This process can be slow, and when large surface areas are involved, infection and fluid loss complicate the situation. The relative speed and effectiveness of skin repair vary depending on the type of wound. A slender, straight cut, or *incision*, may heal relatively quickly compared with a scrape, or *abrasion*, which involves a much greater area.

Figure 5-9 illustrates the four stages in the regeneration of the skin after an injury. When damage extends through the epidermis and into the dermis, bleeding generally occurs. Mast cells in the dermis trigger an *inflammatory response* that will result in enhanced blood flow to the surrounding region and attraction of phagocytes (Step 1). The blood clot, or **scab,** that forms at the surface temporarily restores the integrity of the epidermis and restricts the entry of additional microorganisms (Step 2). Most of the clot consists of an insoluble network of *fibrin*, a fibrous protein that forms from blood proteins during the clotting response. Cells of the stratum germinativum rapidly divide and begin to migrate along the sides of the wound to replace the missing epidermal cells. Meanwhile, macrophages and newly arriving phagocytes patrol the damaged area of the dermis and clear away debris and pathogens.

If the wound covers an extensive area or involves a region covered by thin skin, dermal repairs must be under way before epithelial cells can cover the surface. Fiber-producing cells (*fibroblasts*) and connective tissue stem cells divide to produce mobile cells that invade the deeper areas of injury (see Step 2). Epithelial cells lining damaged blood vessels also begin to divide, and capillaries follow the fibroblasts, providing a circulatory

STEP **1**

Bleeding occurs at the site of injury immediately after the injury, and mast cells in the region trigger an inflammatory response.

- Epidermis

- Dermis

STEP **2**

After several hours, a scab has formed and cells of the stratum germinativum are migrating along the edges of the wound. Phagocytic cells are removing debris, and more of these cells are arriving with the enhanced circulation in the area. Clotting around the edges of the affected area partially isolates the region.

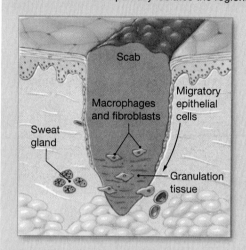

Scab

Macrophages and fibroblasts

Migratory epithelial cells

Sweat gland

Granulation tissue

STEP **3**

One week after the injury, the scab has been undermined by epidermal cells migrating over the meshwork produced by fibroblast activity. Phagocytic activity around the site has almost ended, and the fibrin clot is disintegrating.

Fibroblasts

STEP **4**

After several weeks, the scab has been shed, and the epidermis is complete. A shallow depression marks the injury site, but fibroblasts in the dermis continue to create scar tissue that will gradually elevate the overlying epidermis.

Scar tissue

FIGURE 5-9 **Events in Skin Repair.**

supply. The combination of blood clot, fibroblasts, and an extensive capillary network is called **granulation tissue** (Step 2). Over time, the clot dissolves and the number of capillaries declines. Fibroblast activity has formed an extensive meshwork of collagen fibers in the dermis (Step 3).

These repairs do not restore the integument to its original condition, however, because the dermis now contains an abnormally large number of collagen fibers and relatively few blood vessels. Severely damaged hair follicles, sebaceous or sweat glands, muscle cells, and nerves are seldom repaired, and they too are replaced by fibrous tissue. The formation of this rather inflexible, fibrous, noncellular **scar tissue** can be considered a practical limit to the healing process (Step 4).

The process of scar tissue formation is highly variable. For example, surgical procedures performed on a fetus do not leave scars. In some adults, most often those with dark skin, scar tissue formation may continue beyond the requirements of tissue repair. The result is a flattened mass of scar tissue that begins at the injury site and grows into the surrounding dermis. This thickened area of scar tissue, called a **keloid** (KĒ-loyd), is covered by a shiny, smooth epidermal surface. Keloids most commonly develop on the upper back, shoulders, anterior chest, and earlobes. They are harmless, and some aboriginal cultures intentionally produce keloids as a form of body decoration.

EFFECTS OF BURNS

Burns are relatively common injuries that result from exposure of the skin to heat, radiation, electrical shock, or strong chemical agents. The severity of a burn depends on the depth of penetration and the total area affected. The most common classification of burns is based on the depth of penetration, as detailed in Table 5-1. The larger the area affected, the greater the impact on integumentary function.

5-10 Effects of aging include dermal thinning, wrinkling, and reduced melanocyte activity

Aging affects all the components of the integumentary system. Major age-related changes include the following:

- *Skin injuries and infections become more common.* Such problems are more likely because the epidermis thins as stem cell activity declines.

- *The sensitivity of the immune system is reduced.* The number of macrophages and other immune system cells residing in the skin decreases to around 50 percent of levels seen at maturity (roughly, age 21). This loss further encourages skin damage and infection.

- *Muscles become weaker, and bone strength decreases.* Such changes are related to reduced calcium and phosphate absorption due to a decline in vitamin D_3 production of around 75 percent.

- *Sensitivity to sun exposure increases.* Lesser amounts of melanin are produced because melanocyte activity declines. The skin of light-skinned individuals becomes very pale.

- *The skin becomes dry and often scaly.* Glandular activity declines, reducing sebum production and perspiration.

TABLE 5-1 **A Common Classification of Burns**

CLASSIFICATION	DAMAGE REPORT	APPEARANCE AND SENSATION
First-Degree Burn	*Killed:* superficial cells of epidermis *Injured:* deeper layers of epidermis, papillary dermis	Inflamed; tender
Second-Degree Burn	*Killed:* superficial and deeper cells of epidermis; dermis may be affected *Injured:* damage may extend into reticular layer of the dermis, but many accessory structures are unaffected	Blisters; very painful
Third-Degree Burn	*Killed:* all epidermal and dermal cells *Injured:* hypodermis and deeper tissues and organs	Charred; no sensation at all

- *Hair thins and changes color.* Follicles stop functioning or produce thinner, finer hairs. With decreased melanocyte activity, these hairs are gray or white.

- *Sagging and wrinkling of the skin occur.* The dermis becomes thinner, and the elastic fiber network decreases in size. The integument, therefore, becomes weaker and less resilient. These effects are most pronounced in areas exposed to the sun.

- *The ability to lose heat decreases.* The blood supply to the dermis is reduced at the same time that sweat glands become less active. This combination makes the elderly less able than younger people to lose body heat. As a result, overexertion or overexposure to high temperatures (such as a sauna or hot tub) can cause dangerously high body temperatures.

- *Skin repairs proceed relatively slowly.* For example, it takes 3–4 weeks to complete repairs to an uninfected blister site in a young adult. The same repairs could take 6–8 weeks at ages 65–75. Because repairs are slow, recurrent infections may occur.

CHECKPOINT

24. Older individuals do not tolerate summer heat as well as they did when they were young, and they are more prone to heat-related illnesses. What accounts for these changes?

25. Why does hair turn gray or white with age?

See the blue Answers tab at the back of the book.

5-11 The integumentary system provides protection for all other body systems

The integumentary system forms the external surface of the body and provides protection from dehydration, environmental chemicals, and impacts. The integument is separated and insulated from the rest of the body by the subcutaneous layer, but it is interconnected with the rest of the body by an extensive circulatory network of blood and lymphatic vessels and is richly supplied with sensory nerve endings. As a result, although the protective mechanical functions of the skin can be discussed independently, its physiological activities are always closely integrated with those of other systems. The Integumentary System in Perspective (p. 140) summarizes the interactions of the integumentary system with other body systems.

CHECKPOINT

26. Identify the common purpose that the integumentary system serves for all body systems.

27. Why is the skin important to muscular system activity?

See the blue Answers tab at the back of the book.

RELATED CLINICAL TERMS

acne: A sebaceous gland inflammation caused by an accumulation of secretions.

basal cell carcinoma: A cancer that originates in the stratum germinativum; the most common skin cancer. Roughly two-thirds of cases of this cancer appear in areas subjected to chronic UV exposure. Metastasis seldom occurs.

biopsy (BĪ-op-sē): The removal and examination of tissue from the body for the diagnosis of disease.

cavernous hemangioma (strawberry nevus): A mass of large blood vessels that can occur in the skin or other organs in the body; a "port wine stain" birthmark generally lasts a lifetime.

contact dermatitis: A dermatitis (see below) generally caused by strong chemical irritants. It produces an itchy rash that may spread to other areas as scratching distributes the chemical agent; includes poison ivy.

cyanosis (sī-uh-NŌ-sis): Bluish skin color as a result of reduced oxygenation of the blood in superficial vessels.

dermatitis: An inflammation of the skin that primarily involves the papillary region of the dermis.

dermatology: The branch of medicine concerned with the diagnosis and treatment of diseases of the skin.

granulation tissue: A combination of fibrin, fibroblasts, and capillaries that forms during tissue repair after inflammation.

keloid (KĒ-loyd): A thickened area of scar tissue covered by a shiny, smooth epidermal surface.

lesions (LĒ-zhuns): Changes in tissue structure caused by injury or disease.

male pattern baldness: Hair loss in an adult male due to changes in levels of circulating sex hormones.

malignant melanoma (mel-uh-NŌ-muh): A skin cancer originating in malignant melanocytes.

pruritis (proo-RĪ-tis): An irritating itching sensation, common in skin conditions.

psoriasis (sō-RĪ-uh-sis): A painless condition characterized by rapid stem cell divisions in the stratum germinativum of the scalp, elbows, palms, soles, groin, and nails. Affected areas appear dry and scaly.

sepsis (SEP-sis): A dangerous, widespread bacterial infection; the leading cause of death in burn patients.

squamous cell carcinoma: A form of skin cancer less common than basal cell carcinoma, almost totally restricted to areas of sun-exposed skin. Metastasis seldom occurs.

ulcer: A localized shedding of an epithelium.

xerosis (ze-RŌ-sis): "Dry skin," a common complaint of older persons and almost anyone living in an arid climate.

Chapter 5 Review

KEY TERMS

cutaneous membrane *122*

dermis *122*

epidermis *122*

hair *128*

hair follicle *128*

integument *122*

keratin *124*

melanin *125*

nail *131*

sebaceous glands *130*

stratum germinativum *124*

subcutaneous layer *123*

SUMMARY OUTLINE

An Introduction to the Integumentary System *p. 122*

1. The **integumentary system,** or **integument,** consists of the **cutaneous membrane,** which includes the **epidermis** and **dermis,** and the **accessory structures.** Beneath it lies the **subcutaneous layer** (or **hypodermis**). (*Figure 5-1*)

5-1 The epidermis is composed of strata (layers) with various functions *p. 123*

2. **Thin skin** covers most of the body; heavily abraded body surfaces may be covered by **thick skin.**

3. Cell divisions by the stem cells that make up the **stratum germinativum** replace more superficial cells.

4. As epidermal cells age, they move up through the **stratum spinosum,** the **stratum granulosum,** the **stratum lucidum** (in thick skin), and the **stratum corneum.** In the process, they accumulate large amounts of **keratin.** Ultimately, the cells are shed or lost. (*Figure 5-2*)

5. **Epidermal ridges** interlock with the **dermal papillae** of the dermis. Together, they form superficial ridges on the palms and soles that improve the gripping ability of the hands and feet.

5-2 Factors influencing skin color are epidermal pigmentation and dermal circulation *p. 125*

6. The color of the epidermis depends on two factors: blood supply and the concentrations of **melanin** and **carotene.**

Melanocytes protect stem cells from **ultraviolet (UV) radiation.** (*Figure 5-3*)

5-3 Sunlight has detrimental and beneficial effects on the skin *p. 126*

7. Epidermal cells synthesize **vitamin D$_3$** when exposed to sunlight.

8. Skin cancer is the most common form of cancer. **Basal cell carcinoma** and **squamous cell carcinoma** are not as dangerous as **melanoma.** (*Figure 5-4*)

5-4 The dermis is the tissue layer that supports the epidermis *p. 127*

9. The dermis consists of the **papillary layer** and the deeper **reticular layer.**

10. The papillary layer of the dermis contains blood vessels, lymphatic vessels, and sensory nerves. This layer supports and nourishes the overlying epidermis. The reticular layer consists of a meshwork of collagen and elastic fibers oriented to resist tension in the skin.

11. Components of other organ systems (cardiovascular, lymphoid, and nervous) that communicate with the skin are in the dermis.

5-5 The hypodermis is tissue that connects the dermis to underlying tissues *p. 127*

12. The **hypodermis,** or subcutaneous layer, stabilizes the skin's position against underlying organs and tissues.

5-6 Hair is composed of keratinized dead cells that have been pushed to the surface *p. 128*

13. **Hairs** originate in complex organs called **hair follicles.** Each hair has a **shaft** composed of dead keratinized cells. Hairs have a central **medulla** of soft keratin surrounded by a **cortex** and an outer **cuticle** of hard keratin. (*Figure 5-5*)

14. Each **arrector pili** muscle can raise a single hair.

15. Our hairs grow and are shed according to the *hair growth cycle.* A single hair grows for 2–5 years and is then shed.

5-7 Sebaceous glands and sweat glands are exocrine glands found in the skin *p. 130*

16. Typical **sebaceous glands** discharge waxy **sebum** into hair follicles. *Sebaceous follicles* are sebaceous glands that empty directly onto the skin. *(Figure 5-6)*

17. **Apocrine sweat glands** produce an odorous secretion; the more numerous **merocrine sweat glands** produce perspiration, a watery secretion. *(Figure 5-7)*

5-8 Nails are keratinized epidermal cells that protect the tips of fingers and toes *p. 131*

18. The **nail body** of a **nail** covers the **nail bed.** Nail production occurs at the **nail root.** *(Figure 5-8)*

5-9 Several steps are involved in repairing the integument following an injury *p. 132*

19. The skin can regenerate effectively even after considerable damage. *(Figure 5-9)*

20. Burns are relatively common injuries characterized by damage to layers of the epidermis and perhaps the dermis. *(Table 5-1)*

5-10 Effects of aging include dermal thinning, wrinkling, and reduced melanocyte activity *p. 134*

21. With aging, the integument thins, blood flow decreases, cellular activity decreases, and repairs occur more slowly.

5-11 The integumentary system provides protection for all other body systems *p. 135*

22. The integumentary system has extensive anatomical and physiological connections with other body systems.

REVIEW QUESTIONS

WWW Access more review material online at The Anatomy & Physiology Place (**www.anatomyandphysiology.com**). There, you'll find Chapter Guides, Chapter Quizzes, Chapter Practice Tests, Interactive Flashcards, a Glossary with Pronunciations, and more to help you succeed in the course.

Level 1 • Reviewing Facts and Terms

Match each item in column A with the most closely related item in column B. Place letters for answers in the spaces provided.

COLUMN A

_____ 1. cutaneous membrane
_____ 2. carotene
_____ 3. melanocytes
_____ 4. epidermal layer containing stem cells
_____ 5. smooth muscle
_____ 6. epidermal layer of flattened and dead cells
_____ 7. bluish skin
_____ 8. sebaceous glands
_____ 9. merocrine (eccrine) glands
_____ 10. vitamin D_3

COLUMN B

a. arrector pili
b. cyanosis
c. perspiration
d. sebum
e. stratum corneum
f. skin
g. orange-yellow pigment
h. bone growth
i. pigment cells
j. stratum germinativum

11. The two major components of the integument are
    (a) the cutaneous membrane and the accessory structures.
    (b) the epidermis and the hypodermis.
    (c) the hair and the nails.
    (d) the dermis and the subcutaneous layer.

12. Identify the different portions (a–d) of the cutaneous membrane and the underlying layer of loose connective tissue (e) in the following diagram.

(a) _____   (b) _____
(c) _____   (d) _____
(e) _____

13. The fibrous protein that forms the basic structural component of hair and nails is
    (a) collagen.   (b) melanin.
    (c) elastin.   (d) keratin.

14. The two types of exocrine glands in the skin are
    (a) merocrine and sweat glands.
    (b) sebaceous and sweat glands.
    (c) apocrine and sweat glands.
    (d) eccrine and sweat glands.

15. All of the following are accessory structures of the integumentary system *except*
    (a) nails.   (b) hair.
    (c) dermal papillae.   (d) sweat glands.

16. Sweat glands that communicate with hair follicles in the armpits and produce an odorous secretion are
    (a) apocrine glands.   (b) merocrine glands.
    (c) sebaceous glands. (d) a, b, and c are correct

17. The reason older persons are more sensitive to sun exposure and more likely to get sunburned is that with age
    (a) melanocyte activity declines.
    (b) vitamin D$_3$ production declines.
    (c) glandular activity declines.
    (d) skin thickness decreases.

18. Identify the different portions (a–e) of a hair and hair follicle.

(a) _____   (b) _____
(c) _____   (d) _____
(e) _____

19. Which two skin pigments are found in the epidermis?

20. Which two major layers constitute the dermis, and what components are found in each layer?

21. Which two groups of sweat glands are contained in the integument?

Level 2 • Reviewing Concepts

22. In the elderly, blood supply to the dermis is reduced and sweat glands are less active. This combination of factors would most affect
(a) the ability to thermoregulate.
(b) the ability to heal injured skin.
(c) the ease with which the skin is injured.
(d) the physical characteristics of the skin.
(e) the ability to grow hair.

23. In clinical practice, drugs can be delivered by diffusion across the skin; this delivery method is called transdermal administration. Why are fat-soluble drugs more desirable for transdermal administration than drugs that are water soluble?

24. In our society, a tanned body is associated with good health. However, medical research constantly warns about the dangers of excessive exposure to the sun. What are the benefits of a tan?

25. In some cultures, women must be covered completely, except for their eyes, when they go outside. These women exhibit a high incidence of bone problems. Why?

26. Why is a subcutaneous injection with a hypodermic needle a useful method for administering drugs?

27. Why does skin sag and wrinkle as a person ages?

Level 3 • Critical Thinking and Clinical Applications

28. A new mother notices that her 6-month-old son has a yellow-orange complexion. Fearful that the child may have jaundice (a condition caused by bilirubin, a toxic yellow-orange pigment produced during the destruction of red blood cells), she takes him to her pediatrician. After examining the child, the pediatrician declares him perfectly healthy and advises the mother to watch the child's diet. Why?

29. Vanessa notices that even though her 80-year-old grandmother keeps her thermostat set at 80°F, she still wears a sweater in her house. When Vanessa asks her grandmother why, her grandmother says she is cold. Vanessa can't understand this; how would you explain it to her?

The Integumentary System in Perspective

Functional Relationships Between the Integumentary System and Other Systems

The Skeletal System

- The Skeletal System provides structural support
- The Integumentary System synthesizes vitamin D_3, essential for calcium and phosphorus absorption (bone maintenance and growth)

The Muscular System

- The Muscular System's facial muscles pull against skin of face, producing expressions important in communication
- The Integumentary System synthesizes vitamin D_3, essential for normal calcium absorption (calcium ions play an essential role in muscle contraction)

The Nervous System

- The Nervous System controls blood flow and sweat gland activity for thermoregulation; stimulates contraction of arrector pili muscles to elevate hairs
- The Integumentary System's receptors in dermis and deep epidermis provide sensations of touch, pressure, vibration, temperature, and pain

The Endocrine System

- The Endocrine System includes the sex hormones that stimulate sebaceous and apocrine gland activity, and develop secondary sexual characteristics; suprarenal hormones alter blood flow to skin and mobilize lipids from fat cells
- The Integumentary System synthesizes vitamin D_3, precursor of calcitriol, a hormone produced by the kidneys

The Cardiovascular System

- The Cardiovascular System provides oxygen and nutrients; delivers hormones and cells of immune system; carries away carbon dioxide, waste products, and toxins; provides heat to maintain normal skin temperature
- The Integumentary System's mast cells produce localized changes in blood flow and capillary permeability

The Lymphoid System

- The Lymphoid System assists in defending the integument by providing additional macrophages and mobilizing lymphocytes
- The Integumentary System provides physical barriers that prevent pathogen entry; macrophages resist infection; mast cells trigger inflammation and initiate the immune reponse

The Respiratory System

- The Respiratory System provides oxygen and eliminates carbon dioxide
- The Integumentary System's hairs guard entrance to nasal cavity

The Digestive System

- The Digestive System provides nutrients for all cells and lipids for storage by adipocytes
- The Integumentary System synthesizes vitamin D_3, needed for absorption of calcium and phosphorus

The Urinary System

- The Urinary System excretes waste products, maintains normal body fluid pH and ion composition
- The Integumentary System assists in elimination of water and solutes; keratinized epidermis limits fluid loss through skin

The Reproductive System

- The Reproductive System's sex hormones affect hair distribution, adipose tissue distribution in subcutaneous layer, and mammary gland development
- The Integumentary System covers external genitalia; provides sensations that stimulate sexual behaviors; mammary gland secretions provide nourishment for newborn infant

For All Systems
The Integumentary System provides mechanical protection against environmental hazards

Professional Profile

BURN NURSE SPECIALIST
Cynthia Pronze

> " There are patients in need here, and the work is important. The rewards of working with burns—seeing patients get better—are great. "

Medical professionals who work in trauma units must be ready to handle whatever case comes through the door. The patients are very sick or severely injured, and the days are long and intense.

Cynthia Pronze is a clinical nurse supervisor for the trauma burn intensive care unit and acute care unit of the University of Michigan Hospital. As a nurse supervisor, Cynthia manages a staff of nurses and is in charge of patient care. She begins work early, around 6:15 A.M., checking in with the night-shift nurses before they leave so that she can catch up on the status of all of the patients. She goes unit to unit until she is fully up-to-date. Much of the rest of her day is filled with meetings, either with her direct managers or with doctors or other nurses on the unit. "We're a level 1 trauma burn center, which means this is a vast place. I always check in with staff again, usually before noon, to find out how things are going. What are their needs? Do they need help?"

THE BURN WARD

Working in the burn ward has special challenges. "The number of burns that occur every year in this country is huge. Still, this is not an area that everyone wants to go into." Many people are uncomfortable with burns so they choose other fields.

Cynthia chose to work in trauma because it began to interest her while she was a nursing student. "There are patients in need here, and the work is important. The rewards of working with burns—seeing patients get better—are great. Depending on the percentage of burns, some of these patients are here for many months. We get to know them and their families. We help them deal with stress and the huge gaps in their lives."

A SECOND CAREER

Cynthia began her career after working for 20 years as a hairdresser and raising three children. "I come from a very large family, and college was not an option for me when I was young. But at one point my husband turned to me and said, 'You've always wanted to become a nurse. What are you waiting for?' I enrolled first in the local community college and achieved an A.D.N.—an associate's degree in nursing. Later I took more course work and obtained a master's degree."

Cynthia took anatomy and physiology as an undergraduate and again in her master's program. "A & P course work is very challenging. But I couldn't get enough of it. It's so relevant to nursing. You have to have an in-depth knowledge base when you care for another human being, understanding how the body works, how it responds. A & P answers questions that may be swirling around in your head. And once you're treating patients, you realize, 'Oh, that's why this may or may not have happened with a patient.'"

Like most nurses, Cynthia started in an entry-level "Clin 1" position, doing bedside care for patients. After gaining some experience, nurses can move into the role of charge nurse, making the rounds with physicians and overseeing nursing care for a unit. In Cynthia's case, she eventually became a supervisor. In that role she finds that patient satisfaction and staff satisfaction reflect on each other. "When the patients are doing well, the staff feels good, and vice versa."

What qualities make a successful nurse? "Working well with people, good organizational skills, following directions," she says, "and being able to give of yourself."

6 The Skeletal System

This x-ray image of the hand illustrates the framework of what is considered the most useful structure of the human body. It also shows two of the basic shapes of the bones in the human body—the long bones of the hand and the short bones of the wrist. Our skeletal system is made of bone, a remarkable tissue that is strong and capable of repairing itself even after serious injury.

VOCABULARY DEVELOPMENT

ab- from; *abduction*
acetabulum a vinegar cup; *acetabulum of the hip joint*
ad- toward, to; *adduction*
amphi- on both sides; *amphiarthrosis*
arthros joint; *synarthrosis*
blast precursor; *osteoblast*
circum- around; *circumduction*
clast break; *osteoclast*
clavius clavicle; *clavicle*
concha shell; *middle concha*
corona crown; *coronoid fossa*
cranio- skull; *cranium*
cribrum sieve; *cribriform plate*

dens tooth; *dens*
dia- through; *diarthrosis*
duco to lead; *adduction*
e- out; *eversion*
gennan to produce; *osteogenesis*
gomphosis a bolting together; *gomphosis*
in- into; *inversion*
infra- beneath; *infraspinous fossa*
lacrimae tears; *lacrimal bones*
lamella thin plate; *lamellae of bone*
malleolus little hammer; *medial malleolus*
meniscus crescent; *menisci*

osteon bone; *osteocytes*
penia lacking; *osteopenia*
planta sole; *plantar*
porosus porous; *osteoporosis*
septum wall; *nasal septum*
stylos pillar; *styloid process*
supra- above; *supraspinous fossa*
sutura a sewing together; *suture*
teres cylindrical; *ligamentum teres*
trabecula wall; *trabeculae in spongy bone*
trochlea pulley; *trochlea*
vertere to turn; *inversion*

An Introduction to the Skeletal System

The skeleton has many function, but the most obvious is supporting the weight of the body. This support is provided by bones, structures as strong as reinforced concrete but considerably lighter. Unlike concrete, bones can be remodeled and reshaped to meet changing metabolic demands and patterns of activity. Bones work with muscles to maintain body position and to produce controlled, precise movements. With the skeleton to pull against, contracting muscles can make us sit, stand, walk, or run.

6-1 The skeletal system has five primary functions

The skeletal system includes the bones of the skeleton and the cartilages, joints, ligaments, and other connective tissues that stabilize or connect them. This system has five primary functions:

1. *Support.* The skeletal system provides structural support for the entire body. Individual bones or groups of bones provide a framework for the attachment of soft tissues and organs.

2. *Storage.* The calcium salts of bone represent a valuable mineral reserve that maintains normal concentrations of calcium and phosphate ions in body fluids. In addition, bones store energy reserves as lipids in areas filled with *yellow marrow.*

3. *Blood cell production.* Red blood cells, white blood cells, and other blood elements are produced within the *red marrow,* which fills the internal cavities of many bones. The role of bone marrow in blood cell formation will be discussed when we examine the cardiovascular and lymphoid systems (Chapters 11 and 14).

4. *Protection.* Soft tissues and organs are often surrounded by skeletal elements. The ribs protect the heart and lungs, the skull encloses the brain, the vertebrae shield the spinal cord, and the pelvis cradles delicate digestive and reproductive organs.

5. *Leverage.* Many bones function as levers that change the magnitude and direction of the forces generated by skeletal muscles. The resulting movements range from the delicate motion of a fingertip to powerful changes in the position of the entire body.

CHECKPOINT

1. Name the five primary functions of the skeletal system.

See the blue Answers tab at the back of the book.

6-2 Bones are classified according to shape and structure

Bone, or **osseous tissue,** is a supporting connective tissue that contains specialized cells and a matrix consisting of extracellular protein fibers and a ground substance. ∞ p. 108 The distinctive texture of bone results from the deposition of calcium salts within the matrix. Calcium phosphate, $Ca_3(PO_4)_2$, accounts for almost two-thirds of the weight of bone. The remaining third is dominated by collagen fibers; osteocytes and other cell types make up only around 2 percent of the mass of a bone.

MACROSCOPIC FEATURES OF BONE

The bones of the human skeleton have four general shapes: long, short, flat, and irregular (Figure 6-1). **Long bones** are longer than they are wide, whereas in **short bones** these dimensions are roughly equal. Examples of long bones are bones of the limbs, such as the bones of the arm (*humerus*) and thigh (*femur*). Short bones include the bones of the wrist (*carpal bones*) and ankles (*tarsal bones*). **Flat bones** are thin and relatively broad, such as the parietal bones of the skull, the ribs, and the shoulder blades (*scapulae*). **Irregular bones** have complex shapes that do not fit easily into any other category. An example is any of the vertebrae of the spinal column.

The typical features of a long bone such as the humerus are shown in Figure 6-2. A long bone has a central shaft, or **diaphysis** (dī-AF-i-sis), that surrounds a central *marrow cavity* containing **bone marrow,** a loose connective tissue. The expanded portions at each end, called **epiphyses** (ē-PIF-i-sēz), are cov-

ered by *articular cartilages.* Each epiphysis (ē-PIF-i-sis) of a long bone articulates with an adjacent bone at a joint. As will be discussed shortly, growth in the length of an immature long bone occurs at the junctions between the epiphyses and the diaphysis.

The two types of bone tissue are visible in Figure 6-2. **Compact bone** (or dense bone) is relatively solid, whereas **spongy bone,** or *cancellous* (KAN-se-lus) *bone,* resembles a network of bony rods or struts separated by spaces. Both compact bone and spongy bone are present in the humerus; compact bone forms the diaphysis, and spongy bone fills the epiphyses.

The outer surface of a bone is covered by a **periosteum** (Figure 6-2). The fibers of *tendons* and *ligaments* intermingle with those of the periosteum, attaching skeletal muscles to bones and one bone to another. The periosteum isolates the bone from surrounding tissues, provides a route for circulatory and nervous supplies, and participates in bone growth and repair. Within the bone, a cellular **endosteum** lines the marrow cavity and other inner surfaces. The endosteum is active during bone growth and whenever repair or remodeling is under way.

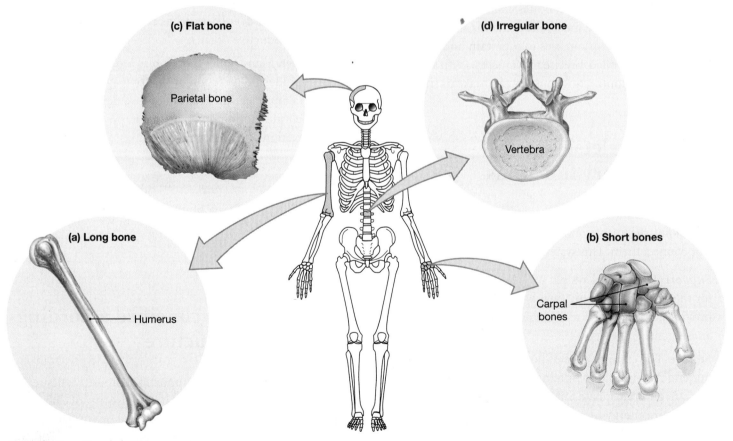

FIGURE 6-1 Shapes of Bones.

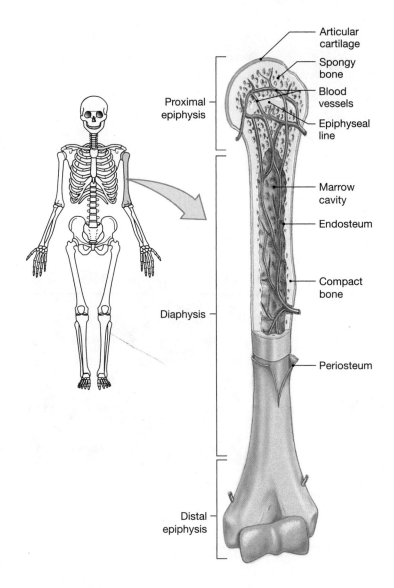

Articular cartilage
Spongy bone
Blood vessels
Epiphyseal line
Proximal epiphysis
Marrow cavity
Endosteum
Compact bone
Diaphysis
Periosteum
Distal epiphysis

FIGURE 6-2 The Structure of a Long Bone.

MICROSCOPIC FEATURES OF BONE

The general histology of bone was introduced in Chapter 4. Figure 6-3 presents the microscopic structure of bone in detail. Histologically, the periosteum consists of a fibrous outer layer and a cellular inner layer (Figure 6-3a). Both compact bone and spongy bone contain bone cells, or **osteocytes** (OS-tē-ō-sīts; *osteon,* bone), in small pockets called **lacunae** (la-KOO-nē) (Figure 6-3b). Lacunae are found between narrow sheets of calcified matrix that are known as **lamellae** (lah-MEL-lē; *lamella,* thin plate). Small channels, called **canaliculi** (ka-na-LIK-ū-lē), radiate through the matrix, interconnecting lacunae and linking them to nearby blood vessels. The canaliculi con-

tain cytoplasmic extensions of the osteocytes. Nutrients from the blood and waste products from osteocytes diffuse through the extracellular fluid that surrounds these cells as well as through their cytoplasmic extensions.

Compact and Spongy Bone

The basic functional unit of compact bone is the **osteon** (OS-tē-on), or *Haversian system* (Figure 6-3). Within an osteon, the osteocytes are arranged in concentric layers around a **central canal,** or *Haversian canal,* that contains one or more blood vessels. The lamellae are cylindrical, oriented parallel to the long axis of the central canal. **Perforating canals** provide passageways for linking the blood vessels of the central canals with those of the periosteum and the marrow cavity.

Spongy bone has a different lamellar arrangement and no osteons. Instead, the lamellae form rods or plates called **trabeculae** (tra-BEK-ū-lē; *trabecula,* wall). Frequent branchings of the thin trabeculae create an open network. Canaliculi radiating from the lacunae of spongy bone end at the exposed surfaces of the trabeculae, where nutrients and wastes diffuse between the marrow and osteocytes.

A layer of compact bone covers bone surfaces everywhere except inside *joint capsules,* where articular cartilages protect opposing surfaces. Compact bone is usually found where stresses come from a limited range of directions. The limb bones, for example, are built to withstand forces applied at either end. Because osteons are parallel to the long axis of the shaft, a limb bone does not bend when a force (even a large one) is applied to either end. However, a much smaller force applied to the side of the shaft can break the bone.

In contrast, spongy bone is found where bones are not heavily stressed or where stresses arrive from many directions. For example, spongy bone is present at the epiphyses of long bones, where stresses are transferred across joints. Spongy bone is also much lighter than compact bone. This reduces the weight of the skeleton and makes it easier for muscles to move the bones. Finally, the trabecular network of spongy bone supports and protects the cells of red bone marrow, important sites of blood cell formation.

Cells in Bone

Although osteocytes are the most abundant cells in bone, other cell types are also present. These cells, called *osteoclasts* and *osteoblasts,* are associated with the endosteum that lines the inner cavities of both compact and spongy bone, and with the

Cellular layer of periosteum

Fibrous layer of periosteum

Spongy bone

Marrow cavity

Compact bone

Small vein

Capillary

Lamellae

Osteons

Endosteum

Canaliculi

Concentric lamellae

Vein

Artery

Lacunae   Central canals   LM × 272

Central canal

Perforating canal

Trabeculae of spongy bone

(a)

(b)

FIGURE 6-3 The Structure of a Typical Bone. (a) This diagrammatic view depicts the structure of a typical long bone. **(b)** In this thin section through compact bone, the intact matrix and central canals appear white, and the lacunae and canaliculi appear black.

cellular layer of the periosteum. Three primary cell types occur in bone:

1. **Osteocytes** are mature bone cells. Osteocytes maintain normal bone structure by recycling the calcium salts in the bony matrix around themselves and by assisting in repairs.

2. **Osteoclasts** (OS-tē-ō-clasts; *clast,* break) are giant cells with 50 or more nuclei. Acids and enzymes secreted by osteoclasts dissolve the bony matrix and release the stored minerals through *osteolysis* (os-tē-OL-i-sis), or *resorption.* This process helps regulate calcium and phosphate concentrations in body fluids.

3. **Osteoblasts** (OS-tē-ō-blasts; *blast,* precursor) are the cells responsible for the production of new bone, a process called *osteogenesis* (os-tē-ō-JEN-e-sis; *gennan,* to produce). Osteoblasts produce new bone matrix and promote the deposition of calcium salts in the organic

matrix. At any given moment, osteoclasts are removing matrix and osteoblasts are adding to it. When an osteoblast becomes completely surrounded by calcified matrix, it differentiates into an osteocyte.

CHECKPOINT

2. Identify the four general shapes of bones.

3. How would the strength of a bone be affected if the ratio of collagen to calcium increased?

4. A sample of a long bone shows concentric layers surrounding a central canal. Is it from the shaft or the end of the bone?

5. Mature bone cells are known as _____, bone-building cells are called _____, and _____ are bone-resorbing cells.

6. If the activity of osteoclasts exceeds that of osteoblasts in a bone, how will the mass of the bone be affected?

See the blue Answers tab at the back of the book.

6-3 Ossification and appositional growth are mechanisms of bone formation and enlargement

The growth of your skeleton determines the size and proportions of your body. Skeletal growth begins about 6 weeks after fertilization, when an embryo is about 12 mm (0.5 in.) long. (At this time, all skeletal elements are made of cartilage.) Bone growth continues through adolescence, and typically portions of the skeleton continue growing until roughly age 25. This section considers the process of osteogenesis (bone formation) and growth. The next section examines the maintenance and turnover of mineral reserves in the adult skeleton.

During development, cartilage or other connective tissues are replaced by bone. The process of replacing other tissues with bone is called **ossification.** (The process of **calcification,** the deposition of calcium salts, occurs during ossification, but it can also occur in tissues other than bone.) There are two major forms of ossification. In *intramembranous ossification,* bone develops within sheets or membranes of connective tissue. In *endochondral ossification,* bone replaces existing cartilage. Figure 6-4 shows some of the bones formed by these two processes in a 16-week-old fetus.

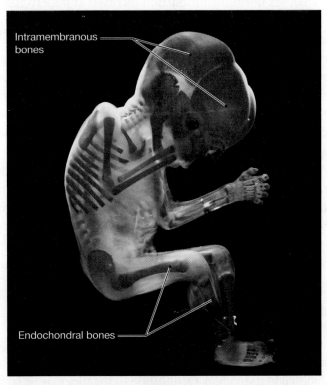

Intramembranous bones

Endochondral bones

FIGURE 6-4 Bone Formation in a 16-Week-Old Fetus.

INTRAMEMBRANOUS OSSIFICATION

Intramembranous (in-tra-MEM-bra-nus) **ossification** begins when osteoblasts differentiate within embryonic or fetal fibrous connective tissue. This type of ossification normally occurs in the deeper layers of the dermis. The osteoblasts differentiate from connective tissue stem cells after the organic components of the matrix secreted by the stem cells become calcified. The place where ossification first occurs is called an **ossification center.** As ossification proceeds and new bone branches outward, some osteoblasts become trapped inside bony pockets and change into osteocytes.

Bone growth is an active process, and osteoblasts require oxygen and a reliable supply of nutrients. Blood vessels begin to grow into the area to meet these demands and over time become trapped within the developing bone. At first, the intramembranous bone resembles spongy bone. Further remodeling around the trapped blood vessels can produce osteons typical of compact bone. The flat bones of the skull, the lower jaw (*mandible*), and the collarbones (*clavicles*) form this way.

ENDOCHONDRAL OSSIFICATION

Most of the bones of the skeleton are formed through **endochondral** (en-dō-KON-drul; *endo,* inside + *chondros,* cartilage) **ossification** of existing hyaline cartilage. The cartilages develop first; they are like miniature cartilage models of the future bone. By the time an embryo is 6 weeks old, the cartilage models of the future limb bones begin to be replaced by true bone. Steps in the growth and ossification of a limb bone are diagrammed in Figure 6-5.

Step 1 Endochondral ossification starts when chondrocytes within the cartilage model enlarge and the surrounding matrix begins to calcify. The chondrocytes die because the diffusion of nutrients slows through the calcified matrix.

Step 2 Bone formation first occurs at the shaft surface. Blood vessels invade the perichondrium, and cells of its inner layer differentiate into osteoblasts that begin producing bone matrix. ∞ p. 108

Step 3 Blood vessels invade the inner region of the cartilage, and newly differentiated osteoblasts form spongy bone within the center of the shaft at a *primary ossification center.* Bone development proceeds toward either end, filling the shaft with spongy bone.

Step 4 As the bone enlarges, osteoclasts break down some of the spongy bone and create a marrow cavity. The

STEP 1
Chondrocytes at the center of the growing cartilage model enlarge and then die as the matrix calcifies.

Enlarging chondrocytes within calcifying matrix

Cartilage model

STEP 2
Newly derived osteoblasts cover the shaft of the cartilage in a thin layer of bone.

Epiphysis

Diaphysis

Bone formation

STEP 3
Blood vessels penetrate the cartilage. New osteoblasts form a primary ossification center.

Marrow cavity

Primary center of ossification

Blood vessel

STEP 4
The bone of the shaft thickens, and the cartilage near each epiphysis is replaced by shafts of bone.

Marrow cavity

Blood vessel

STEP 5
Blood vessels invade the epiphyses and osteoblasts form secondary centers of ossification.

Articular cartilage

Epiphyseal cartilage

Secondary center of ossification

FIGURE 6-5 **Endochondral Ossification.**

cartilage model does not completely fill with bone because the **epiphyseal cartilages,** or *epiphyseal plates,* on the ends continue to enlarge, increasing the length of the developing bone. Although osteoblasts from the shaft continuously invade the epiphyseal cartilages, the bone grows longer because new cartilage is continuously added in front of the advancing osteoblasts. This situation is like a pair of joggers, one in front of the other: As long as they run at the same speed, the one in back will never catch the one in front, no matter how far they travel.

Step 5 The centers of the epiphyses begin to calcify. As blood vessels and osteoblasts enter these areas, *secondary ossification centers* form, and the epiphyses eventually become filled with spongy bone. A thin cap of the original cartilage model remains exposed to the joint cavity as the **articular cartilage.** At this stage, the bone of the shaft and the bone of each epiphysis are still separated by epiphyseal cartilage. As long as the rate of cartilage growth keeps pace with the rate of osteoblast invasion, the epiphyseal cartilage persists, and the bone continues to grow longer.

When sex hormone production increases at puberty, bone growth accelerates dramatically, and osteoblasts begin to produce bone faster than epiphyseal cartilage expands. As a result, the epiphyseal cartilages at each end of the bone get increasingly narrow, until they disappear. In adults, the former location of the epiphyseal cartilage is marked by a distinct *epiphyseal line* (Figure 6-2) that remains evident in x-rays after epiphyseal growth has ended. The end of epiphyseal growth is called *epiphyseal closure.*

While the bone elongates, its diameter also enlarges at its outer surface. This enlargement process, called **appositional growth,** occurs as cells of the periosteum develop into osteoblasts and produce additional bony matrix (Figure 6-6). As new bone is deposited on the outer surface of the shaft, the inner surface is eroded by osteoclasts, and the marrow cavity gradually enlarges.

BONE GROWTH AND BODY PROPORTIONS

The timing of epiphyseal closure varies from bone to bone and individual to individual. Ossification of the toes may be complete by age 11, whereas portions of the pelvis or the wrist may

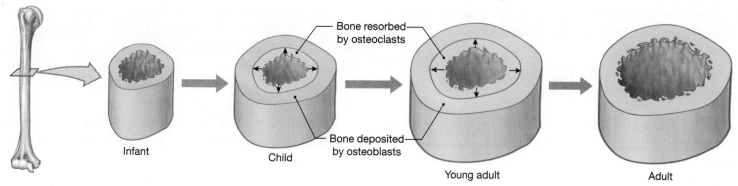

FIGURE 6-6 **Appositional Bone Growth.**

continue to enlarge until age 25. The epiphyseal cartilages in the arms and legs usually close by age 18 (women) or 20 (men). Differences in sex hormones account for variations in body size and proportions between men and women.

REQUIREMENTS FOR NORMAL BONE GROWTH

Normal bone growth and maintenance cannot occur without a reliable source of minerals, especially calcium salts. During prenatal development these minerals are absorbed from the mother's bloodstream. The demands are so great that the maternal skeleton often loses bone mass during pregnancy. From infancy to adulthood, the diet must provide adequate amounts of calcium and phosphate, and the body must be able to absorb and transport these minerals to sites of bone formation.

Vitamin D₃ plays an important role in normal calcium metabolism. This vitamin can be obtained from dietary supplements or manufactured by epidermal cells exposed to UV radiation. ∞ p. 126 After vitamin D₃ has been processed in the liver, the kidneys convert a derivative of this vitamin into *calcitriol,* a hormone that stimulates the absorption of calcium and phosphate ions in the digestive tract. *Rickets* is a condition marked by a softening and bending of bones that occurs in growing children, as a result of vitamin D₃ deficiency. The reduced amounts of calcium salts in the skeleton cause the bones to become very flexible, and affected individuals develop a bowlegged appearance as the leg bones bend under the weight of the body.

Vitamin A and *vitamin C* are also essential for normal bone growth and maintenance. For example, a deficiency of vitamin C can cause *scurvy.* One of the primary features of this condition is a reduction in osteoblast activity that leads to weak and brittle bones. In addition to vitamins, various hormones (including growth hormone, thyroid hormones, sex hormones, and those involved in calcium metabolism) are essential to normal skeletal growth and development.

CHECKPOINT

7. During intramembranous ossification, which type of tissue is replaced by bone?

8. How could x-rays of the femur be used to determine whether a person had reached full height?

9. A child who enters puberty several years later than the average age is generally taller than average as an adult. Why?

10. Why are pregnant women given calcium supplements and encouraged to drink milk even though their skeletons are fully formed?

See the blue Answers tab at the back of the book.

6-4 Bone growth and development depend on a balance between bone formation and resorption, and on calcium availability

Of the five major functions of the skeleton discussed earlier in this chapter, support and storage of minerals depend on the dynamic nature of bone. In adults, osteocytes in lacunae maintain the surrounding matrix, continually removing and replacing the surrounding calcium salts. But osteoclasts and osteoblasts also remain active, even after the epiphyseal cartilages have closed. Normally their activities are balanced: As one osteon forms through the activity of osteoblasts, another is destroyed by osteoclasts. The turnover rate for bone is quite high, and in adults roughly 18 percent of the protein and mineral components are removed and replaced each year through the process of **remodeling.** Not every part of every bone is affected; regional and even local differences in the rate of turnover occur. For example, the spongy bone in the head of the femur may be replaced two or three times each year, whereas the compact bone along the shaft remains largely untouched.

THE ROLE OF REMODELING IN SUPPORT

Regular mineral turnover gives each bone the ability to adapt to new stresses. Heavily stressed bones become thicker and stronger and develop more pronounced surface ridges; bones not subjected to ordinary stresses become thin and brittle. Thus, regular exercise is an important stimulus in maintaining normal bone structure.

Degenerative changes occur in the skeleton after even brief periods of inactivity. For example, using a crutch while wearing a cast takes the weight off the injured leg. After a few weeks, the unstressed leg will lose up to about a third of its bone mass. The bones rebuild just as quickly once they again carry their normal weight.

THE SKELETON AS A CALCIUM RESERVE

The bones of the skeleton are more than just racks to hang muscles on. They are important mineral reservoirs—especially for calcium, the most abundant mineral in the human body. A typical human body contains 1–2 kg (2.2–4.4 lb) of calcium, 99 percent of which is deposited in the skeleton.

Calcium ions play an important role in many physiological processes, so calcium ion concentrations must be closely controlled. Even small variations from normal concentrations affect cellular operations, and larger changes can cause a clinical crisis. Neurons and muscle cells are particularly sensitive to changes in calcium ion concentration. If the calcium concentration in body fluids increases by 30 percent, neurons and muscle cells become relatively unresponsive. If calcium levels decrease by 35 percent, they become so excitable that convulsions may occur. A 50 percent reduction in calcium concentrations usually causes death. Such effects are relatively rare, however, because calcium ion concentrations are so closely regulated that daily fluctuations of more than 10 percent are very unusual.

The Big Picture

What you don't use, you lose. The stresses applied to bones during exercise are essential to maintaining bone strength and bone mass.

The hormones *parathyroid hormone* (PTH) from the parathyroid glands and *calcitriol* from the kidneys work together to elevate calcium levels in body fluids. Their actions are opposed by *calcitonin*, a hormone from the thyroid gland that depresses calcium levels in body fluids. These hormones and their regulation are discussed further in Chapter 10.

By providing a calcium reserve, the skeleton helps maintain calcium homeostasis in body fluids. This function can directly affect the shape and strength of the bones in the skeleton. When large numbers of calcium ions are mobilized, bones become weaker; when calcium salts are deposited, bones become more massive.

REPAIR OF FRACTURES

Despite its strength, bone will crack or even break if subjected to extreme loads, sudden impacts, or stresses from unusual directions. Every such crack or break in a bone constitutes a **fracture**. Fractures are classified according to many features, including their external appearance, the site of the fracture, and the nature of the break. (See "Clinical Note: Types of Fractures" below.)

Bones usually heal even after they have been severely damaged, so long as the blood supply remains and the cellular components of the endosteum and periosteum survive. Steps in

Clinical Note

Types of Fractures

Fractures are named according to several criteria, including their external appearance (open or closed), their location, and the nature of the crack or break in the bone. **Closed** (*simple*) **fractures** are completely internal; they do not involve a break in the skin. **Open** (*compound*) **fractures** project through the skin; they are more dangerous because of the possibility of infection or uncontrolled bleeding. Examples of fractures classified by location are a *Pott fracture,* which occurs at the ankle and affects both bones of the leg, and a *Colles fracture,* a break in the distal portion of the radius (the slender bone of the forearm) that is often the result of reaching out to cushion a fall. Examples of fractures classified by the nature of the break are *transverse fractures,* which break a shaft of a bone across its long axis; *spiral fractures,* which are produced by twisting stresses along the length of the bone; and *comminuted fractures,* which shatter the area into many, smaller fragments. Many fractures fall into more than one category. For example, a Colles fracture is a transverse fracture, but depending on the injury, it may also be a comminuted (fragmented) fracture that can be either open or closed.

the repair process, which may take from 4 months to well over a year following a fracture, are diagrammed in Figure 6-7:

Step 1 In even a small fracture, many blood vessels are broken and extensive bleeding occurs. A large blood clot, called a **fracture hematoma** (*hemato-*, blood; + *tumere,* to swell), soon forms and closes off the injured blood vessels. Because the resulting lack of blood supply kills osteocytes, dead bone extends in either direction from the break.

Step 2 Cells of the periosteum and endosteum undergo mitosis, and the daughter cells migrate into the fracture zone. There they form localized thickenings—an **external callus** (*callum,* hard skin) and an **internal callus,** respectively. At the center of the external callus, cells differentiate into chondrocytes and produce hyaline cartilage.

Step 3 Osteoblasts replace the new central cartilage of the external callus with spongy bone. When this process is complete, the external and internal calluses form a continuous brace of spongy bone at the fracture site. The ends of the fracture are now held firmly in place and can withstand normal stresses from muscle contractions.

Step 4 The remodeling of spongy bone at the fracture site may continue over a period of 4 months to well over a year. When the remodeling is complete, the fragments of dead bone and the spongy bone of the calluses will be gone, and only living compact bone will remain. The repair may be "good as new," with no sign that a fracture occurred, but the bone may be slightly thicker than normal at the fracture site.

CHECKPOINT

11. Describe bone remodeling.

12. Why would you expect the arm bones of a weight lifter to be thicker and heavier than those of a jogger?

13. What general effects do the hormones PTH, calcitriol, and calcitonin secretion have on blood calcium levels?

14. What is the difference between a closed fracture and an open fracture?

See the blue Answers tab at the back of the book.

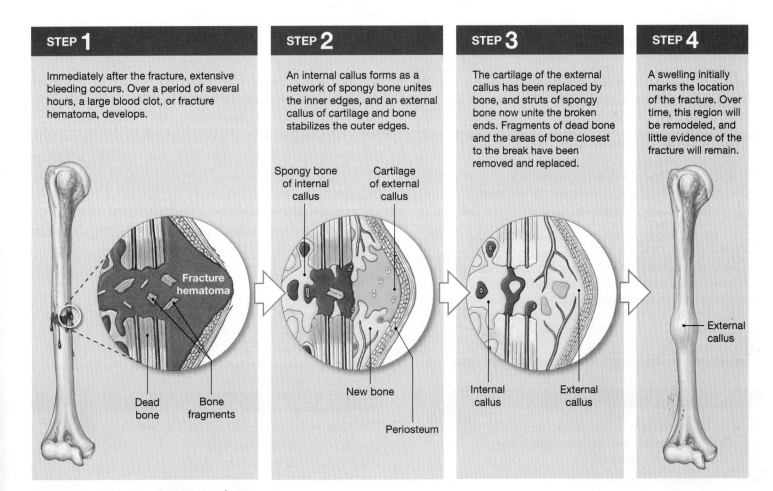

STEP **1**	STEP **2**	STEP **3**	STEP **4**
Immediately after the fracture, extensive bleeding occurs. Over a period of several hours, a large blood clot, or fracture hematoma, develops.	An internal callus forms as a network of spongy bone unites the inner edges, and an external callus of cartilage and bone stabilizes the outer edges.	The cartilage of the external callus has been replaced by bone, and struts of spongy bone now unite the broken ends. Fragments of dead bone and the areas of bone closest to the break have been removed and replaced.	A swelling initially marks the location of the fracture. Over time, this region will be remodeled, and little evidence of the fracture will remain.

FIGURE 6-7 Steps in the Repair of a Fracture.

6-5 Osteopenia has a widespread effect on aging skeletal tissue

Bones become thinner and relatively weaker as a normal part of the aging process. Inadequate ossification is called **osteopenia** (os-tē-ō-PĒ-nē-uh; *penia*, lacking), and all of us become slightly osteopenic as we age. The reduction in bone mass begins between the ages of 30 and 40, as osteoblast activity begins to decline while osteoclast activity continues at normal levels. Once the reduction begins, women lose roughly 8 percent of their skeletal mass every decade, whereas men's skeletons deteriorate at about 3 percent per decade. Not all parts of the skeleton are equally affected. Epiphyses, vertebrae, and the jaws lose more than their fair share, resulting in fragile limbs, a reduction in height, and the loss of teeth.

Clinical Note

Osteoporosis

Osteoporosis (os-tē-ō-po-RŌ-sis; *porosus*, porous) is a condition that produces a reduction in bone mass great enough to compromise normal function. The difference between the "normal" osteopenia of aging and the clinical condition of osteoporosis is a matter of degree.

Sex hormones are important in maintaining normal rates of bone deposition. Among individuals over age 45, an estimated 29 percent of women and 18 percent of men have osteoporosis. In women, the increase in incidence after menopause has been linked to decreases in the production of estrogens (female sex hormones). Because men continue to produce androgens (male sex hormones) until relatively late in life, severe osteoporosis is less common in males under age 60 than in females in that same age group.

Because osteoporotic bones are more fragile, they break easily and do not repair well. Vertebrae may collapse, distorting the vertebral articulations and putting pressure on spinal nerves. Therapies that boost estrogen levels in women, dietary changes that elevate blood calcium levels, and exercise that stresses bones and stimulates osteoblast activity appear to slow, but not completely prevent, the development of osteoporosis.

CHECKPOINT

15. Define osteopenia.

16. Why is osteoporosis more common in older women than in older men?

See the blue Answers tab at the back of the book.

6-6 The bones of the skeleton are distinguished by surface markings and grouped into two skeletal divisions

BONE MARKINGS (SURFACE FEATURES)

Each bone in the human skeleton has not only a distinctive shape but also characteristic external and internal features. For example, elevations or projections form where tendons and ligaments attach and where adjacent bones articulate at joints. Depressions and openings indicate sites where blood vessels and nerves run alongside or penetrate the bone. These landmarks are called **bone markings,** or *surface features.* The most common terms used to describe bone markings are listed and illustrated in Table 6-1.

SKELETAL DIVISIONS

The skeletal system consists of 206 separate bones (Figure 6-8) plus numerous associated cartilages. This system is divided into axial and appendicular divisions (Figure 6-9). The **axial skeleton** forms the longitudinal axis of the body. This division's 80 bones can be subdivided into (1) the 22 bones of the **skull,** plus 7 associated bones (6 **auditory ossicles** and the **hyoid bone**); (2) the **thoracic cage** (*rib cage*), composed of 24 **ribs** and the **sternum;** and (3) the 26 bones of the **vertebral column.**

The **appendicular skeleton** includes the bones of the limbs and those of the **pectoral** and **pelvic girdles,** which attach the limbs to the trunk. All together there are 126 appendicular bones; 32 are associated with each upper limb, and 31 with each lower limb.

CHECKPOINT

17. Define bone markings (surface features).

See the blue Answers tab at the back of the book.

TABLE 6-1 **An Introduction to the Surface Features of Bones**

GENERAL DESCRIPTION	ANATOMICAL TERM	DEFINITION
Elevations and projections (general)	Process	Any projection or bump
	Ramus	An extension of a bone making an angle with the rest of the structure
Processes formed where tendons or ligaments attach	Trochanter	A large, rough projection
	Tuberosity	A smaller, rough projection
	Tubercle	A small, rounded projection
	Crest	A prominent ridge
	Line	A low ridge
	Spine	A pointed process
Processes formed for articulation with adjacent bones	Head	The expanded articular end of an epiphysis, separated from the shaft by a neck
	Neck	A narrow connection between the epiphysis and the diaphysis
	Condyle	A smooth, rounded articular process
	Trochlea	A smooth, grooved articular process shaped like a pulley
	Facet	A small, flat articular surface
Depressions	Fossa	A shallow depression
	Sulcus	A narrow groove
Openings	Foramen	A rounded passageway for blood vessels or nerves
	Canal or Meatus	A passageway through the substance of a bone
	Fissure	An elongate cleft
	Sinus	A chamber within a bone, normally filled with air

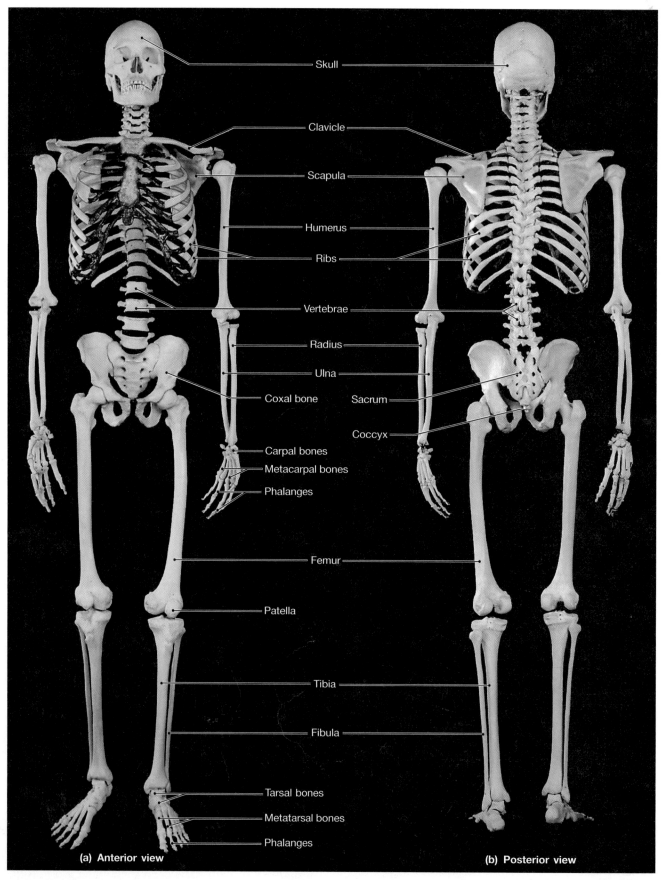

Skull

Clavicle

Scapula

Humerus

Ribs

Vertebrae

Radius

Ulna

Coxal bone — Sacrum

Coccyx

Carpal bones

Metacarpal bones

Phalanges

Femur

Patella

Tibia

Fibula

Tarsal bones

Metatarsal bones

Phalanges

(a) Anterior view

(b) Posterior view

FIGURE 6-8 The Skeleton.

FIGURE 6-9 The Axial and Appendicular Divisions of the Skeleton.

6-7 The bones of the skull, vertebral column, and thoracic cage make up the axial skeleton

The **axial skeleton** creates a framework that supports and protects organ systems in the brain and spinal cavities, and the ventral body cavities. In addition, it provides an extensive surface area for the attachment of muscles that (1) adjust the positions of the head, neck, and trunk; (2) perform respiratory movements; and (3) stabilize or position elements of the appendicular skeleton.

THE SKULL

The bones of the skull protect the brain and support delicate sense organs involved with vision, hearing, balance, olfaction (smell), and gustation (taste). The skull is made up of 22 bones: 8 form the **cranium,** and 14 are associated with the face. Seven

155

additional bones are associated with the skull: Six *auditory ossicles,* tiny bones involved in sound detection, are encased by the *temporal bones* of the cranium, and the *hyoid bone* is connected to the inferior surface of the skull by ligaments.

The cranium encloses the **cranial cavity,** a fluid-filled chamber that cushions and supports the brain. The outer surface of the cranium provides an extensive area for the attachment of muscles that move the eyes, jaws, and head.

The Bones of the Cranium

THE FRONTAL BONE. The **frontal bone** of the cranium forms the forehead and the roof of the **orbits,** the bony recesses that contain the eyes (Figures 6-10 and 6-11a). A **supraorbital foramen** is an opening that pierces the bony ridge above each orbit, forming a passageway for blood vessels and nerves passing to or from the eyebrows and eyelids (Figure 6-10). (Sometimes the ridge has a deep groove, called a *supraorbital notch,* rather than a foramen, but the function is the same.) Above the orbit, the frontal bone contains air-filled internal chambers that communicate with the nasal cavity. These **frontal sinuses** make the bone lighter and produce mucus that cleans and moistens the nasal cavities (Figure 6-12b). The **infraorbital foramen** is an opening for a major sensory nerve from the face (Figures 6-10 and 6-11a).

THE PARIETAL BONES. On both sides of the skull, a **parietal** (pa-RĪ-e-tal) **bone** is posterior to the frontal bone (Figures 6-11a and 6-12a). Together the parietal bones form the roof and the superior walls of the cranium. The parietal bones interlock along the **sagittal suture,** which extends along the midline of the cranium (Figure 6-11a). Anteriorly, the two parietal bones articulate with the frontal bone along the **coronal suture** (Figure 6-10).

THE OCCIPITAL BONE. The **occipital bone** forms the posterior and inferior portions of the cranium (Figures 6-10 and 6-11b). Along its superior margin, the occipital bone contacts the two parietal bones at the **lambdoid** (LAM-doyd) **suture.** The **foramen magnum** connects the cranial cavity with the spinal cavity, which is enclosed by the vertebral column. The spinal cord passes through the foramen magnum to connect with the inferior portion of the brain. On either side of the foramen magnum are the **occipital condyles,** the sites of articulation between the skull and the vertebral column.

THE TEMPORAL BONES. Below the parietal bones and contributing to the sides and base of the cranium are the **temporal bones.** The temporal bones contact the parietal bones along the **squamous** (SKWĀ-mus) **suture** on each side (Figure 6-10).

The temporal bones display a number of distinctive anatomical landmarks. One of them, the **external acoustic meatus,**

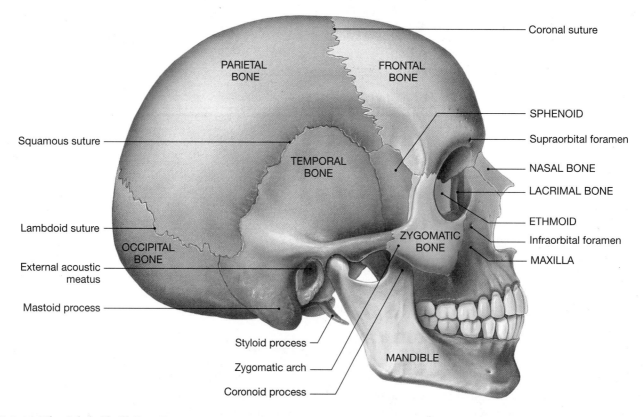

FIGURE 6-10 The Adult Skull, Part I. The adult skull is shown in lateral view.

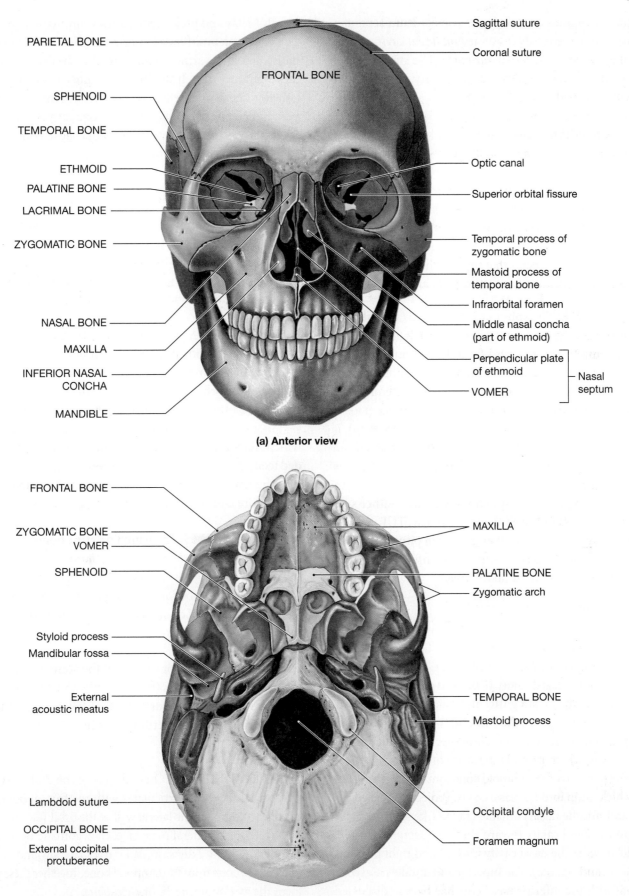

PARIETAL BONE

Sagittal suture

Coronal suture

FRONTAL BONE

SPHENOID

TEMPORAL BONE

ETHMOID
PALATINE BONE
LACRIMAL BONE

ZYGOMATIC BONE

Optic canal

Superior orbital fissure

Temporal process of
zygomatic bone

Mastoid process of
temporal bone

Infraorbital foramen

NASAL BONE

MAXILLA

INFERIOR NASAL
CONCHA

MANDIBLE

Middle nasal concha
(part of ethmoid)

Perpendicular plate
of ethmoid

VOMER

Nasal
septum

(a) Anterior view

FRONTAL BONE

ZYGOMATIC BONE
VOMER

SPHENOID

MAXILLA

PALATINE BONE
Zygomatic arch

Styloid process
Mandibular fossa

External
acoustic meatus

TEMPORAL BONE

Mastoid process

Lambdoid suture

OCCIPITAL BONE

External occipital
protuberance

Occipital condyle

Foramen magnum

FIGURE 6-11 **The Adult Skull, Part II.**

(b) Inferior view

leads to the **tympanum,** or *eardrum.* The eardrum separates the external acoustic meatus from the *middle ear cavity,* which contains the *auditory ossicles,* or *ear bones.* The structure and function of the tympanum, middle ear cavity, and auditory ossicles will be considered in Chapter 9.

Anterior to the external acoustic meatus is a transverse depression, the **mandibular fossa,** which marks the point of articulation with the lower jaw (mandible) (Figure 6-11b). The prominent bulge just posterior and inferior to the entrance to the external acoustic canal is the **mastoid process,** which provides a site for the attachment of muscles that rotate or extend the head. Next to the base of the mastoid process is the long, sharp **styloid** (STĪ-loyd; *stylos,* pillar) **process.** The styloid process is attached to ligaments that support the hyoid bone and anchors muscles associated with the tongue and pharynx.

THE SPHENOID BONE. The **sphenoid** (SFĒ-noyd) **bone** forms part of the floor of the cranium (Figure 6-12b). It also acts like a bridge, uniting the cranial and facial bones, and it braces the sides of the skull. The general shape of the sphenoid has been compared to that of a giant bat with wings extended; the wings can be seen most clearly on the superior surface (Figure 6-12a). From the front (Figure 6-11a) or side (Figure 6-10), it is covered by other bones. Like the frontal bone, the sphenoid bone also contains a pair of sinuses, called **sphenoidal sinuses** (Figures 6-12b,c).

The lateral "wings" of the sphenoid extend to either side from a central depression called the **sella turcica** (TUR-si-kuh) (Turk's saddle) (Figure 6-12a). It encloses the pituitary gland, an endocrine organ that is connected to the inferior surface of the brain by a narrow stalk of neural tissue.

THE ETHMOID BONE. The **ethmoid bone** is anterior to the sphenoid bone. The ethmoid bone consists of two honeycombed masses of bone. It forms part of the cranial floor, contributes to the medial surfaces of the orbit of each eye, and forms the roof and sides of the nasal cavity (Figures 6-11a and 6-12b). A prominent ridge, the **crista galli,** or "cock's comb," projects above the superior surface of the ethmoid (Figure 6-12a). Holes in the **cribriform plate** (*cribrum,* sieve) permit passage of the olfactory nerves, which provide the sense of smell.

The lateral portions of the ethmoid bone contain the **ethmoidal sinuses,** which drain into the nasal cavity. Projections called the **superior** and **middle nasal conchae** (KONG-kē; *concha,* shell) extend into the nasal cavity toward the *nasal septum* (*septum,* wall), which divides the nasal cavity into left and right portions (Figures 6-11a and 6-12b,c). The superior and middle nasal conchae, along with the inferior nasal conchae bones (discussed

shortly), slow and break up the airflow through the nasal cavity. This deflection in airflow allows time for the air to become cleaned, moistened, and warmed before it reaches the delicate portions of the respiratory tract. It also directs air into contact with olfactory (smell) receptors in the superior portions of the nasal cavity. The **perpendicular plate** of the ethmoid bone extends inferiorly from the crista galli, passing between the conchae to contribute to the nasal septum (Figure 6-11a).

The Bones of the Face

The facial bones protect and support the entrances to the digestive and respiratory tracts. They also provide sites for the attachment of muscles that control our facial expressions and help us manipulate food. Of the 14 facial bones, only the lower jaw, or mandible, is movable.

THE MAXILLAE. The **maxillae,** or *maxillary* (MAK-si-ler-ē) *bones,* articulate with all other facial bones except the mandible. The maxillary bones form (1) the floor and medial portion of the rim of the orbit (Figure 6-11a); (2) the walls of the nasal cavity; and (3) the anterior roof of the mouth, or *bony palate* (Figure 6-12c). The maxillae contain large **maxillary sinuses,** which lighten the portion of the maxillae above the embedded teeth. Infections of the gums or teeth can sometimes spread into the maxillary sinuses, increasing pain and making treatment more complicated.

THE PALATINE BONES. The paired **palatine bones** form the posterior surface of the *bony palate,* or *hard palate*—the "roof of the mouth" (Figures 6-11b and 6-12b,c). The superior surfaces of the horizontal portion of each palatine bone contribute to the floor of the nasal cavity. The superior tip of the vertical portion of each palatine bone forms part of the floor of each orbit.

THE VOMER. The inferior margin of the **vomer** articulates with the paired palatine bones (Figures 6-11b and 6-12b). The vomer supports a prominent partition that forms part of the *nasal septum,* along with the ethmoid bone (Figures 6-11a and 6-12b).

THE ZYGOMATIC BONES. On each side of the skull, a **zygomatic** (zī-go-MA-tik) **bone** articulates with the frontal bone and the maxilla to complete the lateral wall of the orbit (Figures 6-10 and 6-11a). Along its lateral margin, each zygomatic bone gives rise to a slender bony extension that curves laterally and posteriorly to meet a process from the temporal bone. Together these processes form the **zygomatic arch,** or *cheekbone.*

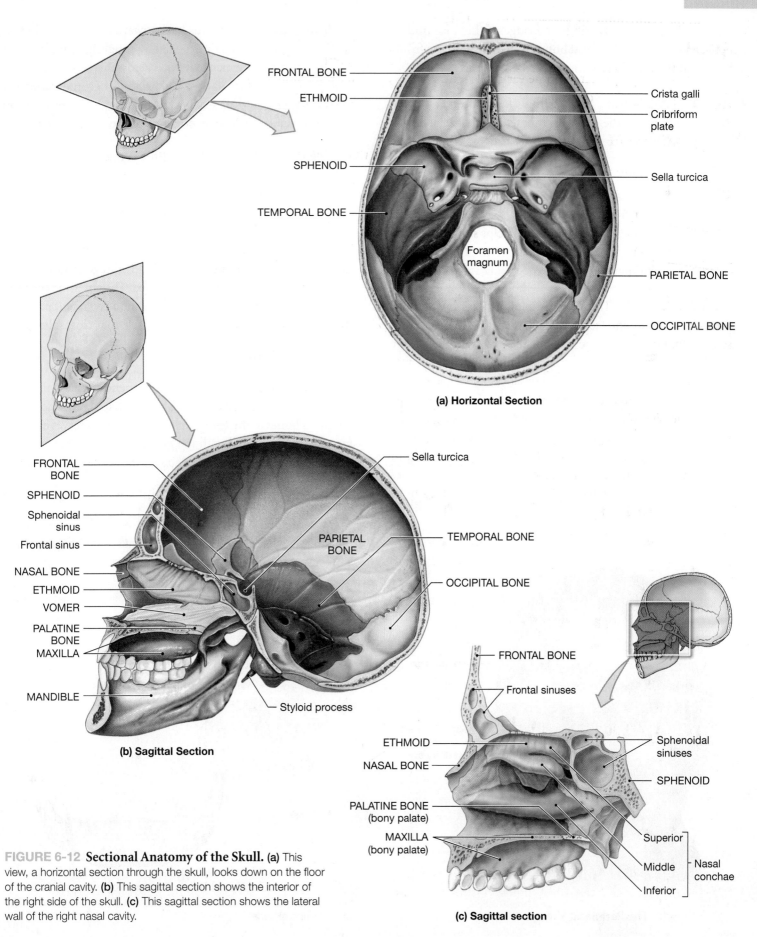

(a) Horizontal Section

FRONTAL BONE
ETHMOID
SPHENOID
TEMPORAL BONE
Foramen magnum

Crista galli
Cribriform plate
Sella turcica
PARIETAL BONE
OCCIPITAL BONE

(b) Sagittal Section

FRONTAL BONE
SPHENOID
Sphenoidal sinus
Frontal sinus
NASAL BONE
ETHMOID
VOMER
PALATINE BONE
MAXILLA
MANDIBLE

Sella turcica
PARIETAL BONE
TEMPORAL BONE
OCCIPITAL BONE
Styloid process

(c) Sagittal section

FRONTAL BONE
Frontal sinuses
ETHMOID
NASAL BONE
PALATINE BONE (bony palate)
MAXILLA (bony palate)

Sphenoidal sinuses
SPHENOID
Superior
Middle
Inferior
Nasal conchae

FIGURE 6-12 Sectional Anatomy of the Skull. (a) This view, a horizontal section through the skull, looks down on the floor of the cranial cavity. **(b)** This sagittal section shows the interior of the right side of the skull. **(c)** This sagittal section shows the lateral wall of the right nasal cavity.

THE NASAL BONES. Forming the bridge of the nose midway between the orbits, the **nasal bones** articulate with the frontal bone and the maxillary bones (Figures 6-10 and 6-11a).

THE LACRIMAL BONES. The **lacrimal** (*lacrimae*, tears) **bones** are located within the orbit on its medial surface. They articulate with the frontal, ethmoid, and maxillary bones (Figures 6-10 and 6-11a).

THE INFERIOR NASAL CONCHAE. The paired **inferior nasal conchae** project from the lateral walls of the nasal cavity (Figures 6-11a and 6-12c). Their shape helps slow airflow and deflects arriving air toward the olfactory (smell) receptors located near the upper portions of the nasal cavity.

THE NASAL COMPLEX. The **nasal complex** includes the bones that form the superior and lateral walls of the nasal cavities and the sinuses that drain into them. The ethmoid bone and vomer form the bony portion of the **nasal septum,** which separates the left and right portions of the nasal cavity (Figure 6-11a). The frontal, sphenoid, ethmoid, palatine, and maxillary bones contain air-filled chambers collectively known as the **paranasal sinuses** (Figure 6-13). (The tiny palatine sinuses, not shown, open into the sphenoid sinuses.) In addition to reducing the weight of the skull, the paranasal sinuses help protect the respiratory system. The paranasal sinuses are connected to the nasal cavities and lined by a mucous membrane. The mucous secretions are released into the nasal cavities, and the ciliated

epithelium passes the mucus back toward the throat, where it is eventually swallowed or expelled by coughing. Incoming air is humidified and warmed as it flows across this carpet of mucus. Foreign particles, such as dust and bacteria, become trapped in the sticky mucus and are swallowed or expelled. This mechanism helps protect more delicate portions of the respiratory tract.

THE MANDIBLE. The broad **mandible** is the bone of the lower jaw. It forms a broad, horizontal curve with vertical processes at either side. Each vertical process, or **ramus,** bears two processes. The more posterior **condylar process** ends at the *mandibular condyle,* a curved surface that articulates with the mandibular fossa of the temporal bone on that side. This articulation is quite mobile, and the disadvantage of such mobility is that the jaw can easily be dislocated. The anterior **coronoid** (kor-Ō-noyd) **process** (Figure 6-10) is the attachment point for the *temporalis muscle,* a powerful muscle that closes the jaws.

The Hyoid Bone

The small, U-shaped **hyoid bone** is suspended below the skull (Figure 6-14). Ligaments extend from the styloid processes of the temporal bones to the *lesser horns.* The hyoid (1) serves as a base for muscles associated with the *larynx* (voicebox), tongue, and pharynx and (2) supports and stabilizes the position of the larynx.

The Skulls of Infants and Children

Many centers of ossification are involved in the formation of the skull. As a fetus develops, the individual centers begin to fuse. This fusion produces a smaller number of composite bones.

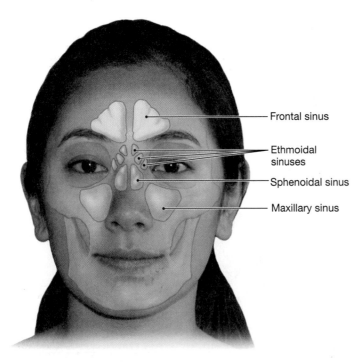

Frontal sinus

Ethmoidal sinuses

Sphenoidal sinus

Maxillary sinus

FIGURE 6-13 The Paranasal Sinuses.

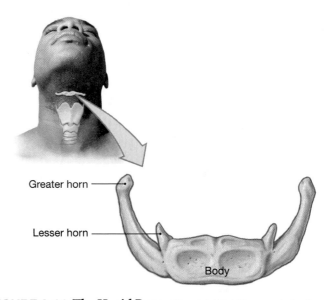

Greater horn

Lesser horn

Body

FIGURE 6-14 The Hyoid Bone. The stylohyoid ligaments (not shown) connect the lesser horns of the hyoid to the styloid processes of the temporal bones.

For example, the sphenoid begins as 14 separate ossification centers but ends as just one bone. At birth, fusion is not yet complete, and there are two frontal bones, four occipital bones, and several sphenoid and temporal elements.

The developing skull organizes around the developing brain, and as the time of birth approaches, the brain enlarges rapidly. Although the bones of the skull are also growing, they fail to keep pace with the brain. At birth the cranial bones are connected by areas of fibrous connective tissue known as **fontanelles** (fon-tah-NELZ). The fontanelles, or "soft spots," are quite flexible and permit distortion of the skull without damage. During delivery such distortion occurs normally and eases the passage of the infant along the birth canal. Figure 6-15 shows the appearance of the skull at birth, including the prominent fontanelles.

THE VERTEBRAL COLUMN AND THORACIC CAGE

The rest of the axial skeleton consists of the thoracic cage, which we will discuss shortly, and the vertebral column, which we discuss next.

The **vertebral column,** or **spine,** consists of 26 bones: the 24 **vertebrae,** the *sacrum* (SĀ-krum), and the *coccyx* (KOK-siks) or *tailbone.* The vertebral column is subdivided on the basis of vertebral structure (Figure 6-16). The **cervical region** of the vertebral column consists of the seven **cervical vertebrae** of the neck (abbreviated as C_1 to C_7). The cervical region begins at the articulation of C_1 with the occipital condyles of the skull and extends inferiorly to the articulation of C_7 with the first thoracic vertebra. The **thoracic region** consists of the 12 **thoracic vertebrae** (T_1 to T_{12}), each of which articulates with one or more pairs of ribs. The **lumbar region** contains the five **lumbar vertebrae** (L_1 to L_5). The first lumbar vertebra articulates with T_{12}, and the fifth lumbar vertebra articulates with the **sacrum.** The sacrum is a single bone formed by the fusion of the five embryonic vertebrae of the **sacral region.** The **coccygeal region** is made up of the small **coccyx,** which also consists of fused vertebrae. The total length of the adult vertebral column averages 71 cm (28 in.).

Spinal Curvature

The vertebral column is not straight and rigid. The lateral view of the spinal column in Figure 6-16 reveals four **spinal curves.** The *thoracic* and *sacral curves* are called **primary curves** because they

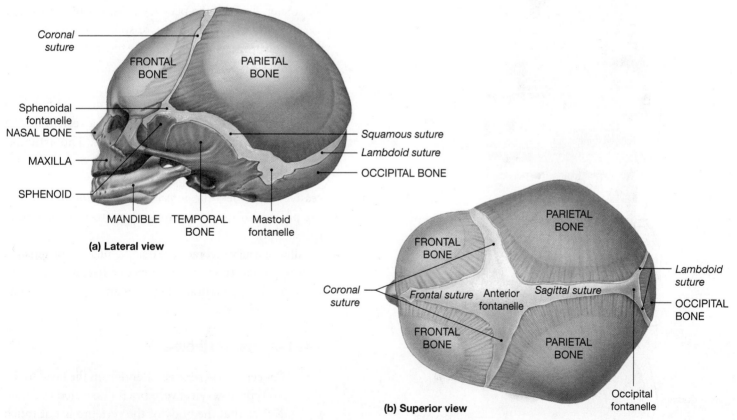

FIGURE 6-15 The Skull of a Newborn. An infant skull contains more individual bones than an adult skull. Many of these bones eventually fuse to create the adult skull. The flat bones of the skull are separated by areas of fibrous connective tissue called fontanelles, which allow for cranial expansion and distortion during birth. By about age 4 these areas disappear, and skull growth is completed.

appear late in fetal development, as the thoracic and abdominal organs enlarge. The *cervical* and *lumbar curves,* known as **secondary curves,** do not appear until months after birth. The cervical curve develops as an infant learns to balance the head upright, and the lumbar curve develops with the ability to stand. When a person is standing, the body's weight must be transmitted through the spinal column to the pelvic girdle and ultimately to the legs. Yet most of the body weight lies in front of the spinal column. The secondary curves bring that weight in line with the body axis. All four spinal curves are fully developed by the time a child is 10 years old.

Several abnormal distortions of spinal curvature may appear during childhood and adolescence. Examples are *kyphosis* (kī-FŌ-sis; exaggerated thoracic curvature), *lordosis* (lor-DŌ-sis; exaggerated lumbar curvature), and *scoliosis* (skō-lē-Ō-sis; an abnormal lateral curvature).

Vertebral Anatomy

Figure 6-17 shows representative vertebrae from three different regions of the vertebral column. Features shared by all vertebrae include a *vertebral body,* a *vertebral arch,* and *articular processes.* The more massive, weight-bearing portion of a vertebra is called the **vertebral body.** The bony faces of the vertebral bodies usually do not contact one another because an **intervertebral disc** of fibrous cartilage lies between them. Intervertebral discs are not found in the sacrum and coccyx, where the vertebrae have fused, or between the first and second cervical vertebrae.

The **vertebral arch** forms the posterior margin of each **vertebral foramen** (plural, *foramina*). Together, the vertebral foramina of successive vertebrae form the **vertebral canal,** which encloses the spinal cord. The vertebral arch has walls, called *pedicles* (PED-i-kulz), and a roof formed by flat layers called *laminae* (LAM-i-nē; singular, *lamina,* a thin plate). *Transverse processes* projecting laterally or dorsolaterally from the pedicles serve as sites for muscle attachment. A *spinous process,* or spinal process, projects posteriorly from where the laminae fuse together. The spinous processes form the bumps that can be felt along the midline of your back.

The **articular processes** arise at the junction between the pedicles and laminae. Each side of a vertebra has a *superior* and *inferior articular process.* The articular processes of successive vertebrae contact one another at the **articular facets.** Gaps between the pedicles of successive vertebrae—the *intervertebral foramina*—permit the passage of nerves running to or from the enclosed spinal cord.

Although all vertebrae have many similar characteristics, some regional structural differences reflect differences in function. The structural differences among the vertebrae are discussed next.

The Cervical Vertebrae

The seven cervical vertebrae extend from the head to the thorax. A typical cervical vertebra is illustrated in **Figure 6-17a.** Notice that the body of the vertebra is not much larger than the size of the vertebral foramen. From the first thoracic vertebra to the sacrum, the diameter of the spinal cord decreases, and so does the size of the verte-

SPINAL CURVES

VERTEBRAL REGIONS

Cervical

Thoracic

Lumbar

Sacral

C₁
C₂
C₃
C₄
C₅
C₆
C₇
T₁
T₂
T₃
T₄
T₅
T₆
T₇
T₈
T₉
T₁₀
T₁₁
T₁₂
L₁
L₂
L₃
L₄
L₅

Cervical

Thoracic

Lumbar

Sacral

Coccygeal

FIGURE 6-16 **The Vertebral Column.** The major regions of the vertebral column and the four spinal curves are shown in this lateral view.

(a) Typical cervical vertebra

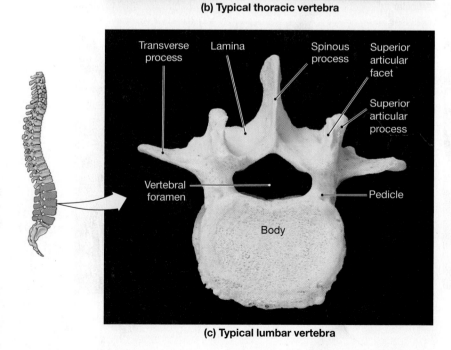

(b) Typical thoracic vertebra

(c) Typical lumbar vertebra

FIGURE 6-17 **Typical Vertebrae of the Cervical, Thoracic, and Lumbar Regions.** Each vertebra is shown in superior view.

bral foramen. At the same time, the vertebral bodies gradually enlarge, because they must bear more weight.

Distinctive features of a typical cervical vertebra include (1) an oval, concave vertebral body; (2) a relatively large vertebral foramen; (3) a stumpy spinous process, usually with a notched tip; and (4) round **transverse foramina** within the transverse processes. These foramina protect important blood vessels supplying the brain.

The first two cervical vertebrae have unique characteristics that allow for specialized movements. The **atlas** (C_1) holds up the head, articulating with the occipital condyles of the skull. It is named after Atlas, who, according to Greek myth, holds the weight of the world on his shoulders. The articulation between the occipital condyles and the atlas permits you to nod (as when indicating "yes"). The atlas, in turn, forms a pivot joint with the **axis** (C_2) through a projection on the axis called the **dens** (*denz*; tooth), or *odontoid process*. This articulation, which permits rotation (as when shaking your head to indicate "no"), is shown in Figure 6-18.

The Thoracic Vertebrae

There are 12 thoracic vertebrae (Figure 6-17b). Distinctive features of a thoracic vertebra include (1) a characteristic heart-shaped body that is more massive than that of a cervical vertebra; (2) a large, slender spinous process that points inferiorly; and (3) *costal facets* on the body (and, in most cases, on the transverse processes) for articulating with the head of one or two pairs of ribs.

The Lumbar Vertebrae

The distinctive features of lumbar vertebrae (Figure 6-17c) include (1) a vertebral body that is thicker and more oval than that of a thoracic vertebra; (2) a relatively massive, stumpy spinous process that projects posteriorly, providing surface area for the attachment of the lower back muscles; and (3) bladelike transverse processes that lack articulations for ribs.

The lumbar vertebrae are the most massive and least mobile, for they support most of the body weight. As you increase the weight on the vertebrae, the intervertebral discs become increasingly important as shock absorbers. The lumbar discs, which are subjected to the most pressure, are the thickest of all. The articulations of lumbar vertebrae limit the stresses on the discs by restricting vertebral motion.

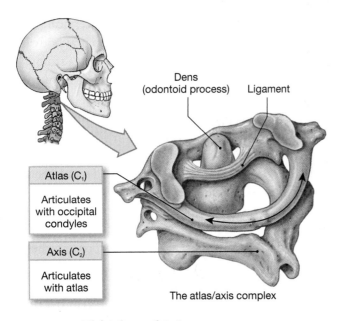

Dens (odontoid process)

Ligament

Atlas (C₁)

Articulates with occipital condyles

Axis (C₂)

Articulates with atlas

The atlas/axis complex

FIGURE 6-18 The Atlas and Axis. The arrows in this drawing indicate the direction of rotation at the articulation between the atlas (C₁) and the axis (C₂).

The Sacrum and Coccyx

The sacrum consists of the fused elements of five sacral vertebrae. It protects the reproductive, digestive, and excretory organs and attaches the axial skeleton to the appendicular skeleton by means of paired articulations with the pelvic girdle. The broad surface area of the sacrum provides an extensive area for the attachment of muscles, especially those responsible for leg movement. Figure 6-19 shows the posterior and anterior surfaces of the sacrum.

Because the sacrum resembles a triangle, the narrow caudal portion is called the **apex,** and the broad superior surface is the **base.** The superior articular processes of the first sacral vertebra articulate with the last lumbar vertebra. The **sacral canal** is a passageway that begins between those processes and extends the length of the sacrum. Nerves and the membranes that line the vertebral canal in the spinal cord continue into the sacral canal. Its inferior end, the *sacral hiatus* (hī-Ā-tus), is covered by connective tissues. A prominent bulge at the anterior tip of the base, the **sacral promontory,** is an important landmark in females during pelvic examinations and during labor and delivery.

The sacral vertebrae begin fusing shortly after puberty and are typically completely fused at ages 25–30. Their fused spinal processes form a series of elevations along the *median sacral crest.* Four pairs of **sacral foramina** open on either side of the median sacral crest.

The coccyx provides an attachment site for a muscle that closes the anal opening. The fusion of the three to five (most

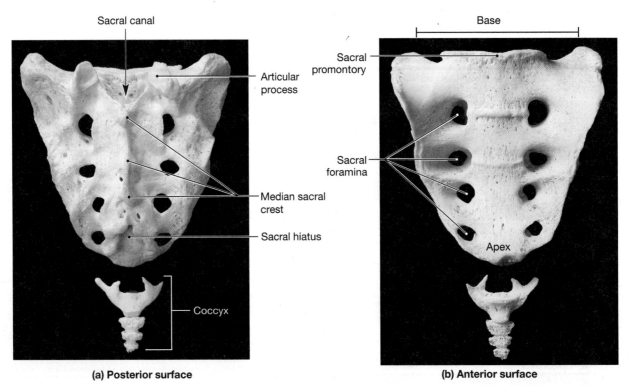

Sacral canal

Articular process

Median sacral crest

Sacral hiatus

Coccyx

(a) Posterior surface

Base

Sacral promontory

Sacral foramina

Apex

(b) Anterior surface

FIGURE 6-19 The Sacrum and Coccyx.

often four) coccygeal vertebrae is not complete until late in adulthood. In elderly people, the coccyx may also fuse with the sacrum.

The Thoracic Cage

The skeleton of the chest, or thoracic cage, consists of the thoracic vertebrae, the ribs, and the sternum (Figure 6-20). It provides bony support for the walls of the thoracic cavity. The ribs and the sternum form the *rib cage*. The thoracic cage protects the heart, lungs, and other internal organs and serves as a base for muscles involved in respiration.

Ribs, or *costal bones,* are elongate, flattened bones that originate on or between the thoracic vertebrae and end in the wall of the thoracic cavity. There are 12 pairs of ribs. The first seven pairs are called **true ribs.** These ribs reach the anterior body wall and are connected to the sternum by separate cartilaginous extensions, the **costal cartilages.** Ribs 8–12 are called the **false ribs** because they do not attach directly to the sternum. The costal cartilages of ribs 8–10 fuse together. This fused cartilage merges with the costal cartilage of rib 7 before it reaches the sternum. The last two pairs of ribs are called **floating ribs** because they have no connection with the sternum.

The adult **sternum,** or breastbone, has three parts. The broad, triangular **manubrium** (ma-NOO-brē-um) articulates with the clavicles of the appendicular skeleton and with the cartilages of the first pair of ribs. The *jugular notch* is the shallow indentation on the superior surface of the manubrium. The elongated **body** ends at the slender **xiphoid** (ZĪ-foyd) **process.** Ossification of the sternum begins at six to ten different centers, and fusion is not complete until at least age 25. The xiphoid process is usually the last of the sternal components to ossify and fuse. Impact or strong pressure can drive it into the liver, causing severe damage. Cardiopulmonary resuscitation (CPR) training strongly emphasizes the proper positioning of the hand to reduce the chances of breaking the xiphoid process or ribs.

With their complex musculature, dual articulations at the vertebrae, and flexible connection to the sternum, the ribs are quite mobile. Because they are curved, their movements affect both the width and the depth of the thoracic cage, increasing or decreasing its volume.

CHECKPOINT

18. The mastoid and styloid processes are found on which skull bones?

19. What bone contains the depression called the sella turcica? What is located in the depression?

20. Which bone of the cranium articulates directly with the vertebral column?

21. During baseball practice, a ball hits Casey in the eye, fracturing the bones directly above and below the orbit. Which bones were broken?

22. What are the functions of the paranasal sinuses?

23. Why would a fracture of the coronoid process of the mandible make it difficult to close the mouth?

24. What signs would you expect to see in a person suffering from a fractured hyoid bone?

25. Joe suffered a hairline fracture at the base of the dens. Which bone is fractured, and where would you find it?

26. In adults, five large vertebrae fuse to form what single structure?

27. Why are the bodies of lumbar vertebrae so large?

28. What are the differences between true ribs and false ribs?

29. Improper administration of CPR (cardiopulmonary resuscitation) could result in a fracture of which bone(s)?

See the blue Answers tab at the back of the book.

6-8 The pectoral girdle and upper limb bones, and the pelvic girdle and lower limb bones, make up the appendicular skeleton

The appendicular skeleton includes the bones of the upper and lower limbs, and the supporting bones of the pectoral and pelvic girdles that connect the limbs to the trunk.

THE PECTORAL GIRDLE

Each upper limb articulates with the trunk at the pectoral girdle, or *shoulder girdle.* The pectoral girdle consists of two broad, flat **scapulae** (SKAP-ū-lē; singular, *scapula,* SKAP-ū-luh; or *shoulder blades*) and two slender, curved **clavicles** (KLAV-i-kulz; or *collarbones*) (Figure 6-9). Each clavicle articulates with the manubrium of the sternum; these are the only direct connections between the pectoral girdle and the axial skeleton. Skeletal muscles support and position each scapula, which has no bony or ligamentous connections to the thoracic cage.

Movements of the clavicle and scapula position the shoulder joint and provide a base for arm movement. Once the shoulder joint is in position, muscles that originate on the pectoral girdle help to move the arm. The surfaces of the scapulae and clavicles are, therefore, extremely important as sites for muscle attachment.

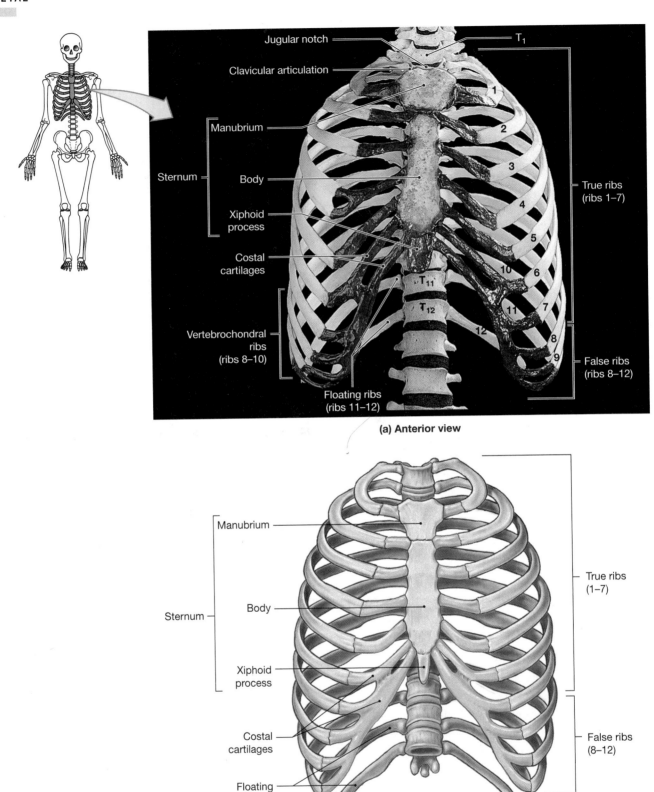

(a) Anterior view

Jugular notch

Clavicular articulation

Manubrium

Sternum

Body

Xiphoid process

Costal cartilages

Vertebrochondral ribs (ribs 8–10)

Floating ribs (ribs 11–12)

T₁

True ribs (ribs 1–7)

T₁₁

T₁₂

False ribs (ribs 8–12)

Manubrium

Sternum

Body

Xiphoid process

Costal cartilages

Floating ribs

True ribs (1–7)

False ribs (8–12)

(b)

FIGURE 6-20 **The Thoracic Cage.** Anterior views of the ribs, sternum, and costal cartilages are shown **(a)** in a photograph of a skeleton and **(b)** diagrammatically.

The Clavicle

The S-shaped clavicle, shown in **Figure 6-21**, articulates with the manubrium of the sternum at its *sternal end* and with the *acromion* (a-KRŌ-mē-on), a process of the scapula, at its *acromial end*. The smooth superior surface of the clavicle lies just beneath the skin. The rough inferior surface of the acromial end is marked by prominent lines and tubercles, attachment sites for muscles and ligaments.

The clavicles are relatively small and fragile, so fractures are fairly common. For example, you can fracture a clavicle in a simple fall if you land on your hand with your arm outstretched. Fortunately, most fractures of the clavicle heal rapidly without a cast.

The Scapula

The anterior surface of the *body* of each scapula forms a broad triangle bounded by the **superior, medial,** and **lateral borders** (**Figure 6-22**). Muscles that position the scapula attach along these edges. The head of the scapula at the intersection of the lateral and superior borders forms a broad process that supports the shallow, cup-shaped **glenoid cavity,** or *glenoid fossa* (FOS-sah). ∞ p. 153 At the glenoid cavity, the scapula articulates with the proximal end of the humerus to form the *shoulder joint.* The depression in the anterior surface of the body of the scapula is called the **subscapular fossa.** The *subscapularis muscle* attaches here and to the humerus, the proximal bone of the upper limb.

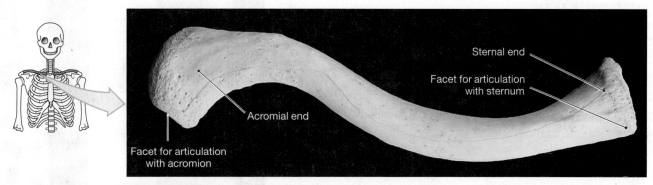

FIGURE 6-21 The Clavicle. The right clavicle is shown in a superior view.

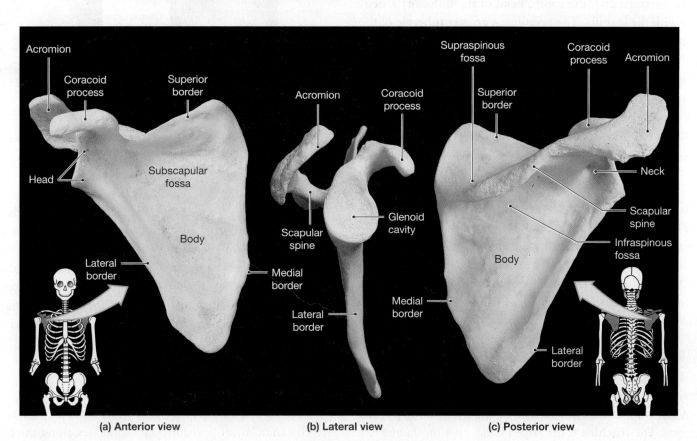

(a) Anterior view   **(b) Lateral view**   **(c) Posterior view**

FIGURE 6-22 The Scapula. This photograph shows the major landmarks on the right scapula.

Figure 6-22b shows a lateral view of the scapula and the two large processes that extend over the glenoid cavity. The smaller, anterior projection is the **coracoid** (KOR-uh-koyd) **process.** The **acromion** is the larger, posterior process. If you run your fingers along the superior surface of the shoulder joint, you will feel this process. The acromion articulates with the distal end of the clavicle.

The **scapular spine** divides the posterior surface of the scapula into two regions (Figure 6-22c). The area superior to the spine is the **supraspinous fossa** (*supra-*, above); the *supraspinatus muscle* attaches here. The region below the spine is the **infraspinous fossa** (*infra-*, beneath), where the *infraspinatus muscle* attaches. Both muscles are also attached to the humerus.

THE UPPER LIMB

The skeleton of each upper limb consists of the bones of the arm, forearm, wrist, and hand. Anatomically, the term *arm* refers only to the proximal portion of the upper limb (from shoulder to elbow), not to the entire limb. ∞ p. 16 The arm, or *brachium*, contains a single bone, the **humerus,** which extends from the scapula to the elbow.

The Humerus

At its proximal end, the round **head** of the humerus articulates with the scapula. The prominent **greater tubercle** of the humerus is a rounded projection near the lateral surface of the head (Figure 6-23). It establishes the lateral contour of the shoulder. The **lesser tubercle** lies more anteriorly, separated from the greater tubercle by a deep *intertubercular groove.* Muscles are attached to both tubercles, and a large tendon runs along the groove. The *anatomical neck* lies between the tubercles and below the surface of the head. Distal to the tubercles, the narrow *surgical neck* corresponds to the region of growing bone, the *epiphyseal cartilage.* ∞ p. 148 The surgical neck earned its name by being a common fracture site.

The proximal shaft of the humerus is round in section. The elevated **deltoid tuberosity** that runs along the lateral border of the shaft is named after the *deltoid muscle,* which attaches to it.

Distally, the posterior surface of the shaft flattens, and the humerus expands to either side, forming a broad triangle. **Medial** and **lateral epicondyles** project to either side, providing additional surface area for muscle attachment, and the smooth **condyle** dominates the inferior surface of the humerus. At the condyle, the humerus articulates with the bones of the forearm, the *radius* and *ulna.*

A low ridge crosses the condyle, dividing it into two distinct regions. The **trochlea** is the large medial portion shaped like

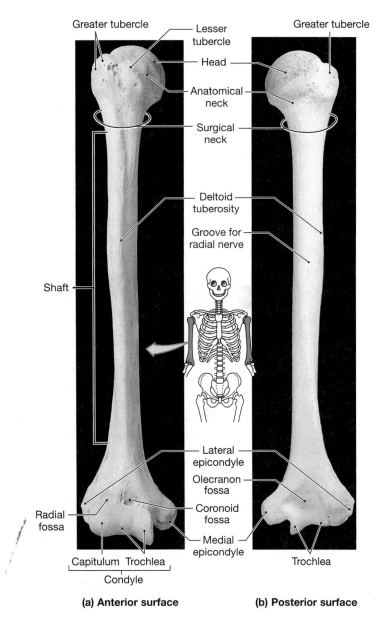

(a) Anterior surface   (b) Posterior surface

FIGURE 6-23 The Humerus. Major landmarks on the right humerus are labeled.

a spool or pulley (*trochlea*, a pulley). The trochlea extends from the base of the **coronoid** (*corona*, crown) **fossa** on the anterior surface to the **olecranon** (ō-LEK-ruh-non) **fossa** on the posterior surface. These depressions accept projections from the surface of the ulna as the elbow reaches its limits of motion. The **capitulum** forms the lateral region of the condyle. A shallow **radial fossa** proximal to the capitulum accommodates a small projection on the radius.

The Radius and Ulna

The **radius** and **ulna** are the bones of the forearm (Figure 6-24). In the anatomical position, the radius lies along the lateral

Olecranon
Head
Neck
RADIUS
Ulnar notch
Styloid process of radius

Trochlear notch
Coronoid process
Radial notch
Ulnar tuberosity
Radial tuberosity
ULNA
Head of ulna
Styloid process of ulna
Articular surface

(a) Anterior view

ULNA — RADIUS

(b) Pronation: Anterior view

FIGURE 6-24 The Radius and Ulna. (a) This photograph provides an anterior view of the bones of the right forearm. **(b)** Notice the changes that occur during pronation.

(thumb) side of the forearm while the ulna provides medial support of the forearm (Figure 6-24a).

The **olecranon** of the ulna is the point of the elbow. On its anterior surface, the **trochlear notch** articulates with the trochlea of the humerus at the elbow joint. The olecranon forms the superior lip of the notch, and the **coronoid process** forms its inferior lip. At the limit of *extension,* when the arm and forearm form a straight line, the olecranon swings into the olecranon fossa on the posterior surface of the humerus. At the limit of *flexion,* when the arm and forearm form a V, the coronoid process projects into the coronoid fossa on the anterior surface of the humerus. Lateral to the coronoid process, a smooth **radial notch** accommodates the head of the radius.

A fibrous sheet connects the lateral margin of the ulna to the radius along its length. Near the wrist, the ulnar shaft ends at a disc-shaped head whose posterior margin bears a short **styloid process.** The distal end of the ulna is separated from the wrist

joint by a pad of cartilage, and only the large distal portion of the radius participates in the wrist joint. The styloid process of the radius assists in the stabilization of the joint by preventing lateral movement of the bones of the wrist (*carpal bones*).

A narrow *neck* extends from the head of the radius to the **radial tuberosity,** which marks the attachment site of the *biceps brachii,* a large muscle on the anterior surface of the arm that flexes the forearm. The disc-shaped head of the radius articulates with the capitulum of the humerus at the elbow joint and with the ulna at the *radial notch.* This proximal articulation with the ulna allows the radius to roll across the ulna, rotating the palm in a movement known as *pronation* (Figure 6-24b). The reverse movement, which returns the forearm to the anatomical position, is called *supination.*

Bones of the Wrist and Hand

The wrist, palm, and fingers are supported by 27 bones (Figure 6-25). The eight **carpal bones** of the wrist, or *carpus,* form two rows. There are four proximal carpal bones: (1) the *scaphoid bone,* (2) the *lunate bone,* (3) the *triquetrum bone,* and (4) the *pisiform* (PIS-i-form) *bone.* There are also four distal carpal bones: (1) the *trapezium,* (2) the *trapezoid bone,* (3) the *capitate bone,* and (4) the *hamate bone.* Joints between the carpal bones permit a limited degree of sliding and twisting.

Five **metacarpal** (met-uh-KAR-pul) **bones** articulate with the distal carpal bones and form the palm of the hand. The metacarpal bones in turn articulate with the finger bones, or **phalanges** (fa-LAN-jēz; singular, *phalanx*). Each hand has 14 phalangeal bones. Four of the fingers contain three phalanges each (proximal, middle, and distal), but the thumb or **pollex** (POL-eks) has only two phalanges (proximal and distal).

THE PELVIC GIRDLE

The pelvic girdle articulates with the thigh bones (Figure 6-9). Because of the stresses involved in weight bearing and locomotion, the bones of the pelvic girdle and lower limbs are more massive than those of the pectoral girdle and upper limbs. The pelvic girdle is also much more firmly attached to the axial skeleton.

The pelvic girdle consists of two large hip bones, or **coxal bones.** Each hip bone, or coxal bone, forms by the fusion of three bones: an **ilium** (IL-ē-um), an **ischium** (IS-kē-um), and a **pubis** (PŪ-bis) (Figure 6-26a,b). Dorsally, the hip bones articulate with

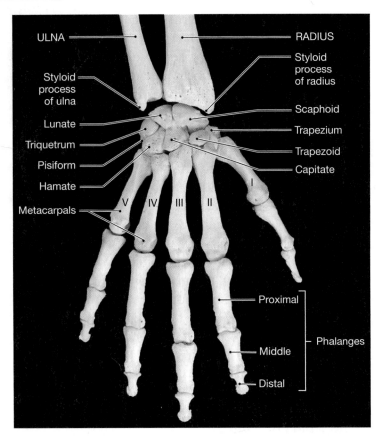

FIGURE 6-25 **Bones of the Wrist and Hand.** A posterior view of the right hand is shown.

the sacrum at the **sacroiliac joint** (Figure 6-26c). Ventrally, the hip bones are connected at the *pubic symphysis*, a fibrous cartilage pad. At the hip joint on either side, the head of the femur (thighbone) articulates with the curved surface of the **acetabulum** (as-ē-TAB-ū-lum; *acetabulum*, a vinegar cup).

The Coxal Bone (Hip Bone)

The ilium is the most superior and largest component of the coxal bone (Figure 6-26a,b). Above the acetabulum, the ilium forms a broad, curved surface that provides an extensive area for the attachment of muscles, tendons, and ligaments. The superior margin of the ilium, the **iliac crest,** marks the sites of attachments of both ligaments and muscles (Figure 6-26c). Near the superior and posterior margin of the acetabulum, the ilium fuses with the ischium. The inferior surface of the ischium, the *ischial tuberosity* (not shown), supports the body's weight when sitting.

The fusion of a narrow branch of the ischium with a branch of the pubis completes the encirclement of the **obturator** (OB-tū-rā-tor) **foramen.** This space is closed by a sheet of collagen fibers whose inner and outer surfaces provide a base for the attachment of muscles and visceral structures.

The anterior and medial surface of the pubis contains a roughened area that marks the **pubic symphysis,** an articulation with the pubis of the opposite side. The pubic symphysis limits movement between the two pubic bones.

(c) Anterior view

FIGURE 6-26 **The Pelvis.** The different colors indicate the components of **(a)** the pelvis in an anterior view and **(b)** the right coxal bone in a lateral view. The photograph in **(c)** shows an anterior view of the pelvis of an adult male.

The Pelvis

The **pelvis** consists of the two hip bones, the sacrum, and the coccyx (Figure 6-26a). It is, thus, a composite structure that includes portions of both the appendicular and axial skeletons. An extensive network of ligaments connects the sacrum with the iliac crests, the ischia, and the pubic bones. Other ligaments tie the ilia to the posterior lumbar vertebrae. These interconnections increase the structural stability of the pelvis.

The shape of the pelvis of a female is somewhat different from that of a male (Figure 6-27). Some of the differences result from variations in body size and muscle mass. For example, in females the pelvis is generally smoother, lighter in weight, and has less prominent markings. Other differences are adaptations for childbearing and are necessary for supporting the weight of the developing fetus and easing passage of the newborn through the pelvic outlet during delivery. The *pelvic outlet* is the inferior opening of the pelvis bounded by the coccyx, the ischia, and the pubic symphysis. Compared to males, females have a relatively broad, low pelvis; a larger pelvic outlet; and a broader *pubic angle* (the angle between the pubic bones).

THE LOWER LIMB

The skeleton of each lower limb consists of a *femur,* the thighbone; a *patella,* the kneecap; a *tibia* and a *fibula,* the bones of the leg; and the bones of the ankle and foot.

The Femur

The **femur,** or *thighbone,* is the longest and heaviest bone in the body (Figure 6-28). The rounded epiphysis, or head, of the femur articulates with the pelvis at the acetabulum. The **greater** and **lesser trochanters** are large, rough projections that extend laterally from the juncture of the neck and the shaft. Both trochanters develop where large tendons attach to the femur. On the posterior surface of the femur, a prominent elevation, the **linea aspera,** marks the attachment of powerful muscles that pull the shaft of the femur toward the midline, a movement called *adduction* (*ad-,* toward + *duco,* to lead).

The proximal shaft of the femur is round in cross section. More distally, the shaft becomes more flattened and ends in two large **epicondyles** (**lateral** and **medial**). The inferior surfaces of the epicondyles form the **lateral** and **medial condyles.** The lateral and medial condyles form part of the knee joint.

The **patella** (*kneecap*) glides over the smooth anterior surface, or *patellar surface,* between the lateral and medial condyles. ∞ p. 155 The patella forms within the tendon of the *quadriceps femoris,* a group of muscles that straighten the knee.

The Tibia and Fibula

The **tibia** (TIB-ē-uh), or *shinbone,* is the large medial bone of the leg (Figure 6-29). The lateral and medial condyles of the femur articulate with the *lateral* and *medial condyles* of the **tibia.** The *patellar ligament* connects the patella to the **tibial tuberosity** just below the knee joint.

Male

90° or less pubic angle

Pelvic outlet, relatively narrow

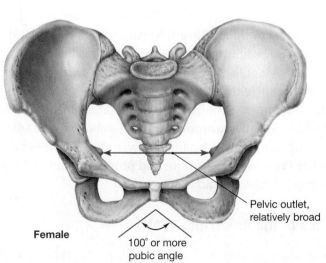

Female

100° or more pubic angle

Pelvic outlet, relatively broad

FIGURE 6-27 **Differences in the Anatomy of the Pelvis in Males and Females.**

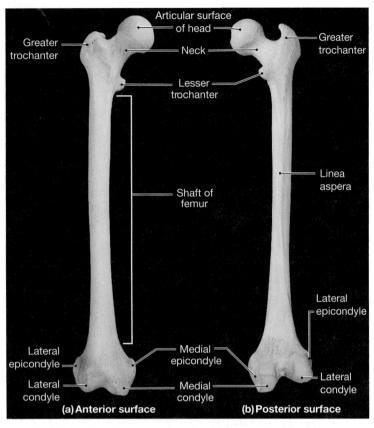

FIGURE 6-28 **The Femur.** The labels indicate the various bone markings on the right femur.

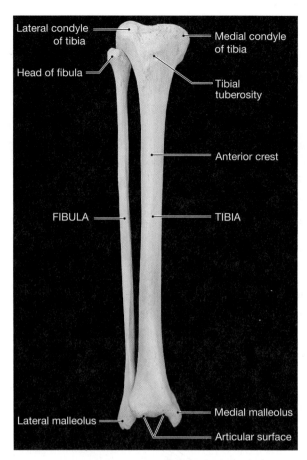

FIGURE 6-29 **The Right Tibia and Fibula.** These bones are shown in an anterior view.

A projecting **anterior crest** extends almost the entire length of the anterior tibial surface. The tibia broadens at its distal end into a large process, the **medial malleolus** (ma-LĒ-o-lus; *malleolus,* hammer). The inferior surface of the tibia forms a joint with the proximal bone of the ankle; the medial malleolus provides medial support for the ankle.

The slender **fibula** (FIB-ū-luh) parallels the lateral border of the tibia. The fibula articulates with the tibia inferior to the lateral condyle of the tibia. The fibula does not articulate with the femur or help transfer weight to the ankle and foot. However, it is an important surface for muscle attachment, and the distal **lateral malleolus** provides lateral stability to the ankle. A fibrous membrane extending between the two bones helps stabilize their relative positions and provides additional surface area for muscle attachment.

Bones of the Ankle and Foot

The ankle, or *tarsus,* includes seven separate **tarsal bones** (Figure 6-30a): (1) the *talus,* (2) the *calcaneus,* (3) the *navicular bone,* (4) the *cuboid bone,* and (5–7) the *first, second,* and *third*

cuneiform bones. Only the proximal tarsal bone, the **talus,** articulates with the tibia and fibula. The talus then passes the body's weight to the ground through bones of the foot.

When you are standing normally, most of your weight is transmitted to the ground through the talus to the large **calcaneus** (kal-KĀ-nē-us), or *heel bone* (Figure 6-30b). The posterior projection of the calcaneus is the attachment site for the *calcaneal tendon,* or *Achilles tendon,* which arises from the calf muscles. These muscles raise the heel and depress the sole, as when you stand on tiptoes. The rest of the body weight is passed through the cuboid bone and cuneiform bones to the **metatarsal bones,** which support the sole of the foot.

The basic organizational pattern of the metatarsals and phalanges of the foot resembles that of the hand. The metatarsals are numbered by Roman numerals I to V from medial to lateral, and their distal ends form the ball of the foot. Like the thumb, the great toe (or **hallux**) has two phalanges; like the fingers, the other toes each contain three phalanges.

(a) Superior view, right foot

FIGURE 6-30 **The Bones of the Ankle and Foot. (a)** This photograph shows the bones of the right foot in superior view. **(b)** This medial view shows the relative positions of the tarsal and metatarsal bones. Notice how the orientation of the tarsal bones conveys the weight of the body to the heel and the sole of the foot.

(b) Medial view, right foot

CHECKPOINT

30. In what way would a broken clavicle affect the mobility of the scapula?

31. The rounded projections on either side of the elbow are parts of which bone?

32. Which bone of the forearm is lateral in the anatomical position?

33. Which three bones make up the hip?

34. The fibula neither participates in the knee joint nor bears weight. When it is fractured, however, walking becomes difficult. Why?

35. While jumping off the back steps at his house, 10-year-old Cesar lands on his right heel and breaks his foot. Which bone is most likely broken?

See the blue Answers tab at the back of the book.

6-9 Joints are categorized according to their range of motion or anatomical organization

Joints, or **articulations,** exist wherever two bones meet. The structure of a joint determines the type of movement that may occur. Each joint reflects a compromise between the need for strength and stability and the need for movement. When movement is not required, or when movement could actually be dangerous, joints can be very strong. For example, the sutures of the skull are such intricate and extensive joints that they lock the elements together as if they were a single bone. At other joints, movement is more important than strength. For example, the articulation at the shoulder permits a range of arm movement that is limited more by the surrounding muscles than by joint structure. The joint itself is relatively weak, and as a result shoulder injuries are rather common.

Joints can be classified according to their structure or function. The structural classification is based on the anatomy of the joint. In this framework, joints are classified as **fibrous, cartilaginous,** or **synovial** (si-NŌ-vē-ul). The first two types reflect the type of connective tissue binding them together. Such joints permit either no movement or slight movements. Synovial joints are surrounded by fibrous tissue, and the ends of bones are covered by cartilage that prevents bone-to-bone contact. Such joints permit free movement.

In a functional classification—one we will emphasize—joints are classified according to the range of motion they permit. An immovable joint is a **synarthrosis** (sin-ar-THRŌ-sis; *syn-,* together + *arthros,* joint); a slightly movable joint is an **amphiarthrosis** (am-fē-ar-THRŌ-sis; *amphi-,* on both sides);

and a freely movable joint is a **diarthrosis** (dī-ar-THRŌ-sis; *dia-*, through), or *synovial joint.* Table 6-2 presents a functional classification of articulations, relates it to the structural classification scheme, and provides some examples.

IMMOVABLE JOINTS (SYNARTHROSES)

At a synarthrosis, the bony edges are quite close together and may even interlock. A synarthrosis can be fibrous or cartilaginous. Two examples of fibrous immovable joints can be found in the skull. In a **suture** (*sutura,* a sewing together), the bones of the skull are interlocked and bound together by dense connective tissue. In a **gomphosis** (gom-FŌ-sis; *gomphosis,* a bolting together), a ligament binds each tooth in the mouth within a bony socket (*alveolus*).

A rigid, cartilaginous connection is called a **synchondrosis** (sin-kon-DRŌ-sis; *syn,* together + *chondros,* cartilage). The connection between the first pair of ribs and the sternum is a synchondrosis. Another example is the epiphyseal cartilage that connects the diaphysis and epiphysis in a growing long bone. ∞ p. 148

SLIGHTLY MOVABLE JOINTS (AMPHIARTHROSES)

An amphiarthrosis permits very limited movement, and the bones are usually farther apart than in a synarthrosis. Structurally, an amphiarthrosis can be fibrous or cartilaginous.

A **syndesmosis** (sin-dez-MŌ-sis; *desmos,* a band or ligament) is a fibrous joint connected by a ligament. The distal articulation between the two bones of the leg, the tibia and fibula, is an example. A **symphysis** is a cartilaginous joint because the bones are separated by a broad disc or pad of fibrous cartilage. The articulations between the spinal vertebrae (at an *intervertebral disc*) and the anterior connection between the two pubic bones are examples of a symphysis.

FREELY MOVABLE JOINTS (DIARTHROSES)

Diarthroses, or **synovial joints,** permit a wide range of motion. The basic structure of a synovial joint was introduced in Chapter 4 in the discussion of synovial membranes. ∞ p. 112 Figure 6-31a shows the structure of a representative synovial joint.

Synovial joints are typically found at the ends of long bones, such as those of the arms and legs. Under normal conditions the bony surfaces do not contact one another, for they are covered with special **articular cartilages.** The joint is surrounded by a fibrous **joint capsule,** or *articular capsule,* and the inner surfaces of the joint cavity are lined with a synovial membrane. **Synovial fluid** within the joint cavity provides lubrication that reduces the friction between the moving surfaces in the joint.

In some complex joints, additional padding lies between the opposing articular surfaces. An example of such shock-absorbing,

TABLE 6-2 **A Functional and Structural Classification of Articulations**

FUNCTIONAL CATEGORY	STRUCTURAL CATEGORY	DESCRIPTION	EXAMPLE
Synarthrosis (no movement)	**Fibrous**		
	Suture	Fibrous connections plus interlocked surfaces	Between the bones of the skull
	Gomphosis	Fibrous connections plus insertion in bony socket (alveolus)	Between the teeth and jaws
	Cartilaginous		
	Synchondrosis	Interposition of cartilage plate	Epiphyseal cartilages
Amphiarthrosis (little movement)	**Fibrous**		
	Syndesmosis	Ligamentous connection	Between the tibia and fibula
	Cartilaginous		
	Symphysis	Connection by a fibrous cartilage pad	Between right and left halves of pelvis; between adjacent vertebrae of spinal column
Diarthrosis (free movement)	**Synovial**	Complex joint bounded by joint capsule and containing synovial fluid	Numerous; subdivided by range of motion (Figure 6-35)

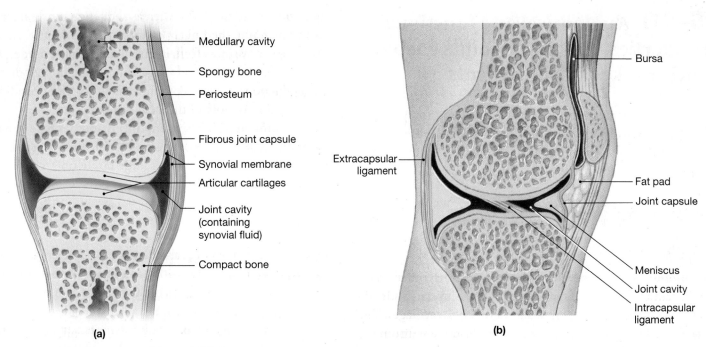

FIGURE 6-31 **The Structure of Synovial Joints.** These diagrammatic sectional views show **(a)** a representative simple articulation and **(b)** the knee joint.

Clinical Note
Rheumatism and Arthritis

Rheumatism (ROO-muh-tizum) is a general term describing pain and stiffness arising in the skeletal or muscular systems, or both. There are several major forms of rheumatism. **Arthritis** (ar-THRĪ-tis) includes all of the rheumatic diseases that affect synovial joints. Arthritis always involves damage to the articular cartilages, but the specific cause can vary. Arthritis can result from bacterial or viral infection, injury to the joint, metabolic problems, or severe physical stresses.

Osteoarthritis (os-tē-ō-ar-THRĪ-tis), also known as *degenerative arthritis,* or *degenerative joint disease (DJD),* usually affects individuals age 60 or older. This disease can result from cumulative wear and tear at the joint surfaces or from genetic factors affecting collagen formation. In the U.S. population, 25 percent of women and 15 percent of men over age 60 show signs of this disease. **Rheumatoid arthritis** is an inflammatory condition that affects roughly 2.5 percent of the adult population. At least some cases result when the immune response mistakenly attacks the joint tissues. Allergies, bacteria, viruses, and genetic factors have all been proposed as contributing to or triggering the destructive inflammation.

Regular exercise, physical therapy, and drugs that reduce inflammation (such as aspirin) can slow the progress of the disease. Surgical procedures can realign or redesign the affected joint, and in extreme cases involving the hip, knee, elbow, or shoulder, the defective joint can be replaced by an artificial one.

fibrocartilage pads are the **menisci** (me-NIS-kē; *meniscus,* crescent) in the knee, shown in Figure 6-31b. Also present in such joints are **fat pads,** which protect the articular cartilages and act as packing material. When the bones move, the fat pads fill in the spaces created as the joint cavity changes shape.

The joint capsule that surrounds the entire joint is continuous with the periostea of the articulating bones. In addition, **ligaments** joining bone to bone may be found outside or inside the joint capsule. Where a tendon or ligament rubs against other tissues, **bursae** (BUR-sē; singular *bursa,* a pouch)—small packets of connective tissue containing synovial fluid—form to reduce friction and act as shock absorbers. Bursae are characteristic of many synovial joints and may also occur surrounding a tendon as a tubular sheath, covering a bone, or within other connective tissues exposed to friction or pressure.

CHECKPOINT

36. Name and describe the three types of joints as classified by the amount of movement possible.

37. In a newborn, the large bones of the skull are joined by fibrous connective tissue. Which type of joint are these? These skull bones later grow, interlock, and form immovable joints. Which type of joint are these?

See the blue Answers tab at the back of the book.

6-10 Anatomical and functional properties of synovial joints enable various skeletal movements

Synovial joints are involved in all of our day-to-day movements. In discussions of motion at synovial joints, phrases such as "bend the leg" or "raise the arm" are not sufficiently precise. Anatomists use descriptive terms that have specific meanings.

TYPES OF MOVEMENT

Gliding

In **gliding,** two opposing surfaces slide past each other. Gliding occurs between the surfaces of articulating carpal bones and articulating tarsal bones, and between the clavicles and sternum. The movement can occur in almost any direction, but the amount of movement is slight. Rotation is usually prevented by the joint capsule and associated ligaments.

Angular Motion

Examples of angular motion are *flexion, extension, adduction, abduction,* and *circumduction.* The description of each movement refers to an individual in the anatomical position.

Flexion (FLEK-shun) is movement in the anterior-posterior plane that reduces the angle between the articulating elements (Figure 6-32a). **Extension** occurs in the same plane, but it increases the angle between articulating elements. When you bring your head toward your chest, you flex the intervertebral joints of the neck. When you bend down to touch your toes, you flex the entire vertebral column. Extension reverses these movements.

Flexion at the shoulder joint or hip joint moves the limbs forward (*anteriorly*), whereas extension moves them back (*posteriorly*). Flexion of the wrist joint moves the hand forward, and extension moves it back. In each of these examples, extension can be continued past the anatomical position, in which case **hyperextension** occurs. You can also hyperextend the neck, a movement that enables you to gaze at the ceiling. Hyperextension of other joints is prevented by ligaments, bony processes, or soft tissues.

Abduction (*ab-,* from) is movement *away from the longitudinal axis of the body* in the frontal plane. For example, swinging the upper limb to the side is abduction of the limb (Figure 6-32b). Moving it back to the anatomical position is **adduction** (*ad,* to). Adduction of the wrist moves the heel of the hand toward the body, whereas abduction moves it farther away. Spreading the fingers or toes apart abducts them, because they move *away* from a central digit (finger or toe), as in Figure 6-32c. Bringing them together is adduction. Abduction and adduction always refer to movements of the appendicular skeleton, not to those of the axial skeleton.

Circumduction (*circum,* around) is another type of angular motion. An example of circumduction is moving your arm in a loop, as when drawing a large circle on a chalkboard (Figure 6-32d).

Rotation

Rotational movements are also described with reference to a figure in the anatomical position. **Rotation** involves turning around the longitudinal axis of the body or a limb. For example, you may rotate your head to look to one side or rotate your arm to screw in a lightbulb. Rotational movements are illustrated in Figure 6-33.

The articulations between the radius and ulna permit the rotation of the distal end of the radius across the anterior surface of the ulna. This rotation moves the wrist and hand from palm-facing-front to palm-facing-back. This motion is called **pronation** (prō-NĀ-shun). The opposing movement, in which the palm is turned forward, is **supination** (soo-pi-NĀ-shun). ∞ p. 169

Special Movements

Some specific terms are used to describe unusual or special types of movement (Figure 6-34).

- **Inversion** (*in-,* into + *vertere,* to turn) is a twisting motion of the foot that turns the sole inward, elevating the medial edge of the sole. The opposite movement is called **eversion** (ē-VER-zhun; *e-,* out).

- **Dorsiflexion** is flexion of the ankle joint and elevation of the sole, as when you dig in your heel. **Plantar flexion** (*planta,* sole), the opposite movement, extends the ankle joint and elevates the heel, as when you stand on tiptoe.

- **Opposition** is the movement of the thumb toward the palm or fingertips that enables you to grasp and hold an object.

- **Protraction** occurs when you move a part of the body anteriorly in the horizontal plane. **Retraction** is the reverse movement. You protract your jaw when you grasp your upper lip with your lower teeth, and you protract your clavicles when you cross your arms.

- **Elevation** and **depression** occur when a structure moves in a superior or inferior direction, respectively. You depress your mandible when you open your mouth and elevate it as you close it.

FIGURE 6-32 Angular Movements. The red dots mark the locations of joints involved in the movements.

(a)

(b)

(c)

(d)

Head rotation

Right rotation

Left rotation

Lateral rotation

Medial rotation

(a)

Supination

Pronation

(b)

FIGURE 6-33 **Rotational Movements.**

Eversion   Inversion

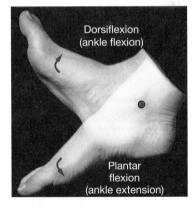

Dorsiflexion (ankle flexion)

Plantar flexion (ankle extension)

Opposition

Retraction   Protraction

Depression

Elevation

FIGURE 6-34 **Special Movements.**

A STRUCTURAL CLASSIFICATION OF SYNOVIAL JOINTS

Based on the shapes of the articulating surfaces, synovial joints can be described as *gliding, hinge, pivot, ellipsoidal, saddle,* or *ball-and-socket joints* (Figure 6-35). Each type of joint permits a different type and range of motion:

- **Gliding joints** have flattened or slightly curved faces (Figure 6-35a). The relatively flat articular surfaces slide across one another, but the amount of movement is very slight. Although rotation is theoretically possible at such a joint, ligaments usually prevent or restrict such movement. Gliding joints are found at the ends of the clavicles, between the carpal bones, between the tarsal bones, and between the articular facets of adjacent vertebrae.

- **Hinge joints** permit angular movement in a single plane, like the opening and closing of a door (Figure 6-35b). Examples are the joint between the occipital bone and the atlas (in the axial skeleton), and the elbow, knee, ankle, and interphalangeal joints of the appendicular skeleton.

- **Pivot joints** permit rotation only (Figure 6-35c). A pivot joint between the atlas and axis enables you to rotate your head to either side, and another between the head of the radius and the proximal shaft of the ulna permits pronation and supination of the palm.

- In an **ellipsoidal joint** (or *condyloid joint*), an oval articular face nestles within a depression on the opposing surface (Figure 6-35d). Angular motion occurs in two planes, along or across the length of the oval. Ellipsoidal joints connect the radius with the proximal carpal bones, the phalanges of the fingers with the metacarpal bones, and the phalanges of the toes with the metatarsal bones.

- **Saddle joints** have articular faces that fit together like a rider in a saddle (Figure 6-35e). Each face is concave on one axis and convex on the other, and the opposing faces nest together. This arrangement permits angular motion, including circumduction, but prevents rotation. The carpometacarpal joint at the base of the thumb is the best example of a saddle joint, and twiddling your thumbs will demonstrate the possible movements.

- In a **ball-and-socket joint,** the round head of one bone rests within a cup-shaped depression in another bone (Figure 6-35f). All combinations of movements, including circumduction and rotation, can be performed at ball-and-socket joints. Examples are the shoulder and hip joints.

The Big Picture

A joint cannot be both highly mobile and very strong. The greater the mobility, the weaker the joint, because mobile joints rely on support from muscles and ligaments rather than solid bone-to-bone connections.

CHECKPOINT

38. Give the proper term for each of the following types of motion: (a) moving the humerus away from the longitudinal axis of the body, (b) turning the palms so that they face forward, and (c) bending the elbow.

39. Which movements are associated with hinge joints?

See the blue Answers tab at the back of the book.

6-11 Intervertebral articulations and appendicular articulations demonstrate functional differences in support and mobility

This section describes examples of articulations that demonstrate important functional principles. We will first consider the *intervertebral articulations* of the axial skeleton. We will then proceed to a discussion of four *synovial articulations* of the appendicular skeleton: the shoulder and elbow of the upper limb, and the hip and knee of the lower limb.

INTERVERTEBRAL ARTICULATIONS

The vertebrae from the axis to the sacrum articulate with one another in two ways: (1) at gliding joints between the *superior* and *inferior articular processes,* and (2) at *symphyseal joints* between the vertebral bodies (Figure 6-36). Articulations between the superior and inferior articular processes of adjacent vertebrae permit small movements that are associated with flexion and rotation of the vertebral column. Little gliding occurs between adjacent vertebral bodies.

Except for the first cervical vertebra, the vertebrae are separated and cushioned by pads called *intervertebral discs.* Each intervertebral disc consists of a tough outer layer of fibrous cartilage. The collagen fibers of that layer attach the discs to adjacent vertebrae. The fibrous cartilage surrounds a soft, elastic,

(a) Gliding joint

(b) Hinge joint

(c) Pivot joint

(d) Ellipsoidal joint

(e) Saddle joint

(f) Ball-and-socket joint

FIGURE 6-35 **A Functional Classification of Synovial Joints.**

and gelatinous core, which gives intervertebral discs resiliency and enables them to act as shock absorbers, compressing and distorting when stressed. This resiliency prevents bone-to-bone contact that might damage the vertebrae or jolt the spinal cord and brain.

Shortly after physical maturity is reached, the gelatinous mass within each disc begins to degenerate, and the "cushion" becomes less effective. Over the same period, the outer fibrous cartilage loses its elasticity. If the stresses are sufficient, the inner mass may break through the surrounding fibrous cartilage and protrude beyond the intervertebral space. This condition, called a *herniated disc,* further reduces disc function. The term *slipped disc* is often used to describe this problem, although the disc does not actually slip. Intervertebral discs also make a significant contribution to an individual's height; they account for roughly one-quarter of the length of the spinal column above the sacrum. As we grow older, the water content of each disc decreases; this loss accounts for the characteristic decrease in height with advancing age.

ARTICULATIONS OF THE UPPER LIMB

The shoulder, elbow, and wrist are responsible for positioning the hand, which performs precise and controlled movements. The shoulder has great mobility, the elbow has great strength, and the wrist makes fine adjustments in the orientation of the palm and fingers.

The Shoulder Joint

The shoulder joint permits the greatest range of motion of any joint in the body. Because it is also the most frequently dislocated joint, it provides an excellent demonstration of the principle that stability must be sacrificed to obtain mobility.

Figure 6-37 shows the ball-and-socket structure of the shoulder joint. The relatively loose joint capsule extends from the scapular neck to the humerus, and this oversized capsule permits an extensive range of motion. Bursae at the shoulder, like those at other joints, reduce friction where large muscles

FIGURE 6-36 Intervertebral Articulations.

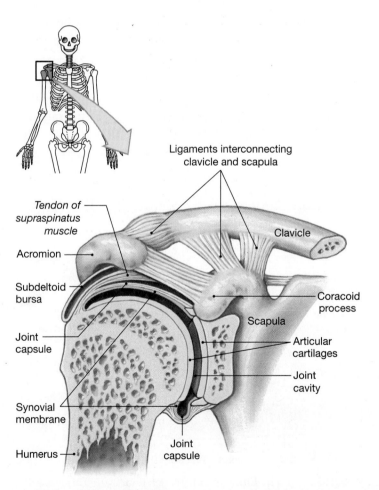

FIGURE 6-37 The Shoulder Joint. The structure of the right shoulder joint is visible in this anterior view of a frontal section.

181

and tendons pass across the joint capsule. The bursae of the shoulder are especially large and numerous. Several bursae are associated with the capsule, the processes of the scapula, and large shoulder muscles. Inflammation of any of these bursae—a condition called *bursitis*—can restrict motion and produce pain.

The muscles that move the humerus do more to stabilize the shoulder joint than all its ligaments and capsular fibers combined. Powerful muscles originating on the trunk, shoulder girdle, and humerus cover the anterior, superior, and posterior surfaces of the capsule. These muscles form the *rotator cuff,* a group of muscles that swing the arm through an impressive range of motion.

The Elbow Joint

The elbow joint consists of two articulations: between the humerus and ulna, and between the humerus and radius (**Figure 6-38**). The larger and stronger articulation is between the humerus and the ulna. This hinge joint provides stability and limits movement at the elbow joint.

The elbow joint is extremely stable because (1) the bony surfaces of the humerus and ulna interlock; (2) the joint capsule is very thick; and (3) the capsule is reinforced by stout ligaments. Nevertheless, the joint can be damaged by severe impacts or unusual stresses. When you fall on your hand with a partially flexed elbow, powerful contractions of the muscles that extend the elbow can break the ulna at the center of the trochlear notch.

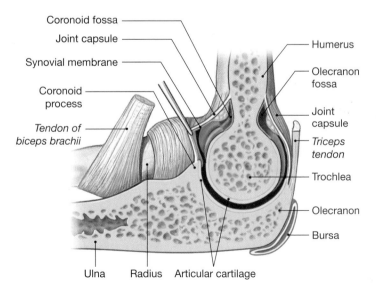

Coronoid fossa
Joint capsule
Synovial membrane
Coronoid process
Tendon of biceps brachii
Humerus
Olecranon fossa
Joint capsule
Triceps tendon
Trochlea
Olecranon
Bursa
Ulna   Radius   Articular cartilage

FIGURE 6-38 The Elbow Joint. This longitudinal section reveals the anatomy of the right elbow joint.

ARTICULATIONS OF THE LOWER LIMB

The joints of the hip, ankle, and foot are sturdier than those at corresponding locations in the upper limb, and they have smaller ranges of motion. The knee has a range of motion comparable to that of the elbow, but it is subjected to much greater forces and, therefore, is less stable.

The Hip Joint

Figure 6-39 shows the structure of the hip joint, a ball-and-socket diarthrosis. The articulating surface of the acetabulum has a fibrous cartilage pad along its edges, a fat pad covered by synovial membrane in its central portion, and a stout central ligament. This combination of coverings and membranes resists compression, absorbs shocks, and stretches and distorts without damage.

Compared with that of the shoulder, the joint capsule of the hip joint is denser and stronger. It extends from the lateral and inferior surfaces of the pelvic girdle to the femur and encloses both the femoral head and neck. This arrangement helps keep the head from moving away from the acetabulum. Three broad ligaments reinforce the joint capsule, while a fourth, the *ligament of the femoral head* (the *ligamentum teres*), is inside the acetabulum and attaches to the center of the femoral head. Additional stabilization comes from the bulk of the surrounding muscles.

The combination of an almost complete bony socket, a strong joint capsule, supporting ligaments, and muscular padding makes this an extremely stable joint. Fractures of the femoral neck or between the trochanters are actually more common than hip dislocations. Although flexion, extension, adduction,

Clinical Note

Hip Fractures

Hip fractures most often occur in individuals over the age of 60, when osteoporosis has weakened the thighbones. These injuries may be accompanied by dislocation of the hip or by pelvic fractures. For individuals with osteoporosis, healing of such fractures proceeds very slowly. In addition, the powerful muscles that surround the joint can easily prevent proper alignment of the bone fragments. Trochanteric fractures usually heal well if the joint can be stabilized; steel frames, pins, screws, or some combination of these devices may be required to preserve alignment and permit normal healing.

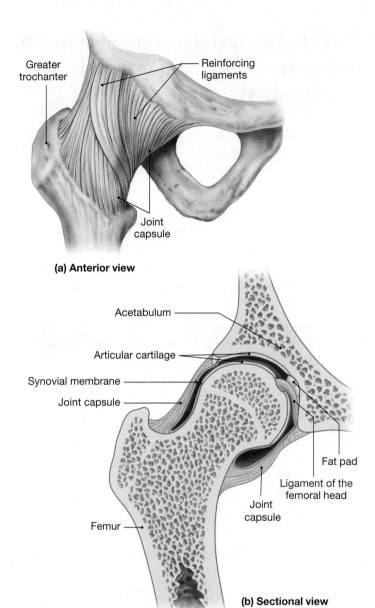

(a) Anterior view

Greater trochanter

Reinforcing ligaments

Joint capsule

Acetabulum

Articular cartilage

Synovial membrane

Joint capsule

Femur

Fat pad

Ligament of the femoral head

Joint capsule

(b) Sectional view

FIGURE 6-39 **The Hip Joint. (a)** The hip joint is extremely strong and stable, in part because of the massive capsule and surrounding ligaments. **(b)** This sectional view of the right hip shows the structure of the joint.

abduction, and rotation are permitted, the total range of motion is considerably less than that of the shoulder. Flexion is the most important normal hip movement, and range of flexion is primarily limited by the surrounding muscles. Other directions of movement are restricted by ligaments and the capsule.

The Knee Joint

The hip joint passes weight to the femur, and at the knee joint the femur transfers the weight to the tibia. Although the knee functions as a hinge joint, the articulation is far more complex than that of the elbow or even the ankle. The rounded condyles of the femur roll across the top of the tibia, so the points of contact are constantly changing. Important features of the knee joint are shown in Figure 6-40.

Structurally, the knee combines three separate articulations—two between the femur and tibia (medial condyle to medial condyle, and lateral condyle to lateral condyle) and one between the patella and the femur. There is no single unified joint capsule, nor is there a common synovial cavity. A pair of fibrous cartilage pads, the **medial** and **lateral menisci,** lies between the femoral and tibial surfaces (Figure 6-40a). They act as cushions and conform to the shape of the articulating surfaces as the femur changes position. Prominent fat pads provide padding around the margins of the joint and assist the bursae in reducing friction between the patella and other tissues (Figure 6-40b).

Ligaments stabilize the anterior, posterior, medial, and lateral surfaces of this joint, and a complete dislocation of the knee is an extremely rare event. The tendon from the muscles responsible for extending the knee passes over the anterior surface of the joint. The patella lies within this tendon, and the **patellar ligament** continues its attachment on the anterior surface of the tibia. This ligament provides support to the front of the knee joint. Posterior ligaments between the femur and the heads of the tibia and fibula reinforce the back of the knee joint. The lateral and medial surfaces of the knee joint are reinforced by another pair of ligaments. These ligaments stabilize the joint at full extension.

Additional ligaments are found inside the joint capsule (Figure 6-40b). Inside the joint a pair of ligaments, the *anterior cruciate* and *posterior cruciate*, cross each other as they attach the tibia to the femur (Figure 6-40a). (The term *cruciate* is derived from the Latin word *crucialis*, meaning a cross.) These ligaments limit the anterior and posterior movement of the femur.

CHECKPOINT

40. Would a tennis player or a jogger be more likely to develop inflammation of the subdeltoid bursa? Why?

41. Daphne falls on her hands with her elbows slightly flexed. After the fall, she can't move her left arm at the elbow. If a fracture exists, which bone is most likely broken?

42. Why is a complete dislocation of the knee joint an infrequent event?

43. What signs would you expect to see in an individual who has damaged the menisci of the knee joint?

See the blue Answers tab at the back of the book.

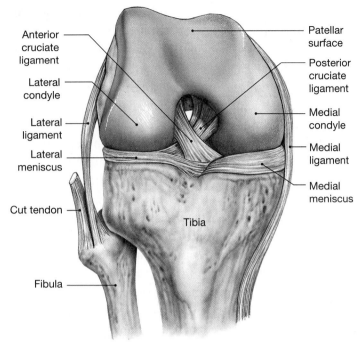

Anterior cruciate ligament

Lateral condyle

Lateral ligament

Lateral meniscus

Cut tendon

Fibula

Patellar surface

Posterior cruciate ligament

Medial condyle

Medial ligament

Medial meniscus

Tibia

(a) Anterior, flexed

Knee extensor muscles

Femur

Bursa

Tendon

Patella

Bursa

Anterior cruciate ligament

Fat pad

Patellar ligament

Bursa

Tibial tuberosity

Tibia

Joint capsule

Synovial membrane

Lateral meniscus

(b) Lateral view of sagittal section through right knee

FIGURE 6-40 The Knee Joint. (a) This anterior view shows the right knee when flexed. **(b)** This sagittal section shows the internal anatomy of the extended right knee.

6-12 The skeletal system supports and stores energy and minerals for other body systems

Although bones may seem inert, you should now realize that they are quite dynamic structures. The entire skeletal system is intimately associated with other organ systems. For example, bones provide attachment sites for the muscular system, and they are extensively interconnected with the cardiovascular and lymphatic systems and largely under the physiological control of the endocrine system. These functional relationships are summarized in the Skeletal System in Perspective (p. 192).

CHECKPOINT

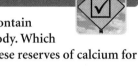

44. The bones of the skeletal system contain 99 percent of the calcium in the body. Which other organ systems depend on these reserves of calcium for normal functioning?

See the blue Answers tab at the back of the book.

RELATED CLINICAL TERMS

ankylosis (ang-ki-LŌ-sis): An abnormal fusion between articulating bones in response to trauma and friction within a joint.

arthritis (ar-THRĪ-tis): Rheumatic diseases that affect synovial joints. Arthritis always involves damage to the articular cartilages, but the specific cause can vary. The diseases of arthritis are usually classified as either *degenerative* or *inflammatory*.

arthroscopic surgery: The surgical modification of a joint using an *arthroscope* (a fiber-optic instrument used to view the inside of joint cavities).

bursitis: Inflammation of a bursa that causes pain whenever the associated tendon or ligament moves.

carpal tunnel syndrome: Inflammation of the tissues at the anterior wrist that causes compression of adjacent tendons and nerves. Symptoms are pain and a loss of wrist mobility.

fracture: A crack or break in a bone.

gigantism: A condition of extreme height resulting from an overproduction of growth hormone before puberty.

herniated disc: A condition caused by intervertebral disc compression severe enough to rupture the outer fibrocartilage layer and release the inner soft, gelatinous core, which may protrude beyond the intervertebral space.

kyphosis (kī-FŌ-sis): An abnormal exaggeration of the thoracic spinal curve that produces a humpback appearance.

lordosis (lor-DŌ-sis): An abnormal lumbar curve of the spine that results in a swayback appearance.

luxation (luks-Ā-shun): A dislocation; a condition in which the articulating surfaces are forced out of position.

orthopedics (or-tho-PĒ-diks): A branch of surgery concerned with disorders of the bones and joints and their associated muscles, tendons, and ligaments.

osteomyelitis (os-tē-ō-mī-e-LĪ-tis): A painful infection in a bone, generally caused by bacteria.

osteopenia (os-tē-ō-PĒ-nē-uh): Inadequate ossification, leading to thinner, weaker bones.

osteoporosis (os-tē-ō-po-RŌ-sis): A reduction in bone mass to a degree that compromises normal function.

rheumatism (ROO-muh-tizum): A general term that indicates pain and stiffness arising in the skeletal system, the muscular system, or both.

rickets: A childhood disorder that reduces the amount of calcium salts in the skeleton; typically characterized by a bowlegged appearance, because the leg bones bend under the body's weight.

scoliosis (skō-lē-Ō-sis): An abnormal lateral curvature of the spine.

scurvy: A condition involving weak, brittle bones as a result of a vitamin C deficiency.

spina bifida (SPĪ-nuh BI-fi-duh): A condition resulting from the failure of the vertebral laminae to unite during development; commonly associated with developmental abnormalities of the brain and spinal cord.

sprain: A condition in which a ligament is stretched to the point at which some of the collagen fibers are torn. The ligament remains functional, and the structure of the joint is not affected.

whiplash: An injury resulting when a sudden change in body position injures the cervical vertebrae.

Chapter **6** Review

KEY TERMS

amphiarthrosis *173*	**marrow** *144*
appendicular skeleton *152*	**meniscus** *175*
articulation *173*	**ossification** *147*
axial skeleton *152*	**osteoblast** *146*
bursa *175*	**osteoclast** *146*
compact bone *144*	**osteocyte** *145*
diaphysis *144*	**osteon** *145*
diarthrosis *174*	**periosteum** *144*
epiphysis *144*	**spongy bone** *144*
fracture *150*	**synarthrosis** *173*
ligament *175*	**synovial fluid** *174*

SUMMARY OUTLINE

An Introduction to the Skeletal System *p. 143*

1. The components of the skeletal system have a variety of purposes, such as providing a framework for body posture and allowing for precise movements.

6-1 The skeletal system has five primary functions *p. 143*

2. The skeletal system includes the bones of the skeleton and the cartilages, ligaments, and other connective tissues that stabilize or interconnect bones. Its functions include structural support, storage, blood cell production, protection, and leverage.

6-2 Bones are classified according to shape and structure *p. 143*

3. **Bone,** or **osseous tissue,** is a supporting connective tissue with a solid *matrix.*

4. General categories of bones are **long bones, short bones, flat bones,** and **irregular bones.** *(Figure 6-1)*

5. The features of a long bone include a **diaphysis,** two **epiphyses,** and a central *marrow cavity. (Figure 6-2)*

6. The two types of bone tissue are **compact** (*dense*) **bone** and **spongy** (*cancellous*) **bone.**

7. A bone is covered by a **periosteum** and lined with an **endosteum.**

8. Both types of bone tissue contain **osteocytes** in **lacunae.** Layers of calcified matrix are **lamellae,** interconnected by **canaliculi.** *(Figure 6-3)*

9. The basic functional unit of compact bone is the **osteon,** containing osteocytes arranged around a **central canal.**

10. Spongy bone contains **trabeculae,** often in an open network.

11. Compact bone is located where stresses come from a limited range of directions; spongy bone is located where stresses are few or come from many different directions.

12. Cells other than osteocytes are also present in bone. **Osteoclasts** dissolve the bony matrix through the process of *osteolysis.* **Osteoblasts** synthesize the matrix in the process of *osteogenesis.*

6-3 Ossification and appositional growth are mechanisms of bone formation and enlargement *p. 147*

13. **Ossification** is the process of converting other tissues to bone.

14. **Intramembranous ossification** begins when stem cells in connective tissue differentiate into osteoblasts and produce spongy or compact bone. *(Figure 6-4)*

15. **Endochondral ossification** begins with the formation of a cartilage model of a bone that is gradually replaced by bone. *(Figure 6-5)*

16. Bone diameter increases through **appositional growth.** *(Figure 6-6)*

17. The timing of epiphyseal closure differs among bones and among individuals.

18. Normal osteogenesis requires a reliable source of minerals, vitamins, and hormones.

6-4 Bone growth and development depend on a balance between bone formation and resorption, and on calcium availability *p. 149*

19. The organic and mineral components of bone are continuously recycled and renewed through the process of **remodeling.**

20. The shapes and thicknesses of bones reflect the stresses applied to them. Mineral turnover enables bone to adapt to new stresses.

21. Calcium is the most abundant mineral in the human body; roughly 99 percent of it is located in the skeleton. The skeleton acts as a calcium reserve.

22. A **fracture** is a crack or break in a bone. Repair of a fracture involves the formation of a **fracture hematoma,** an **external callus,** and an **internal callus.** *(Figure 6-7)*

6-5 Osteopenia has a widespread effect on aging skeletal tissue *p. 152*

23. The effects of aging on the skeleton can include **osteopenia** and **osteoporosis.**

6-6 The bones of the skeleton are distinguished by surface markings and grouped into two skeletal divisions *p. 152*

24. **Bone markings** are surface features that can be used to describe and identify specific bones. *(Table 6-1)*

25. The **axial skeleton** can be subdivided into the **skull** and associated bones (including the **auditory ossicles,** or ear bones, and the **hyoid**); the **thoracic cage,** composed of the **ribs** and **sternum** (*rib cage*) and thoracic vertebrae; and the **vertebral column.** *(Figures 6-8, 6-9)*

26. The **appendicular skeleton** includes the upper and lower limbs and the **pectoral** and **pelvic girdles.**

6-7 The bones of the skull, vertebral column, and thoracic cage make up the axial skeleton *p. 155*

27. The **cranium** encloses the **cranial cavity,** which encloses the brain.

28. The **frontal bone** forms the forehead and superior surface of each **orbit.** *(Figures 6-10, 6-11, 6-12)*

29. The **parietal bones** form the upper sides and roof of the cranium. *(Figures 6-10, 6-12)*

30. The **occipital bone** surrounds the **foramen magnum** and articulates with the sphenoid, temporal, and parietal bones to form the back of the cranium. *(Figures 6-10, 6-11, 6-12)*

31. The **temporal bones** help form the sides and base of the cranium and fuse with the parietal bones along the **squamous suture.** *(Figures 6-10, 6-11, 6-12)*

32. The **sphenoid bone** acts like a bridge that unites the cranial and facial bones. *(Figures 6-10, 6-11, 6-12)*

33. The **ethmoid bone** stabilizes the brain and forms the roof and sides of the nasal cavity. Its **cribriform plate** contains perforations for olfactory nerves, and the **perpendicular plate** forms part of the bony *nasal septum. (Figures 6-10, 6-11, 6-12)*

34. The left and right **maxillae,** or *maxillary bones,* articulate with all the other facial bones except the *mandible. (Figures 6-10, 6-11, 6-12)*

35. The **palatine bones** form the posterior portions of the hard palate and contribute to the walls of the nasal cavity and to the floor of each orbit. (*Figures 6-11, 6-12*)

36. The **vomer** forms the inferior portion of the bony nasal septum. (*Figures 6-11, 6-12*)

37. The **zygomatic bones** help complete the orbit and together with the temporal bones form the **zygomatic arch** (*cheekbone*). (*Figures 6-10, 6-11*)

38. The **nasal bones** articulate with the frontal bone and the maxillary bones. (*Figures 6-10, 6-11, 6-12*)

39. The **lacrimal bones** are within the orbit on its medial surface. (*Figures 6-10, 6-11*)

40. The **inferior nasal conchae** inside the nasal cavity aid the **superior** and **middle nasal conchae** of the ethmoid bone in slowing incoming air. (*Figures 6-11a, 6-12c*)

41. The **nasal complex** includes the bones that form the superior and lateral walls of the nasal cavity and the sinuses that drain into them. The **nasal septum** divides the nasal cavities. Together the **frontal, sphenoidal, ethmoidal, palatine,** and **maxillary sinuses** make up the **paranasal sinuses.** (*Figures 6-11, 6-12, 6-13*)

42. The **mandible** is the bone of the lower jaw. (*Figures 6-10, 6-11, 6-12*)

43. The **hyoid bone** is suspended below the skull by ligaments from the styloid processes of the temporal bones. (*Figure 6-14*)

44. Fibrous tissue connections called **fontanelles** permit the skulls of infants and children to continue growing. (*Figure 6-15*)

45. There are 7 **cervical vertebrae**, 12 **thoracic vertebrae** (which articulate with ribs), and 5 **lumbar vertebrae** (the last articulates with the sacrum). The **sacrum** and **coccyx** consist of fused vertebrae. (*Figure 6-16*)

46. The spinal column has four **spinal curves,** which accommodate the unequal distribution of body weight and keep it in line with the body axis. (*Figure 6-16*)

47. A typical vertebra has a **body** and a **vertebral arch**; it articulates with other vertebrae at the **articular processes.** Adjacent vertebrae are separated by an **intervertebral disc.** (*Figure 6-17*)

48. Cervical vertebrae are distinguished by the oval body and **transverse foramina** on either side. (*Figures 6-17, 6-18*)

49. Thoracic vertebrae have distinctive heart-shaped bodies. (*Figure 6-17*)

50. The lumbar vertebrae are the most massive, least mobile, and are subjected to the greatest strains. (*Figure 6-17*)

51. The sacrum protects reproductive, digestive, and excretory organs. At its **apex,** the sacrum articulates with the coccyx. At its **base,** the sacrum articulates with the last lumbar vertebra. (*Figure 6-19*)

52. The skeleton of the chest, or thoracic cage, consists of the thoracic vertebrae, the ribs, and the sternum. The ribs and sternum form the rib cage. (*Figure 6-20*)

53. Ribs 1 to 7 are **true ribs.** Ribs 8 to 12 lack direct connections to the sternum and are called **false ribs;** they include two pairs of **floating ribs.** The medial end of each rib articulates with a thoracic vertebra. (*Figure 6-20*)

54. The sternum consists of a **manubrium,** a **body,** and a **xiphoid process.** (*Figure 6-20*)

6-8 The pectoral girdle and upper limb bones, and the pelvic girdle and lower limb bones, make up the appendicular skeleton *p. 165*

55. Each arm articulates with the trunk at the pectoral girdle, or shoulder girdle, which consists of the **scapulae** and **clavicles.** (*Figures 6-8, 6-9, 6-21, 6-22*)

56. The clavicle and scapula position the shoulder joint, help move the arm, and provide a base for arm movement and muscle attachment. (*Figures 6-21, 6-22*)

57. Both the **coracoid process** and the **acromion** are attached to ligaments and tendons. The **scapular spine** crosses the posterior surface of the scapular body. (*Figure 6-22*)

58. The **humerus** articulates with the scapula at the shoulder joint. The **greater tubercle** and **lesser tubercle** of the humerus are important sites for muscle attachment. Other prominent landmarks include the **deltoid tuberosity,** the **medial** and **lateral epicondyles,** and the articular **condyle.** (*Figure 6-23*)

59. Distally, the humerus articulates with the radius and ulna. The medial **trochlea** extends from the **coronoid fossa** to the **olecranon fossa.** (*Figure 6-23*)

60. The **radius** and **ulna** are the bones of the forearm. The olecranon fossa accommodates the **olecranon process** during extension of the arm. The coronoid and radial fossae accommodate the **coronoid process** of the ulna. (*Figure 6-24*)

61. The bones of the wrist form two rows of **carpal bones.** The distal carpal bones articulate with the **metacarpal bones** of the palm. The metacarpal bones articulate with the proximal **phalanges,** or finger bones. Four of the fingers contain three phalanges; the **pollex,** or thumb, has only two. (*Figure 6-25*)

62. The pelvic girdle consists of two **coxal bones.** (*Figures 6-8, 6-9, 6-26*)

63. The largest part of the coxal bone, the **ilium,** fuses with the **ischium,** which in turn fuses with the **pubis.** The **pubic symphysis** limits movement between the pubic bones. (*Figure 6-26*)

64. The **pelvis** consists of the hip bones, the sacrum, and the coccyx. (*Figures 6-26, 6-27*)

65. The **femur,** or *thighbone,* is the longest bone in the body. It articulates with the **tibia** at the knee joint. A ligament from the **patella** (the *kneecap*) attaches at the **tibial tuberosity.** (*Figures 6-28, 6-29*)

66. Other tibial landmarks include the **anterior crest** and the **medial malleolus.** The **head** of the **fibula** articulates with

the tibia below the knee, and the **lateral malleolus** stabilizes the ankle. (*Figure 6-29*)

67. The ankle includes seven **tarsal bones;** only the **talus** articulates with the tibia and fibula. When we stand normally, most of our weight is transferred to the **calcaneus,** or *heel bone,* and the rest is passed on to the **metatarsal bones.** (*Figure 6-30*)

68. The basic organizational pattern of the metatarsals and phalanges of the foot resembles that of the hand.

6-9 Joints are categorized according to their range of motion or anatomical organization *p. 173*

69. **Articulations** (joints) exist wherever two bones interact. Immovable joints are **synarthroses,** slightly movable joints are **amphiarthroses,** and those that are freely movable are called **diarthroses.** (*Table 6-2*)

70. Examples of synarthroses are a **suture,** a **gomphosis,** and a **synchondrosis.**

71. Examples of amphiarthroses are a **syndesmosis** and a **symphysis.**

72. The bony surfaces at diarthroses, or **synovial joints,** are covered by **articular cartilages,** lubricated by **synovial fluid,** and enclosed within a **joint capsule.** Other synovial structures include **menisci, fat pads, bursae,** and various **ligaments.** (*Figure 6-31*)

6-10 Anatomical and functional properties of synovial joints enable various skeletal movements *p. 176*

73. Important terms that describe dynamic motion at synovial joints are **flexion, extension, hyperextension, abduction, adduction, circumduction,** and **rotation.** (*Figures 6-32, 6-33*)

74. The bones in the forearm permit **pronation** and **supination.** (*Figure 6-33*)

75. Movements of the foot include **inversion** and **eversion.** The ankle undergoes **dorsiflexion** and **plantar flexion.**

Opposition is the thumb movement that enables us to grasp and hold objects. (*Figure 6-34*)

76. **Protraction** involves moving a part of the body forward; **retraction** involves moving it back. **Depression** and **elevation** occur when we move a structure inferiorly and superiorly, respectively. (*Figure 6-34*)

77. Major types of synovial joints include gliding joints, hinge joints, pivot joints, ellipsoidal joints, saddle joints, and ball-and-socket joints. (*Figure 6-35*)

6-11 Intervertebral articulations and appendicular articulations demonstrate functional differences in support and mobility *p. 179*

78. The articular processes of adjacent vertebrae form gliding joints. *Symphyseal joints* connect adjacent vertebral bodies and are separated by pads called *intervertebral discs.* (*Figure 6-36*)

79. The shoulder joint is formed by the **glenoid cavity** and the head of the humerus. This joint is extremely mobile and, for that reason, it is also unstable and easily dislocated. (*Figure 6-37*)

80. Bursae at the shoulder joint reduce friction from muscles and tendons during movement. (*Figure 6-37*)

81. The elbow joint permits only flexion and extension. It is extremely stable because of extensive ligaments and the shapes of the articulating elements. (*Figure 6-38*)

82. The hip joint is formed by the union of the **acetabulum** with the head of the femur. This ball-and-socket diarthrosis permits flexion and extension, adduction and abduction, circumduction, and rotation. (*Figure 6-39*)

83. The knee joint is a complicated hinge joint. The joint permits flexion-extension and limited rotation. (*Figure 6-40*)

6-12 The skeletal system supports and stores energy and minerals for other body systems *p. 184*

84. The skeletal system is dynamically associated with other systems.

REVIEW QUESTIONS

WWW Access more review material online at The Anatomy & Physiology Place (**www.anatomyandphysiology.com**). There, you'll find Chapter Guides, Chapter Quizzes, Chapter Practice Tests, Interactive Flashcards, a Glossary with Pronunciations, and more to help you succeed in the course.

Level 1 • Reviewing Facts and Terms

Match each item in column A with the most closely related item in column B. Place letters for answers in the spaces provided.

COLUMN A

_____ 1. osteocytes
_____ 2. diaphysis
_____ 3. auditory ossicles
_____ 4. cribriform plate
_____ 5. osteoblasts
_____ 6. C_1
_____ 7. C_2
_____ 8. hip and shoulder
_____ 9. patella
_____ 10. calcaneus
_____ 11. synarthrosis
_____ 12. moving the hand into a palm-front position
_____ 13. osteoclasts
_____ 14. raising the arm laterally
_____ 15. elbow and knee

COLUMN B

a. abduction
b. heel bone
c. ball-and-socket joints
d. bone-dissolving cells
e. hinge joints
f. axis
g. immovable joint
h. bone shaft
i. mature bone cells
j. bone-producing cells
k. atlas
l. olfactory nerves
m. ear bones
n. supination
o. kneecap

16. Skeletal bones store energy reserves as lipids in areas of
    (a) red marrow.
    (b) yellow marrow.
    (c) the matrix of bone tissue.
    (d) the ground substance.

17. The two types of osseous tissue are
    (a) compact bone and spongy bone.
    (b) dense bone and compact bone.
    (c) spongy bone and cancellous bone.
    (d) a, b, and c are correct

18. The basic functional units of mature compact bone are
    (a) lacunae.   (b) osteocytes.
    (c) osteons.   (d) canaliculi.

19. The axial skeleton consists of the bones of the
    (a) pectoral and pelvic girdles.
    (b) skull, thorax, and vertebral column.
    (c) arm, legs, hand, and feet.
    (d) limbs, pectoral girdle, and pelvic girdle.

20. Identify the cranial and facial bones in the diagram below.

Cranial bones   **Facial bones**

(a) _____   (b) _____
(c) _____   (d) _____
(e) _____   (f) _____
(g) _____   (h) _____
(i) _____   (j) _____
(k) _____   (l) _____

21. The appendicular skeleton consists of the bones of the
    (a) pectoral and pelvic girdles.
    (b) skull, thorax, and vertebral column.
    (c) arm, legs, hand, and feet.
    (d) limbs, pectoral girdle, and pelvic girdle.

22. Which of the following lists contains only bones of the cranium?
    (a) frontal, parietal, occipital, sphenoid
    (b) frontal, occipital, zygomatic, parietal
    (c) occipital, sphenoid, temporal, palatine
    (d) mandible, maxilla, nasal, zygomatic

23. Of the following bones, which one is unpaired?
    (a) vomer   (b) maxilla
    (c) palatine   (d) nasal

24. At the glenoid cavity, the scapula articulates with the proximal end of the
    (a) humerus.   (b) radius.
    (c) ulna.   (d) femur.

25. While an individual is in the anatomical position, the ulna lies
    (a) medial to the radius.   (b) lateral to the radius.
    (c) inferior to the radius. (d) superior to the radius.

26. Each coxal bone of the pelvic girdle consists of three fused bones: the
    (a) ulna, radius, humerus.
    (b) ilium, ischium, pubis.
    (c) femur, tibia, fibula.
    (d) hamate, capitate, trapezium.

27. Joints that are typically located at the end of long bones are
    (a) synarthroses.   (b) amphiarthroses.
    (c) diarthroses.   (d) sutures.

28. Label the structures in the following illustration of a synovial joint.

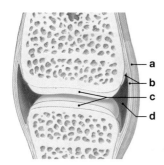

    (a) _____   (b) _____
    (c) _____   (d) _____

29. The function of synovial fluid is
    (a) to nourish chondrocytes.
    (b) to provide lubrication.
    (c) to absorb shock.
    (d) a, b, and c are correct

30. Abduction and adduction always refer to movements of the
    (a) axial skeleton.
    (b) appendicular skeleton.
    (c) skull.
    (d) vertebral column.

31. Standing on tiptoe is an example of a movement called
    (a) elevation.
    (b) dorsiflexion.
    (c) plantar flexion.
    (d) retraction.

32. What is the primary difference between intramembranous ossification and endochondral ossification?

33. What unique characteristic of the hyoid bone makes it different from all the other bones in the body?

34. What two primary functions are performed by the thoracic cage?

35. Which two large scapular processes are associated with the shoulder joint?

Level 2 • Reviewing Concepts

36. Why are stresses or impacts to the side of the shaft of a long bone more dangerous than stress applied along the long axis of the shaft?

37. During the growth of a long bone, how is the epiphysis forced farther from the shaft?

38. Why are ruptured intervertebral discs more common in lumbar vertebrae, and dislocations and fractures more common in cervical vertebrae?

39. Why are clavicular injuries common?

40. What is the difference in skeletal structure between the pelvic girdle and the pelvis?

41. How do articular cartilages differ from other cartilages in the body?

42. What is the significance of the fact that the pubic symphysis is a slightly movable joint?

Level 3 • Critical Thinking and Clinical Applications

43. While playing on her swing set, 10-year-old Yasmin falls and breaks her right leg. At the emergency room, the physician tells Yasmin's parents that the proximal end of the tibia, where the epiphysis meets the diaphysis, is fractured. The fracture is properly set and eventually heals. During a routine physical when she is 18, Yasmin learns that her right leg is 2 cm shorter than her left, probably because of her accident. What might account for this difference?

44. Tess is diagnosed with a disease that affects the membranes surrounding the brain. The physician tells Tess's family that the disease is caused by an airborne virus. Explain how this virus could have entered the cranium.

45. While working at an excavation, an archaeologist finds several small skull bones. She examines the frontal, parietal, and occipital bones and concludes that the skulls are those of children not yet 1 year old. How can she tell their ages from examining these bones?

46. Frank Fireman is fighting a fire in a building when part of the ceiling collapses and a beam strikes him on his left shoulder. He is rescued by his friends, but he has a great deal of pain in his shoulder and cannot move his arm properly, especially anteriorly. His clavicle is not broken, and his humerus is intact. What is the probable nature of Frank's injury?

47. Ed "turns over" his ankle while playing tennis. He experiences swelling and pain, but after examination he is told that there are no torn ligaments and that the structure of the ankle is not affected. On the basis of the signs and symptoms and the examination results, what do you think happened to Ed's ankle?

The Skeletal System in Perspective

Functional Relationships Between the Skeletal System and Other Systems

The Integumentary System

- The Integumentary System synthesizes vitamin D_3, essential for calcium and phosphorus absorption (bone maintenance and growth)
- The Skeletal System provides structural support

The Muscular System

- The Muscular System stabilizes bone positions; tension in tendons stimulates bone growth and maintenence
- The Skeletal System provides calcium needed for normal muscle contraction; bones act as levers to produce body movements

The Nervous System

- The Nervous System regulates bone position by controlling muscle contractions
- The Skeletal System provides calcium for neural function; protects brain, spinal cord; receptors at joints provide information about body position

The Endocrine System

- The Endocrine System regulates skeletal growth with growth hormone, thyroid hormones, and sex hormones; calcium mobilization regulated by parathyroid hormone and calcitonin
- The Skeletal System protects endocrine organs, especially in brain, chest, and pelvic cavity

The Cardiovascular System

- The Cardiovascular System provides oxygen, nutrients, hormones, blood cells; removes waste products and carbon dioxide
- The Skeletal System provides calcium needed for cardiac muscle contraction, blood cells produced in bone marrow; axial skeleton protects heart and great vessels

The Lymphoid System

- The Lymphoid System's lymphocytes assist in the defense and repair of bone following injuries
- The Skeletal System's bone marrow produces and stores lymphocytes and other cells of the immune response

The Respiratory System

- The Respiratory System provides oxygen and eliminates carbon dioxide
- The Skeletal System surrounds and protects lungs; movements of ribs important in breathing

The Digestive System

- The Digestive System provides nutrients, calcium, and phosphate
- The Skeletal System protects portions of liver, stomach, and intestines

The Urinary System

- The Urinary System conserves calcium and phosphate needed for skeletal system growth; disposes of waste products
- The Skeletal System provides some protection for kidneys and ureters; pelvis protects urinary bladder and proximal urethra

The Reproductive System

- The Reproductive System's sex hormones stimulate growth and maintenance of bones; surge of sex hormones at puberty causes acceleration of growth and closure of skeletal system (pelvis)
- The Skeletal System (pelvis) protects reproductive organs of female, protects portion of ductus deferens and accessory glands in males

For All Systems
The Skeletal System provides mechanical support; stores energy reserves; stores calcium and phosphate reserves

Professional Profile

SPORTS TRAINER
Andy Walshe

> " Anatomy and physiology is essential. It teaches you the parts of the engine you're trying to improve, and it's the foundation on which all sports disciplines are based. "

Andy Walshe is the high-performance manager for the athletic program of the U.S. Ski and Snowboard Association. He works closely with over 150 athletes training to become Olympic champions. Andy supervises a staff of physiologists, nutritionists, dieticians, biomechanicists, and sports psychologists.

For trainers at this level, there is no such thing as a typical day. "This profession is full of variety. One day you may be running training camps, and the next you may be on the snow in South America shooting high-speed video for movement analysis."

ELITE TRAINING

In addition to supervising the training team, Andy develops elite sports performance models—frameworks that allow a trainer to analyze athletes in relation to their sport to determine their strengths and weaknesses. His expertise is in biomechanical physiological analysis. This requires a strong background in anatomy and physiology. "You need to understand and analyze movement patterns, and you can't do that without a good understanding of muscles and bones. And you need to understand energy systems as well, so the physiology element is very important."

In fact, says Andy, for all of his staff, "Anatomy and physiology is essential. It teaches you the parts of the engine you're trying to improve, and it's the foundation on which all sports disciplines are based."

Andy is one of a small group of elite-level trainers working with the best athletes in the world. Elite trainers bring to the job a combination of advanced academic work and practical experience. A master's degree is required for this type of job.

Andy worked first as a volunteer assistant physiologist, traveling with teams in an unpaid position, and worked his way up to his current job, which he's had for seven years. "I was always interested in sports and performance. I wanted to use my interests at the elite level. I actually started in summer sports—surfing—and then worked in snowboarding and then skiing."

"To become a sports trainer, it's a good idea to have as much practical training as possible in a variety of sports, working with athletes and coaches. Volunteer your time. Do what it takes to get your foot in the door."

CAREER OPPORTUNITIES

Sports trainers can work at the junior level, college level, or elite level. There are jobs in the United States and chances to work in other countries. At the elite level, most entry-level jobs are unpaid internships, opportunities to learn while showing the trainers what you can do. Andy suggests, "Find out what organizations are associated with sports that interest you. The U.S. Olympic Committee has internship programs, and there are many organizations to investigate for each sport."

Andy loves his job working in the world of elite sports, even though the pace is intense. "You live this job. You are on call all the time, doing anything and everything that involves preparing elite athletes. In a job like this, you're a jack-of-all-trades. It's important to be flexible and be willing to put parts of your life on hold. I travel over 200 days a year and I work 24/7."

However, the rewards are great. "The athletes and the coaches are the best part of this job. It's great being a part of the team that helps athletes chase their dreams. Along the way, you make great friends."

And there's a larger goal as well. "Our number one goal is to get more kids into the sport. Of course, we're here to get our athletes medals, but the impact of those medals is that we get more kids involved in the sport."

7 The Muscular System

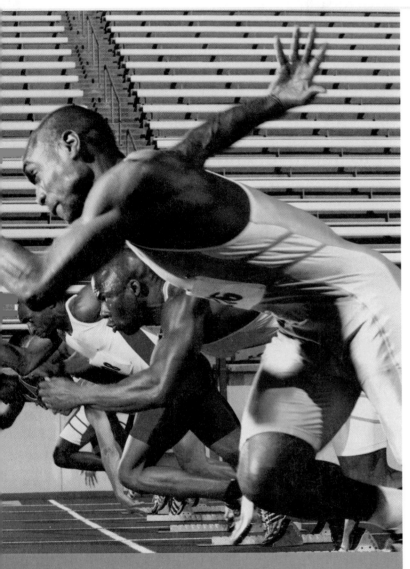

Athletes—such as these sprinters pushing off their starting block—rely on the peak performance of many of the 700 or so skeletal muscles in the body. The contractions of these muscles are responsible for all the movements—whether powerful or delicate—of the axial and appendicular skeletons.

LEARNING OUTCOMES

After completing this chapter, you should be able to do the following:

7-1 Specify the functions of skeletal muscle tissue.

7-2 Describe the organization of muscle at the tissue level.

7-3 Identify the structural components of a sarcomere.

7-4 Explain the key steps involved in the contraction of a skeletal muscle fiber beginning at the neuromuscular junction.

7-5 Compare the different types of muscle contractions.

7-6 Describe the mechanisms by which muscles obtain the energy to power contractions.

7-7 Relate the types of muscle fibers to muscle performance, and distinguish between aerobic and anaerobic endurance.

7-8 Contrast the structures and functions of skeletal, cardiac, and smooth muscle tissues.

7-9 Explain how the name of a muscle can help identify its location, appearance, or function.

7-10 Identify the main axial muscles of the body together with their origins, insertions, and actions.

7-11 Identify the main appendicular muscles of the body together with their origins, insertions, and actions.

7-12 Describe the effects of aging on muscle tissue.

7-13 Discuss the functional relationships between the muscular system and other organ systems.

VOCABULARY DEVELOPMENT

aer air; *aerobic*
an not; *anaerobic*
bi two; *biceps*
caput head; *biceps*
clavius clavicle; *clavicle*
di two; *digastricus*
epi- on; *epimysium*
ergon work; *synergist*
fasciculus a bundle; *fascicle*

gaster stomach; *gastrocnemius*
hyper above; *hypertrophy*
iso- equal; *isometric*
kneme knee; *gastrocnemius*
lemma husk; *sarcolemma*
meros part; *sarcomere*
metron measure; *isometric*
mys muscle; *epimysium*

peri- around; *perimysium*
platys flat; *platysma*
sarkos flesh; *sarcolemma*
syn- together; *synergist*
tetanos convulsive tension; *tetanus*
tonos tension; *isotonic*
trope a turning; *tropomyosin*
-trophy nourishing; *atrophy*

An Introduction to Muscle Tissue

It is hard to imagine what life would be like without muscle tissue. We would be unable to sit, stand, walk, speak, or grasp objects. Blood would not circulate, because there would be no heartbeat to propel it through the vessels. The lungs could not rhythmically empty and fill, nor could food move through the digestive tract. Muscle tissue, one of the four primary tissue types, consists of elongated muscle cells that are highly specialized for contraction. The three types of muscle tissue—*skeletal muscle, cardiac muscle,* and *smooth muscle*—were introduced in Chapter 4. ∞ p. 112

This chapter begins by discussing skeletal muscle tissue, the most abundant muscle tissue in the body. It is followed by an overview of the differences among skeletal, cardiac, and smooth muscle tissue. We will then proceed to a consideration of the muscular system.

7-1 Skeletal muscle performs five primary functions

Skeletal muscles are organs composed primarily of skeletal muscle tissue, but they also contain connective tissues, nerves, and blood vessels. These muscles are directly or indirectly attached to the bones of the skeleton. The muscular system includes approximately 700 skeletal muscles that perform the following functions:

1. *Produce movement of the skeleton.* Skeletal muscle contractions pull on tendons and thereby move the bones. These contractions may produce a simple motion, such as extending the arm, or the highly coordinated movements of swimming, skiing, or typing.

2. *Maintain posture and body position.* Continuous muscle contractions maintain body posture. Without this constant action, you could not sit upright without collapsing, or stand without toppling over.

3. *Support soft tissues.* The abdominal wall and the floor of the pelvic cavity consist of layers of skeletal muscle. These muscles support the weight of visceral organs and shield internal tissues from injury.

4. *Guard entrances and exits.* Skeletal muscles encircle openings to the digestive and urinary tracts. These muscles provide voluntary control over swallowing, defecation, and urination.

5. *Maintain body temperature.* Muscle contractions require energy, and whenever energy is used in the body, some of it is converted to heat. The heat released by working muscles keeps body temperature in the range required for normal functioning.

To understand how skeletal muscle contracts, we must study the structure of skeletal muscle. We begin with the organ-level structure of skeletal muscle before describing its cellular-level structure. In the following discussions we will often encounter the Greek words *sarkos* (flesh) and *mys* (muscle) as word roots in the names of the structural features of muscles and their components.

> **CHECKPOINT**
>
> **1.** Identify the five primary functions of skeletal muscle.
>
> *See the blue Answers tab at the back of the book.*

7-2 A skeletal muscle contains muscle tissue, connective tissues, blood vessels, and nerves

Figure 7-1 illustrates the organization of a typical skeletal muscle. A skeletal muscle contains connective tissues, blood vessels, nerves, and skeletal muscle tissue. Each cell in skeletal muscle tissue is a single muscle *fiber.*

CONNECTIVE TISSUE ORGANIZATION

Three layers of connective tissue are part of each muscle: the epimysium, the perimysium, and the endomysium (**Figure 7-1**).

Surrounding the entire muscle is the **epimysium** (ep-i-MIZ-ē-um; *epi-*, on + *mys*, muscle), a layer of collagen fibers that separates the muscle from surrounding tissues and organs.

The connective tissue fibers of the **perimysium** (per-i-MIZ-ē-um; *peri-*, around) divide the skeletal muscle into compartments, each containing a bundle of muscle fibers called a **fascicle** (FAS-i-kl; *fasciculus*, a bundle). In addition to collagen and elastic fibers, the perimysium contains blood vessels and nerves that supply the fascicles.

Within a fascicle, the **endomysium** (en-dō-MIZ-ē-um; *endo-*, inside) surrounds each skeletal muscle fiber and ties adjacent muscle fibers together. Stem cells scattered among the fibers help repair damaged muscle tissue.

At each end of the muscle, the collagen fibers of all three layers come together to form either a bundle known as a **tendon,** or a broad sheet called an *aponeurosis*. Tendons are bands of collagen fibers that attach skeletal muscles to bones, and aponeuroses connect different skeletal muscles. ∞ p. 104 The tendon fibers are interwoven into the periosteum of the bone, providing a firm attachment. Any contraction of the muscle exerts a pull on its tendon and in turn on the attached bone.

BLOOD VESSELS AND NERVES

The connective tissues of the epimysium and perimysium provide a passageway for the blood vessels and nerves that are necessary for the functioning of muscle fibers. Muscle contraction requires tremendous amounts of energy. An extensive network of blood vessels delivers the necessary oxygen and nutrients and carries away the metabolic wastes generated by active skeletal muscles.

Skeletal muscles contract only under stimulation from the central nervous system. *Axons* (nerve fibers) penetrate the epimysium, branch through the perimysium, and enter the endomysium to control individual muscle fibers. Skeletal muscles are often called *voluntary muscles* because we have voluntary control over their contractions. Many skeletal muscles may also be controlled at a subconscious level. For example, skeletal muscles involved with breathing, such as the *diaphragm*, usually work outside our conscious awareness.

CHECKPOINT

2. Describe the connective tissue layers associated with skeletal muscle tissue.

3. How would severing the tendon attached to a muscle affect the muscle's ability to move a body part?

See the blue Answers tab at the back of the book.

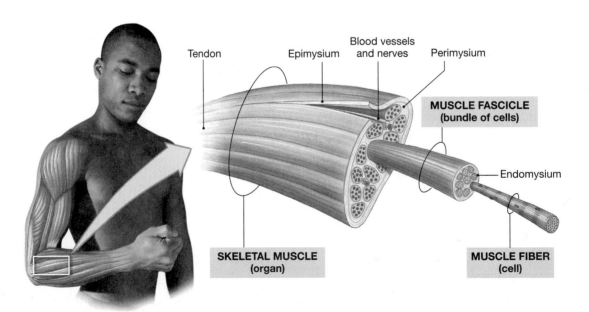

FIGURE 7-1 **The Organization of a Skeletal Muscle.**

7-3 Skeletal muscle fibers have distinctive features

Skeletal muscle fibers are quite different from the "typical" cell described in Chapter 3. One obvious difference is their enormous size. A skeletal muscle fiber from a leg muscle, for example, could have a diameter of 100 μm and a length equal to that of the entire muscle (up to 60 cm, or 24 in.). In addition, each skeletal muscle fiber is *multinucleate*, containing hundreds of nuclei just beneath the cell membrane. In the next sections we will examine the components of a typical skeletal muscle fiber.

THE SARCOLEMMA AND TRANSVERSE TUBULES

The basic structure of a muscle fiber is depicted in Figure 7-2a. The cell membrane, or **sarcolemma** (sar-kō-LEM-uh; *sarkos,* flesh + *lemma,* husk), of a muscle fiber surrounds the cytoplasm, or **sarcoplasm** (SAR-kō-plazm). Openings scattered across the surface of the sarcolemma lead into a network of narrow tubules called **transverse tubules,** or **T tubules.** Filled with extracellular fluid, the T tubules form passageways through the muscle fiber, like a series of tunnels through a mountain.

The T tubules play a major role in coordinating the contraction of the muscle fiber. A muscle fiber contraction occurs through the orderly interaction of both electrical and chemical events. Electrical impulses conducted by the sarcolemma trigger a contraction by altering the chemical environment everywhere inside the muscle fiber. The electrical impulses reach the cell's interior by traveling along the transverse tubules that extend deep into the sarcoplasm of the muscle fiber.

MYOFIBRILS

Inside the muscle fiber, branches of T tubules encircle cylindrical structures called **myofibrils** (Figure 7-2a). A myofibril is 1–2 μm in diameter and as long as the entire muscle fiber. Each muscle fiber contains hundreds to thousands of myofibrils. Myofibrils are bundles of thick and thin **myofilaments,** protein filaments consisting primarily of the proteins *actin* and *myosin* (Figure 7-2a–c). Actin molecules are found in **thin filaments,** and myosin molecules in **thick filaments.** ∞ p. 73

Myofibrils are responsible for muscle fiber contraction. Because they are attached to the sarcolemma at each end of the cell, their contraction shortens the entire cell. Scattered among the myofibrils are mitochondria and granules of glycogen, a source of glucose. The breakdown of glucose and the activity of mitochondria provide the ATP needed to power muscular contractions.

THE SARCOPLASMIC RETICULUM

Wherever a T tubule encircles a myofibril, the tubule is tightly bound to the membranes of the **sarcoplasmic reticulum (SR),** a specialized form of smooth endoplasmic reticulum (Figure 7-2a). The sarcoplasmic reticulum forms a tubular network around each myofibril. On either side of a T tubule lie expanded chambers of the SR called *terminal cisternae* (singular: *cisterna*). As it encircles a myofibril, a transverse tubule lies sandwiched between a pair of terminal cisternae, forming a *triad.*

The terminal cisternae contain high concentrations of calcium ions. The calcium ion concentration in the cytoplasm of all cells is kept very low. Most cells, including skeletal muscle fibers, pump calcium ions across their cell membranes and into the extracellular fluid. Skeletal muscle fibers, however, also actively transport calcium ions into the terminal cisternae of the sarcoplasmic reticulum. A muscle contraction begins when the stored calcium ions are released from the terminal cisternae into the sarcoplasm.

SARCOMERES

Myofilaments (thin and thick filaments) are organized into repeating functional units called **sarcomeres** (SAR-kō-mērz; *sarkos,* flesh + *meros,* part) (Figure 7-2b). Each myofibril consists of approximately 10,000 sarcomeres arranged end to end. *The sarcomere is the smallest functional unit of the muscle fiber. Interactions between the thick and thin filaments of sarcomeres are responsible for muscle contraction.*

The arrangement of thick and thin filaments within a sarcomere produces a banded appearance. All of the myofibrils are arranged parallel to the long axis of the cell, with their sarcomeres lying side by side. As a result, the entire muscle fiber has a banded, or striated, appearance corresponding to the bands of the individual sarcomeres (Figure 7-2a).

Figure 7-2b diagrams the external and internal structure of an individual sarcomere. Each sarcomere has a resting length of about 2 μm. Neither type of filament spans the entire length of a sarcomere. The thick filaments lie in the center of the sarcomere. Thin filaments at either end of the sarcomere are attached to interconnecting proteins that make up the **Z lines,** the boundaries of each sarcomere. From the Z lines, the thin

FIGURE 7-2 The Organization of a Skeletal Muscle Fiber. (a) The structure of a skeletal muscle fiber. **(b)** The organization of a sarcomere, part of a single myofibril. **(c)** The sarcomere in part b, stretched such that thick and thin filaments no longer overlap. (This cannot happen in an intact muscle fiber.) **(d)** The structure of a thin filament. **(e)** The structure of a thick filament.

filaments extend toward the center of the sarcomere, passing among the thick filaments in the *zone of overlap*. Strands of another protein extend from the Z lines to the ends of the thick filaments and keep both types of filaments in alignment. The **M line** is made up of proteins that connect the central portions of each thick filament to its neighbors. The relationships of Z lines and M lines are shown in Figure 7-2c.

Differences in the sizes and densities of thick and thin filaments account for the banded appearance of the sarcomere. The dark **A band** is the area containing thick filaments. The light region between two successive A bands—including the Z line—is the **I band.** (It may help you to remember that in a light micrograph, the A band appears dArk and the I band is lIght.)

Thin and Thick Filaments

Each thin filament consists of a twisted strand of actin molecules (Figure 7-2d). Each actin molecule has an **active site** capable of interacting with myosin. In a resting muscle, the active sites along the thin filaments are covered by strands of the protein **tropomyosin** (trō-pō-MĪ-ō-sin; *trope*, turning). The tropomyosin strands are held in position by molecules of **troponin** (TRŌ-pō-nin) that are bound to the actin strand.

Thick filaments are composed of myosin molecules, each with a *tail* and a globular *head* (Figure 7-2c,e). The myosin molecules are oriented away from the center of the sarcomere, with the heads projecting outward. The myosin heads attach to actin molecules during a contraction. This interaction cannot occur unless the troponin changes position, moving the tropomyosin and exposing the active sites.

Calcium is the "key" that "unlocks" the active sites and starts a contraction. When calcium ions bind to troponin, the protein changes shape, swinging the tropomyosin away from the active sites. Myosin–actin binding can then occur, and a contraction begins. The terminal cisternae of the sarcoplasmic reticulum are the source of the calcium that triggers muscle contraction.

Sliding Filaments and Cross-Bridges

When a sarcomere contracts, the I bands get smaller, the Z lines move closer together, the H bands decrease, and the zones of overlap get larger, but the width of the A bands does not change (Figure 7-3). These observations make sense only if the thin filaments slide toward the center of the sarcomere, alongside the stationary thick filaments. This explanation for sarcomere contraction is called the *sliding filament theory.*

The mechanism responsible for sliding filaments involves the binding of the myosin heads of thick filaments to active sites on the thin filaments. When they connect thick filaments and

Clinical Note

The Muscular Dystrophies

Abnormalities in the genes that code for structural and functional proteins in muscle fibers are responsible for a number of inherited diseases collectively known as the **muscular dystrophies** (DIS-trō-fēz). These conditions, which cause progressive muscular weakness and deterioration, are the result of abnormalities in the sarcolemma or in the structure of internal proteins. The best-known example is *Duchenne muscular dystrophy,* which typically develops in males ages 3 to 7 years.

Sarcomere at rest

Contraction and filament sliding

FIGURE 7-3 Changes in the Appearance of a Sarcomere During Contraction of a Skeletal Muscle Fiber. During a contraction, the A band stays the same width, but the Z lines move closer together and the H band and I band get smaller.

thin filaments, the myosin heads are called **cross-bridges.** When a cross-bridge binds to an active site, it pivots toward the center of the sarcomere (Figure 7-2e), pulling the thin filament in that direction. The cross-bridge then detaches and returns to its original position, ready to repeat a cycle of "attach, pivot, detach, and return," like a person pulling in a rope one-handed.

CHECKPOINT

4. Describe the basic structure of a sarcomere.
5. Why does skeletal muscle appear striated when viewed through a light microscope?
6. Where would you expect the greatest concentration of calcium ions in resting skeletal muscle to be?

See the blue Answers tab at the back of the book.

7-4 Communication between the nervous system and skeletal muscles occurs at neuromuscular junctions

Skeletal muscle fibers contract only under nervous system control. The communication link between the nervous system and a skeletal muscle fiber occurs at a specialized intercellular connection known as a **neuromuscular junction (NMJ)** (Figure 7-4a).

THE NEUROMUSCULAR JUNCTION

Each skeletal muscle fiber is controlled by a nerve cell called a *motor neuron.* A single axon of the neuron branches within the perimysium to form a number of fine branches, each of which ends at an expanded **synaptic terminal.** p. 114 Midway along the fiber's length, the synaptic terminal communicates with it as part of a neuromuscular junction. Figure 7-4b depicts the key features of this structure.

The cytoplasm of the synaptic terminal contains mitochondria and vesicles filled with molecules of **acetylcholine** (as-ē-til-KŌ-lēn), or **ACh.** Acetylcholine is a *neurotransmitter,* a chemical released by a neuron to communicate with other cells. Neurotransmitters change the properties of another cell's membrane, in this case its permeability. The release of ACh from the synaptic terminal results in changes in the sarcolemma that trigger the contraction of the muscle fiber.

A narrow space, the **synaptic cleft,** separates the synaptic terminal from the sarcolemma. This portion of the membrane, which contains receptors that bind ACh, is known as the **motor end plate.** Both the synaptic cleft and the motor end plate contain the enzyme **acetylcholinesterase** (**AChE,** or *cholinesterase*), which breaks down molecules of ACh.

Neurons control skeletal muscle fibers by stimulating the production of an **action potential,** or electrical impulse, in the sarcolemma. In brief, events occur as follows (Figure 7-4c):

Step 1 *Arrival of an action potential at the synaptic terminal.*

Step 2 *Release of acetylcholine.* When an action potential traveling along the axon of a motor neuron reaches the synaptic terminal, vesicles in the synaptic terminal release acetylcholine into the synaptic cleft.

Step 3 *Binding of ACh at the motor end plate.* The ACh molecules diffuse across the synaptic cleft and bind to ACh receptors on the sarcolemma. This event changes the permeability of the membrane to sodium ions. The resulting sudden rush of sodium ions into the sarcoplasm produces an action potential in the sarcolemma. (We will examine the formation and conduction of action potentials more closely in Chapter 8.)

Step 4 *Appearance of an action potential at the sarcolemma.* The action potential spreads over the entire sarcolemma surface. It also travels down all of the transverse tubules toward the terminal cisternae that encircle the sarcomeres of the muscle fiber.

Step 5 *Return to initial state.* The ACh has been broken down by AChE and the sequence of events can now be repeated with another action potential.

Clinical Note

Interference with Neural Control Mechanisms

Any condition that interferes with the generation of an action potential in the sarcolemma will cause muscular paralysis. Two examples are worth noting.

Botulism results from the consumption of foods (often canned or smoked) contaminated with a bacterial toxin. The toxin prevents the release of ACh at the synaptic terminals, leading to a potentially fatal muscular paralysis.

The progressive muscular paralysis seen in **myasthenia gravis** results from the loss of ACh receptors at the motor end plate. The primary cause is a misguided attack on ACh receptors by the immune system. Genetic factors play a role in predisposing individuals to develop this condition.

FIGURE 7-4 The Structure and Function of the Neuromuscular Junction. (a) This colorized SEM shows a neuromuscular junction. **(b)** An action potential (red arrow) carried by the nerve axon arrives at the synaptic terminal. **(c)** The chemical communication between the synaptic terminal and motor end plate triggers an action potential in the sarcolemma.

FIGURE 7-5 Molecular Events of the Contraction Process.

Clinical Note

Rigor Mortis

Upon death, circulation ceases and skeletal muscles are deprived of nutrients and oxygen. Within a few hours, skeletal muscle fibers have run out of ATP, and the sarcoplasmic reticulum becomes unable to remove calcium ions from the sarcoplasm. Calcium ions diffusing into the sarcoplasm from the extracellular fluid or leaking out of the sarcoplasmic reticulum then trigger a sustained contraction. Without ATP, the cross-bridges cannot detach from the active sites, and the muscle locks in the contracted position. All of the body's skeletal muscles are involved, and the individual becomes "stiff as a board." This physical state, called rigor mortis, lasts until the lysosomal enzymes released by autolysis break down the myofilaments 15–25 hours later.

The passage of an action potential along the T tubules triggers a sudden, massive release of calcium ions by the terminal cisternae. As active sites become exposed on the thin filaments, cross-bridge interactions occur, and a contraction begins. Because all of the terminal cisternae in the muscle fiber are affected, this contraction is a combined effort involving every sarcomere on every myofibril. While the contraction process gets under way, ACh is being broken down by AChE.

THE CONTRACTION CYCLE

In the resting sarcomere, each cross-bridge is bound to a molecule of ADP and a phosphate group (PO_4^{3-}), the products released by the breakdown of an ATP molecule. The cross-bridge stores the energy released by the breakage of the high-energy bond. In effect, the resting cross-bridge is "primed" for a contraction, like a cocked pistol or a set mousetrap.

The contraction process involves the following five interlocking steps, which are shown schematically in Figure 7-5:

Step 1 The active site is exposed following the binding of calcium ions (Ca^{2+}) to troponin.

Step 2 The myosin cross-bridge forms and attaches to the exposed active site on the thin filaments.

RESTING SARCOMERE

STEP 5 — MYOSIN REACTIVATION

Step 3 The attached myosin head pivots toward the center of the sarcomere, and ADP and a phosphate group are released. This step uses the energy that was stored in the myosin molecule at rest.

Step 4 The cross-bridges detach when the myosin head binds another ATP molecule.

Step 5 The detached myosin head is reactivated as it splits the ATP and captures the released energy. The entire cycle can now be repeated, beginning with Step 2.

This cycle is broken when calcium ion concentrations return to normal resting levels, primarily through active transport into the sarcoplasmic reticulum. If a single action potential

STEP **1** ACTIVE-SITE EXPOSURE

STEP **2** CROSS-BRIDGE FORMATION

STEP **4** CROSS-BRIDGE DETACHMENT

STEP **3** PIVOTING OF MYOSIN HEAD

The Big Picture

Skeletal muscle fibers shorten as thin filaments interact with thick filaments and sliding occurs. The trigger for contraction is the appearance of free calcium ions in the sarcoplasm; the calcium ions are released by the sarcoplasmic reticulum when the muscle fiber is stimulated by the associated motor neuron. Contraction is an active process; relaxation and the return to resting length are entirely passive.

sweeps across the sarcolemma, calcium ion removal occurs very rapidly, and the contraction will be very brief. A sustained contraction will occur only if action potentials occur one after another, and calcium loss from the terminal cisternae continues.

Table 7-1 (p. 204) provides a summary of the contraction process, from ACh release to the end of the contraction.

CHECKPOINT

7. Describe the neuromuscular junction.

8. How would a drug that blocks acetylcholine release affect muscle contraction?

9. What would you expect to happen to a resting skeletal muscle if the sarcolemma suddenly became very permeable to calcium ions?

See the blue Answers tab at the back of the book.

TABLE 7-1 A Summary of the Steps Involved in Skeletal Muscle Contraction

STEPS THAT START A CONTRACTION

1. At the neuromuscular junction, ACh released by the synaptic terminal binds to receptors on the sarcolemma.

2. The resulting change in the membrane potential of the muscle fiber leads to the production of an action potential that spreads across the entire surface of the muscle fiber and along the T tubules.

3. The sarcoplasmic reticulum (SR) releases stored calcium ions, increasing the calcium concentration of the sarcoplasm in and around the sarcomeres.

4. Calcium ions bind to troponin, resulting in the movement of tropomyosin and the exposure of active sites on the thin (actin) filaments. Cross-bridges form when myosin heads bind to active sites.

5. The contraction begins as repeated cycles of cross-bridge binding, pivoting, and detachment occur, powered by the breakdown of ATP. These events produce filament sliding, and the muscle fiber shortens.

STEPS THAT END A CONTRACTION

6. Action potential generation ceases as ACh is broken down by acetylcholinesterase (AChE).

7. The SR reabsorbs calcium ions, and the concentration of calcium ions in the sarcoplasm declines.

8. When calcium ion concentrations approach normal resting levels, the troponin and tropomyosin molecules return to their normal positions. This change re-covers the active sites and prevents further cross-bridge interaction.

9. Without cross-bridge interactions, further sliding cannot take place and the contraction ends.

10. Muscle relaxation occurs, and the muscle returns passively to its resting length.

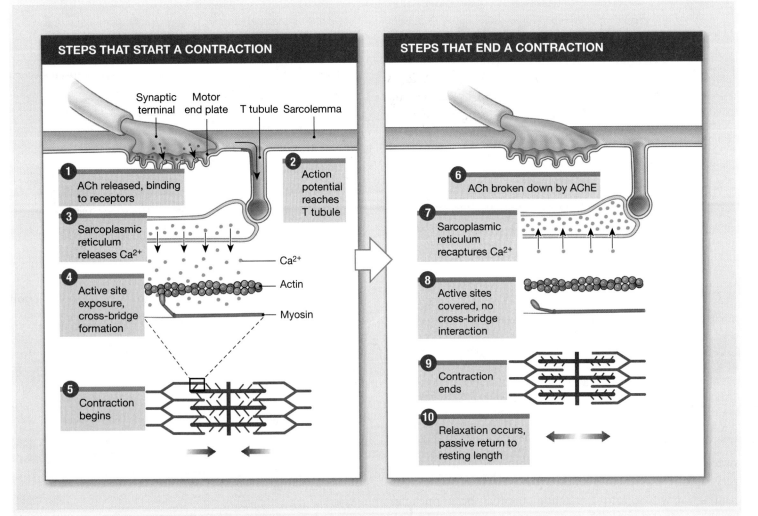

STEPS THAT START A CONTRACTION

Synaptic terminal Motor end plate T tubule Sarcolemma

1 ACh released, binding to receptors

2 Action potential reaches T tubule

3 Sarcoplasmic reticulum releases Ca²⁺

Ca²⁺

4 Active site exposure, cross-bridge formation

Actin

Myosin

5 Contraction begins

STEPS THAT END A CONTRACTION

6 ACh broken down by AChE

7 Sarcoplasmic reticulum recaptures Ca²⁺

8 Active sites covered, no cross-bridge interaction

9 Contraction ends

10 Relaxation occurs, passive return to resting length

7-5 Sarcomere shortening and muscle fiber stimulation produce tension

Now that we are familiar with the contraction of individual muscle fibers, we can examine the performance of skeletal muscles. In this section we will consider the coordinated contractions of an entire population of muscle fibers.

The individual muscle cells in muscle tissue are surrounded and tied together by connective tissue. When muscle cells contract, they pull on collagen fibers, producing an active force called **tension.** Tension applied to an object tends to pull the object toward the source of the tension. However, before movement can occur, the applied tension must overcome the object's **resistance,** a passive force that opposes movement. The amount of resistance can depend on an object's weight and shape, friction, and other factors. In contrast, **compression**— a push applied to an object—tends to force the object away from the source of compression. Muscle cells can only contract (that is, shorten and generate tension); they cannot actively lengthen and generate compression.

The amount of tension produced by an individual muscle fiber depends solely on the number of pivoting cross-bridges it contains. There is no mechanism that regulates the amount of tension produced in that contraction by changing the number of contracting sarcomeres. The muscle fiber is either "on" (producing tension) or "off" (relaxed). Tension production does vary, however, depending on (1) the fiber's resting length at the time of stimulation, which determines the degree of overlap between thick and thin filaments, and (2) the frequency of stimulation, which affects the internal concentration of calcium ions and thus the amount bound to troponin molecules.

An entire skeletal muscle contracts when its component muscle fibers are stimulated. The amount of tension produced in the skeletal muscle *as a whole* is determined by (1) the frequency of muscle fiber stimulation and (2) the number of muscle fibers activated.

FREQUENCY OF MUSCLE FIBER STIMULATION

A **twitch** is a single stimulus-contraction-relaxation sequence in a muscle fiber. Its duration can be as brief as 7.5 msec, as in an eye muscle fiber, or up to 100 msec in fibers of the *soleus,* a small calf muscle. A *myogram* is a graph of tension development in a muscle during a twitch. **Figure 7-6** is a myogram of

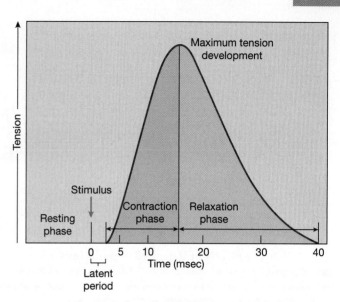

FIGURE 7-6 **The Twitch and Development of Tension.** This myogram plots the time course of a single twitch in the gastrocnemius muscle.

the phases of a 40-msec twitch in the *gastrocnemius muscle,* a prominent calf muscle:

- The **latent period** begins at stimulation and typically lasts about 2 msec. Over this period the action potential sweeps across the sarcolemma, and calcium ions are released by the sarcoplasmic reticulum. No tension is produced by the muscle fiber because contraction has yet to begin.

- In the **contraction phase,** tension rises to a peak. Throughout this period the cross-bridges are interacting with the active sites on the actin filaments. Maximum tension is reached roughly 15 msec after stimulation.

- During the **relaxation phase,** muscle tension falls to resting levels as calcium levels drop, active sites are being covered, and the number of cross-bridges declines. This phase lasts about 25 msec.

A single stimulation produces a single twitch, but twitches in a skeletal muscle do not accomplish anything useful. All normal activities involve sustained muscle contractions. Such contractions result from repeated stimulations.

Summation and Incomplete Tetanus

If a second stimulus arrives before the relaxation phase has ended, a second, more powerful contraction occurs. The addition of one twitch to another in this way is called **summation** (Figure 7-7a). If the muscle is stimulated repeatedly such that it is never allowed to relax completely, the tension rises and

(a) **Summation of twitches**

(b) **Incomplete tetanus**

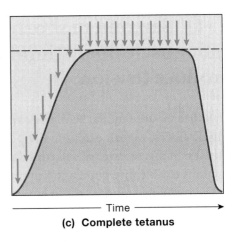

(c) **Complete tetanus**

FIGURE 7-7 **The Effects of Repeated Stimulations. (a)** During summation, tension rises when successive stimuli arrive before the relaxation phase has been completed. **(b)** Incomplete tetanus occurs if the rate of stimulation increases further. Tension production rises to a peak, and the periods of relaxation are very brief. **(c)** In complete tetanus, the frequency of stimulation is so high that the relaxation phase has been completely eliminated, and tension plateaus at the maximal level.

peaks (Figure 7-7b). A muscle producing almost peak tension during rapid cycles of contraction and relaxation is said to be in **incomplete tetanus** (*tetanos*, convulsive tension). Virtually all normal muscular contractions involve incomplete tetanus of the participating muscle fibers.

Complete Tetanus

Complete tetanus occurs when the rate of stimulation is increased until the relaxation phase is completely eliminated, producing maximum tension (Figure 7-7c). In complete tetanus, the action potentials are arriving so fast that the sarcoplasmic

reticulum does not have time to reclaim calcium ions. The high calcium ion concentration in the cytoplasm prolongs the state of contraction, making it continuous.

NUMBER OF MUSCLE FIBERS ACTIVATED

We have a remarkable ability to control the amount of tension exerted by our skeletal muscles so that during a normal movement, our muscles contract smoothly, not jerkily. Such control is accomplished by controlling the number of stimulated muscle fibers in the skeletal muscle.

Clinical Note

The Disease Called Tetanus

Children are often told to be careful around rusty nails. Parents should worry most not about the rust or the nail, but about infection with a very common bacterium, *Clostridium tetani*. This bacterium can cause the disease called **tetanus.** Although they share a name, the disease tetanus has no relation to the normal muscle response to neural stimulation. The *Clostridium* bacteria, although found virtually everywhere, can thrive only in tissues that contain abnormally low amounts of oxygen. For this reason, a deep puncture wound, such as that from a nail, carries a much greater risk than a shallow, open cut that bleeds freely.

When active in body tissues, these bacteria release a powerful toxin that affects the central nervous system. Motor neurons, which control skeletal muscles throughout the body, are particularly sensitive to it. The toxin suppresses the mechanism that regulates motor neuron activity. The result is a sustained, powerful contraction of skeletal muscles throughout the body.

The incubation period (the time between exposure and the onset of symptoms) is usually less than 2 weeks. The most common early complaints are headache, muscle stiffness, and difficulty swallowing. Because it soon becomes difficult to open the mouth, this disease is also called *lockjaw*. Widespread muscle spasms usually develop within 2–3 days of the initial symptoms and continue for a week before subsiding. After 2–4 weeks, surviving patients recover with no aftereffects.

Although severe tetanus has a 40–60 percent mortality rate, immunization is effective in preventing the disease. Of the approximately 500,000 cases of tetanus worldwide each year, only about 100 occur in the United States, thanks to an effective immunization program. ("Tetanus shots," with booster shots every 10 years, are recommended.) Severe symptoms in unimmunized patients can be prevented by early administration of an antitoxin, usually *human tetanus immune globulin*. However, this treatment does not reduce symptoms that have already appeared.

A typical skeletal muscle contains thousands of muscle fibers. Although some motor neurons control a single muscle fiber, most control hundreds or thousands of muscle fibers through multiple synaptic terminals. All the muscle fibers controlled by a single motor neuron constitute a **motor unit.**

The size of a motor unit indicates how fine the control of movement can be. In the muscles of the eye, where precise control is extremely important, a motor neuron may control two or three muscle fibers. We have much less precise control over our leg muscles, where up to 2000 muscle fibers may respond to stimulation by a single motor neuron. The muscle fibers of each motor unit are intermingled with those of other motor units (Figure 7-8). This intermingling ensures that the direction of pull on a tendon does not change despite variations in the number of activated motor units. When you decide to perform a specific arm movement, specific groups of motor neurons within the spinal cord are stimulated. The contraction begins with the activation of the smallest motor units in the stimulated muscle. Over time, the number of activated motor units gradually increases. The activation of more and more motor units is called **recruitment,** and the result is a smooth, steady increase in muscular tension.

Peak tension production occurs when all the motor units in the muscle are contracting in complete tetanus. Such contractions do not last long, however, because the muscle fibers soon use up their available energy supplies. During a sustained contraction, motor units are activated on a rotating basis, so that some are resting while others are contracting. As a result, when your muscles contract for sustained periods, they produce slightly less than maximal tension.

The Big Picture

All voluntary (intentional) movements involve the sustained contractions of skeletal muscle fibers. The force exerted can be increased by increasing the frequency of action potentials or by recruiting additional motor units.

Muscle Tone

Some of the motor units within any particular muscle are always active, even when the entire muscle is not contracting. Their contractions do not produce enough tension to cause movement, but they do tense and firm the muscle. This resting tension in a skeletal muscle is called **muscle tone.** A muscle with little muscle tone is limp and flaccid, whereas one with moderate muscle tone is quite firm and solid. Resting muscle tone stabilizes the positions of bones and joints. For example, in muscles involved with balance and posture, enough motor units are stimulated to produce the tension needed to maintain body position.

A skeletal muscle that is not regularly stimulated by a motor neuron will **atrophy** (AT-rō-fē; *a,* without + *-trophy,* nourishing): Its muscle fibers will become smaller and weaker. Individuals paralyzed by spinal injuries or other damage to the nervous system gradually lose muscle size and tone in the areas affected. Even a temporary reduction in muscle use can lead to muscular atrophy; compare, for example, arm muscles after a cast has been worn to the same muscles in the other arm. Muscle atrophy is initially reversible, but dying muscle fibers are not replaced, and in extreme atrophy the functional losses are permanent. That is why physical therapy is so important for patients who are temporarily unable to move normally.

ISOTONIC AND ISOMETRIC CONTRACTIONS

Muscle contractions may be classified as isotonic or isometric based on the pattern of tension production and overall change in length. In an

SPINAL CORD

Axons of motor neurons

Motor nerve

Muscle fibers

KEY

Motor unit 1

Motor unit 2

Motor unit 3

FIGURE 7-8 **Motor Units.** Each motor unit is made up of the muscle fibers controlled by a single motor neuron. Muscle fibers of different motor units are intermingled, so the forces applied to the tendon remain roughly balanced regardless of which muscle groups are stimulated.

isotonic (*iso-*, equal + *tonos,* tension) **contraction,** tension rises and the skeletal muscle's length changes. Tension in the muscle remains at a constant level until relaxation occurs. Lifting an object off a desk, walking, and running involve isotonic contractions.

In an **isometric** (*metron,* measure) **contraction,** the muscle as a whole does not change length, and the tension produced never exceeds the resistance. Examples of isometric contractions are pushing against a closed door and trying to pick up a car. These examples are rather unusual, but many of the everyday reflexive muscle contractions that keep your body upright when you stand or sit involve isometric contractions of muscles that oppose the force of gravity.

Normal daily activities involve a combination of isotonic and isometric muscular contractions. As you sit reading this text, isometric contractions of postural muscles stabilize your vertebrae and maintain your upright position. When you next turn a page, the movements of your arm, forearm, hand, and fingers are produced by isotonic contractions.

MUSCLE ELONGATION FOLLOWING CONTRACTION

Recall that no active mechanism for muscle fiber elongation exists; contraction is active, but elongation is passive. After a contraction, a muscle fiber usually returns to its original length through a combination of *elastic forces,* the *movements of opposing muscles,* and *gravity.*

Elastic forces are generated when a muscle fiber contracts and tugs on the flexible extracellular fibers of the endomysium, perimysium, epimysium, and tendons. These fibers are also somewhat elastic, and their recoil gradually helps return the muscle fiber to its original resting length.

Much more rapid returns to resting length result from the contraction of opposing muscles. For example, contraction of the *biceps brachii* muscle on the anterior part of the arm flexes the elbow; contraction of the *triceps brachii* muscle on the posterior surface of the arm extends the elbow. When the biceps brachii contracts, the triceps brachii is stretched; when the biceps brachii relaxes, contraction of the triceps brachii extends the elbow and stretches the muscle fibers of the biceps brachii to their original length.

Gravity may also help lengthen a muscle after a contraction. For example, imagine the biceps brachii muscle fully contracted with the elbow pointing at the ground. When the muscle relaxes, gravity will pull the forearm down, stretching the biceps brachii.

7-6 ATP is the energy source for muscular activity

Muscle contraction requires large amounts of energy. For example, an active skeletal muscle fiber may require some 600 trillion molecules of ATP each second, not including the energy needed to pump the calcium ions back into the sarcoplasmic reticulum. This enormous amount of energy is not available before a contraction begins in a resting muscle fiber. Instead, a resting muscle fiber contains only enough energy reserves to sustain a contraction until additional ATP can be generated. Throughout the rest of the contraction, the muscle fiber will generate ATP at roughly the same rate as it is used. This section discusses how muscle fibers meet the demand for ATP.

ATP AND CP RESERVES

The primary function of ATP is the transfer of energy from one location to another, not the long-term storage of energy. At rest, a skeletal muscle fiber produces more ATP than it needs. Under these conditions, ATP transfers energy to *creatine* (KRĒ-uh-tēn), a small molecule assembled from fragments of amino acids in muscle cells. As Figure 7-9a shows, the energy transfer creates another high-energy compound, **creatine phosphate (CP):**

$$\text{ATP} + \text{creatine} \longrightarrow \text{ADP} + \text{creatine phosphate}$$

During a contraction, each cross-bridge breaks down ATP, producing ADP and a phosphate group. The energy stored in creatine phosphate is then used to "recharge" the ADP back to ATP through the reverse reaction:

$$\text{ADP} + \text{creatine phosphate} \longrightarrow \text{ATP} + \text{creatine}$$

(a) Resting muscle

(b) Moderate activity

(c) Peak activity

FIGURE 7-9 **Muscle Metabolism. (a)** A resting muscle generates ATP from the breakdown of fatty acids through aerobic metabolism. The ATP is used to build reserves of ATP, CP, and glycogen. **(b)** A muscle at a modest level of activity meets the ATP demands through the aerobic metabolism of fatty acids and glucose. **(c)** A muscle at peak activity meets the ATP demands primarily through glycolysis, an anaerobic process leading to the production of lactic acid. Mitochondrial activity (not shown) now provides only about one-third of the ATP consumed.

The enzyme that regulates this reaction is **creatine phosphokinase** (**CPK** or **CK**). When muscle cells are damaged, CPK leaks into the bloodstream. Thus, a high blood level of CPK usually indicates serious muscle (cardiac or skeletal muscle) damage.

A resting skeletal muscle fiber contains about six times as much creatine phosphate as ATP. But when a muscle fiber is undergoing a sustained contraction, these energy reserves will be exhausted in about 15 seconds. The muscle fiber must then rely on other mechanisms to convert ADP to ATP.

ATP GENERATION

As you may recall from Chapter 3, cells in the body generate ATP through *aerobic* (oxygen-requiring) *metabolism* in mitochondria and through *glycolysis* in the cytoplasm. ∞ p. 77 Glycolysis is an **anaerobic** (non-oxygen-requiring) process.

Aerobic Metabolism

Aerobic metabolism normally provides 95 percent of the ATP needed by a resting cell. In this process, mitochondria absorb oxygen, ADP, phosphate ions, and small organic substrate molecules from the surrounding cytoplasm. The organic substrates are carbon chains produced by the breakdown of carbohydrates, lipids, or proteins. The substrates enter the *TCA (tricarboxylic acid) cycle* (also known as the *citric acid cycle* or the *Krebs cycle*) and are then completely disassembled by a series of chemical reactions. In brief, the carbon atoms and oxygen atoms are released as carbon dioxide (CO_2). The hydrogen atoms are shuttled to *respiratory enzymes* in the inner mitochondrial membrane, where their electrons are removed. The protons and electrons thus produced ultimately recombine with oxygen to form water (H_2O). Along the way, large amounts of energy are released and used to make ATP. The aerobic metabolism of a common carbohydrate substrate, pyruvic acid, is quite efficient; for each pyruvic acid molecule broken down in the TCA cycle, the cell gains 17 ATP molecules.

Resting skeletal muscle fibers rely primarily on the aerobic metabolism of fatty acids to make ATP (Figure 7-9a). These fatty acids are absorbed from the circulation. When the muscle starts contracting, the mitochondria begin breaking down molecules of pyruvic acid instead of fatty acids. The pyruvic acid is provided through the process of glycolysis (discussed shortly).

The maximum rate of ATP generation within mitochondria is limited by the availability of oxygen. A sufficient supply of oxygen becomes a problem as the energy demands of the muscle fiber increase. Although oxygen consumption and energy production by mitochondria can increase to 40 times resting levels, the energy demands of the muscle fiber may increase by 120 times. Thus, at peak levels of exertion, mitochondrial activity provides only around one-third of the required ATP.

Glycolysis

Glycolysis is the breakdown of glucose to pyruvic acid in the cytoplasm of the cell. The ATP yield of glycolysis is much lower than that of aerobic metabolism; however, because it can proceed in the absence of oxygen, *glycolysis can continue to provide ATP when the availability of oxygen limits the rate of mitochondrial ATP production.*

The glucose broken down under these conditions is obtained from glycogen reserves in the sarcoplasm. Glycogen is a polysaccharide chain of glucose molecules. ∞ p. 42 Typical skeletal muscle fibers contain large glycogen reserves in the form of insoluble granules. When the muscle fiber begins to run short of ATP and CP, enzymes break the glycogen molecules apart, releasing glucose that can be used to generate more ATP.

ENERGY USE AND THE LEVEL OF MUSCLE ACTIVITY

In a resting skeletal muscle cell the demand for ATP is low. More than enough oxygen is available for mitochondria to meet that demand and produce a surplus of ATP. The extra ATP is used to build up reserves of CP and glycogen (Figure 7-9a). At moderate levels of activity, the demand for ATP increases (Figure 7-9b). As the rate of mitochondrial ATP production rises, so does the rate of oxygen consumption. So long as sufficient oxygen is available, the demand for ATP can be met by the mitochondria, and the amount of ATP provided by glycolysis remains relatively minor.

At periods of peak activity, oxygen cannot diffuse into the muscle fiber fast enough to enable the mitochondria to produce the required ATP. Mitochondrial activity can provide only about one-third the ATP needed, and glycolysis becomes the primary source of ATP (Figure 7-9c). The anaerobic process of glycolysis enables the cell to continue generating ATP when mitochondrial activity alone cannot meet the demand. However, this pathway has its drawbacks. For example, when glycolysis produces pyruvic acid faster than it can be used by the mitochondria, pyruvic acid levels rise in the sarcoplasm. Under these conditions, the pyruvic acid is converted to **lactic acid,** a related three-carbon molecule. The conversion of pyruvic acid to lactic acid poses a problem because lactic acid is an or-ganic acid that in body fluids dissociates into a hydrogen ion and a *lactate ion.* The accumulation of hydrogen ions can lower the pH and alter the normal functioning of key enzymes. The muscle fiber then cannot continue to contract.

Glycolysis is also an inefficient way to generate ATP. Under anaerobic conditions, each glucose generates two pyruvic acids, which are converted to lactic acid. In return, the cell gains 2 ATP molecules. Had those 2 pyruvic acid molecules been catabolized aerobically in a mitochondrion, the cell would have gained an additional 34 ATP molecules.

MUSCLE FATIGUE

A skeletal muscle fiber is said to be fatigued when it can no longer contract despite continued neural stimulation. **Muscle fatigue** is caused by the exhaustion of energy reserves or the buildup of lactic acid.

If the muscle contractions use ATP at or below the maximum rate of mitochondrial ATP generation, the muscle fiber can function aerobically. Under these conditions, fatigue will not occur until glycogen and other reserves such as lipids and amino acids are depleted. This type of fatigue affects the muscles of endurance athletes, such as marathon runners, after hours of exertion.

When a muscle produces a sudden, intense burst of activity, the ATP is provided by glycolysis. After a relatively short time (seconds to minutes), the rising lactic acid levels lower the tissue pH, and the muscle can no longer function normally. Athletes running sprints, such as the 100-yard dash, suffer from this type of muscle fatigue.

THE RECOVERY PERIOD

When a muscle fiber contracts, conditions in the sarcoplasm are changed: Energy reserves are consumed, heat is released, and lactic acid may be produced. During the **recovery period,** conditions within the muscle are returned to normal preexertion levels. The muscle's metabolic activity focuses on the removal of lactic acid and the replacement of intracellular energy reserves, and the body as a whole loses the heat generated during intense muscular contraction.

Lactic Acid Recycling

The reaction that converts pyruvic acid to lactic acid is freely reversible. During the recovery period, when oxygen is available, lactic acid can be recycled by converting it back to pyruvic acid. This pyruvic acid can then be used as a building block to synthesize glucose or be used by mitochondria to generate ATP. The ATP is used to convert creatine to creatine phosphate and to store the newly synthesized glucose as glycogen.

During the recovery period, the body's oxygen demand remains elevated above normal resting levels. The additional oxygen required during the recovery period to restore the normal preexertion levels is called the **oxygen debt.** Most of the extra oxygen is consumed by liver cells, as they produce ATP for the conversion of lactic acid back to glucose, and by muscle cells, as they restore their reserves of ATP, creatine phosphate, and glycogen. Other cells, including sweat gland cells, also increase their rate of oxygen use and ATP generation. While the oxygen debt is being repaid, breathing rate and depth are increased. That is why you continue to breathe heavily for a time after you stop exercising.

Heat Loss

Muscular activity generates substantial amounts of heat that warms the sarcoplasm, interstitial fluid, and circulating blood. Because muscle makes up a large portion of total body mass, muscle contractions play an important role in the maintenance of normal body temperature. Shivering, for example, can help keep you warm in a cold environment. But when skeletal muscles are contracting at peak levels, body temperature soon begins to climb. In response, blood flow to the skin increases, promoting heat loss through mechanisms described in Chapters 1 and 5. ∞pp. 13, 126

The Big Picture

Skeletal muscles at rest metabolize fatty acids and store glycogen. During light activity, muscles can generate ATP through the aerobic breakdown of carbohydrates, lipids, or amino acids. At peak levels of activity, most of the energy is provided by anaerobic reactions that generate lactic acid as a by-product.

CHECKPOINT

13. How do muscle cells continuously synthesize ATP?

14. What is muscle fatigue?

15. Define oxygen debt.

See the blue Answers tab at the back of the book.

7-7 Muscle fiber type and physical conditioning determine muscle performance capabilities

Muscle performance can be considered in terms of **force,** the maximum amount of tension produced by a particular muscle or muscle group, and **endurance,** the amount of time over which the individual can perform a particular activity. Two major factors determine the performance capabilities of a particular skeletal muscle: the types of muscle fibers within the muscle, and physical conditioning or training.

TYPES OF SKELETAL MUSCLE FIBERS

The human body contains two contrasting types of skeletal muscle fibers: fast (or fast-twitch) fibers and slow (or slow-twitch) fibers.

Fast Fibers

Most of the skeletal muscle fibers in the body are called **fast fibers** because they can contract in 0.01 second or less following stimulation. Fast fibers are large in diameter and contain densely packed myofibrils, large glycogen reserves, and relatively few mitochondria. The tension produced by a muscle fiber is directly proportional to the number of myofibrils, so fast-fiber muscles produce powerful contractions. However, because these contractions use ATP very quickly, their activity is primarily supported by glycolysis, and fast fibers fatigue rapidly.

Slow Fibers

Slow fibers are only about half the diameter of fast fibers, and they take three times as long to contract after stimulation; however, they can continue contracting for extended periods, long after a fast muscle would have become fatigued. Three specializations related to the availability and use of oxygen make this possible:

1. *Oxygen supply.* Slow muscle tissue contains a more extensive network of capillaries than does typical fast muscle tissue, so oxygen supply is dramatically increased.

2. *Oxygen storage.* Slow muscle fibers contain the red pigment **myoglobin** (MĪ-ō-glō-bin), a globular protein structurally related to hemoglobin, the oxygen-carrying

pigment found in blood. ∞ p. 48 Because myoglobin also binds oxygen molecules, resting slow muscle fibers contain oxygen reserves that can be mobilized during a contraction.

3. *Oxygen use.* Slow muscle fibers contain a relatively larger number of mitochondria than do fast muscle fibers.

The Distribution of Muscle Fibers and Muscle Performance

The percentages of fast and slow muscle fibers can vary considerably among skeletal muscles. Muscles dominated by fast fibers appear pale, and they are often called **white muscles.** Chicken breasts contain "white meat" because chickens use their wings for only brief intervals (as when fleeing from a predator), and the power for flight comes from the anaerobic process of glycolysis in the fast fibers of their breast muscles. The extensive blood vessels and myoglobin in slow muscle fibers give them a reddish color, and muscles dominated by slow fibers are, therefore, known as **red muscles.** Chickens walk around all day, and these movements are powered by aerobic metabolism in the slow muscle fibers of the "dark meat" of their legs.

Most human muscles contain a mixture of fiber types and, therefore, appear pink. However, there are no slow fibers in muscles of the eye and hand, where swift but brief contractions are required. Many back and calf muscles are dominated by slow fibers; these muscles contract almost continuously to maintain an upright posture. The percentage of fast versus slow fibers in each muscle is genetically determined, but the fatigue resistance of fast muscle fibers can be increased through athletic training.

PHYSICAL CONDITIONING

Physical conditioning and training schedules enable athletes to improve both power and endurance. In practice, the training schedule varies depending on whether the activity is primarily supported by aerobic or anaerobic energy production.

Anaerobic endurance is the length of time muscle contractions can be supported by glycolysis and existing energy reserves of ATP and CP. Examples of activities that require anaerobic endurance are a 50-yard dash or swim, a pole vault, and a weight-lifting competition. Such activities involve contractions of fast muscle fibers. Athletes training to develop anaerobic endurance perform frequent, brief, intense workouts. The net effect is an enlargement, or **hypertrophy** (hī-PER-trō-fē), of the stimulated muscles, as seen in champion

The Big Picture

What you don't use, you lose. Muscle tone is an indication of the background level of activity in the motor units in skeletal muscles. When inactive for days or weeks, muscles become flaccid, and the muscle fibers break down their contractile proteins and grow smaller and weaker. If inactive for long periods, muscle fibers may be replaced by fibrous tissue.

weight lifters or bodybuilders. The number of muscle fibers does not change, but the muscle as a whole gets larger because each muscle fiber increases in diameter.

Aerobic endurance is the length of time a muscle can continue to contract while being supported by mitochondrial activities. Aerobic endurance is determined by the availability of substrates for aerobic metabolism from the breakdown of carbohydrates, lipids, or amino acids. Training to improve aerobic endurance usually involves sustained low levels of muscular activity. Examples are jogging, distance swimming, and other exercises that do not require peak tension production. Because glucose is a preferred energy source, endurance athletes often load up on carbohydrates ("carboload") on the day before an event. They may also consume glucose-rich "sports drinks" during an event.

CHECKPOINT

16. Why would a sprinter experience muscle fatigue before a marathon runner would?

17. Which activity would be more likely to create an oxygen debt in an individual who regularly exercises: swimming laps or lifting weights?

18. Which type of muscle fibers would you expect to predominate in the large leg muscles of someone who excels at endurance activities such as cycling or long-distance running?

See the blue Answers tab at the back of the book.

7-8 Cardiac and smooth muscle tissues differ structurally and functionally from skeletal muscle tissue

Cardiac muscle tissue and smooth muscle tissue were first introduced in Chapter 4. Here we consider in greater detail the structural and functional properties of these types of muscle tissue.

CARDIAC MUSCLE TISSUE

Cardiac muscle cells are relatively small and usually have a single, centrally placed nucleus. Cardiac muscle tissue is found only in the heart.

Like skeletal muscle fibers, cardiac muscle cells contain an orderly arrangement of myofibrils and are striated, but significant differences exist in their structures and functions. The most obvious structural difference is that cardiac muscle cells are branched, and each cardiac cell contacts several others at specialized sites called **intercalated** (in-TER-ka-lā-ted) **discs** (Figure 7-10a). These cellular connections contain gap junctions that allow the movement of ions and small molecules and the rapid passage of action potentials from cell to cell, resulting in their simultaneous contraction. Because the myofibrils are also attached to the intercalated discs, the cells "pull together" quite efficiently.

Cardiac muscle and skeletal muscle also have the following important functional differences:

- Cardiac muscle tissue contracts without neural stimulation, a property called *automaticity*. The timing of contractions is normally determined by specialized cardiac muscle cells called **pacemaker cells.**

- Cardiac muscle cell contractions last roughly 10 times longer than those of skeletal muscle fibers.

- The properties of cardiac muscle cell membranes differ from those of skeletal muscle fibers. As a result, cardiac muscle tissue cannot undergo tetanus (sustained contraction). This property is important because a heart in tetany could not pump blood.

- An action potential not only triggers the release of calcium from the sarcoplasmic reticulum but also increases the permeability of the cell membrane to extracellular calcium ions.

- Cardiac muscle cells rely on aerobic metabolism for the energy needed to continue contracting. The sarcoplasm contains large numbers of mitochondria and abundant reserves of myoglobin (to store oxygen).

SMOOTH MUSCLE TISSUE

Smooth muscle cells are similar in size to cardiac muscle cells; they also contain a single, centrally located nucleus within each spindle-shaped cell (Figure 7-10b). Smooth muscle tissue is found within almost every organ, forming sheets, bundles, or sheaths around other tissues. In the skeletal, muscular, ner-

Intercalated discs   Cardiac muscle cell   **(a)**   LM × 315

(b)   LM × 65

FIGURE 7-10 Cardiac and Smooth Muscle Tissues. (a) Notice the striations and the intercalated discs in this LM of cardiac muscle tissue. **(b)** Many visceral organs contain layers or sheets of smooth muscle fibers. This LM view shows smooth muscle cells in longitudinal (L) and transverse (T) sections.

vous, and endocrine systems, smooth muscles around blood vessels regulate blood flow through vital organs. In the digestive and urinary systems, rings of smooth muscles, called *sphincters,* regulate movement along internal passageways.

Actin and myosin are present in all three muscle types. However, the internal organization of a smooth muscle cell differs from that of skeletal or cardiac muscle cells in the following ways:

- Smooth muscle tissue lacks myofibrils, sarcomeres, or striations.

TABLE 7-2 **A Comparison of Skeletal, Cardiac, and Smooth Muscle Tissues**

PROPERTY	SKELETAL MUSCLE FIBER	CARDIAC MUSCLE CELL	SMOOTH MUSCLE CELL
Fiber dimensions (diameter × length)	100 μm × up to 60 cm	10–20 μm × 50-100 μm	5–10 μm × 30–200 μm
Nuclei	Multiple, near sarcolemma	Usually single, centrally located	Single, centrally located
Filament organization	In sarcomeres along myofibrils	In sarcomeres along myofibrils	Scattered throughout sarcoplasm
Control mechanism	Neural, at single neuromuscular junction	Automaticity (pacemaker cells)	Automaticity (pacesetter cells), neural or hormonal control
Ca^{2+} source	Release from sarcoplasmic reticulum	Extracellular fluid and release from sarcoplasmic reticulum	Extracellular fluid and release from sarcoplasmic reticulum
Contraction	Rapid onset; tetanus can occur; rapid fatigue	Slower onset; tetanus cannot occur; resistant to fatigue	Slow onset; tetanus can occur; resistant to fatigue
Energy source	Aerobic metabolism at moderate levels of activity; glycolysis (anaerobic) during peak activity	Aerobic metabolism, usually lipid or carbohydrate substrates	Primarily aerobic metabolism

- In smooth muscle cells, the thick filaments are scattered throughout the sarcoplasm, and the thin filaments are anchored within the cytoplasm and to the sarcolemma.

- Adjacent smooth muscle cells are bound together at these anchoring sites, thereby transmitting the contractile forces throughout the tissue.

Smooth muscle tissue differs from other muscle types in several major ways:

- Calcium ions trigger contractions through a different mechanism than that found in other muscle types. Additionally, most of the calcium ions that trigger contractions enter the cell from the extracellular fluid.

- Smooth muscle cells are able to contract over a greater range of lengths than skeletal or cardiac muscle because the actin and myosin filaments are not rigidly organized. This property is important because layers of smooth muscle are found in the walls of organs that undergo large changes in volume, such as the urinary bladder and stomach.

- Many smooth muscle cells are not innervated by motor neurons, and the muscle cells contract either automatically (in response to *pacesetter cells*) or in response to environmental or hormonal stimulation. When smooth muscle fibers are innervated by motor neurons, the neurons involved are not under voluntary control.

Table 7-2 summarizes the structural and functional properties of skeletal, cardiac, and smooth muscle tissue.

CHECKPOINT

19. How do intercalated discs enhance the functioning of cardiac muscle tissue?

20. Extracellular calcium ions are important for the contraction of what type(s) of muscle tissue?

21. Why can smooth muscle contract over a wider range of resting lengths than skeletal muscle?

See the blue Answers tab at the back of the book.

7-9 Descriptive terms are used to name skeletal muscles

The **muscular system** includes all of the skeletal muscles, which can be controlled voluntarily (Figure 7-11). The general appearance of each of the nearly 700 skeletal muscles provides clues to its primary function. Muscles involved with locomotion and posture work across joints, producing movement of the skeleton. Those that support soft tissue form slings or sheets between relatively stable bony elements, whereas those that guard an entrance or exit completely encircle the opening.

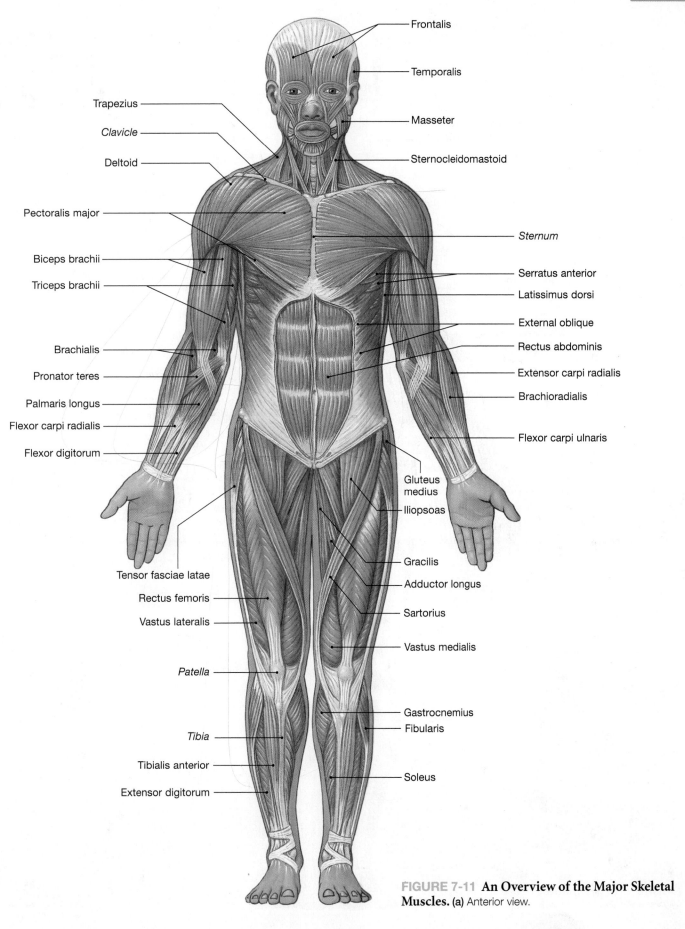

Frontalis

Temporalis

Trapezius

Clavicle

Deltoid

Masseter

Sternocleidomastoid

Pectoralis major

Sternum

Biceps brachii

Serratus anterior

Triceps brachii

Latissimus dorsi

External oblique

Brachialis

Rectus abdominis

Pronator teres

Extensor carpi radialis

Palmaris longus

Brachioradialis

Flexor carpi radialis

Flexor digitorum

Flexor carpi ulnaris

Gluteus medius

Iliopsoas

Tensor fasciae latae

Gracilis

Rectus femoris

Adductor longus

Vastus lateralis

Sartorius

Vastus medialis

Patella

Gastrocnemius

Fibularis

Tibia

Tibialis anterior

Soleus

Extensor digitorum

FIGURE 7-11 **An Overview of the Major Skeletal Muscles. (a)** Anterior view.

Occipitalis

Sternocleidomastoid

Trapezius

Deltoid

Infraspinatus

Teres minor

Teres major

Latissimus dorsi

Triceps brachii

Rhomboid major

Brachioradialis

Extensor carpi
radialis

Flexor carpi ulnaris

Extensor digitorum

Extensor carpi ulnaris

External oblique

Tensor
fasciae
latae

Gluteus
medius

Gluteus
maximus

Adductor
magnus

Semitendinosus

Semimembranosus

Gracilis

Biceps femoris

Sartorius

Gastrocnemius

Soleus

Calcaneal tendon

Calcaneus

FIGURE 7-11 *(continued)*
(b) Posterior view.

Here we consider several features of muscles that are used to name them: their attachment sites, known as origins and insertions, and their actions.

ORIGINS, INSERTIONS, AND ACTIONS

Each muscle begins at an **origin,** ends at an **insertion,** and contracts to produce a specific **action.** In general, a muscle's origin remains stationary while the insertion moves. For example, the *gastrocnemius* muscle (in the calf) has its origin on the distal portion of the femur and inserts on the calcaneus. Its contraction pulls the insertion closer to the origin, resulting in the action called *plantar flexion.* The determinations of origin and insertion are usually based on movement from the anatomical position.

Almost all skeletal muscles either originate or insert on the skeleton. When they contract, they may produce *flexion, extension, adduction, abduction, protraction, retraction, elevation, depression, rotation, circumduction, pronation, supination, inversion,* or *eversion.* (You may wish to review Figures 6-32 to 6-34, pp. 177–178.)

Actions of muscles may be described in two ways. The first describes muscle actions in terms of the bone affected. Accordingly, the *biceps brachii* muscle is said to perform "flexion of the forearm." The second method, which is increasingly used by specialists of human motion *(kinesiologists),* describes muscle action in terms of the joint involved. Thus, the biceps brachii muscle is said to perform "flexion at (or of) the elbow." We will primarily use the second method.

Muscles can also be described by their **primary actions:**

- A **prime mover,** or **agonist** (AG-o-nist), is a muscle whose contraction is chiefly responsible for producing a particular movement. The *biceps brachii* muscle is a prime mover that flexes the elbow.

- **Antagonists** (an-TAG-o-nists) are muscles whose actions oppose the movement produced by another muscle. An antagonist may also be a prime mover. For example, the *triceps brachii* muscle is a prime mover that extends the elbow. It is, therefore, an antagonist of the biceps brachii, and the biceps brachii is an antagonist of the triceps brachii. Agonists and antagonists are functional opposites—if one produces flexion, the other's primary action is extension.

- A **synergist** (*syn-,* together + *ergon,* work) is a muscle that helps a prime mover work efficiently. Synergists may either provide additional pull near the insertion or stabilize the point of origin. For example, the *deltoid muscle* acts to lift the arm away from the body (abduction). A smaller muscle, the *supraspinatus muscle,* assists the deltoid in starting this movement. **Fixators** are synergists that stabilize the origin of a prime mover by preventing movement at another joint.

NAMES OF SKELETAL MUSCLES

You need not learn the name of every skeletal muscle, but you should become familiar with the most important ones. Fortunately, the names assigned to muscles provide clues to their identification. Table 7-3, which summarizes muscle terminology, can be a useful reference as you go through the rest of this chapter. (With the exception of the platysma and the diaphragm, the complete name of every muscle includes the word *muscle.* For simplicity, we have not included the word *muscle* in figures and tables.)

Some names, often those with Greek or Latin roots, refer to the orientation of the muscle fibers. For example, *rectus* means "straight," and *rectus muscles* are parallel muscles whose fibers generally run along the long axis of the body, as in the *rectus abdominis muscle.* In a few cases, a muscle is such a prominent feature that the regional name alone can identify it, such as the *temporalis muscle* of the head. Other muscles are named after structural features. For example, a biceps muscle has two tendons of origin (*bi-,* two + *caput,* head), whereas the *triceps* has three. Table 7-3 also lists names reflecting shape, length, or size, or whether a muscle is visible at the body surface (*externus, superficialis*) or lies beneath (*internus, profundus*). Superficial muscles that position or stabilize an organ are called *extrinsic muscles;* those that operate within an organ are called *intrinsic muscles.*

The first part of many names indicates the muscle's origin, and the second part its insertion. The *sternohyoid muscle,* for example, originates at the sternum and inserts on the hyoid bone. Other names may also indicate the primary function of the muscle. For example, the *extensor carpi radialis muscle* is found along the radial (lateral) border of the forearm, and its contraction produces extension at the wrist (carpal) joint.

The separation of the skeletal system into axial and appendicular divisions provides a useful guideline for subdividing the muscular system as well:

- The **axial musculature** arises on the axial skeleton. It positions the head and spinal column and also moves the rib cage, assisting in the movements that make breathing possible. It does not play a role in movement or support of the pectoral or pelvic girdles or appendages. This category encompasses roughly 60 percent of the skeletal muscles in the body.

- The **appendicular musculature** stabilizes or moves components of the appendicular skeleton.

TABLE 7-3 **Muscle Terminology**

TERMS INDICATING POSITION, DIRECTION, OR MUSCLE FIBER ORIENTATION	TERMS INDICATING SPECIFIC REGIONS OF THE BODY*	TERMS INDICATING STRUCTURAL CHARACTERISTICS OF THE MUSCLE	TERMS INDICATING ACTIONS
Anterior (front)	Abdominis (abdomen)	**Origin**	**General**
Externus (superficial)	Anconeus (elbow)	Biceps (two heads)	Abductor
Extrinsic (outside)	Auricularis (auricle of ear)	Triceps (three heads)	Adductor
Inferioris (inferior)	Brachialis (brachium)	Quadriceps (four heads)	Depressor
Internus (deep, internal)	Capitis (head)		Extensor
Intrinsic (inside)	Carpi (wrist)	**Shape**	Flexor
Lateralis (lateral)	Cervicis (neck)	Deltoid (triangle)	Levator
Medialis/medius (medial, middle)	Cleido-/-clavius (clavicle)	Orbicularis (circle)	Pronator
Obliquus (oblique)	Coccygeus (coccyx)	Pectinate (comblike)	Rotator
Posterior (back)	Costalis (ribs)	Piriformis (pear-shaped)	Supinator
Profundus (deep)	Cutaneous (skin)	Platy- (flat)	Tensor
Rectus (straight, parallel)	Femoris (femur)	Pyramidal (pyramid)	
Superficialis (superficial)	Genio- (chin)	Rhomboid	**Specific**
Superioris (superior)	Glosso-/-glossal (tongue)	Serratus (serrated)	Buccinator (trumpeter)
Transversus (transverse)	Hallucis (great toe)	Splenius (bandage)	Risorius (laughter)
	Ilio- (ilium)	Teres (long and round)	Sartorius (like a tailor)
	Inguinal (groin)	Trapezius (trapezoid)	
	Lumborum (lumbar region)		
	Nasalis (nose)	**Other Striking Features**	
	Nuchal (back of neck)	Alba (white)	
	Oculo- (eye)	Brevis (short)	
	Oris (mouth)	Gracilis (slender)	
	Palpebrae (eyelid)	Lata (wide)	
	Pollicis (thumb)	Latissimus (widest)	
	Popliteus (behind knee)	Longissimus (longest)	
	Psoas (loin)	Longus (long)	
	Radialis (radius)	Magnus (large)	
	Scapularis (scapula)	Major (larger)	
	Temporalis (temples)	Maximus (largest)	
	Thoracis (thoracic region)	Minimus (smallest)	
	Tibialis (tibia)	Minor (smaller)	
	Ulnaris (ulna)	-tendinosus (tendinous)	
	Uro- (urinary)	Vastus (great)	

*For other regional terms, refer to Figure 1-6, p. 16, which shows anatomical landmarks.

CHECKPOINT

22. Identify the kinds of descriptive information used to name skeletal muscles.

23. Which muscle is the antagonist of the biceps brachii?

24. What does the name *flexor carpi radialis longis* tell you about this muscle?

See the blue Answers tab at the back of the book.

7-10 Axial muscles are muscles of the head and neck, vertebral column, trunk, and pelvic floor

The axial muscles fall into four logical groups based on location, function, or both:

1. *Muscles of the head and neck.* These muscles include the muscles responsible for facial expression, chewing, and swallowing.

2. *Muscles of the spine.* This group includes flexors and extensors of the head, neck, and spinal column.

3. *Muscles of the trunk.* The *oblique* and *rectus* muscles form the muscular walls of the thoracic and abdominopelvic cavities.

4. *Muscles of the pelvic floor.* These muscles extend between the sacrum and pelvic girdle and form the muscular *perineum*, which closes the pelvic outlet.

MUSCLES OF THE HEAD AND NECK

The muscles of the head and neck are shown in Figures 7-12 and 7-13 and detailed in Table 7-4 (pp. 200–201). The muscles of

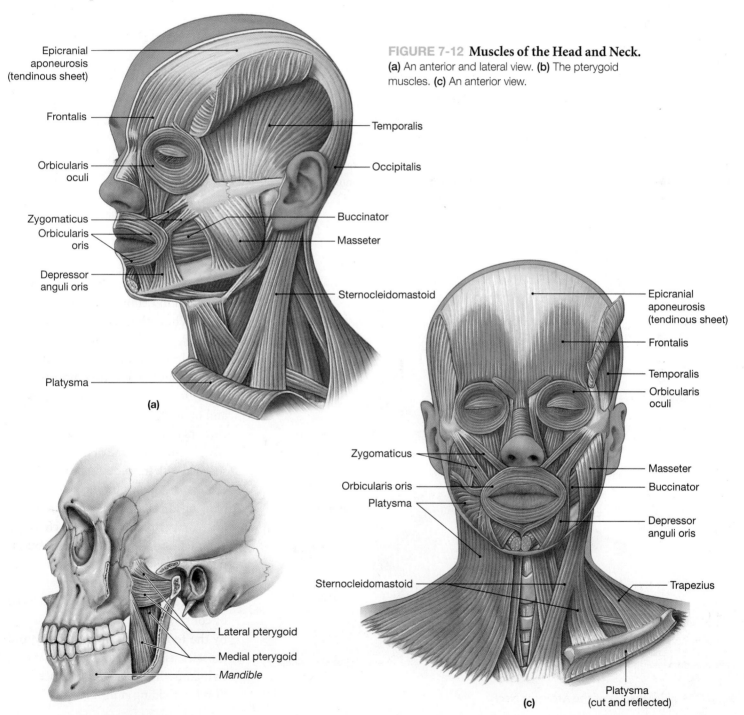

FIGURE 7-12 Muscles of the Head and Neck.
(a) An anterior and lateral view. **(b)** The pterygoid muscles. **(c)** An anterior view.

Epicranial aponeurosis (tendinous sheet)
Frontalis
Orbicularis oculi
Zygomaticus
Orbicularis oris
Depressor anguli oris
Platysma
Temporalis
Occipitalis
Buccinator
Masseter
Sternocleidomastoid

(a)

Lateral pterygoid
Medial pterygoid
Mandible

(b) Lateral view, pterygoid muscles exposed

Zygomaticus
Orbicularis oris
Platysma
Sternocleidomastoid
Epicranial aponeurosis (tendinous sheet)
Frontalis
Temporalis
Orbicularis oculi
Masseter
Buccinator
Depressor anguli oris
Trapezius
Platysma (cut and reflected)

(c)

219

TABLE 7-4 Muscles of the Head and Neck

REGION/MUSCLE	ORIGIN	INSERTION	ACTION
MOUTH			
Buccinator	Maxillary bone and mandible	Blends into fibers of orbicularis oris	Compresses cheeks
Orbicularis oris	Maxillary bone and mandible	Lips	Compresses, purses lips
Depressor anguli oris	Anterolateral surface of mandible	Skin at angle of mouth	Depresses corner of mouth
Zygomaticus	Zygomatic bone	Angle of mouth; upper lip	Draws corner of mouth back and up
EYE			
Orbicularis oculi	Medial margin of orbit	Skin around eyelids	Closes eye
SCALP			
Frontalis	Epicranial aponeurosis	Skin of eyebrow and bridge of nose	Raises eyebrows, wrinkles forehead
Occipitalis	Occipital bone	Epicranial aponeurosis	Tenses and retracts scalp
LOWER JAW			
Masseter	Zygomatic arch	Lateral surface of mandible	Elevates mandible
Temporalis	Along temporal lines of skull	Coronoid process of mandible	Elevates mandible
Pterygoids	Inferior processes of sphenoid	Medial surface of mandible	Elevate, protract, and/or move mandible to either side

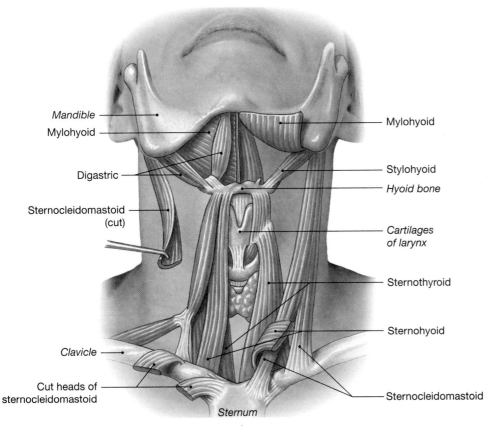

FIGURE 7-13 Muscles of the Anterior Neck.

the face originate on the surface of the skull and insert into the dermis of the skin. When they contract, the skin moves.

The largest group of facial muscles is associated with the mouth. The **orbicularis oris** constricts the opening, and other muscles move the lips or the corners of the mouth. The **buccinator** (BUK-si-nā-tor), one of the muscles associated with the mouth, compresses the cheeks, as when pursing the lips and blowing forcefully. (*Buccinator* translates as "trumpet player.") During chewing, contraction and relaxation of the buccinators move food back across the teeth from the space inside the cheeks. The chewing motions are primarily produced by contractions of the **masseter,** assisted by the **temporalis** and the **pterygoid** muscles used in various combinations. In infants, the buccinator produces suction for suckling at the breast.

TABLE 7-4 **Muscles of the Head and Neck** *(continued)*

REGION/MUSCLE	ORIGIN	INSERTION	ACTION
NECK			
Platysma	From cartilage of second rib to acromion of scapula	Mandible and skin of cheek	Tenses skin of neck, depresses mandible
Digastric	Mastoid region of temporal bone and inferior surface of mandible	Hyoid bone	Depresses mandible and/or elevates larynx
Mylohyoid	Medial surface of mandible	Median connective tissue band that runs to hyoid bone	Elevates floor of mouth and hyoid, and/or depresses mandible
Sternohyoid	Clavicle and sternum	Hyoid bone	Depresses hyoid bone and larynx
Sternothyroid	Dorsal surface of sternum and 1st rib	Thyroid cartilage of larynx	As above
Stylohyoid	Styloid process of temporal bone	Hyoid bone	Elevates larynx
Sternocleidomastoid	Superior margins of sternum and clavicle	Mastoid region of skull	Both sides together flex the neck; one side alone bends head toward shoulder and turns face to opposite side

Smaller groups of muscles control movements of the eyebrows and eyelids, the scalp, the nose, and the external ear. The **epicranium** (ep-i-KRĀ-nē-um), or *scalp*, contains a two part muscle, the *occipitofrontalis*. The anterior **frontalis** muscle and the posterior **occipitalis** muscle of the occipitofrontalis are separated by an *aponeurosis*, or tendinous sheet, called the **epicranial aponeurosis**. The **platysma** (pla-TIZ-muh; *platys*, flat) covers the ventral surface of the neck, extending from the base of the neck to the mandible and the corners of the mouth.

The muscles of the neck control the position of the larynx, depress the mandible, tense the floor of the mouth, and provide a stable foundation for muscles of the tongue and pharynx (Figure 7-13). These muscles include the following:

- The **digastric,** which has two bellies (*di-,* two + *gaster,* stomach), opens the mouth by depressing the mandible.

- The broad, flat **mylohyoid** provides a muscular floor to the mouth and supports the tongue.

- The **stylohyoid** forms a muscular connection between the hyoid bone and the styloid process of the skull.

- The **sternocleidomastoid** (ster-nō-klī-dō-MAS-toyd) extends from the clavicles and the sternum to the mastoid region of the skull. It can rotate the head or flex the neck.

MUSCLES OF THE SPINE

The muscles of the spine are covered by more superficial back muscles, such as the trapezius and latissimus dorsi (Figure 7-11b). The most superior of the spinal muscles are the posterior neck muscles: the superficial **splenius capitis** and the deeper **semispinalis capitis** (Figure 7-14 and Table 7-5). When the left and right pairs of these muscles contract together, they assist each other in extending the head. When both contract on one side, they assist in tilting the head. Because of its more lateral insertion, contraction of the splenius capitis also acts to rotate the head. The *spinal extensors,* or **erector spinae,** act to maintain an erect spinal column and head. Moving laterally from the spine, these muscles can be subdivided into **spinalis, longissimus,** and **iliocostalis** divisions. In the lower lumbar and sacral regions, the border between the longissimus and iliocostalis muscles is indistinct, and they are sometimes known as the *sacrospinalis* muscles. When contracting together, these muscles extend the spinal column. When only the muscles on one side contract, the spine is bent laterally (lateral flexion). Deep to the spinalis muscles, smaller muscles interconnect and stabilize the vertebrae.

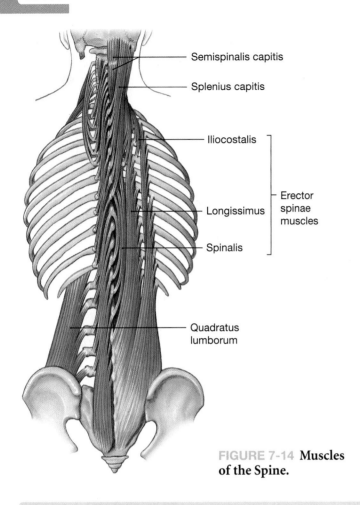

- Semispinalis capitis
- Splenius capitis
- Iliocostalis
- Longissimus — Erector spinae muscles
- Spinalis
- Quadratus lumborum

FIGURE 7-14 **Muscles of the Spine.**

Clinical Note

Hernias

When your abdominal muscles contract forcefully, pressure in your abdominopelvic cavity can skyrocket, and that pressure is applied to internal organs. If you exhale at the same time, the pressure is relieved, because your diaphragm can move upward as the lungs collapse. But during vigorous isometric exercises or when lifting a weight while holding your breath, pressure in the abdominopelvic cavity can rise high enough to cause a variety of problems, among them the development of a hernia.

A **hernia** develops when an organ protrudes through an abnormal opening in the surrounding body cavity wall. The most common hernias are inguinal hernias and diaphragmatic hernias. *Inguinal hernias* typically occur in males, at the *inguinal canal,* the site where blood vessels, nerves, and reproductive ducts pass through the abdominal wall to reach the testes. Elevated abdominal pressure can force open the inguinal canal and push a portion of the intestine into the pocket created. *Diaphragmatic hernias* develop when visceral organs, such as a portion of the stomach, are forced into the left pleural cavity. If herniated structures become trapped or twisted, surgery may be required to prevent serious complications.

TABLE 7-5 Muscles of the Spine

REGION/MUSCLE	ORIGIN	INSERTION	ACTION
SPINAL EXTENSORS			
Splenius capitis	Spinous processes of lower cervical and upper thoracic vertebrae	Mastoid process, base of the skull, and upper cervical vertebrae	The two sides act together to extend the neck; either alone rotates and laterally flexes head to that side
Semispinalis capitis	Spinous processes of lower cervical and upper thoracic vertebrae	Base of skull, upper cervical vertebrae	The two sides act together to extend the neck; either alone laterally flexes head to that side
Spinalis group	Spinous processes and transverse processes of cervical, thoracic, and upper lumbar vertebrae	Base of skull and spinous processes of cervical and upper thoracic vertebrae	The two sides act together to extend vertebral column; either alone extends neck and laterally flexes head or rotates vertebral column to that side
Longissimus group	Processes of lower cervical, thoracic, and upper lumbar vertebrae	Mastoid processes of temporal bone, transverse processes of cervical vertebrae, and inferior surfaces of ribs	The two sides act together to extend vertebral column; either alone rotates and laterally flexes head or vertebral column to that side
Iliocostalis group	Superior borders of ribs and iliac crest	Transverse processes of cervical vertebrae and inferior surfaces of ribs	Extends vertebral column or laterally to that side; moves ribs
SPINAL FLEXOR			
Quadratus lumborum	Iliac crest	Last rib and transverse processes of lumbar vertebrae	Together they depress ribs, flex vertebral column; one side acting alone produces lateral flexion

THE AXIAL MUSCLES OF THE TRUNK

The *oblique muscles* and the *rectus muscles* form the muscular walls of the thoracic and abdominopelvic cavities between the first thoracic vertebra and the pelvis. In the thoracic area, these muscles are partitioned by the ribs, but over the abdominal surface they form broad muscular sheets (Figure 7-15 and Table 7-6). The oblique muscles can compress underlying structures or rotate the spinal column, depending on whether one or both sides are contracting. The rectus muscles are important flexors of the spinal column; they oppose the erector spinae.

The axial muscles of the trunk include (1) the **external** and **internal intercostals,** (2) the muscular **diaphragm** that separates the thoracic and abdominopelvic cavities, (3) the **external** and **internal obliques,** (4) the **transversus abdominis,** (5) the **rectus abdominis,** and (6) the muscles that form the floor of the pelvic cavity.

MUSCLES OF THE PELVIC FLOOR

The floor of the pelvic cavity is called the **perineum** (Figure 7-16 and Table 7-7). It is formed by a broad sheet of muscles that connects the sacrum and coccyx

to the ischium and pubis. These muscles support the organs of the pelvic cavity, flex the coccyx, and control the movement of materials through the urethra and anus.

CHECKPOINT

25. If you were contracting and relaxing your masseter muscle, what would you probably be doing?

26. Which facial muscle would you expect to be well developed in a trumpet player?

27. Damage to the external intercostal muscles would interfere with what important process?

28. If someone were to hit you in your rectus abdominis muscle, how would your body position change?

See the blue Answers tab at the back of the book.

(b) Superior view

(a) Anterior view

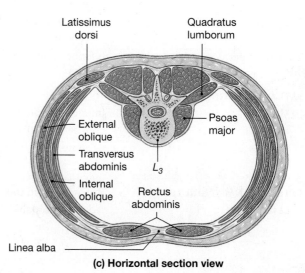

(c) Horizontal section view

FIGURE 7-15 **Oblique and Rectus Muscles and the Diaphragm. (a)** An anterior view. **(b)** A sectional view at the level of the diaphragm. **(c)** A sectional view at the level of the umbilicus.

TABLE 7-6 Axial Muscles of the Trunk

REGION/MUSCLE	ORIGIN	INSERTION	ACTION
THORACIC REGION			
External intercostals	Inferior border of each rib	Superior border of next rib	Elevate ribs
Internal intercostals	Superior border of each rib	Inferior border of the preceding rib	Depress ribs
~~Diaphragm~~	Xiphoid process, cartilages of ribs 4–10, and anterior surfaces of lumbar vertebrae	Central tendinous sheet	Contraction expands thoracic cavity, compresses abdominopelvic cavity
ABDOMINAL REGION			
External oblique	Lower eight ribs	Linea alba and iliac crest	Compresses abdomen, depresses ribs, flexes or laterally flexes vertebral column
Internal oblique	Iliac crest and adjacent connective tissues	Lower ribs, xiphoid of sternum, and linea alba	As above
Transversus abdominis	Cartilages of lower ribs, iliac crest, and adjacent connective tissues	Linea alba and pubis	Compresses abdomen
Rectus abdominis	Superior surface of pubis around symphysis	Inferior surfaces of costal cartilages (ribs 5–7) and xiphoid process	Depresses ribs, flexes vertebral column

TABLE 7-7 Muscles of the Perineum

MUSCLE	ORIGIN	INSERTION	ACTION
BULBOSPONGIOSUS			
Males	Base of penis; fibers cross over urethra	Midline and central tendon of perineum	Compresses base and stiffens penis; ejects urine or semen
Females	Base of clitoris; fibers run on either side of urethral and vaginal openings	Central tendon of perineum	Compresses and stiffens clitoris; narrows vaginal opening
Ischiocavernosus	Inferior medial surface of ischium	Symphysis pubis anterior to base of penis or clitoris	Compresses and stiffens penis or clitoris
Transverse perineus	Inferior medial surface of ischium	Central tendon of perineum	Stabilizes central tendon of perineum
EXTERNAL URETHRAL SPHINCTER			
Males	Inferior medial surfaces of ischium and pubis	Midline at base of penis; inner fibers encircle urethra	Closes urethra, compresses prostate and bulbourethral glands
Females	As above	Midline; inner fibers encircle urethra	Closes urethra, compresses vagina and greater vestibular glands
EXTERNAL ANAL SPHINCTER	By tendon from coccyx	Encircles anal opening	Closes anal opening
Levator ani	Ischial spine, pubis	Coccyx	Tenses floor of pelvis, supports pelvic organs, flexes coccyx, elevates and retracts anus

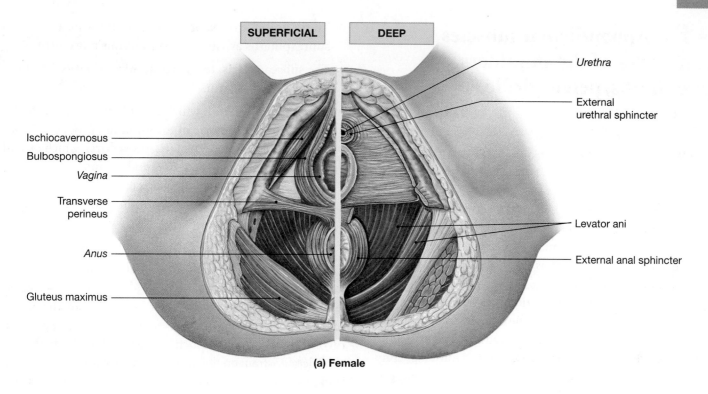

SUPERFICIAL **DEEP**

Urethra

External
urethral sphincter

Ischiocavernosus
Bulbospongiosus
Vagina
Transverse
perineus
Anus

Levator ani

External anal sphincter

Gluteus maximus

(a) Female

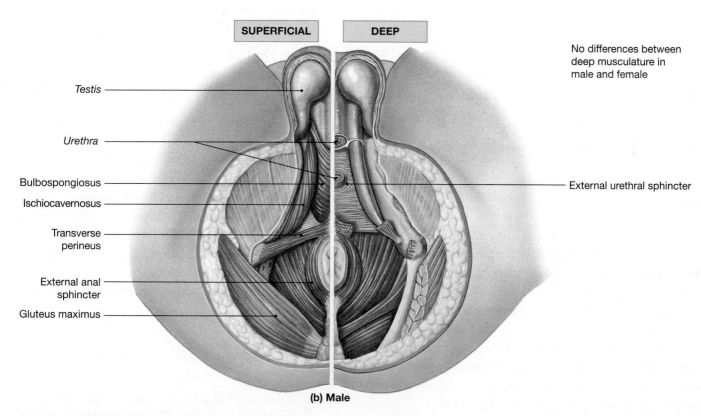

SUPERFICIAL **DEEP**

No differences between
deep musculature in
male and female

Testis

Urethra

Bulbospongiosus
Ischiocavernosus

Transverse
perineus

External anal
sphincter

Gluteus maximus

External urethral sphincter

(b) Male

FIGURE 7-16 **Muscles of the Perineum.**

7-11 Appendicular muscles are muscles of the shoulders, upper limbs, pelvic girdle, and lower limbs

The appendicular musculature includes (1) the muscles of the shoulders and upper limbs and (2) the muscles of the pelvic girdle and lower limbs. Because the functions and required ranges of motion are very different, few similarities exist between the two groups. In addition to increasing the mobility of the upper limb, the muscular connections between the pectoral girdle and the axial skeleton must act as shock absorbers. For example, people can still perform delicate hand movements while jogging because the muscular connections between the axial and appendicular skeleton smooth out the bounces in their stride. In contrast, the pelvic girdle has evolved to transfer weight from the axial to the appendicular skeleton. A muscular connection would reduce the efficiency of the transfer, and the emphasis is on sheer power rather than mobility.

MUSCLES OF THE SHOULDERS AND UPPER LIMBS

Muscles That Position the Pectoral Girdle

The large, superficial **trapezius** muscles cover the back and portions of the neck, reaching to the base of the skull. These muscles form a broad diamond (**Figure 7-17a** and Table 7-8). Its actions are quite varied because specific regions can be made to contract independently. The **rhomboid** muscles and the **levator scapulae** are covered by the trapezius. Both originate on vertebrae and insert on the scapula. Contraction of the rhomboids adducts the scapula, pulling it toward the center of the back. The levator scapulae elevates the scapula, as when you shrug your shoulders.

On the chest, the **serratus anterior** originates along the anterior surfaces of several ribs (**Figure 7-17b**) and inserts along the vertebral border of the scapula. When the serratus anterior contracts, it pulls the shoulder anteriorly. The **pectoralis minor** attaches to the coracoid process of the scapula. When it contracts, it depresses and protracts the scapula.

Muscles That Move the Arm

The muscles that move the arm (**Figure 7-18** and Table 7-9) are easiest to remember when grouped by primary actions:

- The **deltoid** is the major abductor of the arm, and the **supraspinatus** assists at the start of this movement.
- The **subscapularis, teres major, infraspinatus,** and **teres minor** rotate the arm.
- The **pectoralis major,** which extends between the chest and the greater tubercle of the humerus, produces flexion at the shoulder joint. The **latissimus dorsi,** which extends between the thoracic vertebrae and the intertubercular groove of the humerus, produces extension. The two muscles also work together to produce adduction and rotation of the humerus.

These muscles provide substantial support for the shoulder joint. The tendons of the supraspinatus, infraspinatus, teres minor, and subscapularis blend with and support the capsular fibers that enclose the shoulder joint. They are the muscles of the *rotator cuff,* a common site of sports injuries. Sports that involve throwing a ball, such as a baseball or football, place considerable strain on the muscles of the rotator cuff, which can lead to a *muscle strain* (a tear or break in the muscle), *bursitis,* and other painful injuries.

Muscles That Move the Forearm and Wrist

Although most of the muscles that insert on the forearm and wrist (**Figure 7-19** and Table 7-10) originate on the humerus, there are two notable exceptions. The **biceps brachii** and the *long head* tendon of the **triceps brachii** originate on the scapula and insert on the bones of the forearm. Although their contractions can have a secondary effect on the shoulder, their primary actions are at the elbow. The triceps brachii extends the elbow when, for example, you do pushups. The biceps brachii both flexes the elbow and supinates the forearm. With the forearm pronated (palm facing back), the biceps brachii cannot function effectively. As a result, you are strongest when you flex your elbow with a supinated forearm; the biceps brachii then makes a prominent bulge.

Other important muscles include the following:

- The **brachialis** and **brachioradialis** also flex the elbow, opposed by the triceps brachii.
- The **flexor carpi ulnaris,** the **flexor carpi radialis,** and the **palmaris longus** are superficial muscles that work together to produce flexion of the wrist. Because they originate on opposite sides of the humerus, the flexor carpi radialis flexes and abducts the wrist, whereas the flexor carpi ulnaris flexes and adducts the wrist.

| SUPERFICIAL | | DEEP |

- Trapezius
- Infraspinatus
- Deltoid
- Teres minor
- Teres major
- Serratus anterior

- C_1
- C_7
- Levator scapulae
- Rhomboid muscles
- Triceps brachii
- T_{12}

(a) Posterior view

| SUPERFICIAL | | DEEP |

- Trapezius
- Subclavius
- Pectoralis major (cut)
- Pectoralis minor
- Internal intercostals
- External intercostals

- Levator scapulae
- Pectoralis minor (cut)
- Coracobrachialis
- Serratus anterior
- Biceps brachii
- T_{12}

(b) Anterior view

FIGURE 7-17 **Muscles of the Shoulder.**

TABLE 7-8 **Muscles of the Shoulder**

MUSCLE	ORIGIN	INSERTION	ACTION
Levator scapulae	Transverse processes of first 4 cervical vertebrae	Vertebral border of scapula	Elevates scapula
Pectoralis minor	Anterior surfaces of ribs 3–5	Coracoid process of scapula	Depresses and protracts shoulder; rotates scapula laterally (downward); elevates ribs if scapula is stationary
Rhomboid muscles	Spinous processes of lower cervical and upper thoracic vertebrae	Vertebral border of scapula	Adducts and rotates scapula laterally (downward)
Serratus anterior	Anterior and superior margins of ribs 1–9	Anterior surface of vertebral border of scapula	Protracts shoulder, abducts and medially rotates scapula (upward)
Subclavius	First rib	Clavicle	Depresses and protracts shoulder
Trapezius	Occipital bone and spinous processes of thoracic vertebrae	Clavicle and scapula (acromion and scapular spine)	Depends on active region and state of other muscles; may elevate, adduct, depress, or rotate scapula and/or elevate clavicle; can also extend or hyperextend neck

SUPERFICIAL DEEP

Clavicle
Sternum
Deltoid
Pectoralis major

Ribs (cut)
Subscapularis
Coracobrachialis
Teres major
Biceps brachii

(a) Anterior view

FIGURE 7-18 **Muscles That Move the Arm.**

SUPERFICIAL		DEEP

Vertebra T₁

Supraspinatus

Supraspinatus

Deltoid

Infraspinatus

Latissimus dorsi

Supraspinatus

Infraspinatus

Teres minor

Teres major

Triceps brachii

(b) Posterior view

TABLE 7-9 Muscles That Move the Arm

MUSCLE	ORIGIN	INSERTION	ACTION
Coracobrachialis	Coracoid process	Medial margin of shaft of humerus	Adduction and flexion at shoulder
Deltoid	Clavicle and scapula (acromion and adjacent scapular spine)	Deltoid tuberosity of humerus	Abduction at shoulder
Latissimus dorsi	Spinous processes of lower thoracic vertebrae, ribs, and lumbar vertebrae	Intertubercular groove of humerus	Extension, adduction, and medial rotation at shoulder
Pectoralis major	Cartilages of ribs 2–6, body of sternum, and clavicle	Greater tubercle of humerus	Flexion, adduction, and medial rotation at shoulder
Supraspinatus*	Supraspinous fossa of scapula	Greater tubercle of humerus	Abduction at shoulder
Infraspinatus*	Infraspinous fossa of scapula	Greater tubercle of humerus	Lateral rotation at shoulder
Subscapularis*	Subscapular fossa of scapula	Lesser tubercle of humerus	Medial rotation at shoulder
Teres minor*	Lateral border of scapula	Greater tubercle of humerus	Lateral rotation at shoulder
Teres major	Inferior angle of scapula	Intertubercular groove of humerus	Adduction and medial rotation at shoulder

*Rotator cuff muscles

- The **extensor carpi radialis** muscles and the **extensor carpi ulnaris** have a similar relationship; the former produces extension and abduction at the wrist, the latter extension and adduction.

- The **pronators** and the **supinator** rotate the radius at its proximal and distal articulations with the ulna without either flexing or extending the elbow.

Muscles That Move the Hand and Fingers

The muscles of the forearm flex and extend the finger joints (Table 7-10). These muscles end before reaching the hand, and only their tendons cross the wrist. These are relatively large muscles, and keeping them clear of the joints ensures maximum mobility at both the wrist and hand. The tendons that cross the dorsal and ventral surfaces of the wrist are held

FIGURE 7-19 Muscles That Move the Forearm and Wrist. (a) Posterior view of right upper limb. **(b)** Anterior view of right upper limb. **(c)** Anterior view of the muscles of pronation and supination when the limb is supinated.

TABLE 7-10 **Muscles That Move the Forearm, Wrist, and Hand**

MUSCLE	ORIGIN	INSERTION	ACTION
PRIMARY ACTION AT THE ELBOW			
Flexors			
Biceps brachii	*Short head* from the coracoid process and *long head* from the supraglenoid tubercle (both on the scapula)	Tuberosity of radius	Flexion at shoulder and elbow; supination
Brachialis	Anterior, distal surface of humerus	Tuberosity of ulna	Flexion at elbow
Brachioradialis	Lateral epicondyle of humerus	Styloid process of radius	As above
Extensor			
Triceps brachii	Superior, posterior, and lateral margins of humerus, and the scapula	Olecranon of ulna	Extension at elbow
Pronators/Supinator			
Pronator quadratus	Medial surface of distal portion of ulna	Anterior and lateral surface of distal portion of radius	Pronation
Pronator teres	Medial epicondyle of humerus and coronoid process of ulna	Distal lateral surface of radius	As above
Supinator	Lateral epicondyle of humerus and ulna	Anterior and lateral surface of radius distal to the radial tuberosity	Supination
PRIMARY ACTION AT THE WRIST			
Flexors			
Flexor carpi radialis	Medial epicondyle of humerus	Bases of 2nd and 3rd metacarpal bones	Flexion and abduction at wrist
Flexor carpi ulnaris	Medial epicondyle of humerus and adjacent surfaces of ulna	Pisiform bone, hamate bone, and base of 5th metacarpal bone	Flexion and adduction at wrist
Palmaris longus	Medial epicondyle of humerus	A tendinous sheet on the palm	Flexion at wrist
Extensors			
Extensor carpi radialis	Distal lateral surface and lateral epicondyle of humerus	Bases of 2nd and 3rd metacarpal bones	Extension and abduction at wrist
Extensor carpi ulnaris	Lateral epicondyle of humerus and adjacent surface of ulna	Base of 5th metacarpal bone	Extension and adduction at wrist
ACTION AT THE HAND			
Extensor digitorum	Lateral epicondyle of humerus	Posterior surfaces of the phalanges	Extension at finger joints and wrist
Flexor digitorum	Medial epicondyle of humerus; anterior surfaces of ulna and radius; medial and posterior surfaces of ulna	Distal phalanges	Flexion at finger joints and wrist

in place by *tendon sheaths,* wide tubular bursae that reduce friction. p. 175

Inflammation of tendon sheaths can restrict movement and irritate the *median nerve,* a nerve that innervates the palm of the hand. Chronic pain, often associated with weakness in the hand muscles, is the result. This condition is known as *carpal tunnel syndrome.* Fine control of the hand involves small *intrinsic muscles,* which originate on the carpal and metacarpal bones. No muscles originate on the phalanges, and only tendons extend across the distal joints of the fingers.

CHECKPOINT

29. Which muscle do you use to shrug your shoulders?

30. Sometimes baseball pitchers suffer rotator cuff injuries. Which muscles are involved in this type of injury?

31. Injury to the flexor carpi ulnaris would impair which two movements?

See the blue Answers tab at the back of the book.

MUSCLES OF THE PELVIS AND LOWER LIMBS

The muscles of the pelvis and the lower limb can be divided into three functional groups: (1) muscles that work across the hip joint to move the thigh; (2) muscles that work across the knee joint to move the leg; and (3) muscles that work across the various joints of the foot to move the ankles, feet, and toes.

Muscles That Move the Thigh

The muscles that move the thigh are detailed in Figure 7-20 and Table 7-11.

- **Gluteal muscles** cover the lateral surfaces of the ilia (Figure 7-20a). The **gluteus maximus** is the largest and most posterior of the gluteal muscles, which produce extension, rotation, and abduction at the hip.

- The adductors of the thigh include the **adductor magnus,** the **adductor brevis,** the **adductor longus,** the **pectineus** (pek-TI-nē-us), and the **gracilis** (GRAS-i-lis) (Figure 7-20b). When an athlete suffers a *pulled groin,* the problem is a *strain*—a muscle tear or break—in one of these adductor muscles.

- The largest hip flexor is the **iliopsoas** (il-ē-ō-SŌ-us) muscle. The iliopsoas is really two muscles, the **psoas major** and the **iliacus** (il-Ē-ah-kus), which share a common insertion at the lesser trochanter of the femur.

Muscles That Move the Leg

The pattern of muscle distribution in the lower limb is like that in the upper limb: extensors are found along the anterior and lateral surfaces of the limb, and flexors lie along the posterior and medial surfaces (Figure 7-21).

- The four flexors of the knee include three muscles collectively known as the *hamstrings*—the **biceps femoris** (FEM-or-is), the **semimembranosus** (sem-ē-mem-bra-NŌ-sus), and the **semitendinosus** (sem-ē-ten-di-NŌ-sus)—and the **sartorius** (sar-TŌR-ē-us) (Figure 7-21a). A *pulled hamstring* is a relatively common sports injury caused by a strain affecting one of the hamstring muscles.

- Collectively the *knee extensors* are known as the **quadriceps femoris.** The three **vastus** muscles and the **rectus femoris** insert on the patella, which is attached to the tibial tuberosity by the patellar ligament (Figure 7-21b). (Because the vastus intermedius lies under the other quadriceps femoris muscles, it is not visible in Figure 7-21.)

- When you stand, a slight lateral rotation of the tibia can lock the knee in the extended position. This enables you to stand for long periods with minimal muscular effort, but the locked knee cannot be flexed. The **popliteus** (pop-LI-tē-us) muscle medially rotates the tibia back into its normal position, unlocking the joint.

The muscles that move the leg are detailed in Table 7-12 (p. 236).

Muscles That Move the Foot and Toes

Muscles that move the foot and toes are shown in Figure 7-22 and detailed in Table 7-13 (p. 238). Most of the muscles that move the ankle produce the plantar flexion involved with walking and running movements.

- The large **gastrocnemius** (gas-trok-NĒ-mē-us; *gaster,* stomach + *kneme,* knee) of the calf is assisted by the underlying **soleus** (SŌ-lē-us) muscle. These muscles share a common tendon, the **calcaneal tendon,** or *Achilles tendon.*

(b) The gluteal muscle group

(a) Lateral view

FIGURE 7-20 **Muscles That Move the Thigh. (a)** The gluteal muscle group is shown in lateral and posterior views. **(b)** The iliopsoas muscle and the adductor group are shown in an anterior view.

- A pair of deep **fibularis** muscles, or *peroneus* muscles, produces eversion of the foot as well as plantar flexion at the ankle.

- Inversion of the foot is caused by contraction of the **tibialis** (tib-ē-A-lis) muscles; the large **tibialis anterior** dorsiflexes the ankle and opposes the gastrocnemius.

Important digital muscles originate on the surface of the tibia, the fibula, or both, and their tendons pass through tendon sheaths at the ankle joint. Several smaller intrinsic muscles originate on the tarsal and metatarsal bones; their contractions move the toes.

(c) The Iliopsoas muscle and the adductor group

TABLE 7-11 Muscles That Move the Thigh

GROUP/MUSCLE	ORIGIN	INSERTION	ACTION
GLUTEAL GROUP			
Gluteus maximus	Iliac crest of ilium, sacrum, and coccyx	Iliotibial tract and gluteal tuberosity of femur	Extension and lateral rotation at hip
Gluteus medius	Anterior iliac crest and lateral surface of ilium	Greater trochanter of femur	Abduction and medial rotation at hip
Gluteus minimus	Lateral surface of ilium	As above	As above
Tensor fasciae latae	Iliac crest and surface of ilium between anterior iliac spines	Iliotibial tract	Flexion, abduction, and medial rotation at hip; tenses fascia lata, which laterally supports the knee
ADDUCTOR GROUP			
Adductor brevis	Inferior ramus of pubis	Linea aspera of femur	Adduction, flexion, and medial rotation at hip
Adductor longus	Inferior ramus of pubis anterior to adductor brevis	As above	As above
Adductor magnus	Inferior ramus of pubis posterior to adductor brevis	As above	Adduction at hip joint; superior portion produces flexion; inferior portion produces extension
Pectineus	Superior ramus of pubis	Inferior to lesser trochanter of femur	Adduction, flexion, and medial rotation at hip joint
Gracilis	Inferior ramus of pubis	Medial surface of tibia inferior to medial condyle	Flexion at knee; adduction and medial rotation at hip
ILIOPSOAS GROUP			
Iliacus	Medial surface of ilium	Femur distal to lesser trochanter; tendon fused with that of psoas major	Flexion at hip and/or lumbar intervertebral joints
Psoas major	Anterior surfaces and transverse processes of T_{12} and lumbar vertebrae	Lesser trochanter in company with iliacus	As above

Clinical Note

Intramuscular Injections

Drugs are more commonly injected into tissues than directly into the bloodstream. This method enables the physician to introduce a large amount of a drug at one treatment, yet have it enter the circulation gradually. In an **intramuscular (IM) injection,** the drug is introduced into the mass of a large skeletal muscle. Uptake is usually faster and accompanied by less tissue irritation than when drugs are administered *intradermally* or *subcutaneously* (injected into the dermis or subcutaneous layer, respectively). ∞ p. 127 Up to 5 mL of fluid may be injected at one time, and multiple injections are possible.

The most common complications involve accidental injection into a blood vessel or the piercing of a nerve. The sudden entry of massive quantities of a drug into the bloodstream can have unpleasant or even fatal consequences, and damage to a nerve can cause motor paralysis or sensory loss. As a result, the injection site must be selected with care.

Bulky muscles that contain few large vessels or nerves make ideal injection sites, and the gluteus medius or the posterior, lateral, superior portion of the gluteus maximus is often selected. The deltoid muscle of the arm, about 2.5 cm (1 in.) distal to the acromion, is another common site. Probably the most satisfactory from a technical point of view is the vastus lateralis of the thigh, for an injection into this thick muscle will not encounter vessels or nerves. This is the preferred injection site in infants and young children, whose gluteal and deltoid muscles are relatively small. This site is also used in elderly patients or others with atrophied gluteal and deltoid muscles.

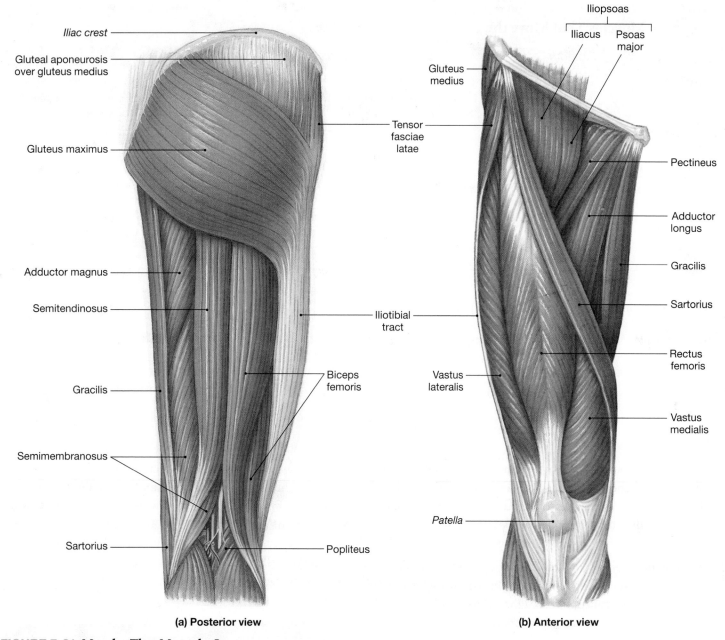

(a) Posterior view

(b) Anterior view

FIGURE 7-21 **Muscles That Move the Leg.**

32. You often hear of athletes suffering a "pulled hamstring." To what does this phrase refer?

33. How would you expect a torn calcaneal tendon to affect movement of the foot?

See the blue Answers tab at the back of the book.

7-12 With advancing age, the size and power of muscle tissue decreases

As the body ages, a general reduction in the size and power of all muscle tissues occurs. The effects of aging on the muscular system can be summarized as follows:

1. *Skeletal muscle fibers become smaller in diameter.* The reduction in size reflects a decrease in the number of my-

TABLE 7-12 Muscles That Move the Leg

MUSCLE	ORIGIN	INSERTION	ACTION
FLEXORS			
Biceps femoris*	Ischial tuberosity and linea aspera of femur	Head of fibula, lateral condyle of tibia	Flexion at knee, extension and lateral rotation at hip
Semimembranosus*	Ischial tuberosity	Posterior surface of medial condyle of tibia	Flexion at knee; extension and medial rotation at hip
Semitendinosus*	As above	Proximal medial surface of tibia	As above
Sartorius	Anterior superior spine of ilium	Medial surface of tibia near tibial tuberosity	Flexion at knee; flexion and lateral rotation at hip
Popliteus	Lateral condyle of femur	Posterior surface of proximal tibial shaft	Rotates tibia medially (or rotates femur laterally); flexion at knee
EXTENSORS			
Rectus femoris	Anterior inferior iliac spine and superior acetabular rim of ilium	Tibial tuberosity by way of patellar ligament	Extension at knee, flexion at hip
Vastus intermedius	Anterior and lateral surface of femur along linea aspera	As above	Extension at knee
Vastus lateralis	Anterior and inferior to greater trochanter of femur and along linea aspera	As above	As above
Vastus medialis	Entire length of linea aspera of femur	As above	As above

*Hamstring muscles

ofibrils. The overall effects are a reduction in muscle strength and endurance and a tendency to fatigue rapidly. Because cardiovascular performance also decreases with age, blood flow to active muscles does not increase with exercise as rapidly as it does in younger people.

2. *Skeletal muscles become less elastic.* Aging skeletal muscles develop increasing amounts of fibrous connective tissue, a process called *fibrosis.* Fibrosis makes the muscle less flexible, and the collagen fibers can restrict movement and circulation.

3. *Tolerance for exercise decreases.* A lower tolerance for exercise as age increases results in part from the tendency to fatigue rapidly and in part from the reduction in thermoregulatory ability described in Chapters 1 and 5. ∞pp. 13, 126 Individuals over age 65 cannot eliminate muscle-generated heat as effectively as younger people, which leads to overheating.

4. *The ability to recover from muscular injuries decreases.* When an injury occurs, repair capabilities are limited, and scar tissue formation is the usual result.

The *rate* of decline in muscular performance is the same in all people, regardless of their exercise patterns or lifestyle. Therefore, to be in good shape late in life, an individual must be in

very good shape early in life. Regular exercise helps control body weight, strengthens bones, and generally improves the quality of life at all ages. Extremely demanding exercise is not as important as regular exercise. In fact, extreme exercise in the elderly can damage tendons, bones, and joints. Although it has obvious effects on the quality of life, there is no clear evidence that exercise prolongs life expectancy.

CHECKPOINT

34. What major structural change occurs in skeletal muscle fibers as we age, and what effects does that change have on muscle performance?

See the blue Answers tab at the back of the book.

7-13 Exercise produces responses in multiple body systems

To operate at maximum efficiency, the muscular system must be supported by many other systems. The changes that occur during exercise provide a good example of such interactions.

(a) Posterior view

Plantaris

Popliteus

Gastrocnemius

Soleus

Soleus

Gastrocnemius
(cut and removed)

Calcaneal
tendon

Calcaneus

SUPERFICIAL

SECOND LAYER

*Head of
fibula*

Tibialis
posterior

Fibularis
longus

Flexor
digitorum longus

Flexor
hallucis longus

Fibularis
brevis

Tendons of
fibularis muscles

Tendon of flexor
hallucis longus

THIRD LAYER

Fibularis

Tibialis
anterior

Extensor
digitorum

Extensor
hallucis

Tendon
sheaths

*Lateral
malleolus*

(b) Anterior view

Iliotibial tract

Head of fibula

Gastrocnemius

Tibialis anterior

Soleus

Fibularis muscles

Extensor digitorum longus

Tendon sheaths

Tendon of extensor
hallucis longus

Calcaneal tendon

(c) Lateral view

FIGURE 7-22 Muscles That Move the Foot and Toes.

TABLE 7-13 Muscles That Move the Foot and Toes

MUSCLE	ORIGIN	INSERTION	ACTION
Dorsiflexor			
Tibialis anterior	Lateral condyle and proximal shaft of tibia	Base of 1st metatarsal bone	Dorsiflexion at ankle; inversion of foot
Plantar flexors			
Gastrocnemius	Femoral condyles	Calcaneus by way of calcaneal tendon	Plantar flexion at ankle; inversion and adduction of foot; flexion at knee
Fibularis	Fibula and lateral condyle of tibia	Bases of 1st and 5th metatarsal bones	Eversion of foot and plantar flexion at ankle
Soleus	Head and proximal shaft of fibula, and adjacent shaft of tibia	Calcaneus by way of calcaneal tendon	Plantar flexion at ankle; adduction of foot
Tibialis posterior	Connective tissue membrane and adjacent shafts of tibia and fibula	Tarsal and metatarsal bones	Adduction and inversion of foot; plantar flexion at ankle
ACTION AT THE TOES			
Flexors			
Flexor digitorum longus	Posterior and medial surface of tibia	Inferior surface of phalanges, toes 2–5	Flexion at joints of toes 2–5
Flexor hallucis longus	Posterior surface of fibula	Inferior surface, distal phalanx of great toe	Flexion at joints of great toe
Extensors			
Extensor digitorum longus	Lateral condyle of tibia, anterior surface of fibula	Superior surfaces of phalanges, toes 2–5	Extension at joints of toes 2–5
Extensor hallucis longus	Anterior surface of fibula	Superior surface, distal phalanx of great toe	Extension at joints of great toe

As noted previously, active muscles consume oxygen and generate carbon dioxide and heat. Responses of other organ systems include the following:

- *Cardiovascular system.* Blood vessels in active muscles and in the skin dilate, and heart rate increases. These adjustments speed up the delivery of oxygen and the removal of carbon dioxide at the muscle and bring heat to the skin for radiation into the environment.

- *Respiratory system.* The rate and depth of respiration increase during exercise. Air moves into and out of the lungs more quickly, keeping pace with the increased rate of blood flow through the lungs.

- *Integumentary system.* Blood vessels dilate, and sweat gland secretion increases. This combination helps promote evaporation at the skin surface and removes the excess heat generated by muscular activity.

- *Nervous and endocrine systems.* These systems direct the responses of other organ systems by controlling heart rate, respiratory rate, and sweat gland activity.

Even when the body is at rest, the muscular system is interacting with other organ systems. The Muscular System in Perspective (p. 244) summarizes the range of interactions between the muscular system and other systems of the body.

CHECKPOINT

35. Identify the physiological effects of exercise on the cardiovascular, respiratory, and integumentary systems, and indicate the relationship between these physiological effects and the nervous and endocrine systems.

See the blue Answers tab at the back of the book.

RELATED CLINICAL TERMS

botulism: A disease characterized by severe, potentially fatal paralysis of skeletal muscles, resulting from the consumption of a bacterial toxin.

carpal tunnel syndrome: Inflammation of the sheath surrounding the flexor tendons of the palm that leads to nerve compression and pain.

compartment syndrome: Ischemia (defined shortly) resulting from accumulated blood and fluid trapped within limb muscle compartments formed by partitions of dense connective tissue.

fibrosis: A process in which a tissue is replaced by fibrous connective tissue. Fibrosis makes muscles weaker and less flexible.

hernia: A condition involving an organ or a body part that protrudes through an abnormal opening in the wall of a body cavity.

intramuscular (IM) injection: The administration of a drug by injecting it into the mass of a large skeletal muscle.

ischemia (is-KĒ-mē-uh): A deficiency of blood ("blood starvation") in a body part, sometimes due to compression of regional blood vessels.

muscle cramps: Prolonged, involuntary, painful muscular contractions.

muscular dystrophies (DIS-trō-fēz): A varied collection of inherited diseases that produce progressive muscle weakness and deterioration.

myalgia (mī-AL-jē-uh): Muscular pain; a common symptom of a wide variety of conditions and infections.

myasthenia gravis (mī-as-THĒ-nē-uh GRA-vis): A general muscular weakness resulting from a reduction in the number of ACh receptors on the motor end plate.

myoma: A benign tumor of muscle tissue.

myositis (mi-ō-SĪ-tis): Inflammation of muscle tissue.

polio: A viral disease in which the destruction of motor neurons produces paralysis and atrophy of motor units.

rigor mortis: A state following death during which muscles are locked in contraction, making the body extremely stiff.

sarcoma: A malignant tumor of masoderm-derived tissue (muscle, bone, or other connective tissue).

strains: Tears or breaks in muscles.

tendinitis: Inflammation of the connective tissue surrounding a tendon.

tetanus: A disease caused by a bacterial toxin that results in sustained, powerful contractions of skeletal muscles throughout the body.

Chapter **7** Review

KEY TERMS

anaerobic *209*
complete tetanus *206*
cross-bridges *200*
glycolysis *210*
insertion *217*
isometric contraction *208*
isotonic contraction *208*
lactic acid *210*
motor unit *207*
myofilaments *197*

myoglobin *211*
neuromuscular junction *200*
origin *217*
prime mover *217*
sarcomere *197*
sarcoplasmic reticulum *197*
synergist *217*
tendon *196*
transverse tubules *197*

SUMMARY OUTLINE

iP Use *Interactive Physiology*® (IP)—available on the IP CD packaged with your new textbook—to help you understand difficult physiological concepts. Follow these navigation paths on IP for concepts in this chapter:

- Muscular System/Sliding Filament Theory
- Muscular System/The Neuromuscular Junction
- Muscular System/Contraction of Motor Units
- Muscular System/Contraction of Whole Muscle
- Muscular System/Muscle Metabolism
- Muscular System/Anatomy Review: Skeletal Muscle Tissue

An Introduction to Muscle Tissue *p. 195*

1. The three types of muscle tissue are *skeletal muscle, cardiac muscle,* and *smooth muscle.* The muscular system includes all of the body's skeletal muscles, which can be controlled voluntarily.

7-1 Skeletal muscle performs five primary functions *p. 195*

2. **Skeletal muscles** attach to bones directly or indirectly and perform the following functions: (1) produce movement of the skeleton, (2) maintain posture and body position, (3) support soft tissues, (4) guard entrances and exits, and (5) maintain body temperature.

7-2 A skeletal muscle contains muscle tissue, connective tissues, blood vessels, and nerves *p. 195*

3. Each muscle fiber is surrounded by an **endomysium.** Bundles of muscle fibers are sheathed by a **perimysium,** and the entire muscle is covered by an **epimysium.** At the end of the muscle is a **tendon.** (*Figure 7-1*)

7-3 Skeletal muscle fibers have distinctive features *p. 197*

4. A muscle cell has a **sarcolemma** (cell membrane), **sarcoplasm** (cytoplasm), and a **sarcoplasmic reticulum,** similar to the

smooth endoplasmic reticulum of other cells. **Transverse tubules (T tubules)** and **myofibrils** aid in contraction. Filaments in a myofibril are organized into repeating functional units called **sarcomeres.** *(Figure 7-2a–c)*

5. **Myofilaments** consist of **thin filaments** *(actin)* and **thick filaments** *(myosin)*. *(Figure 7-2d,e)*

6. The spatial relationships between the thick and thin filaments change as the muscle contracts and shortens. The **Z lines** move closer together as the thin filaments slide past the thick filaments. *(Figure 7-3)*

7. The contraction process involves **active sites** on thin filaments and **cross-bridges** of the thick filaments. For each cross-bridge, sliding involves repeated cycles of "attach, pivot, detach, and return." At rest, the necessary interactions are prevented by **tropomyosin** and **troponin** proteins on the thin filaments.

7-4 Communication between the nervous system and skeletal muscles occurs at neuromuscular junctions *p. 200*

8. Neural control of muscle function involves a link between electrical activity in the sarcolemma and the initiation of a contraction.

9. Each skeletal muscle fiber is controlled by a neuron at a neuromuscular junction; the junction includes the synaptic terminal, the synaptic cleft, and the motor end plate. Acetylcholine (ACh) and acetylcholinesterase (AChE) play roles in the chemical communication between the synaptic terminal and muscle fiber. *(Figure 7-4a,b)*

10. When an **action potential** arrives at the synaptic terminal, acetylcholine is released into the synaptic cleft. The binding of ACh to receptors on the motor end plate leads to the generation of an action potential in the sarcolemma. The passage of an action potential along a transverse tubule triggers the release of calcium ions from the *terminal cisternae* of the sarcoplasmic reticulum. *(Figure 7-4c)*

11. A contraction involves a repeated cycle of "attach, pivot, detach, and return." It begins when calcium ions are released by the sarcoplasmic reticulum. The calcium ions bind to troponin, which changes position and moves tropomyosin away from the active sites of actin. Cross-bridge binding of myosin heads to actin can then occur. After binding, each myosin head pivots at its base, pulling the actin filament toward the center of the sarcomere. *(Figure 7-5)*

12. A summary of the contraction process, from ACh release to the end of the contraction, is shown in *Table 7-1.*

7-5 Sarcomere shortening and muscle fiber stimulation produce tension *p. 205*

13. The amount of tension produced by a muscle fiber depends on the number of cross-bridges formed.

14. Both the number of activated muscle fibers and their rate of stimulation control the tension developed by an entire skeletal muscle.

15. A muscle fiber **twitch** is a cycle of contraction and relaxation produced by a single stimulus. *(Figure 7-6)*

16. Repeated stimulation before the relaxation phase ends can result in the addition of twitches (known as **summation**). The result can be either **incomplete tetanus** (in which tension peaks because the muscle is never allowed to relax completely) or **complete tetanus** (in which the relaxation phase is completely eliminated). *(Figure 7-7)*

17. The number and size of a muscle's **motor units** indicate how precisely the muscle's movements are controlled. *(Figure 7-8)*

18. Muscle tension is increased by increasing the number of motor units involved—a process called **recruitment.**

19. Resting **muscle tone** stabilizes bones and joints. Inadequate stimulation causes muscles to undergo **atrophy.**

20. Normal activities usually include both **isotonic contractions** (in which the tension in a muscle remains constant as the muscle shortens) and **isometric contractions** (in which the muscle's tension rises but the length of the muscle remains constant).

21. Contraction is an active process, but elongation of a muscle fiber is passive. Elongation can result from elastic forces, the contraction of opposing muscles, or the effects of gravity.

7-6 ATP is the energy source for muscular activity *p. 208*

22. Muscle contractions require large amounts of energy from ATP.

23. ATP is an energy-transfer molecule, not an energy-storage molecule. **Creatine phosphate (CP)** can release stored energy to convert ADP to ATP. A resting muscle cell contains many times more CP than ATP. *(Figure 7-9a)*

24. At rest or moderate levels of activity, aerobic metabolism in mitochondria can provide most of the ATP required to support muscle contractions.

25. When a muscle fiber runs short of ATP and CP, enzymes can break down glycogen molecules to release glucose that can be broken down by **glycolysis.** *(Figure 7-9b)*

26. At peak levels of activity the cell relies heavily on the **anaerobic** process of glycolysis to generate ATP, because the mitochondria cannot obtain enough oxygen to meet the existing ATP demands. *(Figure 7-9c)*

27. **Muscle fatigue** occurs when a muscle can no longer contract, because of pH changes due to the buildup of **lactic acid,** a lack of energy, or other problems.

28. The **recovery period** begins immediately after a period of muscle activity and continues until conditions inside the muscle have returned to preexertion levels. The *oxygen debt* created during exercise is the amount of oxygen used during the recovery period to restore normal conditions.

7-7 Muscle fiber type and physical conditioning determine muscle performance capabilities *p. 211*

29. Muscle performance can be considered in terms of **force** (the maximum amount of tension produced by a particular muscle or muscle group) and **endurance** (the duration of muscular activity).

30. The two types of human skeletal muscle fibers are **fast fibers** and **slow fibers.**

31. Fast fibers are large in diameter, contain densely packed myofibrils, large reserves of glycogen, and few mitochondria. They produce rapid and powerful contractions of relatively short duration.

32. Slow fibers are smaller in diameter and take three times as long to contract after stimulation. Specializations such as an extensive capillary supply, abundant mitochondria, and high concentrations of **myoglobin** enable them to contract for long periods of time.

33. **Anaerobic endurance** is the time over which a muscle can support sustained, powerful contractions through anaerobic mechanisms. Training to develop anaerobic endurance can lead to **hypertrophy** (enlargement) of the stimulated muscles.

34. **Aerobic endurance** is the time over which a muscle can continue to contract while supported by mitochondrial activities.

7-8 Cardiac and smooth muscle tissues differ structurally and functionally from skeletal muscle tissue *p. 212*

35. Cardiac muscle cells differ from skeletal muscle fibers in that cardiac muscle cells are smaller, typically have a single central nucleus, have a greater reliance on aerobic metabolism when contracting at peak levels, and have **intercalated discs.** (*Figure 7-10a; Table 7-2*)

36. Cardiac muscle cells have *automaticity* and do not require neural stimulation to contract. Their contractions last longer than those of skeletal muscles, and cardiac muscle cannot undergo tetanus.

37. Smooth muscle is nonstriated, involuntary muscle tissue that can contract over a greater range of lengths than skeletal muscle cells. (*Figure 7-10b; Table 7-2*)

38. Many smooth muscle fibers lack direct connections to motor neurons; those that are innervated are not under voluntary control.

7-9 Descriptive terms are used to name skeletal muscles *p. 214*

39. The **muscular system** includes approximately 700 skeletal muscles, which can be voluntarily controlled. (*Figure 7-11*)

40. Each muscle can be identified by its **origin, insertion,** and **primary action.** A muscle can be classified by its primary action as a **prime mover,** or **agonist;** as a **synergist;** or as an **antagonist.**

41. The names of muscles often provide clues to their location, orientation, or function. (*Table 7-3*)

42. The **axial musculature** arises on the axial skeleton; it positions the head and spinal column and moves the rib cage. The **appendicular musculature** stabilizes or moves components of the appendicular skeleton.

7-10 Axial muscles are muscles of the head and neck, vertebral column, trunk, and pelvic floor *p. 218*

43. The axial muscles fall into four groups based on location and/or function: muscles of (a) the head and neck, (b) the spine, (c) the trunk, and (d) the pelvic floor.

44. The muscles of the head include the **frontalis, orbicularis oris, buccinator, masseter, temporalis,** and **pterygoids.** (*Figure 7-12; Table 7-4*)

45. The muscles of the neck include the **platysma, digastric, mylohyoid, stylohyoid,** and **sternocleidomastoid.** (*Figures 7-12, 7-13; Table 7-4*)

46. The **splenius capitis** and **semispinalis capitis** are the most superior muscles of the spine. The extensor muscles of the spine, or **erector spinae,** can be classified into the **spinalis, longissimus,** and **iliocostalis** groups. In the lower lumbar and sacral regions, the longissimus and iliocostalis are sometimes called the *sacrospinalis* muscles. (*Figure 7-14; Table 7-5*)

47. The muscles of the trunk include the **oblique** and **rectus** muscles. The thoracic region muscles include the **intercostal** and **transversus** muscles. Also important to respiration is the **diaphragm.** (*Figure 7-15; Table 7-6*)

48. The muscular floor of the pelvic cavity is called the **perineum.** These muscles support the organs of the pelvic cavity and control the movement of materials through the urethra and anus. (*Figure 7-16; Table 7-7*)

7-11 Appendicular muscles are muscles of the shoulders, upper limbs, pelvic girdle, and lower limbs *p. 226*

49. Together, the **trapezius** and the sternocleidomastoid affect the position of the shoulder, head, and neck. Other muscles inserting on the scapula include the **rhomboid,** the **levator scapulae,** the **serratus anterior,** and the **pectoralis minor.** (*Figure 7-17; Table 7-8*)

50. The **deltoid** and the **supraspinatus** produce abduction of the arm at the shoulder. The **subscapularis, teres major, infraspinatus,** and **teres minor** rotate the arm at the shoulder. (*Figure 7-18; Table 7-9*)

51. The **pectoralis major** flexes the shoulder joint, and the **latissimus dorsi** extends it. Both of these muscles adduct and rotate the arm at the shoulder joint. (*Figure 7-18; Table 7-9*)

52. The primary actions of the **biceps brachii** and the **triceps brachii** (long head) affect the elbow. The **brachialis** and **brachioradialis** flex the elbow. The **flexor carpi ulnaris**, the **flexor carpi radialis**, and the **palmaris longus** cooperate to flex the wrist. They are opposed by the **extensor carpi radialis** and the **extensor carpi ulnaris**. The **pronator** muscles pronate the forearm, opposed by the **supinator** and the biceps brachii. *(Figure 7-19; Table 7-10)*

53. **Gluteal muscles** cover the lateral surfaces of the ilia. They produce extension, abduction, and rotation at the hip. *(Figure 7-20a; Table 7-11)*

54. Adductors of the thigh work across the hip joint; these muscles include the **adductor magnus, adductor brevis, adductor longus, pectineus,** and **gracilis.** *(Figure 7-20b; Table 7-11)*

55. The **psoas major** and the **iliacus** merge to form the **iliopsoas** muscle, a powerful flexor of the hip. *(Figure 7-20b; Table 7-11)*

56. The flexors of the knee include the hamstrings (**biceps femoris, semimembranosus,** and **semitendinosus**) and **sartorius.** The **popliteus** aids flexion by unlocking the knee. *(Figure 7-21; Table 7-12)*

57. The *knee extensors* are known as the **quadriceps femoris.** This group includes the three **vastus** muscles and the **rectus femoris.** *(Figure 7-21; Table 7-12)*

58. The **gastrocnemius** and **soleus** muscles produce plantar flexion. A pair of **fibularis** muscles produces eversion as well as plantar flexion. The **tibialis anterior** performs dorsiflexion. *(Figure 7-22; Table 7-13)*

59. Control of the phalanges is provided by muscles originating at the tarsal bones and at the metatarsal bones. *(Table 7-13)*

7-12 With advancing age, the size and power of muscle tissue decreases   *p. 235*

60. Aging reduces the size, elasticity, and power of all muscle tissues. Both exercise tolerance and the ability to recover from muscular injuries decrease with age.

7-13 Exercise produces responses in multiple body systems   *p. 236*

61. To operate at maximum efficiency, the muscular system must be supported by many other organ systems. Even at rest, it interacts extensively with other systems.

REVIEW QUESTIONS

WWW   Access more review material online at **The Anatomy & Physiology Place** (**www.anatomyandphysiology.com**). There, you'll find Chapter Guides, Chapter Quizzes, Chapter Practice Tests, Interactive Flashcards, a Glossary with Pronunciations, and more to help you succeed in the course.

Level 1 • Reviewing Facts and Terms

Match each item in column A with the most closely related item in column B. Place letters for answers in the spaces provided.

COLUMN A

_____ 1. epimysium
_____ 2. fascicle
_____ 3. endomysium
_____ 4. motor end plate
_____ 5. transverse tubule
_____ 6. actin
_____ 7. myosin
_____ 8. extensor of the knee
_____ 9. sarcomeres
_____ 10. tropomyosin
_____ 11. recruitment
_____ 12. muscle tone
_____ 13. white muscles
_____ 14. flexor of the leg
_____ 15. red muscles
_____ 16. hypertrophy

COLUMN B

a. resting tension
b. contractile units
c. thin filaments
d. surrounds muscle fiber
e. enlargement
f. surrounds muscle
g. slow fibers
h. thick filaments
i. muscle bundle
j. hamstring muscles
k. covers active sites
l. conducts action potentials
m. fast fibers
n. quadriceps muscles
o. multiple motor units
p. binds ACh

17. Identify the structures in the following figure.

(a) _____   (b) _____
(c) _____   (d) _____
(e) _____   (f) _____
(g) _____   (h) _____

18. A skeletal muscle contains
(a) connective tissues.
(b) blood vessels and nerves.
(c) skeletal muscle tissue.
(d) a, b, and c are correct

19. The type of contraction in which the tension rises but the resistance does not move is called
(a) a wave summation.   (b) a twitch.
(c) an isotonic contraction.   (d) an isometric contraction.

20. Label the three visible muscles of the rotator cuff in the following posterior view of the deep muscles that move the arm.

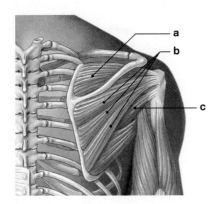

(a) _____   (b) _____
(c) _____

21. What five interlocking steps are involved in the contraction process?

22. What forms of energy reserves are found in resting skeletal muscle cells?

23. What two mechanisms are used to generate ATP from glucose in muscle cells?

24. What is the functional difference between the axial musculature and the appendicular musculature?

Level 2 • Reviewing Concepts

25. Areas of the body where no slow fibers would be found include the
(a) back and calf muscles.   (b) eye and hand.
(c) chest and abdomen.   (d) a, b, and c are correct

26. Describe the basic sequence of events that occurs at a neuromuscular junction.

27. Why is the multinucleate condition important in skeletal muscle fibers?

28. The muscles of the spine include many dorsal extensors but few ventral flexors. Why?

29. What specific structural characteristic makes voluntary control of urination and defecation possible?

30. What types of movements are affected when the hamstrings are injured?

Level 3 • Critical Thinking and Clinical Applications

31. Many potent insecticides contain toxins called *organophosphates,* which interfere with the action of the enzyme acetylcholinesterase. Terry is using an insecticide containing organophosphates and is very careless. He does not use gloves or a mask, so he absorbs some of the chemical through his skin and inhales a large amount as well. What signs would you expect to observe in Terry as a result of organophosphate poisoning?

32. The time of a murder victim's death is commonly estimated by the flexibility/stiffness of the body. Explain why this is possible.

33. Makani is interested in building up his thigh muscles, specifically the quadriceps group. What exercises would you recommend to help him accomplish his goal?

The Muscular System in Perspective

Functional Relationships Between the Muscular System and Other Systems

The Integumentary System

- The Integumentary System removes excess body heat; synthesizes vitamin D_3 for calcium and phosphate absorption; protects underlying muscles
- The Muscular System's skeletal muscles pulling on skin of face produce facial expressions

The Skeletal System

- The Skeletal System maintains normal calcium and phosphate levels in body fluids; supports skeletal muscles; provides sites of attachment
- The Muscular System provides movement and support; stresses exerted by tendons maintain bone mass; stabilizes bones and joints

The Nervous System

- The Nervous System controls skeletal muscle contractions; adjusts activities of respiratory and cardiovascular systems during periods of muscular activity
- The Muscular System's muscle spindles monitor body position; facial muscles express emotion; muscles of the larynx, tongue, lips and cheeks permit speech

The Endocrine System

- The Endocrine System hormones adjust muscle metabolism and growth; parathyroid hormone and calcitonin regulate calcium and phosphate ion concentrations
- The Muscular System's skeletal muscles provide protection for some endocrine organs

The Cardiovascular System

- The Cardiovascular System delivers oxygen and nutrients; removes carbon dioxide, lactic acid, and heat
- The Muscular System's skeletal muscle contractions assist in moving blood through veins; protects deep blood vessels

The Lymphoid System

- The Lymphoid System defends skeletal muscles against infection and assists intissue repairs after injury
- The Muscular System protects superficial lymph nodes and the lymphatic vessels in the abdominopelvic cavity

The Respiratory System

- The Respiratory System provides oxygen and eliminates carbon dioxide
- The Muscular System's muscles generate carbon dioxide; control entrances to respiratory tract, fill and empty lungs, control airflow through larynx, and produce sounds

The Digestive System

- The Digestive System provides nutrients; liver regulates blood glucose and fatty acid levels and removes lactic acid from circulation
- The Muscular System protects and supports soft tissues in abdominal cavity; controls entrances to and exits from digestive tract

The Urinary System

- The Urinary System removes waste products of protein metabolism; assists in regulation of calcium and phosphate concentrations
- The Muscular System's external sphincter controls urination by constricting urethra

The Reproductive System

- The Reproductive System's reproductive hormones accelerate skeletal muscle growth
- The Muscular System's contractions of skeletal muscles eject semen from male reproductive tract; muscle contractions during sex act produce pleasurable sensations

For All Systems
The Muscular System generates heat that maintains normal body temperature

Professional Profile

PHYSICAL THERAPIST
Sydney James

> **Most importantly, I have to know the bones, joints, and muscles. In order to design an exercise program . . . I have to know where the muscles originate, where they attach, and their actions.**

When Sydney James started college at California Polytechnic University, she planned to become a teacher. However, in her senior year Sydney changed her plans. Her interests took her in a different direction to a career as a physical therapist (PT).

As an orthopedic physical therapist at the San Francisco Bay Club, Sydney works closely with patients. "My goal is to help people return back to doing the things that they enjoy, whether that be working, parenting, or being an athlete," she says. "The best part of my job is watching people get better."

TREATMENT AND EDUCATION

The qualities that make a physical therapist effective are similar to those of a good teacher: creativity, compassion, and encouragement. Says Sydney, "You have to be able to look at the therapy situation and adapt to it, trying new things until you find what works. In treatment, it's important to be able to think outside the box."

Patient education is an integral part of treatment. "A big part of physical therapy is about giving patients the information and support they need to prevent a recurrence of their injury. Some patients lack the motivation to improve. You have to encourage them." Being a good role model is another crucial quality. "If you want your patients to improve, you have to model what's appropriate—manage your weight and avoid smoking."

Working at the Bay Club, Sydney typically sees 10 to 12 patients a day. In addition to treating patients, she does community outreach and occasionally attends surgeries performed on patients with whom she's worked.

EDUCATION AND PRACTICE

A career in physical therapy generally requires a master's degree. Prerequisites for the graduate program vary but typically include courses in physics, chemistry, microbiology, and anatomy and physiology. Many physical therapy programs also require students to have completed a certain number of hours of related paid or volunteer work.

Once enrolled in the physical therapy program, students take another anatomy and physiology series, as well as specialized courses in pathology, neurology, and orthopedics, during the two or three years of the program. They work as interns during the summer. After completing their course work, they must pass a state licensing exam in order to practice as a physical therapist.

Sydney uses what she learned in her anatomy and physiology courses every day. "It's about knowing the general systems of the body, what happens in an injury, the disease process, and the injury process. Most importantly, I have to know the bones, joints, and muscles. In order to design an exercise program for someone, I have to know where the muscles originate, where they attach, and their actions. I would say anatomy and physiology is the basis of my job." For instance, she says, "If someone tells me 'This is clicking,' I have to think about what structures might be clicking and what we have to do to get these movement patterns correct in this patient."

Sydney is quick to point out that physical therapy is a broad field with a lot of subfields. For instance, there are orthopedic PTs, neurology PTs, and PTs who specialize in pediatrics. PT assistants, professionals who have completed a two-year program, treat but do not evaluate patients. Physical therapists work in hospitals, doing both inpatient and outpatient work, and in schools, home health care, skilled nursing facilities, and rehab clinics. Says Sydney, "Investigate the many subfields of physical therapy so that you can find a specialty that is right for you." The American Physical Therapy Association is a good place to begin your research.

8 The Nervous System

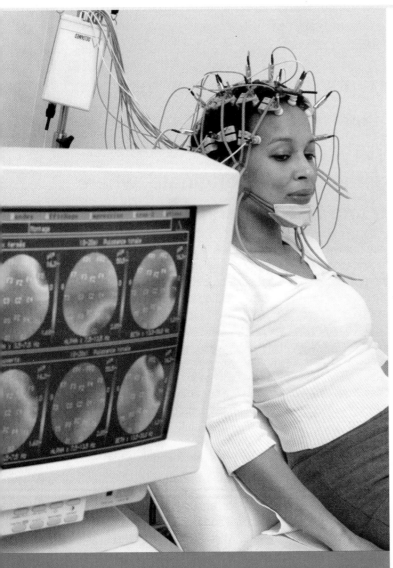

The first EEG, or electroencephalogram recordings, of the electrical activity in human brains were made in the late 1920's. Modern techniques of EEG brain mapping provide a rapid method of visualizing this electrical activity. An EEG is useful in revealing an individual's state of consciousness and measuring how much time is involved in processing various stimuli.

LEARNING OUTCOMES

After completing this chapter, you should be able to do the following:

8-1 Describe the two major anatomical divisions of the nervous system, and list their general functions.

8-2 Distinguish between neurons and neuroglia on the basis of structure and function.

8-3 Describe the events involved in the generation and propagation of an action potential.

8-4 Describe the structure of a synapse, and discuss the mechanism of nerve impulse transmission at a synapse.

8-5 Describe the three meningeal layers that surround the central nervous system.

8-6 Discuss the roles of gray matter and white matter in the spinal cord.

8-7 Name the major regions of the brain, and describe the locations and functions of each.

8-8 Name the cranial nerves, relate each pair of cranial nerves to its principal functions, and relate the distribution pattern of spinal nerves to the regions they innervate.

8-9 Describe the steps in a reflex arc.

8-10 Identify the principal sensory and motor pathways, and explain how it is possible to distinguish among sensations that originate in different areas of the body.

8-11 Describe the structures and functions of the sympathetic and parasympathetic divisions of the autonomic nervous system.

8-12 Summarize the effects of aging on the nervous system.

8-13 Give examples of interactions between the nervous system and each of the other organ systems.

VOCABULARY DEVELOPMENT

a- without; *aphasia*
af to; *afferent*
arachne spider; *arachnoid membrane*
astro- star; *astrocyte*
ataxia a lack of order; *ataxia*
axon axis; *axon*
cauda tail; *cauda equina*
cephalo- head; *diencephalon*
chiasm a crossing; *optic chiasm*
choroid a vascular coat; *choroid plexus*
colliculus a small hill; *superior colliculus*
commissura a joining together; *commissure*
cortex rind; *neural cortex*

cyte cell; *astrocyte*
dia through; *diencephalon*
dura hard; *dura mater*
ef-, ex- from; *efferent*
equus horse; *cauda equina*
ferre to carry; *afferent*
ganglio knot; *ganglion*
glia glue; *neuroglia*
hypo- below; *hypothalamus*
inter- between; *interneurons*
lexis diction; *dyslexia*
limbus a border; *limbic system*
mamilla a little breast; *mamillary bodies*
mater mother; *dura mater*

meninx membrane; *meninges*
meso- middle; *mesencephalon*
neuro- nerve; *neuron*
nigra black; *substantia nigra*
oligo- few; *oligodendrocytes*
phasia speech; *aphasia*
pia delicate; *pia mater*
plexus a network; *choroid plexus*
saltare to leap; *saltatory*
syn- together; *synapse*
vagus wandering; *vagus nerve*
vas vessel; *vasomotor*

An Introduction to the Nervous System

Two organ systems, the *nervous system* and the *endocrine system,* coordinate organ system activities to maintain homeostasis in response to changing environmental conditions. The nervous system responds relatively swiftly but briefly to stimuli, whereas endocrine responses develop more slowly but last much longer. Thus, the nervous system adjusts body position and moves your eyes across this page, while the endocrine system adjusts the entire body's daily rate of energy use and directs such long-term processes as growth and maturation. (We will consider the endocrine system in Chapter 10.)

The nervous system is the most complex organ system. As you read these words and think about them, at the involuntary level your nervous system is also monitoring the external environment and your internal systems and issuing commands as needed to maintain homeostasis. In a few hours—at mealtime or while you are sleeping—the pattern of nervous system activity will be very different. The change from one pattern of activity to another can be almost instantaneous because neural function relies on electrical events that proceed at great speed.

This chapter examines the structure and function of the nervous system, from its cells through their organization into two major divisions: the *central nervous system* and the *peripheral nervous system.* ∞ p. 8

8-1 The nervous system has anatomical and functional divisions

The **nervous system** (1) monitors the internal and external environments, (2) integrates sensory information, and (3) coordinates voluntary and involuntary responses of many other organ systems. These functions are performed by cells called neurons, which are supported and protected by surrounding cells collectively termed *neuroglia.*

The nervous system has two major anatomical divisions. The **central nervous system (CNS),** consisting of the *brain* and the *spinal cord,* integrates and coordinates the processing of sensory data and the transmission of motor commands. The CNS is also the seat of higher functions, such as intelligence, memory, and emotion. All communication between the CNS and the rest of the body occurs over the **peripheral nervous system (PNS),** which includes all the neural tissue *outside* the CNS.

The functional relationships of the two major anatomical divisions of the nervous system are detailed in Figure 8-1. Sensory information detected outside the nervous system—by structures called *receptors*—is transmitted by the **afferent division** (*af-,* to + *ferre,* to carry) of the PNS to sites in the CNS, where the information is processed. The CNS then sends motor commands by means of the **efferent division** (*ef-,* from) of the PNS to smooth muscle, cardiac muscle, and glands, which are called *effectors.*

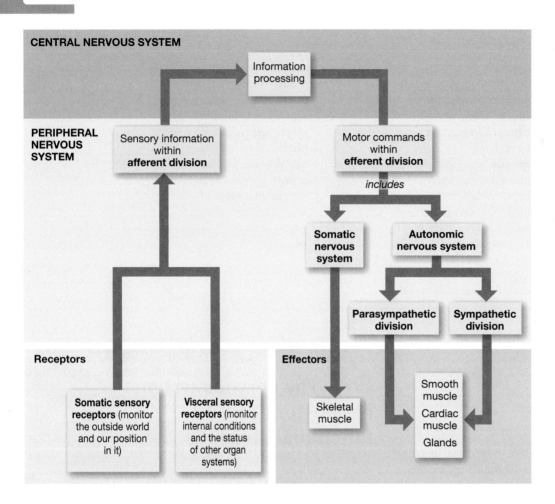

FIGURE 8-1 A Functional
Overview of the Nervous System.

The efferent division of the PNS is subdivided into the **somatic nervous system (SNS),** which provides control over skeletal muscle contractions, and the **autonomic nervous system (ANS)** or *visceral motor system,* which provides automatic involuntary regulation of smooth muscle, cardiac muscle, and glandular secretions. The ANS includes a *sympathetic division* and a *parasympathetic division,* which commonly have opposite effects. For example, activity of the sympathetic division accelerates the heart rate, whereas the parasympathetic division slows the heart rate.

CHECKPOINT

1. Identify the two anatomical divisions of the nervous system.
2. Identify the two functional divisions of the peripheral nervous system, and describe the primary functions of each.
3. What would be the effect of damage to the afferent division of the PNS?

See the blue Answers tab at the back of the book.

8-2 Neurons are specialized for intercellular communication and are supported by cells called neuroglia

The nervous system includes all the neural tissue in the body. Neural tissue, introduced in Chapter 4, consists of two kinds of cells, *neurons* and *neuroglia.* ∞ p. 114 **Neurons** (*neuro-,* nerve) are the basic units of the nervous system. All neural functions involve the communication of neurons with one another and with other cells. The **neuroglia** (noo-RŌG-lē-uh or noo-rō-GLĒ-uh; *glia,* glue) regulate the environment around neurons, provide a supporting framework for neural tissue, and act as phagocytes. Although they are much smaller cells, neuroglia (also called *glial cells*) far outnumber neurons. Unlike most neurons, most glial cells retain the ability to divide.

NEURONS

The General Structure of Neurons

A "representative" neuron has (1) a cell body; (2) several branching, sensitive **dendrites,** which receive incoming signals; and (3) an elongate **axon,** which carries outgoing signals toward (4) one or more **synaptic terminals** (Figure 8-2). At each synaptic terminal, the neuron communicates with another cell. Neurons can have a variety of shapes; Figure 8-2 shows a *multipolar neuron,* the most common type of neuron in the CNS.

The cell body of a typical neuron contains a large, round nucleus with a prominent nucleolus. Most neurons lack centrioles, organelles involved in the movement of chromosomes during mitosis. ∞ p. 74 As a result, typical CNS neurons cannot divide, so they cannot be replaced if lost to injury or disease. Although neural stem cells persist in the adult nervous system, they are typically inactive except in the nose, where the regeneration of olfactory (smell) receptors maintains our sense of smell, and in the *hippocampus,* a portion of the brain involved with memory storage. The mechanisms that trigger neural stem cell activity are now being investigated, with the goal of preventing or reversing neuron loss due to trauma, disease, or aging.

The cell body also contains organelles that provide energy and synthesize organic compounds. The numerous mitochondria, free and fixed ribosomes, and membranes of the rough endoplasmic reticulum (RER) give the cytoplasm a coarse, grainy appearance. Clusters of rough ER and free ribosomes, known as **Nissl bodies,** give a gray color to areas containing neuron cell bodies and account for the color of *gray matter* seen in brain and spinal cord dissections.

Projecting from the cell body are a variable number of dendrites and a single large axon. The plasma membrane of the dendrites and cell body is sensitive to chemical, mechanical, or electrical stimulation. In a process described later, such stimulation often leads to the generation of an electrical impulse, or *action potential,* that travels along the axon. Action potentials begin at a thickened region of the cell body called the *axon hillock.* The axon may branch along its length, producing branches called *collaterals.* Synaptic terminals are found at the tips of each branch. A synaptic terminal is part of a **synapse,** a site where a neuron communicates with another cell.

Structural Classification of Neurons

The billions of neurons in the nervous system are variable in form. Based on the relationship of the dendrites to the cell body and axon, neurons are classified into three types (Figure 8-3):

1. A **multipolar neuron** has two or more dendrites and a single axon (Figure 8-3a). These are the most common neurons in the CNS. All of the motor neurons that control skeletal muscles are multipolar.

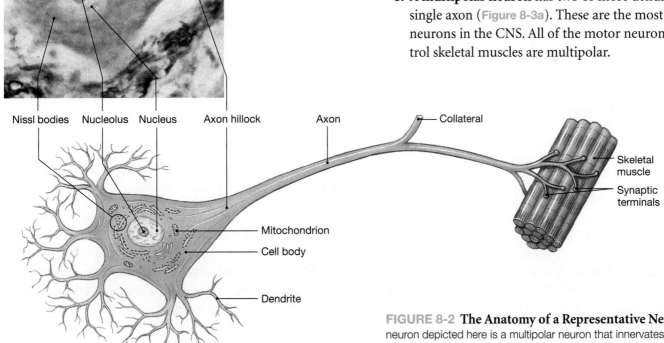

Nissl bodies   Nucleolus   Nucleus   Axon hillock   Axon   Collateral   Skeletal muscle   Synaptic terminals   Mitochondrion   Cell body   Dendrite

FIGURE 8-2 **The Anatomy of a Representative Neuron.** The neuron depicted here is a multipolar neuron that innervates a skeletal muscle. (LM × 1400)

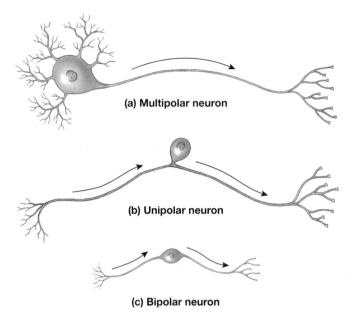

FIGURE 8-3 A Structural Classification of Neurons. The neurons are not drawn to scale; bipolar neurons are many times smaller than typical unipolar and multipolar neurons.

2. In a **unipolar neuron,** the dendrites and axon are continuous, and the cell body lies off to one side (Figure 8-3b). In a unipolar neuron, the action potential begins at the base of the dendrites, and the rest of the process is considered an axon. Most sensory neurons of the peripheral nervous system are unipolar.

3. **Bipolar neurons** have two processes—one dendrite and one axon—with the cell body between them (Figure 8-3c). Bipolar neurons are rare but occur in special sense organs, where they relay information about sight, smell, or hearing from receptor cells to other neurons.

Functional Classification of Neurons

Neurons are sorted into three functional groups: (1) *sensory neurons,* (2) *motor neurons,* and (3) *interneurons.*

SENSORY NEURONS. The approximately 10 million **sensory neurons** in the human body form the afferent division of the PNS. Sensory neurons receive information from *sensory receptors* monitoring the external and internal environments and then relay the information to other neurons in the CNS (spinal cord or brain). The receptor may be a dendrite of a sensory neuron or specialized cells of other tissues that communicate with the sensory neuron.

Receptors may be categorized according to the information they detect. Two types of **somatic sensory receptors** detect in-

formation about the outside world or our physical position within it. (1) **External receptors** provide information about the external environment in the form of touch, temperature, and pressure sensations and the more complex senses of sight, smell, hearing, and touch; and (2) **proprioceptors** (prō-prē-ō-SEP-torz; *proprius,* one's own + *capio,* to take) monitor the position and movement of skeletal muscles and joints. **Visceral receptors,** or **internal receptors,** monitor the activities of the digestive, respiratory, cardiovascular, urinary, and reproductive systems and provide sensations of taste, deep pressure, and pain.

MOTOR NEURONS. The half million **motor neurons** of the efferent division carry instructions from the CNS to other tissues, organs, or organ systems. The peripheral targets are called *effectors* because they respond by *doing* something. For example, a skeletal muscle is an effector that contracts upon neural stimulation. Neurons in the two efferent divisions of the PNS target separate classes of effectors. The **somatic motor neurons** of the somatic nervous system innervate skeletal muscles, whereas the **visceral motor neurons** of the autonomic nervous system innervate all other effectors, including cardiac muscle, smooth muscle, and glands.

INTERNEURONS. The 20 billion **interneurons,** or *association neurons,* are located entirely within the brain and the spinal cord. Interneurons, as the name implies (*inter-,* between), interconnect other neurons. They are responsible for the distribution of sensory information and the coordination of motor activity. The more complex the response to a given stimulus, the greater the number of interneurons involved. Interneurons also play a role in all higher functions, such as memory, planning, and learning.

NEUROGLIA

Neuroglia are found in both the CNS and PNS, but the CNS has a greater variety of glial cells. There are four types of neuroglial cells in the central nervous system (Figure 8-4):

1. **Astrocytes** (AS-trō-sīts; *astro-,* star + *cyte,* cell) are the largest and most numerous neuroglia. Astrocytes secrete chemicals vital to the maintenance of the *blood-brain barrier,* which isolates the CNS from the general circulation. The secretions cause the capillaries of the CNS to become impermeable to many compounds that could interfere with neuron function. Astrocytes also create a structural framework for CNS neurons and perform repairs in damaged neural tissues.

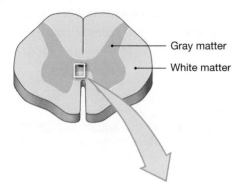

FIGURE 8-4 **Neuroglia in the CNS.** This diagrammatic view of neural tissue in the CNS depicts the relationships between neuroglia and neurons.

2. **Oligodendrocytes** (ol-i-gō-DEN-drō-sīts; *oligo-*, few) have fewer processes (cytoplasmic extensions) than astrocytes. Their thin, expanded tips wrap around axons, creating a membranous sheath of insulation made of **myelin** (MĪ-e-lin). Each oligodendrocyte myelinates short segments of several axons, so many oligodendrocytes are needed to coat an entire axon with myelin. Such an axon is said to be **myelinated.** The gaps between adjacent cell processes are called *nodes,* or the *nodes of Ranvier* (rahn-vē-Ā). The areas covered in myelin are called *internodes.* Myelin increases the speed at which an action potential travels along the axon. Not every axon in the CNS is myelinated, and those without a myelin coating are said to be **unmyelinated.** Myelin is lipid-rich, and on dissection, areas of the CNS containing myelinated axons appear glossy white. These areas constitute the **white matter** of the CNS, whereas areas of **gray matter** are dominated by neuron cell bodies.

3. **Microglia** (mī-KRŌG-lē-uh) are the smallest and rarest of the neuroglia in the CNS. Microglia are phagocytic cells derived from white blood cells that migrated into the CNS as the nervous system formed. They perform protective functions such as engulfing cellular waste and pathogens.

4. **Ependymal** (ep-EN-di-mul) **cells** line both the *central canal* of the spinal cord and the chambers *(ventricles)* of the brain, which are cavities in the CNS that are filled with cerebrospinal fluid (CSF). This lining of epithelial cells is called the **ependyma** (ep-EN-di-muh). In some regions of the brain, the ependyma produces CSF, and the cilia on ependymal cells in other locations help circulate this fluid within and around the CNS.

There are two types of neuroglia in the PNS. **Satellite cells** surround and support neuron cell bodies in the peripheral nervous system, much as astrocytes do in the CNS. The other glial cells in the PNS are **Schwann cells** (Figure 8-5a).

Schwann cells cover every axon outside the CNS. Wherever a Schwann cell covers an axon, the outer surface of the Schwann cell is called the *neurilemma* (noor-i-LEM-uh). Whereas an oligodendrocyte in the CNS may myelinate portions of several adjacent axons, a Schwann cell can myelinate only one segment of a single axon (Figure 8-5a). However, a Schwann cell can enclose portions of several different unmyelinated axons (Figure 8-5b).

The Big Picture

Neurons perform all of the communication, information processing, and control functions of the nervous system. Neuroglia outnumber neurons and have functions essential to preserving the physical and biochemical structure of neural tissue and the survival of neurons.

(a) Myelinated axon

(b) Unmyelinated axon

FIGURE 8-5 Schwann Cells and Peripheral Axons. (a) A myelinated axon in the PNS is covered by several Schwann cells, each of which forms a myelin sheath around a portion of the axon. This arrangement differs from the way myelin forms in the CNS; compare with Figure 8-4. **(b)** A single Schwann cell can encircle several unmyelinated axons. Every axon in the PNS is completely enclosed by Schwann cells. (TEMs × 14,048)

Demyelination Disorders

Demyelination is the progressive destruction of myelin sheaths, accompanied by inflammation, axon damage, and scarring of neural tissue. The result is a gradual loss of sensation and motor control that leaves affected regions numb and paralyzed. In one demyelination disorder, **multiple sclerosis** (skler-Ō-sis; *sklerosis,* hardness), or **MS,** axons in the optic nerve, brain, and/or spinal cord are affected. Common signs and symptoms of MS include partial loss of vision and problems with speech, balance, and general motor coordination. Other important demyelination disorders include *heavy metal poisoning, diphtheria,* and *Guillain-Barré syndrome.*

ORGANIZATION OF NEURONS IN THE NERVOUS SYSTEM

Neuron cell bodies and their axons are not randomly scattered in the CNS and PNS. Instead, they are organized into masses or bundles that have distinct anatomical boundaries and are identified by specific terms (**Figure 8-6**). We will use these terms again, so a brief overview here may prove helpful.

In the PNS:

- Neuron cell bodies (gray matter) are located in **ganglia**.
- The white matter of the PNS contains axons bundled together in **nerves**; *spinal nerves* are connected to the spinal cord, and *cranial nerves* are connected to the brain. Both sensory and motor axons may be present in the same nerve.

FIGURE 8-6 **The Anatomical Organization of the Nervous System.**

In the CNS:

- A collection of neuron cell bodies with a common function is called a **center.** A center with a discrete boundary is called a **nucleus.** Portions of the brain surface are covered by a thick layer of gray matter called **neural cortex** (*cortex,* rind). The term *higher centers* refers to the most complex integration centers, nuclei, and cortical areas in the brain.

- The white matter of the CNS contains bundles of axons that share common origins, destinations, and functions. These bundles are called **tracts.** Tracts in the spinal cord form larger groups called **columns.**

- **Pathways** link the centers of the brain with the rest of the body. For example, **sensory** (*ascending*) **pathways** distribute information from sensory receptors to processing centers in the brain, and **motor** (*descending*) **pathways** begin at CNS centers concerned with motor activity and end at the skeletal muscles they control.

CHECKPOINT

4. Name the structural components of a typical neuron.

5. Examination of a tissue sample reveals unipolar neurons. Are these more likely to be sensory neurons or motor neurons?

6. Identify the neuroglia of the central nervous system.

7. Which type of glial cell would occur in greater-than-normal numbers in the brain tissue of a person with a CNS infection?

8. In the PNS, neuron cell bodies (gray matter) are located in _____.

See the blue Answers tab at the back of the book.

8-3 In neurons, a change in the plasma membrane's electrical potential may result in an action potential (nerve impulse)

The sensory, integrative, and motor functions of the nervous system are dynamic and ever changing. All of the communications between neurons and other cells occur through their membrane surfaces. These membrane changes are electrical events that proceed at great speed.

THE MEMBRANE POTENTIAL

A characteristic feature of a living cell is a *polarized* plasma membrane. An undisturbed cell has a plasma membrane that is polarized because it separates an excess of positive charges on the outside from an excess of negative charges on the inside. When positive and negative charges are held apart, a *potential difference* is said to exist between them. Because the charges are separated by a plasma membrane, this potential difference is called a **membrane potential,** or *transmembrane potential.*

The unit of measurement of potential difference is the *volt* (V). Most cars, for example, have 12 V batteries. The membrane potential of cells is much smaller and is usually reported in *millivolts* (mV, thousandths of a volt). The membrane potential of an undisturbed cell is known as its **resting potential.** The resting potential of a neuron is –70 mV; the minus sign indicates that the inside of the plasma membrane contains an excess of negative charges compared to the outside.

Factors Responsible for the Membrane Potential

In addition to an imbalance of electrical charges, the intracellular and extracellular fluids differ markedly in ionic composition. For example, the extracellular fluid contains relatively high concentrations of sodium ions(Na^+) and chloride ions (Cl^-), whereas the intracellular fluid contains high concentrations of potassium ions (K^+) and negatively charged proteins(Pr^-).

The selective permeability of the plasma membrane maintains these differences between the intracellular and extracellular fluids. The proteins within the cytoplasm are too large to cross the membrane, and the ions can enter or leave the cell only with the aid of membrane channel and/or carrier proteins. ∞ p. 64 There are many different types of membrane channels; some are always open (*leak channels*), whereas others (*gated channels*) open or close under specific circumstances, such as a change in voltage.

Both passive and active processes act across the plasma membrane to determine the membrane potential. The passive forces are chemical and electrical. Chemical concentration gradients move potassium ions out of the cell and sodium ions into the cell (through separate leak channels). However, because it is easier for potassium ions to diffuse through a potassium channel than for sodium ions to diffuse through sodium channels, potassium ions diffuse out of the cell faster than sodium ions enter the cell. The passive movement of sodium and potassium ions is also influenced by electrical forces across the membrane. Positively charged potassium ions are repelled by the overall positive charge on the outer surface of the plasma membrane, whereas the positively charged sodium ions are attracted to the negatively charged inner membrane surface. Potassium ions continue to exit the cell, however, because its chemical concentration gradient is stronger than the repelling electrical force.

To maintain a potential difference across the plasma membrane, active processes are needed both to counter the combined chemical and electrical forces driving sodium ions into the cell and to maintain the potassium concentration gradient. The resting potential remains stable over time because of the actions of a carrier protein, the sodium–potassium exchange pump. ∞ p. 69 This ion pump exchanges three intracellular sodium ions for two extracellular potassium ions. At the normal resting potential of –70 mV, sodium ions are ejected as fast as they enter the cell. The cell, therefore, undergoes a net loss of positive charges, and as a result, the interior of the plasma membrane contains an excess of negative charges, primarily from negatively charged proteins. Figure 8-7 presents a diagrammatic view of the plasma membrane at the resting potential.

The Big Picture

A membrane potential exists across the plasma membrane. It exists because (1) the cytosol differs from extracellular fluid in chemical and ionic composition and (2) the plasma membrane is selectively permeable. The membrane potential can change from moment to moment, as the permeability of the plasma membrane changes in response to chemical or physical stimuli.

Changes in the Membrane Potential

Any stimulus that (1) alters membrane permeability to sodium or potassium or (2) alters the activity of the exchange pump will disturb the resting potential of a cell. Examples of stimuli that can affect membrane potential include exposure to specific chemicals, mechanical pressure, changes in temperature, or shifts in the extracellular ion concentrations. Any change in

FIGURE 8-7 **The Plasma Membrane at the Resting Potential.** The resting potential is the membrane potential of an undisturbed cell. The action of the ATP-driven sodium–potassium exchange pump maintains the concentration gradients of sodium and potassium, as well as the imbalance of electric charges, across the plasma membrane of an undisturbed cell.

KEY

- ⊕ Sodium ion (Na$^+$)
- ⊕ Potassium ion (K$^+$)
- ⊖ Chloride ion (Cl$^-$)

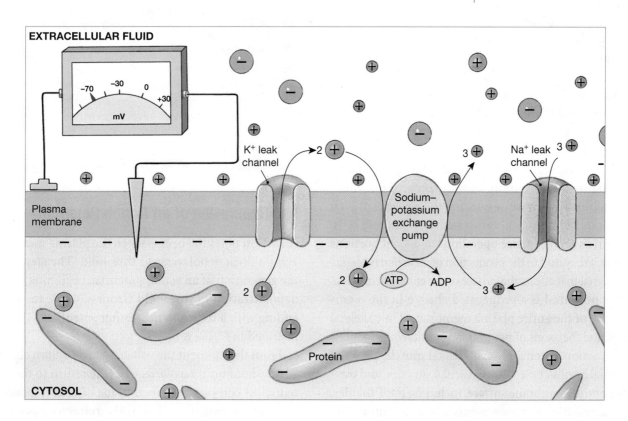

the resting potential can have an immediate effect on the cell. For example, permeability changes in the sarcolemma of a skeletal muscle fiber trigger a contraction. ∞ p. 200

In most cases, a stimulus opens gated ion channels that are closed when the plasma membrane is at its resting potential. The opening of these channels accelerates the movement of ions across the plasma membrane, and this movement changes the membrane potential. For example, the opening of gated sodium channels accelerates the entry of sodium into the cell. As the number of positively charged ions on the inner surface of the plasma membrane increases, the membrane potential shifts toward 0 mV. A shift in this direction is called a **depolarization** of the membrane. A stimulus that opens gated potassium ion channels will shift the membrane potential away from 0 mV, because additional potassium ions will leave the cell. Such a change, which may take the membrane potential from −70 mV to −80 mV, is called a **hyperpolarization.**

Information transfer between neurons and other cells involves graded potentials and action potentials. **Graded potentials** are changes in the membrane potential that cannot spread far from the site of stimulation, thereby affecting only a limited portion of the plasma membrane. For example, if a chemical stimulus applied to the plasma membrane of a neuron opens gated sodium ion channels at a single site, the sodium ions entering the cell will depolarize the membrane at that location. Attracted to surrounding negative ions, the sodium ions move along the inner surface of the membrane in all directions. The degree of depolarization decreases with distance from the point of entry, however, because the cytosol resists ion movement and because some sodium ions are lost as they recross the membrane through leak channels.

Graded potentials occur in the membranes of all cells in response to environmental stimuli. They often trigger specific cell functions. For example, a graded potential in the membrane of a gland cell may trigger secretion. However, graded potentials affect too small an area to have an effect on the activities of such large cells as skeletal muscle fibers or neurons. In these cells, graded potentials can influence operations in distant portions of the cell only if they lead to the production of an *action potential,* an electrical signal that affects the surface of the entire membrane.

An **action potential** is a propagated change in the membrane potential of the entire plasma membrane. Only skeletal muscle fibers and the axons of neurons have *excitable membranes* that conduct action potentials. In a skeletal muscle fiber, the action potential begins at the neuromuscular junction and travels along the entire membrane surface, including the T tubules. ∞ p. 200 The resulting ion movements trigger a contraction.

In an axon, an action potential usually begins near the axon hillock and travels along the length of the axon toward the synaptic terminals, where its arrival activates the synapses. An action potential in a neuron is also known as a **nerve impulse**.

Action potentials are generated by the opening and closing of gated sodium and potassium channels in response to a graded potential (local depolarization). This depolarization acts like pressure on the trigger of a gun. A gun fires only after a certain minimum pressure has been applied to the trigger. It does not matter whether the pressure builds gradually or is exerted suddenly—when the pressure reaches a critical point, the gun will fire. Whenever the gun fires, the forces that were applied to the trigger have no effect on the speed of the bullet leaving the gun. In an axon, the graded potential is the pressure on the trigger, and the action potential is the firing of the gun. An action potential will not appear unless the membrane depolarizes sufficiently to a level known as the **threshold.**

Every stimulus (whether minor or extreme) that brings the membrane to threshold will generate an identical action potential. This is called the **all-or-none principle:** A given stimulus either triggers a typical action potential, or it does not produce one at all.

Clinical Note

Neurotoxins in Seafood

Potentially deadly forms of poisoning result from eating seafood containing *neurotoxins,* poisons that primarily affect neurons. Several neurotoxins, such as *tetrodotoxin* (*TTX*) from puffer fish, *saxitoxin* (*SSX*) from bivalve shellfish, and *ciguatoxin* (*CTX*) from carnivorous, tropical coral reef fish, prevent sodium channels from opening. Motor neurons cannot function under these conditions, and death may result from paralysis of the respiratory muscles.

The Generation of an Action Potential

An action potential begins when the plasma membrane at the axon hillock depolarizes to threshold. The steps involved in the generation of an action potential, beginning with a graded depolarization to threshold (from −70 mV to −60 mV) and ending with a return to the resting potential (−70 mV), are illustrated in **Figure 8-8.**

From the moment the voltage-gated sodium channels open at threshold until *repolarization* (the return to the resting potential) is complete, the membrane cannot respond normally to further stimulation. This is the **refractory period.** The re-

FIGURE 8-8 The Generation of an Action Potential. A sufficiently strong depolarizing stimulus will bring the membrane potential to threshold and trigger an action potential. The numbers on the graph correspond to the steps illustrated at the right.

fractory period limits the rate at which action potentials can be generated in an excitable membrane. (The maximum rate of action potential generation is 500–1000 per second.)

PROPAGATION OF AN ACTION POTENTIAL

An action potential initially involves a relatively small portion of the total membrane surface. But unlike graded potentials,

which diminish rapidly with distance, action potentials affect the entire membrane surface. The basic mechanisms of action potential propagation along unmyelinated and myelinated axons are shown in Figure 8-9.

At a given site, for a brief moment at the peak of the action potential, the inside of the plasma membrane contains an excess of positive ions. Because opposite charges attract, these ions immediately begin spreading along the inner surface of the membrane, drawn to the surrounding negative charges. This

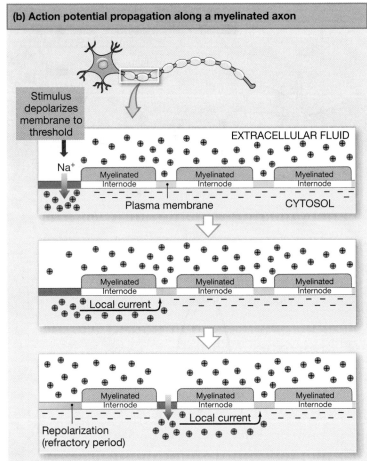

(a) Action potential propagation along an unmyelinated axon

(b) Action potential propagation along a myelinated axon

FIGURE 8-9 **The Propagation of Action Potentials over Unmyelinated and Myelinated Axons. (a)** Continuous propagation occurs along unmyelinated axons. **(b)** Saltatory propagation occurs along myelinated axons.

local current depolarizes adjacent portions of the membrane, and when threshold is reached, action potentials occur at these locations (Figure 8-9a). Each time a local current develops, the action potential moves forward, but not backward, because the previous segment of the axon is still in the refractory period.

The process continues in a chain reaction that soon reaches the most distant portions of the plasma membrane. This form of action potential transmission is known as **continuous propagation.** You might compare continuous propagation to a person walking toward some destination by taking small "baby steps"; progress is made, but slowly. Continuous propagation occurs along unmyelinated axons at a speed of about 1 meter per second (2 mph).

In a myelinated fiber, the axon is wrapped in layers of myelin. This wrapping is complete except at the nodes, where adjacent glial cells contact one another. Between the nodes, the lipids of the myelin sheath block the flow of ions across the membrane. As a result, continuous propagation cannot occur. In-

stead, when an action potential occurs at the axon hillock, the local current skips the internode and depolarizes the closest node to threshold (Figure 8-9b). Thus, the action potential jumps from node to node rather than proceeding in a series of small steps. This process is called **saltatory propagation,** taking its name from *saltare,* the Latin word meaning "to leap." Saltatory propagation carries nerve impulses along an axon at speeds ranging from 18–140 meters per second (40–300 mph). This faster process might be compared to a person jumping over puddles on their way to their destination.

The Big Picture "Information" travels within the nervous system primarily in the form of propagated electrical signals known as action potentials. The most important information, including vision and balance sensations and the motor commands to skeletal muscles, is carried by myelinated axons.

9. What effect would a chemical that blocks the voltage-gated sodium channels in a neuron's plasma membrane have on the neuron's ability to depolarize?

10. What effect would decreasing the concentration of extracellular potassium have on the membrane potential of a neuron?

11. List the steps involved in the generation and propagation of an action potential.

12. Two axons are tested for propagation velocities. One carries action potentials at 50 meters per second, the other at 1 meter per second. Which axon is myelinated?

See the blue Answers tab at the back of the book.

8-4 At synapses, communication occurs among neurons or between neurons and other cells

In the nervous system, information moves from one location to another in the form of action potentials, or nerve impulses, along axons. At the end of an axon, the arrival of an action potential results in the transfer of information to another neuron or to an effector cell. The information transfer occurs through the release of chemicals called **neurotransmitters** from the synaptic terminal.

When one neuron communicates with another, the synapse may occur on a dendrite, on the cell body, or along the length of the axon. Synapses between a neuron and another cell type are called **neuroeffector junctions.** As we saw in Chapter 7, a neuron communicates with a muscle cell at a *neuromuscular junction.* ∞ p. 200 At a *neuroglandular junction*, a neuron controls or regulates the activity of a secretory cell.

STRUCTURE OF A SYNAPSE

Communication between neurons and other cells occurs in only one direction across a synapse. At a synapse between two neurons, the impulse passes from the **synaptic knob** of the **presynaptic neuron** to the **postsynaptic neuron** (Figure 8-10). (The synaptic terminal of a presynaptic neuron at such synapses is called a synaptic knob because of its rounded shape.) The opposing plasma membranes are separated by a narrow space called the **synaptic cleft.**

Each synaptic terminal contains mitochondria, synaptic vesicles, and endoplasmic reticulum. Every synaptic vesicle contains several thousand molecules of a specific neurotransmitter and, upon stimulation, many of these vesicles release their contents into the synaptic cleft. The neurotransmitter then diffuses across the synaptic cleft and binds to receptors on the postsynaptic membrane.

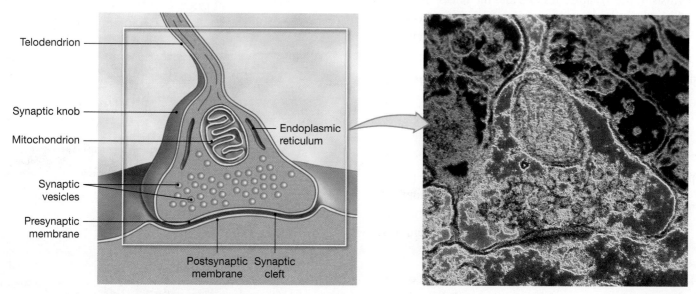

Telodendrion

Synaptic knob

Mitochondrion

Endoplasmic reticulum

Synaptic vesicles

Presynaptic membrane

Postsynaptic membrane   Synaptic cleft

FIGURE 8-10 The Structure of a Typical Synapse. A synapse between two neurons is shown diagrammatically (at left) and in a color-enhanced micrograph (at right, TEM × 222,000).

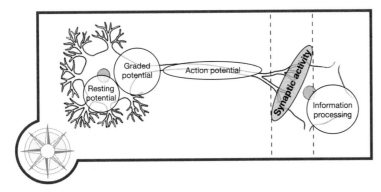

FIGURE 8-11 **The Events at a Cholinergic Synapse.**

SYNAPTIC FUNCTION AND NEUROTRANSMITTERS

There are many different neurotransmitters. The neurotransmitter **acetylcholine,** or **ACh,** is released at **cholinergic synapses.** Cholinergic synapses are widespread inside and outside of the CNS; the neuromuscular junction described in Chapter 7 is one example. Figure 8-11 shows the major events that occur at a cholinergic synapse after an action potential arrives at the presynaptic neuron:

Step 1 *Arrival of an action potential at the synaptic knob.* The arriving action potential depolarizes the presynaptic membrane of the synaptic knob.

Step 2 *Release of the neurotransmitter ACh.* Depolarization of the presynaptic membrane causes the brief opening of calcium channels, allowing extracellular calcium ions to enter the synaptic knob. Their arrival triggers the exocytosis of the synaptic vesicles and the release of ACh. The release of ACh stops very soon thereafter because the calcium ions are rapidly removed from the cytoplasm by active transport mechanisms.

Step 3 *Binding of ACh and the depolarization of the postsynaptic membrane.* The binding of ACh to sodium channels causes them to open and allows sodium ions to enter. If the resulting depolarization of the postsynaptic membrane reaches threshold, an action potential is produced.

Step 4 *Removal of ACh by AChE.* The effects on the postsynaptic membrane are temporary because the synaptic cleft and postsynaptic membrane contain the enzyme acetylcholinesterase (AChE). ∞ p. 201 AChE removes ACh by breaking it into acetate and choline.

Table 8-1 summarizes the sequence of events that occurs at a cholinergic synapse.

Another common neurotransmitter, **norepinephrine** (nor-ep-i-NEF-rin), or **NE,** is important in the brain and in portions

TABLE 8-1 The Sequence of Events at a Typical Cholinergic Synapse

Step 1:
- An arriving action potential depolarizes the synaptic knob and the presynaptic membrane.

Step 2:
- Calcium ions enter the cytoplasm of the synaptic knob.
- ACh release occurs through exocytosis of neurotransmitter vesicles.

Step 3:
- ACh diffuses across the synaptic cleft and binds to receptors on the postsynaptic membrane.
- Sodium channels on the postsynaptic surface are activated, producing a graded depolarization.
- ACh release stops because calcium ions are removed from the cytoplasm of the synaptic knob.

Step 4:
- The depolarization ends as ACh is broken down into acetate and choline by AChE.
- The synaptic knob reabsorbs choline from the synaptic cleft and uses it to resynthesize ACh.

of the autonomic nervous system. It is also called *noradrenaline,* and synapses releasing NE are described as **adrenergic.** The neurotransmitters **dopamine** (DŌ-puh-mēn), **gamma aminobutyric** (GAM-ma a-MĒ-nō-bū-TĒR-ik) **acid** (also known as **GABA**), and **serotonin** (ser-o-TŌ-nin) function in the CNS. There are at least 50 other neurotransmitters whose functions are not well understood. In addition, two gases are now known to be important neurotransmitters: *nitric oxide (NO)* and *carbon monoxide (CO).*

The neurotransmitters released at a synapse may have excitatory or inhibitory effects. Both ACh and NE usually have an excitatory effect due to the depolarization of postsynaptic neurons. Like ACh, NE's effect is temporary; it is broken down by an enzyme called *monoamine oxidase.* The effects of dopamine, GABA, and serotonin are usually inhibitory due to the hyperpolarization of postsynaptic neurons.

Whether or not an action potential appears in the postsynaptic neuron depends on the balance between the depolarizing and hyperpolarizing stimuli arriving at any moment. For example, suppose that a neuron will generate an action potential if it receives 10 depolarizing stimuli. That could mean 10 active synapses if all release excitatory neurotransmitters. But if, at the same moment, 10 other synapses release inhibitory neurotransmitters, the excitatory and inhibitory effects will cancel one another out, and no action potential will develop.

The activity of a neuron thus depends on the balance between excitation and inhibition. The interactions are extremely complex—synapses at the cell body and dendrites may involve tens of thousands of other neurons, some releasing excitatory neurotransmitters and others releasing inhibitory neurotransmitters.

NEURONAL POOLS

As noted earlier, the human body has about 10 million sensory neurons, 20 billion interneurons, and one-half million motor neurons. These individual neurons represent the simplest level of organization within the CNS. However, the integration of sensory and motor information to produce complex responses requires groups of interneurons acting together. A **neuronal pool** is a group of interconnected interneurons with specific functions. Each neuronal pool has a limited number of input sources and output destinations, and each may contain excitatory and inhibitory neurons. The output of one pool may stimulate or depress the activity of other pools, or it may exert direct control over motor neurons or peripheral effectors.

Neurons and neuronal pools communicate with one another in several patterns, or neural circuits. The two simplest circuit patterns are *divergence* and *convergence*. In **divergence,** information spreads from one neuron to several neurons, or from one neuronal pool to multiple neuronal pools (Figure 8-12a). Considerable divergence occurs when sensory neurons bring information into the CNS, because the sensory information is distributed to neuronal pools throughout the spinal cord and brain. For example, visual information arriving from the eyes reaches your conscious awareness at the same time it is carried to areas of the brain that control posture and balance at the subconscious level.

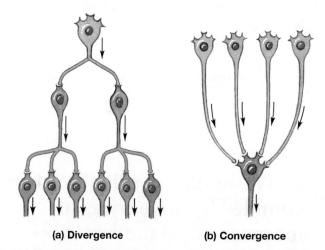

(a) Divergence   **(b) Convergence**

FIGURE 8-12 Two Common Types of Neuronal Pools.
(a) Divergence is a mechanism for spreading stimulation to multiple neurons or neuronal pools in the CNS. **(b)** Convergence is a mechanism for providing input to a single neuron from multiple sources.

The Big Picture

At a chemical synapse, a synaptic terminal releases a neurotransmitter that binds to the postsynaptic plasma membrane. The result is a temporary, localized change in the permeability or function of the postsynaptic cell. This change may have broader effects on the cell, depending on the nature and number of the stimulated receptors. Many drugs affect the nervous system by stimulating receptors that otherwise respond only to neurotransmitters. These drugs can have complex effects on perception, motor control, and emotional states.

Divergence is also involved when you step on a sharp object; that action stimulates sensory neurons that distribute information to a number of neuronal pools. As a result, you might react in several ways—withdraw your foot, shift your weight, move your arms, feel the pain, and shout "Ouch!"—all at the same time.

In **convergence** (Figure 8-12b), several neurons synapse on a single postsynaptic neuron. Convergence makes possible both voluntary and involuntary control of some body processes. For example, right now the movements of your diaphragm and ribs are being involuntarily, or subconsciously, controlled by respiratory centers in the brain. These centers activate or inhibit motor neurons in the spinal cord that control the respiratory muscles. But those same movements can be controlled voluntarily, or consciously, as when you take a deep breath and hold it. Two neuronal pools are involved, and both synapse on the same motor neurons.

CHECKPOINT

13. Describe the general structure of a synapse.

14. What effect would blocking calcium channels at a cholinergic synapse have on synapse function?

15. What type of neural circuit permits both conscious and subconscious control of the same motor neurons?

See the blue Answers tab at the back of the book.

8-5 The brain and spinal cord are surrounded by three layers of membranes called the meninges

The neural tissue of the central nervous system (CNS), which consists of the spinal cord and brain, is delicate, has a very high metabolic rate, and requires abundant nutrients and a con-

stant supply of oxygen. At the same time, CNS tissue must be isolated from a variety of blood-borne compounds that could interfere with its complex operations, and protected against damaging contact with the surrounding bones.

CNS tissue receives physical stability and shock absorption from the **meninges** (me-NIN-jēz), three layers of specialized membranes surrounding the brain and spinal cord (Figure 8-13). Blood vessels branching within these layers deliver needed oxygen and nutrients. At the foramen magnum of the skull, the *cranial meninges* covering the brain are continuous with the *spinal meninges* that surround the spinal cord. The meninges cover cranial and spinal nerves as they penetrate the skull or pass through the intervertebral foramina, becoming continuous with the connective tissues surrounding the peripheral nerves.

The three meningeal layers are the *dura mater*, the *arachnoid*, and the *pia mater*.

THE DURA MATER

The tough, fibrous **dura mater** (DOO-ruh MĀ-ter; *dura*, hard + *mater*, mother) forms the outermost covering of the central nervous system. The dura mater surrounding the brain consists of two fibrous layers. The outer layer is fused to the periosteum of the skull, and the two layers are separated by a slender gap that contains tissue fluids and blood vessels (Figure 8-13a).

At several locations, the inner layer of the dura mater extends deep into the cranial cavity, forming folded membranous sheets called *dural folds*. The dural folds act like seat belts to hold the brain in position. Large collecting veins known as *dural sinuses* lie between the two layers of a dural fold.

In the spinal cord, the outer layer of the dura mater is not fused to bone. Between the dura mater of the spinal cord and the walls of the vertebral canal lies the **epidural space,** which contains loose connective tissue, blood vessels, and adipose tissue (Figure 8-13b). Injecting an anesthetic into the epidural space produces a temporary sensory and motor paralysis known as an *epidural block*. This technique has the advantage of affecting only the spinal nerves in the immediate area of the injection. Epidural blocks in the lower lumbar or sacral regions may be used to control pain during childbirth.

THE ARACHNOID

A narrow **subdural space** separates the inner surface of the dura mater from the second meningeal layer, the **arachnoid** (a-RAK-noyd; *arachne*, spider). This intervening space con-

(a)

(b)

FIGURE 8-13 The Meninges. These drawings illustrate the location and structure of **(a)** the meninges of the brain and **(b)** the meninges of the spinal cord.

tains a small quantity of lymphatic fluid, which reduces friction between the opposing surfaces. The arachnoid is a layer of squamous cells; deep to this epithelial layer lies the **subarachnoid space,** which contains a delicate web of collagen and elastic fibers. The subarachnoid space is filled with *cerebrospinal fluid,* which acts as a shock absorber and transports dissolved gases, nutrients, chemical messengers, and waste products.

THE PIA MATER

The subarachnoid space separates the arachnoid from the innermost meningeal layer, the **pia mater** (*pia,* delicate + *mater,* mother). The pia mater is bound firmly to the underlying neural tissue. The blood vessels servicing the brain and spinal cord run along the surface of this layer, within the subarachnoid space. The pia mater of the brain is highly vascular, and large vessels branch over the surface of the brain, supplying the superficial areas of neural cortex. This extensive circulatory supply is extremely important, for the brain has a very high rate of metabolism; at rest, the 1.4 kg (3.1 lb) brain uses as much oxygen as 28 kg (61.6 lb) of skeletal muscle.

Clinical Note

Epidural and Subdural Damage

A severe head injury may damage cerebral blood vessels and cause bleeding into the cranial cavity. If blood leaks out between the dura mater and the cranium, the condition is known as an *epidural hemorrhage.* The flow of blood into the lower layer of the dura mater and subdural space is called a *subdural hemorrhage.* These are serious conditions because the blood entering these spaces compresses and distorts the relatively soft tissues of the brain. The signs and symptoms vary depending on whether an artery or a vein is damaged. Because arterial blood pressure is higher, bleeding from an artery can cause more rapid and severe distortion of neural tissue.

CHECKPOINT

16. Identify the three meninges surrounding the CNS.

See the blue Answers tab at the back of the book.

(a)

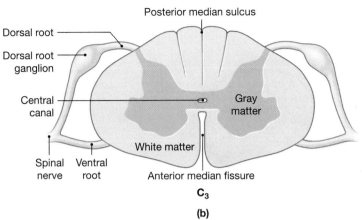

Cervical spinal nerves

C_1
C_2
C_3
C_4
C_5
C_6
C_7
C_8

Cervical enlargement

T_1
T_2
T_3
T_4
T_5
T_6
T_7

Thoracic spinal nerves

T_8
T_9
T_{10}

Posterior median sulcus

T_{11}

Lumbar enlargement

T_{12}

L_1

L_2

Inferior tip of spinal cord

L_3

Lumbar spinal nerves

L_4

Cauda equina

L_5

S_1
S_2
S_3

Sacral spinal nerves

S_4
S_5

Coccygeal nerve (Co_1)

(a)

Posterior median sulcus

Dorsal root

Dorsal root ganglion

Central canal

Gray matter

White matter

Spinal nerve   Ventral root

Anterior median fissure

C_3

(b)

FIGURE 8-14 Gross Anatomy of the Spinal Cord. (a) In this superficial view of the adult spinal cord, the designations to the left identify the spinal nerves. **(b)** This cross section through the cervical region of the spinal cord shows some prominent features and the arrangement of gray matter and white matter.

Clinical Note

Meningitis

Meningitis is inflammation of the meningeal membranes following bacterial or viral infection. Meningitis is dangerous because it can disrupt the supply of blood and cerebrospinal fluid, damaging or killing neurons and glial cells in the affected areas. Although the initial diagnosis may specify the meninges of either the spinal cord (*spinal meningitis*) or brain (*cerebral meningitis*), in later stages the entire meningeal system is usually affected.

8-6 The spinal cord contains gray matter surrounded by white matter and connects to 31 pairs of spinal nerves

The spinal cord serves as the major highway for the passage of sensory impulses to the brain and of motor impulses from the brain. In addition, the spinal cord integrates information on its own and controls *spinal reflexes,* automatic motor responses ranging from withdrawal from pain to complex reflex patterns involved in sitting, standing, walking, and running.

GROSS ANATOMY

The spinal cord is approximately 45 cm (18 in.) long (Figure 8-14a); it has a maximum width of roughly 14 mm (0.55 in.). With two exceptions, the diameter of the cord decreases as it extends toward the sacral region. The two exceptions are regions concerned with the sensory and motor control of the limbs. The *cervical enlargement* supplies nerves to the shoulder girdles and upper limbs, and the *lumbar enlargement* provides innervation to the pelvis and lower limbs. Below the lumbar enlargement, the spinal cord becomes tapered and conical. A slender strand of fibrous tissue extends from the inferior tip of the spinal cord to the coccyx, serving as an anchor that prevents upward movement.

The spinal cord has a **central canal,** a narrow internal passageway filled with cerebrospinal fluid (Figure 8-14b). The posterior surface of the spinal cord has a shallow groove, the *posterior median sulcus,* and the anterior surface has a deeper groove, the *anterior median fissure.*

The entire spinal cord consists of 31 segments, each identified by a letter and number (Figure 8-14a). Every spinal segment is associated with a pair of **dorsal root ganglia** (singular: ganglion), which contain the cell bodies of sensory neurons (Figure 8-14b). The **dorsal roots,** which contain the axons of these neurons, bring sensory information to the spinal cord. A pair of **ventral roots** contains the axons of CNS motor neurons that control muscles and glands. On either side, the dorsal and ventral roots from each segment leave the vertebral column between adjacent vertebrae at the *intervertebral foramen.*

Distal to each dorsal root ganglion, the sensory (dorsal) and motor (ventral) roots are bound together into a single **spinal nerve.** All spinal nerves are classified as *mixed nerves,* because they contain both sensory and motor fibers. The spinal nerves on either side form outside the vertebral canal, where the ventral and dorsal roots unite. ∞ p. 162

In adults, the spinal cord extends only to the level of the first or second lumbar vertebrae. When seen in gross dissection, the long ventral and dorsal roots of spinal nerves inferior to the tip of the spinal cord, plus the cord's threadlike extensions, reminded early anatomists of a horse's tail. With that in mind, they called this complex the *cauda equina* (KAW-duh ek-WĪ-nuh; *cauda,* tail + *equus,* horse).

SECTIONAL ANATOMY

The anterior median fissure and the posterior median sulcus mark the division between left and right sides of the spinal cord (Figure 8-15). The *gray matter* is dominated by the cell bodies of neurons and glial cells. It forms a rough H, or a butterfly shape, around the narrow central canal. Projections of gray matter, called **horns,** extend outward into the *white matter,* which contains large numbers of myelinated and unmyelinated axons.

Figure 8-15a shows the relationship between the function of a particular nucleus (a collection of sensory or motor cell bodies) and its relative position within the gray matter of the spinal cord. The *posterior gray horns* contain sensory nuclei,

whereas the *anterior gray horns* are involved in the motor control of skeletal muscles. Nuclei in the *lateral gray horns* contain the visceral motor neurons that control smooth muscle, cardiac muscle, and glands. The *gray commissures* anterior and posterior to the central canal interconnect the horns on either side of the spinal cord. The gray and white commissures contain axons that cross from one side of the spinal cord to the other.

The white matter on each side can be divided into three regions, or **columns** (Figure 8-15a). The *posterior white columns* extend between the posterior gray horns and the posterior median sulcus. The *anterior white columns* lie between the anterior gray horns and the anterior median fissure; they are interconnected by the *anterior white commissure.* The white matter between the anterior and posterior columns makes up the *lateral white columns.*

Each column contains tracts whose axons carry either sensory data or motor commands. Small tracts carry sensory or motor signals between segments of the spinal cord, and larger tracts connect the spinal cord with the brain. **Ascending tracts** carry sensory information toward the brain, and **descending tracts** convey motor commands into the spinal cord.

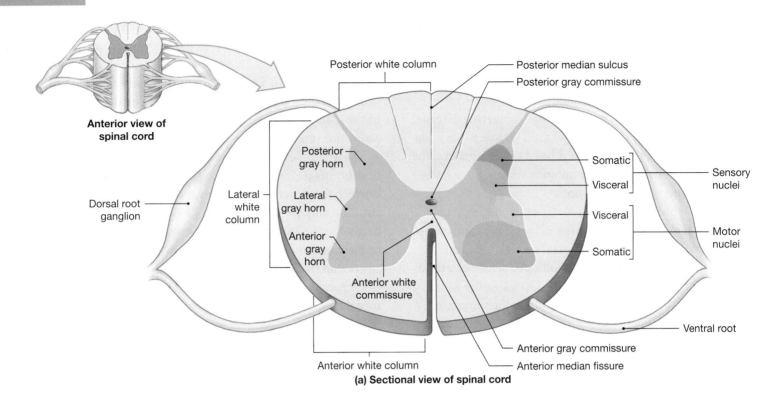

Anterior view of spinal cord

Posterior white column

Posterior median sulcus

Posterior gray commissure

Posterior gray horn

Somatic

Visceral

Sensory nuclei

Dorsal root ganglion

Lateral white column

Lateral gray horn

Visceral

Motor nuclei

Anterior gray horn

Somatic

Anterior white commissure

Ventral root

Anterior white column

Anterior gray commissure

Anterior median fissure

(a) Sectional view of spinal cord

POSTERIOR

Posterior median sulcus

Posterior gray commissure

Dura mater

Posterior gray horn

Arachnoid mater (broken)

Lateral gray horn

Central canal

Dorsal root

Anterior gray commissure

Anterior gray horn

Anterior median fissure

Pia mater

Dorsal root ganglion

Ventral root

ANTERIOR

(b) Micrograph of spinal cord section

FIGURE 8-15 Sectional Anatomy of the Spinal Cord. (a) The left half of this diagrammatic sectional view labels important anatomical landmarks and the major regions of white matter and gray matter. The right half indicates the functional organization of the gray matter in the posterior, lateral, and anterior gray horns. **(b)** This micrograph of a section through the spinal cord shows the major landmarks diagrammed in (a).

The Big Picture

The spinal cord has a narrow central canal surrounded by gray matter containing sensory and motor nuclei. Sensory nuclei are dorsal, motor nuclei are ventral. Gray matter is covered by a thick layer of white matter consisting of ascending and descending axons. These axons are organized in columns that contain axon bundles with specific functions. Because the spinal cord is so highly organized, it is often possible to predict the results of injuries to localized areas.

CHECKPOINT

17. Damage to which root of a spinal nerve would interfere with motor function?

18. A person with polio has lost the use of his leg muscles. In which area of his spinal cord could you locate virus-infected motor neurons?

19. Why are spinal nerves also called mixed nerves?

See the blue Answers tab at the back of the book.

8-7 The brain has several principal structures, each with specific functions

The brain is far more complex than the spinal cord, and its responses to stimuli are more versatile. The brain contains roughly 35 billion neurons organized into hundreds of neuronal pools; it has a complex three-dimensional structure and performs a bewildering array of functions. All of our dreams, passions, plans, and memories are the result of brain activity.

The adult human brain contains almost 98 percent of the neural tissue in the body. A "typical" adult brain weighs 1.4 kg (3 lb) and has a volume of 1200 cc (71 in.³). There is considerable individual variation, and the brains of males are generally about 10 percent larger than those of females, because of differences in average body size. There is no correlation between brain size and intelligence. Individuals with the smallest brains (750 cc) or largest brains (2100 cc) are functionally normal.

THE MAJOR REGIONS OF THE BRAIN

The adult brain has six major regions: (1) the *cerebrum,* (2) the *diencephalon,* (3) the *midbrain,* (4) the *pons,* (5) the *medulla oblongata,* and (6) the *cerebellum.* Major landmarks are indicated in Figure 8-16.

Viewed from the superior surface, the **cerebrum** (SER-e-brum or se-RĒ-brum) can be divided into large, paired **cerebral hemispheres** (Figure 8-16a). Conscious thoughts, sensations, intellectual functions, memory storage and retrieval, and complex movements originate in the cerebrum. The hollow **diencephalon** (dī-en-SEF-a-lon; *dia-*, through + *cephalo,* head) is connected to the cerebrum (Figure 8-16c). Its largest portion, the **thalamus** (THAL-a-mus), contains relay and processing centers for sensory information. A narrow stalk connects the **hypothalamus** (*hypo-,* below) to the *pituitary gland.* The hypothalamus contains centers involved with emotions, autonomic function, and hormone production. The pituitary gland, the primary link between the nervous and endocrine systems, is discussed in Chapter 10. The **epithalamus** contains another endocrine structure, the *pineal gland.*

The **brain stem** contains three major regions of the brain: the midbrain, pons, and medulla oblongata (Figure 8-16c). The brain stem contains important processing centers and relay stations for information headed to or from the cerebrum or cerebellum. Nuclei in the **midbrain,** or *mesencephalon* (mez-en-SEF-a-lon; *meso-,* middle), process visual and auditory information and generate involuntary motor responses. This region also contains centers that help maintain consciousness. The term *pons* refers to a bridge, and the **pons** of the brain connects the cerebellum to the brain stem. In addition to tracts and relay centers, this region of the brain also contains nuclei involved in somatic and visceral motor control. The pons is also connected to the **medulla oblongata,** the segment of the brain that is attached to the spinal cord. The medulla oblongata relays sensory information to the thalamus and other brain stem centers; it also contains major centers that regulate autonomic function, such as heart rate, blood pressure, respiration, and digestive activities.

The large cerebral hemispheres and the smaller hemispheres of the **cerebellum** (ser-e-BEL-um) almost completely cover the brain stem. The cerebellum adjusts voluntary and involuntary motor activities on the basis of sensory information and stored memories of previous movements.

THE VENTRICLES OF THE BRAIN

As previously noted, the brain and spinal cord contain internal cavities filled with cerebrospinal fluid and lined by ependymal cells. ∞ p. 252 The brain has a central passageway that expands to form four chambers called **ventricles** (VEN-tri-kls) (Figure 8-17). Each cerebral hemisphere contains a large **lateral ventricle.** There is no direct connection between the lateral ventricles, but an opening, the *interventricular foramen,* allows each of them to communicate with the **third ventricle** in the

(a) Superior view

Longitudinal fissure

Right cerebral hemisphere
Left cerebral hemisphere ⎤ CEREBRUM

ANTERIOR

POSTERIOR

CEREBELLUM

Cerebral veins and arteries below arachnoid

(b) Lateral view

Central sulcus

Precentral gyrus

Postcentral gyrus

Frontal lobe of left cerebral hemisphere

Parietal lobe

Parieto-occipital sulcus

Lateral sulcus

Occipital lobe

Temporal lobe

CEREBELLUM

PONS

MEDULLA OBLONGATA

(c) Sagittal section

Corpus callosum   Precentral gyrus   Central sulcus   Postcentral gyrus

Frontal lobe

Thalamus
Hypothalamus ⎤ DIENCEPHALON
Pineal gland (part of epithalamus)

Parieto-occipital sulcus

Optic chiasm

Mamillary body

CEREBELLUM

Temporal lobe

Brain stem ⎰ MIDBRAIN
PONS
MEDULLA OBLONGATA

FIGURE 8-16 **The Brain.**

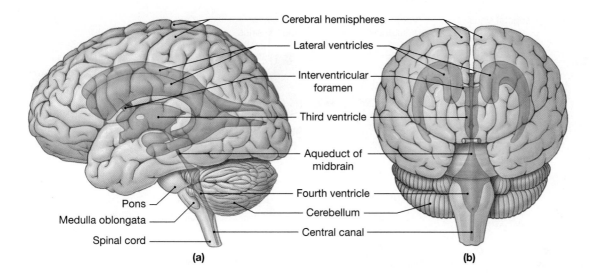

Cerebral hemispheres

Lateral ventricles

Interventricular foramen

Third ventricle

Aqueduct of midbrain

Fourth ventricle

Cerebellum

Central canal

Pons

Medulla oblongata

Spinal cord

(a)

(b)

FIGURE 8-17 The Ventricles of the Brain. These drawings of the brain as if it were transparent show the orientation and extent of the ventricles in **(a)** a lateral view and **(b)** an anterior view.

diencephalon. Instead of a ventricle, the midbrain has a slender canal known as the *aqueduct of midbrain* (or the *mesencephalic aqueduct* or *cerebral aqueduct*), which connects the third ventricle with the **fourth ventricle** in the pons and upper portion of the medulla oblongata. Within the medulla oblongata the fourth ventricle narrows and becomes continuous with the central canal of the spinal cord.

Cerebrospinal Fluid

Completely surrounding and bathing the exposed surfaces of the CNS and cushioning delicate neural structures is **cerebrospinal fluid,** or **CSF.** It also provides support, as the brain essentially floats in the cerebrospinal fluid. A human brain weighs about 1400 g (3.1 lb) in air but only about 50 g (1.76 oz.) when supported by cerebrospinal fluid. Finally, the CSF transports nutrients, chemical messengers, and waste products. Except at the *choroid plexus,* where CSF is produced, the ependymal lining is freely permeable, and CSF is in constant chemical communication with the interstitial fluid of the CNS. Because free exchange occurs between the interstitial fluid and CSF, changes in CNS function may produce changes in the composition of CSF. Samples of CSF can be obtained through a *lumbar puncture,* or *spinal tap,* providing useful clinical information concerning CNS injury, infection, or disease.

Cerebrospinal fluid is produced at the **choroid plexus** (*choroid,* a vascular coat + *plexus,* a network), a network of permeable capillaries that extends into each of the four ventricles (Figure 8-18a). The capillaries of the choroid plexus are covered by large ependymal cells that secrete CSF at a rate of about 500 mL/day. The total volume of CSF at any given moment is approximately 150 mL; this means that the entire vol-

ume of CSF is replaced roughly every 8 hours. Despite this rapid turnover, the composition of CSF is closely regulated, and the rate of removal normally keeps pace with the rate of production. If it does not, a variety of clinical problems may appear.

CSF circulates between the different ventricles, passes along the central canal, and enters the subarachnoid space (Figure 8-18a). Once inside the subarachnoid space, the CSF circulates around the spinal cord and cauda equina and across the surfaces of the brain. Between the cerebral hemispheres, slender extensions of the arachnoid penetrate the inner layer of the dura mater. Clusters of these extensions form **arachnoid granulations,** which project into the *superior sagittal sinus,* a large cerebral vein (Figure 8-18b). Diffusion across the arachnoid granulations returns excess cerebrospinal fluid to the venous circulation.

THE CEREBRUM

The cerebrum, the largest region of the brain, is the site where conscious thought and intellectual functions originate. Much of the cerebrum is involved in receiving somatic sensory information and then exerting voluntary or involuntary control over somatic motor neurons. In general, we are aware of these events. However, most sensory processing and all visceral motor (autonomic) control occur elsewhere in the brain, usually outside our conscious awareness.

The cerebrum includes gray matter and white matter. Gray matter is found in a superficial layer of neural cortex and in deeper *basal nuclei.* The *central white matter,* composed of myelinated axons, lies beneath the neural cortex and surrounds the basal nuclei.

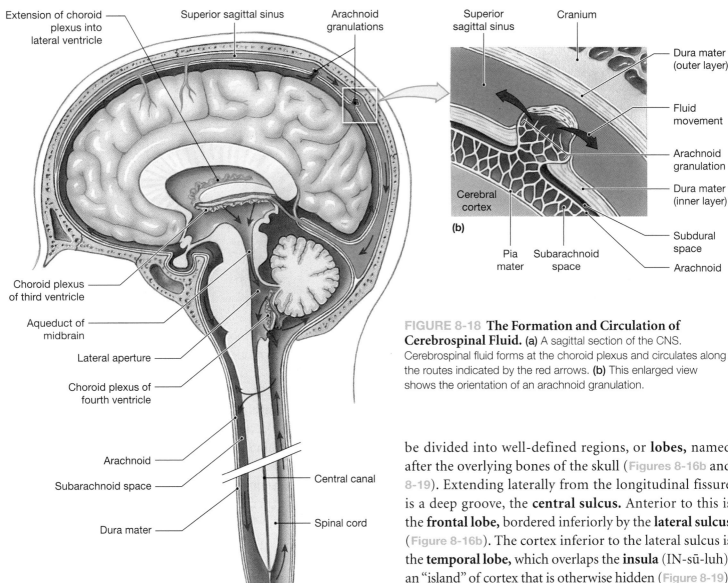

Extension of choroid plexus into lateral ventricle

Superior sagittal sinus

Arachnoid granulations

Superior sagittal sinus

Cranium

Dura mater (outer layer)

Fluid movement

Arachnoid granulation

Dura mater (inner layer)

Cerebral cortex

Subdural space

Pia mater

Subarachnoid space

Arachnoid

(b)

Choroid plexus of third ventricle

Aqueduct of midbrain

Lateral aperture

Choroid plexus of fourth ventricle

Arachnoid

Subarachnoid space

Dura mater

Central canal

Spinal cord

(a)

FIGURE 8-18 **The Formation and Circulation of Cerebrospinal Fluid. (a)** A sagittal section of the CNS. Cerebrospinal fluid forms at the choroid plexus and circulates along the routes indicated by the red arrows. **(b)** This enlarged view shows the orientation of an arachnoid granulation.

Structure of the Cerebral Hemispheres

A thick blanket of neural cortex known as the **cerebral cortex** covers the superior and lateral surfaces of the cerebrum (Figure 8-19). This outer surface forms a series of elevated ridges, or **gyri** (JĪ-rī; singular, *gyrus*), separated by shallow depressions, called **sulci** (SUL-sī), or by deeper grooves, called **fissures.** Gyri increase the surface area of the cerebrum and thus the number of neurons in the cortex; the total surface area of the cerebral hemispheres is roughly equivalent to 2200 cm² (2.5 ft²) of flat surface.

The two cerebral hemispheres are separated by a deep **longitudinal fissure** (Figure 8-16a). Each hemisphere can be divided into well-defined regions, or **lobes,** named after the overlying bones of the skull (Figures 8-16b and 8-19). Extending laterally from the longitudinal fissure is a deep groove, the **central sulcus.** Anterior to this is the **frontal lobe,** bordered inferiorly by the **lateral sulcus** (Figure 8-16b). The cortex inferior to the lateral sulcus is the **temporal lobe,** which overlaps the **insula** (IN-sū-luh), an "island" of cortex that is otherwise hidden (Figure 8-19). The **parietal lobe** extends between the central sulcus and the **parieto-occipital sulcus** (Figure 8-16c). What remains is the **occipital lobe.**

In each lobe, some regions are concerned with sensory information and others with motor commands. Additionally, each hemisphere receives sensory information from, and sends motor commands to, the opposite side of the body. This results in the left cerebral hemisphere controlling the right side of the body and the right cerebral hemisphere controlling the left side. This crossing over has no known functional significance.

Motor and Sensory Areas of the Cortex

Figure 8-19 labels the major motor and sensory regions of the cerebral cortex. The central sulcus separates the motor and sensory portions of the cortex. The **precentral gyrus** of the frontal lobe forms the anterior margin of the central sulcus,

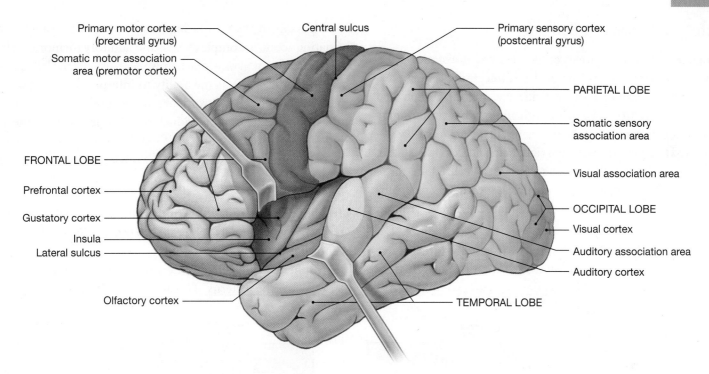

FIGURE 8-19 The Surface of the Cerebral Hemispheres. Major anatomical landmarks on the surface of the left cerebral hemisphere are shown. The colored areas represent various motor, sensory, and association areas of the cerebral cortex.

and its surface is the **primary motor cortex.** Neurons of the primary motor cortex direct voluntary movements by controlling somatic motor neurons in the brain stem and spinal cord.

The **postcentral gyrus** of the parietal lobe forms the posterior margin of the central sulcus, and its surface contains the **primary sensory cortex.** Neurons in this region receive somatic sensory information from touch, pressure, pain, and temperature receptors. We are consciously aware of these sensations because brain stem nuclei relay sensory information to the primary sensory cortex.

Sensations of sight, taste, sound, and smell arrive at other portions of the cerebral cortex. The **visual cortex** of the occipital lobe receives visual information, the **gustatory cortex** of the frontal lobe receives taste sensations, and the **auditory cortex** and **olfactory cortex** of the temporal lobe receive information about hearing and smell, respectively.

Association Areas

The sensory and motor regions of the cortex are connected to nearby **association areas,** regions that interpret incoming data or coordinate a motor response. The **somatic sensory association area** monitors activity in the primary sensory cortex. It is this area that allows you to recognize a touch as light as the arrival of a mosquito on your arm. The special senses of smell, sight, and hearing involve separate areas of sensory cortex, and each has its own association area. The **somatic motor association area,** or **premotor cortex,** is responsible for coordinating learned movements. When you perform a voluntary movement, such as picking up a glass or scanning these lines of type, instructions are relayed to the primary motor cortex by the premotor cortex.

The functional distinctions between the motor and sensory association areas are most evident after localized brain damage has occurred. For example, someone with damage to the premotor cortex might understand written letters and words but be unable to read owing to an inability to track along the lines on a printed page. In contrast, someone with a damaged **visual association area** can scan the lines of a printed page but cannot figure out what the letters mean.

Cortical Connections

The various regions of the cerebral cortex are interconnected by the white matter that lies beneath the cerebral cortex. Axons of different lengths interconnect gyri within a single cerebral hemisphere and link the two hemispheres across the **corpus callosum** (Figure 8-16c). Other bundles of axons link the cerebral cortex with the diencephalon, brain stem, cerebellum, and spinal cord.

Cerebral Processing Centers

"Higher-order" integrative centers receive information from many different association areas. These integrative centers control extremely complex motor activities and perform complicated analytical functions. Even though integrative centers may be found in both cerebral hemispheres, many are *lateralized*—restricted to either the left or the right hemisphere (Figure 8-20). Examples of integrative centers that are lateralized are those concerned with complex processes such as speech, writing, mathematical computation, and understanding spatial relationships.

THE GENERAL INTERPRETIVE AREA.
The **general interpretive area,** or *Wernicke area*, receives information from all the sensory association areas. This region plays an essential role in your personality by integrating sensory information and coordinating access to complex visual and auditory memories. This center is present in only one hemisphere, usually the left. Damage to this area affects the ability to interpret what is read or heard, even though the words are understood as individual entities. For example, an individual might understand the meaning of the spoken words "sit" and "here," because word recognition occurs in the auditory association areas, but be totally bewildered by the instruction "Sit here."

THE SPEECH CENTER.
Some of the neurons in the general interpretive area connect to the **speech center** *(Broca area)*. This center lies along the edge of the premotor cortex in the same hemisphere as the general interpretive area. The speech center regulates the patterns of breathing and vocalization required

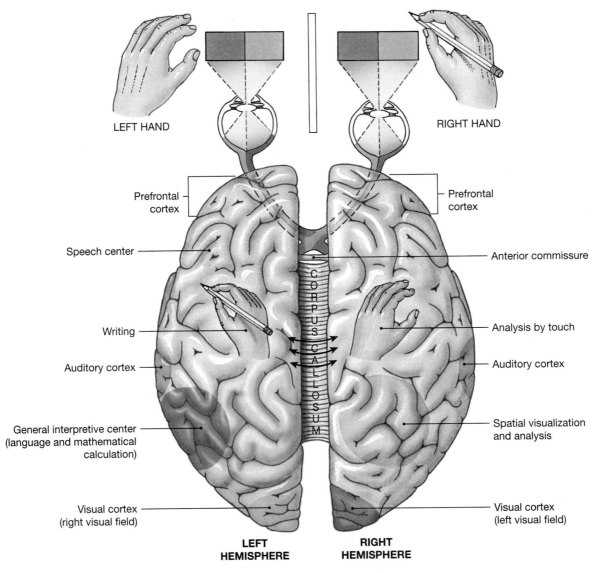

FIGURE 8-20 Hemispheric Lateralization. Some functional differences between the left and right cerebral hemispheres are depicted.

for normal speech. A person with a damaged speech center can make sounds but not words.

The motor commands issued by the speech center are adjusted by feedback from the auditory association area. Damage there can cause a variety of speech-related problems. Some affected individuals have difficulty speaking, even though they know exactly which words to use; others talk constantly but use all the wrong words.

THE PREFRONTAL CORTEX. The **prefrontal cortex** of the frontal lobe (Figure 8-20) coordinates information from the association areas of the entire cortex. In doing so, it performs such abstract intellectual functions as predicting the future consequences of events or actions. Damage to this area leads to problems in estimating time relationships between events. Questions such as "How long ago did this happen?" or "What happened first?" become difficult to answer. The prefrontal cortex also has connections with other cortical areas and with other portions of the brain. Feelings of frustration, tension, and anxiety are generated at the prefrontal cortex as it interprets ongoing events and predicts future situations or consequences. If the connections between the prefrontal cortex and other brain regions are severed, the

Clinical Note

Aphasia and Dyslexia

Aphasia (*a-*, without + *phasia*, speech) is a disorder affecting the ability to speak or read. *Global aphasia* results from extensive damage to the general interpretive area or to the associated sensory tracts. Affected individuals cannot speak, read, understand, or interpret the speech of others. Global aphasia often accompanies a severe stroke or tumor that affects a large area of cortex, including the speech and language areas. Recovery is possible when the condition results from *edema* (an abnormal accumulation of fluid) or hemorrhage, but the process often takes months. Lesser degrees of aphasia often follow minor strokes with no initial period of global aphasia. Such individuals can understand spoken and written words and may recover completely.

Dyslexia (*lexis,* diction) is a disorder affecting the comprehension and use of words. Developmental dyslexia affects children; estimates indicate that up to 15 percent of children in the United States suffer from some degree of dyslexia. These children have difficulty reading and writing, although their other intellectual functions may be normal or above normal. Their writing looks uneven and unorganized; letters are typically written in the wrong order (*dig* becomes *gid*) or reversed (*E* becomes ∃). Recent evidence suggests that at least some forms of dyslexia result from problems in processing and sorting visual information.

tensions, frustrations, and anxieties are removed. Early in the 1900s this rather drastic procedure, called a *prefrontal lobotomy,* was used to "cure" a variety of mental illnesses, especially those associated with violent or antisocial behavior.

Hemispheric Lateralization

As shown in Figure 8-20, each of the two cerebral hemispheres is responsible for specific functions that are not ordinarily performed by the opposite hemisphere. This specialization has been called *hemispheric lateralization.* In most people, the left hemisphere contains the general interpretive and speech centers and is responsible for language-based skills (reading, writing, and speaking). In addition, the premotor cortex involved in the control of hand movements is larger on the left side in right-handed individuals than in left-handed ones. The left hemisphere is also important in performing analytical tasks, such as mathematical calculations and logical decision making. For these reasons, the left hemisphere has been called the dominant hemisphere, or the categorical hemisphere.

The right cerebral hemisphere analyzes sensory information and relates the body to the sensory environment. Interpretive centers in this hemisphere enable you to identify familiar objects by touch, smell, taste, or feel. For example, the right hemisphere plays a dominant role in recognizing faces and in understanding three-dimensional relationships. It is also important in analyzing the emotional context of a conversation—for instance, distinguishing between the threat "Get lost" and the question "Get lost?"

Interestingly, there may be a link between handedness and sensory/spatial abilities. An unusually high percentage of musicians and artists are left-handed; the complex motor activities performed by these individuals are directed by the primary motor cortex and association areas on the right hemisphere, near the association areas involved with spatial visualization and emotions.

Hemispheric lateralization does not mean that the two hemispheres function independently of each other. As previously noted, the white fibers of the corpus callosum link the two hemispheres, including their sensory information and motor commands. The corpus callosum alone contains over 200 million axons, carrying an estimated 4 billion impulses per second!

The Electroencephalogram

The primary sensory cortex and the primary motor cortex have been mapped by direct stimulation in patients undergoing brain surgery. The functions of other regions of the cerebrum can be revealed by the behavioral changes that follow localized injuries or strokes, and the activities of specific regions can be examined by noninvasive techniques such as a PET scan or sequential MRI scans. ∞ p. 24

The electrical activity of the brain is commonly monitored to assess brain activity. Neural function depends on electrical events within the plasma membrane. The brain contains billions of nerve cells, and their activity generates an electrical field that can be measured by placing electrodes on the brain or on the outer surface of the skull. The electrical activity changes constantly as nuclei and cortical areas are stimulated or quiet down. An **electroencephalogram (EEG)** is a printed record of this electrical activity over time. The electrical patterns are called **brain waves,** which can be correlated with the individual's level of consciousness. Electroencephalograms can also provide useful diagnostic information regarding brain disorders. Four types of brain wave patterns are shown in Figure 8-21.

Memory

What was the topic of the last sentence you read? What is your Social Security number? How do you open a screw-top jar? How do you throw a Frisbee? Answering these questions involves accessing memories, stored bits of information gathered through prior experience. Answering the first two questions involves **fact memories,** which are specific bits of information. Answering the last two questions involves **skill memories,** which are learned motor behaviors. With repetition, skill memories become incorporated at the unconscious level. Examples include the complex motor patterns involved in skiing or playing the violin. Skill memories related to programmed behaviors, such as eating, are stored in appropriate portions of the brain stem. Complex skill memories involve an interplay between the cerebellum and the cerebral cortex.

Memories are often classified according to duration. **Short-term memories,** or *primary memories,* do not last long, but while they persist the information can be recalled immediately. Primary memories contain small bits of information, such as a person's name or a telephone number. Repeating a phone number or other bit of information reinforces the original short-term memory and helps ensure its conversion to a long-term memory. **Long-term memories** remain for much longer periods, in some cases for an entire lifetime. The conversion from short-term to long-term memory is called *memory consolidation.* Some long-term memories fade with time and may require considerable effort to recall. Other long-term memories seem to be part of consciousness, such as your name or the contours of your own body.

Most long-term memories are stored in the cerebral cortex. Conscious motor and sensory memories are referred to the appropriate association areas. For example, visual memories are stored in the visual association area, and memories of voluntary motor activity are kept in the premotor cortex. Special portions of the occipital and temporal lobes retain the memories of faces, voices, and words.

Amnesia refers to the loss of memory from disease or trauma. The type of memory loss depends on the specific regions of the brain affected. For example, damage to the auditory asso-

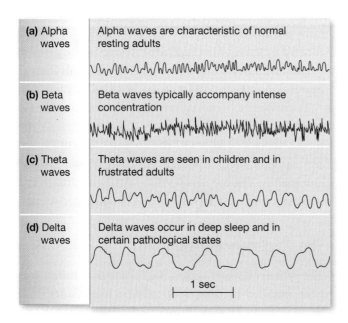

(a) Alpha waves — Alpha waves are characteristic of normal resting adults

(b) Beta waves — Beta waves typically accompany intense concentration

(c) Theta waves — Theta waves are seen in children and in frustrated adults

(d) Delta waves — Delta waves occur in deep sleep and in certain pathological states

1 sec

FIGURE 8-21 **Brain Waves.**

ciation areas may make it difficult to remember sounds. Damage to thalamic and limbic structures, especially the *hippocampus,* will affect memory storage and consolidation.

The Basal Nuclei

While your cerebral cortex is consciously active, other centers of your cerebrum, diencephalon, and brain stem are processing sensory information and issuing motor commands at a subconscious level. Many of these activities outside our conscious awareness are directed by the basal nuclei, or *cerebral nuclei.* The **basal nuclei** are masses of gray matter that lie beneath the lateral ventricles and within the central white matter of each cerebral hemisphere (**Figure 8-22**). The **caudate nucleus** has a massive head and slender, curving tail that fol-

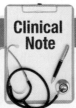
lows the curve of the lateral ventricle. Inferior to the head of the caudate nucleus is the **lentiform** *(lens-shaped)* **nucleus,** which consists of a medial **globus pallidus** (GLŌ-bus PAL-i-dus; pale globe) and a lateral **putamen** (pū-TĀ-men). Together, the caudate and lentiform nuclei are also called the *corpus striatum* (striated body). Inferior to the caudate and lentiform nuclei is another nucleus, the **amygdaloid** (ah-MIG-da-loyd; *amygdale,* almond) **body.** It is a component of the *limbic system* and is discussed in the next section.

The basal nuclei function in the subconscious control of skeletal muscle tone and the coordination of learned movement patterns. These nuclei do not start a movement—that decision is a voluntary one—but once a movement is under way, the basal nuclei provide the general pattern and rhythm. For example, during a simple walk the basal nuclei control the cycles of arm and thigh movements that occur between the time you decide to "start" walking and the time you give the "stop" order.

The Limbic System

The **limbic system** (LIM-bik; *limbus,* a border) includes the olfactory cortex, several basal nuclei, gyri, and tracts along the border between the cerebrum and diencephalon (**Figure 8-23**). This system is a functional grouping rather than an anatomical one. The functions of the limbic system include (1) establishing emotional states and related behavioral drives; (2) linking the conscious, intellectual functions of the cerebral cortex with the unconscious and autonomic functions of the brain stem; and (3) long-term memory storage and retrieval. Whereas the sensory cortex, motor cortex, and association areas of the cerebral

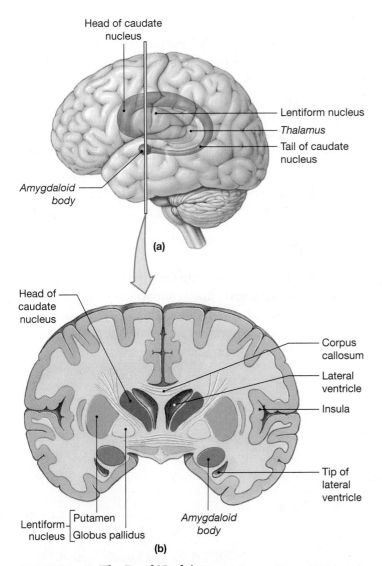

FIGURE 8-22 The Basal Nuclei. The relative positions of the basal nuclei can be seen in **(a)** a lateral view of a transparent brain and **(b)** this frontal section.

cortex enable you to perform complex tasks, it is largely the limbic system that makes you *want* to do them.

The amygdaloid bodies link the limbic system, the cerebrum, and various sensory systems. These nuclei play a role in the regulation of heart rate, in the control of the "fight or flight" response, and in linking emotions with specific memories. The hippocampus is important in learning and in the storage of long-term memories. Damage to the hippocampus that occurs in Alzheimer disease interferes with memory storage and retrieval.

The limbic system also includes hypothalamic centers that control (1) emotional states, such as rage, fear, and sexual arousal, and (2) reflex movements that can be consciously activated. For example, the limbic system includes the *mamillary bodies* (MAM-i-lar-ē; *mamilla*, a little breast) of the hypothalamus. These nuclei process olfactory sensations and control reflex movements associated with eating, such as chewing, licking, and swallowing.

THE DIENCEPHALON

The diencephalon (Figure 8-24) contains switching and relay centers that integrate conscious and unconscious sensory information and motor commands. It surrounds the third ventricle and consists of the *epithalamus*, *thalamus*, and *hypothalamus*.

The Epithalamus

The epithalamus lies superior to the third ventricle, where it forms the roof of the diencephalon. The anterior portion contains an extensive area of choroid plexus. The posterior portion contains the **pineal gland** (Figure 8-24b), an endocrine structure that secretes the hormone *melatonin*. Among other functions, melatonin is important in regulating day–night cycles.

The Thalamus

The left thalamus and right thalamus are separated by the third ventricle, and each contains a rounded mass of thalamic nuclei. The thalamus (Figures 8-16c and 8-24) is the final relay point for all ascending sensory information, other than olfactory, that will reach our conscious awareness. It acts as a filter, passing on to the primary sensory cortex only a small portion of the arriving sensory information. The rest is relayed to the basal nuclei and centers in the brain stem. The thalamus also plays a role in the coordination of voluntary and involuntary motor commands.

The Hypothalamus

The hypothalamus lies inferior to the third ventricle (Figure 8-16c). The hypothalamus contains important control and integrative centers in addition to those associated with the limbic system. Its diverse functions include (1) the subconscious control of skeletal muscle contractions associated with rage, plea-

Cingulate gyrus

Corpus callosum

Thalamic nuclei

Hypothalamic nuclei

Olfactory tract

Amygdaloid body

Hippocampus

Mamillary body

FIGURE 8-23 The Limbic System. This three-dimensional reconstruction of the limbic system shows the relationships among the system's major components.

(a) Lateral view

(b) Posterior view

FIGURE 8-24 **The Diencephalon and Brain Stem.** (a) A lateral view, as seen from the left side. (b) A posterior view.

sure, pain, and sexual arousal; (2) adjusting the activities of autonomic centers in the pons and medulla oblongata (such as heart rate, blood pressure, respiration, and digestive functions); (3) coordinating activities of the nervous and endocrine systems; (4) secreting a variety of hormones, including *antidiuretic hormone (ADH)* and *oxytocin;* (5) producing the behavioral "drives" involved in hunger and thirst; (6) coordinating voluntary and autonomic functions; (7) regulating normal body temperature; and (8) coordinating the daily cycles of activity.

THE MIDBRAIN

The midbrain (Figure 8-24) contains various nuclei and bundles of ascending and descending nerve fibers. It includes two pairs of sensory nuclei, or *colliculi* (ko-LIK-ū-lī; singular: *colliculus,* a small hill), involved in the processing of visual and auditory sensations. The *superior colliculi* control the reflex movements of the eyes, head, and neck in response to visual stimuli, such as a blinding flash of light. The *inferior colliculi* control reflex movements of the head, neck, and trunk in response to auditory stimuli, such as a loud noise. The midbrain also contains motor nuclei for two of the cranial nerves (N III, N IV) involved in the control of eye movements. Descending bundles of nerve fibers on the ventrolateral surface of the midbrain make up the **cerebral peduncles** (*peduncles,* little feet). Some of the descending fibers go to the cerebellum by way of

the pons, and others carry voluntary motor commands from the primary motor cortex of each cerebral hemisphere.

The midbrain is also headquarters to one of the most important brain stem components, the **reticular formation,** which regulates many involuntary functions. The reticular formation is a network of interconnected nuclei that extends the length of the brain stem. The reticular formation of the midbrain contains the *reticular activating system (RAS).* The output of this system directly affects the activity of the cerebral cortex. When the RAS is inactive, so are we; when the RAS is stimulated, so is our state of attention or wakefulness.

The maintenance of muscle tone and posture is controlled by midbrain nuclei that integrate information from the cerebrum and cerebellum and issue the appropriate involuntary motor commands. Other midbrain nuclei play an important role in regulating the motor output of the basal nuclei. For example, the *substantia nigra* (NĪ-gruh; black) inhibit the activity of the basal nuclei by releasing the neurotransmitter dopamine. ∞ p. 261 If the substantia nigra are damaged or the neurons secrete less dopamine, the basal nuclei become more active. The result is a gradual increase in muscle tone and the appearance of symptoms characteristic of *Parkinson disease.* Persons with Parkinson disease have difficulty starting voluntary movements because opposing muscle groups do not relax—they must be overpowered. Once a movement is under way, every aspect must be voluntarily controlled through intense effort and concentration.

THE PONS

The pons (Figure 8-24a) links the cerebellum with the midbrain, diencephalon, cerebrum, and spinal cord. One group of nuclei within the pons includes the sensory and motor nuclei for four of the cranial nerves (N V–N VIII). Other nuclei are concerned with the involuntary control of the pace and depth of respiration. Tracts passing through the pons link the cerebellum with the brain stem, cerebrum, and spinal cord.

THE CEREBELLUM

The cerebellum (Figure 8-16b,c) is an automatic processing center. Its two important functions are (1) adjusting the postural muscles of the body to maintain balance and (2) programming and fine-tuning movements controlled at the conscious and subconscious levels. These functions are performed indirectly by regulating activity along motor pathways at the cerebral cortex, basal nuclei, and brain stem. The cerebellum compares the motor commands with proprioceptive information (position sense) and performs adjustments needed to make the movement smooth. The tracts that link the cerebellum with these different regions are the **cerebellar peduncles** (Figure 8-24). Like the cerebrum, the cerebellum is composed of white matter covered by a layer of neural cortex called the *cerebellar cortex.*

The cerebellum can be permanently damaged by trauma or stroke or temporarily affected by drugs such as alcohol. These alterations can produce *ataxia* (a-TAK-sē-uh; *ataxia*, a lack of order), a disturbance in balance.

THE MEDULLA OBLONGATA

The medulla oblongata (Figure 8-24) connects the brain with the spinal cord. All communication between the brain and spinal cord involves tracts that ascend or descend through the medulla oblongata. These tracts often synapse in the medulla oblongata at sensory or motor nuclei that act as relay stations and processing centers. In addition to these nuclei, the medulla oblongata contains sensory and motor nuclei associated with five of the cranial nerves (N VIII–N XII).

The portion of the reticular system within the medulla oblongata contains nuclei and centers that regulate vital autonomic functions. These *reflex centers* receive inputs from cranial nerves, the cerebral cortex, and the brain stem, and their output controls or adjusts the activities of the cardiovascular and respiratory systems. The **cardiovascular centers** adjust heart rate, the strength of cardiac contractions, and the flow of blood

The Big Picture

The brain is a large, delicate mass of neural tissue that contains internal passageways and chambers filled with cerebrospinal fluid. Each of the six major regions of the brain has specific functions. As you ascend from the medulla oblongata, which connects to the spinal cord, to the cerebrum, those functions become more complex and variable. Conscious thought and intelligence are provided by the neural cortex of the cerebral hemispheres.

through peripheral tissues. In terms of function, the cardiovascular centers are subdivided into a *cardiac center* regulating the heart rate and a *vasomotor center* controlling peripheral blood flow. The **respiratory rhythmicity centers** set the basic pace for respiratory movements, and their activity is adjusted by the *respiratory centers* of the pons.

CHECKPOINT

20. Describe one major function of each of the six regions of the brain.

21. The pituitary gland links the nervous and endocrine systems. To which portion of the diencephalon is it attached?

22. How would decreased diffusion across the arachnoid granulations affect the volume of cerebrospinal fluid in the ventricles?

23. Mary suffers a head injury that damages her primary motor cortex. Where is this area located?

24. What senses would be affected by damage to the temporal lobes of the cerebrum?

25. The thalamus acts as a relay point for all but what type of sensory information?

26. Changes in body temperature stimulate which area of the diencephalon?

27. The medulla oblongata is one of the smallest sections of the brain. Why can damage to it cause death, whereas similar damage in the cerebrum might go unnoticed?

See the blue Answers tab at the back of the book.

8-8 The PNS connects the CNS with the body's external and internal environments

The peripheral nervous system (PNS) is the link between the neurons of the central nervous system (CNS) and the rest of the body; all sensory information and motor commands are carried by axons of the PNS (Figure 8-1, p. 248). These axons, bundled together and wrapped in connective tissue, form **peripheral nerves,** or simply nerves. Cranial nerves originate from the brain, and spinal nerves connect to the spinal cord. The PNS also contains both the cell bodies and the axons of sensory neurons and motor neurons of the autonomic nervous system. The cell bodies are clustered together in masses called **ganglia** (singular: *ganglion*) (Figure 8-6, p. 253).

THE CRANIAL NERVES

Twelve pairs of **cranial nerves** connect to the brain (Figure 8-25). Each cranial nerve has a name related to its appearance or function; each also has a designation consisting of the letter N (for "nerve") and a Roman numeral (for its position along the longitudinal axis of the brain). For example, N I refers to the first pair of cranial nerves, the olfactory nerves.

Distribution and Function of Cranial Nerves

Functionally, each nerve can be classified as primarily sensory, primarily motor, or mixed (sensory and motor). Many cranial nerves, however, have secondary functions. For example, several cranial nerves (N III, N VII, N IX, and N X) also carry autonomic fibers to PNS ganglia, just as spinal nerves deliver them to ganglia along the spinal cord. Next we consider the distribution and functions of the cranial nerves.

Few people are able to remember the names, numbers, and functions of the cranial nerves without some effort. Many people use mnemonic phrases, such as Oh, Once One Takes The Anatomy Final, Very Good Vacations Are Heavenly, in which the first letter of each word represents the names of the cranial nerves.

THE OLFACTORY NERVES (N I). The first pair of cranial nerves, the **olfactory nerves,** are the only cranial nerves attached to

Mamillary body

Basilar artery

Pons

Vertebral artery

Cerebellum

Medulla oblongata

Spinal cord

Olfactory bulb, termination of olfactory nerve (I)

Olfactory tract

Optic chiasm

Optic nerve (II)

Infundibulum

Oculomotor nerve (III)

Trochlear nerve (IV)

Trigeminal nerve (V)

Abducens nerve (VI)

Facial nerve (VII)

Vestibulocochlear nerve (VIII)

Glossopharyngeal nerve (IX)

Vagus nerve (X)

Hypoglossal nerve (XII)

Accessory nerve (XI)

(a)

(b)

FIGURE 8-25 The Cranial Nerves. (a) This photograph provides an inferior view of the brain. **(b)** The attachment of the 12 pairs of cranial nerves is depicted in this diagrammatic view.

the cerebrum. (The rest start or end within nuclei of the diencephalon or brain stem.) These nerves carry special sensory information responsible for the sense of smell. The olfactory nerves originate in the epithelium of the upper nasal cavity and penetrate the cribriform plate of the ethmoid bone to synapse in the olfactory bulbs of the brain. From the olfactory bulbs, the axons of postsynaptic neurons travel within the olfactory tracts to the olfactory centers of the brain.

THE OPTIC NERVES (N II). The **optic nerves** carry visual information from the eyes. After passing through the **optic foramina** of the orbits, these nerves intersect at the **optic chiasm** ("crossing") (Figure 8-25a) before they continue as the *optic tracts* to nuclei of the left and right thalamus.

THE OCULOMOTOR NERVES (N III). The midbrain contains the motor nuclei controlling the third and fourth cranial nerves. Each **oculomotor nerve** innervates four of the six muscles that move an eyeball (the superior, medial, and inferior rectus muscles and the inferior oblique muscle). These nerves also carry autonomic fibers to intrinsic eye muscles that control the amount of light entering the eye and the shape of the lens.

THE TROCHLEAR NERVES (N IV). The **trochlear** (TRŌK-lē-ar; *trochlea,* a pulley) **nerves,** the smallest of the cranial nerves, innervate the superior oblique muscles of the eyes. The motor nuclei that control these nerves lie in the midbrain. The name *trochlear* refers to the pulley-shaped, ligamentous sling through which the tendon of the superior oblique muscle passes to reach its attachment on the eyeball (Figure 9-9a, p. 317).

THE TRIGEMINAL NERVES (N V). The pons contains the nuclei associated with cranial nerve V. The **trigeminal** (trī-JEM-i-nal) **nerves** are the largest of the cranial nerves. These nerves provide sensory information from the head and face and motor control over the chewing muscles, such as the temporalis and masseter. The trigeminal has three major branches. The *ophthalmic branch* provides sensory information from the orbit of the eye, the nasal cavity and sinuses, and the skin of the forehead, eyebrows, eyelids, and nose. The *maxillary branch* provides sensory information from the lower eyelid, upper lip, cheek, nose, upper gums and teeth, palate, and portions of the pharynx. The *mandibular branch,* the largest of the three, provides sensory information from the skin of the temples, the lower gums and teeth, the salivary glands, and the anterior portions of the tongue. It also provides motor control over the chewing muscles (the temporalis, masseter, and pterygoid muscles). ∞ p. 218

THE ABDUCENS NERVES (N VI). The **abducens** (ab-DŪ-senz) **nerves** innervate only the lateral rectus, the sixth of the extrinsic eye muscles. The nuclei of the abducens nerves are in the pons. The nerves emerge at the border between the pons and the medulla oblongata and reach the orbit of the eye along with the oculomotor and trochlear nerves. The name *abducens* is based on the action of this nerve's innervated muscle, which abducts the eyeball, causing it to rotate laterally, away from the midline of the body.

THE FACIAL NERVES (N VII). The **facial nerves** are mixed nerves of the face whose sensory and motor roots emerge from the side of the pons. The sensory fibers monitor proprioceptors in the facial muscles, provide deep pressure sensations over the face, and provide taste information from receptors along the anterior two-thirds of the tongue. The motor fibers produce facial expressions by controlling the superficial muscles of the scalp and face and muscles near the ear. These nerves also carry autonomic fibers that result in control of the tear glands and salivary glands.

THE VESTIBULOCOCHLEAR NERVES (N VIII). The **vestibulocochlear nerves,** also called acoustic nerves, monitor the sensory receptors of the inner ear. The pons and medulla oblongata contain nuclei associated with these nerves. Each vestibulocochlear nerve has two components: (1) a **vestibular nerve** (*vestibulum,* a cavity), which originates at the *vestibule* (the portion of the inner ear concerned with balance sensations) and conveys information on position, movement, and balance; and (2) the **cochlear** (KOK-lē-ar; *cochlea,* snail shell) **nerve,** which monitors the receptors of the cochlea (the portion of the inner ear responsible for the sense of hearing).

THE GLOSSOPHARYNGEAL NERVES (N IX). The **glossopharyngeal** (glos-ō-fah-RIN-jē-al; *glossus,* tongue) **nerves** are mixed nerves innervating the tongue and pharynx. The associated sensory and motor nuclei are in the medulla oblongata. The sensory portion of this nerve provides taste sensations from the posterior third of the tongue and monitors blood pressure and dissolved gas concentrations in major blood vessels. The motor portion controls the pharyngeal muscles involved in swallowing. These nerves also carry autonomic fibers that result in control of the parotid salivary glands.

THE VAGUS NERVES (N X). The **vagus** (VĀ-gus; *vagus,* wandering) **nerves** provide sensory information from the ear canals, the diaphragm, and taste receptors in the pharynx, and from visceral receptors along the esophagus, respiratory tract, and abdominal organs as far away as the last portions of the large intestine. The associated sensory and motor nuclei of the vagus are located in the medulla oblongata. The sensory information provided by N X is vital to the autonomic control of visceral function, but we are not consciously aware of these sensations because they are seldom relayed to the cerebral cortex. The motor components of the vagus nerves control skeletal muscles of the soft palate, pharynx, and esophagus and affect cardiac muscle, smooth muscle, and glands of the esophagus, stomach, intestines, and gallbladder.

THE ACCESSORY NERVES (N XI). The **accessory nerves,** sometimes called the *spinal accessory nerves,* are motor nerves that innervate structures in the neck and back. These nerves differ from other cranial nerves in that some of their motor fibers originate in the lateral gray horns of the first five cervical segments of the spinal cord, as well as in the medulla oblongata. The internal branch joins the vagus nerve and innervates the voluntary swallowing muscles of the soft palate and pharynx, as well as the laryngeal muscles that control the vocal cords and produce speech. The external branch controls the sternocleido-mastoid and trapezius muscles associated with the pectoral girdle. ∞ pp. 221, 226

THE HYPOGLOSSAL NERVES (N XII). The **hypoglossal** (hī-pō-GLOS-al) **nerves** provide voluntary control over the skeletal muscles of the tongue. The nuclei for these motor nerves are located in the medulla oblongata.

The distribution and functions of the cranial nerves are summarized in Table 8-2.

The Big Picture The 12 pairs of cranial nerves are responsible for the special senses of smell, taste, sight, hearing, and balance, and for control over the muscles of the eye, jaw, face, and tongue, and the superficial muscles of the neck, back, and shoulders. The cranial nerves also provide sensory information from the face, neck, and upper chest, and autonomic innervation to organs in the thoracic and abdominopelvic cavities.

TABLE 8-2 **The Cranial Nerves**

CRANIAL NERVES (NUMBER)	PRIMARY FUNCTION	INNERVATION
Olfactory (N I)	Special sensory	Olfactory epithelium
Optic (N II)	Special sensory	Retina of eye
Oculomotor (N III)	Motor	Inferior, medial, superior rectus, inferior oblique, and intrinsic muscles of eye
Trochlear (N IV)	Motor	Superior oblique muscle of eye
Trigeminal (N V)	Mixed	*Sensory:* orbital structures, nasal cavity, skin of forehead, eyelids, eyebrows, nose, lips, gums and teeth; cheek, palate, pharynx, and tongue *Motor:* chewing muscles (temporalis, masseter, pterygoids)
Abducens (N VI)	Motor	Lateral rectus muscle of eye
Facial (N VII)	Mixed	*Sensory:* taste receptors on the anterior 2/3 of tongue *Motor:* muscles of facial expression, lacrimal (tear) gland, and submandibular and sublingual salivary glands
Vestibulocochlear (Acoustic) (N VIII)	Special sensory	Cochlea (receptors for hearing) Vestibule (receptors for motion and balance)
Glossopharyngeal (N IX)	Mixed	*Sensory:* posterior 1/3 of tongue; pharynx and palate (part); receptors for blood pressure, pH, oxygen, and carbon dioxide concentrations *Motor:* pharyngeal muscles, parotid salivary glands
Vagus (N X)	Mixed	*Sensory:* pharynx; auricle and external acoustic meatus; diaphragm; visceral organs in thoracic and abdominopelvic cavities *Motor:* palatal and pharyngeal muscles and visceral organs in thoracic and abdominopelvic cavities
Accessory (Spinal Accessory) (N XI)	Motor	Voluntary muscles of palate, pharynx, and larynx (with vagus nerve); sternocleidomastoid and trapezius muscles
Hypoglossal (N XII)	Motor	Tongue muscles

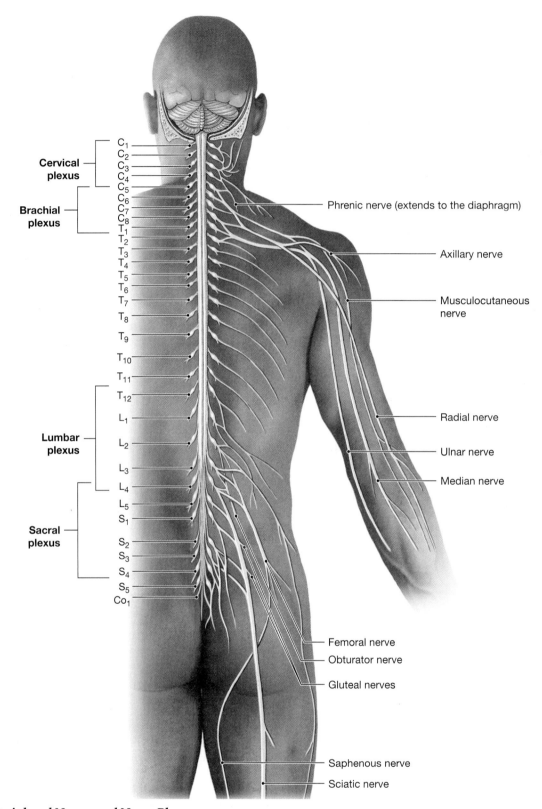

Cervical plexus
- C_1
- C_2
- C_3
- C_4

Brachial plexus
- C_5
- C_6
- C_7
- C_8
- T_1

- T_2
- T_3
- T_4
- T_5
- T_6
- T_7
- T_8
- T_9
- T_{10}
- T_{11}
- T_{12}

Lumbar plexus
- L_1
- L_2
- L_3
- L_4

Sacral plexus
- L_5
- S_1
- S_2
- S_3
- S_4
- S_5
- Co_1

Phrenic nerve (extends to the diaphragm)

Axillary nerve

Musculocutaneous nerve

Radial nerve

Ulnar nerve

Median nerve

Femoral nerve

Obturator nerve

Gluteal nerves

Saphenous nerve

Sciatic nerve

FIGURE 8-26 Peripheral Nerves and Nerve Plexuses.

THE SPINAL NERVES

The 31 pairs of **spinal nerves** are grouped according to the region of the vertebral column from which they originate (Figure 8-26). They include 8 pairs of cervical nerves (C_1–C_8), 12 pairs of thoracic nerves (T_1–T_{12}), 5 pairs of lumbar nerves (L_1–L_5), 5 pairs of sacral nerves (S_1–S_5), and 1 pair of coccygeal nerves (Co_1). Each pair of spinal nerves monitors a specific region of the body surface known as a **dermatome** (Figure 8-27). Dermatomes are clinically important because damage or infection of a spinal nerve or of dorsal root ganglia produces a characteristic loss of sensation in the corresponding region of the skin. For example, in *shingles,* a virus that infects dorsal root ganglia causes a painful rash whose distribution corresponds to that of the affected sensory nerves.

FIGURE 8-27 Dermatomes. Distributions of dermatomes on the surface of the skin, as seen in **(a)** an anterior and **(b)** a posterior view. The face is served by cranial nerves, not spinal nerves.

ANTERIOR

POSTERIOR

NERVE PLEXUSES

During development, skeletal muscles commonly fuse, forming larger muscles innervated by nerve trunks containing axons derived from several spinal nerves. These compound nerve trunks originate at networks called **nerve plexuses.** The four plexuses and the major peripheral nerves are shown in Figure 8-26.

The **cervical plexus** innervates the muscles of the neck and extends into the thoracic cavity to control the diaphragm, a key respiratory muscle. The **brachial plexus** innervates the shoulder girdle and upper limb. The **lumbar plexus** and the **sacral plexus** supply the pelvic girdle and lower limb. These plexuses are sometimes designated the *lumbosacral plexus.* Table 8-3 lists the spinal nerve plexuses and describes the distribution of some of the major nerves.

The nerves arising at the nerve plexuses contain sensory as well as motor fibers. *Peripheral nerve palsies,* also known as *peripheral neuropathies,* are characterized by regional losses of sensory and motor function as the result of nerve trauma or compression. You have experienced a mild, temporary palsy if your arm or leg has ever "fallen asleep."

CHECKPOINT

28. What signs would you associate with damage to the abducens nerve (N VI)?

29. John is having trouble moving his tongue. His physician tells him it is due to pressure on a cranial nerve. Which cranial nerve is involved?

30. Injury to which nerve plexus would interfere with the ability to breathe?

See the blue Answers tab at the back of the book.

8-9 Reflexes are rapid, automatic responses to stimuli

The central and peripheral nervous systems can be studied separately, but they function together. To consider the ways the CNS and PNS interact, we begin with simple reflex responses to stimulation. A **reflex** is an automatic motor response to a specific stimulus. Reflexes help preserve homeostasis by making rapid adjustments in the function of organs or organ systems. The response shows little variability—when a particular reflex is activated, it usually produces the same motor response.

TABLE 8-3 Nerve Plexuses and Major Nerves

PLEXUS	MAJOR NERVE	DISTRIBUTION
Cervical Plexus (C_1–C_5)	Phrenic nerve	Diaphragm
	Other branches	Muscles of the neck; skin of upper chest, neck, and ears
Brachial Plexus (C_5–T_1)	Axillary nerve	Deltoid and teres minor muscles; skin of shoulder
	Musculocutaneous nerve	Flexor muscles of arm and forearm; skin on lateral surface of forearm
	Median nerve	Flexor muscles of forearm and hand; skin over lateral surface of hand
	Radial nerve	Extensor muscles of arm, forearm, and hand; skin over posterolateral surface of the arm
	Ulnar nerve	Flexor muscles of forearm and small digital muscles; skin over medial surface of hand
Lumbosacral Plexus		
Lumbar Plexus (T_{12}–L_4)	Femoral nerve	Flexors and adductors of hip, extensors of knee; skin over medial surfaces of thigh, leg, and foot
	Obturator nerve	Adductors of hip; skin over medial surface of thigh
	Saphenous nerve	Skin over medial surface of leg
Sacral Plexus (L_4–S_4)	Gluteal nerve	Adductors and extensors of hip; skin over posterior surface of thigh
	Sciatic nerve	Flexors of knee and ankle, flexors and extensors of toes; skin over anterior and posterior surfaces of leg and foot

SIMPLE REFLEXES

A reflex involves sensory fibers delivering information from peripheral receptors to the CNS, and motor fibers carrying motor commands to peripheral effectors. The "wiring" of a single reflex is called a **reflex arc.** Figure 8-28 diagrams the five steps involved in the action of a reflex arc: (1) the arrival of a stimulus and activation of a receptor, (2) the activation of a sensory neuron, (3) information processing by an interneuron, (4) the activation of a motor neuron, and (5) the response by an effector (muscle or gland).

A reflex response usually removes or opposes the original stimulus. In Figure 8-28, the contracting muscle pulls the hand away from the painful stimulus. This reflex arc is, therefore, an example of *negative feedback.* ∞ p. 13 By opposing potentially harmful changes in the internal or external environment, reflexes play an important role in maintaining homeostasis.

In the simplest reflex arc, a sensory neuron synapses directly on a motor neuron, which performs the information-processing function. Such a reflex is called a **monosynaptic reflex.** Because there is only one synapse, monosynaptic reflexes control the most rapid, stereotyped motor responses

of the nervous system. The best-known example is the stretch reflex.

The **stretch reflex** provides automatic regulation of skeletal muscle length. The sensory receptors in the stretch reflex are called **muscle spindles,** bundles of small, specialized skeletal muscle fibers scattered throughout skeletal muscles. The stimulus (increasing muscle length) activates a sensory neuron that triggers an immediate motor response (contraction of the stretched muscle) that counteracts the stimulus.

Stretch reflexes are important in maintaining normal posture and balance and in making automatic adjustments in muscle tone. Physicians can use the sensitivity of the stretch reflex to test the general condition of the spinal cord, peripheral nerves, and muscles. For example, in the **knee jerk reflex** (or *patellar reflex*), a sharp rap on the patellar tendon stretches muscle spindles in the quadriceps muscles (Figure 8-29). With so brief a stimulus, the reflexive contraction occurs unopposed and produces a noticeable kick. If this contraction shortens the muscle spindles to below their original resting lengths, the sensory nerve endings are compressed, the sensory neuron is inhibited, and the leg drops back.

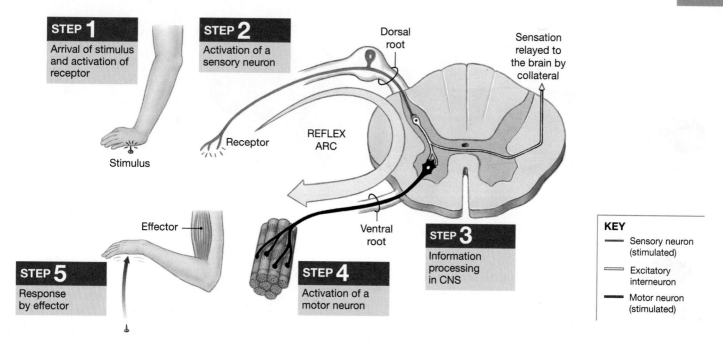

STEP 1
Arrival of stimulus and activation of receptor

STEP 2
Activation of a sensory neuron

Dorsal root

Sensation relayed to the brain by collateral

Receptor

Stimulus

REFLEX ARC

Effector

Ventral root

STEP 5
Response by effector

STEP 4
Activation of a motor neuron

STEP 3
Information processing in CNS

KEY
— Sensory neuron (stimulated)
□ Excitatory interneuron
— Motor neuron (stimulated)

FIGURE 8-28 **The Components of a Reflex Arc.** A simple reflex arc, such as the withdrawal reflex shown here, consists of a sensory neuron, an interneuron, and a motor neuron.

STEP 1
Stretching of muscle tendon stimulates muscle spindles

Muscle spindle (stretch receptor)

Stretch

Spinal cord

REFLEX ARC

Contraction

STEP 2
Activation of motor neuron produces reflex muscle contraction

FIGURE 8-29 **A Stretch Reflex.** The patellar reflex is a stretch reflex controlled by stretch receptors (muscle spindles) in the muscles that straighten the knee. When a reflex hammer strikes the patellar tendon, the muscle spindles are stretched. This stretching results in a sudden increase in the activity of the sensory neurons, which synapse on motor neurons in the spinal cord. The activation of spinal motor neurons produces an immediate muscle contraction and a reflexive kick.

COMPLEX REFLEXES

Many spinal reflexes have at least one interneuron between the sensory (afferent) neuron and the motor (efferent) neuron (**Figure 8-28**). Because there are more synapses, such **polysynaptic reflexes** include a longer delay between stimulus and response. But they can produce far more involved responses because the interneurons can control several muscle groups simultaneously.

Withdrawal reflexes move stimulated parts of the body away from a source of stimulation. The strongest withdrawal reflexes are triggered by painful stimuli, but these reflexes are also initiated by the stimulation of touch or pressure receptors. A **flexor reflex** is a withdrawal reflex affecting the muscles of a limb. If you grab an unexpectedly hot pan on the stove, a dramatic flexor reflex will occur (**Figure 8-30**). When the pain receptors in your hand are stimulated, the sensory neurons activate interneurons in the spinal cord that stimulate motor neurons in the anterior gray horns. The result is a contraction of flexor muscles that yanks your hand away from the stove.

When a specific muscle contracts, opposing (antagonistic) muscles are stretched. The flexor muscles that bend the elbow, for example, are opposed by extensor muscles, which straighten it out. A potential conflict exists here: Contraction of a flexor

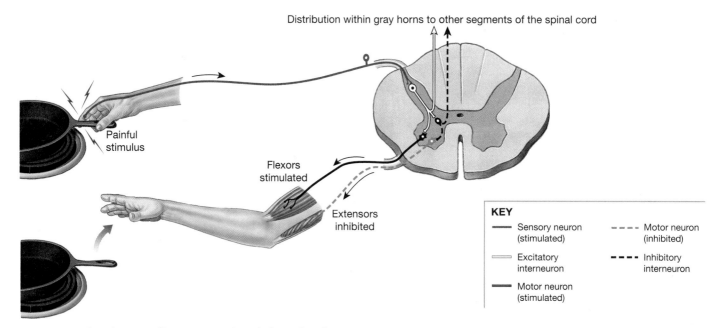

Distribution within gray horns to other segments of the spinal cord

Painful stimulus

Flexors stimulated

Extensors inhibited

KEY
— Sensory neuron (stimulated)
▭ Excitatory interneuron
— Motor neuron (stimulated)
- - - Motor neuron (inhibited)
■■■ Inhibitory interneuron

FIGURE 8-30 The Flexor Reflex, a Type of Withdrawal Reflex.

muscle should trigger in the extensors a stretch reflex that would cause them to contract, opposing the movement that is under way. Interneurons in the spinal cord prevent such competition through **reciprocal inhibition.** When one set of motor neurons is stimulated, those controlling antagonistic muscles are inhibited.

INTEGRATION AND CONTROL OF SPINAL REFLEXES

Although reflexes are automatic, higher centers in the brain influence these responses by stimulating or inhibiting the interneurons and motor neurons involved. The sensitivity of a reflex can thus be modified. For example, a voluntary effort to pull apart clasped hands elevates the general state of stimulation along the spinal cord, leading to an enhancement of all spinal reflexes.

Other descending fibers have an inhibitory effect on spinal reflexes. Stroking an infant's foot on the side of the sole produces a fanning of the toes known as the **Babinski sign,** or *positive Babinski reflex.* This response disappears as descending inhibitory synapses develop, so in adults the same stimulus produces a curling of the toes, called a **plantar reflex,** or *negative Babinski reflex,* after about a one-second delay. If either the higher centers or the descending tracts are damaged, the Babinski sign will reappear. As a result, this reflex is often tested if CNS injury is suspected.

Spinal reflexes produce consistent, stereotyped motor patterns that are triggered by specific external stimuli. However,

the same motor patterns can also be activated as needed by higher centers in the brain. The use of preexisting motor patterns allows a relatively small number of descending fibers to control complex motor functions. For example, the motor patterns for walking, running, and jumping are directed primarily by neuronal pools in the spinal cord. The descending pathways from the brain facilitate, inhibit, or fine-tune the established patterns.

The Big Picture

Reflexes are rapid, automatic responses to stimuli that "buy time" for the planning and execution of more complex responses that are often consciously directed.

CHECKPOINT

31. Define reflex.

32. Which common reflex do physicians use to test the general condition of the spinal cord, peripheral nerves, and muscles?

33. Why can polysynaptic reflexes produce more involved responses than can monosynaptic reflexes?

34. After injuring his back lifting a sofa, Tom exhibits a positive Babinski reflex. What does this imply about Tom's injury?

See the blue Answers tab at the back of the book.

8-10 Separate pathways carry sensory information and motor commands

The communication among the CNS, the PNS, and organs and organ systems occurs over pathways, nerve tracts, and nuclei that relay sensory and motor information. ∞ p. 253 The major sensory (ascending) and motor (descending) tracts of the spinal cord are named with regard to the destinations of the axons. If the name of a tract begins with *spino-,* the tract starts in the spinal cord and ends in the brain, and it therefore carries sensory information. If the name of a tract ends in *-spinal,* its axons start in the higher centers and end in the spinal cord, bearing motor commands. The rest of the tract's name indicates the associated nucleus or cortical area of the brain.

Table 8-4 lists some examples of sensory and motor pathways, and their functions.

SENSORY PATHWAYS

Sensory receptors monitor conditions in the body or the external environment. A **sensation,** the information gathered by a sensory receptor, arrives in the form of action potentials in an afferent (sensory) fiber. Most of the processing of arriving sensations occurs in centers along the sensory pathways in the spinal cord or brain stem; only about 1 percent of the information provided by afferent fibers reaches the cerebral cortex and our conscious awareness. For example, we usually do not feel the clothes we wear or hear the hum of our car's engine.

The Posterior Column Pathway

One example of an ascending sensory pathway is the **posterior column pathway** (Figure 8-31). It sends highly localized ("fine") touch, pressure, vibration, and proprioceptive (position) sensations to the cerebral cortex. In the process, the information is relayed from one neuron to another.

Sensations travel along the axon of a sensory neuron, reaching the CNS through the dorsal roots of spinal nerves. Once inside the spinal cord, the axons ascend within the posterior column pathway to synapse in a sensory nucleus of the medulla oblongata. The axons of the neurons in this nucleus (the second neuron in this pathway) cross over to the opposite side of the brain stem before continuing to the thalamus. The location of the synapse in the thalamus depends on the region of the body involved. The thalamic (in this case, third) neuron then relays the information to an appropriate region of the primary sensory cortex.

The sensations arrive organized such that sensory information from the toes reaches one end of the primary sensory cortex, and information from the head reaches the other. As a result, the sensory cortex contains a miniature map of the body surface called a *sensory homunculus* ("little man"). That map is distorted because the area of sensory cortex devoted to a particular region is proportional not to its size, but to the number of sensory receptors it contains. In other words, it takes many more cortical neurons to process sensory information arriving from the tongue, which has tens of thousands of taste and touch receptors, than it does to analyze sensations originating on the back, where touch receptors are few and far between.

TABLE 8-4 Sensory and Motor Pathways

PATHWAY	FUNCTION
SENSORY	
Posterior column pathway	Delivers highly localized sensations of fine touch, pressure, vibration, and proprioception to the primary sensory cortex
Spinothalamic pathway	Delivers poorly localized sensations of touch, pressure, pain, and temperature to the primary sensory cortex
Spinocerebellar pathway	Delivers proprioceptive information concerning the positions of muscles, bones, and joints to the cerebellar cortex
MOTOR	
Corticospinal pathway	Provides conscious control of skeletal muscles throughout the body
Medial and lateral pathways	Provides subconscious regulation of skeletal muscle tone, controls reflexive skeletal muscle responses to equilibrium sensations and to sudden or strong visual and auditory stimuli

Sensory homunculus of left cerebral hemisphere

KEY

➤ Axon of first-order neuron

⇨ Second-order neuron

➤ Third-order neuron

Nuclei in thalamus

MIDBRAIN

Nucleus in medulla oblongata

MEDULLA OBLONGATA

SPINAL CORD

Dorsal root ganglion

Fine-touch, vibration, pressure, and proprioception sensations from right side of body

FIGURE 8-31 The Posterior Column Pathway. The posterior column pathway delivers fine touch, vibration, and proprioception information to the primary sensory cortex of the cerebral hemisphere on the opposite side of the body. (For clarity, this figure shows only the pathway for sensations originating on the right side of the body.)

MOTOR PATHWAYS

In response to information provided by sensory systems, the CNS issues motor commands that are distributed by the *somatic nervous system (SNS)* and the *autonomic nervous system (ANS)* of the efferent division of the PNS (Figure 8-1). The SNS, under voluntary control, issues somatic motor commands that direct the contractions of skeletal muscles. The motor commands of the ANS, which are issued outside our conscious awareness, control the smooth and cardiac muscles, glands, and fat cells.

Three motor pathways provide control over skeletal muscles: the corticospinal pathway, the medial pathway, and the lateral pathway. The corticospinal pathway provides conscious, voluntary control over skeletal muscles, whereas the medial and lateral pathways exert more indirect, subconscious control. Table 8-4 lists some examples and functions of these motor pathways. We begin our examination of motor pathways with the corticospinal pathway.

The Corticospinal Pathway

The **corticospinal pathway,** sometimes called the *pyramidal system,* provides conscious, voluntary control of skeletal muscles. Figure 8-32 shows the motor pathway providing voluntary control over the right side of the body. As was the case for the sensory map on the primary sensory cortex, the proportions of the neurons of the primary motor cortex reflect the number of motor units present in that portion of the body. For example, the grossly oversized hands of the *motor homunculus* provide an indication of how many different motor units are involved in writing, grasping, and manipulating objects in our environment.

The corticospinal pathway begins at triangular-shaped *pyramidal cells* of the cerebral cortex. The axons of these upper motor neurons extend into the brain stem and spinal cord, where they synapse on lower, somatic motor neurons (Figure 8-32). All axons of the corticospinal tracts eventually cross over to reach motor neurons on the opposite side of the body. As a result, the left side of the body is controlled by the right cerebral hemisphere, and the right side is controlled by the left cerebral hemisphere.

The Medial and Lateral Pathways

The **medial and lateral pathways** provide subconscious, involuntary control of muscle tone and movements of the neck, trunk, and limbs. They also coordinate learned movement patterns and other voluntary motor activities (Table 8-4). Together, these pathways were known as the *extrapyramidal system* because it was thought that they operated independently of and parallel to the *pyramidal system* (the corticospinal pathway). It is now known that the control of the body's motor functions is integrated among all three motor pathways.

The components of the medial and lateral pathways are spread throughout the brain. These components include nuclei in the brain stem (midbrain, pons, and medulla oblon-

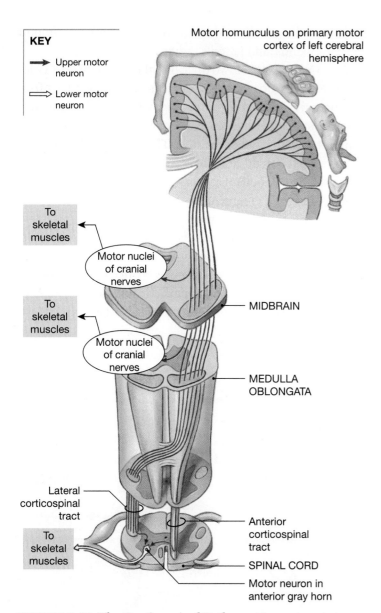

KEY

→ Upper motor neuron

⇒ Lower motor neuron

Motor homunculus on primary motor cortex of left cerebral hemisphere

To skeletal muscles

Motor nuclei of cranial nerves

To skeletal muscles

Motor nuclei of cranial nerves

Lateral corticospinal tract

To skeletal muscles

MIDBRAIN

MEDULLA OBLONGATA

Anterior corticospinal tract

SPINAL CORD

Motor neuron in anterior gray horn

FIGURE 8-32 The Corticospinal Pathway. The corticospinal pathway originates at the primary motor cortex. Axons of the pyramidal cells of the primary motor cortex descend to reach motor nuclei in the brain stem and spinal cord. Most of the fibers cross over in the medulla oblongata before descending into the spinal cord as the corticospinal tracts.

gata), relay stations in the thalamus, the basal nuclei of the cerebrum, and the cerebellum. Output from the basal nuclei and cerebellum exerts the highest level of control. For example, their output can (1) stimulate or inhibit other nuclei of these pathways or (2) stimulate or inhibit the activities of pyramidal cells in the primary motor cortex. Additionally, axons from the upper motor neurons in the medial and lateral pathways synapse on the same motor neurons innervated by the corticospinal pathway.

Clinical Note

Cerebral Palsy

The term **cerebral palsy** refers to a number of disorders affecting voluntary motor performance (including speech, movement, and posture) that appear during infancy or childhood and persist throughout life. The cause may be trauma associated with premature or unusually stressful birth; maternal exposure to drugs, including alcohol; or a genetic defect that causes improper development of the motor pathways. Problems with labor and delivery result from the compression or interruption of placental circulation or oxygen supplies. If the oxygen concentration of fetal blood declines significantly for as little as 5–10 minutes, CNS function can be permanently impaired. The cerebral cortex, cerebellum, basal nuclei, hippocampus, and thalamus are likely targets, producing abnormalities in motor skills, posture and balance, memory, speech, and learning abilities.

CHECKPOINT

35. As a result of pressure on her spinal cord, Jill cannot feel touch or pressure on her legs. What sensory pathway is being compressed?

36. The primary motor cortex of the right cerebral hemisphere controls motor function on which side of the body?

37. An injury to the superior portion of the motor cortex would affect the ability to control muscles of which parts of the body?

See the blue Answers tab at the back of the book.

8-11 The autonomic nervous system, composed of the sympathetic and parasympathetic divisions, is involved in the unconscious regulation of body functions

Using the pathways already discussed, the body can respond to sensory information and exert voluntary control over the activities of skeletal muscles. Yet our conscious sensations, plans, and responses represent only a tiny fraction of the activities of the nervous system. In practical terms, conscious activities have little to do with our immediate or long-term survival, and the adjustments made by the **autonomic nervous system (ANS)** are much more important. Without the ANS, a simple night's sleep would be a life-threatening event.

As parts of the efferent division of the PNS, both the ANS and the somatic nervous system (SNS) carry motor commands to peripheral effectors. ∞ p. 248 However, clear anatomical differences exist between the SNS and ANS (Figure 8-33). In the SNS, lower motor neurons exert direct control over skeletal muscles (Figure 8-33a). In the ANS, a second motor neuron always separates the CNS and the peripheral effector (Figure 8-33b). The ANS motor neurons in the CNS, known as **preganglionic neurons,** send their axons, called *preganglionic fibers,* to autonomic ganglia outside the CNS. In these ganglia, the axons of preganglionic neurons synapse on **ganglionic neurons.** The axons, or **postganglionic fibers,** of these neu-

rons leave the ganglia and innervate cardiac muscle, smooth muscles, glands, and fat cells (adipocytes).

The ANS consists of two divisions: the sympathetic division and the parasympathetic division. Preganglionic fibers from the thoracic and lumbar spinal segments synapse in ganglia near the spinal cord; these axons and ganglia are part of the **sympathetic division** of the ANS. The sympathetic division is often called the "fight or flight" system because it usually stimulates tissue metabolism, increases alertness, and prepares the body to deal with emergencies.

Preganglionic fibers originating in the brain and the sacral spinal segments synapse on neurons of terminal ganglia located near the target organ or *intramural ganglia* (*murus,* wall) embedded within the tissues of visceral organs. These components are part of the **parasympathetic division** of the ANS, often regarded as the "rest and repose" or "rest and digest" sys-

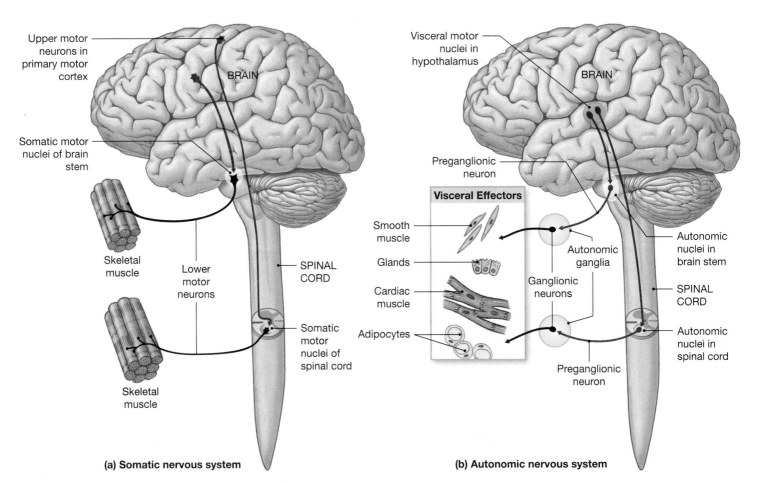

(a) Somatic nervous system

(b) Autonomic nervous system

FIGURE 8-33 The Somatic and Autonomic Nervous Systems. (a) In the SNS, a motor neuron in the CNS has direct control over skeletal muscle fibers. **(b)** In the ANS, visceral motor neurons in the hypothalamus synapse on preganglionic neurons. The preganglionic neurons synapse on ganglionic neurons that innervate effectors, such as smooth and cardiac muscles, glands, and fat cells.

tem because it conserves energy and promotes sedentary activities, such as digestion.

The sympathetic and parasympathetic divisions affect target organs through the controlled release of specific neurotransmitters by the postganglionic fibers. Whether the result is a stimulation or an inhibition of activity depends on the response of the membrane receptor to the presence of the neurotransmitter. Some general patterns are worth noting:

- All preganglionic autonomic fibers are cholinergic: They release acetylcholine (ACh) at their synaptic terminals. ∞ p. 260 The effects are always excitatory.

- Postganglionic parasympathetic fibers are also cholinergic, but the effects are excitatory or inhibitory, depending on the nature of the target cell receptor.

- Most postganglionic sympathetic fibers release norepinephrine (NE). Neurons that release NE are called *adrenergic*. ∞ p. 261 The effects of NE are usually excitatory.

THE SYMPATHETIC DIVISION

The sympathetic division of the ANS (Figure 8-34) consists of the following components:

- *Preganglionic neurons located between segments T_1 and L_2 of the spinal cord.* These neurons are situated in the lateral gray horns, and their short axons enter the ventral roots of these segments.

- *Ganglionic neurons located in ganglia near the vertebral column.* Two types of sympathetic ganglia exist. Paired *sympathetic chain ganglia* on either side of the vertebral column contain neurons that control effectors in the body wall and inside the thoracic cavity. Unpaired *collateral ganglia,* anterior to the vertebral column, contain ganglionic neurons that innervate tissues and organs in the abdominopelvic cavity.

- *The suprarenal medullae.* The center of each suprarenal gland, an area known as the **suprarenal medulla,** is a modified ganglion. Its ganglionic neurons have very short axons.

Organization of the Sympathetic Division

THE SYMPATHETIC CHAIN. From spinal segments T_1 to L_2, sympathetic preganglionic fibers join the ventral root of each spinal nerve. All of these fibers then exit the spinal nerve to enter the sympathetic chain ganglia (Figure 8-34). For motor commands to the body wall, a synapse occurs at the chain ganglia, and then the postganglionic fibers return to the spinal nerve for distribution. For the thoracic cavity, a synapse also occurs at the chain ganglia, but the postganglionic fibers then form nerves that go directly to their targets (Figure 8-34).

THE COLLATERAL GANGLIA. The abdominopelvic tissues and organs receive sympathetic innervation over preganglionic fibers from lower thoracic and upper lumbar segments that pass through the sympathetic chain without synapsing and instead synapse within three unpaired **collateral ganglia** (Figure 8-34). The nerves traveling to the collateral ganglia are known as *splanchnic nerves.* The postganglionic fibers leaving the collateral ganglia innervate organs throughout the abdominopelvic cavity.

THE SUPRARENAL GLANDS. Preganglionic fibers entering each suprarenal gland proceed to its central region, where they synapse on modified neurons that perform an endocrine function. When stimulated, these cells release the neurotransmitters norepinephrine (NE) and epinephrine (E) into surrounding capillaries, which carry them throughout the body. In general, the effects of these neurotransmitters resemble those produced by the stimulation of sympathetic postganglionic fibers.

General Functions of the Sympathetic Division

The sympathetic division stimulates tissue metabolism, increases alertness, and prepares the individual for sudden, intense physical activity. Sympathetic innervation distributed by the spinal nerves stimulates sweat gland activity and arrector pili muscles (producing "goose bumps"), reduces circulation to the skin and body wall, accelerates blood flow to skeletal muscles, releases stored lipids from adipose tissue, and dilates the pupils. The activation of the sympathetic nerves to the thoracic cavity accelerates the heart rate, increases the force of

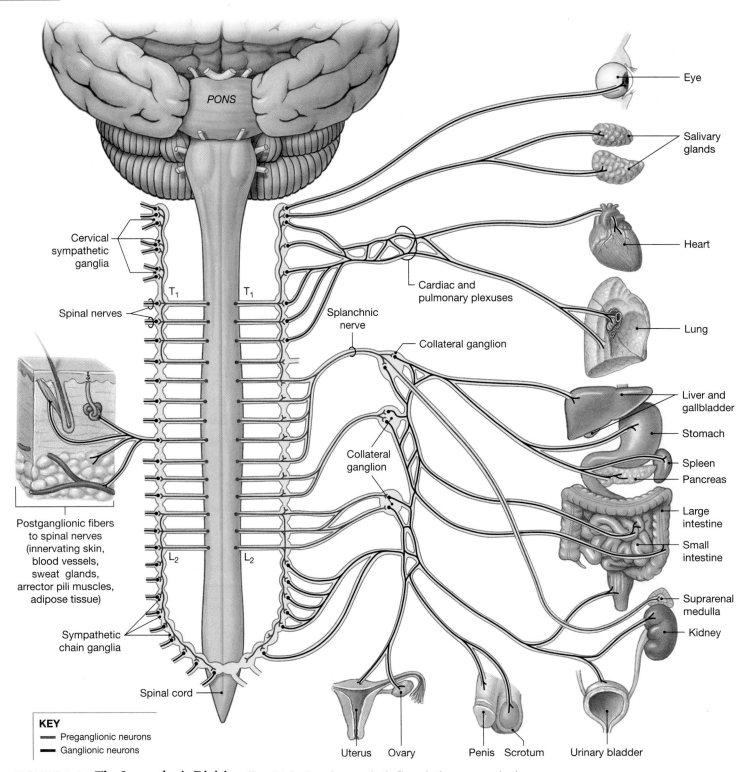

FIGURE 8-34 The Sympathetic Division. The distribution of sympathetic fibers is the same on both sides of the body. For clarity, the innervation of somatic structures is shown to the left, and the innervation of visceral structures to the right.

cardiac contractions, and dilates the respiratory passageways. The postganglionic fibers from the collateral ganglia reduce the blood flow to and energy use by visceral organs that are not important to short-term survival (such as the digestive tract), and they stimulate the release of stored energy reserves. The release of NE and E by the suprarenal medullae broadens the effects of sympathetic activation to cells not innervated by sympathetic postganglionic fibers and also makes the effects last much longer than those produced by direct sympathetic innervation.

THE PARASYMPATHETIC DIVISION

The parasympathetic division of the ANS includes the following structures:

- *Preganglionic neurons in the brain stem and in sacral segments of the spinal cord.* The midbrain, pons, and medulla oblongata contain autonomic nuclei associated with cranial nerves III, VII, IX, and X. Other autonomic nuclei lie in the lateral gray horns of spinal cord segments S_2 to S_4.

- *Ganglionic neurons in peripheral ganglia within or adjacent to the target organs.* Preganglionic fibers of the parasympathetic division do not diverge as extensively as those of the sympathetic division. Thus, the effects of parasympathetic stimulation are more localized and specific than those of the sympathetic division.

Organization of the Parasympathetic Division

Figure 8-35 diagrams the pattern of parasympathetic innervation. Preganglionic fibers leaving the brain travel within cranial nerves III (oculomotor), VII (facial), IX (glossopharyngeal), and X (vagus). These fibers synapse in terminal ganglia located in peripheral tissues, and short postganglionic fibers then continue to their targets. The vagus nerves provide preganglionic parasympathetic innervation to ganglia in organs of the thoracic and abdominopelvic cavities as distant as the last segments of the large intestine. The vagus nerves provide roughly 75 percent of all parasympathetic outflow and innervate most of those organs.

Preganglionic fibers in the sacral segments of the spinal cord carry the sacral parasympathetic output. They do not join the spinal nerves but instead form distinct **pelvic nerves,** which innervate intramural ganglia in the kidney and urinary bladder, the last segments of the large intestine, and the sex organs.

General Functions of the Parasympathetic Division

Among other things, the parasympathetic division constricts the pupils, increases secretions by the digestive glands, increases smooth muscle activity of the digestive tract, stimulates defecation and urination, constricts respiratory passageways, and reduces heart rate and the force of cardiac contractions. These functions center on relaxation, food processing, and energy absorption. Stimulation of the parasympathetic division leads to a general increase in the nutrient content of the blood. Cells throughout the body respond to this increase by absorbing nutrients and using them to support growth and the storage of energy reserves. The effects of parasympathetic stimulation are usually brief and are restricted to specific organs and sites.

RELATIONSHIPS BETWEEN THE SYMPATHETIC AND PARASYMPATHETIC DIVISIONS

The sympathetic division has widespread effects, reaching visceral and somatic structures throughout the body, whereas the parasympathetic division innervates only visceral structures either serviced by cranial nerves or lying within the abdominopelvic cavity. Although some organs are innervated by one division or the other, most vital organs receive **dual innervation**—that is, instructions from both autonomic divisions. Where dual innervation exists, the two divisions often have opposing effects. Table 8-5 provides examples of the effects of either single or dual innervation on selected organs.

CHECKPOINT

38. While out for a brisk walk, Megan is suddenly confronted by an angry dog. Which division of the ANS is responsible for the physiological changes that occur as she turns and runs from the animal?

39. Why is the parasympathetic division of the ANS sometimes referred to as "the anabolic system"?

40. What effect would loss of sympathetic stimulation have on the flow of air into the lungs?

41. What physiological changes would you expect in a patient who is about to undergo a root canal and is quite anxious about it?

See the blue Answers tab at the back of the book.

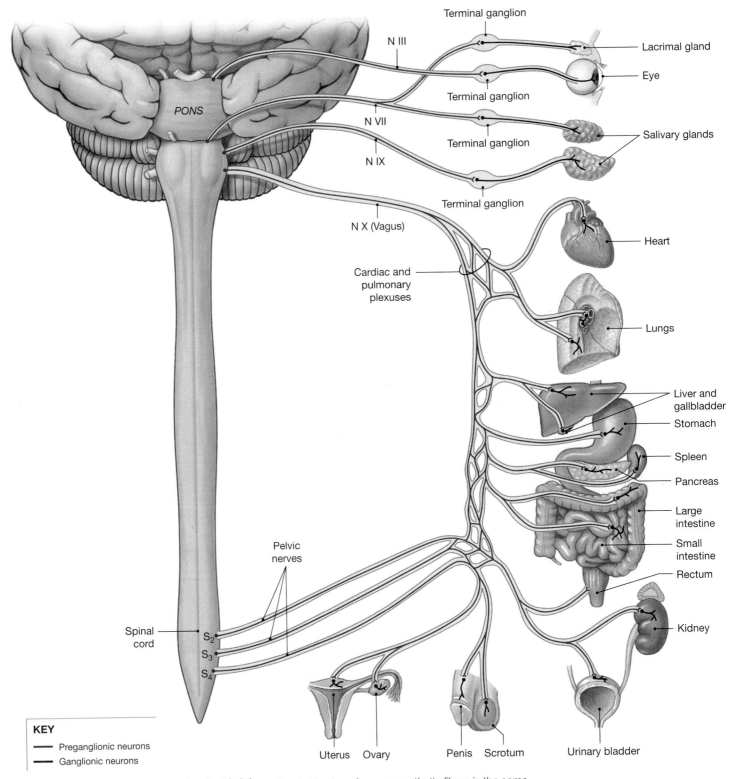

Terminal ganglion

N III

PONS

N VII

N IX

N X (Vagus)

Cardiac and
pulmonary
plexuses

Lacrimal gland

Eye

Terminal ganglion

Salivary glands

Terminal ganglion

Terminal ganglion

Heart

Lungs

Liver and
gallbladder

Stomach

Spleen

Pancreas

Large
intestine

Small
intestine

Rectum

Kidney

Pelvic
nerves

Spinal
cord

S_2

S_3

S_4

Uterus   Ovary

Penis   Scrotum

Urinary bladder

KEY
— Preganglionic neurons
— Ganglionic neurons

FIGURE 8-35 The Parasympathetic Division. The distribution of parasympathetic fibers is the same on both sides of the body.

TABLE 8-5 **The Effects of the Sympathetic and Parasympathetic Divisions of the ANS on Various Body Structures**

STRUCTURE	SYMPATHETIC EFFECTS	PARASYMPATHETIC EFFECTS
EYE	Dilation of pupil	Constriction of pupil
	Focusing for distance vision	Focusing for near vision
Tear Glands	None (not innervated)	Secretion
SKIN		
Sweat glands	Increases secretion	None (not innervated)
Arrector pili muscles	Contraction, erection of hairs	None (not innervated)
CARDIOVASCULAR SYSTEM		
Blood vessels	Vasoconstriction and vasodilation	None (not innervated)
Heart	Increases heart rate, force of contraction, and blood pressure	Decreases heart rate, force of contraction, and blood pressure
SUPRARENAL GLANDS	Secretion of epinephrine and norepinephrine by suprarenal medullae	None (not innervated)
RESPIRATORY SYSTEM		
Airways	Increases diameter	Decreases diameter
Respiratory rate	Increases rate	Decreases rate
DIGESTIVE SYSTEM		
General level of activity	Decreases activity	Increases activity
Liver	Glycogen breakdown, glucose synthesis and release	Glycogen synthesis
SKELETAL MUSCLES	Increases force of contraction, glycogen breakdown	None (not innervated)
ADIPOSE TISSUE	Lipid breakdown, fatty acid release	None (not innervated)
URINARY SYSTEM		
Kidneys	Decreases urine production	Increases urine production
Urinary bladder	Constricts sphincter, relaxes urinary bladder	Tenses urinary bladder, relaxes sphincter to eliminate urine
REPRODUCTIVE SYSTEM	Increased glandular secretions; ejaculation in males	Erection of penis (males) or clitoris (females)

8-12 Aging produces various structural and functional changes in the nervous system

Age-related anatomical and physiological changes in the nervous system begin shortly after maturity (probably by age 30) and accumulate over time. Although an estimated 85 percent of individuals above age 65 lead relatively normal lives, noticeable changes in mental performance and CNS functioning occur. Common age-related anatomical changes include the following:

• *A reduction in brain size and weight.* This change results primarily from a decrease in the volume of the cerebral cortex. The brains of elderly individuals have narrower gyri and wider sulci than those of young persons.

• *A reduction in the number of neurons.* Brain shrinkage has been linked to a loss of cortical neurons. Evidence indicates that the loss of neurons does not occur (at least to the same degree) in brain stem nuclei.

• *A decrease in blood flow to the brain.* With age, the gradual accumulation of fatty deposits in the walls of blood vessels reduces the rate of blood flow through arteries. (This process, called *arteriosclerosis,* affects arteries throughout the body; it is discussed further in Chapter 13.) The reduction in blood flow may not cause a cerebral crisis, but it does increase the chances that the individual will suffer a stroke.

- *Changes in synaptic organization of the brain.* The number of dendritic branchings and interconnections appears to decrease. Synaptic connections are lost, and neurotransmitter production declines.

- *Intracellular and extracellular changes in CNS neurons.* Many neurons in the brain accumulate abnormal intracellular deposits (pigments or abnormal proteins) that have no apparent function. Extracellular accumulations of proteins (plaques) may also occur. These changes appear to occur in all aging brains, but when present in excess they seem to be associated with clinical abnormalities.

Clinical Note

Alzheimer Disease

The most common age-related incapacitating condition of the central nervous system is **Alzheimer disease,** a progressive disorder characterized by the loss of higher cerebral functions. It is the most common cause of **senile dementia,** or *senility.* The first symptoms may appear at 50 to 60 years of age, although the disease occasionally affects younger individuals. The effects of Alzheimer disease are widespread; an estimated 2 million people in the United States, including roughly 15 percent of those over age 65, have some form of the condition, and it causes approximately 100,000 deaths each year. Moreover, the condition can have devastating emotional effects on the patient's immediate family.

In its characteristic form, Alzheimer disease produces a gradual deterioration of mental organization. The afflicted individual loses memories, verbal and reading skills, and emotional control. As memory losses continue to accumulate, problems become more severe. The affected person may forget relatives, a home address, or how to use the telephone. The loss of memory affects both intellectual and motor abilities, and a patient with severe Alzheimer disease has difficulty performing even the simplest motor tasks. There is no cure for Alzheimer disease, but a few medications and supplements slow its progress in many patients.

These anatomical changes are linked to impaired neural function. Memory consolidation—the conversion of short-term memory to long-term memory—often becomes more difficult. Other memories, especially those of the recent past, also become more difficult to access. The sensory systems of the elderly (notably hearing, balance, vision, smell, and taste) become less acute. Light must be brighter, sounds louder, and smells stronger before they are perceived. Reaction times are slowed, and reflexes—even some withdrawal reflexes—weaken or disappear. The precision of motor control decreases, so it takes longer to perform a given motor pattern than it did 20 years earlier.

For roughly 85 percent of the elderly, these changes do not interfere with their abilities to function. But for as yet unknown reasons, many individuals become incapacitated by progressive CNS changes. The most common of such incapacitating conditions is *Alzheimer disease* (see the Clinical Note).

CHECKPOINT

42. What is the major cause of age-related shrinkage of the brain?

See the blue Answers tab at the back of the book.

8-13 The nervous system is closely integrated with other body systems

The relationships between the nervous system and other organ systems are depicted in The Nervous System in Perspective (p. 304). Many of these interactions will be explored in detail in later chapters.

CHECKPOINT

43. How are the nervous system and the integumentary system functionally related?

See the blue Answers tab at the back of the book.

RELATED CLINICAL TERMS

amyotrophic lateral sclerosis (ALS): A progressive, degenerative disorder affecting motor neurons of the spinal cord, brain stem, and cerebral hemispheres; commonly known as Lou Gehrig disease.

aphasia: A disorder affecting the ability to speak or read.

ataxia: A disturbance of balance that in severe cases leaves the individual unable to stand without assistance. It is caused by problems affecting the cerebellum.

cerebrovascular accident (CVA), or *stroke:* A condition in which the blood supply to a portion of the brain is blocked off.

dementia: A stable, chronic state of consciousness characterized by deficits in memory, spatial orientation, language, or personality.

demyelination: The destruction of the myelin sheaths around axons in the CNS and PNS.

diphtheria (dif-THĒ-rē-uh): A disease that results from a bacterial infection of the respiratory tract. Among other effects, the bacterial toxins damage Schwann cells and cause PNS demyelination.

epidural block: The injection of anesthetic into the epidural space of the spinal cord to eliminate sensory and motor innervation by spinal nerves in the area of injection.

Hansen disease (*leprosy*): A bacterial infection that begins in sensory nerves of the skin and gradually progresses to a motor paralysis of the same regions.

Huntington disease: An inherited disease marked by a progressive deterioration of mental abilities and by motor disturbances.

meningitis: Inflammation of the meninges involving the spinal cord (*spinal meningitis*) and/or brain (*cerebral meningitis*); generally caused by bacterial or viral pathogens.

multiple sclerosis (skler-Ō-sis) (MS): A disease marked by recurrent incidents of demyelination affecting axons in the optic nerve, brain, and/or spinal cord.

myelography: A diagnostic procedure in which a radiopaque dye is introduced into the cerebrospinal fluid to obtain an X-ray image of the spinal cord and cauda equina.

neurology: The branch of medicine that deals with the study of the nervous system and its disorders.

neurotoxin: A compound that disrupts normal nervous system function by interfering with the generation or propagation of action potentials. Examples include *tetrodotoxin (TTX), saxitoxin (STX), paralytic shellfish poisoning (PSP),* and *ciguatoxin (CTX).*

paraplegia: Paralysis involving a loss of motor control of the lower (but not the upper) limbs.

paresthesia: An abnormal tingling sensation, usually described as "pins and needles," that accompanies the return of sensation after a temporary palsy.

Parkinson disease: A condition characterized by a pronounced increase in muscle tone, resulting from the excitation of neurons in the basal nuclei.

quadriplegia: Paralysis involving the loss of sensation and motor control of the upper and lower limbs.

sciatica (sī-AT-i-kuh): The painful result of compression of the roots of the sciatic nerve.

seizure: A temporary disorder of cerebral function, accompanied by abnormal movements, unusual sensations, and/or inappropriate behavior.

shingles: A condition caused by the infection of neurons in dorsal root ganglia by the varicella-zoster virus. The primary symptom is a painful rash along the sensory distribution of the affected spinal nerves.

spinal shock: A period of depressed sensory and motor function following any severe injury to the spinal cord.

Chapter **8** Review

KEY TERMS

action potential *256*
autonomic nervous system (ANS) *248*
axon *249*
cerebellum *267*
cerebrospinal fluid *269*
cerebrum *267*
cranial nerves *269*
diencephalon *267*
dual innervation *293*
ganglion/ganglia *253*
hypothalamus *267*
limbic system *275*
medulla oblongata *267*
membrane potential *254*
meninges *262*
midbrain *267*

myelin *252*
nerve plexus *283*
neuroglia *248*
neurotransmitter *259*
parasympathetic division *290*
polysynaptic reflex *285*
postganglionic fiber *290*
preganglionic neuron *290*
pons *267*
reflex *283*
somatic nervous system (SNS) *248*
spinal nerves *283*
sympathetic division *290*
synapse *249*
thalamus *267*

SUMMARY OUTLINE

iP Use *Interactive Physiology*® (IP)—available on the IP CD packaged with your new textbook—to help you understand difficult physiological concepts. Follow these navigation paths on IP for concepts in this chapter:

- Nervous System I/The Membrane Potential
- Nervous System I/Ion Channels
- Nervous System I/The Action Potential
- Nervous System II/Synaptic Transmission

An Introduction to the Nervous System *p. 247*

1. Two organ systems—the nervous and endocrine systems—coordinate organ system activity. The nervous system provides swift but brief responses to stimuli; the endocrine system adjusts metabolic operations and directs long-term changes.

8-1 The nervous system has anatomical and functional divisions *p. 247*

2. The **nervous system** includes all the neural tissue in the body. Its major anatomical divisions include the **central nervous system (CNS)** (the brain and spinal cord) and the **peripheral nervous system (PNS)** (all of the neural tissue outside the CNS).

3. Functionally, the PNS can be divided into an **afferent division,** which brings sensory information to the CNS, and an **efferent division,** which carries motor commands to muscles, glands, and fat cells. The efferent division includes the **somatic nervous system (SNS)** (voluntary control over skeletal muscle contractions) and the **autonomic nervous system**

(ANS) (automatic, involuntary regulation of smooth muscle, cardiac muscle, and glandular activity). *(Figure 8-1)*

8-2 Neurons are specialized for intercellular communication and are supported by cells called neuroglia *p. 248*

4. There are two types of cells in neural tissue: **neurons,** which are responsible for information transfer and processing, and **neuroglia,** or *glial cells,* which provide a supporting framework and act as phagocytes.

5. **Sensory neurons** form the afferent division of the PNS and deliver information to the CNS. **Motor neurons** stimulate or modify the activity of a peripheral tissue, organ, or organ system. **Interneurons (association neurons)** may be located between sensory and motor neurons; they analyze sensory inputs and coordinate motor outputs.

6. A typical neuron has a cell body, an **axon,** several branching **dendrites,** and synaptic terminals. *(Figure 8-2)*

7. Neurons may be described as **unipolar, bipolar,** or **multipolar.** *(Figure 8-3)*

8. The four types of neuroglia in the CNS are (1) **astrocytes,** which are the largest and most numerous; (2) **oligodendrocytes,** which are responsible for the **myelination** of CNS axons; (3) **microglia,** phagocytic cells derived from white blood cells; and (4) **ependymal cells,** with functions related to the *cerebrospinal fluid* (CSF). *(Figure 8-4)*

9. Nerve cell bodies in the PNS are clustered into **ganglia** (singular: *ganglion*). Their axons are covered by myelin wrappings of **Schwann cells.** *(Figure 8-5)*

10. In the CNS, a collection of neuron cell bodies that share a particular function is called a **center.** A center with a discrete anatomical boundary is called a **nucleus.** Portions of the brain surface are covered by a thick layer of gray matter called the **neural cortex.** The white matter of the CNS contains bundles of axons, or **tracts,** that share common origins, destinations, and functions. Tracts in the spinal cord form larger groups, called *columns.* *(Figure 8-6)*

11. **Sensory** *(ascending)* **pathways** carry information from peripheral sensory receptors to processing centers in the brain; **motor** *(descending)* **pathways** extend from CNS centers concerned with motor control to the associated skeletal muscles. *(Figure 8-6)*

8-3 In neurons, a change in the plasma membrane's electrical potential may result in an action potential (nerve impulse) *p. 254*

12. The **resting potential** (or **membrane potential**) of an undisturbed nerve cell results from a balance between the rates of sodium ion entry and potassium ion loss achieved by the sodium–potassium exchange pump. Any stimulus that affects this balance will alter the resting potential of the cell. *(Figure 8-7)*

13. An **action potential** appears when the membrane depolarizes to a level known as the **threshold.** The steps involved include depolarization to threshold, the opening of sodium channels and membrane depolarization, the closing of sodium channels and opening of potassium channels, and the return to normal permeability. *(Figure 8-8)*

14. In **continuous propagation,** an action potential spreads along the entire excitable membrane surface in a series of small steps. During **saltatory propagation,** the action potential appears to leap from node to node, skipping the intervening membrane surface. *(Figure 8-9)*

8-4 At synapses, communication occurs among neurons or between neurons and other cells *p. 259*

15. A **synapse** is a site where intercellular communication occurs through the release of chemicals called **neurotransmitters.** A synapse where neurons communicate with other cell types is a **neuroeffector junction.**

16. Neural communication moves from the **presynaptic neuron** to the **postsynaptic neuron** across the **synaptic cleft.** *(Figure 8-10)*

17. **Cholinergic synapses** release the neurotransmitter **acetylcholine (ACh).** ACh is broken down in the synaptic cleft by the enzyme **acetylcholinesterase (AChE).** *(Figure 8-11; Table 8-1)*

18. The roughly 20 billion interneurons are organized into **neuronal pools** (groups of interconnected neurons with specific functions). **Divergence** is the spread of information from one neuron to several neurons or from one neuronal pool to several pools. In **convergence,** several neurons synapse on the same postsynaptic neuron. *(Figure 8-12)*

8-5 The brain and spinal cord are surrounded by three layers of membranes called the meninges *p. 262*

19. The CNS is made up of the *spinal cord* and *brain.*

20. Special covering membranes, the **meninges,** protect and support the spinal cord and the delicate brain. The *cranial meninges* (dura mater, arachnoid, and pia mater) are continuous with those of the spinal cord, the *spinal meninges.* *(Figure 8-13)*

21. The **dura mater** covers the brain and spinal cord. The **epidural space** separates the spinal dura mater from the walls of the vertebral canal. The subarachnoid space of the arachnoid layer contains **cerebrospinal fluid** (the CSF), which acts as a shock absorber and a diffusion medium for dissolved gases, nutrients, chemical messengers, and waste products. The **pia mater** is bound to the underlying neural tissue.

8-6 The spinal cord contains gray matter surrounded by white matter and connects to 31 pairs of spinal nerves *p. 264*

22. In addition to relaying information to and from the brain, the spinal cord integrates and processes information on its own.

23. The spinal cord has 31 segments, each associated with a pair of **dorsal root ganglia** and their **dorsal roots,** and a pair of **ventral roots.** *(Figures 8-14; 8-15b)*

24. The white matter contains myelinated and unmyelinated axons; the gray matter contains cell bodies of neurons and glial cells. The projections of gray matter toward the outer surface of the spinal cord are called **horns.** *(Figure 8-15a)*

8-7 The brain has several principal structures, each with specific functions *p. 267*

25. There are six regions in the adult brain: cerebrum, diencephalon, midbrain, pons, medulla oblongata, and cerebellum. *(Figure 8-16)*

26. The central passageway of the brain expands to form four chambers called **ventricles.** Cerebrospinal fluid continuously circulates from the ventricles and central canal of the spinal cord into the subarachnoid space of the meninges that surround the CNS. *(Figures 8-17, 8-18)*

27. Conscious thought, intellectual functions, memory, and complex involuntary motor patterns originate in the **cerebrum.** *(Figure 8-17)*

28. The cortical surface of the cerebrum contains **gyri** (elevated ridges) separated by **sulci** (shallow depressions) or deeper grooves (**fissures**). The **longitudinal fissure** separates the two **cerebral hemispheres.** The **central sulcus** marks the boundary between the **frontal lobe** and the **parietal lobe.** Other sulci form the boundaries of the **temporal lobe** and the **occipital lobe.** *(Figures 8-16; 8-19)*

29. Each cerebral hemisphere receives sensory information and generates motor commands that concern the opposite side of the body. The **primary motor cortex** of the **precentral gyrus** directs voluntary movements. The **primary sensory cortex** of the **postcentral gyrus** receives somatic sensory information from touch, pressure, pain, and temperature receptors. **Association areas,** such as the **visual association area** and **premotor cortex** (motor association area), control our ability to understand sensory information and coordinate a motor response. *(Figure 8-19)*

30. The left hemisphere is usually the *categorical hemisphere,* which contains the general interpretive and speech centers and is responsible for language-based skills. The right hemisphere, or *representational hemisphere,* is concerned with spatial relationships and analyses. *(Figure 8-20)*

31. An **electroencephalogram (EEG)** is a printed record of **brain waves.** *(Figure 8-21)*

32. The **basal nuclei** lie within the central white matter and aid in the coordination of learned movement patterns and other somatic motor activities. *(Figure 8-22)*

33. The **limbic system** includes the *hippocampus,* which is involved in memory and learning, and the *mamillary bodies,* which control reflex movements associated with eating. The functions of the limbic system involve emotional states and related behavioral drives. *(Figure 8-23)*

34. The **diencephalon** provides the switching and relay centers needed to integrate the conscious and unconscious sensory and motor pathways. It is made up of the **epithalamus,** which contains the *pineal gland* and *choroid plexus* (a vascular network that produces cerebrospinal fluid), the **thalamus,** and the **hypothalamus.** *(Figure 8-24)*

35. The thalamus is the final relay point for ascending sensory information. Only a small portion of the arriving sensory information is passed to the cerebral cortex; the rest is relayed to the basal nuclei and centers in the brain stem. *(Figures 8-16c; 8-24)*

36. The hypothalamus contains important control and integrative centers. It can produce emotions and behavioral drives, coordinate activities of the nervous and endocrine systems, secrete hormones, coordinate voluntary and autonomic functions, and regulate body temperature.

37. Three regions make up the **brain stem.** (1) The **midbrain** processes visual and auditory information and generates involuntary somatic motor responses. (2) The **pons** connects the cerebellum to the brain stem and is involved with somatic and visceral motor control. (3) The spinal cord connects to the brain at the **medulla oblongata,** which relays sensory information and regulates autonomic functions. *(Figures 8-16c; 8-24)*

38. The **cerebellum** oversees the body's postural muscles and programs and fine-tunes voluntary and involuntary movements. The **cerebellar peduncles** are tracts that link the cerebellum with the brain stem, cerebrum, and spinal cord. *(Figures 8-16; 8-24)*

39. The medulla oblongata connects the brain to the spinal cord. Its nuclei relay information from the spinal cord and brain stem to the cerebral cortex. Its reflex centers, including the **cardiovascular centers** and the **respiratory rhythmicity centers,** control or adjust the activities of one or more peripheral systems. *(Figure 8-24)*

8-8 The PNS connects the CNS with the body's external and internal environments *p. 278*

40. The **peripheral nervous system (PNS)** links the central nervous system (CNS) with the rest of the body; all sensory information and motor commands are carried by axons of the PNS. The sensory and motor axons are bundled together into **peripheral nerves,** or nerves, and clusters of cell bodies, or *ganglia.*

41. The PNS includes cranial nerves and spinal nerves.

42. There are 12 pairs of **cranial nerves,** which connect to the brain, not to the spinal cord. (*Figure 8-25; Table 8-2*)

43. The **olfactory nerves (N I)** carry sensory information responsible for the sense of smell.

44. The **optic nerves (N II)** carry visual information from special sensory receptors in the eyes.

45. The **oculomotor nerves (N III)** are the primary sources of innervation for four of the six muscles that move the eyeball.

46. The **trochlear nerves (N IV),** the smallest cranial nerves, innervate the superior oblique muscles of the eyes.

47. The **trigeminal nerves (N V),** the largest cranial nerves, are mixed nerves with ophthalmic, maxillary, and mandibular branches.

48. The **abducens nerves (N VI)** innervate the sixth extrinsic eye muscle, the lateral rectus.

49. The **facial nerves (N VII)** are mixed nerves that control muscles of the scalp and face. They provide pressure sensations over the face and receive taste information from the tongue.

50. The **vestibulocochlear nerves (N VIII)** contain the vestibular nerves, which monitor sensations of balance, position, and movement, and the cochlear nerves, which monitor hearing receptors.

51. The **glossopharyngeal nerves (N IX)** are mixed nerves that innervate the tongue and pharynx and control swallowing.

52. The **vagus nerves (N X)** are mixed nerves that are vital to the autonomic control of visceral function and have a variety of motor components.

53. The **accessory nerves (N XI)** have an internal branch, which innervates voluntary swallowing muscles of the soft palate and pharynx, and an external branch, which controls muscles associated with the pectoral girdle.

54. The **hypoglossal nerves (N XII)** provide voluntary control over tongue movements.

55. There are 31 pairs of **spinal nerves:** 8 cervical, 12 thoracic, 5 lumbar, 5 sacral, and 1 coccygeal. Each pair monitors a region of the body surface known as a **dermatome** (*Figures 8-26; 8-27*)

56. A **nerve plexus** is a complex, interwoven network of nerves. The four large plexuses are the **cervical plexus,** the **brachial plexus,** the **lumbar plexus,** and the **sacral plexus.** The latter two can be united into a *lumbosacral plexus.* (*Figure 8-26; Table 8-2*)

8-9 Reflexes are rapid, automatic responses to stimuli *p. 283*

57. A **reflex** is an automatic involuntary motor response to a specific stimulus.

58. A **reflex arc** is the "wiring" of a single reflex. Five steps are involved in the action of a reflex arc: (1) arrival of a stimulus and activation of a receptor, (2) activation of a sensory neuron, (3) information processing, (4) activation of a motor neuron, and (5) response by an effector. (*Figure 8-28*)

59. A **monosynaptic reflex** is the simplest reflex arc, in which a sensory neuron synapses directly on a motor neuron that acts as the processing center. A **stretch reflex** is a monosynaptic reflex that automatically regulates skeletal muscle length and muscle tone. The sensory receptors involved are **muscle spindles.** (*Figure 8-29*)

60. **Polysynaptic reflexes,** which have at least one interneuron between the sensory afferent neuron and the motor efferent neuron, have a longer delay between stimulus and response than does a monosynaptic synapse. Polysynaptic reflexes can also produce more involved responses. A **flexor reflex** is a withdrawal reflex affecting the muscles of a limb. (*Figure 8-30*)

61. The brain can facilitate or inhibit reflex motor patterns based in the spinal cord.

8-10 Separate pathways carry sensory information and motor commands *p. 287*

62. The essential communication between the CNS and PNS occurs over pathways that relay sensory information and motor commands. (*Table 8-4*)

63. A **sensation** arrives in the form of an action potential in an afferent fiber. The **posterior column pathway** carries fine touch, pressure, and proprioceptive sensations. The axons ascend within this pathway and synapse with neurons in the medulla oblongata. These axons then cross over and travel on to the thalamus. The thalamus sorts the sensations according to the region of the body involved and projects them to specific regions of the primary sensory cortex. (*Figure 8-31; Table 8-4*)

64. The **corticospinal pathway** provides conscious skeletal muscle control. The **medial** and **lateral pathways** generally exert subconscious control over skeletal muscles. (*Figure 8-32; Table 8-4*)

8-11 The autonomic nervous system, composed of the sympathetic and parasympathetic divisions, is involved in the unconscious regulation of body functions *p. 289*

65. The autonomic nervous system (ANS) coordinates cardiovascular, respiratory, digestive, excretory, and reproductive functions.

66. **Preganglionic neurons** in the CNS send axons to synapse on **ganglionic neurons** in **autonomic ganglia** outside the CNS. The axons of the ganglionic neurons (postganglionic fibers) innervate cardiac muscle, smooth muscles, glands, and fat cells. (*Figure 8-33*)

67. Preganglionic fibers from the thoracic and lumbar segments form the **sympathetic division** ("fight or flight" system) of the ANS. Preganglionic fibers leaving the brain and sacral segments form the **parasympathetic division** ("rest and repose" or "rest and digest" system).

68. The sympathetic division consists of preganglionic neurons between segments T_1 and L_2, ganglionic neurons in ganglia near the vertebral column, and specialized neurons in the adrenal gland. Sympathetic ganglia are paired **sympathetic chain ganglia** or unpaired **collateral ganglia.** *(Figure 8-34)*

69. Preganglionic fibers entering the suprarenal glands synapse within the **suprarenal medullae.** During sympathetic activation these endocrine organs secrete epinephrine and norepinephrine into the bloodstream.

70. In crises, the entire division responds, producing increased alertness, a feeling of energy and euphoria, increased cardiovascular and respiratory activity, and elevation in muscle tone.

71. The parasympathetic division includes preganglionic neurons in the brain stem and sacral segments of the spinal cord, and ganglionic neurons in peripheral ganglia located within or next to target organs. Preganglionic fibers leaving the sacral segments form **pelvic nerves.** *(Figure 8-35)*

72. The effects produced by the parasympathetic division center on relaxation, food processing, and energy absorption; they are usually brief and restricted to specific sites.

73. The sympathetic division has widespread effects, reaching visceral and somatic structures throughout the body. The parasympathetic division innervates only visceral structures either serviced by cranial nerves or lying within the abdominopelvic cavity. Organs with **dual innervation** receive instructions from both divisions. *(Table 8-5)*

8-12 Aging produces various structural and functional changes in the nervous system *p. 295*

74. Age-related changes in the nervous system include (1) a reduction of brain size and weight, (2) a reduction of the number of neurons, (3) decreased blood flow to the brain, (4) changes in synaptic organization of the brain, and (5) intracellular and extracellular changes in CNS neurons.

8-13 The nervous system is closely integrated with other body systems *p. 296*

75. The nervous system monitors pressure, pain, and temperature and adjusts tissue blood flow for all systems.

REVIEW QUESTIONS

WWW Access more review material online at The Anatomy & Physiology Place (www.anatomyandphysiology.com). There, you'll find Chapter Guides, Chapter Quizzes, Chapter Practice Tests, Interactive Flashcards, a Glossary with Pronunciations, and more to help you succeed in the course.

Level 1 • Reviewing Facts and Terms

Match each item in column A with the most closely related item in column B. Place letters for answers in the spaces provided.

COLUMN A
_____ **1.** neuroglia
_____ **2.** autonomic nervous system
_____ **3.** sensory neurons
_____ **4.** dual innervation
_____ **5.** ganglia
_____ **6.** oligodendrocytes
_____ **7.** ascending tracts
_____ **8.** descending tracts
_____ **9.** saltatory propagation
_____ **10.** continuous propagation
_____ **11.** dura mater
_____ **12.** monosynaptic reflex
_____ **13.** sympathetic division
_____ **14.** cerebellum
_____ **15.** somatic nervous system
_____ **16.** hypothalamus
_____ **17.** medulla oblongata
_____ **18.** choroid plexus
_____ **19.** parasympathetic division
_____ **20.** motor neurons

COLUMN B
a. cover CNS axons with myelin
b. carry sensory information to the brain
c. occurs along unmyelinated axons
d. outermost covering of brain and spinal cord
e. production of CSF
f. supporting cells
g. controls smooth and cardiac muscle, glands, and fat cells
h. occurs along myelinated axons
i. link between nervous and endocrine systems
j. carry motor commands to spinal cord
k. efferent division of the PNS
l. controls contractions of skeletal muscles
m. masses of neuron cell bodies
n. connects the brain to the spinal cord
o. stretch reflex
p. afferent division of the PNS
q. maintains muscle tone and posture
r. "rest and repose"
s. opposing effects
t. "fight or flight"

21. Label the structures in the following diagram of a neuron.

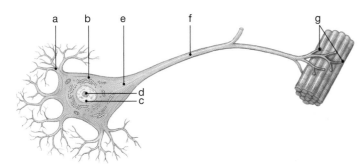

(a) _____ (b) _____
(c) _____ (d) _____
(e) _____ (f) _____
(g) _____

22. Regulation by the nervous system provides
(a) relatively slow but long-lasting responses to stimuli.
(b) swift, long-lasting responses to stimuli.
(c) swift but brief responses to stimuli.
(d) relatively slow, short-lived responses to stimuli.

23. All the motor neurons that control skeletal muscles are
(a) multipolar neurons.
(b) myelinated bipolar neurons.
(c) unipolar, unmyelinated sensory neurons.
(d) proprioceptors.

24. Depolarization of a neuron plasma membrane will shift the membrane potential toward
(a) 0 mV.   (b) –70 mV.
(c) –90 mV.   (d) a, b, and c are correct.

25. Identify the six principal parts of the brain in the following diagram.

(a) _____ (b) _____
(c) _____ (d) _____
(e) _____ (f) _____

26. The structural and functional link between the cerebral hemispheres and the components of the brain stem is the
(a) neural cortex.   (b) medulla oblongata.
(c) midbrain.   (d) diencephalon.

27. The ventricles in the brain are filled with
(a) blood.   (b) cerebrospinal fluid.
(c) air.   (d) neural tissue.

28. Reading, writing, and speaking are dependent on processing in the
(a) right cerebral hemisphere.
(b) left cerebral hemisphere.
(c) prefrontal cortex.
(d) postcentral gyrus.

29. Establishment of emotional states and related behavioral drives are functions of the
(a) limbic system.   (b) pineal gland.
(c) mamillary bodies.   (d) thalamus.

30. The final relay point for ascending sensory information that will be projected to the primary sensory cortex is the
(a) hypothalamus.   (b) thalamus.
(c) spinal cord.   (d) medulla oblongata.

31. Spinal nerves are called mixed nerves because they
(a) are associated with a pair of dorsal root ganglia.
(b) exit at intervertebral foramina.
(c) contain sensory and motor fibers.
(d) are associated with a pair of dorsal and ventral roots.

32. There is always a synapse between the CNS and the peripheral effector in
(a) the ANS.   (b) the SNS.
(c) a reflex arc.   (d) a, b, and c are correct.

33. Approximately 75 percent of parasympathetic outflow is provided by the
(a) pelvic nerves.   (b) sciatic nerve.
(c) glossopharyngeal nerves. (d) vagus nerve.

34. State the all-or-none principle of action potentials.

35. Using the mnemonic device "Oh, Once One Takes The Anatomy Final, Very Good Vacations Are Heavenly," list the 12 pairs of cranial nerves.

36. How does the emergence of sympathetic fibers from the spinal cord differ from the emergence of parasympathetic fibers?

Level 2 • Reviewing Concepts

37. A graded potential
(a) decreases with distance from the point of stimulation.
(b) spreads passively because of local currents.
(c) may involve either depolarization or hyperpolarization.
(d) a, b, and c are correct.

38. The loss of positive ions from the interior of a neuron produces
(a) depolarization.   (b) threshold.
(c) hyperpolarization.   (d) an action potential.

39. Which major part of the brain is associated with respiratory and cardiac activity?

40. Why is response time in a monosynaptic reflex much faster than response time in a polysynaptic reflex?

41. Compare the general effects of the sympathetic and parasympathetic divisions of the ANS.

Level 3 • Critical Thinking and Clinical Applications

42. If neurons in the central nervous system lack centrioles and are unable to divide, how can a person develop brain cancer?

43. A police officer has just stopped Bill on suspicion of driving while intoxicated. The officer asks Bill to walk the yellow line on the road and then asks him to place the tip of his index finger on the tip of his nose. Which part of the brain is being tested by these activities? How would these activities indicate Bill's level of sobriety?

44. In some severe cases of stomach ulcers, the branches of the vagus nerve (N X) that lead to the stomach are surgically severed. How might this procedure control the ulcers?

45. Improper use of crutches can produce a condition known as crutch paralysis, which is characterized by a lack of response by the extensor muscles of the arm and a condition known as wrist drop. Which nerve is involved?

46. While playing football, Ramon is tackled hard and suffers an injury to his left leg. As he tries to get up, he finds that he cannot flex his left hip or extend the knee. Which nerve is damaged, and how would this damage affect sensory perception in his left leg?

The Nervous System in Perspective

Functional Relationships Between the Nervous System and Other Systems

The Integumentary System

- The Integumentary System provides sensations of touch, pressure, pain, vibration, and temperature; hair provides some protection and insulation for skull and brain; protects peripheral nerves.
- The Nervous System controls contraction of arrector pili muscles and secretion of sweat glands.

The Skeletal System

- The Skeletal System provides calcium for neural function; protects brain and spinal cord.
- The Nervous System controls skeletal muscle contractions that produce bone thickening and maintenance, and determine bone position.

The Muscular System

- The Muscular System's facial muscles express emotional state; intrinsic laryngeal muscles permit communication; muscle spindles provide proprioceptive sensations.
- The Nervous System controls skeletal muscle contractions; coordinates respiratory and cardiovascular activities.

The Endocrine System

- The Endocrine System's many hormones affect CNS neural metabolism; the reproductive hormones and thyroid hormone influence CNS development.
- The Nervous System controls pituitary gland and many other endocrine organs; secretes ADH and oxytocin.

The Cardiovascular System

- The Cardiovascular System's capillaries maintain the blood-brain barrier when stimulated by astrocytes; blood vessels (with ependymal cells) produce CSF.
- The Nervous System modifies heart rate and blood pressure; astrocytes stimulate maintenance of blood-brain barrier.

The Lymphoid System

- The Lymphoid System defends against infection and assists in tissue repairs.
- The Nervous System's release of neurotransmitters and hormones affects sensitivity of immune response.

The Respiratory System

- The Respiratory System provides oxygen and eliminates carbon dioxide.
- The Nervous System controls the pace and depth of respiration.

The Digestive System

- The Digestive System provides nutrients for energy production and neurotransmitter synthesis.
- The Nervous System regulates digestive tract movement and secretion.

The Urinary System

- The Urinary System eliminates metabolic wastes; regulates body fluid pH and electrolyte concentrations.
- The Nervous System adjusts renal pressure and controls urination.

The Reproductive System

- The Reproductive System's sex hormones affect CNS development and sexual behaviors.
- The Nervous System controls sexual behaviors and sexual function.

For All Systems
The Nervous System monitors pressure, pain, and temperature; adjusts tissue blood flow patterns

Professional Profile

X-RAY TECHNOLOGIST
Allen Nakagawa

> **"You don't know which area you may end up working in, so get as much A & P as you can."**

If you have ever broken a bone, had a mammogram, or undergone radiation treatment, you have met an x-ray technologist. X-ray technologists, or imaging technologists as they are often called, are the professionals who manage the machines and position the patients for scans and treatments involving radiation.

There are actually four areas of radiologic technology. Radiographers use x-ray equipment, computed tomography (CT) scans, mammography, and magnetic resonance imaging (MRI) to view particular bones, tissues, organs, and vessels within the body. Sonographers obtain images of the body using sound wave technology. Nuclear medicine technologists use radiopharmaceuticals (such as dyes) and special cameras to produce images. Radiation therapists administer therapy to cancer patients and other patients requiring highly focused doses of radiation.

HIGH-TECH TOOLS

Allen Nakagawa is a senior diagnostic radiologic technologist at UCSF Medical Center in San Francisco. Allen specializes in spinal imaging, orthopedics, and pediatric orthopedics.

"A typical day for me begins at about 6:15 a.m.," says Allen. "I check on the incoming patient workload to see what will be happening that day. I also coordinate the workload of the students that I train."

On most days, Allen is assigned to the operating room. "In the OR, we have MRI machines that are built into the room. Before we had this equipment in the OR, the surgeon would have to stabilize and close the patient, and we would move the patient to the imaging department for scans. When we returned, up to an hour later, the surgeon would finish the surgery. You can imagine how much stress that puts on the patient and the surgical team. Now, in the

OR, the surgeon removes any metal in the patient and we do the scan right there with machines that retract back into the wall."

To become an x-ray technologist, you must study in a two-year program. Some programs last four years. Anatomy and physiology is a required course. "You will take intensive anatomy and additional anatomy and physiology in each modality you are considering working in," says Allen. "You don't know which area you may end up working in, so get as much A & P as you can."

After completing the course work, technologists must take a state licensing exam and a national exam. Once they've acquired their licenses, they can specialize in particular areas or work as generalists. "Some people only do diagnostic imaging; others work in the OR, in outpatient care, or in a variety of departments. You can work in a hospital or in an imaging center. Some technologists specialize in doing CT scans, or PET scans, or MRI."

PATIENT CONTACT

Regardless of where a technologist works, contact with patients is the core of the job. "You have to enjoy working with people. It can be hard, because many of your patients are really suffering. We get patients who are terminal, and we get kids who are really sick."

Allen enjoys working in one of the best hospitals in the world, using a variety of equipment to assist physicians and help diagnose their patients' conditions. As an imaging technologist, he is an integral part of the patient care team. "Physicians need to see what is going on inside the body. Even when the body is opened up, physicians still need information they can only get from imaging. For example, patients who have been in auto accidents may behave normally, but they may have a hematoma or a skull fracture that isn't apparent."

9 The General and Special Senses

Our comprehension of the world around us is based on information provided by our senses. For example, our ability to hear our favorite music depends on collecting and directing external sound waves to specialized receptor cells within the inner ear. This chapter examines the way the body's receptors provide sensory information, and the way sensory pathways distribute this information to provide us with our sense of smell, taste, vision, equilibrium, and hearing.

LEARNING OUTCOMES

After completing this chapter, you should be able to do the following:

9-1 Explain how the organization of receptors for the general senses and the special senses affects their sensitivity.

9-2 Identify the receptors for the general senses, and describe how they function.

9-3 Describe the sensory organs of smell, and discuss the processes involved in olfaction.

9-4 Describe the sensory organs of taste, and discuss the processes involved in gustation.

9-5 Identify the internal and accessory structures of the eye, and explain their functions.

9-6 Explain how we form visual images and distinguish colors, and discuss how the central nervous system processes visual information.

9-7 Describe the parts of the external, middle, and inner ear, and the receptors they contain, and discuss the processes involved in the senses of equilibrium and hearing.

9-8 Describe the effects of aging on smell, taste, vision, and hearing.

VOCABULARY DEVELOPMENT

akousis hearing; *acoustic*
baro- pressure; *baroreceptors*
circa about; *circadian*
circum- around; *circumvallate papillae*
cochlea snail shell; *cochlea*
dies day; *circadian*
emmetro- proper measure; *emmetropia*
incus anvil; *incus* (auditory ossicle)
iris colored circle; *iris*

labyrinthos network of canals; *labyrinth*
lacrima tear; *lacrimal gland*
lithos a stone; *otolith*
macula spot; *macula lutea*
malleus a hammer; *malleus* (auditory ossicle)
myein to shut; *myopia*
noceo hurt; *nociceptor*
olfacere to smell; *olfaction*

ops eye; *myopia*
oto- ear; *otolith*
presbys old man; *presbyopia*
skleros hard; *sclera*
stapes stirrup; *stapes* (auditory ossicle)
tectum roof; *tectorial membrane*
tympanon drum; *tympanum*
vallum wall; *circumvallate papillae*
vitreus glassy; *vitreous body*

9-1 Sensory receptors connect our internal and external environments with the nervous system

FIGURE 9-1 **Receptors and Receptive Fields.** Each receptor cell monitors a specific area known as a receptive field.

Our knowledge of the world around us is limited to those characteristics that stimulate our sensory receptors. Although we may not realize it, our picture of the environment is incomplete. Colors invisible to us guide insects to flowers, and sounds and smells we cannot detect provide important information to dolphins, dogs, and cats about their surroundings. Moreover, our senses are sometimes deceptive: In phantom limb pain, a person "feels" pain in a missing limb, and during an epileptic seizure an individual may experience sights, sounds, or smells that have no physical basis.

All sensory information is picked up by *sensory receptors,* specialized cells or cell processes that monitor conditions inside or outside the body. The simplest receptors are the dendrites of sensory neurons. The branching tips of these dendrites are called **free nerve endings.** Free nerve endings are sensitive to many types of stimuli. For example, a given free nerve ending in the skin may provide the sensation of pain in response to crushing, heat, or a cut. Other receptors are especially sensitive to one kind of stimulus. For example, a touch receptor is very sensitive to pressure but relatively insensitive to chemical stimuli; a taste receptor is sensitive to dissolved chemicals but insensitive to pressure. The most complex receptors, such as the visual receptors of the eye, are protected by accessory cells and layers of connective tissue. Not only are these receptor cells specialized to detect light, but also they are seldom exposed to any stimulus *except* light.

The area monitored by a single receptor cell is its *receptive field* (Figure 9-1). Whenever a sufficiently strong stimulus arrives in the receptive field, the CNS receives the information "stimulus arriving at receptor X." The larger the receptive field, the poorer is your ability to localize a stimulus. For example, a touch receptor on the general body surface with a receptive field 7 cm (2.5 in.) in diameter provides less precise information than receptors on the tongue or fingertips, which have receptive fields less than a millimeter in diameter.

All sensory information arrives at the CNS in the form of action potentials in a sensory (afferent) fiber. In general, the stronger the stimulus, the higher the frequency of action potentials. The arriving information is called a **sensation.** When sensory information arrives at the CNS, it is routed according to the location and nature of the stimulus. For example, touch, pressure, pain, temperature, and taste sensations arrive at the primary sensory cortex; visual, auditory, and olfactory information reaches the visual, auditory, and olfactory regions of the cortex, respectively. The conscious awareness of a sensation is called a *perception*.

The CNS interprets the nature of sensory information entirely on the basis of the area of the brain stimulated; it cannot tell the difference between a "true" sensation and a "false" one. For instance, when rubbing your eyes, you may "see" flashes of light. Although the stimulus is mechanical rather than visual, any activity along the optic nerve is projected to the visual cortex and experienced as a visual perception.

Adaptation is a reduction in sensitivity in the presence of a constant stimulus. Familiar examples are stepping into a hot bath or jumping into a cold lake; within moments neither temperature seems as extreme as it did initially. Adaptation reduces the amount of information arriving at the cerebral cortex. Most sensory information is routed to centers along the spinal cord or brain stem, potentially triggering such involuntary reflexes as the withdrawal reflexes. ∞ p. 285 Only about 1 percent of the information provided by afferent fibers reaches the cerebral cortex and our conscious awareness.

Output from higher centers, however, can increase receptor sensitivity or facilitate transmission along a sensory pathway. For example, the *reticular activating system* in the midbrain helps focus attention and, thus, heightens or reduces awareness of arriving sensations. ∞ p. 277 This adjustment of sensitivity can occur under conscious or unconscious direction. When we "listen carefully," our sensitivity to and awareness of auditory stimuli increase. The reverse occurs when we enter a noisy factory or walk along a crowded city street, as we automatically "tune out" the high level of background noise.

The **general senses** include temperature, pain, touch, pressure, vibration, and **proprioception** (body position). The receptors for the general senses are scattered throughout the body. The **special senses** are smell (**olfaction**), taste (**gustation**), vision, balance (**equilibrium**), and hearing. The receptors for the five special senses are concentrated within specific structures—the sense organs. This chapter explores both the general senses and the special senses.

The Big Picture

Stimulation of a receptor produces action potentials along the axon of a sensory neuron. The frequency or pattern of action potentials contains information about the stimulus. Your perception of the nature of that stimulus depends on the path it takes inside the CNS and the region of the cerebral cortex it stimulates.

1. What is adaptation?
2. Receptor A has a circular receptive field with a diameter of 2.5 cm. Receptor B has a circular receptive field 7.0 cm in diameter. Which receptor provides more precise sensory information?
3. List the five special senses.

See the blue Answers tab at the back of the book.

9-2 General sensory receptors can be classified by the type of stimulus that excites them

Receptors for the general senses are scattered throughout the body and are relatively simple in structure. These receptors are classified according to the nature of the stimulus that excites them. Important receptor classes include receptors sensitive to pain *(nociceptors)*; to temperature *(thermoreceptors)*; to physical distortion resulting from touch, pressure, and body position *(mechanoreceptors)*; and to chemical stimuli *(chemoreceptors)*.

PAIN

Pain receptors, or **nociceptors** (nō-sē-SEP-tōrz; *noceo*, hurt), are free nerve endings. They are especially common in the superficial portions of the skin, in joint capsules, within the periostea covering bones, and around blood vessel walls. Other deep tissues and most visceral organs contain few nociceptors. Pain receptors have large receptive fields (**Figure 9-1**), and as a result it is often difficult to determine the exact source of a painful sensation.

Nociceptors may be sensitive to (1) extremes of temperature, (2) mechanical damage, or (3) dissolved chemicals, such as those released by injured cells. Very strong stimuli by any of these sources may excite a nociceptor. For that reason, people describing very painful sensations—whether caused by heat, a deep cut, or inflammatory chemicals—use a similar descriptive term, such as "burning."

Once pain receptors in a region are stimulated, two types of axons carry the painful sensations. Myelinated fibers carry very localized sensations of **fast pain** (or *prickling pain*), such as that caused by an injection or a deep cut. These sensations reach the CNS very quickly, where they often trigger somatic reflexes. They are also relayed to the primary sensory cortex and so receive conscious attention. Slower, unmyelinated fibers carry sensations of **slow pain,** or *burning and aching pain.* Unlike fast pain sensations, slow pain sensations enable you to identify only the general area involved.

Pain sensations from visceral organs are often perceived as originating at the body surface, generally in those regions innervated by the same spinal nerves. The perception of pain coming from parts of the body that are not actually stimulated is called **referred pain.** The precise mechanism responsible for referred pain is not yet clear, but several clinical examples are shown in Figure 9-2. Cardiac pain, for example, is often perceived as originating in the skin of the upper chest and left arm.

Pain receptors continue to respond as long as the painful stimulus remains. However, the perception of the pain can decrease over time because of the inhibition of centers in the thalamus, reticular formation, lower brain stem, and spinal cord.

TEMPERATURE

Temperature receptors, or **thermoreceptors,** are free nerve endings located in the dermis, in skeletal muscles, in the liver, and in the hypothalamus. Cold receptors are three or four times as numerous as warm receptors. There are no known structural differences between warm and cold thermoreceptors.

Temperature sensations are relayed along the same pathways that carry pain sensations. They are sent to the reticular formation, the thalamus, and (to a lesser extent) the primary sensory cortex. Thermoreceptors are very active when the temperature is changing, but they quickly adapt to a stable temperature. When you enter an air-conditioned classroom on a hot summer day or a warm lecture hall on a brisk fall evening, the temperature seems extreme at first, but you quickly become comfortable as adaptation occurs.

TOUCH, PRESSURE, AND POSITION

Mechanoreceptors are sensitive to stimuli such as stretching, compression, or twisting. Distortion of the receptor's cell membrane in response to these stimuli causes mechanically regulated ion channels to open or close. There are three classes of mechanoreceptors: (1) *tactile receptors* (touch), (2) *baroreceptors* (pressure), and (3) *proprioceptors* (position).

Tactile Receptors

Tactile receptors provide sensations of touch, pressure, and vibration. The distinctions between these sensations are hazy, for a touch also represents a pressure, and a vibration consists of an oscillating touch/pressure stimulus. **Fine touch and pressure receptors** provide detailed information about a source of stimulation, including its exact location, shape, size, texture, and movement. **Crude touch and pressure receptors** provide poor localization and little additional information about the stimulus.

Tactile receptors range in complexity from free nerve endings to specialized sensory complexes with accessory cells and supporting structures. Figure 9-3 depicts six types of tactile receptors in the skin:

1. Free nerve endings sensitive to touch and pressure are situated between epidermal cells. No structural differences have been found between these receptors and the

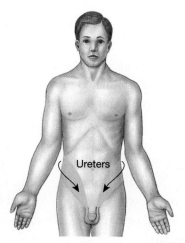

Liver and gallbladder

Heart

Stomach

Small intestine

Appendix

Colon

Ureters

FIGURE 9-2 Referred Pain. In referred pain, sensations originating in visceral organs are perceived as pain in other body regions innervated by the same spinal nerves. Each region of perceived pain is labeled according to the organ at which the pain originates.

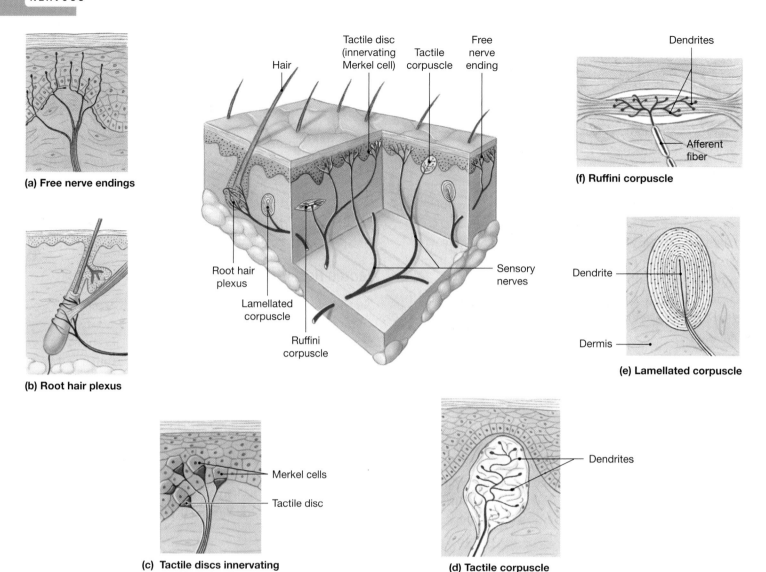

(a) Free nerve endings

(b) Root hair plexus

Hair

Tactile disc (innervating Merkel cell)

Tactile corpuscle

Free nerve ending

Root hair plexus

Lamellated corpuscle

Ruffini corpuscle

Sensory nerves

Dendrites

Afferent fiber

(f) Ruffini corpuscle

Dendrite

Dermis

(e) Lamellated corpuscle

Merkel cells

Tactile disc

(c) Tactile discs innervating Merkel cells

Dendrites

(d) Tactile corpuscle

FIGURE 9-3 **Tactile Receptors in the Skin.**

free nerve endings that provide temperature or pain sensations.

2. The **root hair plexus** is made up of free nerve endings that are stimulated by hair displacement. They monitor distortions and movements across the body surface.

3. **Tactile discs,** or *Merkel* (MER-kel) *discs,* are fine touch and pressure receptors. Hairless skin contains large epithelial cells *(Merkel cells)* in its deepest epidermal layer. The dendrites of a single sensory neuron make close contact with a group of Merkel cells. When compressed, Merkel cells release chemicals that stimulate the neuron.

4. **Tactile corpuscles,** or *Meissner* (MĪS-ner) *corpuscles,* are sensitive to fine touch and pressure and to low-frequency vibration. They are abundant in the eyelids, lips, fingertips, nipples, and external genitalia.

5. **Lamellated** (LAM-e-lāt-ed) **corpuscles,** or *pacinian* (pa-SIN-ē-an) *corpuscles,* are large receptors sensitive to deep pressure and to pulsing or high-frequency vibrations. They are common in the skin of the fingers, breasts, and external genitalia. They are also present in joint capsules, mesenteries, the pancreas, and the walls of the urethra and urinary bladder.

6. **Ruffini** (roo-FĒ-nē) **corpuscles** are sensitive to pressure and distortion of the skin, but they are located in the deepest layer of the dermis.

Tactile sensations travel through the posterior column and spinothalamic pathways. p. 287 Sensitivity to tactile sensations can be altered by infection, disease, and damage to sensory neurons or pathways. The locations of tactile responses may have diagnostic significance. For example, sensory loss along the boundary of a dermatome can help identify the affected spinal nerve or nerves. ∞ p. 283

Baroreceptors

Baroreceptors (bar-ō-rē-SEP-tōrz; *baro-*, pressure) provide information essential to the regulation of autonomic activities by monitoring changes in pressure. These receptors consist of free nerve endings that branch within the elastic tissues in the wall of a distensible organ, such as a blood vessel or a portion of the respiratory, digestive, or urinary tract. When the pressure changes, the elastic walls of these vessels or tracts expand or recoil. This movement distorts the dendritic branches and alters the rate of action potential generation. Although baroreceptors respond immediately to a change in pressure, they also adapt rapidly; the result is that the output along the afferent fibers returns to "normal" gradually.

Figure 9-4 illustrates the locations of some baroreceptors and summarizes their functions in autonomic activities. Baroreceptors monitor blood pressure in the walls of major blood vessels, including the carotid artery (at the *carotid sinus*) and the aorta (at the *aortic sinus*). The information plays a major role in regulating cardiac function and adjusting blood flow to vital tissues. Baroreceptors in the lungs monitor the degree of lung expansion. This information is relayed to the respiratory rhythmicity centers in the brain, which set the pace of respiration. ∞ p. 278 Baroreceptors in the digestive and urinary tracts trigger various visceral reflexes, including those of urination, movement of materials along the digestive tract, and defecation.

Proprioceptors

Proprioceptors monitor the position of joints, the tension in tendons and ligaments, and the state of muscular contraction. *Free nerve endings* in joint capsules detect pressure, tension, and movement at the joint. *Golgi tendon organs* lie between a skeletal muscle and its tendon and monitor the strain on a tendon during muscle contraction. *Muscle spindles* monitor the length of a skeletal muscle and trigger stretch reflexes. ∞ p. 284 Proprioceptors do not adapt to constant stimulation, and each receptor continuously sends information to the CNS. Most of this information is processed subconsciously; only a small proportion of it reaches your conscious awareness. Your sense

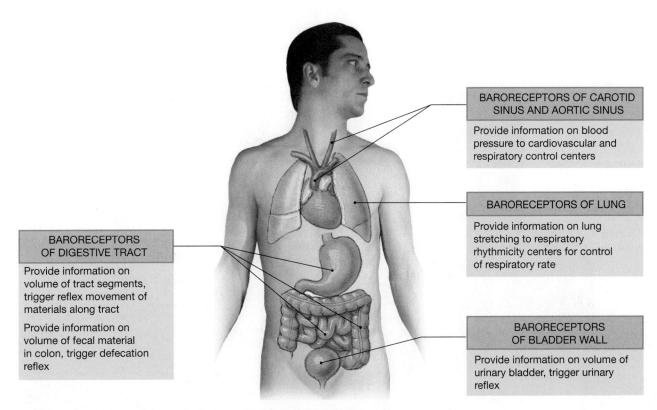

BARORECEPTORS OF CAROTID SINUS AND AORTIC SINUS

Provide information on blood pressure to cardiovascular and respiratory control centers

BARORECEPTORS OF LUNG

Provide information on lung stretching to respiratory rhythmicity centers for control of respiratory rate

BARORECEPTORS OF DIGESTIVE TRACT

Provide information on volume of tract segments, trigger reflex movement of materials along tract

Provide information on volume of fecal material in colon, trigger defecation reflex

BARORECEPTORS OF BLADDER WALL

Provide information on volume of urinary bladder, trigger urinary reflex

FIGURE 9-4 Baroreceptors and the Regulation of Autonomic Functions. Baroreceptors at several sites provide information essential to the regulation of various autonomic activities, including digestion, urination, blood pressure monitoring, respiration, and defecation.

of body position results from the integration of information from these three types of proprioceptors with information from the receptors of the inner ear.

CHEMICAL DETECTION

In general, **chemoreceptors** respond only to water-soluble and lipid-soluble substances that are dissolved in the surrounding fluid. Adaptation usually occurs over a few seconds following stimulation. Except for the special senses of taste and smell, there are no well-defined chemosensory pathways in the brain or spinal cord. The chemoreceptors of the general senses send their information to brain stem centers that participate in the autonomic control of respiratory and cardiovascular functions. The locations of important chemoreceptors are shown in Figure 9-5. Neurons within the respiratory centers of the brain respond to the concentrations of hydrogen ions (pH) and carbon dioxide molecules in the cerebrospinal fluid. Chemoreceptors are also located in the **carotid bodies,** near the origin of the internal carotid arteries on each side of the neck, and in the **aortic bodies,** between the major branches of the aortic arch. These receptors monitor the pH and the carbon dioxide and oxygen concentrations of arterial blood. The afferent fibers leaving the carotid and aortic bodies reach the respiratory centers by traveling along the glossopharyngeal (N IX) and vagus (N X) cranial nerves.

9-3 Olfaction, the sense of smell, involves olfactory receptors responding to chemical stimuli

The sense of smell, or *olfaction,* is provided by paired **olfactory organs** (Figure 9-6). These organs are located in the nasal cavity on either side of the nasal septum just inferior to the cribriform plate of the ethmoid bone. Each olfactory organ consists of an **olfactory epithelium,** which contains **olfactory receptor cells,** supporting cells, and regenerative *basal cells* (stem cells). The underlying layer of loose connective tissue contains large **olfactory glands** whose secretions absorb water and form a pigmented mucus that covers the epithelium. The mucus is produced in a continuous stream that passes across the surface of the olfactory organ, preventing the buildup of poten-

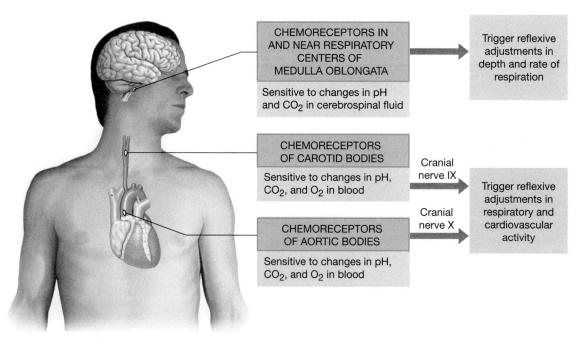

FIGURE 9-5 Locations and Functions of Chemoreceptors. Chemoreceptors are located in the CNS (on the ventrolateral surfaces of the medulla oblongata) and in the aortic and carotid bodies. These receptors are involved in the autonomic regulation of respiratory and cardiovascular function.

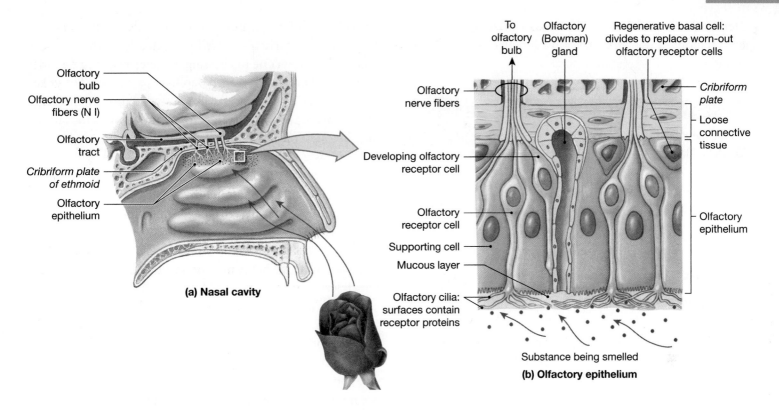

FIGURE 9-6 The Olfactory Organs. (a) The structure and location of the olfactory organ on the left side of the nasal septum is shown. **(b)** An olfactory receptor is a modified neuron with multiple cilia extending from its free surface.

tially dangerous or overpowering stimuli and keeping the area moist and free from dust or other debris.

When you draw air in through your nose, the air swirls within the nasal cavity. A normal, relaxed inhalation carries a small sample (about 2 percent) of the inhaled air to the olfactory organs. Repeated sniffing increases the flow of air across the olfactory epithelium, intensifying the stimulation of the receptors. Once airborne compounds have reached the olfactory organs, water-soluble and lipid-soluble chemicals must diffuse into the mucus before they can stimulate the olfactory receptors.

The olfactory receptor cells are highly modified neurons. The exposed tip of each receptor cell provides a base for cilia that extend into the surrounding mucus. Olfactory reception occurs as dissolved chemicals interact with receptors, called *odorant-binding proteins,* on the surfaces of the cilia. *Odorants* are chemicals that stimulate olfactory receptors. The binding of an odorant changes the permeability of the receptor membrane, producing action potentials. This information is relayed to the central nervous system, which interprets the smell on the basis of the particular pattern of receptor activity.

Approximately 10–20 million olfactory receptor cells are packed into an area of roughly 5 cm². If we take into account the surface area of the exposed cilia, the actual sensory area approaches that of the entire body surface. Nevertheless, our olfactory sensitivities cannot compare with those of other vertebrates such as dogs, cats, or fishes. A German shepherd sniffing for smuggled drugs or explosives has an olfactory receptor surface 72 times greater than that of its human handler.

THE OLFACTORY PATHWAYS

The axons leaving the olfactory epithelium collect into 20 or more bundles that penetrate the cribriform plate of the ethmoid bone to reach the **olfactory bulbs,** where the first synapse occurs. Axons leaving each olfactory bulb travel along the olfactory tract to reach the olfactory cortex of the cerebrum, the hypothalamus, and portions of the limbic system.

Olfactory stimuli are the only type of sensory information that reaches the cerebral cortex without first synapsing in the thalamus. The extensive limbic and hypothalamic connections help explain the profound emotional and behavioral responses that certain smells can produce. The perfume industry, which understands the practical implications of these connections, spends billions of dollars to develop odors that trigger sexual responses.

9-4 Gustation, the sense of taste, involves taste receptors responding to chemical stimuli

Taste receptors, or *gustatory* (GUS-ta-tor-ē) *receptors,* are distributed over the surface of the tongue and adjacent portions of the pharynx and larynx (Figure 9-7). The most important taste receptors are on the tongue; by the time we reach adulthood, those on the pharynx and larynx have decreased in importance and abundance. Taste receptors and specialized epithelial cells form sensory structures called **taste buds.** The taste buds are particularly well protected from the excessive mechanical stress due to chewing, for they lie along the sides of epithelial projections called **papillae** (pa-PIL-lē). The greatest numbers of taste buds are associated with the large *circumvallate papillae,* which form a V that points toward the attached base of the tongue.

Each taste bud contains slender sensory receptors known as **gustatory cells** and supporting cells. Each gustatory cell extends slender microvilli, sometimes called *taste hairs,* into the surrounding fluids through a narrow opening, the **taste pore.** The mechanism behind gustatory reception seems to parallel that of olfaction. Dissolved chemicals contacting the taste hairs stimulate a change in the membrane potential of the taste cell, which leads to action potentials in the sensory neuron.

You are probably already familiar with the four **primary taste sensations:** sweet, salty, sour, and bitter. There is some evidence for differences in sensitivity to tastes along the long axis of the tongue, with greatest sensitivity to salty–sweet anteriorly and to sour–bitter posteriorly (Figure 9-7a). However, there are no differences in the structure of the taste buds, and taste buds in all portions of the tongue provide all four primary taste sensations.

FIGURE 9-7 Gustatory Receptors. **(a)** Tastes are detected by gustatory receptors within taste buds, which form pockets along the sides of epithelial projections called papillae. **(b)** A micrograph of taste buds in a circumvallate papilla. (LM × 280) **(c)** A diagrammatic view of the structure of a taste bud, showing receptor (gustatory) cells and supporting cells.

Two additional tastes, *umami* and *water*, have been discovered in humans. **Umami** (oo-MAH-mē) is a pleasant taste that is characteristic of beef broth, chicken broth, and Parmesan cheese. Most people say water has no flavor, yet **water receptors** are present, especially in the pharynx. Their sensory output is processed in the hypothalamus and affects several systems involved in water balance and the regulation of blood volume.

The threshold for receptor stimulation varies for each of the primary taste sensations, and the taste receptors respond most readily to unpleasant rather than pleasant stimuli. For example, we are much more sensitive to acids, which taste sour, than to either sweet or salty chemicals, and we are more sensitive to bitter compounds than to acids. This sensitivity has survival value, because acids can damage the mucous membranes of the mouth and pharynx, and many biological toxins have an extremely bitter taste.

THE TASTE PATHWAYS

Taste buds are monitored by the facial (N VII), glossopharyngeal (N IX), and vagus (N X) cranial nerves. The sensory afferent fibers of these different nerves synapse within a nucleus in the medulla oblongata, and the axons of the postsynaptic neurons synapse in the thalamus. There the neurons join axons that carry sensory information on touch, pressure, and proprioception. The information is then projected to the appropriate portions of the primary sensory cortex.

A conscious perception of taste is produced as the information received from the taste buds is correlated with other sensory data. Information about the texture of food, along with taste-related sensations such as "peppery" or "spicy hot," is provided by sensory afferents in the trigeminal nerve (V). In addition, information from olfactory receptors plays an overwhelming role in taste perception. You are several thousand times more sensitive to "tastes" when your olfactory organs are fully functional. By contrast, if you have a cold and your nose is stuffed up, airborne molecules cannot reach your olfactory receptors, so meals taste dull and unappealing (even though your taste buds are responding normally).

The Big Picture

Olfactory information is routed directly to the cerebrum, and olfactory stimuli have powerful effects on mood and behavior. Gustatory sensations are strongest and clearest when integrated with olfactory sensations.

9-5 Internal eye structures contribute to vision, while accessory eye structures provide protection

We rely more on vision than on any other special sense. Our visual receptors are contained in the eyes, elaborate structures that enable us to detect not only light but also detailed images. We will begin our discussion of these complex organs by considering the *accessory structures* of the eye, which provide protection, lubrication, and support.

THE ACCESSORY STRUCTURES OF THE EYE

The **accessory structures** of the eye include the (1) eyelids and associated exocrine glands and (2) the superficial epithelium of the eye (**Figure 9-8a**); (3) structures associated with the production, secretion, and removal of tears (**Figure 9-8b**); and (4) the extrinsic eye muscles (**Figure 9-9**).

The **eyelids,** or **palpebrae** (pal-PĒ-brē), are a continuation of the skin. They act like windshield wipers: Their blinking movements keep the surface of the eye lubricated and free from dust and debris. They can also close firmly to protect the delicate surface of the eye. The upper and lower eyelids are connected at the **medial canthus** (KAN-thus) and the **lateral canthus** (**Figure 9-8a**). The eyelashes are very robust hairs that help prevent foreign particles such as dirt and insects from contacting the surface of the eye.

Several types of exocrine glands protect the eye and its accessory structures. Large sebaceous glands are associated with the eyelashes, as they are with other hairs and hair follicles. ⊙ p. 130 Along the inner margins of the eyelids, modified sebaceous glands *(tarsal glands)* secrete a lipid-rich substance that keeps the eyelids from sticking together. At the medial canthus, the **lacrimal caruncle** (KAR-ung-kul), a soft mass of tissue, contains glands that produce thick secretions that contribute

Eyelashes

Pupil

Palpebra (eyelid)

Medial canthus

Lacrimal caruncle

Lateral canthus   Sclera   Iris

(a)

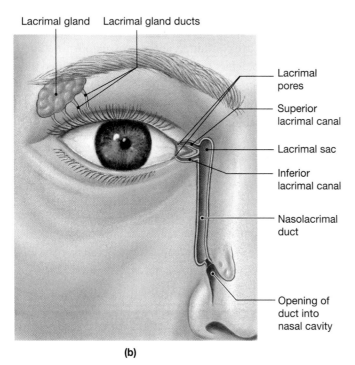

Lacrimal gland   Lacrimal gland ducts

Lacrimal pores

Superior lacrimal canal

Lacrimal sac

Inferior lacrimal canal

Nasolacrimal duct

Opening of duct into nasal cavity

(b)

FIGURE 9-8 The Accessory Structures of the Eye. (a) The gross and superficial anatomies of the accessory structures. **(b)** The details of the lacrimal apparatus.

to the gritty deposits occasionally found after a night's sleep. These various glands sometimes become infected by bacteria. An infection in a sebaceous gland of one of the eyelashes, in a tarsal gland, or in one of the sweat glands between the eyelash follicles produces a painful localized swelling known as a **sty.**

The epithelium covering the inner surfaces of the eyelids and the outer surface of the eye is a mucous membrane called the **conjunctiva** (kon-junk-TĪ-vuh) (Figure 9-10). The conjunctiva extends to the edges of the **cornea** (KOR-nē-uh), a trans-

parent part of the outer layer of the eye. The cornea is covered by a delicate *corneal epithelium,* which is continuous with the conjunctiva. The conjunctiva contains many free nerve endings and is very sensitive. The painful condition of **conjunctivitis,** or pinkeye, results from damage to and irritation of the conjunctival surface. The most obvious sign, redness, is due to the dilation of the blood vessels beneath the conjunctival epithelium.

A constant flow of tears keeps the surface of the eyeball moist and clean. Tears reduce friction, remove debris, prevent bacterial infection, and provide nutrients and oxygen to the conjunctival epithelium. The **lacrimal apparatus** produces, distributes, and removes tears (Figure 9-8b). Superior and lateral to the eyeball is the **lacrimal gland,** or *tear gland,* which has a dozen or more ducts that empty into the pocket between the eyelid and the eye. This gland nestles within a depression in the frontal bone, just inside the orbit. The lacrimal gland normally provides the key ingredients and most of the volume of the tears. Its watery, slightly alkaline secretions also contain *lysozyme,* an enzyme that attacks bacteria. The mixture of secretions from the lacrimal glands, accessory glands, and tarsal glands forms a superficial "oil slick" that assists in lubrication and slows evaporation.

Blinking sweeps tears across the surface of the eye to the medial canthus. Two small pores direct the tears into the **lacrimal canals,** passageways that end at the lacrimal sac (Figure 9-8b). From this sac, the **nasolacrimal duct** carries the tears to the nasal cavity.

Six **extrinsic eye muscles,** or *oculomotor* (ok-ū-lō-MŌ-ter) *muscles,* originate on the surface of the orbit and control the position of the eye (Figure 9-9 and Table 9-1). These muscles are the **inferior rectus, medial rectus, superior rectus, lateral rectus, inferior oblique,** and **superior oblique.**

THE EYE

The eyes are sophisticated visual instruments—more versatile and adaptable than the most expensive cameras, yet compact and durable. Each eye is roughly spherical, has a diameter of nearly 2.5 cm (1 in.), and weighs around 8 g (0.28 oz). The eyeball shares space within the orbit with the extrinsic eye muscles, the lacrimal gland, and the various cranial nerves and blood vessels that service the eye and adjacent areas of the orbit and face. A mass of *orbital fat* cushions and insulates the eye.

The eyeball is hollow (Figure 9-10); its interior can be divided into two cavities: the posterior cavity and the anterior cavity (Figure 9-10b). The large **posterior cavity** is also called

(a) Lateral surface, right eye

(b) Anterior view, right eye

FIGURE 9-9 **The Extrinsic Eye Muscles.**

TABLE 9-1 **The Extrinsic Eye Muscles** (see Figure 9-9)

MUSCLE	ORIGIN	INSERTION	ACTION	INNERVATION
Inferior rectus	Sphenoid bone around optic canal	Inferior, medial surface of eyeball	Eye looks down	Oculomotor nerve (N III)
Medial rectus	As above	Medial surface of eyeball	Eye looks medially	As above
Superior rectus	As above	Superior surface of eyeball	Eye looks up	As above
Lateral rectus	As above	Lateral surface of eyeball	Eye looks laterally	Abducens nerve (N VI)
Inferior oblique	Maxillary bone at anterior portion of orbit	Inferior, lateral surface of eyeball	Eye rolls, looks up and laterally	Oculomotor nerve (N III)
Superior oblique	Sphenoid bone around optic canal	Superior, lateral surface of eyeball	Eye rolls, looks down and laterally	Trochlear nerve (N IV)

the *vitreous chamber* because it contains the gelatinous *vitreous body.* The smaller **anterior cavity** is subdivided into the *anterior chamber* and the *posterior chamber* (Figure 9-10c). The shape of the eye is stabilized in part by the vitreous body and the *aqueous humor,* a clear fluid that fills the anterior cavity. The wall of the eye contains three distinct layers, or *tunics* (Figure 9-10b): an outer *fibrous tunic,* an intermediate *vascular tunic,* and an inner *neural tunic.*

The Fibrous Tunic

The **fibrous tunic,** the outermost layer of the eye, consists of the *sclera* (SKLER-uh) and the *cornea.* The fibrous tunic (1) provides mechanical support and some degree of physical protection, (2) serves as an attachment site for the extrinsic eye muscles, and (3) assists in the focusing process. The **sclera,** or "white of the eye," is a layer of dense fibrous connective tissue containing both collagen and elastic fibers (Figure 9-10c). It is thickest over the posterior surface of the eye and thinnest over the anterior surface. The six extrinsic eye muscles insert on the sclera.

The surface of the sclera contains small blood vessels and nerves that penetrate the sclera to reach internal structures. On the anterior surface of the eye, however, these blood vessels lie under the conjunctiva. Because this network of small capillaries does not carry enough blood to lend an obvious color to the sclera, the white color of the collagen fibers is visible.

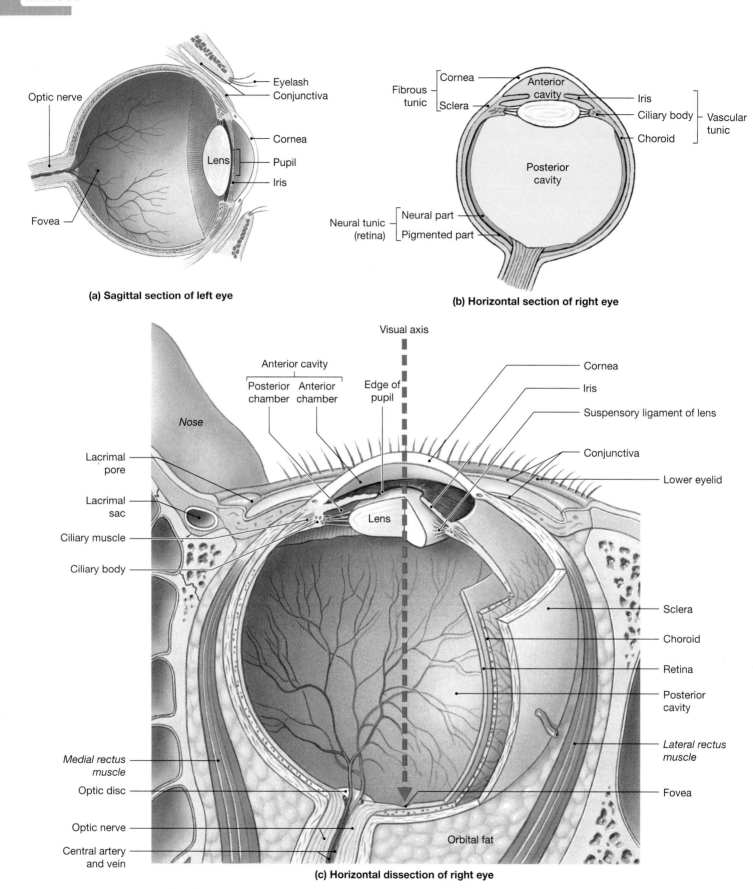

(a) Sagittal section of left eye

(b) Horizontal section of right eye

(c) Horizontal dissection of right eye

FIGURE 9-10 The Sectional Anatomy of the Eye. (a) This sagittal section bisects the left eye. **(b)** This horizontal section reveals the three layers, or tunics, of the right eye. **(c)** This horizontal section of the right eye shows various landmarks and features, including the path light takes (the "visual axis").

The transparent **cornea** is continuous with the sclera, but the collagen fibers of the cornea are organized into a series of layers that does not interfere with the passage of light. The cornea has no blood vessels, and its epithelial cells obtain their oxygen and nutrients from the tears that flow across their surfaces. Because the cornea has only a limited ability to repair itself, corneal injuries must be treated immediately to prevent serious vision losses. Restoration of vision after corneal scarring usually requires replacement of the cornea through a corneal transplant. Such transplants can be performed between unrelated individuals because there are no blood vessels to carry white blood cells, which attack foreign tissues, into the area.

The Vascular Tunic

The **vascular tunic** contains numerous blood vessels, lymphatic vessels, and the *intrinsic eye muscles*. The functions of this layer include (1) providing a route for blood vessels and lymphatic vessels that supply tissues of the eye, (2) regulating the amount of light entering the eye, (3) secreting and reabsorbing the *aqueous humor* that circulates within the eye, and (4) controlling the shape of the lens, an essential part of the focusing process.

The vascular tunic includes the *iris,* the *ciliary body,* and the *choroid* (Figure 9-10b). Visible through the transparent cornea, the **iris** contains blood vessels, pigment cells, loose connective tissue, and two layers of intrinsic smooth muscle fibers. When these *pupillary muscles* contract, they change the diameter of the central opening, or **pupil,** of the iris (Figure 9-11). One layer of these muscles forms concentric circles around the pupil; their contraction decreases, or constricts, the diameter of the pupil. The second layer of muscles extends radially away from the edge of the pupil; their contraction enlarges, or dilates, the pupil. Dilation and constriction are controlled by the autonomic nervous system in response to changes in light intensity. Parasympathetic activation in response to bright light causes the pupils to constrict, and sympathetic activation in response to dim light causes the pupils to dilate.

Eye color is determined by (1) the number of melanocytes in the iris and (2) the presence of melanin granules in the pigmented epithelium on the posterior surface of the iris. (This pigmented epithelium is part of the neural tunic.) When the iris contains no melanocytes, light passes through the iris and bounces off the pigmented epithelium; the eye then appears blue. The irises of green, brown, and black eyes have increasing

Pupillary dilator muscles (radial)

Pupillary constrictor muscles (sphincter)

Dilators contract

Pupil

Constrictors contract

Decreased light intensity
Increased sympathetic stimulation

Increased light intensity
Increased parasympathetic stimulation

FIGURE 9-11 The Pupillary Muscles. Two sets of intrinsic smooth muscle within the iris control the diameter of the pupil. In bright light, the concentric muscle fibers contract, constricting the pupil and reducing the level of incoming light. In dim light, the radial muscle fibers contract and the pupil enlarges, or dilates, to allow the entry of additional light.

numbers of melanocytes. The eyes of albino humans are very pale gray or blue gray.

Along its outer edge, the iris attaches to the anterior portion of the **ciliary body,** most of which consists of the *ciliary muscle,* a ring of smooth muscle that projects into the interior of the eye (Figure 9-10c). The ciliary body begins at the junction between the cornea and sclera and extends to the scalloped border that also marks the anterior edge of the neural tunic. Posterior to the iris, the surface of the ciliary body is thrown into folds called *ciliary processes.* The **suspensory ligaments** of the lens attach to these processes. The connective tissue fibers of these ligaments hold the lens so that light passing through the pupil passes through the center of the lens along the visual axis.

The choroid is a layer that separates the fibrous and neural tunics posterior to the ciliary body (Figure 9-10c). The choroid contains a capillary network that delivers oxygen and nutrients to the neural tunic.

The Neural Tunic

The **neural tunic,** or **retina,** is the innermost layer of the eye. It consists of a thin outer pigment layer called the *pigmented part* and a thick inner layer called the *neural part* (Figure 9-10b). The pigmented part absorbs light after it passes through the neural part. The neural part contains (1) the photoreceptors that respond to light, (2) supporting cells and neurons that perform preliminary processing and integration of visual information, and (3) blood vessels supplying tissues that line the posterior cavity. The two layers of the retina are normally very close together but not tightly interconnected. The pigmented part continues over the ciliary body and iris. The neural part forms a cup that establishes the posterior and lateral boundaries of the posterior cavity.

ORGANIZATION OF THE RETINA. The retina contains several layers of cells (Figure 9-12a). The outermost layer, closest to the wall of the pigmented part of the retina, contains the photoreceptors, the cells that detect light. The eye has two types of photoreceptors: rods and cones. **Rods** do not discriminate among colors of light. These very light-sensitive receptors enable us to see in dimly lit rooms, at twilight, or in pale moonlight. **Cones** provide us with color vision. Three types of cones are present, and their stimulation in various combinations provides the perception of different colors. Cones give us sharper, clearer images, but they require brighter light than do rods. When you watch a sunset, you can notice your vision shifting from cone-based vision (a clear image in full color) to rod-based vision (a less distinct image in black and white).

Rods and cones are not evenly distributed across the retina. If you think of the retina as a cup, approximately 125 million rods are found on the sides, and roughly 6 million cones dominate the bottom. Most of these cones are concentrated in the area where the visual image arrives after passing through the cornea and lens. This region is the **macula lutea** (MAK-ū-luh LOO-tē-uh; yellow spot) (Figure 9-12c). The highest concentration of cones is found in the center of the macula lutea in an area called the **fovea** (FŌ-vē-uh; shallow depression), or *fovea centralis.* The fovea is the center of color vision and the site of sharpest vision. When you look directly at an object, its image falls on this portion of the retina. An imaginary line drawn from the center of that object through the center of the lens to the fovea establishes the **visual axis** of the eye (Figure 9-10).

You are probably already aware of the visual consequences of this distribution. During the day, when there is enough light to stimulate the cones, you see a very clear image. In very dim light, however, cones cannot function. When you try to stare at a dim star, for example, you are unable to see it. But if you look a little to one side rather than directly at the star, you can see it quite clearly. Shifting your gaze moves the image of the star from the fovea, where it does not provide enough light to stimulate the cones, to the sides of the retina, where it stimulates the more sensitive rods.

The rods and cones synapse with roughly 6 million **bipolar cells** (Figure 9-12a). Bipolar cells in turn synapse within the layer of **ganglion cells** adjacent to the posterior cavity. The axons of the ganglion cells deliver the sensory information to the brain. *Horizontal cells* and *amacrine* (AM-a-krin) cells can regulate communication between photoreceptors and ganglion cells, adjusting the sensitivity of the retina. The effect is comparable to adjusting the contrast on a television. These cells play an important role in the eye's adjustment to dim or brightly lit environments.

THE OPTIC DISC. Axons from an estimated 1 million ganglion cells converge on the **optic disc,** a circular region just medial to the fovea. The optic disc is the origin of the optic nerve (N II) (Figure 9-12b). From this point, the axons turn, penetrate the wall of the eye, and proceed toward the diencephalon. Blood vessels that supply the retina pass through the center of the optic nerve and emerge on the surface of the optic disc (Figure 9-12b,c). The optic disc has no photoreceptors or other retinal structures. Because light striking this area goes unnoticed, it is commonly called the **blind spot.** You do not notice

Horizontal cell   Cone   Rod

Choroid

Pigmented part of retina

Rods and cones

Amacrine cell

Bipolar cells

Ganglion cells

LIGHT

Nuclei of ganglion cells   Nuclei of rods and cones   Nuclei of bipolar cells

(a) Cellular organization of the retina

Pigmented part of retina   Neural part of retina

Central retinal vein

Central retinal artery

Optic disc

Sclera

Optic nerve   Choroid

(b)

Fovea   Optic disc (blind spot)

Macula lutea   Central retinal artery and vein emerging from center of optic disc

(c)

FIGURE 9-12 Retinal Organization. (a) The cellular organization of the retina is shown in a drawing and a micrograph. Note that the photoreceptors are closer to the choroid than to the posterior cavity. (LM × 290) **(b)** This diagrammatic section passes through the optic disc. **(c)** This photograph shows the retina as seen through the pupil of the right eye.

a blank spot in your visual field because involuntary eye movements keep the visual image moving and allow your brain to fill in the missing information. A simple activity, shown in Figure 9-13, can demonstrate the presence and location of the blind spot.

The Chambers of the Eye

The ciliary body and lens divide the interior of the eye into a small anterior cavity and a larger posterior cavity, or vitreous chamber (Figure 9-14). The anterior cavity is further subdivided into the **anterior chamber,** which extends from the cornea to the iris, and the **posterior chamber,** between the iris and the ciliary body and lens. The anterior and posterior chambers are filled with **aqueous humor.** This fluid circulates within the anterior cavity, passing from the posterior to the anterior chamber through the pupil. The posterior cavity also contains aqueous humor, but most of this cavity is filled with a clear gelatinous substance known as the **vitreous body,** or *vitreous humor.* The vitreous body helps maintain the shape of the eye and also holds the retina against the choroid.

FIGURE 9-13 **A Demonstration of the Presence of a Blind Spot.** Close your left eye and stare at the cross with your right eye, keeping the cross in the center of your field of vision. Begin with the page a few inches away from your eye and gradually increase the distance. The dot will disappear when its image falls on the blind spot at the optic disc. To check the blind spot in your left eye, close your right eye, stare at the dot, and repeat this sequence.

AQUEOUS HUMOR. Aqueous humor is secreted into the posterior chamber by epithelial cells of the ciliary processes (Figure 9-14). Pressure exerted by this fluid helps maintain the shape of the eye, and the circulation of aqueous humor transports nutrients and wastes. In the anterior chamber near the edge of the iris, the aqueous humor enters a passageway, known as the *canal of Schlemm,* that empties into veins in the sclera and returns this fluid to the venous system.

Interference with the normal circulation and reabsorption of aqueous humor leads to an elevation in pressure inside the eye. If this condition, called **glaucoma,** is left untreated, it can eventually produce blindness by distorting the retina and the optic disc.

The Lens

The **lens** lies posterior to the cornea and is held in place by suspensory ligaments extending from the ciliary body of the choroid. The primary function of the lens is to focus the visual image on the photoreceptors. The lens does so by changing its shape.

THE STRUCTURE OF THE LENS. The transparent lens consists of concentric layers of cells wrapped in a dense fibrous capsule. The cells making up the interior of the lens lack organelles and are filled with transparent proteins. The capsule contains many elastic fibers that, in the absence of any outside force, contract and make the lens spherical. However, tension in the suspensory ligaments can overpower their contraction and pull the lens into a flattened oval.

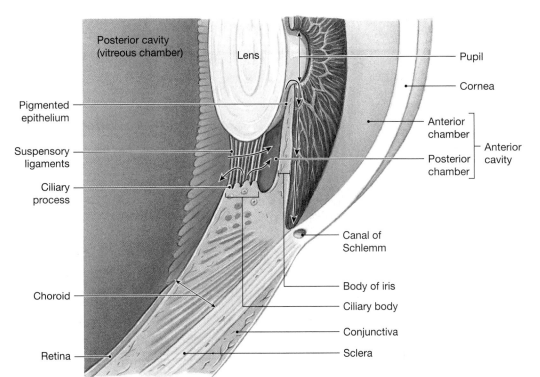

FIGURE 9-14 **Eye Chambers and the Circulation of Aqueous Humor.** The lens is suspended between the vitreous chamber and the posterior chamber. Its position is maintained by suspensory ligaments, which attach the lens to the ciliary body. Aqueous humor secreted at the ciliary body circulates through the posterior and anterior chambers and is reabsorbed after passing along the canal of Schlemm.

Clinical Note

Cataracts

The transparency of the lens depends on a precise combination of structural and biochemical characteristics. When that balance is disturbed, the lens loses its transparency, a condition known as a **cataract**. Cataracts can result from drug reactions, injuries, or radiation, but **senile cataracts** are the most common form. Over time, the lens becomes less elastic, takes on a yellowish hue, and eventually begins to lose its transparency. As the lens becomes opaque, or "cloudy," the individual needs brighter and brighter reading lights, and visual clarity begins to fade. If the lens becomes completely opaque, the person will be functionally blind, even though the photoreceptors are normal. Surgical procedures involve removing the lens, either intact or in pieces after it has been shattered with high-frequency sound. The missing lens is then replaced by an artificial substitute, and vision is fine-tuned with glasses or contact lenses.

LIGHT REFRACTION AND ACCOMMODATION. The eye is often compared to a camera. To provide useful information, the lens of the eye, like a camera lens, must focus the arriving image. To say that an image is "in focus" means that the rays of light arriving from an object strike the sensitive surface of the retina (or of photographic film) so as to form a sharp miniature image of the original. If the rays are not perfectly focused, the image will be blurry. In the eye, focusing normally occurs in two steps, as light passes through first the cornea and then the lens.

Light is bent, or *refracted*, when it passes from one medium to a medium with a different density. In the human eye, the greatest amount of refraction occurs when light passes from the air into the cornea, which has a density close to that of water. As the light enters the relatively dense lens, the lens provides the extra refraction needed to focus the light rays from an object toward a specific **focal point**—the point at which the light rays converge (Figure 9-15a). The distance between the center of the lens and the focal point is the *focal distance*. This distance is determined by two factors: the distance of the object from the lens

FIGURE 9-15 Focal Point, Focal Distance, and Visual Accommodation. A lens refracts light toward a specific focal point. The distance from the center of the lens to that point is the focal distance of the lens. **(a)** Light arrives from a distant source in parallel waves, and the lens is able to focus them over a short focal distance. Light from a nearby source, however, is still spreading out from its source when it strikes the lens; the result is a longer focal distance. **(b)** Lens shape also affects focal distance: The rounder the lens, the shorter the focal distance. **(c)** For the eye to form a sharp image, the focal distance must equal the distance between the center of the lens and the retina. The lens compensates for variations in the distance between the eye and the object in view by changing its shape. This process is called accommodation. **(d)** For close objects, the ciliary muscle contracts, and the suspensory ligaments allow the lens to round up. **(e)** For distant objects, the ciliary muscle relaxes, and the ligaments pull against the margins of the lens and flatten it.

and the shape of the lens. The closer the object, the longer the focal distance (Figure 9-15a,b); the rounder the lens, the more refraction occurs, and the shorter is the focal distance (Figure 9-15b,c). In the eye, the lens changes shape to keep the focal distance constant, thereby keeping the image focused on the retina.

Accommodation is the process of focusing an image on the retina by changing the shape of the lens (Figure 9-15d,e). During accommodation, the lens either becomes rounder (to focus the image of a nearby object on the retina) or flattens (to focus the image of a distant object on the retina).

The lens is held in place by the suspensory ligaments that originate at the ciliary body. Smooth muscle fibers in the ciliary body encircle the lens and act like sphincter muscles. As you view a nearby object, the ciliary muscle contracts, and the ciliary body moves toward the lens (Figure 9-15d). This movement reduces the tension in the suspensory ligaments, and the elastic capsule pulls the lens into a more spherical shape. When you view a distant object, the ciliary muscle relaxes, the suspensory ligaments pull at the circumference of the lens, and the lens becomes flatter (Figure 9-15e).

IMAGE FORMATION. The image of an object reaching the retina is a miniature image of the original, but it is upside down and backward. This makes sense if an object in view can be treated as a large number of individual light sources. Figure 9-16a shows why an image formed on the retina is upside down. Light from

The Big Picture

Light passes through the conjunctiva and cornea, crosses the anterior cavity to reach the lens, transits the lens, crosses the posterior chamber, and then penetrates the neural tissue of the retina before reaching and stimulating the photoreceptors. Cones are most abundant at the fovea and macula lutea, and they provide high-resolution color vision in brightly lit environments. Rods dominate the peripheral areas of the retina, and they provide relatively low-resolution black and white vision in dimly lit environments.

the top of the pole lands at the bottom of the retina, and light from the bottom of the pole hits the top of the retina. Figure 9-16b illustrates why an image formed on the retina is backward. Light from the left side of the fence falls on the right side of the retina, and light from the right side of the fence falls on the left side of the retina. The brain compensates for both aspects of image reversal without our conscious awareness.

CHECKPOINT

11. Which layer of the eye would be the first to be affected by inadequate tear production?

12. When the lens is more rounded, are you looking at an object that is close to you or far from you?

13. As Malia enters a dimly lit room, most of the available light becomes focused on the fovea of her eye. Will she be able to see very clearly?

See the blue Answers tab at the back of the book.

9-6 Photoreceptors respond to light and change it into electrical signals essential to visual physiology

The rods and cones of the retina are called **photoreceptors** because they detect *photons*, basic units of visible light. Light is a form of radiant energy that travels in waves with a characteristic wavelength (distance between wave peaks). Our eyes are sensitive to wavelengths that make up the spectrum of **visible light** (700–400 nm). This spectrum, seen in a rainbow, can be remembered by the acronym ROY G. BIV (*Red, Orange, Yellow, Green, Blue, Indigo, Violet*). Color depends on the wavelength of the light. Photons of red light have the longest wavelength and carry the least energy. Photons from the violet portion of the spectrum have the shortest wavelength and carry the most energy.

(a)

(b)

FIGURE 9-16 Image Formation. Light from each portion of an object is focused on a different part of the retina. The resulting image arrives **(a)** upside down and **(b)** backward.

Clinical Note

Accommodation Problems

In the normal eye, when the ciliary muscles are relaxed and the lens is flattened, a distant image will be focused on the retinal surface (Figure 9-17a), a condition called *emmetropia* (*emmetro-*, proper measure). However, irregularities in the shape of the lens or cornea can affect refraction and the clarity of the resulting visual image. This condition, called *astigmatism,* can usually be corrected by glasses or special contact lenses.

Figure 9-17 also diagrams two common accommodation problems. If the eyeball is too deep, the image of a distant object will form in front of the retina, and the image will be blurry and out of focus (Figure 9-17b). Vision at close range will be normal, because the lens will be able to round up enough to focus the image on the retina. As a result, such individuals are said to be "nearsighted." Their condition is more formally termed *myopia* (*myein,* to shut + *ops,* eye). Myopia can be corrected by placing a diverging lens in front of the eye (Figure 9-17c).

If the eyeball is too shallow, *hyperopia* results (Figure 9-17d). The ciliary muscles must contract to focus even a distant object on the retina, and at close range the lens cannot provide enough refraction. These individuals are said to be "farsighted" because they can see distant objects most clearly. Older individuals become farsighted as their lenses lose elasticity; this form of hyperopia is called *presbyopia* (*presbys,* old man). Hyperopia can be treated by placing a converging lens in front of the eye (Figure 9-17e).

Myopia and hyperopia may be corrected by surgically reshaping the cornea to alter its refractive powers. In **photorefractive keratectomy (PRK),** a computer-guided laser reshapes the cornea by removing tissue to a depth of 10–20 μm—about 10 percent of the cornea's thickness. The entire procedure can be done in less than a minute. Each year, an estimated 100,000 people undergo the PRK procedure in the United States. Many still need reading glasses, however, and both immediate and long-term visual problems can occur.

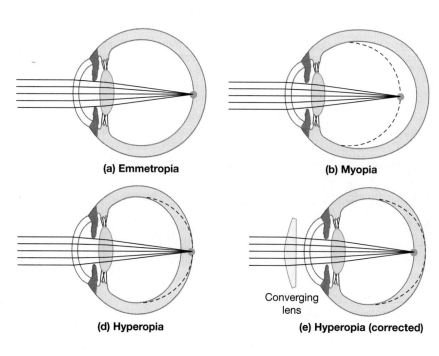

(a) Emmetropia

(b) Myopia

(c) Myopia (corrected)

(d) Hyperopia

(e) Hyperopia (corrected)

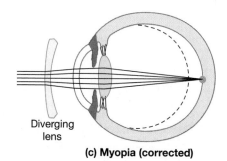

FIGURE 9-17 Visual Abnormalities. (a) In normal vision (emmetropia), the lens focuses the visual image on the retina. Common problems with the accommodation mechanism are **(b)** myopia, an inability to lengthen the focal distance enough to focus the image of a distant object on the retina, and **(c)** hyperopia, an inability to shorten the focal distance adequately for nearby objects. **(d)** A diverging lens is used to correct myopia, whereas **(e)** a converging lens is used to correct hyperopia.

RODS AND CONES

Rods provide the CNS with information about the presence or absence of photons, without regard to wavelength. As a result, they do not discriminate among colors of light. They are very sensitive, however, and enable us to see in dim conditions.

Cones provide information about the wavelength of photons. Because cones are less sensitive than rods, they function only in relatively bright light. We have three types of cones: *blue cones, green cones,* and *red cones.* Each type of cone contains pigments sensitive to blue, green, or red wavelengths of light; their stimulation in various combinations accounts for our perception of colors.

Persons unable to distinguish certain colors have a form of *color blindness.* The standard tests for color vision involve picking numbers or letters out of a complex image, such as the one in Figure 9-18. Color blindness occurs because one or more classes of cones are absent or nonfunctional. In the most common condition, the red cones are missing and the individual cannot distinguish red light from green light. Ten percent of men have some color blindness, whereas the incidence among women is only around 0.67 percent. Total color blindness is extremely rare; only 1 person in 300,000 has no cone pigments of any kind.

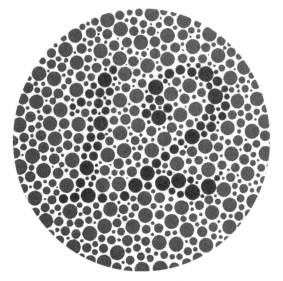

FIGURE 9-18 **A Standard Test for Color Vision.** Individuals who lack one or more populations of cones are unable to distinguish the patterned image (the number 12).

PHOTORECEPTOR STRUCTURE

Figure 9-19a compares the structure of rods and cones. The *outer segment* of a photoreceptor contains hundreds to thousands of flattened membranous discs. The names *rod* and *cone* refer to the outer segment's shape. The *inner segment* of a photoreceptor contains typical cellular organelles and forms synapses with other cells. In the dark, each photoreceptor continually releases neurotransmitters. The arrival of a photon initiates a chain of events that alters the membrane potential of the photoreceptor and changes the rate of neurotransmitter release.

The discs of the outer segment in both rods and cones contain special organic compounds called **visual pigments.** The absorption of photons by visual pigments is the first key step in the process of *photoreception,* the detection of light. The visual pigments are derived from the compound **rhodopsin** (rō-DOP-sin). Rhodopsin consists of a protein,

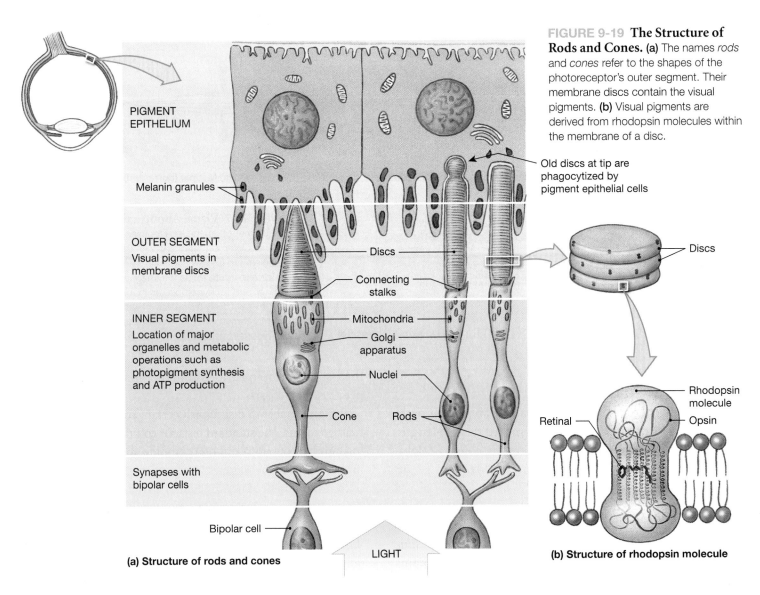

FIGURE 9-19 **The Structure of Rods and Cones. (a)** The names *rods* and *cones* refer to the shapes of the photoreceptor's outer segment. Their membrane discs contain the visual pigments. **(b)** Visual pigments are derived from rhodopsin molecules within the membrane of a disc.

PIGMENT EPITHELIUM

Melanin granules

Old discs at tip are phagocytized by pigment epithelial cells

OUTER SEGMENT
Visual pigments in membrane discs

Discs

Connecting stalks

Discs

INNER SEGMENT
Location of major organelles and metabolic operations such as photopigment synthesis and ATP production

Mitochondria

Golgi apparatus

Nuclei

Cone   Rods

Synapses with bipolar cells

Bipolar cell

LIGHT

Retinal

Rhodopsin molecule

Opsin

(a) Structure of rods and cones

(b) Structure of rhodopsin molecule

Clinical Note

Visual Acuity

Clarity of vision, or visual acuity, is rated on the basis of the sight of a "normal" person. A person whose vision is rated 20/20 can see details at a distance of 20 feet as clearly as a "normal" individual would. Vision rated 20/15 is better than average, for at 20 feet the person is able to see details that would be clear to a "normal" eye only at a distance of 15 feet. Conversely, a person with 20/30 vision must be 20 feet from an object to discern details that a person with "normal" vision could make out at a distance of 30 feet.

When visual acuity falls below 20/200, even with the help of glasses or contact lenses, the individual is considered legally blind. There are probably fewer than 400,000 legally blind people in the United States; more than half are over 65 years of age. The term *blindness* implies a total absence of vision due to damage to the eyes or to the optic pathways. Common causes of blindness include diabetes mellitus, cataracts, glaucoma, corneal scarring, retinal detachment, accidental injuries, and hereditary factors that are as yet poorly understood.

opsin, bound to the pigment **retinal** (RET-i-nal) (Figure 9-19b). Retinal is synthesized from **vitamin A.** Retinal is identical in both rods and cones, but a different form of opsin is found in the rods and in each of the three types of cones (red, blue, and green).

PHOTORECEPTION

Photoreception begins when a photon strikes a rhodopsin molecule in the outer segment of a photoreceptor. When the photon is absorbed, a change in the shape of the retinal component activates opsin, starting a chain of enzymatic events that alters the rate of neurotransmitter release. This change is the signal that light has struck a photoreceptor at that particular location on the retina.

Shortly after the retinal changes shape, the rhodopsin molecule begins to break down into retinal and opsin, a process known as *bleaching* (Figure 9-20). The retinal must be converted to its former shape before it can recombine with opsin. This conversion requires energy in the form of ATP, and it takes time. Bleaching contributes to the lingering visual impression that you have after a camera flash goes off. After an intense exposure to light, a photoreceptor cannot respond to further stimulation until its rhodopsin molecules have been regenerated. As a result, a "ghost" image remains on the retina.

THE VISUAL PATHWAY

The visual pathway begins at the photoreceptors and ends at the visual cortex of the cerebral hemispheres. In other sensory pathways we have examined, at most one synapse lies between a receptor and a sensory neuron that delivers information to the CNS. In the visual pathway, the message must cross two synapses

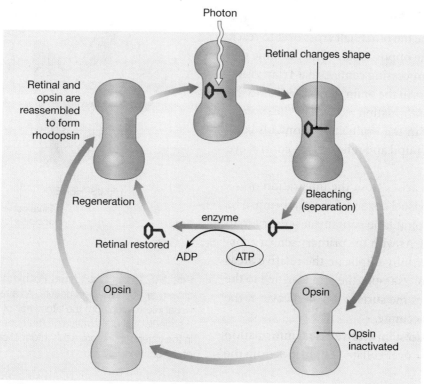

FIGURE 9-20 **The Bleaching and Regeneration of Visual Pigments.**

Clinical Note

Night Blindness

The visual pigments of the photoreceptors are synthesized from vitamin A. The body contains vitamin A reserves sufficient for several months, and a significant amount is stored in the cells of the pigmented part of the retina. If dietary sources are inadequate, these reserves are gradually exhausted, and the amount of visual pigment in the photoreceptors begins to decline. Daylight vision is affected, but in daytime the light is usually bright enough to stimulate any remaining visual pigments in the densely packed cone population. As a result, the problem first becomes apparent at night, when the dim light proves insufficient to activate the rods. This condition, known as **night blindness,** can be treated by administration of vitamin A. The body can convert the carotene pigments in many vegetables to vitamin A. Carrots are a particularly good source of carotene, which explains the old adage that carrots are good for your eyesight.

(photoreceptor to bipolar cell, and bipolar cell to ganglion cell) before it moves toward the brain. Axons from the entire population of ganglion cells converge on the optic disc, penetrate the wall of the eye, and proceed toward the diencephalon as the optic nerve (N II). The two optic nerves (one from each eye) meet at the optic chiasm (Figure 9-21). From this point, approximately half of the fibers of each optic nerve proceed within the optic tracts toward the thalamic nucleus on the same side of the brain, while the other half cross over to reach the thalamic nucleus on the opposite side. The thalamic nuclei act as switching and processing centers that relay visual information to reflex centers in the brain stem as well as to the cerebral cortex. The visual information received by the *superior colliculi* (midbrain nuclei in the brain stem) controls constriction or dilation of the pupil and reflexes that control eye movement. ∞ p. 277

The sensation of vision arises from the integration of information arriving at the visual cortex of the cerebrum. The visual cortex of each occipital lobe contains a sensory map of the entire field of vision. As with the primary sensory cortex, the map does not faithfully duplicate the relative areas within the sensory field. For example, the area assigned to the fovea covers about 35 times the surface it would cover if the map were proportionally accurate.

Many centers in the brain stem receive visual information from the thalamic nuclei or over collateral branches from the

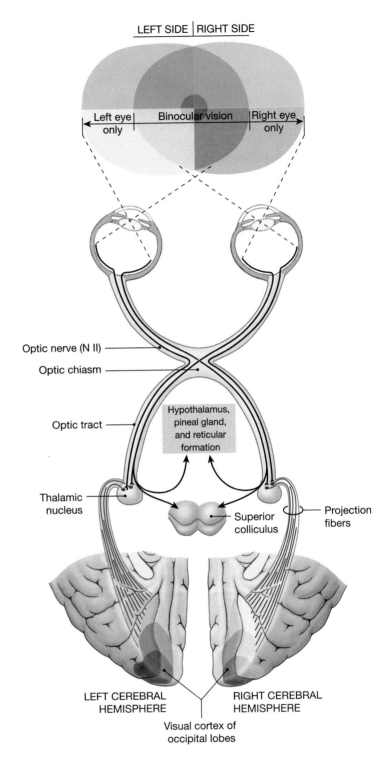

FIGURE 9-21 The Visual Pathway. At the optic chiasm, a partial crossover of nerve fibers occurs. As a result, each hemisphere receives visual information from the lateral half of the retina on that side and from the medial half of the retina on the opposite side. Visual association areas in the cerebrum integrate this information to develop a composite picture of the entire visual field.

optic tracts. For example, some collaterals bypass the thalamic nuclei synapse in the hypothalamus. Visual inputs there and at the pineal gland establish a daily pattern of activity that is tied to the day–night cycle. This *circadian*(*circa,* about + *dies,* day) *rhythm* affects your metabolic rate, endocrine function, blood pressure, digestive activities, awake–sleep cycle, and other processes.

CHECKPOINT

14. Are individuals born without cone cells able to see? Explain.

15. How would a diet deficient in vitamin A affect vision?

See the blue Answers tab at the back of the book.

9-7 Equilibrium sensations originate within the inner ear, while hearing involves the detection and interpretation of sound waves

The special senses of equilibrium and hearing are provided by the *inner ear,* a receptor complex located in the temporal bone of the skull. ∞ p. 156 *Equilibrium* informs us of the position of the body in space by monitoring gravity, linear acceleration, and rotation; *hearing* enables us to detect and interpret sound waves. The basic receptor mechanism for these senses is the same. The receptors—*hair cells*—are simple mechanoreceptors. The complex structure of the inner ear and the different arrangements of accessory structures permit hair cells to respond to different stimuli and, thus, to provide the input for both senses.

ANATOMY OF THE EAR

The ear is divided into three anatomical regions: the *external ear,* the *middle ear,* and the *inner ear* (Figure 9-22). The external ear—the visible portion of the ear—collects and directs sound waves toward the middle ear, a chamber located in a thickened portion of the temporal bone. Structures of the middle ear collect and amplify sound waves and transmit them to an appropriate portion of the inner ear. The inner ear contains the sensory organs for hearing and equilibrium.

The External Ear

The **external ear** includes the fleshy **auricle,** or *pinna,* which surrounds the entrance to the **external acoustic meatus,** or *ear canal.* The auricle, which is supported by elastic cartilage, protects the opening of the canal. It also provides directional sensitivity to the ear: Sounds coming from behind the head are partially blocked by the auricle; sounds coming from the side are collected and channeled into the external auditory meatus. (When you "cup" your ear with your hand to hear a faint sound more clearly, you are exaggerating this effect.) **Ceruminous** (se-ROO-mi-nus) **glands** along the external acoustic meatus secrete a waxy material *(cerumen)* that helps prevent the entry of foreign objects and insects, as do many small, outwardly projecting hairs. The waxy cerumen also slows the growth of microorganisms in the ear canal and reduces the likelihood of infection. The external acoustic meatus ends at the **tympanic membrane,** also called the *tympanum* or *eardrum.* The tympanic membrane is a thin sheet that separates the external ear from the middle ear (Figure 9-22).

The Middle Ear

The **middle ear,** or *tympanic cavity,* is an air-filled chamber separated from the external acoustic meatus by the tympanum. The middle ear communicates with the superior portion of the pharynx, a region known as the *nasopharynx,* and with *air cells* in the mastoid process of the temporal bone. The connection with the nasopharynx is the **auditory tube,** also called the *pharyngotympanic tube* or the *Eustachian tube* (Figure 9-22). The auditory tube enables the equalization of pressure on either side of the eardrum. Unfortunately, it can also allow microorganisms to travel from the nasopharynx into the tympanic cavity, leading to an unpleasant middle ear infection known as *otitis media.*

THE AUDITORY OSSICLES. The middle ear contains three tiny ear bones, collectively called **auditory ossicles.** The ear bones connect the tympanum with the receptor complex of the inner ear (Figure 9-23). The three auditory ossicles are the malleus, the incus, and the stapes. The **malleus** (*malleus,* hammer) attaches at three points to the interior surface of the tympanum. The middle bone—the **incus** (*incus,* anvil)—attaches the malleus to the inner bone, the **stapes** (*stapes,* stirrup). The base of the stapes almost completely fills the

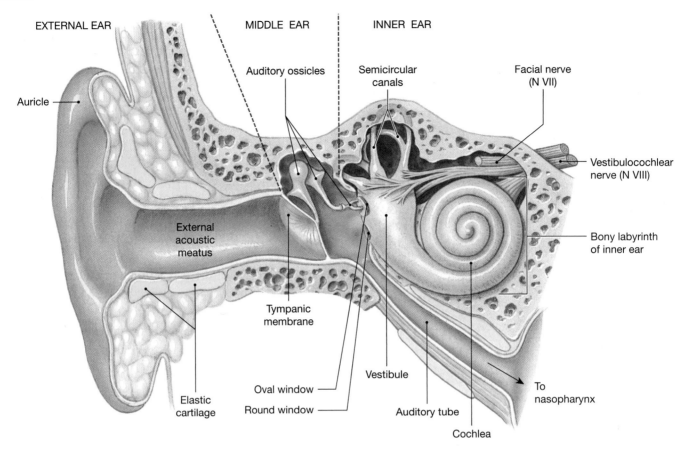

EXTERNAL EAR   MIDDLE EAR   INNER EAR

Auricle

Auditory ossicles

Semicircular canals

Facial nerve (N VII)

Vestibulocochlear nerve (N VIII)

Bony labyrinth of inner ear

External acoustic meatus

Tympanic membrane

Oval window

Round window

Vestibule

Auditory tube

To nasopharynx

Cochlea

Elastic cartilage

FIGURE 9-22 **The Anatomy of the Ear.** The boundaries separating the three regions of the ear (external, middle, and inner) are roughly marked by the dashed lines.

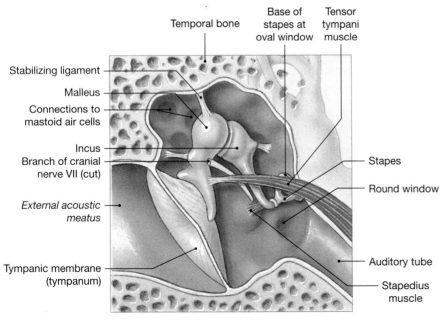

Temporal bone

Base of stapes at oval window

Tensor tympani muscle

Stabilizing ligament

Malleus

Connections to mastoid air cells

Incus

Branch of cranial nerve VII (cut)

External acoustic meatus

Stapes

Round window

Tympanic membrane (tympanum)

Auditory tube

Stapedius muscle

FIGURE 9-23 **The Structure of the Middle Ear.**

oval window, a small opening in the bone that encloses the inner ear.

The in-and-out vibrations of the tympanic membrane convert arriving sound energy into mechanical movements of the auditory ossicles. The ossicles act as levers that conduct the vibrations to the inner ear. The tympanum is larger and heavier than the delicate membrane spanning the oval window, so the amount of movement increases markedly from tympanum to oval window.

This magnification in movement enables us to hear very faint sounds. It can also be a problem, however, when we are exposed to very loud noises. In the middle ear, two small muscles protect the eardrum and ossicles from violent movements under noisy conditions. The *tensor tympani* (TEN-sor tim-PAN-ē) *muscle* pulls on the malleus, which increases the stiffness of the tympanum and reduces the amount of possible movement. The *stapedius* (sta-PĒ-dē-us) *muscle* pulls on the stapes, thereby reducing its movement at the oval window.

KEY

| | Membranous labyrinth |
| | Bony labyrinth |

(a)

Semicircular canal

Semicircular ducts
- Anterior
- Lateral
- Posterior

Vestibule

Perilymph

Bony labyrinth

Endolymph

Membranous labyrinth

(b)

Utricle

Saccule

Vestibular duct

Cochlear duct

Tympanic duct

Organ of Corti

Cochlea

FIGURE 9-24 The Inner Ear and a Hair Cell. (a) Part of this anterior view of the bony labyrinth has been removed to show the outline of the enclosed membranous labyrinth. **(b)** A section through one of the semicircular canals, showing the relationship between the bony and membranous labyrinths and the locations of the perilymph and endolymph. **(c)** A representative hair cell (receptor) from the vestibular complex. Bending the strereocilia in one direction results in stimulating its sensory neuron. Displacement in the opposite direction results in inhibition of its sensory neuron.

The Inner Ear

The senses of equilibrium and hearing are provided by the receptors within the **inner ear.** These receptors are protected by the **bony labyrinth** (Figure 9-24); its outer walls are fused with the surrounding temporal bone (Figure 9-22). The bony labyrinth surrounds and protects the **membranous labyrinth** (*labyrinthos*, network of canals), a collection of tubes and chambers that follow the contours of the surrounding bony labyrinth and are filled with a fluid called **endolymph** (EN-dō-limf). Between the bony and membranous labyrinths flows another fluid, the **perilymph** (PER-i-limf) (Figure 9-24b). The receptors lie within the membranous labyrinth.

Displacement in this direction stimulates hair cell

Displacement in this direction inhibits hair cell

Stereocilia

Hair cell

Sensory nerve ending

Supporting cell

(c) Hair cell

The bony labyrinth can be subdivided into three parts (Figure 9-24a):

1. *Vestibule.* The **vestibule** (VES-ti-bŭl) includes a pair of membranous sacs, the **saccule** (SAK-ŭl) and the **utricle** (Ū-tri-kul). Receptors in these sacs provide sensations of gravity and linear acceleration.

2. *Semicircular canals.* The **semicircular canals** enclose slender *semicircular ducts.* Receptors in the semicircular ducts are stimulated by rotation of the head. The combination of vestibule and semicircular canals is called the **vestibular complex,** because the fluid-filled chambers within the vestibule are continuous with those of the semicircular canals.

3. *Cochlea.* The bony, spiral-shaped **cochlea** (KOK-lē-uh; *cochlea,* snail shell) contains the **cochlear duct** of the membranous labyrinth. Receptors in the cochlear duct provide the sense of hearing. The cochlear duct is sandwiched between a pair of perilymph-filled chambers, and the entire complex is coiled around a central bony hub.

The bony labyrinth's walls are dense bone everywhere except at two small areas near the base of the cochlea. The round window is an opening in the bone of the cochlea. A thin membrane spans the opening and separates perilymph in the cochlea from the air in the middle ear. The membrane spanning the oval window is firmly attached to the base of the stapes. When a sound vibrates the tympanic membrane, the movements are conducted over the malleus and incus to the stapes. Movement of the stapes ultimately leads to the stimulation of receptors in the cochlear duct, and we hear the sound.

RECEPTOR FUNCTION IN THE INNER EAR. The receptors of the inner ear are called **hair cells** (Figure 9-24c). Regardless of location, they are always surrounded by supporting cells and monitored by the dendrites of sensory neurons. Each hair cell communicates with a sensory neuron by continually releasing small quantities of neurotransmitter. The free surface of this receptor supports 80–100 long microvilli called *stereocilia.* Hair cells do not actively move these processes. Instead, when some external force causes the stereocilia to move, their movement distorts the cell surface and alters its rate of neurotransmitter release. Displacement of the stereocilia in one direction stimulates the hair cells (and increases neurotransmitter release); displacement in the opposite direction inhibits the hair cells (and decreases neurotransmitter release).

EQUILIBRIUM

There are two aspects of equilibrium: (1) **dynamic equilibrium,** which aids us in maintaining our balance when the head and body are moved suddenly, and (2) **static equilibrium,** which maintains our posture and stability when the body is motionless. All equilibrium sensations are provided by hair cells of the vestibular complex. The semicircular ducts, which monitor dynamic equilibrium, provide information about rotational movements of the head. For example, when you turn your head to the left, receptors in the semicircular ducts tell you how rapid the movement is and in which direction. The saccule and the utricle, which monitor static equilibrium, provide information about your position with respect to gravity. If you stand with your head tilted to one side, receptors in the saccule and utricle will report the angle involved and whether your head is tilting forward or backward. These receptors are also stimulated by sudden changes in velocity. For example, when your car accelerates, the saccular and utricular receptors give you the sensation of increasing speed.

The Semicircular Ducts: Rotational Motion

Sensory receptors in the semicircular ducts respond to rotational movements of the head. Figure 9-24a shows the **anterior, posterior,** and **lateral semicircular ducts** and their continuity with the utricle. Each semicircular duct contains a swollen region, the **ampulla,** which contains the sensory receptors (Figure 9-25a). Hair cells attached to the wall of the ampulla form a raised structure known as a *crista* (Figure 9-25b). The stereocilia of the hair cells are embedded in a gelatinous structure called the *cupula* (KŪ-pū-luh), which nearly fills the ampulla. When the head rotates in the plane of the semicircular duct, movement of the endolymph pushes against this structure and stimulates the hair cells (Figure 9-25c).

Each semicircular duct responds to one of three possible rotational movements. To distort the cupula and stimulate the receptors, endolymph must flow along the axis of the duct; such flow will occur only when there is rotation in that plane. A horizontal rotation, as in shaking the head "no," stimulates the hair cells of the lateral semicircular duct. Nodding "yes" excites receptors of the anterior duct, and tilting the head from side to side activates receptors in the posterior duct. The three planes monitored by the semicircular ducts correspond to the three dimensions in the world around us, and they provide accurate information about even the most complex movements.

FIGURE 9-25 The Vestibular Complex. **(a)** This anterior view of the right semicircular ducts, utricle, and saccule shows the location of the sensory receptors. **(b)** A cross section through the ampulla of a semicircular duct reveals the relationship of hair cells to the cupula and the crista. **(c)** Endolymph movement along the axis of the semicircular duct moves the cupula and stimulates the hair cells. **(d)** This enlargement reveals the structure of a macula. **(e)** This diagram depicts the function of an otolith when the head is level and tilted back.

The Vestibule: Gravity and Linear Acceleration

Receptors in the utricle and saccule respond to gravity and linear acceleration. As depicted in Figure 9-25a, the hair cells of the utricle and saccule are clustered in oval **maculae** (MAK-ū-lē; *macula,* spot). As in the ampullae, the hair cell processes in the maculae are embedded in a gelatinous mass, but the surface of this gelatinous material contains a thin layer of densely packed calcium carbonate crystals. The complex as a whole (gelatinous mass and crystals) is called an *otolith* (*oto-,* ear + *lithos,* a stone) (Figure 9-25d). When the head is in the normal, upright position, the otolith crystals sit atop the macula. Their weight presses down on the macular surface, pushing the sensory hairs downward rather than to one side or another (Figure 9-25e). When the head is tilted, the pull of gravity on the otolith crystals shifts their weight to the side, distorting the sensory hairs. The change in receptor activity tells the CNS that the head is no longer level.

Otolith crystals are relatively dense and heavy, and they are connected to the rest of the body only by the sensory processes of the macular cells. So whenever the rest of the body makes a sudden movement, the otolith crystals lag behind. When an elevator starts downward, for example, we are immediately aware of it because the otolith crystals no longer push so forcefully against the surfaces of the receptor cells. Once they catch up and the elevator has reached a constant speed, we are no longer aware of any movement until the elevator brakes to a halt. As the body slows down, the otolith crystals press harder against the hair cells and we "feel" the force of gravity increase.

A similar mechanism accounts for our perception of linear acceleration in a car that speeds up suddenly. The otoliths lag behind, distorting the sensory hairs and changing the activity in the sensory neurons. A comparable otolith movement occurs when the chin is raised and gravity pulls the otoliths backward. On the basis of visual information, the brain decides whether the arriving sensations indicate acceleration or a change in head position.

Pathways for Equilibrium Sensations

Hair cells of the vestibule and of the semicircular canals are monitored by sensory neurons whose fibers form the **vestibular branch** of the vestibulocochlear nerve (N VIII). These fibers synapse on neurons in the *vestibular nuclei* located at the boundary between the pons and the medulla oblongata. The two vestibular nuclei (1) integrate sensory information arriving from each side of the head; (2) relay information to the cerebellum; (3) relay information to the cerebral cortex, providing a conscious sense of position and movement; and (4) send commands to motor nuclei in the brain stem and in the spinal cord. These reflexive motor commands are distributed to the motor nuclei for cranial nerves involved with eye, head, and neck movements (N III, N IV, N VI, and N XI). Descending instructions along the *vestibulospinal tracts* of the spinal cord adjust peripheral muscle tone to complement the reflexive movements of the head or neck.

HEARING

The receptors of the cochlear duct provide us with a sense of hearing that enables us to detect the quietest whisper, yet remain functional in a crowded, noisy room. The receptors responsible for auditory sensations are hair cells similar to those of the vestibular complex. However, both their placement within the cochlear duct and the organization of the surrounding accessory structures shield them from stimuli other than sound. In conveying vibrations from the tympanic membrane to the oval window, the auditory ossicles convert sound energy (pressure waves) in air to pressure pulses in the perilymph of the cochlea. These pressure pulses stimulate hair cells along the cochlear spiral. The *frequency* (pitch) of the perceived sound is determined by *which part* of the cochlear duct is stimulated. The *intensity* (volume) of the perceived sound is determined by *how many* hair cells at that location are stimulated.

The Cochlear Duct

In sectional view, the cochlear duct, or *scala media,* lies between a pair of chambers containing perilymph: the **vestibular duct** *(scala vestibuli)* and the **tympanic duct** *(scala tympani)* (Figure 9-26a). The vestibular and tympanic ducts are interconnected at the tip of the cochlear spiral. The outer surfaces of these ducts are encased by the bony labyrinth everywhere except at the oval window (the base of the vestibular duct) and the round window (the base of the tympanic duct).

THE ORGAN OF CORTI. The hair cells of the cochlear duct are located in the **organ of Corti** (Figure 9-26b). This sensory structure sits above the **basilar membrane,** which separates the cochlear duct from the underlying tympanic duct. The hair cells are arranged in a series of longitudinal rows, with their stereocilia in contact with the overlying **tectorial membrane** (tek-TOR-ē-al; *tectum,* roof). This membrane is firmly attached to the inner wall of the cochlear duct. When a portion of the

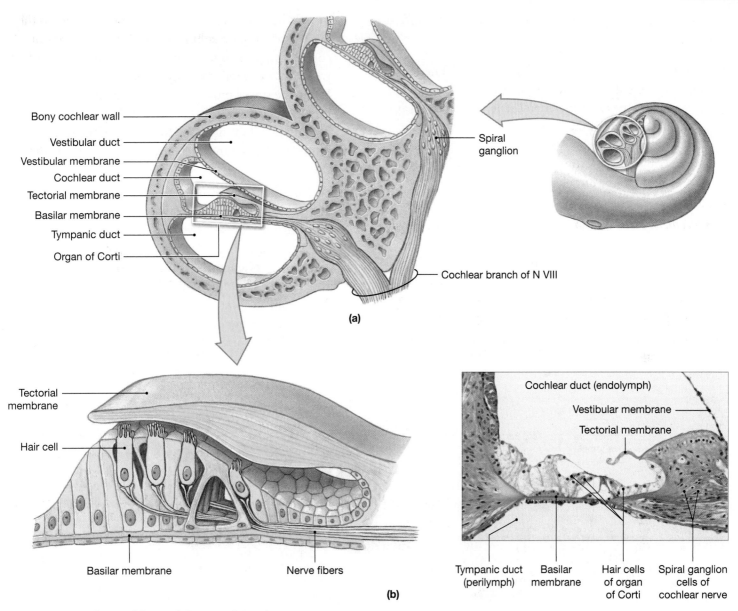

FIGURE 9-26 **The Cochlea and Organ of Corti. (a)** A section of the cochlea reveals its internal structures, including the organ of Corti. **(b)** The drawing shows the three-dimensional structure of the tectorial membrane and hair cell complex of the organ of Corti; the photomicrograph shows the actual structures. (LM × 1233)

basilar membrane bounces up and down in response to pressure waves in the perilymph, the stereocilia of the hair cells are distorted as they are pushed up against the tectorial membrane.

The Hearing Process

Hearing is the detection of sound, which consists of waves of pressure that are conducted through a medium such as air or water. Physicists use the term **cycles** rather than waves, and the number of cycles per second (cps)—or **hertz (Hz)**—represents

the **frequency** of the sound. What we perceive as the **pitch** of a sound (how high or low it is) is our sensory response to its frequency. A sound of high frequency (high pitch) might have a frequency of 15,000 Hz or more; a sound of low frequency (low pitch) could have a frequency of 100 Hz or less. The amount of energy, or power, of a sound determines its *intensity,* or volume. Intensity is reported in **decibels** (DES-i-belz). Some examples of different sounds and their intensities include a soft whisper (30 decibels), a refrigerator (50 decibels), a gas lawnmower (90 decibels), a chain saw (100 decibels), and a jet plane (140 decibels).

Hearing can be divided into six basic steps, diagrammed in Figure 9-27.

Step 1 *Sound waves arrive at the tympanic membrane.*
Sound waves enter the external acoustic meatus and travel toward the tympanic membrane. Sound waves approaching the side of the head have direct access to the tympanic membrane on that side, whereas sounds arriving from another direction must bend around corners or pass through the auricle or other body tissues.

Step 2 *Movement of the tympanic membrane causes displacement of the auditory ossicles.* The tympanic membrane provides the surface for sound collection. It vibrates to sound waves with frequencies between approximately 20 and 20,000 Hz (in a young child). When the tympanic membrane vibrates, so do the malleus and (through their articulations) the incus and stapes.

Step 3 *The movement of the stapes at the oval window establishes pressure waves in the perilymph of the vestibular*

duct. When the stapes moves, it applies pressure to the perilymph of the vestibular duct. Because the rest of the cochlea is sheathed in bone, pressure applied at the oval window can be relieved only at the round window. When the stapes moves inward, the membrane spanning the round window bulges outward. As the stapes moves in and out, vibrating at the frequency of the sound at the tympanic membrane, it creates pressure waves within the perilymph.

Step 4 *The pressure waves distort the basilar membrane on their way to the round window of the tympanic duct.* These pressure waves cause movement in the basilar membrane. The basilar membrane does not have the same structure throughout its length. Near the oval window, it is narrow and stiff; at its terminal end, it is wider and more flexible. As a result, the location of maximum stimulation varies with the frequency of the sound. High-frequency sounds vibrate the basilar membrane near the oval window. The lower the frequency of the sound, the farther from the oval

STEP 1	STEP 2	STEP 3	STEP 4	STEP 5	STEP 6
Sound waves arrive at tympanic membrane.	Movement of the tympanic membrane causes displacement of the auditory ossicles.	Movement of the stapes at the oval window establishes pressure waves in the perilymph of the vestibular duct.	The pressure waves distort the basilar membrane on their way to the round window of the tympanic duct.	Vibration of the basilar membrane causes vibration of hair cells against the tectorial membrane.	Information about the region and the intensity of stimulation is relayed to the CNS over the cochlear branch of cranial nerve VIII.

FIGURE 9-27 Sound and Hearing. This drawing presents the steps in the reception of sound and the process of hearing.

window is the area of maximum distortion. The actual *amount* of movement at a given location depends on the amount of force applied by the stapes. The louder the sound, the more the basilar membrane moves.

Step 5 *Vibration of the basilar membrane causes vibration of hair cells against the tectorial membrane.* The vibration of the affected region of the basilar membrane moves hair cells against the tectorial membrane. The displacement of the hair cells results in the release of neurotransmitters and the stimulation of sensory neurons. The hair cells are arranged in several rows; a very soft sound may stimulate only a few hair cells in a portion of one row. As the volume of a sound increases, not only do these hair cells become more active, but also additional hair cells—at first in the same row and then in adjacent rows—are stimulated as well. The number of hair cells responding in a given region of the organ of Corti thus provides information on the intensity of the sound.

Step 6 *Information about the region and intensity of stimulation is relayed to the CNS over the cochlear branch of cranial nerve VIII.* The cell bodies of the sensory neurons that monitor the cochlear hair cells are located at the center of the bony cochlea (Figure 9-26a) in the *spiral ganglion*. From there, the information is carried by the cochlear branch of cranial nerve VIII to the cochlear nuclei of the medulla oblongata for distribution to other centers in the brain.

Auditory Pathways

Hair cell stimulation activates sensory neurons whose cell bodies are in the nearby spiral ganglion. Their afferent fibers (axons) form the **cochlear branch** of the vestibulocochlear nerve (N VIII) (Figure 9-28). These axons enter the medulla

Auditory cortex (temporal lobe)

Low-frequency sounds

High-frequency sounds

Thalamus

Thalamic nucleus

Inferior colliculus (midbrain)

Motor output to cranial nerve nuclei

Motor output to spinal cord

Cochlea

Low-frequency sounds

High-frequency sounds

Vestibular branch

Cochlear branch

Vestibulocochlear nerve (N VIII)

Cochlear nucleus

FIGURE 9-28 Pathways for Auditory Sensations. Auditory sensations are carried by the cochlear branch of N VIII to the cochlear nuclei of the medulla oblongata. From there the information is relayed to the midbrain, which directs unconscious motor responses to sounds. Ascending acoustic information goes to the thalamus before being forwarded to the auditory cortex of the temporal lobe.

Clinical Note

Hearing Deficits

Probably more than 6 million people in the United States alone have at least a partial hearing deficit. **Conductive deafness** results from conditions in the outer or middle ear that block the normal transfer of vibration from the tympanic membrane to the oval window. An external acoustic meatus plugged by accumulated wax or trapped water may cause a temporary hearing loss. Scarring or perforation of the tympanum and immobilization of one or more of the auditory ossicles are more serious causes of conductive deafness.

In **nerve deafness,** the problem lies within the cochlea or somewhere along the auditory pathway. The vibrations are reaching the oval window and entering the perilymph, but the receptors either cannot respond or their response cannot reach its CNS destinations. Very loud (high-intensity) sounds,

for example, can produce nerve deafness by breaking stereocilia off the surfaces of the hair cells. (The reflex contraction of the tensor tympani and stapedius muscles in response to a dangerously loud noise occurs in less than 0.1 second, but this may not be fast enough.) Drugs such as the aminoglycoside antibiotics (*neomycin* or *gentamicin*) may diffuse into the endolymph and kill hair cells. Because hair cells and sensory nerves can also be damaged by bacterial infection, the potential side effects must be balanced against the severity of infection.

Many treatment options are available for conductive deafness; treatment options for nerve deafness are relatively limited. Because many of these problems become progressively worse, early diagnosis improves the chances for successful treatment.

---

oblongata, where they split into two groups and synapse at the left and right *cochlear nuclei*. From there, information ascends to the *inferior colliculus* of the midbrain. This processing center coordinates a number of responses to acoustic stimuli, including auditory reflexes involving skeletal muscles of the head, face, and trunk. For example, these reflexes automatically change the position of your head in response to a sudden loud noise.

Before reaching the cerebral cortex and your conscious awareness, ascending auditory sensations synapse in the thalamus. Thalamic fibers then deliver the information to the auditory cortex of the temporal lobe. In effect, the auditory cortex contains a map of the organ of Corti. High-frequency sounds activate one portion of the cortex, and low-frequency sounds affect another. If the auditory cortex is damaged, the individual will respond to sounds and have normal acoustic reflexes, but sound interpretation and pattern recognition will be difficult or impossible. Damage to the adjacent association area leaves the ability to detect the tones and patterns unaffected but produces an inability to comprehend their meaning.

Auditory Sensitivity

Our hearing abilities are remarkable, but it is difficult to assess the absolute sensitivity of the system. The range from the

The Big Picture

Balance and hearing rely on the same basic types of sensory receptors (hair cells). The nature of the stimulus that stimulates a particular group of hair cells depends on the structure of the associated sense organ. In the semicircular ducts, the stimulus is fluid movement caused by head rotation in the horizontal, sagittal, or frontal planes. In the utricle and saccule, the stimulus is gravity-induced shifts in the position of attached otoliths. In the cochlea, the stimulus is movement of the basilar membrane by pressure waves.

softest audible sound to the loudest tolerable blast represents a trillionfold increase in power. The receptor mechanism is so sensitive that if we were to remove the stapes, we could, in theory, hear air molecules bouncing off the oval window. We never utilize the full potential of this system, because body movements and our internal organs produce squeaks, groans, thumps, and other sounds that are tuned out by adaptation. When other environmental noises fade away, the level of adaptation drops and the system becomes increasingly sensitive. If we relax in a quiet room, our heartbeat seems to get louder and louder as the auditory system adjusts to the lower level of background noise.

16. If the round window were not able to bulge out with increased pressure in the perilymph, how would sound perception be affected?

17. How would the loss of stereocilia from the hair cells of the organ of Corti affect hearing?

See the blue Answers tab at the back of the book.

9-8 Aging is accompanied by a noticeable decline in the special senses

The general lack of replacement of neurons leads to an inevitable decline in sensory function with age. Although increases in stimulus strength can compensate for part of this functional decline, the loss of axons necessary for conducting sensory action potentials cannot be compensated for to the same degree. Next we consider the toll aging takes on various special senses.

SMELL AND AGING

Unlike populations of other neurons, the population of olfactory receptor cells is regularly replaced by the division of stem cells in the olfactory epithelium. Despite this process, the total number of receptors declines with age, and the remaining receptors become less sensitive. As a result, elderly individuals have difficulty detecting odors in low concentrations. This drop in the number of receptors explains "Grandmother's" tendency to apply too much perfume and why "Grandfather's" aftershave lotion seems so overpowering. They must apply more to be able to smell it.

TASTE AND AGING

Tasting ability declines with age due to the thinning of mucous membranes and a reduction in the number and sensitivity of taste buds. We begin life with more than 10,000 taste buds, but that number begins declining dramatically by age 50. The sensory loss becomes especially significant because aging individuals also experience a decline in the number of olfactory receptors. As a result, many of the elderly find that their food tastes bland and unappetizing. Children, however, find the same food too spicy.

VISION AND AGING

Various disorders of vision are associated with normal aging; the most common involve the lens and the neural part of the retina. With age, the lens loses its elasticity and stiffens. As a result, seeing close-up objects becomes more difficult, and older individuals become farsighted—a condition called *presbyopia*. ∞ p. 325 For example, the inner limit of clear vision, known as the *near point of vision*, changes from 7–9 cm in children to 15–20 cm in young adults and typically reaches 83 cm by age 60. As noted earlier, the most common cause of the development of a cataract (the loss of transparency in the lens) is advancing age. Such cataracts are called *senile cataracts*. ∞ p. 321 In addition to changes in the near point of vision and some changes in lens transparency, a gradual loss of rods occurs with age. This reduction explains why individuals over age 60 need almost twice as much light for reading than individuals at age 40.

Another contributor to the loss of vision with age is *macular degeneration*, the leading cause of blindness in persons over 50. This condition is typically associated with the growth and proliferation of blood vessels in the retina. The leakage of blood from these abnormal vessels causes retinal scarring and a loss of photoreceptors. The vascular proliferation begins in the macula lutea, the area of the retina correlated with acute vision. Color vision is affected as the cones deteriorate.

HEARING AND AGING

Hearing is generally affected less by aging than are the other senses. However, because the tympanic membrane loses some of its elasticity, it becomes more difficult to hear high-pitched sounds. The progressive loss of hearing that occurs with aging is called *presbycusis* (prez-bē-KŪ-sis; *presbys*, old man + *akousis*, hearing).

18. How can a given food be both too spicy for a child and too bland for an elderly individual?

19. Explain why we have an increasingly difficult time seeing close-up objects as we age.

See the blue Answers tab at the back of the book.

RELATED CLINICAL TERMS

analgesic: A drug that relieves pain without eliminating sensitivity to other stimuli, such as touch or pressure.

anesthesia: A total or partial loss of sensation.

cataract: Opacity (loss of transparency) of the lens.

color blindness: A condition in which a person is unable to distinguish certain colors.

conductive deafness: Deafness resulting from conditions in the outer or middle ear that block the transfer of vibrations from the tympanic membrane to the oval window.

glaucoma: A condition characterized by increased fluid pressure within the eye due to the impaired reabsorption of aqueous humor; can result in blindness.

hyperopia, or *farsightedness:* A condition in which nearby objects are blurry but distant objects are clear.

Ménière disease: A condition in which high fluid pressures rupture the walls of the membranous labyrinth, resulting in acute vertigo (an inappropriate sense of motion) and inappropriate auditory sensations.

myopia, or *nearsightedness:* A condition in which vision at close range is normal but distant objects appear blurry.

nerve deafness: Deafness resulting from problems within the cochlea or along the auditory pathway.

nystagmus: Abnormal eye movements that may appear after the brain stem or inner ear is damaged.

opthalmology (of-thal-MOL-o-jē): The study of the eye and its diseases.

presbyopia: A type of hyperopia that develops with age as the lens becomes less elastic.

retinitis pigmentosa: A group of inherited retinopathies (see the next term) characterized by the progressive deterioration of photoreceptors, eventually resulting in blindness.

retinopathy (ret-i-NOP-ah-thē): A disease or disorder of the retina.

scotomas (skō-TŌ-muhz): Abnormal blind spots in the field of vision (that is, those not caused by the optic disc).

strabismus: Deviations in the alignment of the eyes to each other; one or both eyes turn inward or outward.

Chapter 9 Review

KEY TERMS

accommodation *324*	nociceptors *308*
cochlea *332*	olfaction *308*
fovea *320*	proprioception *308*
gustation *308*	pupil *319*
iris *319*	retina *320*
macula *334*	sclera *317*

SUMMARY OUTLINE

9-1 Sensory receptors connect our internal and external environments with the nervous system *p. 307*

1. The **general senses** are temperature, pain, touch, pressure, vibration, and proprioception; receptors for these sensations are distributed throughout the body. Receptors for the **special senses** (smell, taste, vision, balance, and hearing) are located in specialized areas or in sense organs.

2. A *sensory receptor* is a specialized cell that, when stimulated, sends a sensation to the CNS. The simplest receptors are **free nerve endings;** the most complex have specialized accessory structures that isolate the receptors from all but a specific type of stimulus.

3. Each receptor cell monitors a specific *receptive field. (Figure 9-1)*

4. Sensory information is relayed in the form of action potentials in a sensory (afferent) fiber. In general, the larger the stimulus, the greater is the frequency of action potentials. The CNS interprets the nature of the arriving sensory information on the basis of the area of the brain stimulated.

5. **Adaptation**—a reduction in sensitivity in the presence of a constant stimulus—involves changes in receptor sensitivity or inhibition along sensory pathways.

9-2 General sensory receptors can be classified by the type of stimulus that excites them *p. 308*

6. **Nociceptors** respond to a variety of stimuli usually associated with tissue damage. The two types of these painful sensations are **fast pain,** or *prickling pain,* and **slow pain,** or *burning and aching pain.*

7. The perception of pain in parts of the body that are not actually stimulated is called **referred pain.** *(Figure 9-2)*

8. **Thermoreceptors** respond to changes in temperature.

9. **Mechanoreceptors** respond to physical distortion of, contact with, or pressure on their cell membranes; **tactile receptors** respond to touch, pressure, and vibration; **baroreceptors** respond to pressure changes in the walls of blood vessels, the digestive and urinary tracts, and the lungs; and **proprioceptors** respond to positions of joints and muscles.

10. **Fine touch and pressure receptors** provide detailed information about a source of stimulation; **crude touch**

and **pressure receptors** are poorly localized. Important tactile receptors include the *root hair plexus, tactile discs, tactile corpuscles, lamellated corpuscles,* and *Ruffini corpuscles.* (*Figure 9-3*)

11. Baroreceptors in the walls of major arteries and veins respond to changes in blood pressure, and those along the digestive tract help coordinate reflex activities of digestion. (*Figure 9-4*)

12. Proprioceptors monitor the position of joints, tension in tendons and ligaments, and the state of muscular contraction. Proprioceptors include Golgi tendon organs and muscle spindles.

13. In general, **chemoreceptors** respond to water-soluble and lipid-soluble substances dissolved in the surrounding fluid. They monitor the chemical composition of body fluids. (*Figure 9-5*)

9-3 Olfaction, the sense of smell, involves olfactory receptors responding to chemical stimuli *p. 312*

14. The **olfactory organs** consist of an **olfactory epithelium** containing **olfactory receptor cells** (neurons sensitive to chemicals dissolved in the overlying mucus), supporting cells, and *basal cells* (stem cells). Their surfaces are coated with the secretions of the **olfactory glands.** (*Figure 9-6*)

15. The olfactory receptors are modified neurons.

16. The olfactory system has extensive limbic and hypothalamic connections.

9-4 Gustation, the sense of taste, involves taste receptors responding to chemical stimuli *p. 314*

17. **Taste (gustatory) receptors** are clustered in **taste buds;** each taste bud contains **gustatory cells,** which extend *taste hairs* through a narrow **taste pore.** (*Figure 9-7*)

18. Taste buds are associated with **papillae,** epithelial projections on the superior surface of the tongue. (*Figure 9-7*)

19. The **primary taste sensations** are sweet, salty, sour, and bitter; umami and water receptors are also present. (*Figure 9-7*)

20. The taste buds are monitored by cranial nerves that synapse within a nucleus of the medulla oblongata.

9-5 Internal eye structures contribute to vision, while accessory eye structures provide protection *p. 315*

21. The **accessory structures** of the eye include the eyelids and associated exocrine glands, the superficial epithelium of the eye, structures associated with the production and removal of tears, and the extrinsic eye muscles.

22. An epithelium called the **conjunctiva** covers most of the exposed surface of the eye except the transparent **cornea.**

23. The secretions of the **lacrimal gland** bathe the conjunctiva; these secretions contain *lysozyme* (an enzyme that attacks bacteria). Tears reach the nasal cavity after passing through the **lacrimal canals,** the **lacrimal sac,** and the **nasolacrimal duct.** (*Figure 9-8*)

24. Six **extrinsic eye muscles** control external eye movements: the **inferior** and **superior rectus,** the **lateral** and **medial rectus,** and the **superior** and **inferior obliques.** (*Figure 9-9; Table 9-1*)

25. The eye has three layers: an outer fibrous tunic, a vascular tunic, and an inner neural tunic. Most of the ocular surface is covered by the **sclera** (a dense fibrous connective tissue), which is continuous with the cornea, both of which are part of the **fibrous tunic.** (*Figure 9-10*)

26. The **vascular tunic** includes the **iris,** the **ciliary body,** and the **choroid.** The iris forms the boundary between the eye's anterior and posterior chambers. The iris regulates the amount of light entering the eye. The ciliary body contains the *ciliary muscle* and the *ciliary processes,* which attach to the **suspensory ligaments** of the **lens.** (*Figures 9-10, 9-11*)

27. The **neural tunic** consists of an outer *pigmented part* and an inner *neural part;* the latter contains visual receptors and associated neurons. (*Figures 9-10, 9-12*)

28. From the photoreceptors, the information is relayed to **bipolar cells,** then to **ganglion cells,** and to the brain by the optic nerve. Horizontal cells and amacrine cells modify the signals passed between other retinal components. (*Figure 9-12*)

29. The ciliary body and lens divide the interior of the eye into a large **posterior cavity** and a smaller **anterior cavity.** The anterior cavity is subdivided into the **anterior chamber,** which extends from the cornea to the iris, and a **posterior chamber** between the iris and the ciliary body and lens. The posterior cavity contains the *vitreous body,* a gelatinous mass that helps stabilize the shape of the eye and supports the retina. (*Figure 9-14*)

30. **Aqueous humor** circulates within the eye and reenters the circulation after diffusing through the walls of the anterior chamber and into veins of the sclera through the *canal of Schlemm.* (*Figure 9-14*)

31. The lens, held in place by the suspensory ligaments, focuses a visual image on the retinal receptors. Light is refracted (bent) when it passes through the cornea and lens. During **accommodation,** the shape of the lens changes to focus an image on the retina. (*Figures 9-15, 9-16, 9-17*)

9-6 Photoreceptors respond to light and change it into electrical signals essential to visual physiology *p. 324*

32. Light is radiated in waves with a characteristic wavelength. A *photon* is a single energy packet of visible light. The two

types of **photoreceptors** (visual receptors of the retina) are **rods** and **cones.** Rods respond to almost any photon, regardless of its energy content; cones have characteristic ranges of sensitivity. Many cones are densely packed within the **fovea** (the central portion of the **macula lutea**), the site of sharpest vision. (*Figure 9-19*)

33. Each photoreceptor contains an outer segment with membranous **discs** containing **visual pigments.** Light absorption occurs in the visual pigments, which are derivatives of **rhodopsin** (**opsin** plus the pigment **retinal,** which is synthesized from **vitamin A**). A photoreceptor responds to light by changing its rate of neurotransmitter release and thereby altering the activity of a bipolar cell. (*Figures 9-19, 9-20*)

34. The message is relayed from photoreceptors to bipolar cells to ganglion cells within the retina. The axons of ganglion cells converge at the optic disc and leave the eye as the optic nerve. A partial crossover occurs at the optic chiasm before the information reaches a nucleus in the thalamus on each side of the brain. From these nuclei, visual information is relayed to the visual cortex of the occipital lobe, which contains a sensory map of the field of vision. (*Figure 9-21*)

9-7 Equilibrium sensations originate within the inner ear, while hearing involves the detection and interpretation of sound waves *p. 329*

35. The senses of equilibrium (**dynamic equilibrium** and **static equilibrium**) and hearing are provided by the receptors of the **inner ear.** Its chambers and canals contain the fluid **endolymph.** The **bony labyrinth** surrounds and protects the **membranous labyrinth,** and the space between them contains the fluid **perilymph.** The bony labyrinth consists of the **vestibule,** the **semicircular canals** (receptors in the vestibule and semicircular canals provide the sense of equilibrium), and the **cochlea** (these receptors provide the sense of hearing). The structures and air spaces of the **external ear** and **middle ear** help capture and transmit sound to the cochlea. (*Figures 9-22, 9-23, 9-24*)

36. The external ear includes the **auricle** (*pinna*), which surrounds the entrance to the **external acoustic meatus,** which ends at the **tympanic membrane** (*tympanum* or *eardrum*). (*Figures 9-22, 9-23*)

37. The middle ear is connected to the nasopharynx by the **auditory tube** (*pharyngotympanic tube* or *Eustachian tube*). The middle ear encloses and protects the **auditory ossicles,** which connect the tympanic membrane with the receptor complex of the inner ear. (*Figures 9-22, 9-23*)

38. The vestibule includes a pair of membranous sacs, the **saccule** and **utricle,** whose receptors provide sensations of gravity and linear acceleration. The semicircular canals contain the **semicircular ducts,** whose receptors provide sensations of rotation. The cochlea contains the **cochlear duct,** an elongated portion of the membranous labyrinth. (*Figure 9-24a*)

39. The basic receptors of the inner ear are **hair cells,** whose surfaces support *stereocilia.* Hair cells provide information about the direction and strength of mechanical stimuli. (*Figure 9-24c*)

40. The **anterior, posterior,** and **lateral semicircular ducts** are attached to the utricle. Each semicircular duct contains an **ampulla** with sensory receptors. There the stereocilia contact the *cupula,* a gelatinous mass that is distorted when endolymph flows along the axis of the duct. (*Figures 9-24, 9-25a, b, c*)

41. In the saccule and utricle, hair cells cluster within **maculae,** where their cilia contact the *otolith* (densely packed mineral crystals in a gelatinous mass). When the head tilts, the otoliths shift, and the resulting distortion in the sensory hairs signals the CNS. (*Figure 9-25d,e*)

42. The vestibular receptors activate sensory neurons whose axons form the **vestibular branch** of the vestibulocochlear nerve (N VIII).

43. Sound waves travel toward the tympanic membrane, which vibrates; the auditory ossicles amplify and conduct the vibrations to the inner ear. Movement at the oval window applies pressure to the perilymph of the **vestibular duct.** (*Figures 9-26, 9-27*)

44. Pressure waves distort the **basilar membrane** and push the hair cells of the **organ of Corti** against the **tectorial membrane.** (*Figure 9-27*)

45. The sensory neurons are located in the **spiral ganglion** of the cochlea. Afferent fibers of sensory neurons form the **cochlear branch** of the vestibulocochlear nerve (N VIII), synapsing at the left and right cochlear nuclei. (*Figure 9-28*)

9-8 Aging is accompanied by a noticeable decline in the special senses *p. 339*

46. As part of the aging process, there are (1) gradual reductions in smell and taste sensitivity, (2) a tendency toward *presbyopia* and cataract formation in the eyes, and (3) a progressive loss of hearing (*presbycusis*).

REVIEW QUESTIONS

WWW Access more review material online at The Anatomy & Physiology Place (www.anatomyandphysiology.com). There, you'll find Chapter Guides, Chapter Quizzes, Chapter Practice Tests, Interactive Flashcards, a Glossary with Pronunciations, and more to help you succeed in the course.

Level 1 • Reviewing Facts and Terms

Match each item in column A with the most closely related item in column B. Place letters for answers in the spaces provided.

COLUMN A

_____ 1. myopia
_____ 2. fibrous tunic
_____ 3. nociceptors
_____ 4. proprioceptors
_____ 5. cones
_____ 6. accommodation
_____ 7. tympanic membrane
_____ 8. thermoreceptors
_____ 9. rods
_____ 10. olfaction
_____ 11. fovea
_____ 12. hyperopia
_____ 13. maculae
_____ 14. semicircular ducts

COLUMN B

a. pain receptors
b. free nerve endings
c. sclera and cornea
d. rotational movements
e. provide information on joint position
f. color vision
g. site of sharpest vision
h. active in dim light
i. eardrum
j. change in lens shape to focus retinal image
k. nearsighted
l. farsighted
m. smell
n. gravity and acceleration receptors

15. Identify the structures in the following horizontal section of the right eye.

(b) Horizontal section of right eye

(a) _____   (b) _____
(c) _____   (d) _____
(e) _____   (f) _____
(g) _____   (h) _____
(i) _____   (j) _____

16. Regardless of the nature of a stimulus, sensory information must be sent to the central nervous system in the form of
    (a) dendritic processes.
    (b) action potentials.
    (c) neurotransmitter molecules.
    (d) generator potentials.

17. A reduction in sensitivity in the presence of constant stimulus is called
    (a) transduction.   (b) sensory coding.
    (c) line labeling.   (d) adaptation.

18. Mechanoreceptors that detect pressure changes in the walls of blood vessels and in portions of the digestive, reproductive, and urinary tracts are
    (a) tactile receptors.   (b) baroreceptors.
    (c) proprioceptors.   (d) free nerve endings.

19. Examples of proprioceptors that monitor the position of joints and the state of muscular contraction are
    (a) lamellated and Meissner corpuscles.
    (b) carotid and aortic sinuses.
    (c) Merkel discs and Ruffini corpuscles.
    (d) Golgi tendon organs and muscle spindles.

20. When chemicals dissolve in the nasal cavity, they stimulate
    (a) gustatory cells.   (b) olfactory hairs.
    (c) rod cells.   (d) tactile receptors.

21. Taste receptors are also known as
    (a) tactile discs.   (b) gustatory receptors.
    (c) hair cells.   (d) olfactory receptors.

22. The purpose of tears produced by the lacrimal apparatus is to
    (a) keep conjunctival surfaces moist and clean.
    (b) reduce friction and remove debris from the eye.
    (c) provide nutrients and oxygen to the conjunctival epithelium.
    (d) a, b, and c are correct.

23. The thickened gel-like substance that helps support the structure of the eyeball is the
    (a) vitreous body.   (b) aqueous humor.
    (c) cupula.   (d) perilymph.

24. The retina is considered to be a component of the
    (a) vascular tunic.   (b) fibrous tunic.
    (c) neural tunic.   (d) a, b, and c are correct.

25. At sunset your visual system adapts to
    (a) fovea vision.   (b) rod-based vision.
    (c) macular vision.   (d) cone-based vision.

26. The malleus, incus, and stapes are the tiny ear bones located in the
    (a) outer ear.   (b) middle ear.
    (c) inner ear.   (d) membranous labyrinth.

27. Receptors in the saccule and utricle provide sensations of
    (a) balance and equilibrium.
    (b) hearing.
    (c) vibration.
    (d) gravity and linear acceleration.

28. Identify the structures of the external, middle, and inner ear in the following figure.

    (a) _____   (b) _____
    (c) _____   (d) _____
    (e) _____   (f) _____
    (g) _____   (h) _____
    (i) _____

29. The organ of Corti is located within the _____ of the inner ear.
    (a) utricle   (b) bony labyrinth
    (c) vestibule   (d) cochlea

30. What three types of mechanoreceptors respond to stretching, compression, twisting, or other distortions of the cell membrane?

31. Identify six types of tactile receptors found in the skin and their sensitivities.

32. (a) What structures make up the fibrous tunic of the eye?
    (b) What are the functions of the fibrous tunic?

33. What structures are parts of the vascular tunic of the eye?

34. What six basic steps are involved in the process of hearing?

Level 2 • Reviewing Concepts

35. The CNS interprets sensory information entirely on the basis of the
    (a) strength of the action potential.
    (b) number of generator potentials.
    (c) area of brain stimulated.
    (d) a, b, and c are correct

36. If the auditory cortex is damaged, the individual will respond to sounds and have normal acoustic reflexes, but
    (a) the sounds may produce nerve deafness.
    (b) the auditory ossicle may be immobilized.
    (c) sound interpretation and pattern recognition may be impossible.
    (d) normal transfer of vibration to the oval window is inhibited.

37. Distinguish between the general senses and the special senses in the human body.

38. In what form does the CNS receive a stimulus detected by a sensory receptor?

39. Why are olfactory sensations long lasting and an important part of our memories and emotions?

40. Jane makes an appointment with the optometrist for a vision test. Her test results for visual acuity are reported as 20/15. What does this test result mean? Is a rating of 20/20 better or worse?

Level 3 • Critical Thinking and Clinical Applications

41. You are at a park watching some deer 35 feet away from you. Your friend taps you on the shoulder to ask a question. As you turn to look at your friend, who is standing 2 feet away, what changes will occur regarding your eyes?

42. After attending a Fourth of July fireworks extravaganza, Millie finds it difficult to hear normal conversation, and her ears keep "ringing." What is causing her hearing problems?

43. After riding the express elevator from the twentieth floor to the ground floor, for a few seconds you still feel as if you are descending, even though you have obviously come to a stop. Why?

10 The Endocrine System

These three preadolescent boys are poised at the threshold of puberty, a period of rapid growth and developing sexual maturity. The changes that will occur in their facial features, voice, height, and sexual organs are initiated by the genetically programmed release of sex hormones.

10-1 Homeostasis is preserved through intercellular communication

To maintain homeostasis, every cell in the body must communicate with its neighbors and with cells and tissues in distant portions of the body. Most of this communication involves the release and receipt of chemical messages. Each living cell is continually "talking" to its neighbors by releasing chemicals into the extracellular fluid. These chemicals tell cells what their neighbors are doing at any given moment, and the result is the coordination of tissue function at the local level.

Cellular communication over greater distances is coordinated by the nervous and endocrine systems. The nervous system functions somewhat like a telephone company, carrying specific "messages" from one location to another inside the body. The source and the destination are quite specific, and the effects are short lived. This form of communication is ideal for crisis management; if you are in danger of being hit by a speeding bus, the nervous system can coordinate and direct your leap to safety.

Many life processes, however, require long-term cellular communication. This type of regulation is provided by the endocrine system, which uses chemical messengers called *hormones* to relay information and instructions between cells. In such communication, hormones are like addressed letters, and the cardiovascular system is the postal service. Each hormone released into and distributed by the circulation has specific *target cells* that will respond to its presence. These target cells possess the receptors required for binding and "reading" the hormonal message when it arrives. But hormones are really like bulk mail advertisements—cells throughout the body are exposed to them whether or not they have the necessary receptors. At any moment, each individual cell can respond to only a few of the hormones present. The other hormones are ignored, because the cell lacks the receptors needed to read the messages they contain.

Because target cells can be anywhere in the body, a single hormone can alter the metabolic activities of multiple tissues and organs simultaneously. The effects may be slow to appear, but they often persist for days. This persistence makes hormones effective in coordinating cell, tissue, and organ activities on a sustained, long-term basis. For example, circulating hormones keep body water content and levels of electrolytes and organic nutrients within normal limits 24 hours a day throughout our entire lives.

While the effects of a single hormone persist, a cell may receive additional instructions from other hormones. The result is a further modification in cellular operations. Gradual changes in the quantities and identities of circulating hormones can produce complex changes in physical structure and physiological capabilities. Examples are the processes of embryological and fetal development, growth, and puberty.

When viewed from a broad perspective, the differences between the nervous and endocrine systems seem relatively clear. In fact, these broad organizational and functional distinctions are the basis for treating them as two separate systems. Yet when considered in detail, the two systems function in parallel ways:

- Both systems rely on the release of chemicals that bind to specific receptors on target cells.

- Both systems share various chemical messengers; for example, norepinephrine and epinephrine are called *hormones* when released into the bloodstream, and *neurotransmitters* when released across synapses.

- Both systems are primarily regulated by negative feedback control mechanisms.

- Both systems coordinate and regulate the activities of other cells, tissues, organs, and systems to maintain homeostasis.

This chapter introduces the components and functions of the endocrine system and explores the interactions between the nervous and endocrine systems.

1. List four similarities between the nervous and endocrine systems.

See the blue Answers tab at the back of the book.

10-2 The endocrine system regulates physiological processes through the binding of hormones to receptors

The endocrine system includes all of the endocrine cells and tissues of the body. As noted in Chapter 4, **endocrine cells** are glandular secretory cells that release their secretions into the extracellular fluid. This feature distinguishes them from *exocrine cells*, which secrete onto epithelial surfaces. ⟳ p. 94 The chemicals released by endocrine cells may affect adjacent cells only—as is the case of *cytokines* (or *local hormones*) such as *prostaglandins*—or they may affect cells throughout the body. We define **hormones** as chemical messengers that are released in one tissue and transported by the bloodstream to reach target cells in other tissues.

The tissues and organs of the endocrine system, and some of the major hormones they produce, are introduced in Figure 10-1. Some of these organs, such as the pituitary gland, have endocrine secretion as a primary function. Others, such as the pancreas, have many other functions besides endocrine secretion; chapters on other organ systems consider such endocrine organs in more detail.

THE STRUCTURE OF HORMONES

Based on their chemical structures, hormones can be divided into the following three groups:

1. *Amino acid derivatives.* Some hormones are relatively small molecules that are structurally similar to amino acids. (Amino acids, the building blocks of proteins, were introduced in Chapter 2.) ⟳ p. 46 This group includes *epinephrine, norepinephrine,* the *thyroid hormones,* and *melatonin.*

2. *Peptide hormones.* **Peptide hormones** consist of chains of amino acids. These molecules range from short amino acid chains, such as *ADH* and *oxytocin,* to small proteins such as *growth hormone* and *prolactin.* This is the largest class of hormones and includes all of the hor-

mones secreted by the hypothalamus, pituitary gland, heart, kidneys, thymus, digestive tract, and pancreas.

3. *Lipid derivatives.* There are two classes of lipid-based hormones: steroid hormones and eicosanoids (ī-KŌ-sa-noydz). **Steroid hormones** are lipids that are derived from (and, thus, are structurally similar to) cholesterol, a lipid introduced in Chapter 2. ⟳ p. 45 Steroid hormones are released by the reproductive organs and the suprarenal glands. Insoluble in water, steroid hormones are bound to specific transport proteins in blood. *Eicosanoids* are fatty acid-based compounds derived from the 20-carbon fatty acid *arachidonic* (a-rak-i-DON-ik) *acid.* Eicosanoids, which include the **prostaglandins,** coordinate local cellular activities and affect enzymatic processes in extracellular fluids, including blood clotting.

THE MECHANISMS OF HORMONAL ACTION

All cellular structures and functions are determined by proteins: Structural proteins determine the general shape and internal structure of a cell, and enzymes direct the cell's metabolism. Hormones alter cellular operations by changing the *identities, activities, locations,* or *quantities* of important enzymes and structural proteins in various **target cells.** What determines a target cell's sensitivity to a given hormone is the presence or absence of a specific target cell **receptor** for that hormone (Figure 10-2). The mechanisms of hormone action (Figure 10-3) depend on whether hormone receptors are located on the plasma membrane or inside the cell.

Hormonal Action at the Plasma Membrane

The receptors for epinephrine, norepinephrine, peptide hormones, and eicosanoids are in the plasma membranes of their respective target cells (Figure 10-3a). Because epinephrine, norepinephrine, and the peptide hormones are not lipid soluble, they cannot diffuse through a plasma membrane, and they bind to receptor proteins on the *outer* surface of the plasma membrane. Eicosanoids, which *are* lipid soluble, diffuse across the plasma membrane and bind to receptor proteins on the *inner* surface of the cell membrane.

Hormones that bind to plasma membrane receptors do not have direct effects on the target cell. Instead, when these hormones bind to an appropriate receptor, they are considered **first messengers** that then trigger the appearance of a **second messenger** in the cytoplasm. The link between the first messenger and the second messenger usually involves a **G protein,** an enzyme

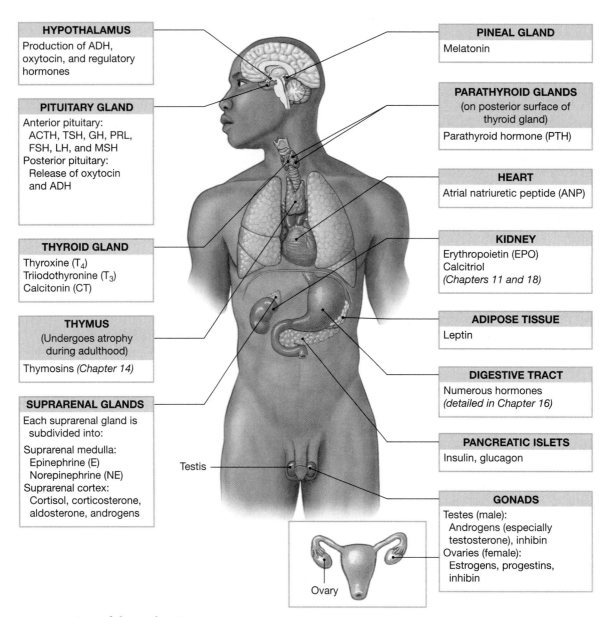

HYPOTHALAMUS
Production of ADH, oxytocin, and regulatory hormones

PITUITARY GLAND
Anterior pituitary:
  ACTH, TSH, GH, PRL, FSH, LH, and MSH
Posterior pituitary:
  Release of oxytocin and ADH

THYROID GLAND
Thyroxine (T_4)
Triiodothyronine (T_3)
Calcitonin (CT)

THYMUS
(Undergoes atrophy during adulthood)
Thymosins *(Chapter 14)*

SUPRARENAL GLANDS
Each suprarenal gland is subdivided into:
Suprarenal medulla:
  Epinephrine (E)
  Norepinephrine (NE)
Suprarenal cortex:
  Cortisol, corticosterone, aldosterone, androgens

Testis

PINEAL GLAND
Melatonin

PARATHYROID GLANDS
(on posterior surface of thyroid gland)
Parathyroid hormone (PTH)

HEART
Atrial natriuretic peptide (ANP)

KIDNEY
Erythropoietin (EPO)
Calcitriol
(Chapters 11 and 18)

ADIPOSE TISSUE
Leptin

DIGESTIVE TRACT
Numerous hormones
(detailed in Chapter 16)

PANCREATIC ISLETS
Insulin, glucagon

GONADS
Testes (male):
  Androgens (especially testosterone), inhibin
Ovaries (female):
  Estrogens, progestins, inhibin

Ovary

FIGURE 10-1 An Overview of the Endocrine System.

complex that is coupled to a membrane receptor. The G protein is activated when a hormone binds to the hormone's receptor at the membrane surface. The second messenger may function as an enzyme activator or inhibitor, but the net result is a change in the cell's metabolic activities.

One of the most important second messengers is **cyclic-AMP (cAMP)** (Figure 10-3a). Its appearance depends on an activated G protein, which activates an enzyme called **adenylate cyclase.** In turn, adenylate cyclase converts ATP to a ring-shaped molecule of cAMP. Cyclic-AMP activates *kinase* enzymes, which attach a high-energy phosphate group (PO_4^{3-}) to another molecule in a process called *phosphorylation.*

The effect on the target cell depends on the nature of the proteins affected. The phosphorylation of membrane proteins can open ion channels, and in the cytoplasm many enzymes can be activated only by phosphorylation. As a result, a single hormone can have one effect in one target tissue and quite different effects in other target tissues. The effects of cAMP are usually very short-lived, because another enzyme in the cell, *phosphodiesterase (PDE)*, inactivates cAMP by converting it to AMP (adenosine monophosphate). In a few instances, the activation of a G protein can *lower* the concentration of cAMP within the cell by stimulating PDE activity. The decline in cAMP has an inhibitory effect on the cell because without phosphorylation, key enzymes remain inactive.

Although cyclic-AMP is one of the most common second messengers, there are many others. Important examples are *calcium ions* and *cyclic-GMP*, a derivative of the high-energy compound *guanosine triphosphate (GTP)*.

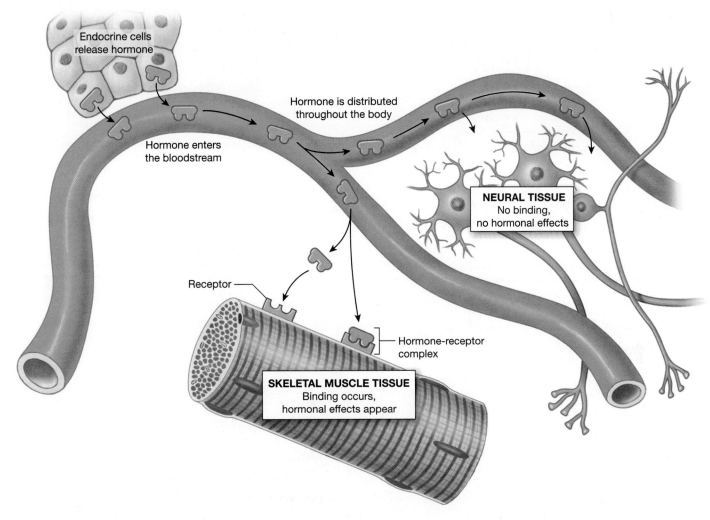

Endocrine cells
release hormone

Hormone is distributed
throughout the body

Hormone enters
the bloodstream

NEURAL TISSUE
No binding,
no hormonal effects

Receptor

Hormone-receptor
complex

SKELETAL MUSCLE TISSUE
Binding occurs,
hormonal effects appear

FIGURE 10-2 **The Role of Target Cell Receptors in Hormonal Action.** For a hormone to affect a target cell, that cell must have receptors that can bind the hormone and initiate a change in cellular activity. The hormone in this illustration affects skeletal muscle tissue but not neural tissue because only the muscle tissue has the appropriate receptors.

Hormone Interaction with Intracellular Receptors

Steroid hormones and thyroid hormones cross the plasma membrane before binding to receptors inside the cell (Figure 10-3b). Steroid hormones diffuse rapidly through the lipid portion of the plasma membrane and bind to receptors in the cytoplasm or nucleus. The resulting *hormone-receptor complex* then activates or inactivates specific genes in the nucleus. By this mechanism, steroid hormones can alter the rate of mRNA transcription, thereby changing the structure or function of the cell. The steroid hormone testosterone, for example, stimulates the production of enzymes and proteins in skeletal muscle fibers, increasing muscle size and strength.

Thyroid hormones cross the plasma membrane either by diffusion or by a transport mechanism. Once within the cell, thyroid hormones bind to receptors within the nucleus or on mitochondria. The hormone-receptor complexes in the nucleus activate specific genes or change the rate of mRNA transcription. The result is an increase in metabolic activity due to changes in the nature or number of enzymes in the cytoplasm. Thyroid hormones bound to mitochondria increase the mitochondrial rates of ATP production.

THE SECRETION AND DISTRIBUTION OF HORMONES

Hormone release occurs where capillaries are abundant, and the hormones quickly enter the bloodstream for distribution throughout the body. Within the blood, hormones may circulate freely or attach to special transport proteins. A freely circulating hormone remains functional for less than one hour, and sometimes for as little as two minutes. Free hormones are inactivated when (1) they diffuse out of the bloodstream and bind to receptors on target cells, (2) they are absorbed and broken down by certain

(a) Mechanisms of action for nonsteroidal hormones

(b) Mechanisms of action for steroid and thyroid hormones

FIGURE 10-3 **Mechanisms of Hormone Action.** (a) Nonsteroidal hormones, such as epinephrine (E), norepinephrine (NE), peptide hormones, and eicosanoids, bind to membrane receptors and activate G proteins. They exert their effects on target cells through a second messenger, such as cAMP, which alters the activity of enzymes present in the cell. (b) Both steroid hormones and thyroid hormones pass directly through target cell membranes. Steroid hormones bind to receptors in the cytoplasm or nucleus. Thyroid hormones either proceed directly to receptors in the nucleus or bind to receptors on mitochondria in the cytoplasm. In the nucleus, both steroid and thyroid hormone-receptor complexes directly affect gene activity and protein synthesis. Thyroid hormones also increase the rate of ATP production in the cell.

liver or kidney cells, or (3) they are broken down by enzymes in the plasma or interstitial fluids.

Steroid hormones and thyroid hormones remain in circulation much longer because almost all become attached to

The Big Picture

Hormones coordinate cell, tissue, and organ activities on a sustained basis. They circulate in the bloodstream and bind to specific receptors on or in target cells. They then modify cellular activities by altering membrane permeability, activating or inactivating key enzymes, or changing genetic activity.

special transport proteins. For each hormone an equilibrium occurs between the bound hormones and the small number remaining in a free state. As the free hormones are removed, they are replaced by the release of bound hormones.

THE CONTROL OF ENDOCRINE ACTIVITY

Endocrine activity—specifically, hormonal secretion—is controlled by negative feedback mechanisms. In this case, a stimulus triggers the production of a hormone whose direct or indirect effects reduce the intensity of the stimulus. ⟲ p. 13 In the simplest case, endocrine activity may be controlled by *humoral* ("liq-

HYPOTHALAMUS

1 Secretion of regulatory hormones to control activity of anterior pituitary gland

2 Production of ADH and oxytocin

3 Control of sympathetic output to suprarenal medullae

Preganglionic motor fibers

Suprarenal gland

Suprarenal medulla

Posterior pituitary gland

Anterior pituitary gland

Hormones secreted by anterior pituitary gland control other endocrine organs

Release of ADH and oxytocin

Secretion of epinephrine and norepinephrine

FIGURE 10-4 **Three Mechanisms of Hypothalamic Control over Endocrine Organs.**

uid") *stimuli*—changes in the composition of the extracellular fluid. Consider, for example, the control of blood calcium levels by two hormones, *parathyroid hormone* and *calcitonin.* When calcium levels in the blood decline, parathyroid hormone is released, and the responses of target cells elevate blood calcium levels. When calcium levels in the blood rise, calcitonin is released, and the responses of target cells lower blood calcium levels. Endocrine activity may also be controlled by *hormonal stimuli*—changes in the levels of circulating hormones. Such control may involve one or more intermediary steps and two or more hormones. Finally, endocrine control can also occur through *neural stimulation* resulting from the arrival of neurotransmitter at a neuroglandular junction. An important example of endocrine control involves the activity of the hypothalamus.

The hypothalamus provides the highest level of endocrine control by acting as an important link between the nervous and endocrine systems. Coordinating centers in the hypothalamus regulate the activities of the nervous and endocrine systems in three ways (**Figure 10-4**):

1. The hypothalamus secretes **regulatory hormones,** special hormones that control the activity of endocrine cells in the anterior pituitary gland. There are two classes of regulatory hormones: **Releasing hormones (RH)** stimulate the production of one or more hormones in the anterior pituitary, whereas **inhibiting hormones (IH)**

prevent the synthesis and secretion of pituitary hormones. The hormones released by the anterior pituitary gland control other endocrine glands.

2. The hypothalamus acts as an endocrine organ by synthesizing two hormones, ADH and oxytocin, which are then released into the circulation at the posterior pituitary gland.

3. The hypothalamus contains autonomic nervous system centers that control the endocrine cells of the suprarenal medullae (the interior of the suprarenal glands) through sympathetic innervation. ∞ p. 291 When the sympathetic division is activated, the suprarenal medullae release hormones into the bloodstream.

CHECKPOINT

2. Define hormone.

3. What is the primary factor that determines each cell's sensitivities to hormones?

4. How would the presence of a molecule that blocks adenylate cyclase affect the activity of a hormone that produces cellular effects through cAMP?

5. Why is cAMP described as a second messenger?

6. What are the three types of stimuli that control hormone secretion?

See the blue Answers tab at the back of the book.

10-3 The bilobed pituitary gland is an endocrine organ that releases nine peptide hormones

The **pituitary gland,** or **hypophysis** (hī-POF-i-sis), secretes nine different hormones. All are peptides or small proteins that bind to membrane receptors, and all use cAMP as a second messenger. The pituitary gland is a small, oval gland nestled within the *sella turcica,* a depression in the sphenoid bone of the skull (**Figure 10-5**). It hangs beneath the hypothalamus, connected by a slender stalk, the **infundibulum** (in-fun-DIB-ū-lum; funnel). The pituitary gland has a complex structure, including distinct anterior and posterior regions.

THE ANTERIOR PITUITARY GLAND

The **anterior pituitary gland** contains endocrine cells surrounded by an extensive capillary network. This capillary network, which provides entry into the circulatory system for the hormones secreted by endocrine cells of the anterior pituitary, is part of the *hypophyseal portal system.*

The Hypophyseal Portal System

As previously noted, regulatory hormones produced by the hypothalamus control the activities of the anterior pituitary.

These hormones, released by hypothalamic neurons near the attachment of the infundibulum, enter a network of highly permeable capillaries. Before leaving the hypothalamus, this capillary network unites to form a series of slightly larger vessels that descend to the anterior pituitary before forming a second capillary network (**Figure 10-6**).

The circulatory arrangement illustrated in Figure 10-6, in which blood flows from one capillary bed to another, is very unusual. Typically, blood flows from the heart through increasingly smaller arteries to a capillary network and then returns to the heart through increasingly larger veins. Blood vessels that link two capillary networks—including the vessels between the hypothalamus and the anterior pituitary—are called *portal vessels;* in this case, they have the structure of veins. The entire complex is termed a **portal system.**

Portal systems ensure that all of the blood entering the portal vessels reaches certain target cells before returning to the general circulation. Portal systems are named after their destinations, so this particular network is called the **hypophyseal** (hī-po-FI-sē-al) **portal system.**

Hypothalamic Control of the Anterior Pituitary

An endocrine cell in the anterior pituitary may be controlled by releasing hormones (RH), inhibiting hormones (IH), or some combination of the two. The regulatory hormones released at the hypothalamus are transported directly to the anterior pituitary by the hypophyseal portal system.

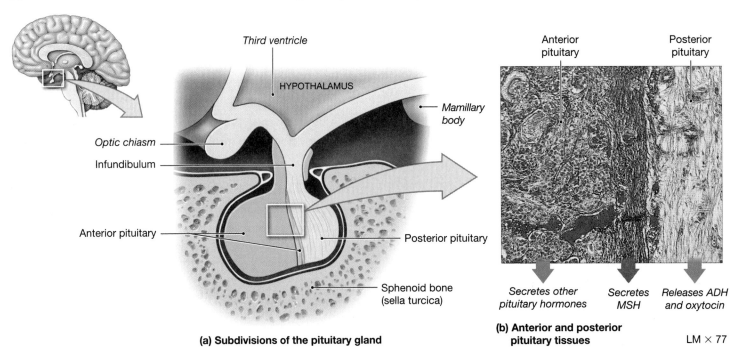

(a) Subdivisions of the pituitary gland

(b) Anterior and posterior pituitary tissues

LM × 77

FIGURE 10-5 **The Location and Anatomy of the Pituitary Gland.**

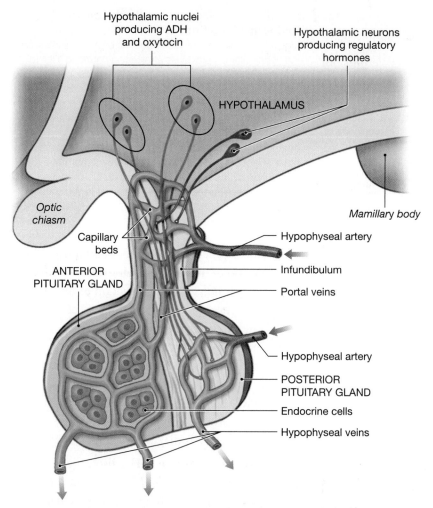

Hypothalamic nuclei producing ADH and oxytocin

Hypothalamic neurons producing regulatory hormones

HYPOTHALAMUS

Optic chiasm

Mamillary body

Capillary beds

Hypophyseal artery

ANTERIOR PITUITARY GLAND

Infundibulum

Portal veins

Hypophyseal artery

POSTERIOR PITUITARY GLAND

Endocrine cells

Hypophyseal veins

FIGURE 10-6 **The Hypophyseal Portal System and the Blood Supply to the Pituitary Gland.**

The rate of regulatory hormone secretion by the hypothalamus is regulated through negative feedback mechanisms. The basic regulatory patterns are diagrammed in Figure 10-7; these will be referenced in the following description of pituitary hormones. Many of these regulatory hormones are called *tropic hormones* (*tropos,* a turning) because they "turn on" other endocrine glands or support the functions of other organs.

Hormones of the Anterior Pituitary

The anterior pituitary gland produces seven hormones. The first four described in the following list regulate the production of hormones by other endocrine glands.

1. **Thyroid-stimulating hormone (TSH),** or *thyrotropin,* targets the thyroid gland and triggers the release of thyroid hormones. TSH is released in response to *thyrotropin-releasing hormone* (*TRH*) from the hypothalamus. As circulating concentrations of thyroid hormones

rise, the rates of TRH and TSH production decline (Figure 10-7a).

2. **Adrenocorticotropic hormone (ACTH)** stimulates the release of steroid hormones by the *suprarenal cortex,* the outer portion of the suprarenal glands. ACTH specifically targets cells producing hormones called *glucocorticoids* (gloo-kō-KOR-ti-koydz), which affect glucose metabolism. ACTH release occurs under the stimulation of *corticotropin-releasing hormone* (*CRH*) from the hypothalamus. A rise in glucocorticoid levels causes a decline in the production of ACTH and CRH. This type of negative feedback control is comparable to that for TSH (Figure 10-7a).

A group of hormones called **gonadotropins** (gō-nad-ō-TRŌ-pinz) regulates the activities of the male and female sex organs, or *gonads.* The production of gonadotropins is stimulated by *gonadotropin-releasing hormone* (*GnRH*) from the hypothalamus. An abnormally low production of gonadotropins produces *hypogonadism.* Children with this condition will not undergo sexual maturation, and adults with hypogonadism cannot produce functional sperm or ova. The anterior pituitary produces two gonadotropins: follicle-stimulating hormone (FSH) and luteinizing hormone (LH).

3. **Follicle-stimulating hormone (FSH)** promotes follicle (and egg) development in females, and it stimulates the secretion of estrogens—steroid hormones produced by ovarian cells. In males, FSH production supports sperm production in the testes. A peptide hormone called *inhibin,* released by the cells of the testes and ovaries, inhibits the release of FSH and GnRH through a negative feedback control mechanism comparable to that for TSH (Figure 10-7a).

4. **Luteinizing** (LOO-tē-in-ī-zing) **hormone (LH)** induces *ovulation,* the production of reproductive cells in females. It also promotes the secretion by the ovaries of estrogens and **progestins** (such as *progesterone*), which prepare the body for possible pregnancy. In males, LH is sometimes called *interstitial cell-stimulating hormone* (*ICSH*) because it stimulates the interstitial cells of the testes to produce sex hormones. These sex hormones are called **androgens** (AN-drō-jenz; *andros,* man); the most important is *testosterone.* GnRH production is inhibited

Releasing Hormone (RH)	Hormone 1 (from pituitary)	Endocrine target organ	Hormone 2 (from target organ)
TRH	TSH	Thyroid gland	Thyroid hormones
CRH	ACTH	Suprarenal cortex	Gluco-corticoids
GnRH	FSH	Testes	Inhibin
		Ovaries	Inhibin Estrogens
	LH	Ovaries	Progestins Estrogens
		Testes	Androgens

(a) General pattern

KEY

→ Stimulation

—‖ Inhibition

(b) Pattern variations

FIGURE 10-7 **Negative Feedback Control of Endocrine Secretion.** **(a)** In the typical pattern of regulation (in which multiple endocrine organs are involved), the hypothalamus produces a releasing hormone (RH) to stimulate hormone production by other glands; control occurs via negative feedback. **(b)** Shown here are two variations on the theme outlined in part (a). For the regulation of prolactin (PRL) production by the anterior pituitary (at left), the hypothalamus produces both a releasing factor (PRF) and an inhibiting hormone (PIH); when one is stimulated, the other is inhibited. In the regulation of growth hormone (GH) production by the anterior pituitary (at right), whenever GH–RH release is inhibited, GH–IH release is stimulated.

development. In pregnancy and during the period of nursing following delivery, PRL also stimulates the production of milk by the mammary glands. Prolactin's effects in human males are poorly understood, but it may help regulate androgen production. The regulation of prolactin release involves inter-actions between prolactin-releasing factor (PRF) and prolactin-inhibiting hormone (PIH) from the hypothalamus. The regula-tory pattern is diagrammed in Figure 10-7b.

6. **Growth hormone (GH),** also called *human growth hormone* (*hGH*) or *somatotropin* (*soma,* body), stimulates cell growth and replication by accelerating the rate of pro-tein synthesis. Although virtually every tis-sue responds to some degree, skeletal muscle cells and chondrocytes (cartilage cells) are particularly sensitive to growth hormone.

The stimulation of growth by GH in-volves two mechanisms. The indirect, pri-mary mechanism is best understood. Liver cells respond to the presence of growth hor-mone by synthesizing and releasing **somatomedins,** or *insulin-like growth fac-tors* (*IGFs*), which are peptide hormones that bind to receptor sites on a variety of cell membranes. Somatomedins increase the rates at which amino acids are taken up and incorporated into new proteins. These ef-fects develop almost immediately after GH release occurs, and they are particularly im-portant after a meal, when blood glucose and amino acid concentrations are high.

by estrogens, progestins, and androgens through a nega-tive feedback control mechanism comparable to that of TSH (Figure 10-7a).

5. **Prolactin** (prō-LAK-tin; *pro-,* before + *lac,* milk), or **PRL,** works with other hormones to stimulate mammary gland

The direct actions of GH usually do not appear until after blood glucose and amino acid concentrations have returned to normal levels. In epithelia and connective tissues, GH stimulates stem cell divisions and the differentiation of daughter cells. GH also has metabolic effects in adipose tissue and in the liver. In adipose tissue, it stimulates the breakdown of stored fats and the release of fatty acids into the blood. In turn, many tissues stop breaking down glucose and start breaking down fatty acids to generate ATP. This process is termed a *glucose-sparing effect*. In the liver, GH stimulates the breakdown of glycogen reserves and the release of glucose into the circulation. Thus, GH plays a role in mobilizing energy reserves.

The production of GH is regulated by *growth hormone–releasing hormone (GH–RH)* and *growth hormone–inhibiting hormone (GH–IH)* from the hypothalamus. Somatomedins stimulate GH–IH and inhibit GH–RH. This regulatory mechanism is summarized in Figure 10-7b.

7. **Melanocyte-stimulating hormone (MSH)** stimulates the melanocytes in the skin to increase their production of melanin. MSH is important in the control of skin and hair pigmentation in fishes, amphibians, reptiles, and many mammals other than primates. The MSH-producing cells of the pituitary gland in adult humans are virtually nonfunctional, and the circulating blood usually does not contain MSH. However, the human pituitary secretes MSH (1) during fetal development, (2) in very young children, (3) in pregnant women, and (4) in some diseases. The functions of MSH under these circumstances are not known. The administration of a synthetic form of MSH causes darkening of the skin, so MSH has been suggested as a means of obtaining a "sunless tan."

THE POSTERIOR PITUITARY GLAND

The **posterior pituitary gland** contains axons from two different groups of neurons located within the hypothalamus. One group manufactures antidiuretic hormone (ADH) and the other oxytocin. These products are transported within axons along the infundibulum to the posterior pituitary, as indicated in Figure 10-6.

Antidiuretic hormone (ADH) is released when the body is low on water. Stimuli for its release include a rise in the concentration of electrolytes in the blood (an increased osmotic pressure) or a fall in blood volume or pressure. The primary function of ADH is to decrease the amount of water lost in the urine. With losses minimized, any water absorbed from the digestive tract will be retained, reducing the concentration of electrolytes. ADH also causes *vasoconstriction,* a constriction of peripheral blood vessels that helps increase blood pressure. ADH release is inhibited by alcohol, which explains the increased fluid excretion that follows the consumption of alcoholic beverages.

In women, **oxytocin** (*okytokos,* swift birth), or **OXT,** stimulates smooth muscle contractions in the wall of the uterus during labor and delivery and in special contractile cells associated with the mammary glands. Until the final stages of pregnancy, the uterine muscles are insensitive to oxytocin, but they become more sensitive as the time of delivery approaches. The stimulation of uterine muscles by oxytocin helps maintain and complete normal labor and childbirth (discussed in Chapter 20). After delivery, oxytocin also stimulates the contraction of special cells surrounding the secretory cells and ducts of the mammary glands. In the "milk let-down" reflex, oxytocin secreted in response to suckling triggers the release of milk from the breasts.

Although oxytocin's functions in sexual activity remain uncertain, circulating oxytocin levels are known to rise during sexual arousal and peak at orgasm in both sexes. In men, oxytocin stimulates smooth muscle contraction in the walls of the sperm duct and prostate gland. These actions may be important in *emission,* the ejection of prostatic secretions, sperm, and the secretions of other glands into the male reproductive tract before ejaculation. In women, oxytocin released during intercourse

Clinical Note

Diabetes Insipidus

Diabetes (*diabetes,* to pass through) occurs in several forms, all characterized by excessive urine production (*polyuria*). Although diabetes can be caused by physical damage to the kidneys, most forms are the result of endocrine abnormalities. The two most important forms are diabetes mellitus and diabetes insipidus. Diabetes mellitus is described on p. 366.

Diabetes insipidus (*insipidus,* tasteless) develops when the posterior pituitary no longer releases adequate amounts of ADH or the kidneys fail to respond to ADH. Water conservation at the kidneys is impaired, and excessive amounts of water are lost in the urine. As a result, the individual is constantly thirsty—a condition known as *polydipsia* (*dipsa,* thirst)—but the body does not retain the fluids consumed. Mild cases may not require treatment, so long as fluid and electrolyte intake keeps pace with urinary losses. In severe cases, fluid losses can reach 10 liters per day, and a fatal dehydration will occur unless treatment is provided.

KEY TO PITUITARY HORMONES:

ACTH	Adrenocorticotropic hormone
TSH	Thyroid-stimulating hormone
GH	Growth hormone
PRL	Prolactin
FSH	Follicle-stimulating hormone
LH	Luteinizing hormone
MSH	Melanocyte-stimulating hormone
ADH	Antidiuretic hormone
OXT	Oxytocin

FIGURE 10-8 Pituitary Hormones and Their Targets.

may stimulate smooth muscle contractions in the uterus and vagina that promote the transport of sperm toward the uterine tubes.

Figure 10-8 and Table 10-1 (p. 357) summarize important information concerning the hormones produced by the pituitary gland.

The Big Picture

The hypothalamus produces regulatory factors that adjust the activities of the anterior pituitary gland, which produces seven hormones. Most of these hormones control other endocrine organs, including the thyroid gland, suprarenal gland, and gonads. It also produces growth hormone, which stimulates cell growth and protein synthesis. The posterior pituitary gland releases two hormones produced in the hypothalamus: ADH restricts water loss and promotes thirst, and oxytocin stimulates smooth muscle contractions in the mammary glands and uterus (in females) and in the prostate gland (in males).

CHECKPOINT

7. If a person were dehydrated, how would the amount of ADH released by the posterior pituitary change?

8. A blood sample contains elevated levels of somatomedins. Which pituitary hormone would you also expect to be elevated?

9. What effect would elevated circulating levels of cortisol, a hormone from the suprarenal cortex, have on the pituitary secretion of ACTH?

See the blue Answers tab at the back of the book.

TABLE 10-1 **The Pituitary Hormones**

REGION	HORMONE	TARGET	HORMONAL EFFECTS
Anterior pituitary	Thyroid-stimulating hormone (TSH)	Thyroid gland	Secretion of thyroid hormones
	Adrenocorticotropic hormone (ACTH)	Suprarenal cortex	Glucocorticoid secretion (cortisol, corticosterone)
	Gonadotropins:		
	Follicle-stimulating hormone (FSH)	Follicle cells of ovaries	Estrogen secretion, follicle development
		Nurse cells of testes	Sperm maturation
	Luteinizing hormone (LH)	Follicle cells of ovaries	Ovulation, formation of corpus luteum, and progesterone secretion
		Interstitial cells of testes	Testosterone secretion
	Prolactin (PRL)	Mammary glands	Production of milk
	Growth hormone (GH)	All cells	Growth, protein synthesis, lipid mobilization and catabolism
	Melanocyte-stimulating hormone (MSH)	Melanocytes of skin	Increased melanin synthesis in epidermis
Posterior pituitary	Antidiuretic hormone (ADH)	Kidneys	Reabsorption of water, elevation of blood volume and pressure
	Oxytocin	Uterus, mammary glands (females)	Labor contractions, milk ejection
		Sperm duct and prostate gland (males)	Contractions of sperm duct and prostate gland

10-4 The thyroid gland lies inferior to the larynx and requires iodine for hormone synthesis

The **thyroid gland** lies anterior to the trachea and just inferior to the **thyroid** ("shield-shaped") **cartilage,** which forms most of the anterior surface of the larynx (Figure 10-9a). The two lobes of the thyroid gland are united by a slender connection, the *isthmus* (IS-mus). An extensive blood supply gives the thyroid gland a deep red color.

THYROID FOLLICLES AND THYROID HORMONES

The thyroid gland contains numerous **thyroid follicles,** spheres lined by a simple cuboidal epithelium (Figure 10-9b). The cavity within each follicle contains a viscous *colloid,* a fluid containing large amounts of suspended proteins and thyroid hormones. A network of capillaries surrounds each follicle, delivering nutrients and regulatory hormones to the glandular cells and picking up their secretory products and metabolic wastes.

Thyroid hormones are manufactured by the follicular epithelial cells and stored within the follicle cavities. Under TSH stimulation from the anterior pituitary, the epithelial cells remove hormones from the follicle cavities and release them into the circulation. However, almost all of the released thyroid hormones are unavailable because they become attached to plasma proteins in the bloodstream. Only the remaining unbound thyroid hormones, a small percentage of the total released, are free to diffuse into target cells in body tissues. As the concentration of unbound hormone molecules decreases, the plasma proteins release additional bound hormone. The bound thyroid hormones are a substantial reserve; in fact, the bloodstream normally contains more than a week's supply of thyroid hormones.

The thyroid hormones are derived from molecules of the amino acid tyrosine to which iodine atoms have been attached. The hormone **thyroxine** (thī-ROKS-ēn) contains four atoms of iodine; it is also known as *tetraiodothyronine* (tet-ra-ī-ō-dō-THĪ-rō-nēn), or T_4. Thyroxine accounts for roughly 90 percent of all thyroid secretions. **Triiodothyronine,** or T_3, is a related, more potent molecule containing three iodine atoms.

Thyroid hormones readily cross plasma membranes, and they affect almost every cell in the body. Inside a cell, they bind to receptor sites on mitochondria and in the nucleus (Figure 10-3b). The binding of thyroid hormones to mitochondria increases the rate of ATP production. Thyroid hormone-receptor complexes in the nucleus activate genes coding for the synthesis of enzymes involved in glycolysis and energy production, resulting in increased rates of metabolism and oxygen

Thyroid follicle

Cuboidal epithelium of follicle

C cell

Thyroid hormones stored in colloid of follicle

(b) Thyroid follicles   LM × 260

Hyoid bone

Thyroid artery

Internal jugular vein

Thyroid cartilage

Thyroid vein

Right lobe of thyroid gland

Left lobe of thyroid gland

Isthmus of thyroid gland

Common carotid artery

Thyroid veins

Trachea

Outline of sternum

(a) Location of thyroid gland, anterior view

FIGURE 10-9 **The Thyroid Gland. (a)** This drawing shows the location and gross anatomy of the thyroid gland. **(b)** This micrograph reveals histological details, including the thyroid follicles.

consumption in the cell. Because the cell consumes more energy, and energy use is measured in *calories,* the effect is called the **calorigenic effect** of thyroid hormones. When the metabolic rate increases, more heat is generated and body temperature rises. In growing children, thyroid hormones are essential to normal development of the skeletal, muscular, and nervous systems.

Normal production of thyroid hormones establishes the background rates of cellular metabolism. These hormones exert their primary effects on active tissues and organs, including skeletal muscles, the liver, the heart, and the kidneys. Overproduction or underproduction of thyroid hormones can, therefore, cause very serious metabolic problems. In many parts of the world, inadequate dietary iodine intake leads to an inability to synthesize thyroid hormones. Under these conditions, TSH stimulation continues, and the thyroid follicles become distended with nonfunctional secretions. The result is an enlarged thyroid gland, or *goiter.* Goiters vary in size, and

a large goiter can interfere with breathing and swallowing. This is seldom a problem in the United States because the typical American diet provides roughly three times the minimum daily requirement of iodine, thanks to the addition of iodine to table salt ("iodized salt").

THE C CELLS OF THE THYROID GLAND: CALCITONIN

C cells, or *parafollicular cells,* are endocrine cells sandwiched between the follicle cells and their basement membrane (see Figure 10-9b). C cells produce the hormone **calcitonin (CT).** Calcitonin helps regulate calcium ion concentrations in body fluids. The control of calcitonin secretion is independent of the hypothalamus or pituitary gland. As Figure 10-10 illustrates, C cells release calcitonin when the calcium ion (Ca^{2+}) concentration of the blood rises above normal. The target organs are the bones and the kidneys. Calcitonin inhibits osteoclasts

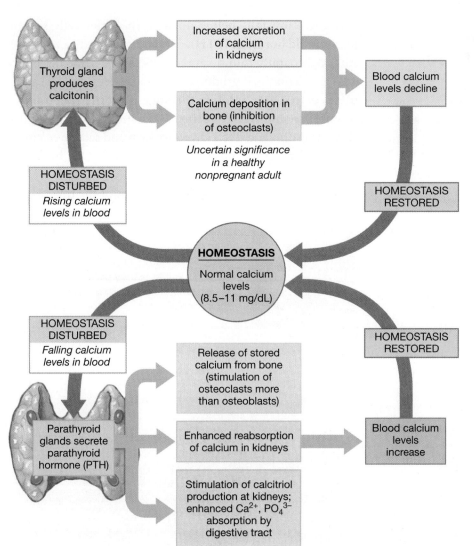

FIGURE 10-10 The Homeostatic Regulation of Calcium Ion Concentrations.

(which slows the release of calcium from bone) and stimulates calcium excretion at the kidneys. The resulting reduction in blood calcium levels eliminates the stimulus and "turns off" the C cells.

Calcitonin is most important during childhood, when it stimulates active bone growth and calcium deposition in the skeleton. It also acts to reduce the loss of bone mass during prolonged starvation and during late pregnancy, when the maternal skeleton competes with the developing fetus for absorbed calcium ions. The role of calcitonin in healthy nonpregnant adults is unclear.

We have seen the importance of calcium ions in controlling muscle cell and nerve cell activities. ∞ pp. 200, 260 Calcium ion concentrations also affect the sodium permeabilities of excitable membranes. At high calcium levels, sodium permeability decreases, and membranes become less responsive. Such problems are relatively rare, because under normal conditions, calcium levels seldom rise enough to trigger calcitonin secretion.

Most homeostatic adjustments prevent lower-than-normal calcium ion concentrations. Low calcium concentrations are dangerous because sodium permeabilities then increase, and muscle cells and neurons become extremely excitable. If calcium levels fall too far, convulsions or muscular spasms can result. Such disastrous events are prevented by the actions of the parathyroid glands.

CHECKPOINT

10. Identify the hormones of the thyroid gland.

11. What signs and symptoms would you expect to see in an individual whose diet lacks iodine?

12. When a person's thyroid gland is removed, signs of decreased thyroid hormone concentration do not appear until about one week later. Why?

See the blue Answers tab at the back of the book.

10-5 The four parathyroid glands, embedded in the posterior surface of the thyroid gland, secrete parathyroid hormone to elevate blood calcium levels

Two tiny pairs of **parathyroid glands** are embedded in the posterior surfaces of the thyroid gland (Figure 10-11a). The cells of the two adjacent glands are separated by connective tissue fibers surrounding each parathyroid gland (Figure 10-11b). At least two cell populations are found in the parathyroid gland. **Chief cells** produce parathyroid hormone; the functions of the other cell type are unknown.

Like the C cells of the thyroid, the chief cells monitor the concentration of circulating calcium ions. When the Ca^{2+} concentration falls below normal, the chief cells secrete **parathyroid hormone (PTH),** or *parathormone* (Figure 10-10). Although parathyroid hormone acts on the same target organs as calcitonin, it produces the opposite effects. PTH stimulates osteoclasts, inhibits the bone-building functions of osteoblasts, and reduces urinary excretion of calcium ions. PTH also stimulates the kidneys to form and secrete *calcitriol,* which promotes the absorption of Ca^{2+} and PO_4^{3-} by the digestive tract.

Information concerning the hormones of the thyroid and parathyroid glands is summarized in Table 10-2.

The Big Picture

The thyroid gland produces (1) hormones that adjust tissue metabolic rates and (2) a hormone that usually plays a minor role in calcium ion homeostasis by opposing the action of parathyroid hormone.

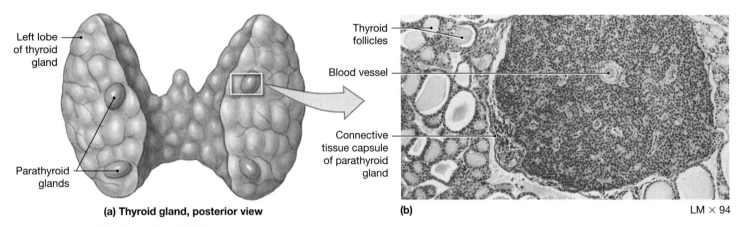

Left lobe of thyroid gland

Parathyroid glands

(a) Thyroid gland, posterior view

Thyroid follicles

Blood vessel

Connective tissue capsule of parathyroid gland

(b)

LM × 94

FIGURE 10-11 The Parathyroid Glands. (a) The parathyroid glands lie embedded in the posterior surface of the thyroid lobes. **(b)** This photomicrograph shows the histologic features of parathyroid and thyroid tissues.

TABLE 10-2 Hormones of the Thyroid Gland and Parathyroid Glands

GLAND/CELLS	HORMONE(S)	TARGETS	HORMONAL EFFECTS
THYROID			
Follicular epithelium	Thyroxine (T_4), triiodothyronine (T_3)	Most cells	Increased energy utilization, oxygen consumption, growth, and development
C cells	Calcitonin (CT)	Bone, kidneys	Decreased calcium concentrations in body fluids (see Figure 10-10)
PARATHYROIDS			
Chief cells	Parathyroid hormone (PTH)	Bone, kidneys	Increased calcium concentrations in body fluids (see Figure 10-10)

13. Identify the hormone secreted by the parathyroid glands.

14. Removal of the parathyroid glands would result in decreased blood concentrations of what important mineral?

See the blue Answers tab at the back of the book.

10-6 The suprarenal glands, consisting of a cortex and a medulla, cap each kidney and secrete several hormones

A yellow, pyramid-shaped **suprarenal** (soo-pra-RĒ-nal; *supra-*, above + *renes*, kidneys) **gland,** or *adrenal gland*, or sits on the superior border of each kidney (Figure 10-12a). Each suprarenal gland has two parts: an outer *suprarenal cortex* and an inner *suprarenal medulla* (Figure 10-12b).

THE SUPRARENAL CORTEX

The yellowish color of the **suprarenal cortex** is due to the presence of stored lipids, especially cholesterol and various fatty acids. The suprarenal cortex produces more than two dozen steroid hormones, collectively called *adrenocortical steroids,* or simply **corticosteroids.** In the bloodstream, these hormones are bound to transport proteins. These hormones are vital; if the suprarenal glands are destroyed or removed, the individual will die unless corticosteroids are administered. Overproduction or underproduction of any of the corticosteroids will have severe consequences because these hormones affect metabolism in many different tissues.

Each of the three distinct regions or zones of the suprarenal cortex synthesizes specific corticosteroids: the outer zone produces *mineralocorticoids,* the middle zone produces *glucocorticoids,* and the inner zone produces *androgens* (Figure 10-12c).

Mineralocorticoids (MCs)

The **mineralocorticoids** affect the electrolyte composition of body fluids. **Aldosterone** (al-DOS-ter-ōn), the principal MC, stimulates the conservation of sodium ions and the elimination of potassium ions by targeting cells that regulate the ionic composition of excreted fluids.

Specifically, aldosterone causes the retention of sodium by preventing the loss of sodium ions in urine, sweat, saliva, and digestive secretions. The retention of sodium ions is accompanied by a loss of potassium ions. Secondarily, the reabsorption of sodium ions results in the osmotic reabsorption of water at the kidneys, sweat glands, salivary glands, and pancreas. Aldosterone also increases the sensitivity of salt receptors in the tongue, resulting in greater interest in consuming salty foods.

Aldosterone secretion occurs in response to a drop in blood sodium content, blood volume, or blood pressure, or to a rise in blood potassium levels. Aldosterone release also occurs in response to the hormone *angiotensin II* (*angeion*, vessel + *teinein*, to stretch). This hormone will be discussed later in the chapter.

Glucocorticoids (GCs)

The steroid hormones collectively known as **glucocorticoids** affect glucose metabolism. The three most important glucocorticoids are **cortisol** (KOR-ti-sol; also called *hydrocortisone*), **corticosterone** (kor-ti-KOS-te-rōn), and **cortisone.**

Glucocorticoid secretion occurs under ACTH stimulation and is regulated by negative feedback (Figure 10-7a). These hormones accelerate the rates of glucose synthesis and glycogen formation, especially within the liver. Simultaneously, adipose tissue responds by releasing fatty acids into the blood, and other tissues begin to break down fatty acids instead of glucose. This *glucose-sparing effect* results in an increase in blood glucose levels. Glucocorticoids also have *anti-inflammatory* effects; they suppress the activities of white blood cells and other components of the immune system. "Steroid creams" are often used to control irritating allergic rashes, such as those produced by poison ivy, and injections of glucocorticoids may be used to control more severe allergic reactions. Because they slow wound healing and suppress immune defenses against infectious organisms, topical steroids are used to treat superficial rashes but are never applied to open wounds.

Androgens

The suprarenal cortex in both sexes produces small quantities of **androgens,** the sex hormones produced in large quantities by the testes in males. Once in the bloodstream, some of the androgens are converted to estrogens, the dominant sex hormone in females. When secreted in normal amounts, neither androgens nor estrogens affect sexual characteristics, so the importance of the small suprarenal production of androgens in both sexes remains unclear.

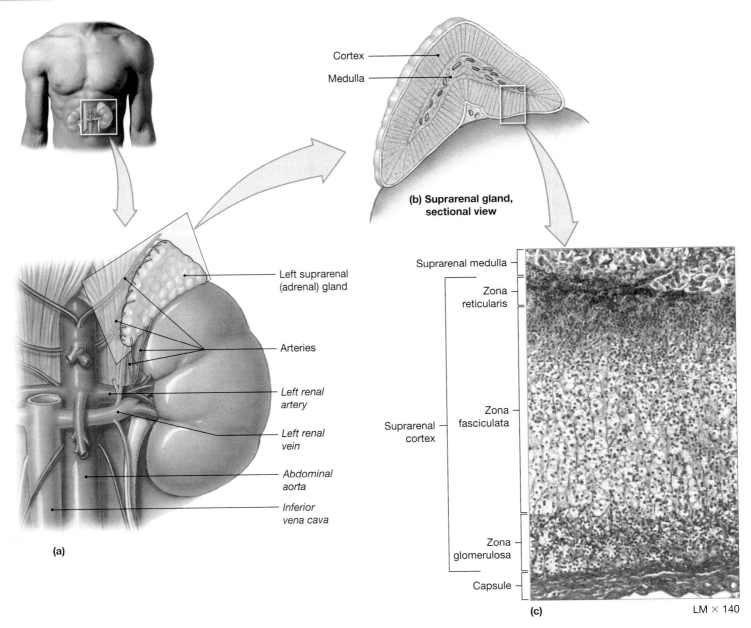

FIGURE 10-12 The Suprarenal Gland. (a) This superficial view depicts the location of the suprarenal gland atop the left kidney. **(b)** The cortex and medulla are visible in this section of a suprarenal gland. **(c)** The labels indicate the sources of the major suprarenal cortex hormones.

THE SUPRARENAL MEDULLA

The **suprarenal medulla** is a pale gray or pink, due in part to the many blood vessels within it. It contains large, rounded cells similar to those found in other sympathetic ganglia, and these cells are innervated by preganglionic sympathetic fibers. The secretory activities of the suprarenal medullae are controlled by the sympathetic division of the ANS. ⊂⊃ p. 291

The suprarenal medulla contains two populations of secretory cells, one producing **epinephrine** (**E,** or *adrenaline*) and the other **norepinephrine** (**NE,** or *noradrenaline*). These hormones are continuously released at a low rate, but sympathetic stimulation accelerates the rate of discharge dramatically.

Epinephrine makes up 75–80 percent of the secretions from the medulla; the rest is norepinephrine. Receptors for epinephrine and norepinephrine are found on skeletal muscle fibers, adipocytes, liver cells, and cardiac muscle fibers. In skeletal muscles, suprarenal medulla secretions trigger a mobilization of glycogen reserves and accelerate the breakdown of glucose to provide ATP; this combination results in

TABLE 10-3 The Suprarenal Hormones

REGION	HORMONE	TARGET	EFFECTS
Suprarenal cortex	Mineralocorticoids, primarily aldosterone	Kidneys	Increases reabsorption of sodium ions and water by the kidneys; accelerates urinary loss of potassium ions
	Glucocorticoids: cortisol (hydrocortisone), corticosterone, cortisone	Most cells	Release of amino acids from skeletal muscles and lipids from adipose tissues; promotes liver formation of glycogen and glucose; promotes peripheral use of lipids; anti-inflammatory effects
	Androgens		Uncertain significance under normal conditions
Suprarenal medulla	Epinephrine (E, adrenaline), norepinephrine (NE, noradrenaline)	Most cells	Increases cardiac activity, blood pressure, glycogen breakdown, and blood glucose levels; release of lipids by adipose tissue (see Table 8-5, p. 295)

increased muscular power and endurance. In adipose tissue, stored fats are broken down to fatty acids, and in the liver, glycogen molecules are converted to glucose. The fatty acids and glucose are then released into the circulation for use by peripheral tissues. The heart responds to suprarenal medulla hormones with an increase in the rate and force of cardiac contractions.

The metabolic changes that follow epinephrine and norepinephrine release peak 30 seconds after suprarenal stimulation and linger for several minutes thereafter. Thus, the effects produced by stimulation of the suprarenal medullae outlast the other results of sympathetic activation.

The characteristics of the suprarenal hormones are summarized in Table 10-3.

The Big Picture

The suprarenal glands produce hormones that adjust metabolic activities at specific sites, affecting the pattern of nutrient use, the balance of mineral ion levels, or the rate of energy consumption by active tissues.

CHECKPOINT

15. Identify the two regions of the suprarenal gland, and list the hormones secreted by each.

16. What effect would elevated cortisol levels have on blood glucose levels?

See the blue Answers tab at the back of the book.

10-7 The pineal gland, attached to the third ventricle, secretes melatonin

The **pineal gland** lies in the posterior portion of the roof of the third ventricle. ∞ p. 276 It contains neurons, glial cells, and secretory cells that synthesize the hormone **melatonin** (mel-a-TŌ-nin). Branches of the axons of neurons making up the visual pathways enter the pineal gland and affect the rate of melatonin production, which is lowest during daylight hours and highest at night.

Several functions have been suggested for melatonin in humans:

- *Inhibition of reproductive function.* In some mammals, melatonin slows the maturation of sperm, ova, and reproductive organs. The significance of this effect remains unclear, but circumstantial evidence suggests that melatonin may play a role in the timing of human sexual maturation. Melatonin levels in the blood decline at puberty, and pineal tumors that eliminate melatonin production cause premature puberty in young children.

- *Antioxidant activity.* Melatonin is a very effective antioxidant that may protect CNS neurons from *free radicals,* such as nitric oxide (NO) or hydrogen peroxide (H_2O_2), that may be generated in active neural tissue. (Free radicals are highly reactive atoms or molecules that contain unpaired electrons in their outer electron shell.) ∞ p. 261

- *Establishment of day–night cycles of activity.* Because of the cyclical nature of its rate of secretion, the pineal gland may also be involved in maintaining basic *circadian rhythms*—daily changes in physiological processes that follow a regular day–night pattern. Increased melatonin secretion in darkness has been suggested as a primary cause of *seasonal affective disorder* (*SAD*). This condition, characterized by changes in mood, eating habits, and sleeping patterns, can develop during the winter in high latitudes, where sunshine is scarce or lacking.

CHECKPOINT

17. Increased amounts of light would inhibit the production of which hormone by which structure?

18. List three functions of melatonin.

See the blue Answers tab at the back of the book.

10-8 The endocrine pancreas produces insulin and glucagon, hormones that regulate blood glucose levels

The **pancreas** lies in the J-shaped loop between the stomach and proximal portion of the small intestine (Figure 10-13). It is a slender, pale organ with a nodular (lumpy) consistency (Figure 10-13a) that contains both exocrine and endocrine cells. The pancreas is primarily a digestive organ whose exocrine cells make digestive enzymes. The **exocrine pancreas** is discussed further in Chapter 16.

Cells of the **endocrine pancreas** form clusters known as **pancreatic islets,** or the *islets of Langerhans* (LAN-ger-hanz). The islets are scattered among the exocrine cells (Figure 10-13b) and account for only about 1 percent of all pancreatic cells. Each islet contains several cell types. The two most important are **alpha cells,** which produce the hormone **glucagon** (GLOO-ka-gon), and **beta cells,** which secrete **insulin** (IN-suh-lin). Glucagon and insulin regulate blood glucose concentrations in much the same way parathyroid hormone and calcitonin control blood calcium levels.

Figure 10-14 diagrams the mechanism of hormonal regulation of blood glucose levels. Glucose is the preferred energy source for most cells in the body, and under normal conditions it is the only energy source for neurons. When blood glucose concentrations rise above normal homeostatic levels, beta cells release insulin, which then stimulates glucose transport and utilization in its target cells. The plasma membranes of almost all cells in the body contain insulin receptors; the only exceptions are (1) neurons and red blood cells, which cannot metabolize nutrients other than glucose; (2) epithelial cells of the kidney tubules, where glucose is reabsorbed; and (3) epithelial cells of the intestinal lining, where glucose is obtained from the diet. When glucose is abundant, all cells use it as an energy source and stop breaking down amino acids and lipids.

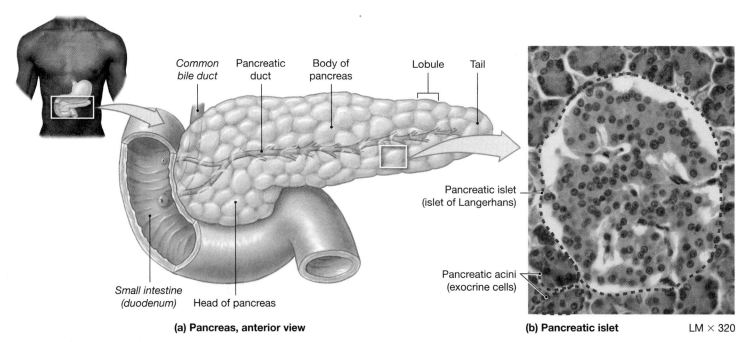

(a) Pancreas, anterior view

Common bile duct — Pancreatic duct — Body of pancreas — Lobule — Tail

Small intestine (duodenum) — Head of pancreas

(b) Pancreatic islet   LM × 320

Pancreatic islet (islet of Langerhans)

Pancreatic acini (exocrine cells)

FIGURE 10-13 **The Endocrine Pancreas. (a)** This drawing depicts the location and gross anatomy of the pancreas. **(b)** Each pancreatic islet is surrounded by exocrine cells.

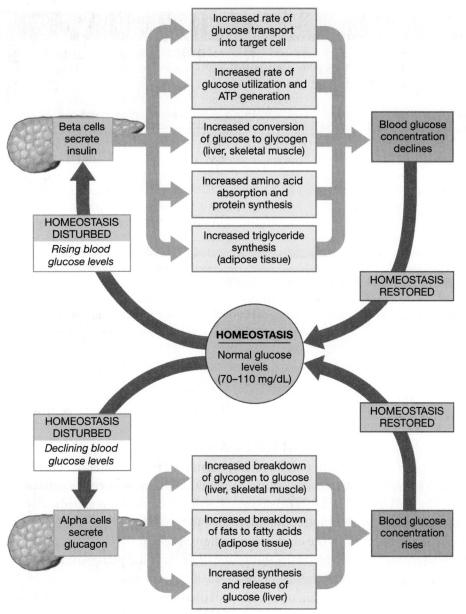

FIGURE 10-14 **The Regulation of Blood Glucose Concentrations.**

also accelerates the formation of glycogen. In summary, when glucose is abundant, insulin secretion by beta cells stimulates glucose utilization to support growth and to establish glycogen and fat reserves (Figure 10-14).

When glucose concentrations fall below normal homeostatic levels, insulin secretion is suppressed, as is glucose transport into its target cells. These cells now shift over to other energy sources, such as fatty acids. At the same time, alpha cells release glucagon, and energy reserves are mobilized. Skeletal muscles and liver cells break down glycogen into glucose (for energy in the muscle or for release by the liver), adipose tissue releases fatty acids for use by other tissues, and proteins are broken down into their component amino acids (Figure 10-14). The liver takes in the amino acids and converts them to glucose that can be released into the circulation. As a result, blood glucose concentrations rise toward normal levels. The interplay between insulin and glucagon both stabilizes blood glucose levels and prevents competition between neural tissue and other tissues for limited glucose supplies.

Pancreatic alpha and beta cells are sensitive to blood glucose concentrations, and the secretion of glucagon and insulin can occur without endocrine or nervous system instructions. Yet because the islet cells are very sensitive to variations in blood glucose levels, any hormone that affects blood glucose concentrations will indirectly affect the production of insulin and glucagon. Insulin and glucagon production are also influenced by autonomic activity. Parasympathetic stimulation enhances insulin release, whereas sympathetic stimulation inhibits it. Sympathetic stimulation promotes glucagon release.

ATP generated by the breakdown of glucose molecules is used to build proteins and to increase energy reserves, and most cells increase their rates of protein synthesis in response to insulin. A secondary effect is an increase in the rate of amino acid transport across plasma membranes. Insulin also stimulates fat cells to increase their rates of triglyceride (fat) synthesis and storage. In the liver and in skeletal muscle fibers, insulin

CHECKPOINT

19. Identify two important types of cells in the pancreatic islets and the hormones produced by each.

20. Which pancreatic hormone causes skeletal muscle and liver cells to convert glucose to glycogen?

21. What effect would increased levels of glucagon have on the amount of glycogen stored in the liver?

See the blue Answers tab at the back of the book.

The Big Picture

The pancreatic islets of the endocrine pancreas produce insulin and glucagon. Insulin is released when blood glucose levels rise, and it stimulates glucose transport into, and utilization by, peripheral tissues. Glucagon is released when blood glucose levels decline, and it stimulates glycogen breakdown, glucose synthesis, and fatty acid release.

Clinical Note

Diabetes Mellitus

Whether glucose is absorbed across the digestive tract or manufactured and released by the liver, very little glucose leaves the body intact once it has entered the circulation. Glucose does get filtered out of the blood at the kidneys, but virtually all of it is reabsorbed, so urinary glucose losses are negligible.

Diabetes mellitus (MEL-ī-tus; *mellitum,* honey) is characterized by blood glucose concentrations that are high enough to overwhelm the reabsorption capabilities of the kidneys. (The term **hyperglycemia** [hī-per-glī-SĒ-mē-ah] refers to the presence of high glucose levels in the blood.) Glucose appears in the urine (*glycosuria*), and urine production becomes excessive (*polyuria*). Other metabolic products, such as fatty acids and other lipids, are also present in abnormally high concentrations.

Diabetes mellitus can be caused by genetic abnormalities, and some of the genes responsible have been identified. Mutations that result in inadequate insulin production, the synthesis of abnormal insulin molecules, or the production of defective insulin receptor proteins will produce the same

basic signs and symptoms. Diabetes mellitus can also result from other pathological conditions, injuries, immune disorders, or hormonal imbalances.

There are two major types of diabetes mellitus: *type 1 diabetes mellitus* (*insulin-dependent*) and *type 2 diabetes mellitus* (*non-insulin-dependent*). In type 1 diabetes mellitus, the primary cause is inadequate insulin production. Type 1 diabetes mellitus most often appears in individuals under 40 years of age. Because it frequently appears in childhood, it has been called *juvenile-onset diabetes.* Long-term treatment involves dietary control and the administration of insulin. Type 2 diabetes mellitus typically affects obese individuals over 40 years of age and, consequently, is often called *maturity-onset diabetes.* In this condition, insulin levels are normal or elevated, but cells in peripheral tissues no longer take up glucose. The cause of this resistance to insulin is unknown, although a reduction in the number of insulin receptors may be the problem. Treatment consists of weight loss, dietary restrictions, and drugs (oral hypoglycemic agents) that may elevate insulin production and tissue response to it.

10-9 Many organs have secondary endocrine functions

Many organs that are part of other body systems have secondary endocrine functions. Examples include the intestines (digestive system), the kidneys (urinary system), the heart (cardiovascular system), the thymus (lymphoid system), and the gonads—the testes in males and ovaries in females (reproductive system). Recent discoveries have led to the realization that the body's adipose tissue has important endocrine functions, which are also considered in this section.

THE INTESTINES

The intestines, which process and absorb nutrients, release a variety of hormones that coordinate the activities of the digestive system. Although the pace of digestive activities can be affected by the autonomic nervous system, most digestive processes are controlled locally. The hormones involved will be discussed in Chapter 16.

THE KIDNEYS

The kidneys release the steroid hormone *calcitriol,* the peptide hormone *erythropoietin,* and the enzyme *renin.* Calcitriol is important to calcium ion homeostasis. Erythropoietin and

renin are involved in the regulation of blood pressure and blood volume.

Calcitriol is secreted by the kidneys in response to the presence of parathyroid hormone (PTH). Its synthesis depends on the availability of vitamin D_3, which may be synthesized in the skin or absorbed from the diet. Vitamin D_3 is absorbed by the liver and converted to an intermediary product that is released into the circulation and absorbed by the kidneys. Calcitriol stimulates the absorption of calcium and phosphate ions across the intestinal lining of the digestive tract.

Erythropoietin (e-rith-rō-POY-e-tin); *erythros,* red + *poiesis,* making), or **EPO,** is released by the kidneys in response to low oxygen levels in kidney tissues. EPO stimulates the production of red blood cells by the bone marrow. The increase in the number of red blood cells elevates blood volume. Because these cells transport oxygen, their increased abundance improves oxygen delivery to peripheral tissues. EPO will be considered again when we discuss the formation of blood cells in Chapter 11.

Renin (RĒ-nin) is released by specialized kidney cells in response to a decline in blood volume, blood pressure, or both. Once in the bloodstream, renin starts an enzymatic chain reaction, known as the *renin-angiotensin system,* that leads to the formation of the hormone **angiotensin II.** Angiotensin II stimulates the production of aldosterone (by the suprarenal cortex) and ADH (in the posterior pituitary gland). This combination restricts salt and water loss at the kidneys. Angiotensin II also stimulates thirst and elevates blood pressure. (Because renin plays a leading role in the formation of angiotensin II, many physiological and endocrinological references consider renin to be a hormone.) The *renin-angiotensin system* will be detailed in Chapters 13 and 18.

THE HEART

The endocrine cells in the heart are cardiac muscle cells in the walls of the *right atrium,* the chamber that receives blood from the largest veins. If blood volume becomes too great, these cardiac muscle cells are excessively stretched, stimulating them to release the hormone *atrial natriuretic peptide* (*ANP*) (nā-trē-ū-RET-ik; *natrium,* sodium + *ouresis,* making water). In general, the effects of ANP oppose those of angiotensin II: ANP promotes the loss of sodium ions and water at the kidneys and inhibits renin release and the secretion of ADH and aldosterone. ANP secretion results in a reduction in both blood volume and pressure. We will consider the actions of this hormone further when we discuss the control of blood pressure and volume in Chapter 13.

THE THYMUS

The **thymus** is located in the *mediastinum,* usually just posterior to the sternum. In a newborn infant, the thymus is relatively enormous, often extending from the base of the neck to the superior border of the heart. As the child grows, the thymus continues to enlarge slowly, reaching its maximum size just before puberty, at a weight of about 40 g (1.4 oz.). After puberty, it gradually diminishes in size; by age 50, the thymus may weigh less than 12 g (0.4 oz.).

The thymus produces several hormones collectively known as the **thymosins** (THĪ-mō-sinz), which play a key role in the development and maintenance of normal immune defenses. It has been suggested that the gradual decrease in the size and secretory abilities of the thymus may make the elderly more susceptible to disease. The structure of the thymus and the functions of the thymosins will be considered in more detail in Chapter 14.

THE GONADS

The Testes

In males, the **interstitial cells** of the testes produce the steroid hormones known as androgens, of which **testosterone** (tes-TOS-ter-ōn) is the most important. Testosterone promotes the production of functional sperm, maintains the secretory glands of the male reproductive tract, and determines secondary sex characteristics such as the distribution of facial hair and body

fat. Testosterone also affects metabolic operations throughout the body. It stimulates protein synthesis and muscle growth, and it produces aggressive behavioral responses. During embryonic development, the production of testosterone affects the development of male reproductive ducts, external genitalia, and CNS structures, including hypothalamic nuclei that will later affect sexual behaviors.

Nurse (sustentacular) cells in the testes support the formation of functional sperm. Under FSH stimulation, these cells secrete the hormone **inhibin,** which inhibits the secretion of FSH by the anterior pituitary. Throughout adult life, these two hormones interact to maintain sperm production at normal levels.

The Ovaries

In the ovaries, female sex cells (*ova*) develop in specialized structures called **follicles,** under stimulation by FSH. Follicle cells surrounding the ova produce **estrogens** (ES-trō-jenz), steroid hormones that support the maturation of the eggs and stimulate the growth of the lining of the uterus. Under FSH stimulation, follicle cells secrete inhibin, which suppresses FSH release through a negative feedback mechanism comparable to that in males. After ovulation has occurred, the follicular cells reorganize into a **corpus luteum.** The cells of the corpus luteum then begin to release a mixture of estrogens and progestins, especially **progesterone** (prō-JES-ter-ōn). Progesterone accelerates the movement of fertilized eggs along the uterine tubes and prepares the uterus for the arrival of a developing embryo. In combination with other hormones, it also causes an enlargement of the mammary glands.

The production of androgens, estrogens, and progestins is controlled by regulatory hormones released by the anterior pituitary gland. During pregnancy, the placenta functions as an endocrine organ, working with the ovaries and the pituitary gland to promote normal fetal development and delivery.

Table 10-4 summarizes the characteristics of the reproductive hormones.

ADIPOSE TISSUE

Adipose tissue is a type of loose connective tissue introduced in Chapter 4. p. 106 Adipose tissue is known to produce a peptide hormone called **leptin,** which has several functions, the best known being the negative feedback control of appetite. When you eat, adipose tissue absorbs glucose and lipids and synthesizes triglycerides (fats) for storage. At the same time, it releases leptin into the bloodstream. Leptin binds to neurons in the hypothalamus involved with emotion and appetite control. The result is a sense of satiation and the suppression of appetite.

TABLE 10-4 Hormones of the Reproductive System

STRUCTURE/CELLS	HORMONE	PRIMARY TARGET	EFFECTS
TESTES **Interstitial cells**	Androgens	Most cells	Support functional maturation of sperm, protein synthesis in skeletal muscles, male secondary sex characteristics, and associated behaviors
Nurse cells	Inhibin	Anterior pituitary	Inhibits secretion of FSH
OVARIES **Follicular cells**	Estrogens	Most cells	Support follicle maturation, female secondary sex characteristics, and associated behaviors
	Inhibin	Anterior pituitary	Inhibits secretion of FSH
Corpus luteum	Progestins	Uterus, mammary glands	Prepare uterus for implantation; prepare mammary glands for secretory functions

Leptin also enhances GnRH and gonadotropin synthesis. This effect explains why (1) thin girls commonly enter puberty relatively late, (2) an increase in body fat content can improve fertility, and (3) women stop menstruating when their body fat content becomes very low.

CHECKPOINT

22. Identify the two hormones secreted by the kidneys, and describe their functions.

23. Identify a hormone released by adipose tissue.

24. Describe the action of renin.

See the blue Answers tab at the back of the book.

10-10 Hormones interact to produce coordinated physiological responses

Even though hormones are usually studied individually, extracellular fluids contain a mixture of hormones whose concentrations change daily and even hourly. When a cell receives instructions from two different hormones at the same time, four outcomes are possible:

- The two hormones may have **antagonistic** (opposing) **effects,** as is the case for parathyroid hormone and calcitonin, or insulin and glucagon.

Clinical Note — Hormones and Athletic Performance

Medical research involving humans is generally subject to tight ethical constraints and meticulous scientific scrutiny. Yet a hidden, unscientific, and potentially dangerous program of "experimentation" with hormones is being pursued by athletes around the world.

The use of hormones to improve athletic performance is banned by the International Olympic Committee, the U.S. Olympic Committee, the National Collegiate Athletic Association, and the National Football League, and it is condemned by the American Medical Association and the American College of Sports Medicine. A significant number of amateur and professional athletes, however, persist in this dangerous practice. Synthetic forms of testosterone are used most often, but athletes may use any combination of testosterone, growth hormone (GH), erythropoietin (EPO), and a variety of synthetic hormones.

The use of anabolic steroids or androgens such as *androstenedione,* which the body can convert to testosterone, was highlighted during 2004 when several prominent sports trainers, including the trainer of baseball slugger Barry Bonds, were arrested for providing synthetic steroids to their clients. (Performance-enhancing drugs were banned by Major League Baseball in 1999.)

One justification for this practice has been the unfounded opinion that compounds manufactured in the body are not only safe but also good for you. In reality, the use of natural or synthetic androgens in abnormal amounts carries unacceptable health risks. Androgens are known to produce several complications, including (1) premature closure of epiphyseal cartilages; (2) various liver dysfunctions, including jaundice and liver tumors; (3) in males, prostate gland enlargement, urinary tract obstructions, testicular atrophy, and infertility; and (4) in females, irregular menstrual periods and changes in body hair distribution. Links to heart attacks, impaired heart function, and strokes have also been suggested. Finally, androgen abuse can cause a generalized depression of the immune system.

- The two hormones may have additive effects, in which case the net result is greater than the effect that each would produce acting alone. In some cases, the net result is greater than the *sum* of their individual effects. An example of such a **synergistic** (sin-er-JIS-tik; *syn*, together + *ergon*, work) **effect** is the glucose-sparing action of GH and glucocorticoids. ∞ pp. 355, 361

- Hormones can have a **permissive effect** on other hormones. In such cases, one hormone must be present if a second hormone is to produce its effects. Thus, epinephrine, for example, has no apparent effect on energy consumption unless thyroid hormones are also present in normal concentrations.

- Hormones may also produce different but complementary results in a given tissue or organ. These **integrative effects** are important in coordinating the activities of diverse physiological systems. The differing effects of calcitriol and parathyroid hormone on tissues involved in calcium metabolism are an example.

The next few sections will discuss how hormones interact to control normal growth, reactions to stress, alterations of behavior, and the effects of aging. More detailed discussions can be found in chapters on cardiovascular function, metabolism, excretion, and reproduction.

HORMONES AND GROWTH

Normal growth requires the cooperation of several endocrine organs. Six hormones—growth hormone, thyroid hormones, insulin, parathyroid hormone, calcitriol, and reproductive hormones—are especially important, although many others have secondary effects on growth rates and patterns:

- *Growth hormone (GH).* The effects of GH on protein synthesis and cellular growth are most apparent in children, in whom GH supports muscular and skeletal development. In adults, GH helps maintain normal blood glucose concentrations and mobilizes lipid reserves stored in adipose tissues. It is not the primary hormone involved, however, and an adult with a GH deficiency but normal levels of thyroxine, insulin, and glucocorticoids will have no physiological problems. Undersecretion or oversecretion of GH can lead to *pituitary dwarfism* or *gigantism*, respectively.

- *Thyroid hormones.* Normal growth also requires appropriate levels of thyroid hormones. If these hormones are absent for the first year after birth, the nervous system fails to develop normally, producing mental retardation. If thyroxine concentrations decline later in life but before puberty, normal skeletal development will not continue.

- *Insulin.* Growing cells need adequate supplies of energy and nutrients. Without insulin, the passage of glucose and amino acids across cell membranes is drastically reduced or eliminated.

- *Parathyroid hormone (PTH) and calcitriol.* Parathyroid hormone and calcitriol promote the absorption of calcium for building bone. Without adequate levels of both hormones, bones can enlarge but will be poorly mineralized, weak, and flexible. For example, in *rickets,* a condition typically resulting from inadequate production of calcitriol in growing children, the limb bones are so weak that they bend under the body's weight. ∞ p. 149

- *Reproductive hormones.* Both the activity of osteoblasts in key locations and the growth of specific cell populations are affected by the presence or absence of sex hormones (androgens in males, estrogens in females). The targets differ for androgens and estrogens, and the differential growth induced by these hormonal changes accounts for sex-related differences in skeletal proportions and secondary sex characteristics.

HORMONES AND STRESS

Any condition—whether physical or emotional—that threatens homeostasis is a form of **stress.** Stresses produced by the action of *stressors* may be (1) physical, such as illness or injury; (2) emotional, such as depression or anxiety; (3) environmental, such as extreme heat or cold; or (4) metabolic, such as acute starvation. Many stresses are opposed by specific homeostatic adjustments. For example, a decline in body temperature leads to shivering or changes in the pattern of blood flow, which act to restore normal body temperature.

In addition, the body has a general response to stress that can occur while other, more specific, responses are under way. *All stress-causing factors produce the same basic pattern of hormonal and physiological adjustments.* These responses are part of the **general adaptation syndrome (GAS),** also known as the **stress response.** The GAS has three basic phases: the *alarm phase,* the *resistance phase,* and the *exhaustion phase* (Figure 10-15).

The **alarm phase** is an immediate response to stress; it is under the direction of the sympathetic division of the autonomic nervous system. During this phase, energy reserves (mainly in the form of glucose) are mobilized, and the body prepares for any physical activities needed to eliminate or escape from the source of the stress. Epinephrine is the dominant hormone of the alarm phase, and its secretion accompanies the sympathetic activation that produces the "fight or flight" response. ∞ p. 290 Even though the effects of epinephrine are most apparent during the alarm phase, other hormones play

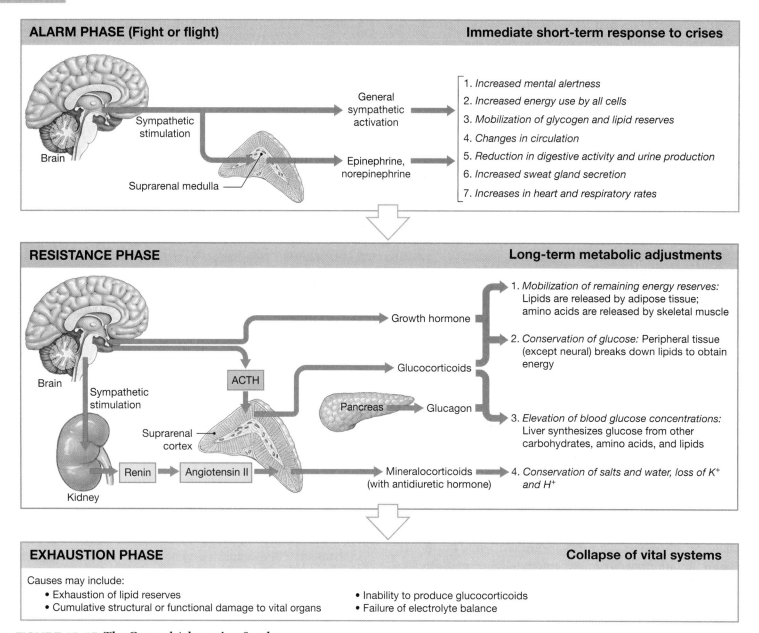

FIGURE 10-15 The General Adaptation Syndrome.

supporting roles. For example, the reduction of water losses resulting from ADH production and aldosterone secretion can be very important if the stress involves a loss of blood.

The temporary adjustments of the alarm phase often remove or overcome the stress. But some stresses, including starvation, acute illness, or severe anxiety, can persist for hours, days, or even weeks. If stress lasts longer than a few hours, the individual enters the **resistance phase** of the GAS. Glucocorticoids (GCs) are the dominant hormones of the resistance phase. Epinephrine, GH, and thyroid hormones are also involved. Energy demands in the resistance phase remain higher than normal, owing to the combined effects of these hormones.

Neural tissue has a high demand for energy, and if blood glucose concentrations fall too far, neural function deteriorates. The endocrine secretions of the resistance phase coordinate three integrated actions to maintain adequate levels of glucose in the blood: (1) mobilization of lipid and protein reserves, (2) conservation of glucose for neural tissues, and (3) synthesis and release of glucose by the liver. In addition, blood volume is maintained by the actions of ADH and aldosterone.

When the resistance phase ends, homeostatic regulation breaks down, and the **exhaustion phase** begins. Unless corrective actions are taken almost immediately, the ensuing failure of one or more organ systems will prove fatal. Mineral imbalances

Clinical Note

Endocrine Disorders

Endocrine disorders fall into two basic categories: inadequate hormonal effects and excessive hormonal effects. The observed signs and symptoms may reflect either abnormal hormone production (hyposecretion or hypersecretion) or abnormal target cell sensitivity. Figure 10-16 shows the characteristic features of some important endocrine disorders.

(a) *Acromegaly* results from the over-production of growth hormone after puberty, when most of the epiphyseal cartilages have fused. Bone shapes change, and cartilaginous areas of the skeleton enlarge. Notice the broad facial features and the enlarged lower jaw.

(b) *Cretinism* or *congenital hypothy-roidism* results from thyroid hormone insufficiency in infancy.

(c) An enlarged thyroid gland, or *goiter*, can be associated with thyroid hyposecretion due to iodine insufficiency in adults.

(d) *Addison disease* is caused by hyposecretion of corticosteroids, especially glucocorticoids. Pigment changes result from stimulation of melanocytes by ACTH, which is structurally similar to MSH.

(e) *Cushing disease* is caused by hypersecretion of glucocorticoids. Lipid reserves are mobilized, and adipose tissue accumulates in the cheeks and at the base of the neck.

FIGURE 10-16 **Endocrine Disorders.**

contribute to the existing problems with major systems. The production of aldosterone throughout the resistance phase results in a conservation of sodium ions at the expense of potassium ions. As the body's potassium content declines, a variety of cells—notably neurons and muscle fibers—begin to malfunction. Although a single cause, such as heart failure, may be listed as the cause of death, the underlying problem is the inability to support the endocrine and metabolic adjustments of the resistance phase.

HORMONES AND BEHAVIOR

The hypothalamus regulates many endocrine functions, and its neurons monitor the levels of many circulating hormones. Other portions of the brain that affect how we act, or behave, are also quite sensitive to hormonal stimulation.

The clearest demonstrations of the behavioral effects of specific hormones involve individuals whose endocrine glands are oversecreting or undersecreting. But even normal changes in circulating hormone levels can cause behavioral changes. In *precocious* (premature) *puberty*, sex hormones are produced at an inappropriate time, perhaps as early as age 5 or 6. An affected child not only begins to develop adult secondary sex characteristics but also undergoes significant behavioral changes. The "nice little kid" disappears, and the child becomes aggressive and assertive due to the effects of sex hormones on CNS function. Thus, behaviors that in normal teenagers are usually attributed to environmental stimuli, such as peer pressure, can have a physiological basis as well. In adults, changes in the mixture of hormones reaching the CNS can have significant effects on intellectual capabilities, memory, learning, and emotional states.

HORMONES AND AGING

The endocrine system undergoes relatively few functional changes with age. The most dramatic exception is the decline in the concentration of reproductive hormones. Effects of these hormonal changes on the skeletal system were noted in Chapter 6; further discussion can be found in Chapter 20. ∞ p. 152

Blood and tissue concentrations of many other hormones, including TSH, thyroid hormones, ADH, PTH, prolactin, and glucocorticoids, remain unchanged with increasing age. Although circulating hormone levels may remain within normal limits, some endocrine tissues become less responsive to stimulation. For example, in elderly individuals, less GH and insulin are secreted after a carbohydrate-rich meal. The reduction in levels of GH and other tropic hormones affects tissues throughout the body; these hormonal effects are associated with the reductions in bone density and muscle mass noted in earlier chapters.

Finally, it should be noted that age-related changes in peripheral tissues may make them less responsive to some hormones. This loss of sensitivity has been documented for glucocorticoids and ADH.

CHECKPOINT

25. What type of hormonal interaction occurs when insulin lowers blood glucose levels while glucagon elevates blood glucose levels?

26. The lack of which hormones would inhibit skeletal formation and development?

27. What are the dominant hormones of the resistance phase of the general adaptation syndrome, and in what ways do they act?

See the blue Answers tab at the back of the book.

10-11 Extensive integration occurs between the endocrine system and other body systems

The endocrine system provides long-term regulation and adjustments of homeostatic mechanisms that affect many body functions. These functional relationships are summarized in the Endocrine System in Perspective (p. 378). (The System in Perspective excludes all the hormones associated with the digestive system and the control of digestive functions. These hormones will be discussed in Chapter 16.)

CHECKPOINT

28. Discuss the general role of the endocrine system in the functioning of other body systems.

See the blue Answers tab at the back of the book.

RELATED CLINICAL TERMS

Addison disease: A condition caused by the hyposecretion of glucocorticoids and mineralocorticoids; characterized by an inability to mobilize energy reserves and maintain normal blood glucose levels.

cretinism (KRĒ-tin-ism): A condition caused by hypothyroidism at birth or in infancy; marked by inadequate skeletal and nervous development and a metabolic rate as much as 40 percent below normal levels.

Cushing disease: A condition caused by the hypersecretion of glucocorticoids; characterized by the excessive breakdown of lipid reserves and proteins, and relocation of lipids.

diabetes insipidus: A disorder that develops either when the posterior pituitary no longer releases adequate amounts of ADH or when the kidneys cannot respond to ADH.

diabetes mellitus (MEL-ī-tus): A disorder characterized by glucose concentrations high enough to overwhelm the kidneys' reabsorption capabilities.

diabetic retinopathy, nephropathy, neuropathy: Disorders of the retina, kidneys, and peripheral nerves, respectively, related to diabetes mellitus; these conditions most often afflict middle-aged or older diabetics.

endocrinology (EN-dō-kri-NOL-ō-jē): The study of hormones and hormone-secreting tissues and glands and their roles in physiological and disease processes in the body.

general adaptation syndrome (GAS): The pattern of hormonal and physiological adjustments with which the body responds to all forms of stress.

glycosuria (glī-ko-SOO-rē-a): The presence of glucose in the urine.

goiter: An abnormal enlargement of the thyroid gland.

hyperglycemia: Abnormally high glucose levels in the blood.

hypoglycemia: Abnormally low glucose levels in the blood.

insulin-dependent diabetes or *type 1 diabetes,* or *juvenile-onset diabetes*: A type of diabetes mellitus; the primary cause is inadequate insulin production by beta cells of the pancreatic islets.

myxedema: In adults, the effects of hyposecretion of thyroid hormones, including subcutaneous swelling, hair loss, dry skin, low body temperature, muscle weakness, and slowed reflexes.

non-insulin-dependent diabetes or *type 2 diabetes,* or *maturity-onset diabetes:* A type of diabetes mellitus in which insulin levels are normal or elevated, but peripheral tissues no longer respond normally to insulin.

polyuria: The production of excessive amounts of urine; a clinical sign of diabetes.

thyrotoxicosis: A condition caused by the oversecretion of thyroid hormones (*hyperthyroidism*). Signs and symptoms include increases in metabolic rate, blood pressure, and heart rate; excitability and emotional instability; and lowered energy reserves.

Chapter **10** Review

KEY TERMS

endocrine cell *347*
first messenger *347*
general adaptation syndrome *369*
glucagon *364*
hormone *347*
hypophyseal portal system *352*
hypophysis *352*
insulin *364*
pancreas *364*
peptide hormone *347*
pituitary gland *352*
second messenger *347*
steroid hormone *347*
suprarenal cortex *361*
suprarenal medulla *362*

SUMMARY OUTLINE

IP Use *Interactive Physiology*® (**IP**) —available on the IP CD packaged with your new textbook—to help you understand difficult physiological concepts. Follow these navigation paths on IP for concepts in this chapter:

- Endocrine System/The Hypothalamic-Pituitary Axis
- Endocrine System/Endocrine System Review
- Endocrine System/Response to Stress

10-1 Homeostasis is preserved through intercellular communication *p. 346*

1. In general, the nervous system performs short-term "crisis management," whereas the endocrine system regulates longer-term, ongoing metabolic processes. Endocrine cells release **hormones,** chemicals that alter the metabolic activities of many different tissues and organs. (*Figure 10-1*)

10-2 The endocrine system regulates physiological processes through the binding of hormones to receptors *p. 347*

2. Hormones can be divided into three groups based on chemical structure: amino acid derivatives, peptide hormones, and lipid derivatives.

3. *Amino acid derivatives* are structurally similar to amino acids; they include *epinephrine, norepinephrine, thyroid hormones,* and *melatonin.*

4. **Peptide hormones** are chains of amino acids.

5. There are two classes of *lipid derivatives:* **steroid hormones,** lipids that are structurally similar to cholesterol, and *eicosanoids,* fatty acid–based hormones that include **prostaglandins.**

6. Hormones exert their effects by modifying the activities of **target cells** (peripheral cells that are sensitive to that particular hormone). *(Figure 10-2)*

7. Receptors for amino acid–derived hormones, peptide hormones, and fatty acid–derived hormones are located on the plasma membranes of target cells; in this case, the hormone acts as a **first messenger** that causes the formation of a **second messenger** in the cytoplasm. Thyroid and steroid hormones cross the cell membrane and bind to receptors in the cytoplasm or nucleus. Thyroid hormones also bind to mitochondria, where they increase the rate of ATP production. *(Figure 10-3)*

8. Hormones may circulate freely or be carried by transport proteins. Free hormones are rapidly removed from the bloodstream.

9. The most direct patterns of endocrine control involve negative feedback on the endocrine cells resulting from changes in the extracellular fluid.

10. The most complex endocrine responses involve the hypothalamus, which regulates the activities of the nervous and endocrine systems by three mechanisms: (1) It acts as an endocrine organ by releasing hormones into the circulation; (2) it secretes **regulatory hormones** that control the activities of endocrine cells in the pituitary gland; and (3) its autonomic centers exert direct neural control over the endocrine cells of the suprarenal medullae. *(Figure 10-4)*

10-3 The bilobed pituitary gland is an endocrine organ that releases nine peptide hormones *p. 352*

11. The **pituitary gland** (*hypopohysis*) releases nine important peptide hormones; all bind to membrane receptors, and most use cyclic-AMP as a second messenger. *(Figure 10-5)*

12. Hypothalamic neurons release regulatory factors into the surrounding interstitial fluids, which then enter highly permeable capillaries.

13. The **hypophyseal portal system** ensures that all of the blood entering the *portal vessels* will reach target cells in the anterior pituitary before returning to the general circulation. *(Figure 10-6)*

14. The rate of regulatory hormone secretion by the hypothalamus is regulated through negative feedback mechanisms. *(Figure 10-7)*

15. The seven hormones of the **anterior pituitary gland** are (1) **thyroid-stimulating hormone (TSH),** which triggers the release of thyroid hormones; (2) **adrenocorticotropic hormone (ACTH),** which stimulates the release of **glucocorticoids** by the suprarenal gland; (3) **follicle-stimulating hormone (FSH),** which stimulates estrogen secretion and egg development in females and sperm production in males; (4) **luteinizing hormone (LH),** which causes ovulation and **progestin** production in females and **androgen** production in males; (5) **prolactin (PRL),** which stimulates the development of the mammary glands and the production of milk; (6) **growth hormone (GH),** which stimulates cell growth and replication by triggering the release of **somatomedins** from liver cells; and (7) **melanocyte-stimulating hormone (MSH),** which stimulates melanocytes to produce melanin (but is not normally secreted by nonpregnant women).

16. The **posterior pituitary gland** contains the axons of hypothalamic neurons that manufacture **antidiuretic hormone (ADH)** and **oxytocin (OXT).** ADH decreases the amount of water lost at the kidneys. In females, oxytocin stimulates smooth muscle cells in the uterus and contractile cells in the mammary glands. In males, it stimulates sperm duct and prostate gland smooth muscle contractions. *(Figure 10-8; Table 10-1)*

10-4 The thyroid gland lies inferior to the larynx and requires iodine for hormone synthesis *p. 357*

17. The **thyroid gland** lies near the **thyroid cartilage** of the larynx and consists of two lobes. *(Figure 10-9)*

18. The thyroid gland contains numerous **thyroid follicles.** Thyroid follicles release several hormones, including **thyroxine** (T_4) and **triiodothyronine** (T_3). *(Table 10-2)*

19. Thyroid hormones exert a **calorigenic effect,** which enables us to adapt to cold temperatures.

20. The **C cells** of the follicles produce **calcitonin (CT),** which helps lower calcium ion concentrations in body fluids. *(Table 10-2)*

10-5 The four parathyroid glands, embedded in the posterior surface of the thyroid gland, secrete parathyroid hormone to elevate blood calcium levels *p. 360*

21. Four **parathyroid glands** are embedded in the posterior surface of the thyroid gland. The **chief cells** of the parathyroid produce **parathyroid hormone (PTH)** in response to lower than normal concentrations of calcium ions. Chief cells and the C cells of the thyroid gland maintain calcium levels within relatively narrow limits. *(Figures 10-10, 10-11; Table 10-2)*

10-6 The suprarenal glands, consisting of a cortex and a medulla, cap each kidney and secrete several hormones *p. 361*

22. A single **suprarenal gland,** or *adrenal gland,* lies along the superior border of each kidney. Each gland, which is surrounded by a fibrous capsule, can be subdivided into the superficial suprarenal cortex and the inner suprarenal medulla. *(Figure 10-12)*

23. The **suprarenal cortex** manufactures steroid hormones called *adrenocortical steroids* (**corticosteroids**). The cortex produces

(1) **glucocorticoids**—notably, **cortisol, corticosterone,** and **cortisone,** which, in response to ACTH, affect glucose metabolism; (2) **mineralocorticoids**—principally **aldosterone,** which, in response to *angiotensin II,* restricts sodium and water losses at the kidneys, sweat glands, digestive tract, and salivary glands; and (3) androgens of uncertain significance. *(Figure 10-12; Table 10-3)*

24. The **suprarenal medulla** produces **epinephrine** and **norepinephrine.** *(Figure 10-12; Table 10-3)*

10-7 The pineal gland, attached to the third ventricle, secretes melatonin   *p. 363*

25. The **pineal gland** synthesizes **melatonin.** Melatonin appears to (1) slow the maturation of sperm, eggs, and reproductive organs; (2) protect neural tissue from free radicals; and (3) establish daily circadian rhythms.

10-8 The endocrine pancreas produces insulin and glucagon, hormones that regulate blood glucose levels   *p. 364*

26. The **pancreas** contains both exocrine and endocrine cells. The **exocrine pancreas** secretes an enzyme-rich fluid that functions in the digestive tract. Cells of the **endocrine pancreas** form clusters called **pancreatic islets** (*islets of Langerhans*), containing **alpha cells** (which produce the hormone **glucagon**) and **beta cells** (which secrete **insulin**). *(Figure 10-13)*

27. Insulin lowers blood glucose by increasing the rate of glucose uptake and utilization; glucagon raises blood glucose by increasing the rates of glycogen breakdown and glucose synthesis in the liver. *(Figure 10-14)*

10-9 Many organs have secondary endocrine functions   *p. 366*

28. The intestines release hormones that coordinate digestive activities.

29. Endocrine cells in the kidneys produce two hormones and an enzyme important in calcium metabolism and in the maintenance of blood volume and blood pressure.

30. **Calcitriol** stimulates calcium and phosphate ion absorption along the digestive tract.

31. **Erythropoietin (EPO)** stimulates red blood cell production by the bone marrow.

32. **Renin** activity leads to the formation of **angiotensin II,** the hormone that stimulates the production of aldosterone in the suprarenal cortex.

33. Specialized muscle cells in the heart produce **atrial natriuretic peptide (ANP)** when blood pressure or blood volume becomes excessive.

34. The **thymus** produces several hormones called **thymosins,** which play a role in developing and maintaining normal immunological defenses.

35. The **interstitial cells** of the paired testes in males produce androgens and **inhibin.** The androgen testosterone is the most important sex hormone in males. *(Table 10-4)*

36. In females, ova (eggs) develop in **follicles;** follicle cells surrounding the eggs produce **estrogens** and inhibin. After ovulation, the cells reorganize into a **corpus luteum** that releases a mixture of estrogens and progestins, especially **progesterone.** If pregnancy occurs, the placenta functions as an endocrine organ. *(Table 10-4)*

37. Adipose tissue secretes **leptin,** which functions in the negative feedback control of appetite.

10-10 Hormones interact to produce coordinated physiological responses   *p. 368*

38. The endocrine system functions as an integrated unit, and hormones often interact. These interactions may have (1) **antagonistic** (opposing) effects, (2) **synergistic** (additive) effects, (3) **permissive** effects, or (4) **integrative** effects, in which hormones produce different but complementary results.

39. Normal growth requires the cooperation of several endocrine organs. Six hormones are especially important: growth hormone, thyroid hormones, insulin, parathyroid hormone, calcitriol, and reproductive hormones.

40. Any condition that threatens homeostasis produces **stress.** Our bodies respond to stress through the **general adaptation syndrome (GAS).** The GAS is divided into three phases: (1) the **alarm phase,** under the direction of the sympathetic division of the ANS; (2) the **resistance phase,** dominated by glucocorticoids; and (3) the **exhaustion phase,** the eventual breakdown of homeostatic regulation and failure of one or more organ systems. *(Figure 10-15)*

41. Many hormones affect the functional state of the nervous system, producing changes in mood, emotional states, and various behaviors.

42. The endocrine system undergoes relatively few functional changes with advancing age. The most dramatic endocrine change is a decline in the concentration of reproductive hormones.

10-11 Extensive integration occurs between the endocrine system and other body systems   *p. 372*

43. The endocrine system affects all organ systems by adjusting metabolic rates and regulating growth and development.

REVIEW QUESTIONS

WWW • Access more review material online at The Anatomy & Physiology Place (www.anatomyandphysiology.com). There, you'll find Chapter Guides, Chapter Quizzes, Chapter Practice Tests, Interactive Flashcards, a Glossary with Pronunciations, and more to help you succeed in the course.

Level 1 • Reviewing Facts and Terms

Match each item in column A with the most closely related item in column B. Place letters for answers in the spaces provided.

COLUMN A

_____ **1.** thyroid gland
_____ **2.** pineal gland
_____ **3.** polyuria
_____ **4.** parathyroid gland
_____ **5.** thymus gland
_____ **6.** suprarenal cortex
_____ **7.** heart
_____ **8.** endocrine pancreas
_____ **9.** gonadotropins
_____ **10.** hypothalamus
_____ **11.** pituitary gland
_____ **12.** growth hormone

COLUMN B

a. islets of Langerhans
b. atrophies by adulthood
c. atrial natriuretic peptide
d. cell growth
e. melatonin
f. hypophysis
g. excessive urine production
h. calcitonin
i. secretes regulatory hormones
j. FSH and LH
k. secretes androgens, mineralocorticoids, and glucocorticoids
l. stimulated by low calcium levels

---

13. Identify the endocrine glands and tissues in the following diagram.

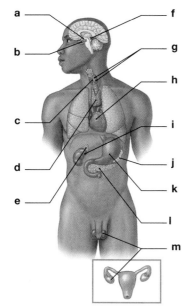

(a) _____	(b) _____	(c) _____
(d) _____	(e) _____	(f) _____
(g) _____	(h) _____	(i) _____
(j) _____	(k) _____	
(l) _____	(m) _____	

14. Adrenocorticotropic hormone (ACTH) stimulates the release of
  (a) thyroid hormones by the hypothalamus.
  (b) gonadotropins by the suprarenal glands.
  (c) somatotropins by the hypothalamus.
  (d) steroid hormones by the suprarenal glands.

15. FSH production in males supports
  (a) maturation of sperm by stimulating sustentacular cells.
  (b) development of muscles and strength.
  (c) production of male sex hormones.
  (d) increased desire for sexual activity.

16. The hormone that induces ovulation in women and promotes the ovarian secretion of progesterone is
  (a) interstitial cell-stimulating hormone.
  (b) estradiol.
  (c) luteinizing hormone.
  (d) prolactin.

17. The two hormones released by the posterior pituitary are
  (a) somatotropin and gonadotropin.
  (b) estrogen and progesterone.
  (c) growth hormone and prolactin.
  (d) antidiuretic hormone and oxytocin.

18. The primary function of antidiuretic hormone (ADH) is to
  (a) increase the amount of water lost at the kidneys.
  (b) decrease the amount of water lost at the kidneys.
  (c) dilate peripheral blood vessels to decrease blood pressure.
  (d) increase absorption along the digestive tract.

19. The element required for normal thyroid function is
    (a) magnesium.
    (b) calcium.
    (c) potassium.
    (d) iodine.

20. Reduced fluid losses in the urine due to retention of sodium ions and water is a result of the action of
    (a) insulin.
    (b) calcitonin.
    (c) aldosterone.
    (d) cortisone.

21. The suprarenal medullae produce the hormones
    (a) cortisol and cortisone.
    (b) epinephrine and norepinephrine.
    (c) corticosterone and testosterone.
    (d) androgens and progesterone.

22. What seven hormones are released by the anterior pituitary gland?

23. What are the effects of calcitonin and parathyroid hormone on blood calcium levels?

24. (a) What three phases of the general adaptation syndrome (GAS) constitute the body's response to stress? (b) What endocrine secretions play dominant roles in each of the first two phases?

Level 2 • Reviewing Concepts

25. What is the primary difference in the ways the nervous and endocrine systems communicate with their target cells?

26. In what ways can hormones modify the activities of their target cells?

27. What possible results occur when a cell receives instructions from two different hormones at the same time?

28. How would blocking the activity of phosphodiesterase affect a cell that responds to hormonal stimulation by the cAMP second messenger system?

Level 3 • Critical Thinking and Clinical Applications

29. Roger has been suffering from extreme thirst; he drinks numerous glasses of water every day and urinates a great deal. Name two disorders that could produce these signs and symptoms. What test could a clinician perform to determine which disorder is present?

30. Julie is pregnant and is not receiving any prenatal care. She has a poor diet consisting mostly of fast food. She drinks no milk, preferring colas instead. How will this situation affect Julie's level of parathyroid hormone?

The Endocrine System in Perspective

Functional Relationships Between the Endocrine System and Other Systems

The Integumentary System

- The Integumentary System protects superficial endocrine organs; epidermis synthesizes vitamin D_3

- The Endocrine System's sex hormones stimulate sebaceous glands, influence hair growth, fat distribution, and apocrine sweat glands; PRL stimulates development of mammary glands; suprarenal hormones alter dermal blood flow, stimulate release of lipids from adipocytes; MSH stimulates melanocytes

The Skeletal System

- The Skeletal System protects endocrine organs, especially in the brain, chest, and pelvic cavity

- The Endocrine System regulates skeletal growth: PTH and calcitonin mobilize calcium; sex hormones speed growth and close epiphyseal cartilages at puberty, and help maintain bone mass in adults

The Muscular System

- The Muscular System provides protection for some endocrine organs

- The Endocrine System adjusts muscle metabolism, energy production, and growth; regulates calcium and phosphate levels in body fluids; speeds skeletal muscle growth

The Nervous System

- The Nervous System's hormones control secretions by the pituitary, other endocrine organs, and suprarenal medullae; secretes ADH and oxytocin

- The Endocrine System's hormones affect neural metabolism; help regulate fluid and electrolyte balance; reproductive hormones influence CNS development and behaviors

The Cardiovascular System

- The Cardiovascular System's vessels distribute hormones throughout the body; heart secretes ANP

- The Endocrine System's hormone EPO regulates production of RBCs; several hormones elevate blood pressure; E elevates heart rate and contraction force

For All Systems
The Endocrine System adjusts metabolic rates and substrate utilization; regulates growth and development

The Lymphoid System

- The Lymphoid System's lymphocytes defend against infection and, with other WBCs, assist in repair after injury

- The Endocrine System's hormones have anti-inflammatory effects (gluco-corticoids), stimulate development of lymphocytes (thymosins), and affect immune function

The Respiratory System

- The Respiratory System provides oxygen and eliminates carbon dioxide generated by endocrine cells

- The Endocrine System's hormones E and NE stimulate respiration and dilate respiratory passageways

The Digestive System

- The Digestive System provides nutrients to endocrine cells; Pancreas secretes insulin and glucagon; liver produces angiotensinogen

- The Endocrine System's hormones E and NE constrict sphincters and depress activity along digestive tract; digestive tract hormones coordinate secretions along tract

The Urinary System

- The Urinary System's kidney cells (1) release renin and EPO when local blood pressure declines and (2) produce calcitriol

- The Endocrine System's hormones (aldosterone, ADH, and ANP) adjust fluid and electrolyte reabsorption in kidneys

The Reproductive System

- The Reproductive System's steroid sex hormones and inhibin suppress secretion in hypothalamus and pituitary

- The Endocrine System's hypothalamic and pituitary hormones regulate sexual development and function; oxytocin stimulates contractions of the uterus and mammary glands

Professional Profile

OCCUPATIONAL THERAPIST
Lynn Dorsey

❝ **Understanding the anatomy and physiology of how joints move and why muscles are impaired is the basis for occupational therapy."**

Occupational therapists are trained to help people regain their independence after an injury, accident, or illness. Patients who need occupational therapy come from all walks of life and include those who have suffered a stroke or spinal cord injury, are recovering from an accident, have mental health problems, or are living with arthritis, multiple sclerosis, or other diseases that limit their abilities in some way.

REWARDING WORK

For Lynn Dorsey, an occupational therapist (OT) working in California, helping people regain some or all of what they have lost is the job's biggest reward. "As an occupational therapist, I work to get people back to functioning the best they can, to be independent and enjoy life again. It's incredibly gratifying to see people improve in strength and endurance and to regain the ability to get to the bathroom or into a chair on their own."

Lynn has worked as an occupational therapist for more than 20 years, most of the time in a community hospital. On a typical day, she sees eight or nine patients, either evaluating them or treating them. Many of her patients have had strokes or suffered head injuries. For these patients, she concentrates on basic quality-of-life skills such as bathing, dressing, oral hygiene, and grooming, as well as strengthening the muscles, improving visual perception, and developing fine motor coordination. "We want people to be safe, more independent, and more functional," she says.

The goal of all occupational therapy is to get the patient to the next level of independence, whether that is moving to a rehabilitation center or assisted living situation or returning home. "Seeing their progress is very rewarding," says Lynn.

ANATOMY AND PHYSIOLOGY ARE FUNDAMENTAL

Occupational therapists must be familiar with the interactions of the muscles, bones, and nerves.

According to Lynn, "We have to know how to strengthen the arms and reeducate the muscles. We also have to understand how the nerves work to make the muscles function. Understanding the anatomy and physiology of how joints move and why muscles are impaired is the basis for occupational therapy." Hand therapy is a subspecialty of occupational therapy. OTs apply their knowledge of anatomy when working with nerve and muscle damage, tendon repairs, and other types of hand injuries. They also perform vocational retraining.

Lynn lists the qualities that a good OT should have as "problem-solving ability, versatility, friendliness, and an encouraging nature."

Lynn studied occupational therapy at the University of Puget Sound, where she received a bachelor of science degree. After college, Lynn worked in a physical rehabilitation center and an adult day care setting before joining the hospital where she works now.

Like many health care programs, OT programs usually require students to have volunteered in a related area for at least 40 hours. Lynn encourages students to volunteer in an OT setting, if possible. "This is a great way to get to know what the field is all about and find out whether it's a match for you."

After completing their course work, students must practice in at least two "affiliations," training in physical disabilities and psychiatry, for periods of three months each. They can then take the tests required to get their state licenses and national certification. OTs interested in a particular area may also complete affiliations in pediatrics, hand therapy, or another specialty. Entry-level jobs are available in hospitals, skilled nursing facilities, home care, burn wards, pediatrics, nursing homes, and outpatient clinics.

For more information about a career as an occupational therapist, contact the American Occupational Therapy Association.

11 The Cardiovascular System: Blood

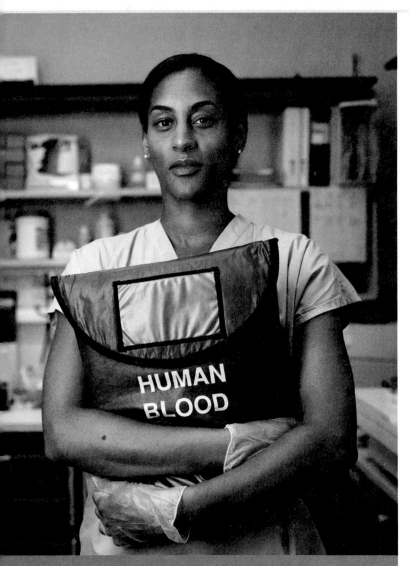

The old saying "Out of sight, out of mind" applies quite well to blood. As long as we don't see blood, we don't think or worry much about it. But looking at vials or bags of it in a hospital—or worse, watching our own blood oozing from a cut—makes most of us feel uneasy. This anxiety probably comes from being reminded of how dependent we are on our relatively small supply of the precious fluid. A sudden loss of 15 to 20 percent of a person's total blood volume is a clinical emergency—the person needs to receive some blood in a hurry. Fortunately, blood transfusions are now fairly routine matters—but as we will learn in this chapter, not just any blood will do.

VOCABULARY DEVELOPMENT

agglutinins gluing; *agglutinization*
embolos plug; *embolus*
erythros red; *erythrocytes*
haima blood; *hemostasis*
hypo- below; *hypoxia*
karyon nucleus; *megakaryocyte*

leukos white; *leukocyte*
megas big; *megakaryocyte*
myelos marrow; *myeloid*
-osis condition; *leukocytosis*
oxy- presence of oxygen; *hypoxia*
penia poverty; *leukopenia*

poiesis making; *hemopoiesis*
punctura a piercing; *venipuncture*
stasis halt; *hemostasis*
thrombos clot; *thrombocytes*
vena vein; *venipuncture*

An Introduction to the Cardiovascular System

The living body is in constant chemical communication with its external environment. Nutrients are absorbed through the lining of the digestive tract, gases move across the thin epithelium of the lungs, and wastes are excreted in the feces and urine. Even though these chemical exchanges occur at specialized sites, they affect every cell, tissue, and organ in a matter of moments because all parts of the body are linked by the **cardiovascular system,** an internal transport network.

The cardiovascular system can be compared to the cooling system of a car. Both systems have a circulating fluid (blood versus water), a pump (the heart versus a water pump), and flexible tubing to carry the fluid (the blood vessels versus radiator hoses). Although the cardiovascular system is far more complicated and versatile, both mechanical and biological systems can malfunction from fluid losses, pump failures, or damaged tubing.

Small embryos don't need cardiovascular systems because diffusion across their exposed surfaces can exchange materials rapidly enough to meet their demands. By the time an embryo has reached a few millimeters in length, however, developing tissues consume oxygen and nutrients and generate waste products faster than they can be provided or removed through simple diffusion. At that stage, the cardiovascular system must begin functioning to provide a rapid-transport system for oxygen, nutrients, and waste products. It is the first organ system to become fully operational: The heart begins beating by the end of the third week of embryonic life, when most other systems have barely begun to develop. When the heart starts beating, blood begins circulating. The embryo can now make more efficient use of the nutrients obtained from the maternal bloodstream, and its size doubles in the next week.

This chapter considers the nature of the circulating blood. Chapter 12 focuses on the structure and function of the heart, and Chapter 13 examines the organization of blood vessels and the integrated functions of the cardiovascular system.

Chapter 14 considers the lymphoid system, a defense system intimately connected to the cardiovascular system.

11-1 Blood has several important functions and unique physical characteristics

The circulating fluid of the body is **blood,** a specialized connective tissue that contains cells suspended in a fluid matrix. ∞ p. 106 Blood has five major functions:

1. *Transportation of dissolved gases, nutrients, hormones, and metabolic wastes.* Blood carries oxygen from the lungs to the tissues, and carbon dioxide from the tissues to the lungs. It distributes nutrients that are either absorbed at the digestive tract or released from storage in adipose tissue or in the liver. Blood carries hormones from endocrine glands toward their target cells. It also absorbs the wastes produced by active cells and carries these wastes to the kidneys for excretion.

2. *Regulation of the pH and ion composition of interstitial fluids throughout the body.* Diffusion between interstitial fluids and blood eliminates local deficiencies or excesses of ions such as calcium or potassium. Blood also absorbs and neutralizes the acids generated by active tissues, such as lactic acid produced by skeletal muscle contractions.

3. *Restriction of fluid losses at injury sites.* Blood contains enzymes and factors that respond to breaks in vessel walls by initiating the process of *blood clotting.* The resulting blood clot acts as a temporary patch that prevents further reductions in blood volume.

4. *Defense against toxins and pathogens.* Blood transports white blood cells, specialized cells that migrate into body tissues to fight infections or remove debris. Blood also delivers *antibodies,* special proteins that attack invading organisms or foreign compounds.

5. *Stabilization of body temperature.* Blood absorbs the heat generated by active skeletal muscles and redistributes it to other tissues. When body temperature is high, blood is directed to the skin surface, where heat is lost to the environment. When body temperature is too low, the flow of warm blood is restricted to crucial structures—to the brain and to other temperature-sensitive organs.

COMPOSITION OF BLOOD

Blood has a unique composition (Figure 11-1). It is a fluid connective tissue with a matrix called *plasma* (PLAZ-muh) and several *formed elements.* **Plasma** contains dissolved proteins rather than the network of insoluble fibers like those in loose connective tissue or cartilage. Because these proteins are in solution, plasma is slightly denser than water.

Formed elements are blood cells and cell fragments (platelets) suspended in the plasma. **Red blood cells (RBCs),** or **erythrocytes** (e-RITH-rō-sīts; *erythros,* red), transport oxygen and carbon dioxide. The less numerous **white blood cells (WBCs),** or **leukocytes** (LOO-kō-sīts; *leukos,* white), function as part of the body's defense mechanisms. **Platelets** are small, membrane-enclosed packets of cytoplasm that contain enzymes and factors important to blood clotting.

Formed elements are produced through the process of **hemopoiesis** (hē-mō-poy-Ē-sis), or *hematopoiesis.* Two populations of stem cells—*myeloid stem cells* and *lymphoid stem cells*—are responsible for the production of all the kinds of formed elements. We will consider the fates of the myeloid and lymphoid stem cells as we discuss the formation of each type of formed element.

Together, the plasma and formed elements constitute **whole blood.** The volume of whole blood ranges from 5 to 6 liters (5.3–6.4 quarts) in the cardiovascular system of an adult man, and from 4 to 5 liters (4.2–5.3 quarts) in that of an adult woman. Whole blood components may be separated, or **fractionated,** for analytical or clinical purposes.

BLOOD COLLECTION AND ANALYSIS

Fresh whole blood is usually collected from a superficial vein, such as the median cubital vein on the anterior surface of the elbow (Figure 11-1a). This procedure is called **venipuncture** (VĒN-i-punk-chur; *vena,* vein + *punctura,* a piercing). It is a common sampling technique because superficial veins are easy to locate, the walls of veins are thinner than those of arteries of comparable size, and blood pressure in the venous system is relatively low, so the puncture wound seals quickly. The most common clinical procedures examine venous blood.

Blood from peripheral capillaries can be obtained by puncturing the tip of a finger, an ear lobe, or (in infants) the great toe or heel of the foot. A small drop of capillary blood can be used to prepare a *blood smear,* a thin film of blood on a microscope slide. The blood smear is then stained with special dyes to show different types of formed elements.

An **arterial puncture,** or "arterial stick," may be required for evaluating the efficiency of gas exchange at the lungs. Samples are usually drawn from the radial artery at the wrist or the brachial artery at the elbow.

Whole blood from any of these sources has the same basic physical characteristics:

- *Temperature.* The temperature of blood is roughly 38°C (100.4°F), slightly above normal body temperature.

- *Viscosity.* Blood is five times as viscous as water—that is, five times stickier, more cohesive, and resistant to flow than water. The high viscosity results from interactions among the dissolved proteins, formed elements, and water molecules in plasma.

- *pH.* Blood is slightly alkaline, with a pH between 7.35 and 7.45 (average: 7.4). ∞ p. 39

CHECKPOINT

1. List five major functions of blood.

2. What two components make up whole blood?

3. Why is venipuncture a common technique for obtaining a blood sample?

See the blue Answers tab at the back of the book.

11-2 Plasma, the fluid portion of blood, contains significant quantities of plasma proteins

Plasma and interstitial fluid account for most of the volume of extracellular fluid (ECF) in the body. In this section we consider the composition of plasma and examine the proteins it contains.

THE COMPOSITION OF PLASMA

Plasma makes up 46–63% of the volume of whole blood, and water accounts for 92 percent of plasma volume (Figure 11-1b). In many respects, the composition of plasma resembles that of interstitial fluid (IF). The concentrations of the major plasma ions (electrolytes), for example, are similar to those of the IF

(a) Blood collection from a superficial vein

PLASMA PROTEINS

Albumins (60%)	Major contributors to osmotic pressure of plasma; transport lipids, steroid hormones
Globulins (35%)	Transport ions, hormones, lipids; immune function
Fibrinogen (4%)	Essential component of clotting system; can be converted to insoluble fibrin
Regulatory proteins (<1%)	Enzymes, proenzymes, hormones, prohormones

PLASMA COMPOSITION

Plasma proteins	7%
Other solutes	1%
Water	92%
Transports organic and inorganic molecules, formed elements, and heat	

(b) Components of plasma

OTHER SOLUTES

Electrolytes	Normal extracellular fluid ion composition essential for vital cellular activities Na^+, K^+, Ca^{2+}, Cl^-, HCO_3^-
Organic nutrients	Used for ATP production, growth, and maintenance of cells
Organic wastes	Carried to sites of breakdown or excretion

Sample of whole blood

consists of

Plasma (46–63%)

+

Formed elements (37–54%)

FORMED ELEMENTS

Platelets	0.1%
White blood cells	
Red blood cells	99.9%

(c) Formed elements of blood

PLATELETS

WHITE BLOOD CELLS

Neutrophils (50–70%)

Eosinophils (2–4%)

Basophils (<1%)

Lymphocytes (20–30%)

μm 0 5 10 15

Monocytes (2–8%)

RED BLOOD CELLS

FIGURE 11-1 The Composition of Whole Blood. (a) A sample of whole blood, as collected as shown in the photograph, contains plasma and formed elements. **(b)** Plasma, the liquid portion of blood, consists of plasma proteins and other solutes dissolved in water. **(c)** Formed elements include red blood cells, white blood cells, and platelets.

and differ from those inside cells. The similarity is understandable because a constant exchange of water, ions, and small solutes occurs between the interstitial fluid and plasma across the walls of capillaries (considered in Chapter 13). The primary differences between plasma and interstitial fluid involve the levels of respiratory gases (oxygen and carbon dioxide) and the concentrations of dissolved proteins. The differences in the levels of respiratory gases are due to the respiratory activities of cells (as discussed in Chapter 15). The protein concentrations differ because plasma proteins are too large to cross the walls of capillaries.

PLASMA PROTEINS

Plasma contains considerable quantities of dissolved proteins. On average, each 100 mL of plasma contains about 7 g of protein (**Figure 11-1b**), almost five times the concentration in interstitial fluid. The large size of most blood proteins prevents them from crossing capillary walls, so they remain confined to the circulatory system. The three primary types of plasma proteins are *albumins* (al-BŪ-minz), *globulins* (GLOB-ū-linz), and *fibrinogen* (fī-BRIN-ō-jen).

Albumins constitute roughly 60 percent of all plasma proteins. As the most abundant proteins, they are major contributors to the osmotic pressure of the plasma. **Globulins,** accounting for another 35 percent of plasma proteins, include antibodies and transport proteins. **Antibodies,** also called **immunoglobulins** (i-mū-nō-GLOB-ū-linz), attack foreign proteins and pathogens. **Transport proteins** bind small ions, hormones, or compounds that might otherwise be lost at the kidneys or that have very low solubility in water. One example is thyroid-binding globulin, which binds and transports thyroid hormones.

Both albumins and globulins can bind to lipids, such as triglycerides, fatty acids, or cholesterol. These lipids are not themselves water soluble, but the protein-lipid combination readily dissolves in plasma. In this way, the cardiovascular system transports insoluble lipids to peripheral tissues. Globulins involved in lipid transport are called *lipoproteins* (LĪ-pō-prō-tēnz).

The third type of plasma protein, **fibrinogen,** functions in blood clotting. Under certain conditions, fibrinogen molecules interact and convert to form large, insoluble strands of **fibrin** (FĪ-brin). These fibers provide the basic framework for a blood clot. If steps are not taken to prevent clotting in a plasma sample, fibrinogen will convert to fibrin. The fluid left after the clotting proteins are removed is known as **serum.**

The liver synthesizes more than 90 percent of the plasma proteins, including all albumins and fibrinogen and most of the globulins. Antibodies (immunoglobulins) are produced by

The Big Picture

Approximately half of the volume of whole blood consists of cells and cell products. Plasma resembles interstitial fluid but it contains a unique mixture of proteins not found in other extracellular fluids.

plasma cells of the lymphoid system. Because the liver is the primary source of plasma proteins, liver disorders can alter the composition and functional properties of the blood. For example, some forms of liver disease can lead to uncontrolled bleeding resulting from the inadequate synthesis of fibrinogen and other plasma proteins involved in the clotting response.

CHECKPOINT

4. List the three major types of plasma proteins.
5. What would be the effects of a decrease in the amount of plasma proteins?

See the blue Answers tab at the back of the book.

11-3 Red blood cells, formed by erythropoiesis, contain hemoglobin that can be recycled

Red blood cells (RBCs) are the most abundant blood cells, accounting for 99.9 percent of the formed elements. RBCs contain the pigment *hemoglobin,* which binds and transports oxygen and carbon dioxide.

ABUNDANCE OF RED BLOOD CELLS

The number of RBCs in the blood of a normal individual staggers the imagination. A standard blood test reports the number of RBCs per microliter (μL) of whole blood as the *red blood cell count*. In adult males, 1 microliter, or 1 cubic millimeter (mm^3), of whole blood contains roughly 5.4 million erythrocytes; in adult females, 1 microliter contains about 4.8 million. A single drop of whole blood contains some 260 million RBCs. Roughly one-third of the 75 trillion cells in the human body are red blood cells.

The **hematocrit** (he-MA-tō-krit) is the percentage of whole blood volume occupied by cellular elements. The hematocrit is measured after a blood sample has been spun in a centrifuge so that all the formed elements come out of suspension. In adult males, it averages 46 percent (range: 40–54); in adult females, 42 percent (range: 37–47). The sex difference in hematocrit reflects the fact that androgens (male hormones) stimulate red blood cell production, whereas estrogens (female hormones) do not. Because whole blood contains roughly 1000 red blood cells for each white blood cell, the hematocrit closely approximates the volume of RBCs. For this reason, hematocrit values are often reported as the *volume of packed red cells* (*VPRC*), or simply the *packed cell volume* (*PCV*).

Many conditions can affect the hematocrit. The hematocrit increases, for example, during dehydration (owing to a reduction in plasma volume) or after *erythropoietin* (*EPO*) stimulation. ∞ p. 366 The hematocrit decreases as a result of internal bleeding or problems with RBC formation. As a result, the hematocrit alone does not provide specific diagnostic information. However, a change in hematocrit is an indication that more specific tests are needed. (Some of those tests are discussed on p. 391.)

STRUCTURE OF RBCS

Red blood cells are specialized to transport oxygen and carbon dioxide within the bloodstream. As Figure 11-2 shows, each RBC is a biconcave disc with a thin central region and a thick outer margin. This unusual shape has two important effects on RBC function: (1) It gives each RBC a relatively large surface area to volume ratio that increases the rate of diffusion between its cytoplasm and the surrounding plasma, and (2) it enables RBCs to bend and flex to squeeze through narrow capillaries.

During their formation, RBCs lose most of their organelles, including mitochondria, ribosomes, and nuclei. Without a nucleus or ribosomes, RBCs can neither undergo cell division nor synthesize structural proteins or enzymes. Without mitochondria, they can obtain energy only through anaerobic metabolism, relying on glucose obtained from the surrounding plasma. This characteristic makes RBCs relatively inefficient in terms of energy use, but it ensures that any oxygen they absorb will be carried to peripheral tissues, not "stolen" by mitochondria in the cytoplasm.

HEMOGLOBIN STRUCTURE AND FUNCTION

A mature red blood cell consists of a cell membrane enclosing a mass of transport proteins. Molecules of **hemoglobin** (HĒ-mō-glō-bin) (**Hb**) account for over 95 percent of an RBC's intracellular proteins. Hemoglobin is responsible for the cell's ability to transport oxygen and carbon dioxide.

Two pairs of globular proteins (each pair composed of slightly different polypeptide chains) combine to form a single hemoglobin molecule. ∞ p. 48 Each of the four subunits contains a single molecule of an organic pigment called **heme.** Each heme molecule holds an iron ion in such a way that it can interact with an oxygen molecule (O_2). The iron–oxygen interaction is very weak, and the two can easily separate. RBCs containing hemoglobin with bound oxygen give blood a bright red color. The RBCs give blood a dark red, almost burgundy, color when oxygen is not bound to hemoglobin.

The amount of oxygen bound in each RBC depends on the conditions in the surrounding plasma. When oxygen is abundant in the plasma, hemoglobin molecules gain oxygen until all the heme molecules are occupied. As plasma oxygen levels decline, plasma carbon dioxide levels are usually rising.

(a) Blood smear

(b) SEM of RBCs

0.45–1.16 µm

2.31–2.85 µm

7.2–8.4 µm

(c) Sectional view of RBC

FIGURE 11-2 **The Anatomy of Red Blood Cells. (a)** When viewed in a standard blood smear, red blood cells appear as two-dimensional objects because they are flattened against the surface of the slide. (LM × 320) **(b)** A scanning electron micrograph of red blood cells reveals their three-dimensional structure. (SEM × 1195) **(c)** The average dimensions of a mature red blood cell are indicated in this sectional view.

Abnormal Hemoglobin

Clinical Note

Several inherited disorders are characterized by the production of abnormal hemoglobin. Two of the best known are *thalassemia* and *sickle cell anemia* (SCA).

The various forms of **thalassemia** (thal-ah-SĒ-mē-uh) result from an inability to produce adequate amounts of the globular protein components of hemoglobin. As a result, the rate of RBC production is slowed, and mature RBCs are frag-

ile and short lived. The scarcity of healthy RBCs reduces the oxygen-carrying capacity of the blood and leads to problems in growth and development. Individuals with severe thalassemia must undergo frequent *transfusions*—the administration of blood components—to maintain adequate numbers of RBCs in the blood.

Sickle cell anemia (SCA) results from a mutation affecting the amino acid sequence of one pair of the globular proteins of the hemoglobin molecule. When blood contains an abundance of oxygen, the hemoglobin molecules and the RBCs that carry them appear normal (Figure 11-3a). But when the defective hemoglobin gives up enough of its stored oxygen, the adjacent hemoglobin molecules interact and the cells change shape, becoming stiff and markedly curved (Figure 11-3b). This "sickling" does not affect the oxygen-carrying capabilities of the RBCs, but it makes them more fragile and easily damaged. The untimely breakdown of such "sickled" RBCs produces a characteristic hemolytic anemia. Moreover, when an RBC that has folded to squeeze into a narrow capillary delivers its oxygen to the surrounding tissue, the cell can become stuck as sickling occurs. This blocks blood flow, and nearby tissues become oxygen starved.

(a) Normal RBC   **(b) Sickled RBC**

FIGURE 11-3 Sickling in Red Blood Cells. (a) When fully oxygenated, the red blood cells of an individual with sickle cell trait have the same appearance as normal RBCs. **(b)** At lower oxygen concentrations the RBCs change shape, becoming more rigid and sharply curved ("sickled"). (SEM × 5200)

Under these conditions, hemoglobin molecules release their oxygen reserves, and the globin portion of each hemoglobin molecule begins to bind carbon dioxide molecules in a process that is just as reversible as the binding of oxygen to heme.

As red blood cells circulate, they are exposed to varying concentrations of oxygen and carbon dioxide. At the lungs, where diffusion brings oxygen into the plasma and removes carbon dioxide, the hemoglobin molecules in red blood cells respond by absorbing oxygen and releasing carbon dioxide. In peripheral tissues, the situation is reversed; active cells consume oxygen and produce carbon dioxide. As blood flows through these areas, oxygen diffuses out of the plasma, and carbon dioxide diffuses in. Under these conditions, hemoglobin releases its bound oxygen and binds carbon dioxide.

Normal activity levels can be sustained only when tissue oxygen levels are kept within normal limits. The blood of a person who has a low hematocrit, or whose RBCs have a reduced hemoglobin content, has a reduced oxygen-carrying capacity. This condition is called **anemia.** Anemia causes a variety of symptoms, including premature muscle fatigue, weakness, and a general lack of energy.

RBC LIFE SPAN AND CIRCULATION

RBCs are exposed to severe physical stresses. A single round-trip through the circulatory system usually takes less than a minute, but in that time a red blood cell is forced along vessels where it bounces off the walls, collides with other red blood cells, and is squeezed through tiny capillaries. With all this mechanical battering and no repair mechanisms, an RBC has a relatively short life span—only about 120 days. The continuous elimination of RBCs usually goes unnoticed because new ones enter the circulation at a comparable rate. About 1 percent of the circulating RBCs are replaced each day, and approximately 3 million new RBCs enter the circulation each second!

Hemoglobin Recycling

As red blood cells age or are damaged, some of them rupture. When this occurs, the hemoglobin breaks down in the blood, and the individual polypeptide chains are filtered from the blood by the kidneys and lost in the urine. When large numbers of RBCs break down in the circulation, the urine can turn reddish or brown, a condition called **hemoglobinuria.**

Fortunately, only about 10 percent of RBCs survive long enough to rupture, or **hemolyze** (HĒ-mō-līz), within the bloodstream. Instead, phagocytic cells (macrophages) in the liver, spleen, and bone marrow usually recognize and engulf RBCs before they undergo *hemolysis,* in the process recycling hemoglobin and other components of RBCs. (Phagocytosis and phagocytic cells were introduced in Chapter 3; additional details are given in Chapter 14.) ∞ p. 71

The recycling of hemoglobin and turnover of red blood cells is shown in Figure 11-4. Once a red blood cell has been engulfed and broken down by a macrophage, each component of a hemoglobin molecule has a different fate:

1. The four globular proteins of each hemoglobin molecule are disassembled into their component amino acids. These amino acids are either metabolized by the cell or released into the circulation for use by other cells.

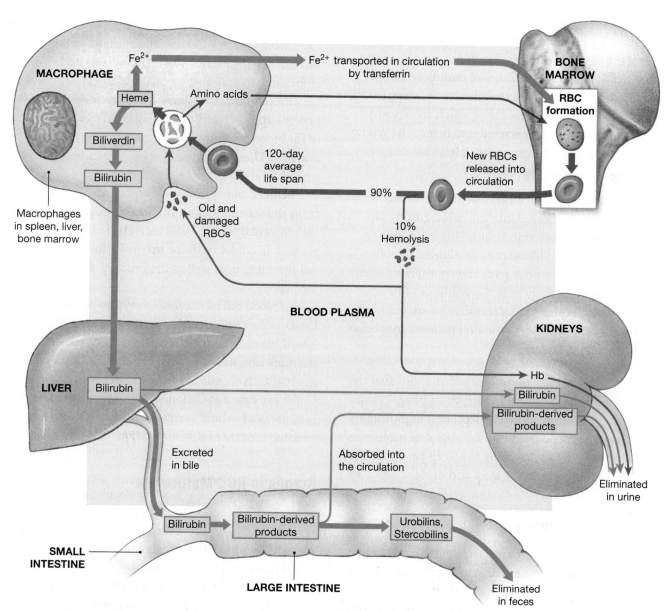

FIGURE 11-4 Hemoglobin Recycling. Macrophages in the spleen, liver, and bone marrow phagocytize and break down old and damaged RBCs, releasing the components of the hemoglobin molecules they contain. The breakdown of the protein portion of hemoglobin releases amino acids into the bloodstream for use by other cells, including RBCs developing in the red bone marrow. Iron from the heme units is either used in the formation of new hemoglobin or stored in the liver, spleen, and bone marrow. After removal of the iron, the remaining portions of the heme units are converted to bilirubin. Bilirubin in the circulation is absorbed by the liver and excreted within bile, which is released into the intestine. Bilirubin-derived products are excreted in urine or feces.

2. Each heme molecule is stripped of its iron and converted to **biliverdin** (bil-i-VER-din), an organic compound with a green color. (Bad bruises commonly appear greenish because biliverdin forms in the blood-filled tissues.) Biliverdin is then converted to **bilirubin** (bil-i-ROO-bin), an orange-yellow pigment, and released into the circulation. Liver cells absorb the bilirubin and normally release it into the small intestine within the bile. If, however, the bile ducts are blocked (by gallstones, for example), bilirubin then diffuses into peripheral tissues, giving them a yellow color that is most apparent in the skin and the sclera of the eyes. The condition characterized by yellow skin and eyes is called **jaundice** (JAWN-dis). Bilirubin reaching the large intestine is converted to related pigment molecules, some of which are absorbed into the bloodstream and excreted into urine. The yellow color of urine and the brown color of feces are due to these bilirubin-derived pigments.

3. Iron extracted from heme molecules may be stored in the macrophage or released into the bloodstream, where it binds to **transferrin** (tranz-FER-in), a plasma transport protein. Red blood cells developing in the bone marrow absorb amino acids and transferrins from the circulation and use them in the synthesis of new hemoglobin molecules. Excess transferrins are removed in the liver and spleen, where the iron is stored in special protein–iron complexes.

In summary, most of the components of an individual red blood cell are recycled following hemolysis or phagocytosis. The entire system is remarkably efficient; although roughly 26 mg of iron are incorporated into hemoglobin molecules each day, a dietary supply of 1–2 mg can keep pace with the incidental losses that occur in the feces and urine.

Gender and Iron Reserves

Any impairment in iron uptake or metabolism can cause serious clinical problems because RBC formation will be affected. Women are especially dependent on a normal dietary supply of iron because their iron reserves are smaller than those of men. The body of a normal man contains around 3.5 g of iron in the ionic form Fe^{2+}. Of that amount, 2.5 g is bound to the hemoglobin of circulating red blood cells, and the rest is stored in the liver and bone marrow. In women, total body iron content averages 2.4 g, with roughly 1.9 g incorporated into red blood cells. Thus, a woman's iron reserves consist of only 0.5 g, half that of a typ-

ical man. If dietary supplies of iron are inadequate, hemoglobin production slows, and symptoms of *iron deficiency anemia* appear. The accumulation of too much iron in the liver and in cardiac muscle tissue can also cause problems. Excessive iron deposition in cardiac muscle cells has recently been linked to heart disease.

RBC FORMATION

Embryonic blood cells appear in the bloodstream during the third week of development. These cells divide repeatedly, rapidly increasing in number. The vessels of the *yolk sac,* an embryonic membrane, are the primary sites of blood formation for the first eight weeks of development. As other organ systems appear, some of the embryonic blood cells move out of the bloodstream and into the liver, spleen, thymus, and bone marrow. These embryonic cells differentiate into stem cells whose divisions produce blood cells.

The liver and spleen are the primary sites of hemopoiesis from the second to fifth months of development, but as the skeleton enlarges, the bone marrow becomes increasingly important. In adults, red bone marrow is the only site of red blood cell production, as well as the primary site of white blood cell formation.

Red blood cell formation, or **erythropoiesis** (e-rith-rō-poy-Ē-sis), occurs only in *red bone marrow,* or **myeloid tissue** (MĪ-e-loyd; *myelos,* marrow). This tissue is located in the vertebrae, sternum, ribs, scapulae, pelvis, and proximal limb bones. Other marrow areas contain a fatty tissue known as *yellow bone marrow.* Under extreme stimulation, such as a severe and sustained blood loss, areas of yellow marrow can convert to red marrow, increasing the rate of RBC formation.

Stages in RBC Maturation

Specialists in blood formation and function—**hematologists** (hē-ma-TOL-o-jists)—give specific names to key stages in the maturation of the formed elements. Like all formed elements, RBCs result from the divisions of hemocytoblasts (pluripotent stem cells) in red bone marrow (Figure 11-5). In giving rise to the cells that ultimately become RBCs, the hemocytoblasts produce **myeloid stem cells,** some of which proceed through a series of stages in their development to mature erythrocytes (see left side of Figure 11-5).

Erythroblasts are very immature red blood cells that are actively synthesizing hemoglobin. After roughly 4 days of differentiation, each erythroblast sheds its nucleus and becomes

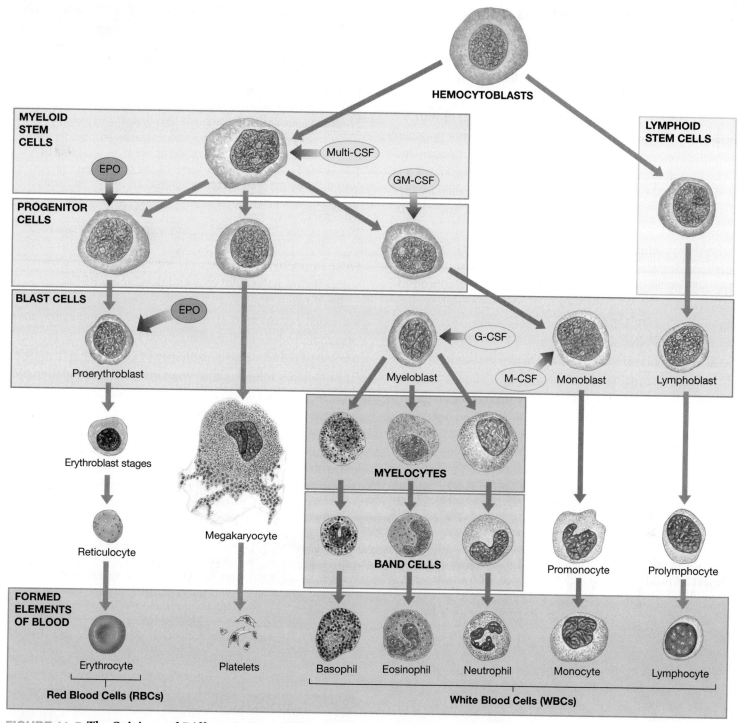

FIGURE 11-5 **The Origins and Differentiation of RBCs, Platelets, and WBCs.** Hemocytoblast divisions give rise to (1) lymphoid stem cells, which produce the various lymphocytes, and (2) myeloid stem cells, which produce cells that ultimately become red blood cells, platelets, and the other types of white blood cells. Hematologists use specific terms for the various key stages the formed elements pass through on the way to maturity. The targets of EPO and four colony-stimulating factors (CSFs) are also indicated.

a **reticulocyte** (re-TIK-ū-lō-sīt). After 2 or 3 more days in the bone marrow synthesizing proteins, reticulocytes enter the bloodstream. At this time they can still be detected in a blood smear with stains that specifically combine with RNA.

Normally, reticulocytes account for about 0.8 percent of the circulating erythrocytes. After 24 hours in circulation, the reticulocytes complete their maturation and become indistinguishable from other mature RBCs.

The Regulation of Erythropoiesis

For erythropoiesis to proceed normally, the red bone marrow must receive adequate supplies of amino acids, iron, and vitamins (including B_{12}, B_6, and folic acid) required for protein synthesis. We obtain **vitamin B_{12}** from dairy products and meat, and its absorption requires the presence of *intrinsic factor* produced in the stomach. If vitamin B_{12} is not obtained from the diet, normal stem cell divisions cannot occur, and *pernicious anemia* results. Erythropoiesis is stimulated directly by the hormone erythropoietin and indirectly by several hormones, including thyroxine, androgens, and growth hormone.

Erythropoietin (EPO), also called *erythropoiesis-stimulating hormone,* appears in the plasma when peripheral tissues—especially the kidneys—are exposed to low oxygen concentrations (**Figure 11-6**). The state of low tissue oxygen levels is called **hypoxia** (hī-POKS-ē-uh; *hypo-*, below + *oxy-*, presence of oxygen). EPO is released (1) during anemia, (2) when blood flow to the kidneys declines, (3) when the oxygen content of air in the lungs declines (owing to disease or high altitude), and (4) when the respiratory surfaces of the lungs are damaged.

Clinical Note

Blood Tests and RBCs

Blood tests provide information about the general health of an individual, usually with a minimum of trouble and expense.

Several common blood tests focus on red blood cells, the most abundant formed element. These RBC tests assess the number, size, shape, and maturity of circulating RBCs. This information provides an indication of the bone marrow's RBC-forming activities and can also be useful in detecting problems, such as internal bleeding, that may not produce obvious signs. Table 11-1 lists some important blood tests and the terms associated with abnormal values.

Once in the bloodstream, EPO travels to red bone marrow, where it stimulates stem cells and developing RBCs.

Erythropoietin has two major effects: (1) It stimulates increased cell division rates in erythroblasts and in the stem cells that produce erythroblasts, and (2) it speeds up the maturation of red blood cells, primarily by accelerating the rate of hemoglobin synthesis. Under maximum EPO stimulation, the bone marrow can increase the rate of RBC formation tenfold, to around 30 million cells per second.

This ability is important to a person recovering from a severe blood loss. However, if EPO is administered to a healthy person, the hematocrit may rise to 65 or more, and the resulting increase in blood viscosity increases the workload on the

The Big Picture

Red blood cells (RBCs) are the most numerous cells in the body. They remain in circulation for approximately 4 months before being recycled; several million are produced each second. The hemoglobin inside RBCs transports oxygen from the lungs to peripheral tissues; it also carries carbon dioxide from those tissues to the lungs.

FIGURE 11-6 The Role of EPO in the Control of Erythropoiesis. Tissues deprived of oxygen release EPO, which accelerates division of stem cells and the maturation of erythroblasts. More red blood cells then enter the circulation, improving the delivery of oxygen to peripheral tissues.

CHECKPOINT

6. Describe hemoglobin.

7. What effect does dehydration have on an individual's hematocrit?

8. In what way would a disease that causes liver damage affect the level of bilirubin in the blood?

9. What effect does a reduction in oxygen supply to the kidneys have on levels of erythropoietin in the blood?

See the blue Answers tab at the back of the book.

TABLE 11-1 **Common RBC Tests and Related Terminology**

TEST	DETERMINES	TERMS ASSOCIATED WITH ABNORMAL VALUES	
		ELEVATED	DEPRESSED
HEMATOCRIT (HCT)	Percentage of formed elements in whole blood Normal = 37–54%	Polycythemia (may result from erythrocytosis or leukocytosis)	Anemia
COMPLETE BLOOD COUNT (CBC) RBC count	Number of RBCs per mL of whole blood Normal = 4.2–6.3 million/μL	Erythrocytosis/polycythemia	Anemia
Hemoglobin concentration (Hb)	Concentration of hemoglobin in blood Normal = 12–18 g/dL		Anemia
Reticulocyte count (Retic.)	Circulating percentage of reticulocytes Normal = 0.8%	Reticulocytosis	
Mean corpuscular volume (MCV)	Average volume of a single RBC Normal = 82–101μm³ (normocytic)	Macrocytic	Microcytic
Mean corpuscular hemoglobin concentration (MCHC)	Average amount of Hb in one RBC Normal = 27–34 pg/μL (normochromic)	Hyperchromic	Hypochromic

heart, which can lead to sudden death from heart failure. Similar risks result from *blood doping,* in which athletes reinfuse packed RBCs removed at an earlier date for the purpose of improving performance by increasing oxygen delivery to muscles.

11-4 The ABO blood types and Rh system are based on antigen-antibody responses

Antigens are substances (most often proteins) that can trigger an *immune response,* a defense mechanism that protects the body from infection. The membranes of all your cells contain surface antigens, substances that your immune defenses recognize as "normal." In other words, your immune system ignores these substances rather than attacking them as "foreign."

Red blood cells have at least 50 kinds of surface antigens. Which antigens your RBCs have is genetically determined. The presence or absence of three antigens on the surface of RBCs—A, B, and Rh—determines your **blood type.**

All of the red blood cells of a given individual have the same pattern of surface antigens. **Type A** blood has antigen A only, **Type B** has antigen B only, **Type AB** has both A and B, and **Type O** has neither A nor B (Figure 11-7a). Variations in these values differ by ethnic group and by region (Table 11-2).

The term **Rh positive** (Rh⁺) indicates the presence of the Rh antigen on the surface of RBCs. The absence of this antigen is indicated as **Rh negative** (Rh⁻). When an individual's

TABLE 11-2 **The Distribution of Blood Types in Selected Populations**

POPULATION	PERCENTAGE WITH EACH BLOOD TYPE				
	O	A	B	AB	Rh⁺
U.S. (AVERAGE)	46	40	10	4	85
African American	49	27	20	4	95
Caucasian	45	40	11	4	85
Chinese American	42	27	25	6	100
Filipino American	44	22	29	6	100
Hawaiian	46	46	5	3	100
Japanese American	31	39	21	10	100
Korean American	32	28	30	10	100
NATIVE NORTH AMERICAN	79	16	4	<1	100
NATIVE SOUTH AMERICAN	100	0	0	0	100
AUSTRALIAN ABORIGINE	44	56	0	0	100

complete blood type is recorded, the term *Rh* is usually omitted, and the data are reported as O negative (O⁻), A positive (A⁺) and so on. In the general U.S. population, blood types are distributed approximately as follows: O⁺, 38 percent; A⁺, 34 percent; B⁺, 9 percent; O⁻, 7 percent; A⁻, 6 percent; AB⁺, 3 percent; B⁻, 2 percent; and AB⁻, 1 percent.

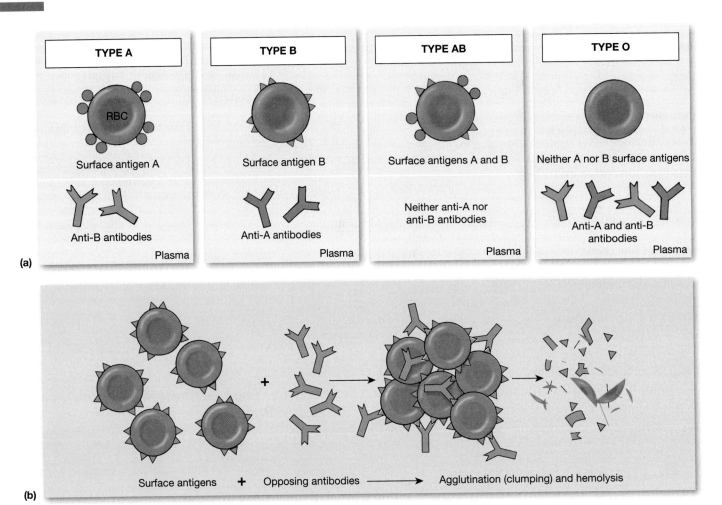

FIGURE 11-7 Blood Types and Cross-Reactions. (a) Blood type depends on the presence or absence of antigens on the surfaces of RBCs. For each blood type except Type AB, plasma contains antibodies that will react with foreign RBC antigens. **(b)** A cross-reaction occurs when antibodies in plasma encounter their target antigens on RBCs. The result is extensive clumping (agglutination) and hemolysis of the affected RBCs.

CROSS-REACTIONS IN TRANSFUSIONS

We noted previously that your immune system ignores the surface antigens—also called *agglutinogens* (a-gloo-TIN-ō-jenz)—on your own RBCs. However, your plasma contains antibodies, or *agglutinins* (a-GLOO-ti-ninz), that will attack surface antigens on RBCs of a different blood type (Figure 11-7a). Thus, the plasma of individuals with Type A blood contains circulating anti-B antibodies, which will attack Type B surface antigens, and the plasma of Type B individuals contains anti-A antibodies, which will attack Type A surface antigens. Similarly, Type AB individuals lack antibodies against either A or B surface antigens, whereas the plasma of individuals with Type O blood contains both anti-A and anti-B antibodies.

The presence of these antibodies is why, before blood is transfused, the blood types of donor and recipient are identified. If an individual receives blood of a different blood type, antibodies in the recipient's plasma meet their specific antigen on the donated RBCs, and a **cross-reaction** occurs (Figure 11-7b). Initially the binding of antigens and antibodies causes the foreign RBCs to clump together—a process called **agglutination** (a-gloo-ti-NĀ-shun). Subsequently, the RBCs may break up, or *hemolyze*. Clumps and fragments of RBCs under attack from antibodies form drifting masses that can plug small vessels in the kidneys, lungs, heart, or brain, damaging or destroying tissues. Such cross-reactions, or *transfusion reactions,* can be avoided by ensuring that the blood types of donor and recipient are **compatible.**

In practice, the surface antigens on the donor's cells are more important in determining compatibility than are the antibod-

Clinical Note

Testing for Blood Compatibility

Testing for blood compatibility normally involves two steps: a determination of blood type and a *cross-match test.* Although some 50 RBC surface antigens are known, the standard test for blood type categorizes a blood sample on the basis of the three most likely to produce dangerous cross-reactions. The test involves mixing drops of blood with solutions containing anti-A, anti-B, and anti-Rh antibodies and noting any cross-reactions. For example, if the RBCs clump together when exposed to anti-A and anti-B, the individual has Type AB blood. If no reactions occur, the person must be Type O. The presence or absence of the Rh antigen is also noted, and the individual is classified as Rh-positive or Rh-negative. In the most common type—Type O-positive (O⁺)—the RBCs lack surface antigens A and B, but they do have the Rh antigen. Standard blood typing of both donor and recipient can be completed in a matter of minutes.

In an emergency (such as a severe gunshot wound), a patient may require 5 *liters* or more of blood before the damage can be repaired. Under these circumstances, Type O blood can be safely administered to a victim of any blood type because Type O RBCs lack A and B surface antigens. Because their blood cells are unlikely to produce severe cross-reactions in a recipient, Type O (especially O⁻) individuals are sometimes

called *universal donors.* Type AB individuals were once called *universal recipients* because they lack anti-A or anti-B antibodies, which would attack donated RBCs. This term has been dropped from usage largely because reliable blood supplies and quick compatibility testing typically allow the administration of Type AB blood to Type AB recipients.

With at least 48 other possible antigens on the cell surface, however, cross-reactions can occur, even to Type O blood. Whenever time and facilities permit, further testing is performed to ensure complete compatibility. **Cross-match testing** involves exposing the donor's RBCs to a sample of the recipient's plasma under controlled conditions. This procedure reveals the presence of significant cross-reactions involving other antigens and antibodies. Another way to avoid compatibility problems is to replace lost blood with synthetic blood substitutes, which do not contain surface antigens that can trigger a cross-reaction.

Other applications of blood compatibility—for example, paternity tests and crime detection—stem from the fact that blood groups are inherited. Results from such tests cannot prove that a particular individual is the criminal or the father involved, but it can prove that he is not involved. For example, a man with Type AB blood cannot be the father of an infant with Type O blood.

ies in the donor's plasma. Unless large volumes of whole blood or plasma are transferred, cross-reactions between the donor's plasma and the recipient's blood cells will fail to produce significant agglutination. Packed RBCs, with a minimal amount of plasma, are commonly transfused. Even when whole blood is transfused, the plasma is diluted through mixing with the recipient's relatively large plasma volume.

Unlike the case for Type A and Type B individuals, the plasma of an Rh-negative individual does not normally contain anti-Rh antibodies. These antibodies are present only if the individual has been *sensitized* by previous exposure to Rh-positive RBCs. Such exposure can occur accidentally, during a transfusion, but it can also occur in a normal pregnancy when an Rh-negative mother carries an Rh-positive fetus.

CHECKPOINT

10. Which blood type(s) can be safely transfused into a person with Type AB blood?

11. Why can't a person with Type A blood safely receive blood from a person with Type B blood?

See the blue Answers tab at the back of the book.

11-5 The various types of white blood cells contribute to the body's defenses

White blood cells, also known as WBCs or **leukocytes,** can be distinguished from RBCs by their larger size and by the presence of a nucleus and other organelles. WBCs also lack hemoglobin. White blood cells help defend the body against invasion by pathogens, and they remove toxins, wastes, and abnormal or damaged cells. Traditionally, WBCs have been divided into two groups based on their appearance after staining: (1) *granulocytes,* which contain abundant stained "granules" (which are secretory vesicles and lysosomes), and (2) *agranulocytes,* in which few if any stained granules are apparent. This categorization is convenient but somewhat misleading because each agranulocyte also contains vesicles and lysosomes, but they are quite small and difficult to see using a light microscope.

Typical WBCs in the circulating blood are shown in Figure 11-8. *Neutrophils, eosinophils,* and *basophils* are granulocytes; *monocytes* and *lymphocytes* are agranulocytes. Even though a microliter of blood typically contains 6000–9000

(a) Neutrophil

(b) Eosinophil

(c) Basophil

(d) Monocyte

(e) Lymphocyte

RBC

Platelets

FIGURE 11-8 **White Blood Cells.** (LMs × 1500)

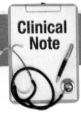

Clinical Note

Hemolytic Disease of the Newborn

Genes controlling the presence or absence of any surface antigen in the membrane of an RBC are provided by both parents, so a child's blood type can differ from that of either parent. During pregnancy, when fetal and maternal circulatory systems are closely intertwined, certain kinds of the mother's antibodies may cross the placenta, attacking and destroying fetal RBCs. The resulting potentially fatal condition is called **hemolytic disease of the newborn (HDN).**

The sensitization that causes this condition usually occurs during delivery, when bleeding at the placenta and uterus exposes an Rh-negative mother to an Rh-positive fetus's Rh antigens. This event can trigger the production of anti-Rh antibodies in the mother. Because these antibodies are not produced in significant amounts until after delivery, the first Rh-positive infant is not affected. However, a sensitized Rh-negative mother will respond to a second Rh-positive fetus by producing massive amounts of anti-Rh antibodies. These antibodies attack and hemolyze the fetal RBCs, producing a dangerous anemia, which increases the fetal demand for blood cells. The resulting RBCs leave the bone marrow and enter the circulation before completing their development. Because these immature RBCs are erythroblasts, HDN is also known as *erythroblastosis fetalis* (e-rith-rō-blas-TŌ-sis fe-TAL-is).

WBCs, circulating WBCs represent only a small fraction of the total population. Most of the WBCs in the body are located in connective tissue proper or in organs of the lymphoid system.

WBC CIRCULATION AND MOVEMENT

Unlike RBCs, WBCs circulate for only a short portion of their life span. White blood cells migrate through the loose and dense connective tissues of the body, using the bloodstream to travel from one organ to another and for rapid transportation to areas of invasion or injury. WBCs are sensitive to the chemical signs of damage to surrounding tissues. When problems are detected, these cells leave the bloodstream and enter the damaged area.

Circulating WBCs have four characteristics:

1. They are capable of *amoeboid movement,* a gliding motion accomplished by the flow of cytoplasm into slender cellular processes extended out from the cell. This mobility allows WBCs to move along the walls of blood vessels and, when outside the bloodstream, through surrounding tissues.

2. They can migrate out of the bloodstream. WBCs can enter surrounding tissue by squeezing between adjacent epithelial cells in the capillary wall. This process is called *diapedesis* (dī-a-pe-DĒ-sis).

3. They are attracted to specific chemical stimuli. This characteristic, called **positive chemotaxis** (kē-mō-TAK-sis), guides WBCs to invading pathogens, damaged tissues, and other active WBCs.

4. Neutrophils, eosinophils, and monocytes are capable of *phagocytosis.* ∞ p. 71 These cells can engulf pathogens, cell debris, or other materials. Neutrophils and eosinophils are sometimes called *microphages* to distinguish them from the larger macrophages in connective tissues. Macrophages are monocytes that have moved out of the bloodstream and become actively phagocytic.

TYPES OF WBCs

Neutrophils, eosinophils, basophils, and monocytes contribute to the body's *nonspecific defenses.* These defenses respond to a variety of stimuli but always in the same way—they do not discriminate between one type of threat and another. Lymphocytes, in contrast, are the cells responsible for *specific defenses:* the body's ability to attack invading pathogens or foreign proteins *on a specific, individual basis.* The interactions between WBCs, and the relationships between specific and nonspecific defenses, will be discussed in Chapter 14.

Neutrophils

Fifty to 70 percent of the circulating white blood cells are **neutrophils** (NOO-trō-filz). This name reflects the fact that their granules are chemically neutral and thus are difficult to stain with either acidic or basic dyes. A mature neutrophil has a very dense, contorted nucleus with two to five lobes resembling beads on a string (Figure 11-8a).

Neutrophils are usually the first WBCs to arrive at an injury site. They are very active phagocytes, specializing in attacking and digesting bacteria. Most neutrophils have a short life span (about 10 hours). After engulfing one to two dozen bacteria, a neutrophil dies, but its breakdown releases chemicals that attract other neutrophils to the site. A mixture of dead neutrophils, cellular debris, and other waste products form the *pus* associated with infected wounds.

Eosinophils

Eosinophils (ē-ō-SIN-ō-filz) were so named because their granules stain darkly with the red dye eosin (Figure 11-8b). They usually represent 2–4 percent of circulating WBCs and are similar in size to neutrophils. Their deep red granules and a two-lobed nucleus make them easy to identify. Eosinophils at-

tack objects that are coated with antibodies. Although they will engulf antibody-marked bacteria, protozoa, or cellular debris, their primary mode of attack is the exocytosis of toxic compounds, including nitric oxide and cytotoxic enzymes. Their numbers increase dramatically during a parasitic infection or an allergic reaction.

Basophils

Basophils (BĀ-sō-filz) have numerous granules that stain darkly with basic dyes. In a standard blood smear, the granules are a deep purple or blue (Figure 11-8c). These cells are somewhat smaller than neutrophils or eosinophils and are relatively rare, accounting for less than 1 percent of the circulating WBC population. Basophils migrate to sites of injury and cross the capillary wall to accumulate within damaged tissues, where they discharge their granules into the interstitial fluids. The granules contain the chemicals *heparin,* which prevents blood clotting, and *histamine.* The release of histamine by basophils enhances the local inflammation initiated by mast cells within damaged connective tissues. ∞ p. 115 Other chemicals released by stimulated basophils attract eosinophils and other basophils to the area.

Monocytes

Monocytes (MON-ō-sīts) are nearly twice the size of a typical erythrocyte (Figure 11-8d). The nucleus is large and commonly oval or shaped like a kidney bean. Monocytes normally account for 2–8 percent of circulating WBCs. They remain in circulation for only about 24 hours before entering peripheral tissues to become tissue macrophages. These migrating monocytes are called *free macrophages* to distinguish them from the immobile *fixed macrophages* present in many connective tissues. ∞ p. 104 They are aggressive phagocytes, often attempting to engulf items as large as or larger than themselves. Active monocytes release chemicals that attract and stimulate neutrophils, additional monocytes, and other phagocytes, and that draw fibroblasts to the region. The fibroblasts then begin to produce scar tissue, which walls off the injured area.

Lymphocytes

Typical **lymphocytes** (LIM-fō-sīts) are slightly larger than RBCs and contain a relatively large nucleus surrounded by a thin halo of cytoplasm (Figure 11-8e). Lymphocytes account for 20–30 percent of the WBC population in blood. Lymphocytes are continuously migrating from the bloodstream, through peripheral tissues, and back to the bloodstream. Circulating lymphocytes represent a very small fraction of the entire WBC population, for at any moment most lymphocytes are in other connective tissues and in organs of the lymphoid system. They also protect the body and its tissues, but they do not rely on phagocytosis. Some kinds of lymphocytes attack foreign cells and abnormal body cells; other kinds secrete antibodies into the circulation. The antibodies can attack foreign cells or proteins in distant parts of the body.

THE DIFFERENTIAL COUNT AND CHANGES IN WBC ABUNDANCE

A variety of disorders, including infections, inflammation, and allergic reactions, cause characteristic changes in the circulating populations of WBCs. By examining a stained blood smear, we can obtain a **differential count** of the WBC population. The values reported indicate the number of each type of cell in a sample of 100 WBCs.

The normal range for the differential count for each WBC type is included in Table 11-3. The term **leukopenia** (loo-kō-PĒ-ne-uh; *penia*, poverty) indicates reduced numbers of WBCs. **Leukocytosis** (loo-kō-sī-TO-sis) refers to excessive numbers of WBCs. Extreme leukocytosis (WBC counts of 100,000/μL or more) usually indicates the presence of some form of **leukemia** (loo-KĒ-mē-uh), a cancer of blood-forming tissues. Only some of the many types of leukemia are characterized by leukocytosis; other indications are the presence of abnormal or immature WBCs. Treatment helps in some cases; unless treated, all are fatal.

WBC FORMATION

As previously noted, hemocytoblasts—the cells from which all the formed elements develop—are present in red bone marrow. Hemocytoblasts produce (1) lymphoid stem cells, which give rise to lymphocytes, and (2) myeloid stem cells, which give rise to all the other types of formed elements (Figure 11-5, p. 389). Basophils, eosinophils, and neutrophils complete their development in myeloid (marrow) tissue; monocytes begin their differentiation in the bone marrow, enter the circulation, and complete their development when they become free macrophages in peripheral tissues. Each of these cell types goes through a characteristic series of developmental stages.

Many of the lymphoid stem cells responsible for the production of lymphocytes migrate from the bone marrow to peripheral **lymphoid tissues,** including the thymus, spleen, and lymph nodes. As a result, lymphocytes are produced in these organs as well as in the bone marrow. The process of lymphocyte production is called **lymphopoiesis.**

Various hormones are involved in the regulation of white blood cell populations. WBCs other than lymphocytes are regulated by hormones called *colony-stimulating factors* (*CSFs*). Four CSFs have been identified, each targeting single stem cell lines or groups of stem cell lines (Figure 11-5, p. 389). Prior to an individual's maturity, hormones produced by the thymus gland (thymosins) promote the differentiation of one type of lymphocyte, the *T cells*. (In adults, the production of lymphocytes is regulated by exposure to antigens such as foreign proteins, cells, and toxins. We will describe the control mechanisms in Chapter 14.)

Many aspects of the body's defenses depend on the effects of lymphocyte hormones on the production of other WBCs. For example, active macrophages release chemicals that make lymphocytes more sensitive to antigens and accelerate the development of specific immunity. In turn, active lymphocytes release CSFs, which reinforce nonspecific defenses by stimulating the production of other WBCs. Because of their potential clinical importance, immune system hormones are being studied intensively. Several CSFs are now produced by genetic engineering; one of them is used to stimulate the production of neutrophils in patients undergoing cancer chemotherapy.

The Big Picture

White blood cells (WBCs) are usually outnumbered by RBCs by a ratio of 1000:1. WBCs are responsible for defending the body against infection, foreign cells, or toxins, and for assisting in the cleanup and repair of damaged tissues. The most numerous are neutrophils, which engulf bacteria, and lymphocytes, which are responsible for the specific defenses of the immune response.

CHECKPOINT

12. Identify the five types of white blood cells.

13. Which type of white blood cell would you expect to find in the greatest numbers in an infected cut?

14. Which type of cell would you find in elevated numbers in a person producing large amounts of circulating antibodies to combat a virus?

15. How do basophils respond during inflammation?

See the blue Answers tab at the back of the book.

TABLE 11-3 A Review of the Formed Elements of the Blood

	CELL	ABUNDANCE (AVERAGE PER μL)	FUNCTIONS	REMARKS
	RED BLOOD CELLS	5.2 million (range: 4.4–6.0 million)	Transport oxygen from lungs to tissues, and carbon dioxide from tissues to lungs	Remain in bloodstream; 120-day life expectancy; amino acids and iron recycled; produced in bone marrow
	WHITE BLOOD CELLS	7000 (range: 6000–9000)		
	Neutrophils	4150 (range: 1800–7300) Differential count: 50–70%	Phagocytic: Engulf pathogens or debris in tissues, release cytotoxic enzymes and chemicals	Move into tissues after several hours; survive minutes to days, depending on tissue activity; produced in bone marrow
	Eosinophils	165 (range: 0–700) Differential count: 2–4%	Attack antibody-labeled materials through release of cytotoxic enzymes and/or phagocytosis	Move into tissues after several hours; survive minutes to days, depending on tissue activity; produced in bone marrow
	Basophils	44 (range: 0–150) Differential count: < 1%	Enter damaged tissues and release histamine and other chemicals that promote inflammation	Survival time unknown; assist mast cells of tissues in producing inflammation; produced in bone marrow
	Monocytes	456 (range: 200–950) Differential count: 2–8%	Enter tissues to become macrophages; engulf pathogens or debris	Move into tissues after 1–2 days; survive months or longer; primarily produced in bone marrow
	Lymphocytes	2185 (range: 1500–4000) Differential count: 20–30%	Cells of lymphoid system; provide defense against specific pathogens or toxins	Survive months to decades; circulate from blood to tissues and back; produced in bone marrow and lymphoid tissues
	PLATELETS	350,000 (range: 150,000–500,000)	Hemostasis: Clump together and stick to vessel wall (platelet phase); initiate coagulation phase	Remain in circulation or in vascular organs; survive 7–12 days; produced by megakaryocytes in bone marrow

11-6 Platelets, disc-shaped structures formed from megakaryocytes, function in the clotting process

Platelets (PLĀT-lets) are another component of the formed elements. In nonmammalian vertebrates, platelets are nucleated cells called **thrombocytes** (THROM-bō-sīts; *thrombos*, clot). Because in humans these formed elements are cell fragments rather than individual cells, the term *platelet* is preferred when referring to our blood.

Bone marrow contains enormous cells with large nuclei called **megakaryocytes** (meg-a-KAR-ē-ō-sīts; *megas*, big + *karyon*, nucleus + *-cyte*, cell) (Figure 11-5). Megakaryocytes continuously shed cytoplasm in small membrane-enclosed packets. These packets are the platelets that enter the bloodstream. Platelets initiate the clotting process and help close injured blood vessels. They are a major participant in a vascular *clotting system*, detailed in the next section.

Platelets are continuously replaced. An individual platelet circulates for 9–12 days before being removed by phagocytes. Each microliter of circulating blood contains 150,000–500,000 platelets; 350,000/μL is the average concentration. An abnormally low platelet count (80,000/μL or less) is known as *thrombocytopenia* (throm-bō-sī-tō-PĒ-nē-uh), and this condition usually results from excessive platelet destruction or inadequate platelet production. Clinical signs include bleeding along the digestive tract, within the skin, and occasionally inside the CNS.

In *thrombocytosis* (throm-bō-sī-TŌ-sis), platelet counts can exceed 1,000,000/μL. Thrombocytosis usually results from accelerated platelet formation in response to infection, inflammation, or cancer.

CHECKPOINT

16. Explain the difference between platelets and thrombocytes.

17. List the primary functions of platelets.

See the blue Answers tab at the back of the book.

11-7 Hemostasis involves vascular spasm, platelet plug formation, and blood coagulation

Hemostasis (*haima*, blood + *stasis*, halt), the process that halts bleeding, prevents the loss of blood through the walls of dam-aged vessels. In restricting blood loss, this process also establishes a framework for tissue repairs.

PHASES OF HEMOSTASIS

Hemostasis is a process consisting of three overlapping phases:

1. *The Vascular Phase:* The walls of blood vessels contain smooth muscle and an inner lining of simple squamous epithelium known as an **endothelium** (en-dō-THĒ-lē-um). Cutting the wall of a blood vessel triggers a contraction in the smooth muscle fibers in the vessel wall that decreases the vessel's diameter. This local contraction, called a *vascular spasm,* can slow or even stop the loss of blood through the wall of a small vessel. The vascular spasm lasts about 30 minutes, a period that constitutes the **vascular phase** of hemostasis. Changes also occur in the vessel's endothelium; the membranes of endothelial cells at the injury site become "sticky," and in small capillaries the cells may stick together and block the opening completely.

2. *The Platelet Phase:* The platelets begin to attach to the sticky endothelial surfaces and exposed collagen fibers within 15 seconds of the injury. These attachments mark the start of the **platelet phase** of hemostasis. As more platelets arrive, they begin sticking to one another as well. This process forms a *platelet plug,* a mass that may close the break in the vessel wall, if the damage is not severe or occurs in a small blood vessel.

3. *The Coagulation Phase:* The vascular and platelet phases begin within a few seconds after the injury. The **coagulation** (cō-ag-ū-LĀ-shun) **phase** does not start until 30 seconds or more after the vessel has been damaged. **Coagulation,** or *blood clotting,* involves a complex sequence of steps leading to the conversion of circulating fibrinogen into the insoluble protein fibrin. As the fibrin network grows, blood cells and additional platelets are trapped within the fibrous tangle, forming a **blood clot** that effectively seals off the damaged portion of the vessel (Figure 11-9).

THE CLOTTING PROCESS

Normal blood clotting cannot occur unless the plasma contains the necessary **clotting factors,** which include calcium ions and 11 different plasma proteins. These proteins are converted from inactive *proenzymes* to active enzymes that direct essential reactions in the clotting response. Most of the circulating clotting proteins are synthesized by the liver.

During the coagulation phase, the clotting proteins interact in sequence, such that one protein is converted into an enzyme that activates a second protein and so on, in a chain reaction, or *cascade*. Figure 11-10 provides an overview of the cascades involved in the *extrinsic, intrinsic,* and *common pathways,* which result in the formation of a blood clot. The extrinsic pathway begins outside the bloodstream, in the vessel wall; the intrinsic pathway begins inside the bloodstream. These pathways join at the common pathway through the activation of Factor X, a clotting protein produced by the liver.

The Extrinsic, Intrinsic, and Common Pathways

When a blood vessel is damaged, both the extrinsic and intrinsic pathways are activated. Clotting usually begins in 15 seconds and is initiated by the shorter and faster extrinsic pathway. The slower, intrinsic pathway reinforces the initial clot, making it larger and more effective.

The **extrinsic pathway** begins with the release of a lipoprotein called **tissue factor** by damaged endothelial cells or peripheral tissues. The greater the damage, the more tissue factor is released and the faster clotting occurs. Tissue factor then combines with calcium ions and another clotting protein (Factor VII) to form an enzyme capable of activating Factor X.

The **intrinsic pathway** begins with the activation of proenzymes exposed to collagen fibers at the injury site. This pathway proceeds with the assistance of a *platelet factor* released by

FIGURE 11-9 **The Structure of a Blood Clot.** This colorized scanning electron micrograph shows the fibrin network that forms the framework of a clot. (SEM × 4120) Red blood cells trapped in those fibers add to the mass of the blood clot and make it red. Platelets that stick to the fibrin strands gradually contract, shrinking the clot and tightly packing the RBCs within it.

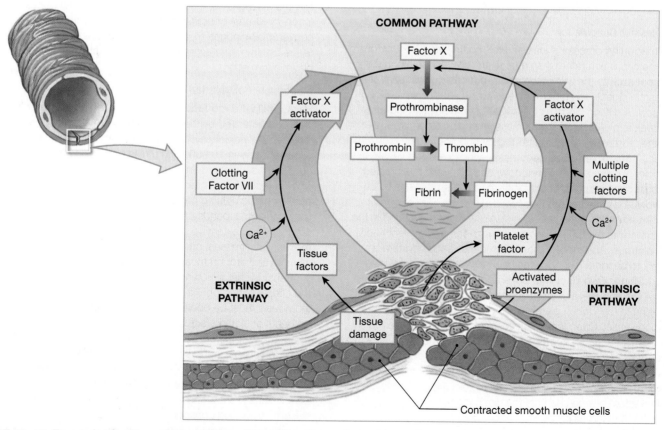

FIGURE 11-10 **Events in the Coagulation Phase of Hemostasis.**

aggregating platelets. Platelets also release a variety of other factors that speed up the reactions of the intrinsic pathway. After a series of linked reactions, activated clotting proteins combine to form an enzyme capable of activating Factor X.

The **common pathway** begins when enzymes from either the extrinsic or the intrinsic pathway activate Factor X, forming the enzyme prothrombinase. Prothrombinase converts the clotting protein **prothrombin** into the enzyme **thrombin** (THROM-bin). Thrombin then completes the clotting process by converting fibrinogen to fibrin.

The thrombin formed in the common pathway also acts to increase the rate of clot formation. Thrombin stimulates the formation of tissue factor and the release of platelet factor by platelets. The presence of these factors further stimulates both the extrinsic and intrinsic pathways. This positive feedback loop accelerates the clotting process, and speed is important in reducing blood loss after a severe injury. ∞ p. 14

Calcium ions and a single vitamin, **vitamin K,** affect almost every aspect of the clotting process. Because all three pathways (intrinsic, extrinsic, and common) require the presence of calcium ions, any disorder that lowers plasma calcium ion concentrations will also impair blood clotting. Because adequate amounts of vitamin K must be present for the liver to synthesize four of the clotting factors (including prothrombin), a vitamin K deficiency leads to the breakdown of the common pathway, inactivating the clotting system. Roughly half of the vitamin K the body needs is absorbed directly from the diet, and the rest is synthesized by intestinal bacteria.

CLOT RETRACTION AND REMOVAL

Once the fibrin network has appeared, platelets and red blood cells stick to the fibrin strands. The platelets then contract, pulling the torn edges of the wound closer together as the en-

---

Clinical Note

Abnormal Hemostasis

Hemostasis involves a complex chain of events, and any disorder that affects any individual clotting factor can disrupt the entire process. As a result, many clinical conditions affect the clotting process.

Excessive Coagulation

If the clotting process is inadequately controlled, clots will form in the circulation rather than at an injury site. These blood clots do not stick to the wall of the vessel but drift downstream until plasmin digests them or they become lodged in a small blood vessel. A drifting blood clot is a type of embolus (EM-bo-lus; *embolos,* plug), an abnormal mass within the bloodstream. (Other common emboli are drifting air bubbles and fat globules.) When an embolus becomes lodged in a blood vessel, it blocks circulation to the area downstream, killing the affected tissues. The condition resulting from vascular blockage by an embolus is called **embolism.**

An embolus in the arterial system can become lodged in the capillaries in the brain, causing a tissue-damaging event known as a *stroke.* An embolus that forms in the venous system is likely to become lodged in the capillaries in the lung, causing a condition known as *pulmonary embolism.*

A **thrombus**—a blood clot attached to a vessel wall— begins to form when platelets stick to the wall of an intact blood vessel. Often the platelets are attracted to roughened areas called *plaques,* where endothelial and smooth muscle cells contain large quantities of lipids. The blood clot gradually enlarges, projecting into the vessel's channel (or *lumen*) and reducing its diameter. Eventually the vessel may be completely blocked, or a large chunk of the clot can break off, creating an equally dangerous embolus.

Treatment of these conditions must be prompt to prevent irreparable damage to tissues whose vessels have been restricted or blocked by emboli or thrombi. The clots can be surgically removed, or they can be attacked by administering anticoagulants—such as the enzymes *streptokinase* (strep-tō-KĪ-nās) or *urokinase* (ū-rō-KĪ-nās), which convert plasminogen to plasmin—or by administering *tissue plasminogen activator* (*t-PA*), which stimulates plasmin formation.

Inadequate Coagulation

Hemophilia (hē-mō-FĒL-ē-uh) is one of many inherited disorders characterized by the inadequate production of clotting factors. The incidence of this condition in the general population is about 1 in 10,000, with males accounting for 80–90 percent of those affected. In hemophilia, the production of a single clotting factor (most often Factor VIII, an essential component of the intrinsic clotting pathway) is inadequate; the severity of the condition depends on the degree of underproduction. In severe cases, extensive bleeding accompanies the slightest mechanical stresses, and hemorrhages occur spontaneously at joints and around muscles.

Transfusions of clotting factors can reduce or control the effects of hemophilia, but plasma samples from many individuals must be pooled (combined) to obtain adequate amounts of clotting factors. This procedure makes treatment very expensive and increases the risk of blood-borne infections such as hepatitis or AIDS. Gene-splicing techniques have been used to manufacture Factor VIII. As methods are developed to synthesize other clotting factors, treatment of the various forms of hemophilia will become safer and cheaper.

tire clot begins to undergo **clot retraction.** This process reduces the size of the damaged area, making it easier for the fibroblasts, smooth muscle cells, and endothelial cells in the area to make the necessary repairs.

As repairs proceed, the clot gradually dissolves. This process, called **fibrinolysis** (fī-bri-NOL-i-sis), begins with the activation of the plasma protein **plasminogen** (plaz-MIN-ō-jen) by

thrombin and **tissue plasminogen activator,** or **t-PA,** which is released by damaged tissues. The activation of plasminogen produces the enzyme **plasmin** (PLAZ-min), which begins digesting the fibrin strands and breaking down the clot.

The Big Picture

Platelets are involved in the coordination of hemostasis (blood clotting). When platelets are activated by abnormal changes in their local environment, they release clotting factors and other chemicals. Hemostasis is a complex cascade that establishes a fibrous patch that can subsequently be remodeled and then removed as the damaged area is repaired.

CHECKPOINT

18. If a sample of bone marrow has fewer than normal numbers of megakaryocytes, what body process would you expect to be impaired as a result?

19. Two alternate pathways of interacting clotting proteins lead to coagulation, or blood clotting. How is each pathway initiated?

20. What are the effects of a vitamin K deficiency on blood clotting (coagulation)?

See the blue Answers tab at the back of the book.

RELATED CLINICAL TERMS

anemia (a-NĒ-mē-uh): A condition in which the oxygen-carrying capacity of blood is reduced due to low hematocrit or low blood hemoglobin concentrations.

embolism: A condition in which a drifting blood clot (embolus) becomes stuck in a blood vessel, blocking circulation to the area downstream.

erythrocytosis (e-rith-rō-sī-TŌ-sis): A polycythemia involving red blood cells only.

hematocrit (he-MAT-ō-krit): The percentage of whole blood volume occupied by cellular elements.

hematology (HĒM-ah-tol-o-jē): The study of blood and its disorders.

hematuria (hē-ma-TOO-rē-uh): The presence of red blood cells in the urine.

hemolytic disease of the newborn (HDN): A condition in which fetal red blood cells are destroyed by maternal antibodies.

hemophilia (hē-mō-FĒL-ē-uh): Inherited disorders characterized by inadequate production of clotting factors.

heterologous marrow transplant: The transplantation of bone marrow from one individual to another to replace bone marrow destroyed during cancer therapy.

hypoxia (hī-POKS-ē-uh): Low tissue oxygen levels.

jaundice (JAWN-dis): A condition characterized by yellow skin and eyes, resulting from abnormally high levels of bilirubin in the plasma.

leukemia (loo-KĒ-mē-uh): A cancer of blood-forming tissues characterized by extremely elevated levels of circulating white blood cells; in-

cludes both *myeloid leukemia* (abnormal granulocytes or other cells of the bone marrow) and *lymphoid leukemia* (abnormal lymphocytes).

leukopenia (loo-kō-PĒ-ne-uh): Inadequate numbers of white blood cells in the bloodstream.

normovolemic (nor-mō-vō-LĒ-mik): Having a normal blood volume.

phlebotomy (fle-BOT-o-mē): The process of withdrawing blood from a vein.

polycythemia (po-lē-sī-THĒ-mē-uh): An elevated hematocrit accompanied by a normal blood volume.

septicemia: A dangerous condition in which bacteria and bacterial toxins are distributed throughout the body in the bloodstream.

sickle cell anemia: An anemia resulting from the production of an abnormal form of hemoglobin; causes red blood cells to become sickle shaped at low oxygen levels.

thalassemia: An inherited blood disorder resulting from the production of an abnormal form of hemoglobin.

thrombus: A blood clot attached to the internal surface of a blood vessel.

transfusion: A procedure in which blood components are given to someone to restore blood volume or to remedy some deficiency in blood composition.

venipuncture (VĒN-i-punk-chur): The puncturing of a vein for any purpose, including the withdrawal of blood or the administration of medication.

Chapter 11 Review

KEY TERMS

blood *381*

cardiovascular system *381*

coagulation *398*

embolus *400*

erythrocyte *382*

fibrin *384*

fibrinolysis *401*

hematocrit *384*

hemoglobin *385*

hemopoiesis *382*

hemostasis *398*

leukocyte *382*

plasma *382*

platelets *382*

serum *384*

SUMMARY OUTLINE

An Introduction to the Cardiovascular System

p. 381

1. The **cardiovascular system** provides a mechanism for the rapid transport of nutrients, waste products, respiratory gases, and cells within the body.

11-1 Blood has several important functions and unique physical characteristics *p. 381*

2. **Blood** is a specialized fluid connective tissue. Its functions include (1) transporting dissolved gases, nutrients, hormones, and metabolic wastes; (2) regulating the pH and electrolyte composition of the interstitial fluids; (3) restricting fluid losses through damaged vessels; (4) defending against pathogens and toxins; and (5) regulating body temperature by absorbing and redistributing heat.

3. Blood contains **plasma, red blood cells (RBCs), white blood cells (WBCs),** and **platelets.** The plasma and formed elements constitute whole blood, which can be **fractionated** for analytical or clinical purposes. *(Figure 11-1a)*

4. **Hemopoiesis** is the process by which all formed elements are produced. *Myeloid stem cells* and *lymphoid stem cells* divide to form all three types of formed elements.

11-2 Plasma, the fluid portion of blood, contains significant quantities of plasma proteins *p. 382*

5. Plasma accounts for about 55 percent of the volume of blood; roughly 92 percent of plasma is water. *(Figure 11-1b)*

6. Compared with interstitial fluid, plasma has a higher dissolved oxygen concentration and more dissolved proteins. The three classes of plasma proteins are *albumins, globulins,* and *fibrinogen.*

7. **Albumins** constitute about 60 percent of plasma proteins. **Globulins** constitute roughly 35 percent of plasma proteins;

they include **antibodies (immunoglobulins),** which attack foreign proteins and pathogens, and **transport proteins,** which bind ions, hormones, and other compounds. In the clotting reaction, **fibrinogen** molecules are converted to **fibrin.** The removal of clotting proteins from plasma leaves a fluid called **serum.**

11-3 Red blood cells, formed by erythropoiesis, contain hemoglobin that can be recycled *p. 384*

8. Red blood cells (**RBCs**), or **erythrocytes,** account for slightly less than half of the blood volume and 99.9 percent of the formed elements. The **hematocrit** is the percentage of whole blood volume occupied by cellular elements. *(Figure 11-1c; Table 11-1)*

9. RBCs transport oxygen and carbon dioxide within the bloodstream. They are highly specialized cells with a large surface area to volume ratio. They lack many organelles and usually degenerate after 120 days in the bloodstream. *(Figure 11-2)*

10. Molecules of **hemoglobin (Hb)** account for over 95 percent of RBC proteins. Hemoglobin is a globular protein formed from four subunits. Each subunit contains a single molecule of **heme** and can reversibly bind an oxygen molecule. Hemoglobin from damaged or dead RBCs is recycled by phagocytes. *(Figure 11-4)*

11. **Erythropoiesis,** the formation of RBCs, occurs mainly in the **red bone marrow (myeloid tissue)** in adults. RBC formation increases under stimulation by **erythropoietin (EPO),** or erythropoiesis-stimulating hormone, which occurs when peripheral tissues are exposed to low oxygen concentrations. Stages in RBC development include **erythroblasts** and **reticulocytes.** *(Figures 11-5, 11-6)*

11-4 The ABO blood types and Rh system are based on antigen-antibody responses *p. 391*

12. **Blood type** is determined by the presence or absence of three specific **surface antigens** (*agglutinogens*) in the cell membranes of RBCs: antigens A, B, and Rh. Antibodies (*agglutinins*) in the plasma of individuals of some blood types can react with surface antigens on the RBCs of different blood types. Anti-Rh antibodies are synthesized only after an Rh-negative individual becomes sensitized to the Rh surface antigen. *(Figure 11-7; Table 11-2)*

11-5 The various types of white blood cells contribute to the body's defenses *p. 393*

13. White blood cells (WBCs), or **leukocytes,** defend the body against pathogens and remove toxins, wastes, and abnormal or damaged cells.

14. Leukocytes exhibit *diapedesis* (the ability to move through vessel walls) and **chemotaxis** (an attraction to specific chemicals).

15. *Granulocytes* (granular leukocytes) are *neutrophils, eosinophils,* and *basophils.* Fifty to 70 percent of circulating WBCs are **neutrophils,** which are highly mobile phagocytes. The much less common **eosinophils** are phagocytes attracted to foreign substances that have reacted with circulating antibodies. The relatively rare **basophils** migrate to damaged tissues and release histamine, aiding the inflammation response. *(Figure 11-8)*

16. *Agranulocytes* (agranular leukocytes) are *monocytes* and *lymphocytes.* **Monocytes** that migrate into peripheral tissues become free macrophages. Most **lymphocytes** are in the tissues and organs of the **lymphoid system,** where they function in the body's specific defenses. Different classes of lymphocytes attack foreign cells directly, produce antibodies, and destroy abnormal body cells. *(Figure 11-8)*

17. Granulocytes and monocytes are produced by **myeloid stem cells** in the bone marrow. **Lymphoid stem cells** responsible for **lymphopoiesis** (production of lymphocytes) also originate in the bone marrow, but many migrate to lymphoid tissues. *(Figure 11-5)*

18. Factors that regulate lymphocyte maturation are not completely understood. *Colony-stimulating factors* (*CSFs*) are hormones involved in regulating other WBC populations.

11-6 Platelets, disc-shaped structures formed from megakaryocytes, function in the clotting process *p. 398*

19. **Megakaryocytes** in the bone marrow release packets of cytoplasm (platelets) into the circulating blood. Platelets are essential to the clotting process. *(Figure 11-5)*

11-7 Hemostasis involves vascular spasm, platelet plug formation, and blood coagulation
p. 398

20. **Hemostasis** prevents the loss of blood through the walls of damaged vessels.

21. The initial step of hemostasis, the **vascular phase,** is a period of local contraction of vessel walls resulting from a vascular spasm at the injury site. The **platelet phase** follows as platelets stick to damaged surfaces. The third phase of hemostasis is the **coagulation phase.**

22. The coagulation phase occurs as factors released by endothelial cells or peripheral tissues (**extrinsic pathway**) and platelets (**intrinsic pathway**) interact with **clotting factors** to form a **blood clot.** *(Figures 11-9, 11-10)*

23. During **clot retraction,** platelets contract, pulling the torn edges of a damaged blood vessel closer together. During **fibrinolysis,** the clot gradually dissolves through the action of **plasmin,** the activated form of circulating **plasminogen.**

REVIEW QUESTIONS

WWW Access more review material online at The Anatomy & Physiology Place (**www.anatomyandphysiology.com**). There, you'll find Chapter Guides, Chapter Quizzes, Chapter Practice Tests, Interactive Flashcards, a Glossary with Pronunciations, and more to help you succeed in the course.

Level 1: • Reviewing Facts and Terms

Match each item in column A with the most closely related item in column B. Place letters for answers in the spaces provided.

COLUMN A

_____ 1. interstitial fluid
_____ 2. hemopoiesis
_____ 3. stem cells
_____ 4. hypoxia
_____ 5. surface antigens
_____ 6. antibodies
_____ 7. diapedesis
_____ 8. leukopenia
_____ 9. agranulocyte
_____ 10. leukocytosis
_____ 11. granulocyte
_____ 12. thrombocytopenia

COLUMN B

a. hemocytoblasts
b. abundant WBCs
c. agglutinogens
d. neutrophil
e. WBC migration
f. extracellular fluid
g. monocyte
h. few WBCs
i. low platelet count
j. agglutinins
k. blood cell formation
l. low oxygen concentration

13. Identify the five types of white blood cells in the following micrographs.

(a)   (b)   (c)

(d)   (e)

(a) _____   (b) _____
(c) _____   (d) _____
(e) _____

14. The formed elements of the blood include
   (a) plasma, fibrin, and serum.
   (b) albumins, globulins, and fibrinogen.
   (c) WBCs, RBCs, and platelets.
   (d) a, b, and c are correct.

15. Blood temperature is approximately _____, and the blood pH averages _____.
   (a) 98.6°F, 7.0   (b) 104°F, 7.8
   (c) 100.4°F, 7.4   (d) 96.8°F, 7.0

16. Plasma contributes approximately _____ percent of the volume of whole blood, and water accounts for _____ percent of the plasma volume.
   (a) 55, 92   (b) 25, 55
   (c) 92, 55   (d) 35, 72

17. When the clotting proteins are removed from plasma, _____ remains.
   (a) fibrinogen   (b) fibrin
   (c) serum   (d) heme

18. In an adult, the only site of red blood cell production, and the primary site of white blood cell formation, is the
   (a) liver.   (b) spleen.
   (c) thymus.   (d) red bone marrow.

19. The most numerous WBCs found in a differential count of a "normal" individual are
   (a) neutrophils.   (b) basophils.
   (c) lymphocytes.   (d) monocytes.

20. Stem cells responsible for the process of lymphopoiesis are located in the
   (a) thymus and spleen.   (b) lymph nodes.
   (c) red bone marrow.   (d) a, b, and c are correct.

21. The first step in the process of hemostasis is
   (a) coagulation.   (b) the platelet phase.
   (c) fibrinolysis.   (d) vascular spasm.

22. The complex sequence of steps leading to the conversion of fibrinogen to fibrin is called
   (a) fibrinolysis.   (b) clotting.
   (c) retraction.   (d) the platelet phase.

23. What three primary classes of plasma proteins are found in the blood? What is the major function of each?

24. What type(s) of antibodies does the plasma contain for each of the following blood types?
   (a) Type A   (b) Type B
   (c) Type AB   (d) Type O

25. What four characteristics of WBCs are important to their response to tissue invasion or injury?

26. What contribution from the intrinsic and/or extrinsic pathways is necessary for the common pathway to begin?

27. Distinguish between an embolus and a thrombus.

Level 2: • Reviewing Concepts

28. Dehydration would cause
   (a) an increase in the hematocrit.
   (b) a decrease in the hematocrit.
   (c) no effect in the hematocrit.
   (d) an increase in plasma volume.

29. Erythropoietin directly stimulates RBC formation by
   (a) increasing rates of mitotic divisions in erythroblasts.
   (b) speeding up the maturation of red blood cells.
   (c) accelerating the rate of hemoglobin synthesis.
   (d) a, b, and c are correct.

30. A person with Type A blood has
   (a) anti-A antibodies in the plasma.
   (b) B antigens in the plasma.
   (c) A antigens on red blood cells.
   (d) anti-B antibodies on red blood cells.

31. Hemolytic disease of the newborn can result if
   (a) the mother is Rh-positive and the father is Rh-negative.
   (b) both the father and the mother are Rh-negative.
   (c) both the father and the mother are Rh-positive.
   (d) an Rh-negative woman carries an Rh-positive fetus.

32. How do red blood cells differ from typical body cells?

Level 3: • Critical Thinking and Clinical Applications

33. Which of the formed elements would you expect to increase after you have donated a pint of blood?

34. Why do many individuals with advanced kidney disease become anemic?

35. In the disease mononucleosis ("mono"), the spleen enlarges because of increased numbers of phagocytes and other cells. Common signs and symptoms of this disease include pale complexion, a tired feeling, and a lack of energy sometimes to the point of not being able to get out of bed. What might cause each of these signs and symptoms?

12 The Cardiovascular System: The Heart

The hardworking muscles of this off-road cyclist require a steady supply of blood for their nutrients and oxygen. This is especially true of the hardest-working muscle of all: your heart. Any major interruption in the flow of blood to this organ has grave consequences—what we commonly call a heart attack. Such attacks typically occur when there is an obstruction in one of the coronary arteries that supply the heart muscle. An exercise stress test can aid a physician in determining the presence of a coronary artery blockage which may not be apparent while an individual is at rest.

LEARNING OUTCOMES

After completing this chapter, you should be able to do the following:

12-1 Describe the anatomy of the heart—including its surface features; the structure of the pericardium, heart wall, and cardiac skeleton; and the heart's blood supply—and trace the flow of blood through the heart, identifying the major blood vessels, chambers, and heart valves.

12-2 Explain the events of an action potential in cardiac muscle, describe the conducting system of the heart, and identify the electrical events recorded in an electrocardiogram.

12-3 Explain the events of the cardiac cycle, and relate the heart sounds to specific events in this cycle.

12-4 Define cardiac output, describe the factors that influence heart rate and stroke volume, and explain how adjustments in stroke volume and cardiac output are coordinated at different levels of physical activity.

VOCABULARY DEVELOPMENT

anastomosis outlet; *anastomoses*
atrion hall; *atrium*
auris ear; *auricle*
bi- two; *bicuspid*
bradys slow; *bradycardia*
cuspis point; *bicuspid valve*

diastole expansion; *diastole*
-gram record; *electrocardiogram*
luna moon; *semilunar valve*
mitre a bishop's hat; *mitral valve*
papilla nipple-shaped elevation; *papillary muscles*

semi- half; *semilunar valve*
septum wall; *interatrial septum*
systole a drawing together; *systole*
tachys swift; *tachycardia*
tri- three; *tricuspid valve*
ventricle little belly; *ventricle*

The Heart's Role in the Cardiovascular System

Our body cells rely on the surrounding interstitial fluid for oxygen, nutrients, and waste disposal. Conditions in the interstitial fluid are kept stable through continuous exchange between the peripheral tissues and circulating blood. If the blood stops moving, its oxygen and nutrient supplies are quickly exhausted, its capacity to absorb wastes is soon saturated, and neither hormones nor white blood cells can reach their intended targets. Thus, all cardiovascular functions ultimately depend on the heart. This muscular organ beats approximately 100,000 times each day, pumping roughly 8000 liters of blood—enough to fill forty 55-gallon drums, or nearly 8500 quart-sized milk cartons.

Blood flows through a network of blood vessels that extends between the heart and peripheral tissues. Blood vessels are subdivided into a **pulmonary circuit,** which carries blood to and from the exchange surfaces of the lungs, and a **systemic circuit,** which transports blood to and from the rest of the body (**Figure 12-1**). Each circuit begins and ends at the heart, and blood travels through these circuits in sequence. Thus, blood returning to the heart from the systemic circuit must complete the pulmonary circuit before reentering the systemic circuit.

Arteries, or *efferent* vessels, carry blood away from the heart; **veins,** or *afferent* vessels, return blood to the heart. **Capillaries** are small, thin-walled vessels between the smallest arteries and the smallest veins. The thin walls of capillaries permit the exchange of nutrients, dissolved gases, and waste products between the blood and surrounding tissues.

Despite its impressive workload, the heart is a small organ, roughly the size of a clenched fist. The heart contains four chambers, two associated with each circuit. The **right atrium** (Ā-trē-um; hall; plural, *atria*) receives blood from the systemic circuit, and the **right ventricle** (VEN-tri-kl; "little belly") dis-

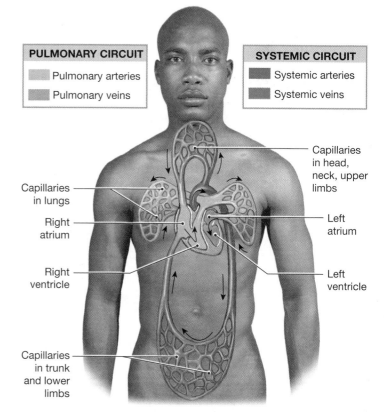

PULMONARY CIRCUIT	
	Pulmonary arteries
	Pulmonary veins

SYSTEMIC CIRCUIT	
	Systemic arteries
	Systemic veins

Capillaries in head, neck, upper limbs

Capillaries in lungs

Right atrium

Left atrium

Right ventricle

Left ventricle

Capillaries in trunk and lower limbs

FIGURE 12-1 An Overview of the Cardiovascular System.
Driven by the pumping of the heart, blood flows through separate pulmonary and systemic circuits. Each circuit begins and ends at the heart and contains arteries, capillaries, and veins.

charges blood into the pulmonary circuit. The **left atrium** collects blood from the pulmonary circuit, and the **left ventricle** ejects it into the systemic circuit. When the heart beats, the two atria contract first, then the ventricles. The two ventricles contract at the same time and eject equal volumes of blood.

We begin this chapter by examining the structural features that enable the heart to perform so reliably. We will then consider the physiological mechanisms that regulate the activities of the heart to meet the body's ever-changing needs.

12-1 The heart is a four-chambered organ, supplied by coronary circulation, that pumps oxygen-poor blood to the lungs and oxygen-rich blood to the rest of the body

The heart lies near the anterior chest wall, directly behind the sternum (Figure 12-2a). It is enclosed by the *mediastinum,* the connective tissue mass that divides the thoracic cavity into two pleural cavities (see Figure 1-10c, p. 21) and also contains the thymus, esophagus, and trachea.

The heart is surrounded by the **pericardial** (per-i-KAR-dē-al) **cavity.** The lining of the pericardial cavity is a serous membrane called the **pericardium.** ∞ p. 111 To visualize the relationship

between the heart and the pericardial cavity, imagine pushing your fist toward the center of a large balloon (Figure 12-2b). The balloon represents the pericardium, and your fist represents the heart. Your wrist, where the balloon folds back on itself, corresponds to the **base** of the heart (Figure 12-2a). The air space inside the balloon corresponds to the pericardial cavity.

The pericardium can be subdivided into the visceral pericardium and the parietal pericardium. The **visceral pericardium,** or **epicardium,** covers the outer surface of the heart, whereas the **parietal pericardium** lines the inner surface of the *pericardial sac,* which surrounds the heart (Figure 12-2b). The pericardial sac consists of a dense network of collagen fibers that stabilizes the positions of the pericardium, heart, and associated vessels in the mediastinum. The space between the parietal and visceral surfaces is the pericardial cavity. It normally contains a small quantity of *pericardial fluid* secreted by the pericardial membranes. The fluid acts as a lubricant, reducing friction between the opposing surfaces as the heart beats.

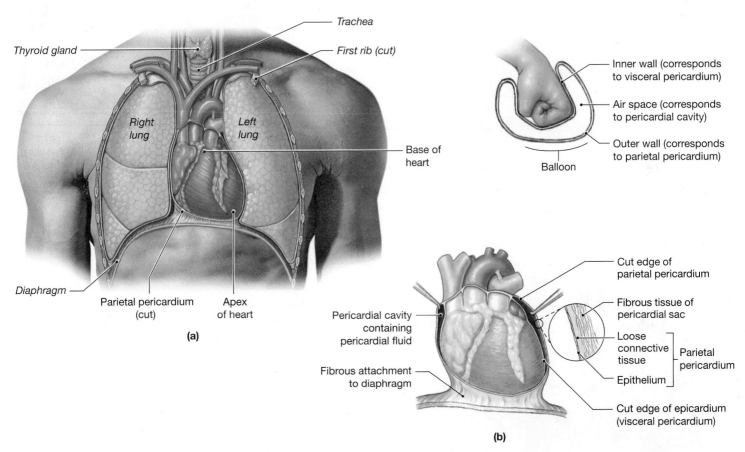

FIGURE 12-2 The Location of the Heart in the Thoracic Cavity. (a) This anterior view of the open chest cavity shows the position of the heart and major vessels relative to the lungs. **(b)** The pericardial cavity surrounding the heart is formed by the visceral epicardium and the parietal epicardium. The relationship between the heart and the pericardial cavity can be likened to a fist pushed into a balloon.

THE SURFACE ANATOMY
OF THE HEART

Several external features of the heart can be used to identify its four chambers (Figure 12-3). The two atria have relatively thin muscular walls and are highly expandable, so when an atrium is not filled with blood, its outer portion deflates into a lumpy, wrinkled flap called an **auricle** (AW-ri-kl; *auris*, ear). The **coronary sulcus,** a deep groove usually filled with substantial amounts of fat, marks the border between the atria and the ventricles. Shallower depressions—the **anterior interventricular sulcus** and **posterior interventricular sulcus**—mark the boundary between the left and right ventricles. In addition to fat, the sulci (SUL-sī) also contain the major arteries and veins that supply blood to the cardiac muscle.

The great veins and arteries of the circulatory system are connected to the superior end of the heart at the base. The inferior, pointed tip of the heart is the **apex** (Ā-peks)

(a) Anterior surface

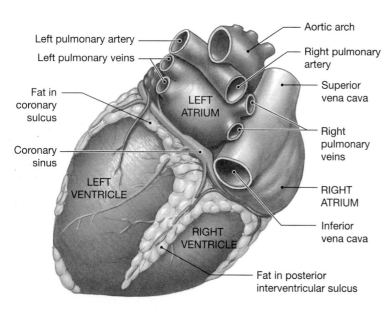

(b) Posterior surface

FIGURE 12-3 The Surface Anatomy of the Heart. The heart's major surface features are shown in **(a)** two anterior views and **(b)** a posterior view.

(Figure 12-2a). A typical heart measures approximately 12.5 cm (5 in.) from the attached base to the apex.

The heart sits at an angle to the longitudinal axis of the body. It is also rotated slightly toward the left, so the anterior surface primarily consists of the right atrium and right ventricle (Figure 12-3a). The wall of the left ventricle forms much of the posterior surface between the base and the apex of the heart (Figure 12-3b).

THE HEART WALL

The wall of the heart contains three distinct layers: the epicardium (visceral pericardium), the myocardium, and the endocardium (Figure 12-4a). The **epicardium** covers the outer surface of the heart. This serous membrane consists of an exposed epithelium and an underlying layer of loose connective tissue that is attached to the myocardium. The **myocardium,** or muscular wall of the heart, contains cardiac muscle tissue, blood vessels, and nerves. The cardiac muscle tissue of the myocardium forms concentric layers that wrap around the atria and spiral into the walls of the ventricles (Figure 12-4b). This arrangement results in squeezing and twisting contractions that increase the pumping efficiency of the heart. The heart's inner surfaces, including the heart valves, are covered by the **endocardium** (en-dō-KAR-dē-um), a simple squamous epithelium that is continuous with the endothelium (epithelial lining) of the attached blood vessels.

Cardiac Muscle Cells

Typical cardiac muscle cells are shown in Figure 12-4c,d. These cells are smaller than skeletal muscle fibers and contain a single, centrally located nucleus. Like skeletal muscle fibers, each cardiac muscle cell contains myofibrils, and contraction involves the shortening of individual sarcomeres. Because cardiac muscle cells are almost totally dependent on aerobic metabolism to obtain the energy needed to continue contracting, they have many mitochondria and abundant reserves of myoglobin (to store oxygen). Energy reserves are stored as glycogen and lipids.

Each cardiac muscle cell is in contact with several others at specialized sites known as **intercalated** (in-TER-ka-lā-ted) **discs.** ∞ p. 112 At an intercalated disc, the interlocking membranes of adjacent cells are held together by desmosomes and linked by gap junctions. ∞ p. 96 The desmosomes help convey the force of contraction from cell to cell, increasing their efficiency as they "pull together" during a contraction. The

gap junctions provide for the movement of ions and small molecules, enabling action potentials to travel rapidly from cell to cell.

Connective Tissue in the Heart

The connective tissues of the heart include abundant collagen and elastic fibers that wrap around each cardiac muscle cell and tie together adjacent cells. These fibers (1) provide support for cardiac muscle fibers, blood vessels, and nerves of the myocardium, (2) add strength and prevent overexpansion of the heart, and (3) help the heart return to normal shape after contractions. Connective tissue also forms the *cardiac skeleton* of the heart, discussed in a later section.

INTERNAL ANATOMY AND ORGANIZATION

The four chambers of the heart are shown in sectional view in Figure 12-5. The two atria are separated by the **interatrial septum** (*septum,* wall), and the two ventricles are divided by the **interventricular septum.** Each atrium opens into the ventricle on the same side through an **atrioventricular (AV) valve,** folds of fibrous tissue that ensure a one-way flow of blood from the atria into the ventricles.

The right atrium receives blood from the systemic circuit through two large veins, the superior vena cava (VĒ-na KĀ-vuh) and the inferior vena cava. The **superior vena cava** delivers blood from the head, neck, upper limbs, and chest. The **inferior vena cava** carries blood from the rest of the trunk, the viscera, and the lower limbs. The *cardiac veins* of the heart return venous blood to the **coronary sinus,** which opens into the right atrium slightly below the connection with the inferior vena cava.

A small depression called the *fossa ovalis* (Figure 12-5) persists where an oval opening—the *foramen ovale*—penetrated the interatrial septum from the fifth week of embryonic development until birth. The foramen ovale (see Figure 13-25, p. 460) allowed blood to flow from the right atrium to the left atrium while the lungs were developing; at birth, the foramen ovale closes, and after 48 hours it is permanently sealed. Occasionally, the foramen ovale remains open even after birth. Under these conditions, contractions of the left atrium push blood back into the pulmonary circuit. This leads to heart enlargement and eventual heart failure and death if the condition is not surgically corrected.

Blood travels from the right atrium into the right ventricle through a broad opening bounded by three flaps of fibrous

FIGURE 12-4 **The Heart Wall and Cardiac Muscle Tissue.** (a) This diagrammatic section through the heart wall illustrates the relative positions of the epicardium, myocardium, and endocardium. (b) Cardiac muscle tissue forms concentric layers that wrap around the atria and spiral within the walls of the ventricles. (c, d) These sectional and diagrammatic views of cardiac muscle tissue show the characteristic single central nucleus, branching interconnections, and intercalated discs of cardiac muscle cells. (LM × 575)

Parietal pericardium
Dense fibrous layer
Loose connective tissue
Epithelium

MYOCARDIUM (cardiac muscle tissue)

Pericardial cavity

Epithelium
Loose connective tissue
EPICARDIUM (visceral pericardium)

Connective tissues

ENDOCARDIUM
Loose connective tissue
Endothelium

(a)

(b)

Cardiac muscle cell
Mitochondria
Intercalated disc (sectioned)

Nucleus

Cardiac muscle cell (sectioned)

Bundles of myofibrils

Intercalated discs

(c) Cardiac muscle tissue

(d) Cardiac muscle cells

FIGURE 12-5 Sectional Anatomy of the Heart. The heart's major internal landmarks and the path of blood flow through the atria and ventricles are shown in this diagrammatic frontal section. Red arrows represent oxygenated blood, and blue arrows represent deoxygenated blood.

Labels (left, top to bottom): Superior vena cava · Right pulmonary arteries · Fossa ovalis · Opening of coronary sinus · RIGHT ATRIUM · Cusp of right AV (tricuspid) valve · Chordae tendineae · Papillary muscles · RIGHT VENTRICLE · Inferior vena cava

Labels (top and right): Aortic arch · Aorta · Pulmonary trunk · Pulmonary semilunar valve · Left pulmonary arteries · Left pulmonary veins · LEFT ATRIUM · Interatrial septum · Aortic semilunar valve · Cusp of left AV bicuspid valve · LEFT VENTRICLE · Interventricular septum · Aorta

tissue. These flaps, or **cusps,** are part of the **right atrioventricular (AV) valve,** also known as the **tricuspid** (trī-KUS-pid; *tri-,* three + *cuspis,* point) **valve** (Figure 12-5). Each cusp is braced by connective tissue fibers called **chordae tendineae** (KOR-dē TEN-di-nē-ē; "tendinous cords"). These fibers are connected to **papillary** (PAP-i-ler-ē) **muscles,** cone-shaped projections on the inner surface of the ventricle. The contraction of these muscles tenses the chordae tendineae, limiting the movement of the cusps and preventing the backflow of blood into the right atrium.

Blood leaving the right ventricle flows into the **pulmonary trunk,** the start of the pulmonary circuit. The **pulmonary semilunar** (*semi-,* half + *luna,* moon; a crescent, or half-moon, shape) **valve** (*pulmonary valve*) guards the entrance to this efferent trunk. Within the pulmonary trunk, blood flows into the **left** and **right pulmonary arteries.** These vessels branch repeatedly in the lungs before supplying the capillaries where gas exchange occurs. From these respiratory capillaries, oxygenated blood moves intō the **left** and **right pulmonary veins,** which deliver it to the left atrium.

Like the right atrium, the left atrium has an external auricle and a valve, the **left atrioventricular (AV) valve,** or **bicuspid** (bī-KUS-pid) **valve.** As the name *bicuspid* implies, the left AV valve contains a pair, not a trio, of cusps. Clinicians often call this valve the **mitral** (MĪ-tral; *mitre,* a bishop's hat) **valve.**

The internal organization of the left ventricle resembles that of the right ventricle. A pair of papillary muscles braces the chordae tendineae that insert on the bicuspid valve. Blood leaving the left ventricle passes through the **aortic semilunar valve** (*aortic valve*) and into the **aorta,** the start of the systemic circuit.

Structural Differences Between the Left and Right Ventricles

The function of either atrium is to collect blood returning to the heart and deliver that blood to the attached ventricle. Thus, the demands on the two atria are very similar, and they look almost identical. But the demands on the right and left ventricles are very different, as the significant structural differences between the two suggest.

The lungs are close to the heart, and the pulmonary arteries and veins are relatively short and wide. Thus, the right ventricle normally does not need to push very hard to propel blood through the pulmonary circuit. The wall of the right ventricle is relatively thin (Figure 12-5), and in sectional view it resembles a pouch attached to the massive wall of the left ventricle. When the right ventricle contracts, it acts like a bellows pump, squeezing the blood against the left ventricle and then out through the pulmonary semilunar valve. This mechanism moves blood very efficiently with minimal effort, but it develops relatively low pressures.

A comparable pumping arrangement would not be suitable for the left ventricle, because four to six times as much pressure must be exerted to push blood around the systemic circuit as around the pulmonary circuit. The left ventricle has an extremely thick muscular wall and is round in cross section. When this ventricle contracts, two things happen: (1) The distance between the heart's base and apex decreases, and (2) the diameter of the ventricular chamber decreases. (If you can imagine the effects of simultaneously squeezing and rolling up the end of a toothpaste tube, you get the idea.) As the powerful left ventricle contracts, it also bulges into the right ventricular cavity, an action that helps force blood out of the right ventricle. An individual whose right ventricular musculature has been severely damaged may survive because the contraction of the left ventricle helps push blood through the pulmonary circuit.

The Heart Valves

Details of the structure and function of the heart valves are depicted in Figure 12-6.

THE ATRIOVENTRICULAR VALVES. The atrioventricular valves prevent the backflow of blood from the ventricles into the atria. The chordae tendineae and papillary muscles play important roles in the normal function of the AV valves. When the ventricles are relaxed (Figure 12-6a), the chordae tendineae are loose and the AV valve offers no resistance to the flow of blood from atrium to ventricle. When the ventricles contract (Figure 12-6b), blood moving back toward the atrium swings the cusps together, closing the valves. During ventricular contraction, tension in the papillary muscles and chordae tendineae keeps the cusps from swinging into the atrium. This action prevents the backflow, or **regurgitation,** of blood into the atrium each time the ventricle contracts. A small amount of regurgitation often occurs, even in normal individuals. The swirling blood creates a soft but distinctive sound called a *heart murmur.*

Mitral Valve Prolapse

Clinical Note

Minor abnormalities in valve shape are relatively common. For example, an estimated 10 percent of normal individuals ages 14–30 have some degree of **mitral valve prolapse.** In this condition, the cusps of the left AV valve (the mitral valve) do not close properly. The problem may stem from abnormally long (or short) chordae tendineae or malfunctioning papillary muscles. Because the valve does not work perfectly, some regurgitation occurs during the contraction of the left ventricle. Most individuals with mitral valve prolapse are completely asymptomatic; they live normal healthy lives unaware of any circulatory malfunction.

THE SEMILUNAR VALVES. The pulmonary and aortic semilunar valves prevent the backflow of blood from the pulmonary trunk and aorta into the right and left ventricles, respectively. The semilunar valves do not require muscular bracing as the AV valves do, because the arterial walls do not contract and the relative positions of the cusps are stable. When the semilunar valves close, the three symmetrical cusps in each valve support one another like the legs of a tripod, preventing the movement of blood back into the ventricles (Figure 12-6a).

Saclike expansions of the base of the ascending aorta occur next to each cusp of the aortic semilunar valve. These sacs, called **aortic sinuses** (Figure 12-6b), prevent the cusps from sticking to the wall of the aorta when the valve opens. The *right* and *left coronary arteries* originate at the aortic sinuses.

Valvular Heart Disease

Clinical Note

Serious valve problems are very dangerous because they reduce pumping efficiency. If valve function deteriorates such that the heart cannot maintain adequate circulatory flow, symptoms of **valvular heart disease (VHD)** appear. Congenital defects may be responsible, but in many cases the condition develops following *carditis,* an inflammation of the heart.

One relatively common cause of carditis is **rheumatic** (roo-MA-tik) **fever,** an acute childhood reaction to streptococcal bacteria. Valve problems serious enough to reduce cardiac function may not appear until 10–20 years after the initial infection. The resulting disorder is known as *rheumatic heart disease* (RHD). Rheumatic fever is seldom seen in the United States, due to the widespread availability and use of antibiotics.

Transverse section, superior view, atria and vessels removed

Cardiac skeleton

Left AV (bicuspid) valve (open)

LEFT VENTRICLE

RIGHT VENTRICLE

Right AV (tricuspid) valve (open)

Aortic valve (closed)

Pulmonary valve (closed)

Frontal section through left atrium and ventricle

Pulmonary veins

LEFT ATRIUM

Aortic valve (closed)

Left AV (bicuspid) valve (open)

Chordae tendineae (loose)

Papillary muscles (relaxed)

LEFT VENTRICLE (dilated)

(a) Relaxed ventricles

Right AV (tricuspid) valve (closed)

Cardiac skeleton

Left AV (bicuspid) valve (closed)

RIGHT VENTRICLE

LEFT VENTRICLE

Aortic valve (open)

Pulmonary valve (open)

Aorta

Aortic sinus

Aortic valve (open)

LEFT ATRIUM

Left AV (bicuspid) valve (closed)

Chordae tendineae (tense)

Papillary muscles (contracted)

Left ventricle (contracted)

(b) Contracting ventricles

FIGURE 12-6 The Valves of the Heart. Red (oxygenated) and blue (deoxygenated) arrows indicate blood flow into and out of the ventricle; black arrows, blood flow into an atrium; and, green arrows, ventricular contraction. **(a)** When the ventricles are relaxed, the AV valves are open, and the semilunar valves are closed. The chordae tendineae are loose, and the papillary muscles are relaxed. **(b)** When the ventricles contract, the AV valves are closed, and the semilunar valves are open. In the frontal section, notice that the chordae tendineae and papillary muscles prevent backflow through the left AV valve.

The Cardiac Skeleton of the Heart

The **cardiac skeleton,** or *fibrous skeleton,* of the heart consists of dense bands of tough, elastic connective tissue that encircle the bases of the large blood vessels carrying blood away from the heart (*pulmonary trunk* and *aorta*) and each of the heart valves (Figure 12-6). The cardiac skeleton stabilizes the position of the heart valves and also physically isolates the atrial muscle tissue from the ventricular muscle tissue. This isolation is important to normal heart function because it means that the timing of ventricular contraction relative to atrial contraction can be precisely controlled.

The Big Picture

The heart has four chambers, two associated with the pulmonary circuit (right atrium and right ventricle) and two with the systemic circuit (left atrium and left ventricle). The left ventricle has a greater workload and is much more massive than the right ventricle, but the two chambers pump equal amounts of blood. AV valves prevent backflow from the ventricles into the atria, and semilunar valves prevent backflow from the aortic and pulmonary trunks into the ventricles.

The Blood Supply to the Heart

The heart works continuously, so cardiac muscle cells require reliable supplies of oxygen and nutrients. The **coronary circulation** (Figure 12-7) supplies blood to the muscle tissue of the heart. During exertion, the oxygen demand rises considerably, and blood flow to the heart may increase to up to nine times that of resting levels.

The left and right **coronary arteries** originate at the base of the aorta at the aortic sinuses (Figure 12-7a). Blood pressure here is the highest of any place in the systemic circuit. This high pressure ensures a continuous flow of blood to meet the demands of active cardiac muscle. The right coronary artery (RCA) supplies blood to the right atrium and to portions of both ventricles. The left coronary artery (LCA) supplies blood to the left ventricle, left atrium, and interventricular septum.

Each coronary artery gives rise to two branches. The right coronary artery forms the *marginal* and *posterior interventricular* (*descending*) arteries, and the left coronary artery forms the *circumflex* and *anterior interventricular* (*descending*) arteries. Small tributaries from these branches of the left and right coronary arteries form interconnections called **anastomoses** (a-nas-tō-MŌ-sēz; *anastomosis,* outlet). Because the arteries are interconnected in this way, alternate pathways exist for the blood supply to reach cardiac muscle. The **great** and **middle cardiac veins** carry blood away from the coronary capillaries. They drain into the **coronary sinus,** a large, thin-walled vein in the posterior portion of the coronary sulcus. The coronary sinus opens into the right atrium near the base of the inferior vena cava (Figure 12-5).

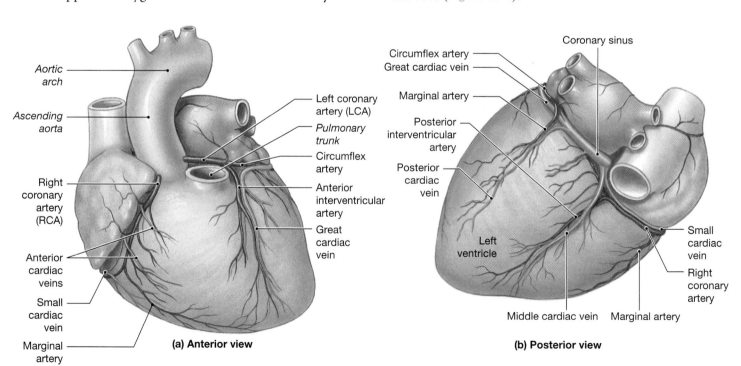

(a) Anterior view

(b) Posterior view

FIGURE 12-7 The Coronary Circulation. The blood vessels that constitute the coronary circulation are labeled in **(a)** anterior and **(b)** posterior views.

An area of dead tissue caused by an interruption in blood flow is called an **infarct.** In a **myocardial** (mī-ō-KAR-dē-al) **infarction (MI),** or *heart attack,* the coronary circulation becomes blocked, and cardiac muscle cells die from a lack of oxygen. Heart attacks most often result from severe *coronary artery disease,* a condition characterized by the buildup of fatty deposits in the walls of the coronary arteries.

12-2 Contractile cells and the conducting system produce each heartbeat, and an electrocardiogram records the associated electrical events

In a single **heartbeat,** the entire heart—atria and ventricles—contracts in a coordinated manner so that blood flows in the correct direction at the proper time. Each time the heart beats, the contractions of individual cardiac muscle cells in the atria and ventricles must occur in a specific sequence. Two types of cardiac muscle cells are involved in a normal heartbeat: (1) *contractile cells,* which produce the powerful contractions that propel blood, and (2) specialized noncontractile muscle cells of the *conducting system,* which control and coordinate the activities of the contractile cells.

CONTRACTILE CELLS

Contractile cells form the bulk of the heart's muscle tissue (about 99 percent of all cardiac muscle cells). In both cardiac muscle cells and skeletal muscle fibers, an action potential leads to the appearance of Ca^{2+} among the myofibrils, and its binding to troponin on the thin filaments begins a contraction. However, skeletal and cardiac muscle cells differ in terms of the duration of action potentials, the source of Ca^{2+}, and the duration of the resulting contraction. Figure 12-8a shows the sequence of events in an action potential in a cardiac muscle cell, and Figure 12-8b compares the action potentials and twitch contractions in skeletal and cardiac muscle.

An action potential in a ventricular contractile cell begins when the membrane is brought to threshold by a stimulus (typically by the excitation of an adjacent muscle cell). The action potential then proceeds in three steps (Figure 12-8a):

Step 1 *Rapid Depolarization.* At threshold, voltage-gated sodium channels open, and the influx of sodium ions rapidly depolarizes the sarcolemma (plasma membrane). The sodium channels close when the transmembrane potential reaches +30 mV.

Step 2 *The Plateau.* As the cell now begins to actively pump sodium ions out, voltage-gated calcium channels open and *extracellular* calcium ions enter the sarcoplasm. The calcium channels remain open for a relatively long period, and the entering positive charges (Ca^{2+}) roughly balance the loss of Na^+ from the cell. The extracellular calcium ions (1) delay repolarization (their positive charges maintain a transmembrane potential near 0 mV—the *plateau*) and (2) initiate contraction. Their increased concentration within the cell also triggers the release of Ca^{2+} from reserves in the sarcoplasmic reticulum (SR), which continue the contraction.

Step 3 *Repolarization.* As the calcium channels begin to close, potassium channels open and potassium ions (K^+) rush out of the cell. The net result is a repolarization that restores the resting potential.

In a skeletal muscle fiber, the 10-msec (millisecond) action potential of a rapid depolarization is immediately followed by a rapid repolarization. This brief action potential ends as the related twitch contraction begins (Figure 12-8b). The twitch contraction is short and ends as the SR reclaims the Ca^{2+} it released. The action potential is prolonged in a cardiac muscle cell because calcium ions continue to enter the cell throughout the plateau. As a result, the period of muscle contraction continues until the plateau ends. As the calcium channels close, the intracellular calcium ions are absorbed by the SR or are pumped out of the cell, and the muscle cell relaxes.

The complete depolarization–repolarization process in a cardiac muscle cell lasts 250–300 msec, some 25–30 times as long as an action potential in a skeletal muscle fiber (Figure 12-8b). Until the membrane repolarizes, it cannot respond to further stimulation, so the refractory period of a cardiac muscle cell membrane is relatively long. Thus, a normal cardiac muscle cell is limited to a maximum rate of about 200 contractions per minute.

In skeletal muscle fibers, the refractory period ends before the muscle fiber develops peak tension and relaxes. As a result, twitches

① Rapid Depolarization

Cause: Na+ entry
Duration: 3–5 msec
Ends with: Closure of voltage-gated sodium channels

② The Plateau

Cause: Ca2+ entry
Duration: ~175 msec
Ends with: Closure of calcium channels

③ Repolarization

Cause: K+ loss
Duration: 75 msec
Ends with: Closure of potassium channels

(a) Cardiac muscle

(b)

FIGURE 12-8 Action Potentials and Muscle Cell Contraction in Skeletal and Cardiac Muscle. (a) This graph indicates the events of an action potential in a ventricular cardiac muscle cell. **(b)** In skeletal muscle fibers, an action potential is relatively brief and ends as the related twitch contraction begins. In cardiac muscle cells, both the action potential and twitch contraction are prolonged. The shaded areas indicate the duration of the refractory period.

can build on one another until tension reaches a sustained peak; this state is called *tetanus.* ∞ p. 206 In cardiac muscle cells, the refractory period continues until relaxation is under way. A summation of twitches is, therefore, not possible, and tetanic contractions cannot occur in a normal cardiac muscle cell, regardless of the frequency and intensity of stimulation. This feature is absolutely vital because a heart in tetany could not pump blood.

THE CONDUCTING SYSTEM

In contrast to skeletal muscle, cardiac muscle tissue contracts on its own in the absence of neural or hormonal stimulation. (This property, called *automaticity,* or *autorhythmicity,* also characterizes some types of smooth muscle tissue discussed in Chapter 7. ∞ p. 213)

In the heart's normal pattern of activity, each contraction follows a precise sequence: The atria contract first, followed by the ventricles. Cardiac contractions are coordinated by the heart's **conducting system,** a network of specialized cardiac muscle cells that initiates and distributes electrical impulses (Figure 12-9a). The network is made up of two types of cardiac muscle cells that do not contract: (1) **nodal cells,** which are responsible for establishing the rate of cardiac contraction

and are located at the *sinoatrial* (*SA*) and *atrioventricular* (*AV*) *nodes;* and (2) **conducting cells,** which distribute the contractile stimulus to the general myocardium. The ventricular conducting cells include those in the *AV bundle* and the *bundle branches,* as well as the *Purkinje fibers.*

Nodal cells are unusual because their cell membranes depolarize spontaneously and generate action potentials at regular intervals. Nodal cells are electrically coupled to one another, to conducting cells, and to normal cardiac muscle cells. As a result, when an action potential is initiated in a nodal cell, it sweeps through the conducting system, reaching all of the cardiac muscle tissue and causing a coordinated contraction. In this way, nodal cells determine the heart rate.

Not all nodal cells depolarize at the same rate, and the normal rate of contraction is established by **pacemaker cells,** the nodal cells that reach threshold first. These pacemaker cells are located in the **sinoatrial** (sī-nō-Ā-trē-al) **node (SA node),** or *cardiac pacemaker,* a tissue mass embedded in the posterior wall of the right atrium near the entrance of the superior vena cava (Figure 12-9a). Pacemaker cells depolarize rapidly and spontaneously, generating 70–80 action potentials per minute. This results in a heart rate of 70–80 beats per minute (bpm).

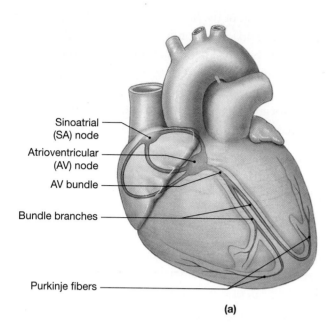

(a)

FIGURE 12-9 The Conducting System of the Heart. (a) The locations of the elements of the conducting system and pathways of electrical impulses are shown in this diagrammatic view of the heart. **(b)** The stimulus for contraction moves through the heart in a predictable sequence of events (steps 1–5 as diagrammed).

After the stimulus for a contraction is generated at the SA node, it must be distributed so that (1) the atria contract together, before the ventricles; and (2) the ventricles contract together, in a wave that begins at the apex and spreads toward the base. When the ventricles contract in this way, blood is pushed toward the base of the heart into the aorta and pulmonary trunk.

The cells of the SA node are electrically connected to those of the larger **atrioventricular** (ā-trē-ō-ven-TRIK-ū-lar) **node (AV node)** by conducting cells in the atrial walls (Figure 12-9a). Although the AV nodal cells also depolarize spontaneously, they generate only 40–60 action potentials per minute. Under normal circumstances, before an AV cell depolarizes to threshold spontaneously, it is stimulated by an action potential generated by the SA node. However, if the AV node does not receive this action potential, it will then become the pacemaker of the heart and establish a heart rate of 40–60 beats per minute.

The AV node is located in the floor of the right atrium near the opening of the coronary sinus. From there the action potentials travel to the **AV bundle,** also known as the *bundle of His* (pronounced *hiss*). This bundle of conducting cells extends along the interventricular septum before dividing into **left** and **right bundle branches,** which radiate across the inner surfaces of the left and right ventricles. At this point, specialized **Purkinje**

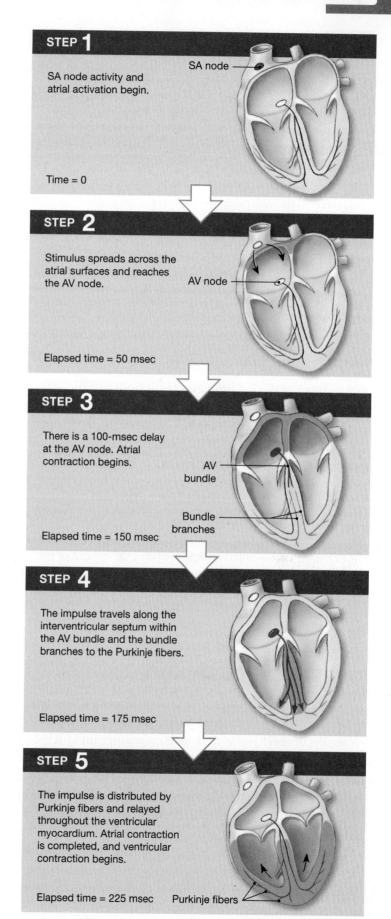

STEP 1

SA node activity and atrial activation begin.

Time = 0

STEP 2

Stimulus spreads across the atrial surfaces and reaches the AV node.

Elapsed time = 50 msec

STEP 3

There is a 100-msec delay at the AV node. Atrial contraction begins.

Elapsed time = 150 msec

STEP 4

The impulse travels along the interventricular septum within the AV bundle and the bundle branches to the Purkinje fibers.

Elapsed time = 175 msec

STEP 5

The impulse is distributed by Purkinje fibers and relayed throughout the ventricular myocardium. Atrial contraction is completed, and ventricular contraction begins.

Elapsed time = 225 msec

(b)

(pur-KIN-jē) **fibers** (*Purkinje cells*) convey the impulses to the contractile cells of the ventricular myocardium.

As shown in Figure 12-9b, it takes an action potential roughly 50 msec to travel from the SA node to the AV node over the conducting pathways. Along the way, the conducting cells pass the contractile stimulus to cardiac muscle cells of the right and left atria. The action potential then spreads across the atrial surfaces through cell-to-cell contact. The stimulus affects only the atria because the cardiac skeleton (Figure 12-6b) electrically isolates the atria from the ventricles everywhere except at the AV bundle.

At the AV node, the impulse slows down, and another 100 msec pass before it reaches the AV bundle. This delay is important because the atria must be contracting, and blood must be moving, before the ventricles are stimulated. Once the impulse enters the AV bundle, it flashes down the interventricular septum, along the bundle branches, and into the ventricular myocardium along the Purkinje fibers. Within another 75 msec, the stimulus to begin a contraction has reached all of the ventricular muscle cells.

A number of clinical problems result from deviations from normal pacemaker function, which produces a heart rate that averages 70–80 bpm. **Bradycardia** (brād-ē-KAR-dē-uh; *bradys*, slow) is a condition in which the heart rate is slower than normal (less than 60 bpm). **Tachycardia** (tak-ē-KAR-dē-uh; *tachys*, swift) is a faster than normal heart rate (100 bpm or more). In some cases, an abnormal conducting cell or ventricular muscle cell may begin generating action potentials so rapidly that they override those of the SA or AV node. The origin of such abnormal signals is called an **ectopic** (ek-TOP-ik; out of place) **pacemaker.** The action potentials may completely bypass the conducting system and disrupt the timing of ventricular contractions. Such conditions are commonly diagnosed with the aid of an *electrocardiogram,* which we will discuss next.

THE ELECTROCARDIOGRAM

The electrical events occurring in the heart are powerful enough to be detected by electrodes placed on the body surface. A recording of these events is an **electrocardiogram** (ē-lek-trō-KAR-dē-ō-gram), also called an **ECG** or **EKG.** Each time the heart beats, a wave of depolarization radiates through the atria, reaches the AV node, travels down the interventricular septum to the apex, turns, and spreads through the ventricular myocardium toward the base.

By comparing the information obtained from electrodes placed at different locations, a clinician can monitor the electrical activity of the heart and check the performance of specific nodal, conducting, and contractile components. When, for

example, a portion of the heart has been damaged, the affected muscle cells will no longer conduct action potentials, so an ECG will reveal an abnormal pattern of impulse conduction.

The appearance of the ECG tracing varies with the placement of the monitoring electrodes, or *leads.* The important features of an electrocardiogram as analyzed with the leads in one of the standard configurations are shown in Figure 12-10:

- A small **P wave** accompanies the depolarization of the atria. The atria begin contracting around 100 msec after the start of the P wave.

- A **QRS complex** appears as the ventricles depolarize. This portion of the electrical signal is relatively strong because the mass of the ventricular muscle is much larger than that of the atria. The ventricles begin contracting shortly after the peak of the R wave.

- A smaller **T wave** indicates ventricular repolarization. Atrial repolarization is not apparent because it occurs while the ventricles are depolarizing, and the electrical events there are masked by the QRS complex.

Analyzing an ECG involves measuring the size of the voltage changes and determining the temporal relationships of the various components. Attention usually focuses on the amount of depolarization occurring during the P wave and the QRS complex. For example, a smaller than normal electrical signal can mean that the mass of the heart muscle has decreased, whereas excessively strong depolarizations can mean that the heart muscle has become enlarged.

Electrocardiogram analysis is useful in detecting and diagnosing **cardiac arrhythmias** (ā-RITH-mē-az), abnormal patterns of cardiac activity. Momentary arrhythmias are not inherently dangerous, and about 5 percent of the normal population experiences a few abnormal heartbeats each day. Clinical problems appear when the arrhythmias reduce the heart's pumping efficiency. Serious arrhythmias can indicate damage to the myocardium, injuries to the pacemaker or conduction pathways, exposure to drugs, or variations in the electrolyte composition of the extracellular fluids.

The Big Picture

The heart rate is normally established by the cells of the SA node, but that rate can be modified by autonomic activity, hormones, and other factors. From the SA node, the stimulus is conducted to the AV node, the AV bundle, the bundle branches, and Purkinje fibers before reaching the ventricular muscle cells. The electrical events associated with the heartbeat can be monitored in an electrocardiogram (ECG).

FIGURE 12-10 An Electrocardiogram.
An ECG printout is a strip of graph paper containing a continuous record of the electrical events in the heart as monitored by electrodes attached to the body surface. **(a)** The placement of electrodes affects the size and shape of the waves recorded. The electrode placement for a standard ECG is shown here. **(b)** The enlarged section indicates the major components of the ECG and the events that correspond to them.

800 msec

+1
Millivolts
0

ECG rhythm strip

(a)

R

T wave
Ventricles return to resting state

P

T

P wave
Impulse spreads across atria, triggering atrial contractions

Q

QRS complex
Impulse spreads to ventricles, triggering ventricular contractions

S

CHECKPOINT

4. How does the fact that cardiac muscle does not undergo tetanus (as skeletal muscle does) affect the functioning of the heart?

5. If the cells of the SA node were not functioning, how would the heart rate be affected?

6. Why is it important for the impulses from the atria to be delayed at the AV node before passing into the ventricles?

7. What might cause an increase in the size of the QRS complex in an electrocardiogram?

See the blue Answers tab at the back of the book.

12-3 Events during a complete heartbeat make up a cardiac cycle

The period between the start of one heartbeat and the start of the next is a single **cardiac cycle** (Figure 12-11). Each cardiac cycle, therefore, includes a period of contraction and one of relaxation. For any one chamber of the heart, the cardiac cycle can be divided into two phases. During contraction, or **systole** (SIS-tō-lē), the chamber squeezes blood into an adjacent chamber or into an arterial trunk. Systole is followed by the second phase—relaxation, or **diastole** (dī-AS-tō-lē)—when the chamber fills with blood and prepares for the start of the next cardiac cycle.

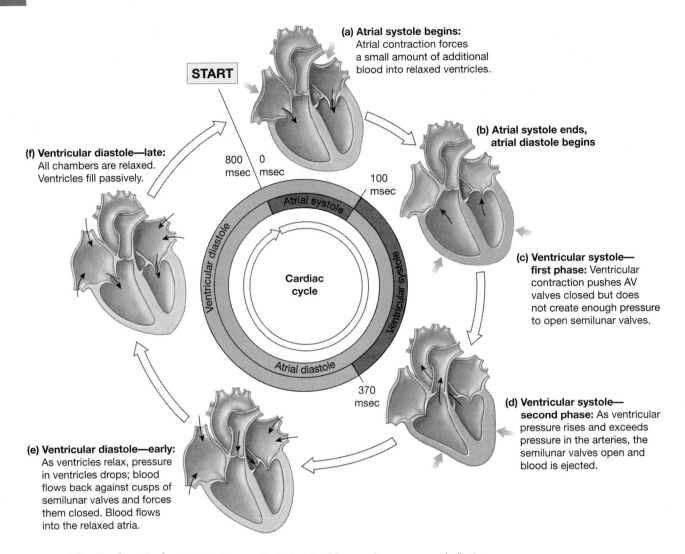

(a) Atrial systole begins: Atrial contraction forces a small amount of additional blood into relaxed ventricles.

START

(b) Atrial systole ends, atrial diastole begins

(f) Ventricular diastole—late: All chambers are relaxed. Ventricles fill passively.

(c) Ventricular systole— first phase: Ventricular contraction pushes AV valves closed but does not create enough pressure to open semilunar valves.

(d) Ventricular systole— second phase: As ventricular pressure rises and exceeds pressure in the arteries, the semilunar valves open and blood is ejected.

(e) Ventricular diastole—early: As ventricles relax, pressure in ventricles drops; blood flows back against cusps of semilunar valves and forces them closed. Blood flows into the relaxed atria.

800 msec · 0 msec · 100 msec · 370 msec

Atrial systole · Ventricular diastole · Ventricular systole · Atrial diastole

Cardiac cycle

FIGURE 12-11 **The Cardiac Cycle.** Thin black arrows indicate blood flow, and green arrows indicate contractions. Times noted in the figure are for a heart rate of 75 bpm.

Fluids tend to move from an area of higher pressure to one of lower pressure. During the cardiac cycle, the pressure within each chamber rises during systole and falls during diastole. An increase in pressure in one chamber causes the blood to flow to another chamber (or vessel) where the pressure is lower. The atrioventricular and semilunar valves ensure that blood flows in one direction only during the cardiac cycle.

PHASES OF THE CARDIAC CYCLE

The correct pressure relationships among the heart chambers are maintained by the careful timing of contractions. The elaborate pacemaking and conduction systems normally provide the required interval of time between atrial systole and ventricular systole. If the atria and ventricles were to contract simultaneously, blood could not leave the atria because the AV valves would be closed. In the normal heart, atrial systole and

atrial diastole are slightly out of phase with ventricular systole and diastole. Figure 12-11 shows the duration and timing of systole and diastole for a heart rate of 75 bpm.

The cardiac cycle begins with atrial systole. At the start of a cardiac cycle, the ventricles are partially filled with blood. During atrial systole, the atria contract and the ventricles become completely filled with blood (Figure 12-11a). As atrial systole ends (Figure 12-11b), atrial diastole and ventricular systole begin. As pressures in the ventricles rise above those in the atria, the AV valves swing shut (Figure 12-11c). But blood cannot begin moving into the arterial trunks until ventricular pressures exceed the arterial pressures. At this point, the blood pushes open the semilunar valves and flows into the aorta and pulmonary trunk (Figure 12-11d). This blood flow continues for the duration of ventricular systole, and lasts approximately 270 msec in a resting adult.

When ventricular diastole begins (Figure 12-11e), ventricular pressures decline rapidly. As they fall below the pressures of the arterial trunks, the semilunar valves close. Ventricular pressures continue to drop; as they fall below atrial pressures, the AV valves open and blood flows from the atria into the ventricles. Both atria and ventricles are now in diastole; blood now flows from the major veins through the relaxed atria and into the ventricles (**Figure 12-11f**). By the time atrial systole marks the start of another cardiac cycle, the ventricles are roughly 70 percent filled. The relatively minor contribution atrial systole makes to ventricular volume explains why individuals can survive quite normally when their atria have been so severely damaged that they can no longer function. In contrast, damage to one or both ventricles can leave the heart unable to maintain adequate cardiac output. A condition of *heart failure* then exists.

HEART SOUNDS

Physicians use an instrument called a **stethoscope** to listen for four **heart sounds.** When you listen to your own heart, you hear the familiar "lubb-dupp" that accompanies each heartbeat. These two sounds accompany the actions of the heart valves. The *first heart sound* ("lubb") is produced as the AV valves close and the semilunar valves open. It marks the start of ventricular systole and lasts a little longer than the second sound. The *second heart sound,* "dupp," occurs at the beginning of ventricular diastole, when the semilunar valves close.

Third and *fourth heart sounds* may be audible as well, but they are usually very faint and are seldom detectable in healthy adults. These sounds are associated with atrial contraction and blood flowing into the ventricles rather than with valve action.

CHECKPOINT

8. Provide the alternate terms for heart contraction and heart relaxation.

9. Is the heart always pumping blood when pressure in the left ventricle is rising? Explain.

10. What events cause the "lubb-dupp" heart sounds as heard with a stethoscope?

See the blue Answers tab at the back of the book.

12-4 Heart dynamics examines the factors that affect cardiac output

The term *heart dynamics,* or *cardiodynamics,* refers to the movements and forces generated during cardiac contractions. Each time the heart beats, the two ventricles eject equal amounts of blood. The amount ejected by a ventricle during a single beat is the **stroke volume (SV).** The stroke volume can vary from beat to beat, so physicians are often more interested in the **cardiac output (CO),** or the amount of blood pumped by each ventricle in 1 minute. Cardiac output provides an indication of the blood flow through peripheral tissues; without adequate blood flow, homeostasis cannot be maintained.

Cardiac output can be calculated by multiplying the heart rate (HR) by the average stroke volume:

$$\begin{array}{ccccc} \text{CO} & = & \text{HR} & \times & \text{SV} \\ \text{cardiac output} & & \text{heart rate} & \times & \text{stroke volume} \\ \text{(mL/min)} & & \text{(beats/min)} & & \text{(mL/beat)} \end{array}$$

For example, if the heart rate is 75 beats per minute (bpm) and the average stroke volume is 80 mL per beat, the cardiac output will be:

$$\text{CO} = 75 \text{ beats/min} \times 80 \text{ mL/beat}$$
$$= 6000 \text{ mL/min (6 L/min)}$$

This value represents a cardiac output equivalent to the total volume of blood of an average adult every minute. Cardiac output is highly variable, however, because a normal heart can increase both its rate of contraction and its stroke volume. When necessary, stroke volume in a normal heart can almost double, and the heart rate can increase by 250 percent. When both increase together, the cardiac output can increase by 500 to 700 percent, or up to 30 liters per minute.

Cardiac output is precisely regulated so that peripheral tissues receive an adequate blood supply under a variety of conditions. The major factors that regulate cardiac output often affect both heart rate and stroke volume simultaneously. These primary factors include *blood volume reflexes, autonomic innervation,* and *hormones.* Secondary factors include the concentration of ions in the extracellular fluid and body temperature (see the Clinical Note "Extracellular Ions, Temperature, and Cardiac Output").

BLOOD VOLUME REFLEXES

Cardiac muscle contraction is an active process, but relaxation is entirely passive. The force needed to return cardiac muscle to its precontracted length is provided by the blood pouring into the heart, aided by the elasticity of the cardiac skeleton. As a result, there is a direct relationship between the amount of blood entering the heart and the amount of blood ejected during the next contraction.

Two heart reflexes respond to changes in blood volume. One of these occurs in the right atrium and affects heart rate. The other is a ventricular reflex that affects stroke volume.

The **atrial reflex** (*Bainbridge reflex*) involves adjustments in heart rate in response to an increase in the **venous return,** the flow of venous blood into the heart. The entry of blood stimulates stretch receptors in the right atrial walls, triggering a reflexive increase in heart rate through increased sympathetic activity. As a result of sympathetic stimulation, the cells of the SA node depolarize faster and heart rate increases.

The amount of blood pumped out of a ventricle each heartbeat (the stroke volume) depends not only on venous return but also on the **filling time**—the duration of ventricular diastole, when blood can flow into the ventricles. Filling time depends primarily on the heart rate: The faster the heart rate, the shorter the available filling time. Venous return changes in response to alterations in cardiac output, peripheral circulation, and other factors that affect the rate of blood flow through the venae cavae.

Over the range of normal activities, the greater the volume of blood entering the ventricles, the more powerful the contraction (and the more pumping force is produced) and the greater the stroke volume. In a resting individual, venous return is relatively low and the walls are not stretched much, so the ventricles develop little power, and stroke volume is low. If venous return suddenly increases (that is, more blood flows into the heart), the myocardium stretches farther, the ventricles produce greater force upon contraction, and stroke volume increases. This general rule of "more in = more out" is often called the **Frank-Starling principle,** in honor of the physiologists who first demonstrated the relationship. The major effect of the Frank-Starling principle is that the output of blood from both ventricles is balanced under a variety of conditions.

AUTONOMIC INNERVATION

As previously noted, the pacemaker cells of the SA node establish the basic heart rate, but this rate can be modified by the autonomic nervous system (ANS). As shown in Figure 12-12, both the sympathetic and parasympathetic divisions of the ANS innervate the heart. Postganglionic sympathetic fibers extend from neuron cell bodies located in the cervical and upper thoracic ganglia. The vagus nerves (N X) carry parasympathetic preganglionic fibers to small ganglia near the heart. Both ANS divisions innervate the SA and AV nodes as well as the atrial and ventricular cardiac muscle cells.

Autonomic Effects on Heart Rate

Autonomic effects on heart rate primarily reflect the responses of the SA node to acetylcholine (ACh) and to norepinephrine (NE). Acetylcholine released by

parasympathetic motor neurons results in a lowering of the heart rate. Norepinephrine released by sympathetic neurons increases the heart rate. A more sustained rise in heart rate follows the release of epinephrine (E) and norepinephrine by the suprarenal medullae during sympathetic activation.

Autonomic Effects on Stroke Volume

The ANS also affects stroke volume by altering the force of myocardial contractions through the release of NE, E, and ACh:

- *The effects of NE and E.* The sympathetic release of NE at synapses in the myocardium and the release of NE and E by the suprarenal medullae stimulate cardiac muscle cell metabolism and increase the force and degree of contraction. The result is an increase in stroke volume.

- *The effects of ACh.* The primary effect of parasympathetic ACh release is inhibition, resulting in a decrease in the

FIGURE 12-12 **Autonomic Innervation of the Heart.**

force of cardiac contractions. Because parasympathetic innervation of the ventricles is relatively limited, the greatest reduction in contractile force occurs in the atria.

Both autonomic divisions are normally active at a steady background level, releasing ACh and NE both at the nodes and into the myocardium. Thus, cutting the vagus nerves increases heart rate, and sympathetic blocking agents slow heart rate. Through dual innervation and adjustments in autonomic tone, the ANS can make very delicate adjustments in cardiovascular function.

The Coordination of Autonomic Activity

The *cardiac centers* of the medulla oblongata contain the autonomic headquarters for cardiac control. ⊙ p. 278 The **cardioacceleratory center** controls sympathetic motor neurons that increase heart rate; the nearby **cardioinhibitory center** controls the parasympathetic motor neurons that slow heart rate (**Figure 12-12**). Information concerning the status of the cardiovascular system arrives at the cardiac centers over sensory fibers from the vagus nerves and from the sympathetic nerves of the cardiac plexus.

The cardiac centers respond to changes in blood pressure and in the arterial concentrations of dissolved oxygen and carbon dioxide. These properties are monitored by baroreceptors and chemoreceptors innervated by the glossopharyngeal (N IX) and vagus nerves. A decline in blood pressure or oxygen concentrations or an increase in carbon dioxide levels usually indicates that the oxygen demands of peripheral tissues have increased. The cardiac centers then call for an increase in cardiac output, and the heart works harder.

In addition to making automatic adjustments in response to sensory information, the cardiac centers can be influenced by higher centers, especially centers in the hypothalamus. As a result, changes in emotional state (such as rage, fear, or arousal) have an immediate effect on heart rate.

HORMONES

As previously noted, epinephrine and norepinephrine secreted by the suprarenal medullae act to increase both heart rate and force of contraction. Thyroid hormones and glucagon also act to increase force of contraction. Before synthetic drugs were available, glucagon was widely used to stimulate heart function.

Various drugs that affect the contractility of the heart have been developed for use in cardiac emergencies and to treat heart disease. Those that act by increasing the Ca^{2+} concentration within cardiac muscle cells, such as *digitalis* and related drugs, result in an increase in the force of contractions. Many

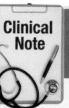

Clinical Note

Extracellular Ions, Temperature, and Cardiac Output

Changes in extracellular calcium ion concentrations primarily affect the strength and duration of cardiac contractions, and thus stroke volume. If such calcium concentrations are elevated (**hypercalcemia**), cardiac muscle cells become extremely excitable, and their contractions become powerful and prolonged. In extreme cases, the heart goes into an extended state of contraction that is usually fatal. When calcium levels are abnormally low (**hypocalcemia**), the contractions become very weak and may cease altogether.

Abnormal extracellular potassium ion concentrations alter the resting potential at the SA node and primarily change heart rate. When potassium concentrations are high (**hyperkalemia**), cardiac contractions become weak and irregular. When the extracellular concentration of potassium is abnormally low (**hypokalemia**), heart rate is reduced.

Temperature changes affect metabolic operations throughout the body. For example, a lowered body temperature slows the rate of depolarization at the SA node, lowers heart rate, and reduces the strength of cardiac contractions. An elevated body temperature increases heart rate and contractile force—one reason why your heart seems to race and pound when you have a fever.

drugs used to treat hypertension (high blood pressure) have a negative effect on contractility.

The Big Picture

Cardiac output is the amount of blood pumped by the left ventricle each minute. It is adjusted on a moment-to-moment basis by the ANS, and in response to circulating hormones, changes in blood volume, and alterations in venous return. In most healthy people, cardiac output can increase by 300–500 percent.

CHECKPOINT

11. Define cardiac output.

12. If the cardioinhibitory center of the medulla oblongata were damaged, which part of the autonomic nervous system would be affected, and how would the heart be influenced?

13. What effect does stimulation of the acetylcholine receptors of the heart have on cardiac output?

14. What effect does increased venous return have on stroke volume?

15. Why is it a potential problem if the heart beats too rapidly?

See the blue Answers tab at the back of the book.

RELATED CLINICAL TERMS

angina pectoris (an-JĪ-nuh PEK-tor-is): Severe chest pain resulting from temporary ischemia (local loss of blood supply) whenever the heart's workload increases (as during exertion or stress).

balloon angioplasty: A technique for reducing the size of a coronary plaque by compressing it against the arterial walls using a catheter with an inflatable collar.

bradycardia (brăd-ē-KAR-de-uh): A slower than normal heart rate.

cardiac arrhythmias (ā-RITH-mē-az): Abnormal patterns of cardiac electrical activity, indicating abnormal contractions.

cardiac tamponade: A condition, resulting from pericardial irritation and inflammation, in which fluid collects in the pericardial sac and restricts cardiac output.

cardiology (kar-dē-OL-o-jē): The study of the heart, its functions, and its diseases.

carditis (kar-DĪ-tis): Inflammation of the heart.

coronary arteriography: The production of an x-ray image of coronary circulation after the introduction of a radiopaque dye into one of the coronary arteries through a catheter; the resulting image is a *coronary angiogram.*

coronary artery bypass graft (CABG): The routing of blood around an obstructed coronary artery (or one of its branches) by a vessel transplanted from another site in the body.

coronary artery disease (CAD): A disorder resulting from the obstruction of coronary circulation.

coronary ischemia: A deficiency of blood supply to the heart due to restricted circulation; may cause cardiac tissue damage and a reduction in cardiac efficiency.

coronary thrombosis: The presence of a thrombus (clot) in a coronary artery; may cause circulatory blockage resulting in a heart attack.

defibrillator: A device used to eliminate atrial or ventricular fibrillation (uncoordinated contractions) and restore normal cardiac rhythm.

echocardiography: Ultrasound analysis of the heart and of the blood flow through the great vessels.

electrocardiogram (ē-lek-trō-KAR-dē-ō-gram) (**ECG** or **EKG**): A recording of the electrical activities of the heart over time.

heart block: An impairment of conduction in the heart in which damage to conduction pathways (due to mechanical distortion, ischemia, infection, or inflammation) disrupts the heart's normal rhythm.

heart failure: A condition in which the heart weakens and peripheral tissues suffer from oxygen and nutrient deprivation.

myocardial (mī-ō-KAR-dē-al) **infarction (MI):** A condition in which blockage of the coronary circulation causes cardiac muscle cells to die from oxygen starvation; also called a *heart attack.*

pericarditis: Inflammation of the pericardium.

rheumatic heart disease (RHD): A disorder in which the heart valves become thickened and stiffen into a partially closed position, reducing the efficiency of the heart.

tachycardia (tak-ē-KAR-dē-uh): A faster than normal heart rate.

valvular heart disease (VHD): A disorder caused by abnormal functioning of one of the cardiac valves; its severity depends on the degree of damage and the valve involved.

Chapter 12 Review

KEY TERMS

atrioventricular valve *409*	**intercalated disc** *409*
atrium *406*	**myocardium** *409*
cardiac cycle *419*	**pericardium** *407*
cardiac output *421*	**Purkinje fibers** *417*
diastole *419*	**sinoatrial node** *416*
electrocardiogram (EKG) *418*	**systole** *419*
endocardium *409*	**ventricle** *406*
epicardium *407*	

SUMMARY OUTLINE

IP Use *Interactive Physiology*® (**IP**) —available on the IP CD packaged with your new textbook—to help you understand difficult physiological concepts. Follow these navigation paths on IP for concepts in this chapter:

- Cardiovascular System/Cardiac Action Potential
- Cardiovascular System/Intrinsic Conduction System
- Cardiovascular System/Cardiac Cycle
- Cardiovascular System/Cardiac Output

The Heart's Role in the Cardiovascular System *p. 406*

1. The blood vessels of the cardiovascular system can be subdivided into the **pulmonary circuit** (which carries blood to and from the lungs) and the **systemic circuit** (which transports blood to and from the rest of the body). **Arteries** carry blood away from the heart; **veins** return blood to the heart. **Capillaries** are tiny vessels between the smallest arteries and smallest veins. *(Figure 12-1)*

2. The heart has four chambers: the **right atrium, right ventricle, left atrium,** and **left ventricle.**

12-1 The heart is a four-chambered organ, supplied by coronary circulation, that pumps oxygen-poor blood to the lungs and oxygen-rich blood to the rest of the body *p. 407*

3. The heart is surrounded by the **pericardial cavity** (lined by the **pericardium**). The **visceral pericardium (epicardium)** covers the heart's outer surface, whereas the **parietal pericardium** lines the inner surface of the *pericardial sac,* which surrounds the heart. *(Figure 12-2)*

4. The **coronary sulcus,** a deep groove, marks the boundary between the atria and ventricles. *(Figure 12-3)*

5. The bulk of the heart consists of the muscular **myocardium.** The **endocardium** lines the inner surfaces of the heart. *(Figure 12-4a,b)*

6. **Cardiac muscle cells** are interconnected by **intercalated discs,** which convey the force of contraction from cell to cell and conduct action potentials. *(Figure 12-4c,d)*

7. The atria are separated by the **interatrial septum,** and the ventricles are divided by the **interventricular septum.** The right atrium receives blood from the systemic circuit via two large veins, the **superior vena cava** and **inferior vena cava.** *(Figure 12-5)*

8. Blood flows from the right atrium into the right ventricle through the **right atrioventricular (AV) valve (tricuspid valve).** This opening is bounded by three **cusps** of fibrous tissue braced by the tendinous **chordae tendineae,** which are connected to **papillary muscles.**

9. Blood leaving the right ventricle enters the **pulmonary trunk** after passing through the **pulmonary semilunar valve.** The pulmonary trunk divides to form the **left** and **right pulmonary arteries.** The **left** and **right pulmonary veins** return oxygenated blood to the left atrium. Blood leaving the left atrium flows into the left ventricle through the **left atrioventricular (AV) valve (bicuspid valve** or **mitral valve).** Blood leaving the left ventricle passes through the **aortic semilunar valve** and into the systemic circuit through the **aorta.** *(Figure 12-5)*

10. Anatomical differences between the ventricles reflect the functional demands on them. The wall of the right ventricle is relatively thin, whereas the left ventricle has a massive muscular wall.

11. Valves normally permit blood flow in only one direction, preventing the **regurgitation** (backflow) of blood. *(Figure 12-6)*

12. The connective tissues of the heart and **cardiac skeleton** support the heart's contractile cells and valves. *(Figure 12-6)*

13. The **coronary circulation** meets the high oxygen and nutrient demands of cardiac muscle cells. The coronary arteries originate at the base of the aorta. Arterial **anastomoses**—interconnections between arteries—ensure a constant blood supply. The **great** and **middle cardiac veins** carry blood from the coronary capillaries to the **coronary sinus.** *(Figure 12-7)*

12-2 Contractile cells and the conducting system produce each heartbeat, and an electrocardiogram records the associated electrical events *p. 415*

14. Two general classes of cardiac cells are involved in the normal heartbeat: *contractile cells* and cells of the conducting system.

15. Cardiac muscle cells have a long refractory period, so rapid stimulation produces isolated contractions (twitches) rather than tetanic contractions. *(Figure 12-8)*

16. The conducting system includes **nodal cells** and **conducting cells.** The conducting system initiates and distributes electrical impulses within the heart. Nodal cells establish the rate of cardiac contraction; **pacemaker cells** are nodal cells that reach threshold first. Conducting cells distribute the contractile stimulus to the general myocardium.

17. Unlike skeletal muscle, cardiac muscle contracts without neural or hormonal stimulation. Pacemaker cells in the **sinoatrial (SA) node** (*cardiac pacemaker*) normally establish the rate of contraction. From the SA node, impulses travel to the **atrioventricular (AV) node** and then to the **AV bundle,** which divides into **bundle branches.** From there, **Purkinje fibers** convey the impulses to the ventricular myocardium. *(Figure 12-9)*

18. A recording of electrical activities in the heart is an **electrocardiogram (ECG** or **EKG).** Important landmarks of an ECG include the **P wave** (atrial depolarization), **QRS complex** (ventricular depolarization), and **T wave** (ventricular repolarization). *(Figure 12-10)*

12-3 Events during a complete heartbeat make up a cardiac cycle *p. 419*

19. A **cardiac cycle** consists of **systole** (contraction) followed by **diastole** (relaxation). Both ventricles contract at the same time, and they eject equal volumes of blood. *(Figure 12-11)*

20. The closing of the heart valves and the rushing of blood through the heart cause characteristic **heart sounds.**

12-4 Heart dynamics examines the factors that affect cardiac output *p. 421*

21. *Heart dynamics* refers to the movements and forces generated during contractions. The amount of blood ejected by a ventricle during a single beat is the **stroke volume (SV);** the amount of blood pumped by a ventricle each minute is the **cardiac output (CO).**

22. The major factors that affect cardiac output are blood volume reflexes, autonomic innervation, and hormones.

23. Blood volume reflexes are stimulated by changes in **venous return,** the amount of blood entering the heart. The **atrial reflex** accelerates the heart rate when entering blood stretches the walls of the right atrium. Ventricular contractions become more powerful and increase stroke volume when the ventricular walls are stretched (the **Frank-Starling principle**).

24. The basic heart rate is established by pacemaker cells, but it can be modified by the ANS. *(Figure 12-12)*

25. Acetylcholine (ACh) released by parasympathetic motor neurons lowers heart rate and stroke volume. Norepinephrine (NE) released by sympathetic neurons increases heart rate and stroke volume.

26. Epinephrine (E) and norepinephrine, hormones released by the suprarenal medullae during sympathetic activation, increase both heart rate and stroke volume. Thyroid hormones and glucagon also act to increase cardiac output.

27. The **cardioacceleratory center** in the medulla oblongata activates sympathetic neurons; the **cardioinhibitory center** governs the activities of the parasympathetic neurons. These cardiac centers receive inputs from higher centers and from receptors monitoring blood pressure and the levels of dissolved gases.

REVIEW QUESTIONS

WWW Access more review material online at The Anatomy & Physiology Place (**www.anatomyandphysiology.com**). There, you'll find Chapter Guides, Chapter Quizzes, Chapter Practice Tests, Interactive Flashcards, a Glossary with Pronunciations, and more to help you succeed in the course.

Level 1 • Reviewing Facts and Terms

Match each item in column A with the most closely related item in column B. Place letters for answers in the spaces provided.

COLUMN A	COLUMN B
_____ 1. epicardium	a. heart attack
_____ 2. right AV valve	b. cardiac pacemaker
_____ 3. left AV valve	c. tachycardia
_____ 4. anastomoses	d. SV × HR
_____ 5. myocardial infarction	e. tricuspid valve
_____ 6. SA node	f. bradycardia
_____ 7. systole	g. mitral valve
_____ 8. diastole	h. interconnections between arteries
_____ 9. cardiac output	i. visceral pericardium
_____ 10. HR slower than usual	j. increased venous return
_____ 11. HR faster than normal	k. contractions of heart chambers
_____ 12. atrial reflex	l. relaxation of heart chambers

13. Identify the superficial structures in the following diagram of the heart.

(a) _____	(b) _____
(c) _____	(d) _____
(e) _____	(f) _____
(g) _____	(h) _____

14. The blood supply to the muscles of the heart is provided by the
    (a) systemic circulation.   (b) pulmonary circulation.
    (c) coronary circulation.   (d) coronary portal system.

15. The autonomic centers for cardiac function are located in
    (a) myocardial tissue of the heart.
    (b) cardiac centers of the medulla oblongata.
    (c) the cerebral cortex.
    (d) a, b, and c are correct

16. The simple squamous epithelium covering the valves of the heart constitutes the
    (a) epicardium.   (b) endocardium.
    (c) myocardium.   (d) cardiac skeleton.

17. The structure that permits blood flow from the right atrium to the left atrium while the lungs are developing is the
    (a) foramen ovale.   (b) interatrial septum.
    (c) coronary sinus.   (d) fossa ovalis.

18. Identify the structures in the following diagram of a sectional view of the heart.

(a) _____ (b) _____
(c) _____ (d) _____
(e) _____ (f) _____
(g) _____ (h) _____
(i) _____ (j) _____
(k) _____ (l) _____
(m) _____

19. Blood leaves the left ventricle by passing through the
    (a) aortic semilunar valve.
    (b) pulmonary semilunar valve.
    (c) mitral valve.
    (d) tricuspid valve.

20. The QRS complex of the ECG is produced when the
    (a) atria depolarize.
    (b) ventricles depolarize.
    (c) ventricles repolarize.
    (d) atria repolarize.

21. During diastole, the chambers of the heart
    (a) undergo a sharp increase in pressure.
    (b) contract and push blood into an adjacent chamber.
    (c) relax and fill with blood.
    (d) reach a pressure of approximately 120 mm Hg.

22. What roles do the chordae tendineae and papillary muscles have in the normal function of the AV valves?

23. What are the principal heart valves, and what is the function of each?

24. Trace the normal path of an electrical impulse through the conducting system of the heart.

25. (a) What is the cardiac cycle? (b) What phases and events are necessary to complete the cardiac cycle?

Level 2 • Reviewing Concepts

26. Tetanic muscle contractions cannot occur in a normal cardiac muscle cell because
    (a) cardiac muscle tissue contracts on its own.
    (b) there is no neural or hormonal stimulation.
    (c) the refractory period lasts until the muscle cell relaxes.
    (d) the refractory period ends before the muscle cell reaches peak tension.

27. The amount of blood forced out of the heart depends on the
    (a) degree of stretching at the end of ventricular diastole.
    (b) contractility of the ventricle.
    (c) amount of pressure required to eject blood.
    (d) a, b, and c are correct.

28. Cardiac output cannot increase indefinitely because
    (a) available filling time becomes shorter as the heart rate increases.
    (b) cardiovascular centers adjust the heart rate.
    (c) the rate of spontaneous depolarization decreases.
    (d) the ion concentrations surrounding pacemaker cell membranes decrease.

29. Describe the relationships of the four chambers of the heart to the pulmonary and systemic circuits.

30. What are the sources and clinical significance of the heart sounds?

31. (a) What effect does sympathetic stimulation have on the heart? (b) What effect does parasympathetic stimulation have on the heart?

Level 3 • Critical Thinking and Clinical Applications

32. A patient's ECG tracing shows a consistent pattern of two P waves followed by a normal QRS complex and T wave. What is the cause of this abnormal wave pattern?

33. The following measurements were made on two individuals (the values recorded remained stable for 1 hour):

    Person A: heart rate, 75 bpm; stroke volume, 60 mL

    Person B: heart rate, 90 bpm; stroke volume, 95 mL

    Which person has the greater venous return? Which person has the longer ventricular filling time?

34. Karen is taking the medication *verapamil*, a drug that blocks the calcium channels in cardiac muscle cells. What effect should this medication have on Karen's stroke volume?

13 The Cardiovascular System: Blood Vessels and Circulation

One of the vital signs measured in a physical examination is blood pressure. Blood pressure is determined with a stethoscope and blood pressure cuff (sphygmomanometer). Unusually high or low readings can alert the examiner to potential problems with heart or blood vessel function.

LEARNING OUTCOMES

After completing this chapter, you should be able to do the following:

13-1 Distinguish among the types of blood vessels based on their structure and function.

13-2 Explain the mechanisms that regulate blood flow through blood vessels, and discuss the mechanisms that regulate movement of fluids between capillaries and interstitial spaces.

13-3 Describe the control mechanisms that interact to regulate blood flow and pressure in tissues, and explain how the activities of the cardiac, vasomotor, and respiratory centers are coordinated to control blood flow through tissues.

13-4 Explain how the cardiovascular system responds to the stresses of exercise and hemorrhage.

13-5 Describe the three general functional patterns in the pulmonary and systemic circuits.

13-6 Identify the major arteries and veins of the pulmonary circuit.

13-7 Identify the major arteries and veins of the systemic circuit.

13-8 Identify the differences between fetal and adult circulation patterns, and describe the changes in the patterns of blood flow that occur at birth.

13-9 Discuss the effects of aging on the cardiovascular system.

13-10 Give examples of interactions between the cardiovascular system and the other organ systems.

An Introduction to Blood Vessels and Circulation

The previous two chapters examined the composition of blood and the structure and function of the heart, whose pumping action keeps blood in motion. Here we will consider the vessels that carry blood to peripheral tissues, and the nature of the exchange that occurs between the blood and interstitial fluids.

This chapter first examines the structure of arteries, capillaries, and veins. Then it discusses their functions and the basic principles of cardiovascular regulation before examining the distribution of the body's major blood vessels.

13-1 Arteries, arterioles, capillaries, venules, and veins differ in size, structure, and function

Blood leaves the heart by way of the pulmonary trunk and aorta, each with a diameter of around 2.5 cm (1 in.). These vessels branch repeatedly, forming the major **arteries** that distribute blood to body organs. Within these organs further branching occurs, creating several hundred million tiny arteries, or **arterioles** (ar-TĒR-e-ōls). The arterioles provide blood to more than 10 billion **capillaries.** These capillaries, barely the diameter of a single red blood cell, form extensive, branching networks. If all the capillaries in an average adult's body were placed end to end, they would circle the globe in an unbroken chain 25,000 miles long.

The vital functions of the cardiovascular system occur at the capillary level: *Chemical and gaseous exchange between the blood and interstitial fluid occurs across capillary walls.* Tissue cells rely on capillary diffusion to obtain nutrients and oxygen and to remove metabolic wastes such as carbon dioxide and urea.

Blood flowing out of a capillary network first enters **venules** (VEN-ūls), the smallest vessels of the venous system. These slender vessels subsequently merge to form small **veins.** Blood then passes through medium-sized and large veins before reaching the venae cavae (in the systemic circuit) or the pulmonary veins (in the pulmonary circuit) (see Figure 12-1, p. 406).

THE STRUCTURE OF VESSEL WALLS

The walls of arteries and veins contain three distinct layers (Figure 13-1):

1. The **tunica intima** (IN-ti-muh), or *tunica interna,* is the innermost layer of a blood vessel. It includes the endothelial lining of the vessel and an underlying layer of connective tissue dominated by elastic fibers.

2. The **tunica media,** the middle layer, contains smooth muscle tissue in a framework of collagen and elastic fibers. When these smooth muscles contract, vessel diameter decreases; when they relax, vessel diameter increases.

3. The outer **tunica externa** (eks-TER-nuh), or *tunica adventitia* (ad-ven-TISH-a), forms a sheath of connective tissue around the vessel. Its collagen fibers may intertwine with those of adjacent tissues, stabilizing and anchoring the blood vessel.

Arteries and veins often lie side by side in a narrow band of connective tissue, as shown in Figure 13-1. Such a sectional view clearly shows the greater wall thickness characteristic of arteries. The thicker tunica media of an artery contains more elastic fibers and smooth muscle cells than does that of a vein. The elastic components enable arterial vessels to resist the pressure generated by the heart as it forces blood into the arterial network. The smooth muscle provides a means of actively controlling vessel diameter. Arterial smooth muscle is under the control of the sympathetic division of the autonomic nervous system. When stimulated, these muscles in the vessel wall contract and the artery constricts in a process called **vasoconstriction.** Relaxation increases the diameter of the artery and its central opening, or *lumen,* in a process called **vasodilation.**

ARTERIES

In traveling from the heart to the capillaries, blood passes through elastic arteries, muscular arteries, and arterioles (Figure 13-2).

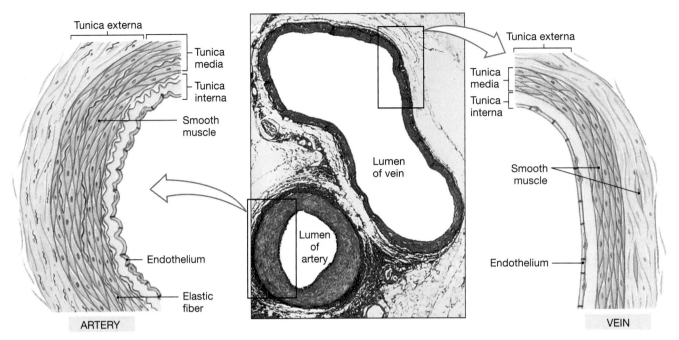

FIGURE 13-1 A Comparison of a Typical Artery and a Typical Vein. The walls of both arteries and veins are made up of three layers containing different tissues. The inner layer, or tunica intima, includes an endothelium with its basement membrane and an underlying connective tissue layer with elastic fibers; the middle layer, or tunica media, contains sheets of smooth muscle fibers within loose connective tissue; the outer layer, or tunica externa, forms a connective tissue covering around the vessel. In general, for a vessel of a given size, an artery has a thicker wall and smaller lumen than a vein. (LM × 74)

Elastic arteries are large, extremely resilient vessels with diameters of up to 2.5 cm (1 in.). Some examples are the pulmonary trunk and aorta, and their major arterial branches. The walls of elastic arteries contain a tunica media dominated by elastic fibers rather than smooth muscle cells. As a result, elastic arteries are able to absorb the pressure changes that occur during the cardiac cycle. During ventricular systole, blood pressure rises quickly as additional blood is pushed into the systemic circuit. Over this period, the elastic arteries are stretched, and their diameter increases. During ventricular diastole, arterial blood pressure declines, and the elastic fibers recoil to their original dimensions. The net result is that the expansion of the arteries dampens the rise in pressure during ventricular systole, and the ensuing arterial recoil slows the decline in pressure during ventricular diastole. If the arteries were solid pipes rather than elastic tubes, pressures would rise much higher during systole and would fall much lower during diastole.

Muscular arteries, also known as *medium-sized arteries* or *distribution arteries,* distribute blood to skeletal muscles and internal organs. A typical muscular artery has a diameter of approximately 0.4 cm (0.15 in.). The external carotid arteries of the neck are one example. The thick tunica media in a muscular artery contains more smooth muscle cells and fewer elastic fibers than does an elastic artery (Figure 13-2).

Arterioles, with an internal diameter of about 30 μm, are much smaller than muscular arteries. The tunica media of an arteriole consists of one to two layers of smooth muscle cells. These muscle layers enable muscular arteries and arterioles to change the diameter of the lumen, thereby altering blood pressure and the rate of flow through dependent tissues.

CAPILLARIES

Capillaries are the *only* blood vessels whose walls permit exchange between the blood and the surrounding interstitial fluid. Because capillary walls are relatively thin, diffusion distances are small, and exchange can occur quickly. In addition, the small diameter of capillaries slows blood flow, allowing sufficient time for the diffusion or active transport of materials across capillary walls.

A typical capillary consists of a single layer of endothelial cells inside a basement membrane (Figure 13-2). Neither a tunica externa nor a tunica media is present. The average diameter of a capillary is 8 μm, very close to that of a red blood cell. In most regions of the body, the endothelium forms a complete lining, and most substances enter or leave the capillary by diffusing across endothelial cells or through gaps between adjacent endothelial cells. Water, small solutes, and lipid-soluble materials can easily diffuse into the surrounding interstitial

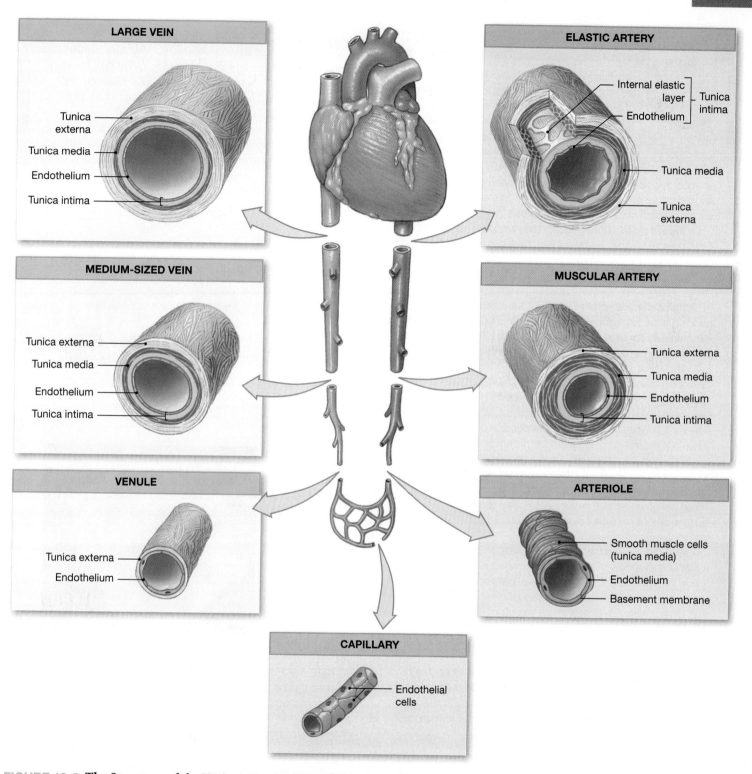

FIGURE 13-2 **The Structure of the Various Types of Blood Vessels.** The different types of blood vessels have different diameters, wall thicknesses, and lumen sizes. Note that the wall of a capillary is only one cell thick; it consists of an endothelium and a basement membrane.

fluid. In other areas (notably, the choroid plexus of the brain, the hypothalamus, and filtration sites in the kidneys), small pores in the endothelial cells also permit the passage of relatively large molecules, including proteins.

Capillaries do not function as individual units but as part of an interconnected network called a **capillary bed** (Figure 13-4). A single arteriole usually gives rise to dozens of capillaries, which in turn collect into several *venules,* the smallest vessels of the

Clinical Note

Arteriosclerosis

Arteriosclerosis (ar-tē-rē-ō-skle-RŌ-sis; *skleros,* hard) is a thickening and toughening of arterial walls. Complications related to arteriosclerosis account for roughly half of all deaths in the United States. The effects of arteriosclerosis are varied; for example, arteriosclerosis of coronary vessels is responsible for *coronary artery disease* (*CAD*), and arteriosclerosis of arteries supplying the brain can lead to strokes. ∞ p. 414 There are two major forms of arteriosclerosis: *focal calcification* and *atherosclerosis.*

In **focal calcification,** degenerating smooth muscle in the tunica media is replaced by calcium deposits. It occurs as part of the aging process, in association with atherosclerosis, and as a complication of diabetes mellitus, an endocrine disorder. ∞ p. 366

Atherosclerosis (ath-er-ō-skle-RŌ-sis; *athero-,* a pasty deposit) is the formation of lipid deposits in the tunica media associated with damage to the endothelial lining. Many factors may contribute to the development of atherosclerosis. One major factor is lipid levels in the blood. Atherosclerosis tends to develop in individuals whose blood contains elevated levels of plasma lipids, specifically cholesterol. Circulating cholesterol is transported to peripheral tissues in protein–lipid complexes called *lipoproteins.* (The various types of lipoproteins are discussed in Chapter 17.) When cholesterol-rich lipoproteins remain in circulation for an extended period, circulating monocytes begin removing them from the bloodstream. Eventually the monocytes, now filled with lipid droplets, attach themselves to the endothelia of blood vessels. These cells then release growth factors that stimulate the divisions of smooth muscle cells near the tunica interna. The vessel wall thickens and stiffens.

Other monocytes then invade the area, migrating between the endothelial cells. As these changes occur, the monocytes, smooth muscle fibers, and endothelial cells begin phagocytizing lipids as well. The result is a **plaque,** a fatty mass of tissue that projects into the lumen of the vessel. At this point, the plaque has a relatively simple structure, and evidence indicates that the process can be reversed if appropriate dietary adjustments are made.

If these conditions persist, the endothelial cells become swollen with lipids, and gaps appear in the endothelial lining. Platelets now begin sticking to the exposed collagen fibers, and platelet adhesion and aggregation lead to the formation of

a localized blood clot that further restricts blood flow through the vessel. The structure of the plaque is now relatively complex (**Figure 13-3**); plaque growth can be halted, but the structural changes are permanent.

Elderly individuals, especially elderly men, are most likely to develop atherosclerotic plaques. In addition to age, sex, and high blood cholesterol levels, other important risk factors include high blood pressure, cigarette smoking, diabetes mellitus, obesity, and stress.

(a)

(b)

FIGURE 13-3 A Plaque Within an Artery. (a) This photomicrograph provides a cross-sectional view of a large plaque. **(b)** This photograph shows a section of a coronary artery narrowed by plaque formation.

venous system. The entrance to each capillary is guarded by a **precapillary sphincter,** a band of smooth muscle. Contraction of the smooth muscle fibers narrows the diameter of the capillary's entrance and reduces the flow of blood. The relaxation of the sphincter dilates the opening, allowing blood to enter the capillary more rapidly.

Although blood usually flows from arterioles to venules at a constant rate, the blood flow within any single capillary can

be quite variable. Each precapillary sphincter undergoes cycles of activity, alternately contracting and relaxing perhaps a dozen times each minute. As a result of this cyclical change—called **vasomotion** (*vaso-,* vessel)—blood flow within any given capillary is intermittent rather than a steady and constant stream. The net effect is that blood may reach the venules by one route now and by a quite different route later. This process is controlled at the tissue level, as smooth muscle fibers re-

FIGURE 13-4 **The Organization of a Capillary Bed. (a)** In this diagram showing the basic features of a typical capillary bed, solid arrows indicate consistent blood flow, and dashed arrows indicate variable blood flow. **(b)** This micrograph shows several capillary beds.

spond to local changes in the concentrations of chemicals and dissolved gases in the interstitial fluid. For example, when dissolved oxygen levels decline within a tissue, the capillary sphincters relax, and blood flow to the area increases. Such control at the tissue level is called *autoregulation.*

Sometimes blood vessels provide alternate routes for blood flow by forming an **anastomosis** (a-nas-tō-MŌ-sis; "outlet"; plural, *anastomoses*), the joining of two tubes. Under certain conditions, blood completely bypasses a capillary bed through an **arteriovenous** (ar-tēr-ē-ō-VĒ-nus) **anastomosis,** a vessel that connects an arteriole to a venule (Figure 13-4a). In other cases, a single capillary bed is supplied by an **arterial anastomosis,** in which more than one artery fuses before giving rise to arterioles. An arterial anastomosis in effect provides an insurance policy for capillary beds: If one artery is compressed or blocked, the others can continue to deliver blood to the capillary bed, and dependent tissues will not be damaged. Arterial anastomoses occur in the brain, in the coronary circulation, and in many other sites as well. ∞ p. 414

VEINS

Veins collect blood from all tissues and organs and return it to the heart. Veins are classified on the basis of their internal diameters. The smallest—**venules**—resemble expanded capil-

laries, and venules with diameters smaller than 50 μm lack a tunica media altogether (Figure 13-2). **Medium-sized veins** range from 2 mm to 9 mm in diameter, comparable in size to muscular arteries. In these veins, the tunica media contains several smooth muscle layers, and the relatively thick tunica externa has longitudinal bundles of elastic and collagen fibers. **Large veins** include the two venae cavae and their tributaries in the abdominopelvic and thoracic cavities. In these vessels, the thin tunica media is surrounded by a thick tunica externa composed of elastic and collagenous fibers.

Veins have relatively thin walls because they need not withstand much pressure. In venules and medium-sized veins, the pressure is so low that it cannot overcome the force of gravity. In the limbs, medium-sized veins contain **valves,** folds of endothelium that function like the valves in the heart, preventing the backflow of blood (Figure 13-5). As long as the valves function normally, any body movement that compresses a vein will push blood toward the heart, improving *venous return.* ∞ p. 421 If the walls of the veins near the valves weaken or become stretched and distorted, the valves may not work properly. Blood then pools in the veins, which become distended. The effects range from mild discomfort and a cosmetic problem (as in superficial *varicose veins* in the thighs and legs) to painful distortion of adjacent tissues (as in *hemorrhoids,* swollen veins in the lining of the anal canal).

Valve opened

Valve closed

Valve closed

Valve opened

FIGURE 13-5 The Function of Valves in the Venous System.
Valves in the walls of medium-sized veins prevent the backflow of blood. The compression of veins by the contraction of adjacent skeletal muscles helps maintain venous blood flow.

CHECKPOINT

1. List the five general classes of blood vessels.

2. A cross section of tissue shows several small, thin-walled vessels with very little smooth muscle tissue in the tunica media. Which type of vessels are these?

3. What effect would relaxation of precapillary sphincters have on blood flow through a tissue?

4. Why are valves found in veins, but not in arteries?

See the blue Answers tab at the back of the book.

13-2 Pressure and resistance determine blood flow and affect rates of capillary exchange

The primary function of the components of the cardiovascular system (the blood, heart, and blood vessels) is to maintain an adequate blood flow through the capillaries in all tissues of the body. The capillaries are the sites of nutrient and waste exchange for the body's cells. Under normal circumstances, blood flow equals cardiac output. When cardiac output goes up, so does blood flow through capillary beds; when cardiac output declines, blood flow is reduced. Next we consider how the flow of blood through capillaries also depends on two additional factors—*pressure* and *resistance.*

FACTORS AFFECTING BLOOD FLOW

Pressure and resistance both affect blood flow to the tissues, but they have opposing effects. Blood flow and pressure are directly related: When pressure increases, flow increases. Blood flow and resistance are inversely related: When resistance increases, flow decreases. To keep blood moving in the body, the heart must generate enough pressure to overcome the resistance to blood flow in the pulmonary and systemic circuits.

Pressure

Liquids, including blood, cannot be compressed. As a result, a force exerted against a liquid generates a fluid (or hydrostatic) pressure that is conducted in all directions. If a pressure difference exists, a liquid will flow from an area of higher pressure toward an area of lower pressure. The flow rate is directly proportional to the pressure difference: the greater the difference in pressure, the faster the flow.

The largest pressure difference, or *pressure gradient,* is found in the systemic circuit between the base of the aorta (where blood leaves the left ventricle) and the entrance to the right atrium (where blood returns to the heart). This pressure difference, called the *circulatory pressure,* averages about 100 mm Hg (millimeters of mercury, a standard unit of pressure). This relatively high circulatory pressure is needed primarily to force blood through the arterioles and into the capillaries.

Circulatory pressure is divided into three components: (1) *arterial pressure* (routinely measured on a person's arm and commonly referred to as **blood pressure**), (2) *capillary pressure,* and (3) *venous pressure.* Each component of circulatory pressure will be discussed in some detail shortly.

Resistance

Resistance is any force that opposes movement. In the cardiovascular system, resistance opposes the movement of blood. For blood to flow, the circulatory pressure must be great enough to overcome the **total peripheral resistance,** the resistance of the entire cardiovascular system. The greatest pressure difference within the cardiovascular system—about 65 mm Hg—occurs in the arterial network because of the high resistance of the arterioles. The resistance of the arterial system is termed **peripheral resistance.** Sources of peripheral resistance include *vascular resistance, viscosity,* and *turbulence.*

VASCULAR RESISTANCE. The largest component of peripheral resistance is **vascular resistance,** the resistance of the blood vessels to blood flow. *The most important factor in vascular resistance is friction between the blood and the vessel walls.* The amount of friction depends on the length and diameter of the vessel. Friction increases with increasing vessel length (longer vessels have a larger surface area in contact with the blood) and with decreasing vessel diameter (in small-diameter vessels, nearly all the blood is slowed down by friction with the walls). Vessel length cannot ordinarily be changed, so vascular resistance is controlled by changing the diameter of blood vessels—through the contraction or relaxation of smooth muscle in the vessel walls.

Most of the vascular resistance occurs in arterioles, which are extremely muscular. The walls of an arteriole with a 30-μm internal diameter, for example, can have a 20-μm-thick layer of smooth muscle. Local, neural, and hormonal stimuli that stimulate or inhibit contractions of this smooth muscle tissue can adjust the diameters of these vessels, and a small change in diameter can produce a very large change in resistance.

VISCOSITY. The property called **viscosity** is the resistance to flow resulting from interactions among molecules and suspended materials in a liquid. Liquids of low viscosity, such as water, flow at low pressures, whereas thick, syrupy liquids such as molasses flow only under higher pressures. Because whole blood contains plasma proteins and suspended blood cells, it has a viscosity about five times that of water.

Under normal conditions, the viscosity of blood remains stable. But disorders that affect the hematocrit or the plasma protein content can change blood viscosity and increase or decrease peripheral resistance. For example, in **anemia,** the hematocrit is reduced due to inadequate production of hemoglobin, RBCs, or both. As a result, both the oxygen-carrying capacity and the viscosity of the blood are reduced. A reduction in blood viscosity can also result from protein deficiency diseases, in which the liver cannot synthesize normal amounts of plasma proteins.

TURBULENCE. Blood usually flows through a vessel smoothly, with the slowest flow near the walls, and the fastest flow at the center of the vessel. High flow rates, irregular surfaces caused by injury or disease processes, or sudden changes in vessel diameter upset this smooth flow, creating eddies and swirls. This phenomenon, called **turbulence,** slows flow and increases resistance.

Turbulence normally occurs when blood flows between the heart's chambers and from the heart into the aorta and pulmonary trunk. In addition to increasing resistance, this turbulence generates the *third* and *fourth heart sounds* often heard through a stethoscope. Turbulent blood flow across damaged or misaligned heart valves produces the sound of *heart murmurs.*
∞ p. 412

The Interplay Between Pressure and Resistance

Neural and hormonal control mechanisms regulate blood pressure, keeping it relatively stable. Adjustments in the peripheral resistance of vessels supplying specific organs allow the rate of blood flow to be precisely controlled. An example is the increase in blood flow to skeletal muscles during exercise, discussed in Chapter 7. ∞ p. 238 That increase results from a drop in the peripheral resistance of the arteries supplying active muscles. Of the three sources of resistance, only vascular resistance can be adjusted by the nervous or endocrine system to regulate blood flow. Viscosity and turbulence, which affect peripheral resistance, are normally constant.

CARDIOVASCULAR PRESSURES WITHIN THE SYSTEMIC CIRCUIT

Pressure varies along the path of blood flow within the systemic circuit. Systemic pressures are highest in the aorta, peaking at around 120 mm Hg, and lowest at the venae cavae, averaging about 2 mm Hg (**Figure 13-6**). Next we consider pressures in the arterial network; then we examine how pressure in the capillaries drives the exchange of substances between the bloodstream and body tissues before considering pressures in the venous system.

Blood Pressure (Arterial Pressure)

As **Figure 13-6** shows, the pressure in large and small arteries fluctuates, rising during ventricular systole and falling during ventricular diastole. **Systolic pressure** is the peak blood pressure measured during ventricular systole, and **diastolic pressure** is the minimum blood pressure at the end of ventricular diastole. In recording blood pressure, we separate systolic and diastolic pressures by a slash mark, as in "120/80" (read as "one twenty over eighty"). A *pulse* is a rhythmic pressure oscillation that accompanies each heartbeat. The difference between the systolic and diastolic pressures is the **pulse pressure** (*pulsus,* stroke).

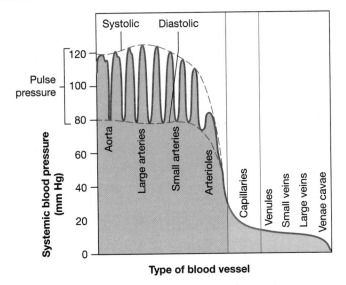

FIGURE 13-6 **Pressures Within the Circulatory System.** Notice the general reduction of circulatory pressures within the systemic circuit and the elimination of the pulse pressure in the arterioles.

Pulse pressure lessens as the distance from the heart increases. As already discussed, the average pressure declines as a result of friction between the blood and the vessel walls. The pulse pressure fades because arteries are elastic tubes rather than solid pipes. Much as a balloon's walls expand upon the entry of air, the elasticity of the arteries allows them to expand with blood during systole. When diastole begins and blood pressures fall, the arteries recoil to their original dimensions. Because the aortic semilunar valve prevents the return of blood to the heart, arterial recoil adds an extra push to the flow of blood. The magnitude of this phenomenon, called *elastic rebound,* is greatest near the heart and drops in succeeding arterial sections.

By the time blood reaches a precapillary sphincter, no pressure oscillations remain, and the blood pressure is about 35 mm Hg (Figure 13-6). Along the length of a typical capillary, blood pressure gradually falls from about 35 mm Hg to roughly 18 mm Hg, the pressure at the start of the venous system.

Capillary Pressures and Capillary Exchange

The pressure of blood within a capillary bed, or **capillary pressure,** pushes against capillary walls, just as it does in arteries. But unlike other blood vessels, capillary walls are quite permeable to small ions, nutrients, organic wastes, dissolved gases, and water. Most of these materials are reabsorbed by the capillaries, but about 3.6 liters (0.95 gallons) of water and solutes flow through peripheral tissues each day and enter the **lymphatic vessels** of the lymphoid system, which empty into the bloodstream (Figure 13-7).

This continuous movement and exchange of water and solutes from the capillaries through the body tissues and back into the bloodstream plays an important role in homeostasis. Capillary exchange has four important functions: (1) maintaining constant communication between plasma and interstitial fluid; (2) speeding the distribution of nutrients, hormones, and dissolved gases throughout tissues; (3) assisting the movement of insoluble lipids and tissue proteins that cannot cross capillary walls; and (4) flushing bacterial toxins and other chemical stimuli to lymphoid tissues and organs that function in providing immunity to disease.

FIGURE 13-7 **Forces Acting Across Capillary Walls.** At the arteriolar end of the capillary, capillary hydrostatic pressure (CHP) is greater than blood osmotic pressure (BOP), so fluid moves out of the capillary (filtration). Near the venule, CHP is lower than BOP, so fluid moves into the capillary (reabsorption).

The movement of materials across capillary walls occurs by diffusion, filtration, and osmosis. Chapter 3 described these processes, so only a brief overview is provided here. ∞ p. 64 Solute molecules tend to diffuse across the capillary lining, driven by their individual concentration gradients. Water-soluble materials—including ions and small organic molecules such as glucose, amino acids, or urea—diffuse through small spaces between adjacent endothelial cells. Larger water-soluble molecules, such as plasma proteins, cannot normally leave the bloodstream. Lipid-soluble materials—including steroids, fatty acids, and dissolved gases—diffuse across the endothelial lining, passing through the membrane lipids.

Water molecules will move when driven by either hydrostatic (fluid) pressure or osmotic pressure. ∞ p. 66 In filtration, hydrostatic pressure pushes water molecules from an area of high pressure to an area of lower pressure. At a capillary, the hydrostatic pressure, or *capillary hydrostatic pressure (CHP)*, is greatest at the arteriolar end (35 mm Hg) and least at the venous end (18 mm Hg). The tendency for water and small solutes to move out of the blood is, therefore, greatest at the start of a capillary, where the CHP is highest, and declines along the length of the capillary as CHP falls.

Osmosis, in contrast, is the movement of water across a selectively permeable membrane separating two solutions with different solute concentrations. Water moves into the solution with the higher solute concentration, and the force of this water movement is called osmotic pressure. Because blood contains more dissolved proteins than does interstitial fluid, its osmotic pressure is higher, and water tends to move from the interstitial fluid into the blood. ∞ p. 66 The osmotic pressure of blood (25 mm Hg) is constant along the length of the capillaries. Thus, capillary hydrostatic pressure (CHP) tends to push water out of the capillary, whereas blood osmotic pressure (BOP) forces tends to reabsorb water, or pull it back in (**Figure 13-7**).

Venous Pressure

Although pressure at the start of the venous system is only about one-tenth that at the start of the arterial system (**Figure 13-6**), the blood must still travel through a vascular network as complex as the arterial system before returning to the heart. However, venous pressures are low, and the veins offer little resistance. As a result, once blood enters the venous system, pressure declines very slowly.

As blood travels through the venous system toward the heart, the veins become larger, resistance drops further, and the flow rate increases. Pressures at the entrance to the right atrium fluctuate, but they average approximately 2 mm Hg. This means that the driving force pushing blood through the venous system is a mere 16 mm Hg (18 mm Hg in the venules – 2 mm Hg in the venae cavae = 16 mm Hg) as compared to the 65 mm Hg pressure acting along the arterial system (100 mm Hg at the aorta – 35 mm Hg at the capillaries = 65 mm Hg).

When you are lying down, a pressure gradient of 16 mm Hg is sufficient to maintain venous flow. But when you are standing, venous blood in regions below the heart must overcome gravity as it ascends within the inferior vena

Clinical Note — Capillary Dynamics and Blood Volume

Any condition that affects hydrostatic or osmotic pressures in the blood or tissues will shift the direction of fluid movement. For example, consider what happens at the capillary level to a bleeding accident victim or a dehydrated person lost in the desert. In both cases, the decrease in blood volume causes a drop in blood pressure. In the second case, however, the loss in blood volume is also accompanied by a rise in blood osmotic pressure, because as water is lost, the blood becomes more concentrated. In either case, a net movement of water from the interstitial fluid to the bloodstream occurs, and blood volume increases. This process is known as a *recall of fluids*.

The converse situation is **edema** (e-DĒ-muh), an abnormal accumulation of interstitial fluid in the tissues. Localized edema often occurs around a bruise, for example. Damage to capillaries at the injury site allows plasma proteins to leak into the interstitial fluid, which decreases the osmotic pressure of the blood and elevates that of the tissues. More water then moves into the tissue, resulting in edema. In the U.S. population, serious cases of edema most often result from an increase in pressure in the arterial system, the venous system, or both. This condition often occurs during **congestive heart failure (CHF).**

Heart failure occurs when cardiac output is insufficient to meet the circulatory demands of the body. In congestive heart failure, the left ventricle can no longer keep up with the right ventricle, and blood flow backs up (becomes congested) in the pulmonary circuit. This situation makes the right ventricle work harder, further elevating pulmonary arterial pressures and forcing blood through the lungs and into the weakened left ventricle. The increased blood pressure in the pulmonary vessels leads to *pulmonary edema,* a buildup of fluids in the lungs.

Clinical Note

Checking the Pulse and Blood Pressure

The pulse can be felt within any of the large or medium-sized arteries. The usual procedure involves using the fingertips to compress an artery against a relatively solid mass, preferably a bone. When the vessel is compressed, the pulse is felt as a pressure against the fingertips.

Figure 13-8a indicates the locations used to check the pulse. The inside of the wrist is often used because the *radial artery* can easily be pressed against the distal portion of the radius. Other accessible arteries include the *temporal, facial, external carotid, brachial, femoral, popliteal, posterior tibial,* and *dorsalis pedis arteries.* Firm pressure exerted on an artery near the base of a limb can reduce or eliminate arterial bleeding in more distal portions of the limb. These sites are called *pressure points.*

Blood pressure is measured using a *sphygmomanometer* (sfig-mō-ma-NOM-e-ter; *sphygmos,* pulse + *manometer,* device for measuring pressure), as shown in Figure 13-8b. An inflatable cuff is placed around the arm such that inflation of the cuff squeezes the brachial artery. A stethoscope is placed over the artery distal to the cuff, and the cuff is then inflated. A tube connects the cuff to a pressure gauge that measures the pressure inside the cuff in millimeters of mercury (mm Hg). Inflation continues until cuff pressure is roughly 30 mm Hg above the pressure sufficient to collapse the brachial artery, stop the flow of blood, and eliminate the sound of the pulse.

The practitioner then slowly lets air out of the cuff. When the pressure in the cuff falls below systolic pressure, blood can again enter the artery. At first, blood enters only at peak systolic pressures, and the sound of blood pulsing through the artery becomes audible through the stethoscope. As the pressure falls further, the sound changes because the vessel is remaining open for longer and longer periods. When the cuff pressure falls below diastolic pressure, blood flow becomes continuous, and the sound of the pulse becomes muffled or disappears completely. Thus, the pressure at which the pulse can first be heard corresponds to the peak systolic pressure; when the pulse fades, the pressure has reached diastolic levels. The distinctive sounds heard during this test are called **sounds of Korotkoff** (sometimes spelled *Korotkov* or *Korotkow*). When the blood pressure is recorded, systolic and diastolic pressures are usually separated by a slash, as in "120/80" ("one twenty over eighty") or "110/75." A reading of 120/80 corresponds to a pulse pressure of 40 (mm Hg).

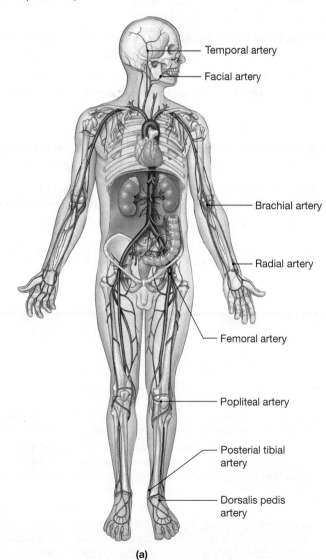

- Temporal artery
- Facial artery
- Brachial artery
- Radial artery
- Femoral artery
- Popliteal artery
- Posterial tibial artery
- Dorsalis pedis artery

(a)

FIGURE 13-8 Checking the Pulse and Blood Pressure.
(a) Several pressure points can be used to monitor the pulse or control peripheral bleeding. **(b)** A sphygmomanometer and a stethoscope are used to check an individual's blood pressure.

(b)

cava. Two factors help overcome gravity and propel venous blood toward the heart:

1. **Muscular compression.** The contractions of skeletal muscles near a vein compress it, helping push blood toward the heart. The valves in medium-sized veins ensure that blood flow occurs in one direction only (Figure 13-5, p. 434).

2. The **respiratory pump.** As you inhale, decreased pressure in the thoracic cavity draws air into the lungs. This drop in pressure causes the inferior vena cava and right atrium to expand and fill with blood, thus increasing venous return. During exhalation, the increased pressure that forces air out of the lungs compresses the venae cavae, pushing blood into the right atrium.

During exercise, both factors cooperate to increase venous return and push cardiac output to maximal levels. However, when an individual stands at attention, with knees locked and leg muscles immobile, these mechanisms are impaired, and the reduction in venous return leads to a fall in cardiac output. The blood supply to the brain is in turn reduced, sometimes enough to cause *fainting,* a temporary loss of consciousness. The person then collapses; once the body is horizontal, both venous return and cardiac output return to normal.

The Big Picture

It is blood flow that's the goal, and total peripheral blood flow is equal to cardiac output. Blood pressure is needed to overcome friction and elastic forces and sustain blood flow. If blood pressure is too low, vessels collapse, blood flow stops, and tissues die; if blood pressure is too high, vessel walls stiffen and capillary beds may rupture.

CHECKPOINT

5. Identify the factors that contribute to total peripheral resistance.

6. In a healthy individual, where is blood pressure greater: at the aorta or at the inferior vena cava? Explain.

7. While standing in the hot sun, Sally begins to feel light-headed and then faints. Explain what happened.

See the blue Answers tab at the back of the book.

13-3 Cardiovascular regulation involves autoregulation, neural mechanisms, and endocrine responses

Homeostatic mechanisms regulate cardiovascular activity to ensure that tissue blood flow, also called *tissue perfusion,* meets the demand for oxygen and nutrients. Three variable factors influence tissue blood flow: cardiac output, peripheral resistance, and blood pressure. We discussed cardiac output in Chapter 12 (∞ p. 421) and considered peripheral resistance and pressure earlier in this chapter.

Most cells are relatively close to capillaries. When a group of cells becomes active, the circulation to that region must increase to deliver the oxygen and nutrients they need and to carry away the waste products and carbon dioxide they generate. The goal of cardiovascular regulation is to ensure that these blood flow changes occur (1) at an appropriate time, (2) in the right area, and (3) without drastically altering blood pressure and blood flow to vital organs.

The mechanisms involved in the regulation of cardiovascular function include the following (Figure 13-9):

- *Autoregulation.* Changes in tissue conditions act directly on precapillary sphincters to alter peripheral resistance, producing local changes in the pattern of blood flow within capillary beds. Such autoregulation causes immediate, localized homeostatic adjustments. If autoregulation is unable to normalize tissue conditions, neural and endocrine mechanisms are activated.

- *Neural mechanisms.* Neural mechanisms respond to changes in arterial pressure or blood gas levels at specific sites. When those changes occur, the autonomic nervous system adjusts cardiac output and peripheral resistance to maintain adequate blood flow.

- *Endocrine mechanisms.* The endocrine system releases hormones that enhance short-term adjustments and direct long-term changes in cardiovascular performance.

Short-term responses adjust cardiac output and peripheral resistance to stabilize blood pressure and blood flow to tissues. Long-term adjustments involve alterations in blood volume that affect cardiac output and the transport of oxygen and carbon dioxide to and from active tissues.

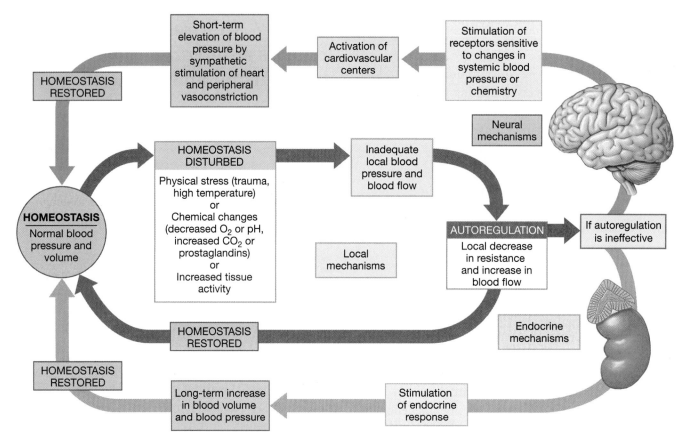

FIGURE 13-9 Local, Neural, and Endocrine Adjustments That Maintain Blood Pressure and Blood Flow.

AUTOREGULATION OF BLOOD FLOW WITHIN TISSUES

Under normal resting conditions, cardiac output remains stable, and precapillary sphincters control local blood flow by automatically adjusting peripheral resistance in individual tissues. The smooth muscles of precapillary sphincters respond automatically to certain alterations in the local environment, such as changes in oxygen and carbon dioxide levels or the presence of specific chemicals. For example, when oxygen is abundant, the smooth muscle cells in the sphincters contract and slow the flow of blood. As the cells take up and use O_2 for aerobic respiration, tissue oxygen supplies dwindle, carbon dioxide levels rise, and pH falls. These changes signal the smooth muscle cells in the precapillary sphincters to relax, and blood flow increases. Similarly, the release of nitric oxide (NO) by capillary endothelial cells stimulated by high shear forces along the capillary walls or the presence of histamine at an injury site during inflammation triggers the relaxation of precapillary sphincters, increasing blood flow.

Factors that promote the dilation of precapillary sphincters are called **vasodilators,** and those that stimulate the constriction of

precapillary sphincters are called **vasoconstrictors.** Together, such factors control blood flow in a single capillary bed. When present in high concentrations, these factors also affect arterioles, increasing or decreasing blood flow to all the capillary beds in a given region. Such an event often triggers a neural response, because significant changes in blood flow to one region of the body have an immediate effect on circulation to other regions.

NEURAL CONTROL OF BLOOD PRESSURE AND BLOOD FLOW

The nervous system adjusts cardiac output and peripheral resistance to maintain adequate blood flow to vital tissues and organs. The *cardiac centers* and *vasomotor center* of the medulla oblongata are the *cardiovascular (CV) centers* responsible for these regulatory activities. As noted in Chapter 12, each cardiac center includes a *cardioacceleratory center,* which increases cardiac output through sympathetic innervation, and a *cardioinhibitory center,* which reduces cardiac output through parasympathetic innervation. ∞ p. 423

The vasomotor center of the medulla oblongata primarily controls the diameters of arterioles through sympathetic innervation. Inhibition of the vasomotor center leads to vasodilation (dilation of arterioles), reducing peripheral resistance. Stimulation of the vasomotor center causes vasoconstriction (constriction of peripheral arterioles) and, with very strong stimulation, **venoconstriction** (constriction of peripheral veins), both of which increase peripheral resistance.

The cardiovascular centers detect changes in tissue demand by monitoring arterial blood, especially blood pressure, pH, and dissolved gas concentrations. *Baroreceptor reflexes* respond to changes in blood pressure, and *chemoreceptor reflexes* respond to changes in chemical composition. These reflexes are regulated through negative feedback: The stimulation of a receptor by an abnormal condition leads to a response that counteracts the stimulus and restores normal conditions.

Baroreceptor Reflexes

Baroreceptors monitor the degree of stretch in the walls of expandable organs. ∞ p. 311 The baroreceptors involved in cardiovascular regulation are located (1) in the **aortic sinuses,** pockets in the walls of the aorta adjacent to the heart (see Figure 12-6b; p. 413); (2) in the walls of the **carotid sinuses,** expanded

chambers near the bases of the *internal carotid arteries* of the neck (Figure 13-18a, p. 452); and (3) in the wall of the right atrium. These receptors initiate **baroreceptor reflexes** (*baro-*, pressure), autonomic reflexes that adjust cardiac output and peripheral resistance to maintain normal arterial pressures.

Aortic baroreceptors monitor blood pressure within the ascending aorta. There the *aortic reflex* adjusts blood pressure in response to changes in pressure. The purpose of the aortic reflex is to maintain adequate blood pressure and blood flow through the systemic circuit. Carotid sinus baroreceptors respond to changes in blood pressure at the carotid sinuses. These receptors trigger reflexes that maintain adequate blood flow to the brain. Blood flow to the brain must remain constant, and the *carotid sinus reflex* is extremely sensitive. The baroreceptor reflexes triggered by changes in blood pressure at these locations are diagrammed in Figure 13-10.

When blood pressure climbs (Figure 13-10a), increased output from the baroreceptors travels to the cardiovascular centers of the medulla oblongata, where it inhibits the cardioacceleratory center, stimulates the cardioinhibitory center, and inhibits the vasomotor center. Two effects are produced: (1) Under the command of the cardioinhibitory center,

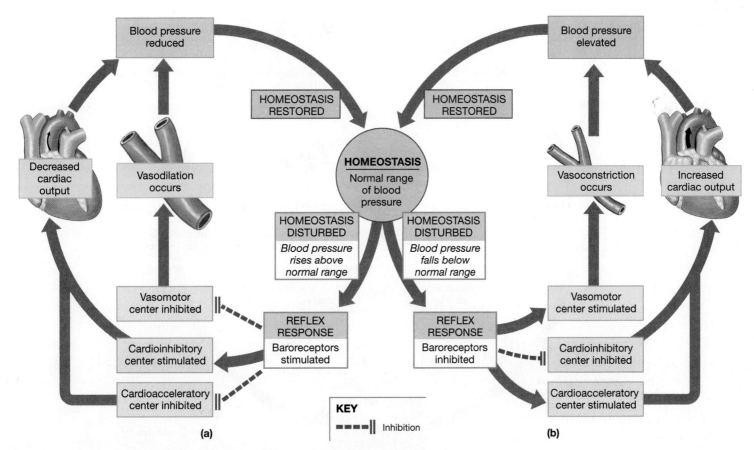

FIGURE 13-10 **The Baroreceptor Reflexes of the Carotid and Aortic Sinuses.**

the vagus nerves release acetylcholine (ACh), which reduces the rate and strength of cardiac contractions, decreasing cardiac output; and (2) the inhibition of the vasomotor center leads to dilation of peripheral arterioles throughout the body. This combination of reduced cardiac output and decreased peripheral resistance then lowers blood pressure.

If blood pressure falls below normal (Figure 13-10b), inhibition of baroreceptor output produces the opposite effects: (1) an increase in cardiac output and (2) widespread peripheral vasoconstriction. Reduced baroreceptor activity stimulates the cardioacceleratory center, inhibits the cardioinhibitory center, and stimulates the vasomotor center. The cardioacceleratory center stimulates sympathetic neurons innervating the sinoatrial (SA) node, atrioventricular (AV) node, and general myocardium. This stimulation increases heart rate and stroke volume, leading to an immediate increase in cardiac output. Vasomotor activity, also carried by sympathetic motor neurons, produces rapid vasoconstriction, increasing peripheral resistance. These adjustments—increased cardiac output and increased peripheral resistance—work together to elevate blood pressure.

Atrial baroreceptors monitor blood pressure at the end of the systemic circuit—at the venae cavae and the right atrium. The atrial reflex responds to the stretching of the wall of the right atrium. ∞ p. 421 Under normal circumstances, the heart pumps blood into the aorta at the same rate at which it arrives at the right atrium. A rise in blood pressure at the atrium means that blood is arriving at the heart faster than it is being pumped out. The atrial baroreceptors correct the situation by stimulating the cardioacceleratory center, increasing cardiac output until the backlog of venous blood is removed. Atrial pressure then returns to normal.

Chemoreceptor Reflexes

The **chemoreceptor reflexes** respond to changes in carbon dioxide, oxygen, or pH in blood and cerebrospinal fluid (Figure 13-11). The chemoreceptors involved are sensory neurons found in the **carotid bodies** (located in the neck near the carotid sinuses) and in the **aortic bodies** (near the arch of the aorta), where they monitor the chemical composition of the arterial blood. Additional chemoreceptors on the surface of the medulla oblongata monitor the composition of the cerebrospinal fluid (CSF).

FIGURE 13-11 The Chemoreceptor Reflexes.

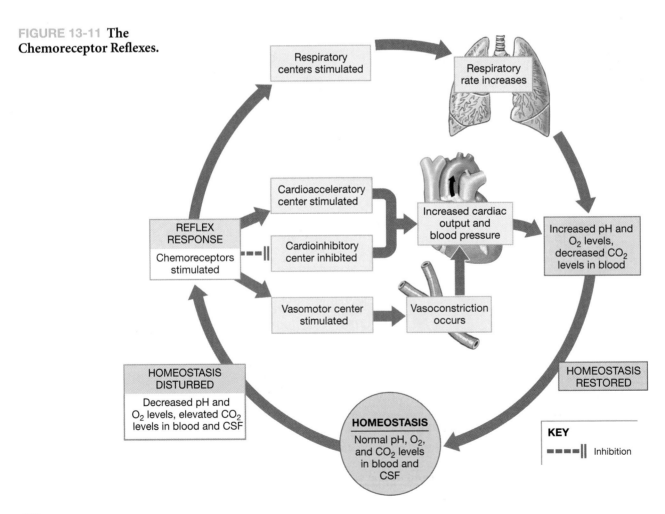

Chemoreceptors are activated by a drop in pH or in plasma O_2, or by a rise in CO_2. Any of these changes leads to a stimulation of the cardioacceleratory and vasomotor centers. This elevates arterial pressure and increases blood flow through peripheral tissues. Chemoreceptor output also affects the respiratory centers in the medulla oblongata. As a result, a rise in blood flow and blood pressure is associated with an elevated respiratory rate. The coordination of cardiovascular and respiratory activity is vital, because accelerating tissue blood flow is useful only if the circulating blood contains adequate oxygen. In addition, a rise in the respiratory rate accelerates venous return through the action of the respiratory pump. ∞ p. 439

HORMONES AND CARDIOVASCULAR REGULATION

The endocrine system provides both short-term and long-term regulation of cardiovascular performance. In the short term, epinephrine (E) and norepinephrine (NE) from the suprarenal medullae stimulate cardiac output and peripheral vasoconstriction. Long-term cardiovascular regulation involves the participation of other hormones—antidiuretic hormone (ADH), angiotensin II, erythropoietin (EPO), and atrial natriuretic peptide (ANP), introduced in Chapter 10. ∞ pp. 355, 366, 367 The roles of these hormones in the regulation of blood pressure and blood volume are diagrammed in **Figure 13-12**.

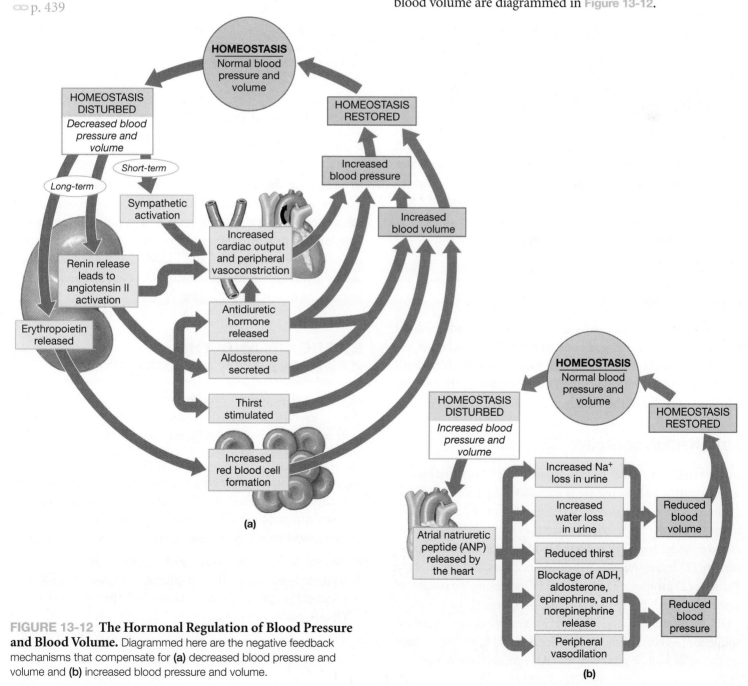

FIGURE 13-12 The Hormonal Regulation of Blood Pressure and Blood Volume. Diagrammed here are the negative feedback mechanisms that compensate for **(a)** decreased blood pressure and volume and **(b)** increased blood pressure and volume.

Antidiuretic Hormone

Antidiuretic hormone (ADH) is released at the posterior pituitary gland in response to a decrease in blood volume, an increase in the osmotic concentration of the plasma, or the presence of angiotensin II (Figure 13-12a). The immediate result is peripheral vasoconstriction that elevates blood pressure. ADH also has a water-conserving effect on the kidneys, thereby preventing a reduction in blood volume.

Angiotensin II

Angiotensin II is formed in the blood following the release of the enzyme renin by specialized kidney cells in response to a fall in blood pressure (Figure 13-12a). Renin starts a chain reaction that ultimately converts an inactive plasma protein, *angiotensinogen*, to the hormone angiotensin II. Angiotensin II stimulates cardiac output and triggers arteriole constriction, which in turn elevates systemic blood pressure almost immediately. It also stimulates the secretion of ADH by the pituitary gland, and of aldosterone by the suprarenal cortex. The effects of these hormones are complementary: ADH stimulates water conservation at the kidneys, and aldosterone stimulates the reabsorption of sodium ions and water from the urine. In addition, angiotensin II stimulates thirst, and the presence of ADH and aldosterone ensures that the additional water consumed will be retained, elevating blood volume.

Erythropoietin

Erythropoietin (EPO) is released by the kidneys when blood pressure falls or the oxygen content of the blood becomes abnormally low (Figure 13-12a). EPO stimulates red blood cell production, elevating blood volume and improving the oxygen-carrying capacity of the blood.

Atrial Natriuretic Peptide

In contrast to the three hormones just described, atrial natriuretic peptide (ANP) release is stimulated by *increased* blood pressure (Figure 13-12b). ANP is produced by cardiac muscle cells in the wall of the right atrium when they are stretched by excessive venous return. ANP reduces blood volume and blood pressure by (1) increasing the loss of sodium ions and water at the kidneys, (2) promoting water losses by increasing the volume of urine produced, (3) reducing thirst, (4) blocking the release of ADH, aldosterone, E, and NE, and (5) stimulating peripheral vasodilation. As blood volume and blood pressure decline, tension on the atrial walls is removed, and ANP production ceases.

The Big Picture Cardiac output cannot increase indefinitely, and blood flow to active versus inactive tissues must be differentially controlled. Such control is accomplished by a combination of autoregulation, neural regulation, and hormone release.

CHECKPOINT

8. Describe the actions of vasodilators and vasoconstrictors.

9. How would slightly compressing the common carotid artery affect your heart rate?

10. What effect would vasoconstriction of the renal artery have on systemic blood pressure and blood volume?

See the blue Answers tab at the back of the book.

13-4 The cardiovascular system adapts to physiological stress

In our day-to-day lives, the components of the cardiovascular system—the blood, heart, and blood vessels—operate in an integrated way. In this section we will examine this system's adaptability in maintaining homeostasis in response to two common stresses: exercise and blood loss. We will also consider the physiological mechanisms involved in shock, an important cardiovascular disorder.

EXERCISE AND THE CARDIOVASCULAR SYSTEM

At rest, cardiac output averages about 5.8 liters per minute. During exercise, both cardiac output and the pattern of blood distribution change markedly. As exercise begins, several interrelated changes take place:

- *Extensive vasodilation occurs* as the rate of oxygen consumption in skeletal muscles increases. Peripheral resistance drops, blood flow through the capillaries increases, and blood enters the venous system at an accelerated rate.

- *Venous return increases* as skeletal muscle contractions squeeze blood along the peripheral veins, and an increased breathing rate pulls blood into the venae cavae (the respiratory pump).

- *Cardiac output rises* as a result of the increased venous return. This increase occurs in direct response to ventricular stretching (the Frank-Starling principle) and in a reflexive response to atrial stretching (the atrial reflex). ∞ p. 422 The increased cardiac output keeps pace with the elevated demand, and arterial pressures are maintained despite the drop in peripheral resistance.

This regulation by venous feedback gradually increases cardiac output to about double resting levels. Over this range, which is typical of light exercise, the pattern of blood distribution remains relatively unchanged.

At higher levels of exertion, other physiological adjustments occur as the cardiac and vasomotor centers activate the sympathetic nervous system. Cardiac output increases (up to 20–25 liters per minute), blood pressure increases, and blood flow is severely restricted to "nonessential" organs (such as those of the digestive system) in order to increase blood flow to active skeletal muscles. When you exercise at maximal levels, your blood essentially races among your skeletal muscles, lungs, and heart. Although blood flow to most other organs is diminished, that to the skin increases further, because body temperature continues to climb. Only the blood supply to the brain is unaffected.

Clinical Note

Exercise, Cardiovascular Fitness, and Health

Cardiovascular performance improves significantly with training. Trained athletes have larger hearts and stroke volumes than do nonathletes. These functional changes are important. Cardiac output is equal to stroke volume times heart rate, so for a given cardiac output, an individual with a larger stroke volume has a lower heart rate. A professional athlete at rest can maintain normal blood flow to peripheral tissues at a heart rate as low as 32 bpm (beats per minute), compared with about 80 bpm for a nonathlete. And, when necessary, the athlete's cardiac output can increase to levels 50 percent higher than those of nonathletes.

Regular exercise has several beneficial effects. Even a modest exercise routine (jogging 5 miles per week, for example) can lower total blood cholesterol levels. High cholesterol is one of the major risk factors for atherosclerosis, which leads to cardiovascular disease and strokes. In addition, a healthy lifestyle—regular exercise, a balanced diet, weight control, and no smoking—reduces stress, lowers blood pressure, and slows plaque formation. Large-scale statistical studies indicate that regular moderate exercise can cut the incidence of heart attacks almost in half.

THE CARDIOVASCULAR RESPONSE TO HEMORRHAGE

In Chapter 11 we considered the local circulatory reaction to a break in the wall of a blood vessel. ∞ p. 398 When the clotting response fails to prevent a significant blood loss and blood pressure falls, the entire cardiovascular system begins making adjustments. The immediate goal is to maintain adequate blood pressure and peripheral blood flow; the long-term goal is to restore normal blood volume (**Figure 13-12**).

The Short-Term Elevation of Blood Pressure

Short-term responses appear almost as soon as blood pressure starts to decline, when the carotid and aortic reflexes increase cardiac output and cause peripheral vasoconstriction. When you donate blood at a blood bank, the amount collected is usually 500 mL, roughly 10 percent of your total blood volume. Such a loss initially causes a drop in cardiac output, but the vasomotor center quickly improves venous return and restores cardiac output to normal levels by mobilizing the **venous reserve** (large reservoirs of slowly moving venous blood in the liver, bone marrow, and skin) through venoconstriction (see p. 439). This venous compensation can restore normal arterial pressures and peripheral blood flow after losses of 15–20 percent of total blood volume. With a more substantial blood loss, cardiac output is maintained by increasing the heart rate, often to 180–200 bpm. Sympathetic activation assists by constricting the muscular arteries and arterioles, which elevates blood pressure.

Sympathetic activation also causes the secretion of E and NE by the suprarenal medullae. At the same time, ADH is released by the posterior pituitary gland, and the fall in blood pressure in the kidneys causes the release of renin, initiating the activation of angiotensin II. Both E and NE increase cardiac output, and in combination with ADH and angiotensin II, they cause a powerful vasoconstriction that elevates blood pressure and improves peripheral blood flow.

The Long-Term Restoration of Blood Volume

After serious hemorrhaging, several days may pass before blood volume returns to normal. When short-term responses are unable to maintain normal cardiac output and blood pressure, the decline in capillary blood pressure triggers a recall of fluids from the interstitial spaces. ∞ p. 437 Over this period, ADH and aldosterone promote fluid retention and reabsorption at the kidneys, preventing further reductions in blood volume. Thirst increases, and additional water is absorbed across the digestive tract. This intake of fluid elevates blood volume and ultimately replaces the interstitial fluids "borrowed" at the capillaries. Erythropoietin targets the bone marrow, stimulating the maturation of red blood cells, which increases blood volume and improves oxygen delivery to peripheral tissues.

Clinical Note

Shock

Shock is an acute circulatory crisis marked by low blood pressure (hypotension) and inadequate peripheral blood flow. Severe and potentially fatal effects develop as vital tissues become starved for oxygen and nutrients. Common causes of shock are (1) a fall in cardiac output after hemorrhage or other fluid losses, (2) damage to the heart, (3) external pressure on the heart, or (4) extensive peripheral vasodilation.

One important form of shock, called **circulatory shock,** is caused by a reduction in total blood volume of about 30 percent. All such cases share six basic signs or symptoms:

1. Hypotension, with systolic pressures below 90 mm Hg.

2. Pale, cool, and moist ("clammy") skin. The skin is pale and cool because of peripheral vasoconstriction; the moisture reflects sympathetic activation of the sweat glands.

3. Confusion and disorientation, caused by a drop in blood pressure at the brain.

4. A rise in heart rate and a rapid, weak pulse.

5. Cessation of urination, because the reduced blood flow to the kidneys slows or stops urine production.

6. A drop in blood pH (acidosis), due to lactic acid generated in oxygen-deprived tissues.

When blood volume declines by more than 35 percent, homeostatic mechanisms become unable to cope with the situation, and a vicious cycle begins: Low blood pressure and low venous return lead to decreased cardiac output and myocardial damage, further reducing cardiac output. When the mean arterial pressure falls to about 50 mm Hg, carotid sinus baroreceptors trigger a massive activation of sympathetic vasoconstrictors. The resulting vasoconstriction reduces blood flow to peripheral tissues in order to maintain adequate blood flow to the brain. The prevention of fatal consequences requires immediate treatment that concentrates on (1) preventing further fluid losses and (2) increasing blood volume through transfusions.

Several other forms of shock also exist. In *cardiogenic shock* and *obstructive shock,* the heart is unable to maintain normal cardiac output. *Septic shock, toxic shock syndrome,* and *anaphylactic shock* result from a widespread, uncontrolled vasodilation. All share similar effects and consequences with circulatory shock.

11. Why does blood pressure increase during exercise?

12. Name the immediate and long-term problems related to the cardiovascular response to hemorrhaging.

13. Explain the role of aldosterone and ADH in long-term restoration of blood volume.

See the blue Answers tab at the back of the book.

13-5 The pulmonary and systemic circuits of the cardiovascular system exhibit three general functional patterns

As previously discussed, the cardiovascular system is divided into the **pulmonary circuit** and the **systemic circuit.** ⊃ p. 406 The pulmonary circuit is composed of arteries and veins that transport blood between the heart and the lungs; this circuit begins at the right ventricle and ends at the left atrium. The systemic circuit is composed of arteries that transport oxygenated blood and nutrients to all other organs and tissues, and veins that return deoxygenated blood to the heart; this circuit begins at the left ventricle and ends at the right atrium. **Figure 13-13** summarizes the primary circulatory routes within the pulmonary and systemic circuits.

Three general functional patterns of blood vessels are worth noting:

1. The distribution of arteries and veins on the left and right sides of the body is usually identical—except near the heart, where large vessels connect to the atria or ventricles. For example, the distribution of the *left* and *right subclavian, axillary, brachial,* and *radial arteries* parallels the *left* and *right subclavian, axillary, brachial,* and *radial veins.*

2. A single vessel may undergo several name changes as it crosses specific anatomical boundaries. For example, the *external iliac artery* becomes the *femoral artery* as it leaves the trunk and enters the thigh.

3. Tissues and organs are usually serviced by several arteries and veins. Often, anastomoses between adjacent arteries or veins reduce the impact of a temporary or even permanent occlusion (blockage) of a single blood vessel.

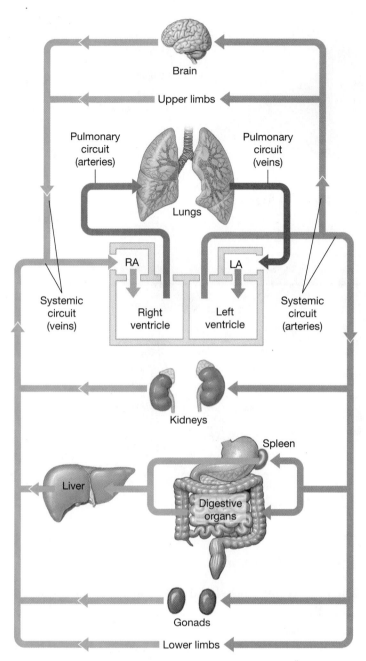

FIGURE 13-13 **An Overview of the Pattern of Circulation.**
RA stands for right atrium; LA for left atrium.

13-6 In the pulmonary circuit, deoxygenated blood enters the lungs in arteries, and oxygenated blood leaves the lungs in veins

Blood entering the right atrium has just returned from peripheral capillary beds, where oxygen was released and carbon dioxide was absorbed. After traveling through the right atrium and ventricle, blood enters the **pulmonary trunk** (*pulmo-,* lung), the start of the pulmonary circuit (Figure 13-14). In this circuit, carbon dioxide is released, oxygen stores are replenished, and the oxygenated blood is returned to the heart for distribution in the systemic circuit.

The arteries of the pulmonary circuit differ from those of the systemic circuit in that they carry deoxygenated blood. (For this reason, color-coded diagrams usually show the pulmonary arteries in blue, the same color as systemic veins.) As the pulmonary trunk curves over the superior border of the heart, it gives rise to the **left** and **right pulmonary arteries.** These large arteries enter the lungs before branching repeatedly, giving rise to smaller and smaller arteries. The smallest branches, the pulmonary arterioles, provide blood to capillary networks that surround small air pockets, or **alveoli** (al-VĒ-ō-lī; *alveolus,* sac). The walls of alveoli are thin enough for gas exchange to occur between the capillary blood and inspired air, a process detailed in Chapter 15. As oxygenated blood leaves the alveolar capillaries, it enters venules, which in turn unite to form larger vessels leading to the **pulmonary veins.** These four veins (two from each lung) empty into the left atrium, completing the pulmonary circuit.

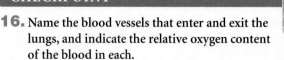

CHECKPOINT

14. Identify the two circulatory circuits of the cardiovascular system.

15. Identify the three general functional patterns of the body's blood vessels.

See the blue Answers tab at the back of the book.

CHECKPOINT

16. Name the blood vessels that enter and exit the lungs, and indicate the relative oxygen content of the blood in each.

17. Trace a drop of blood through the lungs, beginning at the right ventricle and ending at the left atrium.

See the blue Answers tab at the back of the book.

FIGURE 13-14 The Pulmonary Circuit.

13-7 The systemic circuit carries oxygenated blood from the left ventricle to tissues other than the lungs' exchange surfaces, and returns deoxygenated blood to the right atrium

The systemic circuit supplies the capillary beds in all parts of the body not serviced by the pulmonary circuit. The systemic circuit, which at any moment contains about 84 percent of total blood volume, begins at the left ventricle and ends at the right atrium,

SYSTEMIC ARTERIES

Figure 13-15 provides an overview of the locations of the major systemic arteries.

The Ascending Aorta

The first systemic vessel and largest artery is the aorta. The **ascending aorta** begins at the aortic semilunar valve of the left ventricle, and the *left* and *right coronary arteries* originate near its base (see Figure 12-7, p. 414). The **aortic arch** curves across the superior surface of the heart, connecting the ascending aorta with the **descending aorta** (Figure 13-16).

Arteries of the Aortic Arch

Three elastic arteries—the **brachiocephalic** (brā-kē-ō-se-FAL-ik) **trunk,** the **left common carotid,** and the **left subclavian** (sub-CLĀ-vē-an)—originate along the aortic arch and deliver blood to the head, neck, shoulders, and upper limbs (Figures 13-16 and 13-17). The brachiocephalic trunk ascends for a short distance before branching to form the **right common carotid artery** and the **right subclavian artery.** Note that we have only one brachiocephalic trunk and that the left common carotid and left subclavian arteries arise separately from the aortic arch. In

FIGURE 13-15 **An Overview of the Arterial System.**

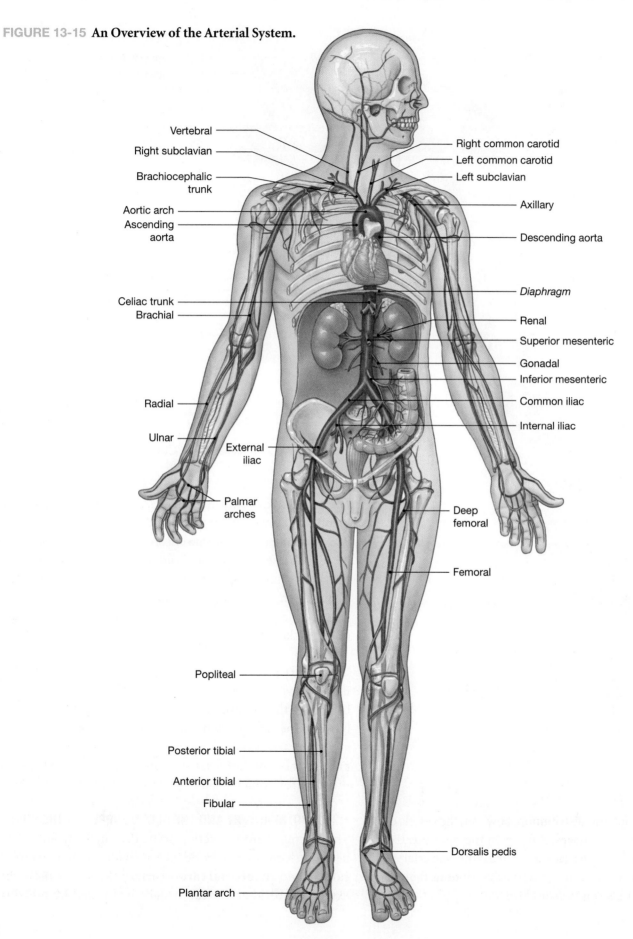

Vertebral
Right subclavian
Brachiocephalic trunk
Aortic arch
Ascending aorta
Celiac trunk
Brachial
Radial
Ulnar
External iliac
Palmar arches

Right common carotid
Left common carotid
Left subclavian
Axillary
Descending aorta
Diaphragm
Renal
Superior mesenteric
Gonadal
Inferior mesenteric
Common iliac
Internal iliac
Deep femoral
Femoral

Popliteal
Posterior tibial
Anterior tibial
Fibular
Plantar arch
Dorsalis pedis

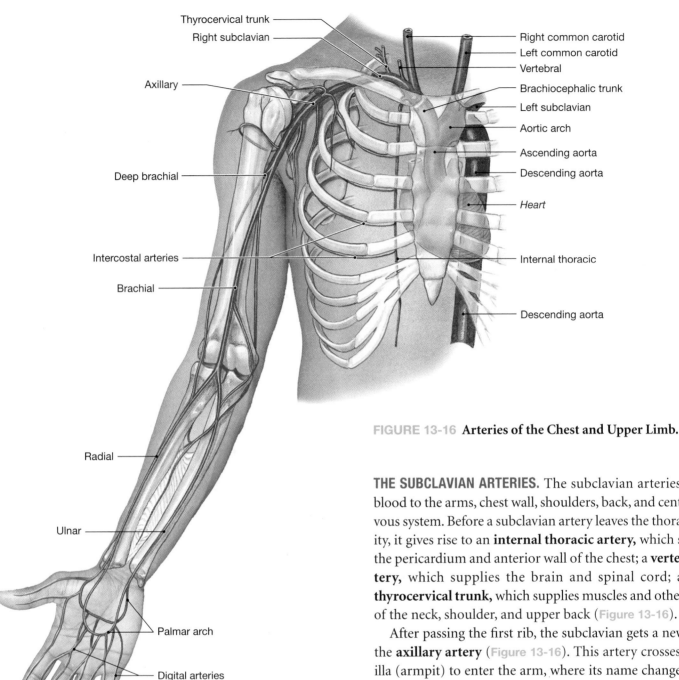

Thyrocervical trunk

Right subclavian

Axillary

Deep brachial

Intercostal arteries

Brachial

Radial

Ulnar

Palmar arch

Digital arteries

Right common carotid

Left common carotid

Vertebral

Brachiocephalic trunk

Left subclavian

Aortic arch

Ascending aorta

Descending aorta

Heart

Internal thoracic

Descending aorta

FIGURE 13-16 **Arteries of the Chest and Upper Limb.**

THE SUBCLAVIAN ARTERIES. The subclavian arteries supply blood to the arms, chest wall, shoulders, back, and central nervous system. Before a subclavian artery leaves the thoracic cavity, it gives rise to an **internal thoracic artery,** which supplies the pericardium and anterior wall of the chest; a **vertebral artery,** which supplies the brain and spinal cord; and the **thyrocervical trunk,** which supplies muscles and other tissues of the neck, shoulder, and upper back (Figure 13-16).

After passing the first rib, the subclavian gets a new name: the **axillary artery** (Figure 13-16). This artery crosses the axilla (armpit) to enter the arm, where its name changes again, becoming the **brachial artery.** The brachial artery provides blood to the arm before branching to create the **radial artery** and **ulnar artery** of the forearm. These arteries connect at the palm to form anastomoses—the superficial and deep *palmar arches*—from which the *digital arteries* originate.

THE CAROTID ARTERY AND THE BLOOD SUPPLY TO THE BRAIN. The common carotid arteries ascend deep in the tissues of the neck. Each common carotid artery divides into an **external carotid** and an **internal carotid artery** (Figure 13-18a). The external carotid artery can usually be located by pressing

terms of their peripheral distribution, however, the vessels on the left side are mirror images of those on the right side. Because most of the major arteries are paired, with one artery of each pair on either side of the body, the descriptions that follow will not use the terms *right* and *left*.

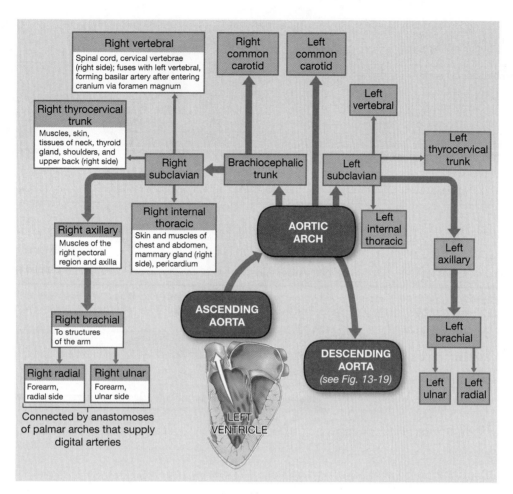

FIGURE 13-17 **A Flow Chart Showing the Arterial Distribution to the Head, Chest, and Upper Limbs.**

gently along either side of the windpipe (trachea) until a strong pulse is felt. The external carotid arteries supply blood to the pharynx, esophagus, larynx, and face. The internal carotid arteries enter the skull to deliver blood to the brain and the eyes.

The brain is extremely sensitive to changes in blood supply. An interruption of blood flow for several seconds will produce unconsciousness, and after 4 minutes permanent neural damage may result. Such circulatory crises are rare, however, because blood reaches the brain by two routes: through the vertebral arteries, and through the internal carotid arteries.

The vertebral arteries ascend within the transverse foramina of the cervical vertebrae, penetrating the skull at the foramen magnum. Inside the cranium, they fuse to form a large **basilar artery,** which continues along the ventral surface of the brain. This artery gives rise to the vessels shown in Figure 13-18b.

Normally, the internal carotid arteries supply the arteries of the anterior half of the cerebrum, and the rest of the brain receives blood from the vertebral arteries. But this circulatory pattern can easily change, because the internal carotids and the basilar artery are interconnected in the **cerebral arterial circle,** or *circle of Willis,* a ring-shaped anastomosis that encircles the infundibulum (stalk) of the pituitary gland. With this arrangement, the brain can receive blood from either the carotid or the vertebral arteries, and the chances for a serious interruption of circulation are reduced.

The Descending Aorta

The **descending aorta** is continuous with the aortic arch. The diaphragm divides the descending aorta into a superior **thoracic aorta** and an inferior **abdominal aorta** (Figure 13-19). The thoracic aorta travels within the mediastinum, providing blood to the intercostal arteries, which carry blood to the vertebral column area and the body wall. The thoracic aorta also gives rise to small arteries that end in capillary beds in the esophagus, pericardium, and other mediastinal structures. Near the diaphragm, the **phrenic** (FREN-ik) **arteries** deliver blood to the

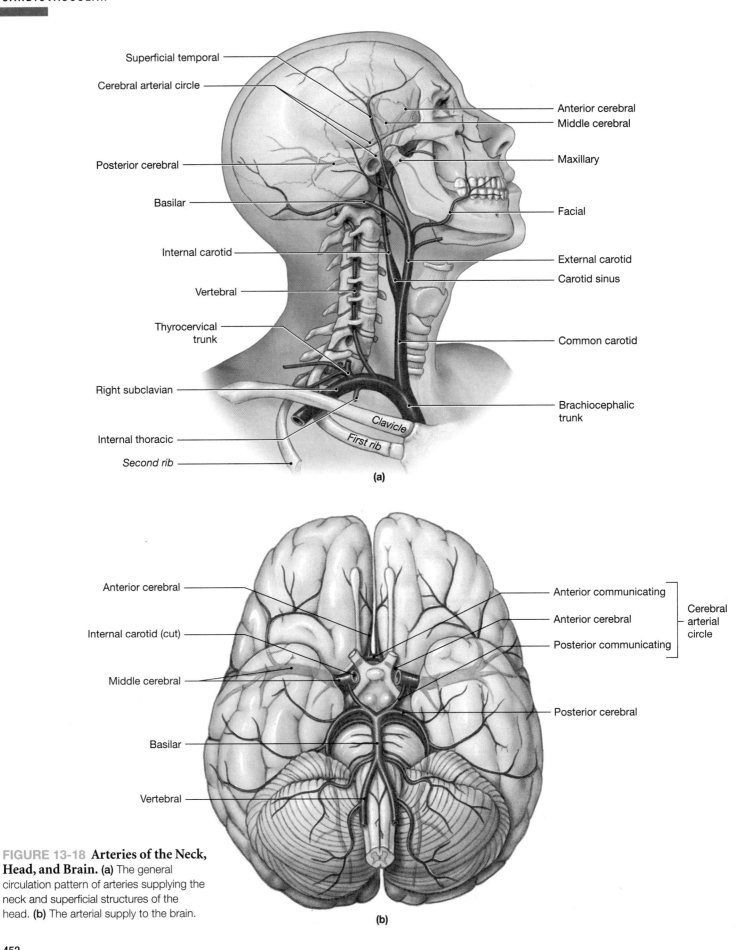

FIGURE 13-18 Arteries of the Neck, Head, and Brain. (a) The general circulation pattern of arteries supplying the neck and superficial structures of the head. **(b)** The arterial supply to the brain.

Vertebral
Thyrocervical trunk
Common carotid
Subclavian
Axillary
Internal thoracic
Bronchials
Mediastinals
Pericardials
Intercostals
Descending aorta (thoracic aorta)
Phrenics
Celiac trunk
Diaphragm
Common hepatic
Left gastric
Suprarenal
Splenic
Renal
Superior mesenteric
Descending aorta (abdominal aorta)
Lumbar
Gonadal
Inferior mesenteric
Common iliac
Terminal segment of the aorta
External iliac
Internal iliac

(a)

FIGURE 13-19 **Major Arteries of the Trunk.** **(a)** A diagrammatic view. **(b)** A flow chart.

muscular diaphragm, which separates the thoracic and abdominopelvic cavities.

The abdominal aorta delivers blood to all the abdominopelvic organs and structures (**Figure 13-19**). The **celiac** (SĒ-lē-ak) **trunk, superior mesenteric** (mez-en-TER-ik) **artery,** and **inferior mesenteric artery** arise on the anterior surface of the abdominal aorta and branch in the connective tissues of the mesenteries. These three vessels provide blood to all of the digestive organs in the abdominopelvic cavity. The celiac trunk

divides into three branches that deliver blood to the liver, gallbladder, stomach, and spleen. The superior mesenteric artery supplies the pancreas, small intestine, and most of the large intestine. The inferior mesenteric delivers blood to the last portion of the large intestine and rectum.

Paired **gonadal** (gō-NAD-al) **arteries** originate between the superior and inferior mesenteric arteries. In males they are called *testicular arteries;* in females, *ovarian arteries.* The **suprarenal arteries** and **renal arteries** arise along the lateral

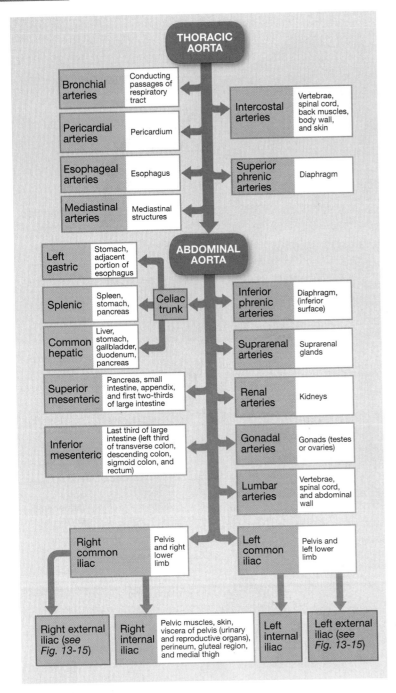

FIGURE 13-19 **Major Arteries of the Trunk.** (continued)
(b) A flow chart.

surface of the abdominal aorta and travel behind the peritoneal lining to reach the suprarenal glands and kidneys. Small **lumbar arteries** begin on the posterior surface of the aorta and supply the spinal cord and the abdominal wall.

Near the level of vertebra L_4, the abdominal aorta divides to form a pair of muscular arteries. These **common iliac** (IL-ē-ak) **arteries** carry blood to the pelvis and lower limbs (**Figure 13-15**). As it travels along the inner surface of the ilium, each common iliac divides to form an **internal iliac artery,**

which supplies smaller arteries of the pelvis, and an **external iliac artery,** which enters the lower limb.

Once in the thigh, the external iliac artery branches, forming the **femoral artery** and the **deep femoral artery.** When it reaches the back of the knee, the femoral artery becomes the **popliteal artery,** which almost immediately branches to form the **anterior tibial, posterior tibial,** and **fibular arteries.** At the ankle, the anterior tibial artery becomes the *dorsalis pedis artery,* and the posterior tibial artery divides in two. These three arteries are connected by two anastomoses. The arrangement produces a *dorsal arch* on the top of the foot and a *plantar arch* on the bottom.

SYSTEMIC VEINS

Blood from each of the body's tissues and organs returns to the heart by means of a venous network that drains into the right atrium through the superior and inferior venae cavae. **Figure 13-20** illustrates the major vessels of the venous system. Complementary arteries and veins often run side by side, and in many cases they have comparable names. For example, the axillary arteries run alongside the axillary veins. In addition, arteries and veins often travel in the company of peripheral nerves that have the same names and innervate the same structures.

One significant difference between the arterial and venous systems concerns the distribution of major veins in the neck and limbs. Arteries in these areas are located deep beneath the skin, protected by bones and surrounding soft tissues. In contrast, the neck and limbs usually have two sets of peripheral veins, one superficial and the other deep. This dual venous drainage helps control body temperature. In a hot environment, venous blood flows in superficial veins, through which heat loss can occur; in a cold environment, blood is routed to the deep veins to minimize heat loss.

The Superior Vena Cava

The **superior vena cava (SVC)** receives blood from two regions: the head and neck (**Figure 13-21**), and the upper limbs, shoulders, and chest (**Figure 13-22**).

VENOUS RETURN FROM THE HEAD AND NECK. Small veins in the neural tissue of the brain empty into a network of thin-walled channels called the **dural sinuses.** ∞ p. 262 The largest, the **superior sagittal sinus,** is located within the fold of dura mater lying between the cerebral hemispheres. Most of the blood leaving the brain passes through one of the dural sinuses and leaves the skull in one of the **internal jugular veins,** descending parallel to the common carotid artery in the neck.

Vertebral

External jugular

Subclavian

Axillary

Cephalic

Brachial

Basilic

Hepatic veins

Median cubital

Radial

Median antebrachial

Ulnar

Palmar venous arches

Digital veins

Great saphenous

Popliteal

Small saphenous

Fibular

Plantar venous arch

Dorsal venous arch

Internal jugular

Brachiocephalic

Superior vena cava

Intercostal veins

Inferior vena cava

Renal

Gonadal

Lumbar veins

Left and right
common iliac

External iliac

Internal iliac

Deep
femoral

Femoral

Posterior tibial

Anterior tibial

KEY

Superficial veins

Deep veins

FIGURE 13-20 **An Overview of the Venous System.**

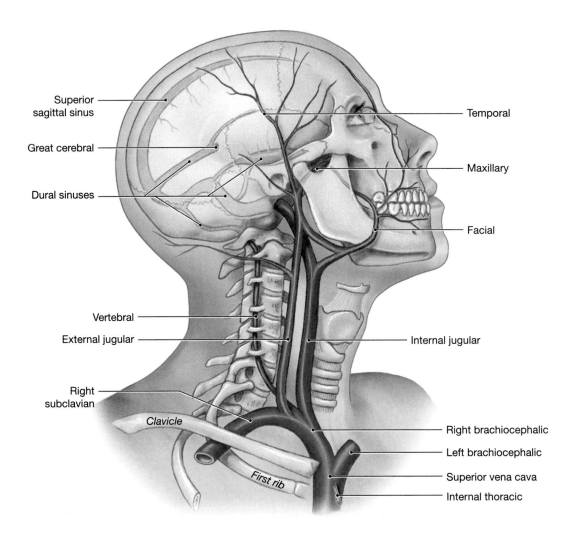

FIGURE 13-21 **Major Veins of the Head and Neck.** Veins draining superficial and deep portions of the head and neck.

The more superficial **external jugular veins** collect blood from the superficial structures of the head and neck. These veins travel just beneath the skin, and a *jugular venous pulse (JVP)* can sometimes be detected at the base of the neck. **Vertebral veins** drain the cervical spinal cord and the posterior surface of the skull, descending within the transverse foramina of the cervical vertebrae alongside the vertebral arteries.

VENOUS RETURN FROM THE UPPER LIMBS AND CHEST. The major veins of the upper body are illustrated in Figure 13-22, and a flow chart indicating the venous tributaries of the superior vena cava is provided in (Figure 13-23a, p. 458). A venous network in the palms collects blood from the digital veins. These vessels drain into the **cephalic vein** and the **basilic vein.** The superficial **median cubital vein** passes from the cephalic vein, medially and at an oblique angle, to connect to the basilic vein. (The median cubital is the vein from which venous blood samples are typically collected.) The deeper veins of the forearm consist of a **radial vein** and an **ulnar vein.** After crossing the elbow, these

veins fuse to form the **brachial vein.** As the brachial vein continues toward the trunk, it joins the basilic vein before entering the axilla as the **axillary vein.** The cephalic vein drains into the axillary vein at the shoulder.

The axillary vein then continues into the trunk; at the level of the first rib it becomes the **subclavian vein.** After traveling a short distance inside the thoracic cavity, the subclavian meets and merges with the external and internal jugular veins of that side. This fusion creates the large **brachiocephalic vein,** also known as the *innominate vein.* Near the heart, the two brachiocephalic veins (one from each side of the body) combine to create the superior vena cava. The SVC receives blood from the thoracic body wall through the **azygos** (AZ-i-gos) **vein** before arriving at the right atrium.

The Inferior Vena Cava

The **inferior vena cava (IVC)** collects most of the venous blood from organs inferior to the diaphragm. (A small amount reaches

FIGURE 13-22 **The Venous Drainage of the Abdomen and Chest.**

the superior vena cava through the azygos vein.) A flow chart of the tributaries of the IVC is provided in Figure 13-23b, and the veins of the abdomen are illustrated in Figure 13-22. Refer to Figure 13-20 to see the veins of the lower limbs.

Blood leaving the capillaries in the sole of each foot collects into a network of *plantar veins,* which supply the *plantar venous arch.* The plantar network provides blood to the **anterior tibial vein,** the **posterior tibial vein,** and the **fibular vein,** the deep veins of the leg. A *dorsal venous arch* drains blood from capillaries on the superior surface of the foot. This arch is drained by two superficial veins, the **great saphenous vein** (sa-FĒ-nus; *saphenes,* prominent) and the **small saphenous vein.** (Surgeons often use segments of the great saphenous vein, the largest superficial vein, as a bypass vessel during *coronary bypass surgery.*) The plantar arch and the dorsal arch

interconnect extensively, so blood flow can easily shift from superficial veins to deep veins.

Behind the knee, the small saphenous, tibial, and fibular veins unite to form the **popliteal vein.** When the popliteal vein reaches the femur, it becomes the **femoral vein.** Before penetrating the abdominal wall, the great saphenous and **deep femoral** veins join the femoral vein. The femoral vein penetrates

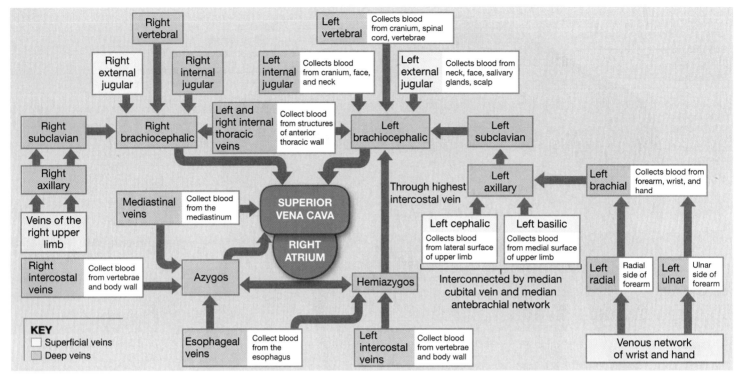

(a) Tributaries of the superior vena cava

FIGURE 13-23 **A Flow Chart of the Tributaries of the Superior and Inferior Venae Cavae.**

the body wall and emerges into the pelvic cavity as the **external iliac vein.** As the external iliac travels across the inner surface of the ilium, it is joined by the **internal iliac vein,** which drains the pelvic organs. The resulting **common iliac vein** then meets its counterpart from the opposite side to form the IVC.

Like the aorta, the IVC lies posterior to the abdominopelvic cavity. As it ascends to the heart, it collects blood from several lumbar veins. In addition, the IVC receives blood from the *gonadal, renal, suprarenal, phrenic,* and *hepatic veins* before reaching the right atrium (**Figure 13-22**).

The Hepatic Portal System

You may have noticed that the list of veins did not include any names that refer to digestive organs other than the liver. Instead of traveling directly to the inferior vena cava, blood leaving the capillaries supplied by the celiac, superior, and inferior mesenteric arteries flows to the liver through the **hepatic portal system** (*porta*, a gate). A blood vessel connecting two capillary beds is called a *portal vessel,* and the network formed is called a *portal system.* p. 352

Blood in the hepatic portal vessels is quite different in composition from that in other systemic veins because it contains

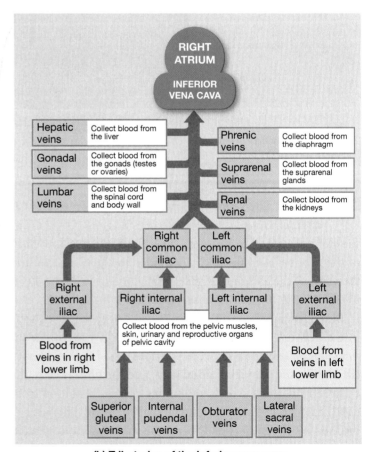

(b) Tributaries of the inferior vena cava

substances absorbed by the digestive tract, including high concentrations of glucose and amino acids, various wastes, and an occasional toxin. Because a portal system carries blood from one capillary bed to another, the blood within it does not immediately mix with blood in the general circulation. Instead, the hepatic portal system delivers blood containing these compounds to the liver, where liver cells absorb them for storage, metabolic conversion, or excretion. In the process, the liver regulates the concentrations of nutrients in the circulating blood.

Figure 13-24 shows the anatomy of the hepatic portal system. The system begins in the capillaries of the digestive organs. Blood from capillaries along the lower portion of the large intestine enters the **inferior mesenteric vein.** On their way toward the liver, veins from the spleen, the lateral border of the stomach, and the pancreas fuse with the inferior mesenteric, forming the **splenic vein.** The **superior mesenteric vein** also drains the lat-

eral border of the stomach, through an anastomosis with one of the branches of the splenic vein. In addition, the superior mesenteric collects blood from the entire small intestine and two-thirds of the large intestine. The **hepatic portal vein** forms through the fusion of the superior mesenteric and splenic veins. Of the two, the superior mesenteric normally contributes the greater volume of blood and most of the nutrients. As it proceeds, the hepatic portal vein receives blood from the **gastric veins,** which drain the medial border of the stomach, and the **cystic vein** from the gallbladder. The hepatic portal system ends where the hepatic portal vein empties into the liver capillaries.

After passing through the liver capillaries, blood collects in the hepatic veins, which empty into the inferior vena cava. Because blood goes to the liver before returning to the heart, the composition of the blood in the systemic circulation remains relatively stable, regardless of the digestive activities under way.

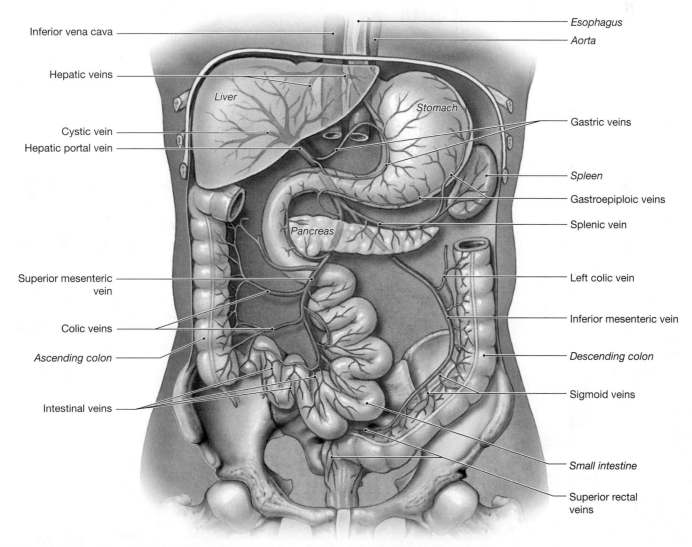

FIGURE 13-24 The Hepatic Portal System.

18. Blockage of which branch of the aortic arch would interfere with blood flow to the left arm?

19. Why would compression of the common carotid arteries cause a person to lose consciousness?

20. Grace is in an automobile accident, and her celiac trunk is ruptured. Which organs will be affected most directly by this injury?

21. Describe the general distribution of major arteries and veins in the neck and limbs. What functional advantage does this distribution provide?

See the blue Answers tab at the back of the book.

13-8 Modifications of fetal and maternal cardiovascular systems promote exchange of materials, and independence is achieved at birth

The fetal and adult cardiovascular systems have significant differences reflecting different sources of respiratory and nutri-tional support. The embryonic lungs are collapsed and nonfunctional, and the embryonic digestive tract has nothing to digest. All of the embryo's nutritional and respiratory needs are provided by diffusion across the *placenta,* a structure within the uterine wall where the maternal and fetal circulatory systems are in close contact. Circulation in a full-term (9-month-old) fetus is diagrammed in Figure 13-25a.

PLACENTAL BLOOD SUPPLY

The fetus's blood reaches the placenta through a pair of **umbilical arteries,** which arise from the internal iliac arteries before entering the umbilical cord. At the placenta, the blood gives up CO_2 and wastes and picks up oxygen and nutrients. Blood returning from the placenta flows through a single **umbilical vein** before reaching the developing liver. Some of the blood flows through capillary networks within the liver; the rest bypasses the liver capillaries and reaches the inferior vena cava within the **ductus venosus.** When the placental connection is broken at birth, blood flow through the umbilical vessels ceases, and they soon degenerate.

FIGURE 13-25 Fetal Circulation. (a) Blood flow to and from the placenta. **(b)** Blood flow through the heart of a newborn baby.

(a) Full-term fetus (before birth)

(b) After delivery

FETAL CIRCULATION IN THE HEART AND GREAT VESSELS

One of the most interesting aspects of circulatory development reflects the differences between the life of an embryo or fetus and that of an infant. Throughout embryonic and fetal life, the lungs are collapsed; yet after delivery, the newborn infant must be able to extract oxygen from inspired air rather than across the placenta.

Although the interatrial and interventricular septa of the heart develop early in fetal life, the interatrial partition remains functionally incomplete until birth. The interatrial opening, or **foramen ovale,** is associated with an elongate flap that acts as a valve. Blood can flow freely from the right atrium to the left atrium, but any backflow will close the valve and isolate the two chambers. Thus, blood can enter the heart at the right atrium and bypass the pulmonary circuit. A second short-circuit exists between the pulmonary and aortic trunks. This connection, the **ductus arteriosus,** consists of a short, muscular vessel.

With the lungs collapsed, the capillaries are compressed and little blood flows through the lungs. During diastole, blood enters the right atrium and flows into the right ventricle, but it also passes into the left atrium through the foramen ovale. About 25 percent of the blood arriving at the right atrium bypasses the pulmonary circuit in this way. In addition, over 90 percent of the blood leaving the right ventricle passes through the ductus arteriosus and enters the systemic circuit rather than continuing to the lungs.

CIRCULATORY CHANGES AT BIRTH

At birth, dramatic changes occur. When an infant takes its first breath, the lungs expand, and so do the pulmonary vessels. Within a few seconds, the smooth muscles in the ductus arteriosus contract, isolating the pulmonary and aortic trunks, and blood begins flowing through the pulmonary circuit. As pressures rise in the left atrium, the valvular flap closes the foramen ovale (Figure 13-25b). In adults, the interatrial septum bears a shallow depression, the *fossa ovalis,* that marks the site of the foramen ovale (see Figure 12-5, p. 411). The remnants of the ductus arteriosus persist as a fibrous cord, the *ligamentum arteriosum.*

If the proper vascular changes do not occur at birth or shortly thereafter, problems will eventually develop because the heart will have to work too hard to provide adequate amounts of oxygen to the systemic circuit. Treatment may involve surgical closure of the foramen ovale, the ductus arteriosus, or both. Other forms of congenital heart defects result from abnormal cardiac development or inappropriate connections between the heart and major arteries and veins.

CHECKPOINT

22. Name the umbilical vessels that constitute the placental blood supply.
23. A blood sample taken from the umbilical cord contains high levels of oxygen and nutrients, and low levels of carbon dioxide and waste products. Is this sample from an umbilical artery or from the umbilical vein? Explain.
24. Name the structures that are vital to fetal circulation but cease to function at birth. What becomes of each of these structures?

See the blue Answers tab at the back of the book.

13-9 Aging affects the blood, heart, and blood vessels

The capabilities of the cardiovascular system gradually decline with age. Major changes affect all parts of the cardiovascular system: blood, heart, and vessels.

In the blood, age-related changes may include (1) decreased hematocrit; (2) the constriction or blockage of peripheral veins by the formation of a *thrombus* (stationary blood clot), which can become detached, pass through the heart, and become wedged in a small artery (most often in the lungs, causing *pulmonary embolism*); and (3) the pooling of blood in the veins of the legs because valves are not working effectively.

In the heart, age-related changes include (1) a reduction in maximum cardiac output; (2) changes in the activities of the nodal and conducting cells; (3) a reduction in the elasticity of the fibrous skeleton; (4) progressive atherosclerosis, which can restrict coronary circulation; and (5) the replacement of damaged cardiac muscle cells by scar tissue.

In blood vessels, age-related changes are often related to arteriosclerosis, a thickening and toughening of arterial walls. For example, (1) the inelastic walls of arteries become less tolerant of sudden pressure increases, which can lead to a localized dilation, or *aneurysm,* whose rupture may cause a stroke, myocardial infarction, or massive blood loss (depending on the vessel); (2) calcium salts can be deposited on weakened vascular walls, increasing the risk of a stroke or myocardial infarction; and (3) thrombi can form at atherosclerotic plaques.

CHECKPOINT

25. Identify components of the cardiovascular system that are affected by age.
26. Define thrombus.
27. Define aneurysm.

See the blue Answers tab at the back of the book.

13-10 The cardiovascular system is both structurally and functionally linked to all other systems

The Cardiovascular System in Perspective (p. 468) summarizes the physiological relationships between the cardiovascular system and other organ systems. The most extensive communication occurs between the cardiovascular system and the lymphoid system. Not only are the two systems physically interconnected, but cells of the lymphoid system use the cardiovascular system as a highway to move from one part of the body to another. Chapter 14 examines the lymphoid system in detail.

CHECKPOINT

28. What does the cardiovascular system provide for all other body systems?
29. The cardiovascular system is most closely interconnected with what other organ system?
30. What is the relationship between the skeletal system and the cardiovascular system?

See the blue Answers tab at the back of the book.

RELATED CLINICAL TERMS

aneurysm (AN-ū-rizm): A bulge in the weakened wall of a blood vessel, generally an artery.

arteriosclerosis (ar-tē-rē-ō-skle-RŌ-sis): A condition characterized by the thickening and toughening of arterial walls.

atherosclerosis (ath-er-ō-skle-RŌ-sis): A type of arteriosclerosis characterized by changes in the endothelial lining and the formation of a plaque.

edema (e-DĒ-muh): An abnormal accumulation of fluid in peripheral tissues.

hypertension: Abnormally high blood pressure; usually defined in adults as blood pressure higher than 140/90.

hypervolemic (hī-per-vō-LĒ-mik): Having an excessive blood volume.

hypotension: Blood pressure so low that circulation to vital organs may be impaired.

hypovolemic (hī-pō-vō-LĒ-mik): Having a low blood volume.

orthostatic hypotension: Low blood pressure upon standing, often accompanied by dizziness or fainting; results from a failure of the regulatory mechanisms that increase blood pressure to maintain adequate blood flow to the brain.

phlebitis: Inflammation of a vein.

pulmonary embolism: Circulatory blockage caused by the trapping of an embolus (often a detached thrombus) in a pulmonary artery.

shock: An acute circulatory crisis marked by hypotension and inadequate peripheral blood flow.

sphygmomanometer: A device that measures blood pressure using an inflatable cuff placed around a limb.

thrombus: A stationary blood clot within a blood vessel.

varicose (VAR-i-kōs) **veins:** Sagging, swollen veins distorted by gravity and by failure of the venous valves.

Chapter 13 Review

KEY TERMS

SUMMARY OUTLINE

iP Use *Interactive Physiology* ® (**IP**)—available on the IP CD packaged with your new textbook—to help you understand difficult physiological concepts. Follow these navigation paths on IP for concepts in this chapter:

- Cardiovascular System/Anatomy Review: Blood Vessel Structure and Function
- Cardiovascular System/Factors That Affect Blood Pressure
- Cardiovascular System/Measuring Blood Pressure
- Cardiovascular System/Autoregulation and Capillary Dynamics
- Cardiovascular System/Blood Pressure Regulation

13-1 Arteries, arterioles, capillaries, venules, and veins differ in size, structure, and function *p. 429*

1. Blood flows through a network of arteries, capillaries, and veins. The vital functions of the cardiovascular system depend on events at the capillary level: All chemical and gaseous exchange between the blood and interstitial fluid takes place across **capillary** walls.

2. Arteries and veins form an internal distribution system, propelled by the heart. **Arteries** branch repeatedly, decreasing in size until they become **arterioles;** from the arterioles, blood enters the capillary networks. Blood flowing from the capillaries enters small **venules** before entering larger **veins.**

3. The walls of arteries and veins contain three layers: the **tunica intima, tunica media,** and outermost **tunica externa.** (*Figure 13-1*)

4. The walls of arteries are usually thicker than the walls of veins. The arterial system includes the large **elastic arteries,** medium-sized **muscular arteries,** and smaller arterioles. As blood proceeds toward the capillaries, the number of vessels increases, but the diameter of the individual vessels decreases and the walls become thinner. (*Figure 13-2*)

5. Capillaries are the only blood vessels whose walls permit exchange between blood and interstitial fluid.

6. Capillaries form interconnected networks called **capillary beds.** A **precapillary sphincter** (a band of smooth muscle) adjusts blood flow into each capillary. Blood flow in a capillary changes as **vasomotion** occurs. (*Figure 13-4*)

7. Venules collect blood from capillaries and merge into **medium-sized veins** and then **large veins.** The arterial system is a high-pressure system; pressure in veins is much lower. **Valves** in these vessels prevent backflow of blood. (*Figure 13-5*)

13-2 Pressure and resistance determine blood flow and affect rates of capillary exchange *p. 434*

8. Flow is proportional to the difference in pressure (pressure gradient); blood will flow from an area of higher pressure to one of lower pressure.

9. For circulation to occur, the *circulatory pressure* must be greater than the *total peripheral resistance* (the resistance of the entire cardiovascular system). For blood to flow into peripheral capillaries, **blood pressure** (arterial pressure) must be greater than the **peripheral resistance** (the resistance of the arterial system). Neural and hormonal control mechanisms regulate blood pressure.

10. The most important determinant of peripheral resistance is arteriole diameter.

11. High arterial pressures overcome peripheral resistance and maintain blood flow through peripheral tissues. **Capillary pressures** are normally low; small changes in capillary pressure determine the rate of fluid movement into or out of the bloodstream. Venous pressure, normally low, determines ve-nous return and affects cardiac output and peripheral blood flow.

12. Arterial pressure rises in ventricular systole and falls in ventricular diastole. The difference between the **systolic** and **diastolic pressures** is **pulse pressure.** (*Figures 13-6, 13-8*)

13. At the capillaries, solute molecules diffuse across the capillary lining, and water-soluble materials diffuse through small spaces between endothelial cells. Water will move when driven by either hydrostatic pressure or osmotic pressure. The direction of water movement is determined by the balance between these two opposing pressures. (*Figure 13-7*)

14. Valves, **muscular compression,** and the **respiratory pump** help the relatively low venous pressures propel blood toward the heart. (*Figure 13-5*)

13-3 Cardiovascular regulation involves autoregulation, neural mechanisms, and endocrine responses *p. 439*

15. Homeostatic mechanisms ensure that tissue blood flow (*tissue perfusion*) delivers adequate oxygen and nutrients.

16. Blood flow varies with cardiac output, peripheral resistance, and blood pressure.

17. Autoregulation, neural mechanisms, and endocrine mechanisms influence the coordinated regulation of cardiovascular function. Autoregulation involves local factors changing the pattern of blood flow within capillary beds in response to chemical changes in interstitial fluids. Central nervous system mechanisms respond to changes in arterial pressure or blood gas levels. Hormones can assist in short-term adjustments (changes in cardiac output and peripheral resistance) and long-term adjustments (changes in blood volume that affect cardiac output and gas transport). (*Figure 13-9*)

18. Peripheral resistance is adjusted at the tissues by the dilation or constriction of precapillary sphincters.

19. **Baroreceptor reflexes** are autonomic reflexes that adjust cardiac output and peripheral resistance to maintain normal arterial pressures. Baroreceptor populations include the **aortic** and **carotid sinuses** and *atrial baroreceptors*. (*Figure 13-10*)

20. **Chemoreceptor reflexes** respond to changes in oxygen or carbon dioxide levels in blood and cerebrospinal fluid. Sympathetic activation leads to stimulation of the *cardioacceleratory* and *vasomotor centers;* parasympathetic activation stimulates the *cardioinhibitory center.* (*Figure 13-11*)

21. Short-term endocrine regulation of cardiac output and peripheral resistance is achieved by epinephrine and norepinephrine from the suprarenal medullae. Hormones involved in long-term regulation of blood pressure and volume are antidiuretic hormone (ADH), angiotensin II, erythropoietin (EPO), and atrial natriuretic peptide (ANP). (*Figure 13-12*)

22. ADH and angiotensin II also promote peripheral vasoconstriction in addition to their other functions. ADH and

aldosterone promote water and electrolyte retention and stimulate thirst. EPO stimulates red blood cell production. ANP encourages sodium loss and fluid loss, reduces blood pressure, inhibits thirst, and lowers peripheral resistance.

13-4 The cardiovascular system adapts to physiological stress *p. 444*

23. During exercise, blood flow to skeletal muscles increases at the expense of circulation to nonessential organs, and cardiac output rises. Cardiovascular performance improves with training. Athletes have larger stroke volumes, lower resting heart rates, and greater cardiac reserves than do nonathletes.

24. Blood loss causes an increase in cardiac output, mobilization of venous reserves, peripheral vasoconstriction, and the liberation of hormones that promote fluid retention and red blood cell production.

13-5 The pulmonary and systemic circuits of the cardiovascular system exhibit three general functional patterns *p. 446*

25. The peripheral distributions of arteries and veins are generally identical on both sides of the body except near the heart.

13-6 In the pulmonary circuit, deoxygenated blood enters the lungs in arteries, and oxygenated blood leaves the lungs in veins *p. 447*

26. The **pulmonary circuit** includes the **pulmonary trunk,** the **left** and **right pulmonary arteries,** and the **pulmonary veins,** which empty into the left atrium. (*Figures 13-13 and 13-14*)

13-7 The systemic circuit carries oxygenated blood from the left ventricle to tissues other than the lungs' exchange surfaces, and returns deoxygenated blood to the right atrium *p. 448*

27. In the **systemic circuit,** the **ascending aorta** gives rise to the coronary circulation. The **aortic arch** communicates with the **descending aorta.** (*Figures 13-15 to 13-19*)

28. Arteries in the neck and limbs are deep beneath the skin; in contrast, two sets of peripheral veins usually occur in those sites, one superficial and one deep. This dual-venous drainage is important for controlling body temperature.

29. The **superior vena cava (SVC)** receives blood from the head, neck, chest, shoulders, and arms. (*Figures 13-20 to 13-23*)

30. The **inferior vena cava (IVC)** collects most of the venous blood from organs inferior to the diaphragm. (*Figure 13-23*)

31. The **hepatic portal system** directs blood from the other digestive organs to the liver before the blood returns to the heart. (*Figure 13-24*)

13-8 Modifications of fetal and maternal cardiovascular systems promote exchange of materials, and independence is achieved at birth *p. 460*

32. The placenta receives blood from the two **umbilical arteries.** Blood returns to the fetus through the **umbilical vein,** which delivers blood to the **ductus venosus** in the liver. (*Figure 13-25a*)

33. Prior to delivery, blood bypasses the pulmonary circuit by flowing (1) from the right atrium into the left atrium through the **foramen ovale,** and (2) from the pulmonary trunk into the aortic arch via the **ductus arteriosus.** (*Figure 13-25b*)

13-9 Aging affects the blood, heart, and blood vessels *p. 461*

34. Age-related changes in the blood can include (1) decreased hematocrit, (2) constriction or blockage of peripheral veins by a *thrombus* (stationary blood clot), and (3) pooling of blood in veins of the legs because the valves are not working effectively.

35. Age-related changes in the heart include (1) a reduction in maximum cardiac output, (2) changes in the activities of the nodal and conducting cells, (3) a reduction in the elasticity of the fibrous skeleton, (4) progressive **atherosclerosis** that can restrict coronary circulation, and (5) replacement of damaged cardiac muscle cells by scar tissue.

36. Age-related changes in blood vessels, often related to **arteriosclerosis,** include (1) reduced tolerance of inelastic walls of arteries to sudden pressure increases, which can lead to an aneurysm; (2) the deposition of calcium salts on weakened vascular walls, increasing the risk of stroke or infarction; and (3) the formation of thrombi at atherosclerotic plaques.

13-10 The cardiovascular system is both structurally and functionally linked to all other systems *p. 462*

37. The cardiovascular system delivers oxygen, nutrients, and hormones to all body systems.

REVIEW QUESTIONS

WWW Access more review material online at The Anatomy & Physiology Place (**www.anatomyandphysiology.com**). There, you'll find Chapter Guides, Chapter Quizzes, Chapter Practice Tests, Interactive Flashcards, a Glossary with Pronunciations, and more to help you succeed in the course.

Level 1 • Reviewing Facts and Terms

Match each item in column A with the most closely related item in column B. Place letters for answers in the spaces provided.

COLUMN A

_____ 1. diastolic pressure
_____ 2. arterioles
_____ 3. hepatic vein
_____ 4. renal vein
_____ 5. aorta
_____ 6. precapillary sphincter
_____ 7. medulla oblongata
_____ 8. internal iliac artery
_____ 9. external iliac artery
_____ 10. baroreceptors
_____ 11. systolic pressure
_____ 12. saphenous vein

COLUMN B

a. drains the liver
b. largest superficial vein in body
c. carotid sinus
d. minimum blood pressure
e. blood supply to leg
f. blood supply to pelvis
g. peak blood pressure
h. vasomotion
i. largest artery in body
j. drains the kidney
k. vasomotor center
l. smallest arterial vessels

---

13. Identify the major arteries in the following diagram.

(a) _____
(c) _____
(e) _____
(g) _____
(i) _____
(b) _____
(d) _____
(f) _____
(h) _____

14. Blood vessels that carry blood away from the heart are called
   (a) veins.
   (b) arterioles.
   (c) venules.
   (d) arteries.

15. The layer of the arteriole wall that provides the properties of contractility and elasticity is the
   (a) tunica adventitia.
   (b) tunica media.
   (c) tunica intima.
   (d) tunica externa.

16. The two-way exchange of substances between blood and body cells occurs only through
   (a) arterioles.
   (b) capillaries.
   (c) venules.
   (d) a, b, and c are correct.

17. The blood vessels that collect blood from all tissues and organs and return it to the heart are the
   (a) veins.
   (b) arteries.
   (c) capillaries.
   (d) arterioles.

18. Blood is compartmentalized within the veins because of the presence of
   (a) venous reservoirs.
   (b) muscular walls.
   (c) clots.
   (d) valves.

19. The most important factor in vascular resistance is
   (a) the viscosity of the blood.
   (b) friction between the blood and vessel walls.
   (c) turbulence due to irregular surfaces of blood vessels.
   (d) the length of the blood vessels.

20. In a blood pressure reading of 120/80, the 120 represents _____ and the 80 represents _____.
    (a) diastolic pressure; systolic pressure
    (b) pulse pressure; mean arterial pressure
    (c) systolic pressure; diastolic pressure
    (d) mean arterial pressure; pulse pressure

21. Hydrostatic pressure forces water _____ a solution; osmotic pressure forces water _____ a solution.
    (a) into; out of   (b) out of; into
    (c) out of; out of   (d) a, b, and c are incorrect

22. The two factors that assist the relatively low venous pressures in propelling blood toward the heart are
    (a) ventricular systole and valve closure.
    (b) gravity and vasomotion.
    (c) muscular compression and the respiratory pump.
    (d) atrial and ventricular contractions.

23. Identify the major veins in the following diagram.

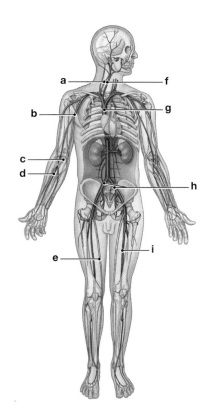

    (a) _____   (b) _____
    (c) _____   (d) _____
    (e) _____   (f) _____
    (g) _____   (h) _____
    (i) _____

24. Arteries of the pulmonary circuit differ from those of the systemic circuit in that they carry
    (a) oxygen and nutrients.
    (b) deoxygenated blood.
    (c) oxygenated blood.
    (d) oxygen, carbon dioxide, and nutrients.

25. The two arteries formed by the division of the brachiocephalic trunk are the
    (a) aorta and internal carotid.
    (b) axillary and brachial.
    (c) external and internal carotid.
    (d) common carotid and subclavian.

26. The unpaired arteries supplying blood to the visceral organs include the
    (a) suprarenal, renal, and lumbar arteries.
    (b) iliac, gonadal, and femoral arteries.
    (c) celiac trunk and superior and inferior mesenteric arteries.
    (d) a, b, and c are correct.

27. The artery generally used to feel the pulse at the wrist is the
    (a) ulnar artery.   (b) radial artery.
    (c) fibular artery.   (d) dorsalis artery.

28. The vein that drains the dural sinuses of the brain is the
    (a) cephalic vein.   (b) great saphenous vein.
    (c) internal jugular vein. (d) superior vena cava.

29. The vein that collects most of the venous blood from below the diaphragm is the
    (a) superior vena cava.   (b) great saphenous vein.
    (c) inferior vena cava.   (d) azygos vein.

30. (a) What are the primary forces that cause fluid to move out of a capillary and into the interstitial fluid at its arterial end? (b) What are the primary forces that cause fluid to move into a capillary from the interstitial fluid at its venous end?

31. What two effects result when the baroreceptor response to elevated blood pressure (BP) is triggered?

32. What factors affect the activity of chemoreceptors in the carotid and aortic bodies?

33. What circulatory changes occur at birth?

34. What age-related changes take place in the blood, heart, and blood vessels?

Level 2 • Reviewing Concepts

35. When dehydration occurs,
    (a) water reabsorption at the kidneys accelerates.
    (b) fluids are reabsorbed from the interstitial fluid.
    (c) blood osmotic pressure increases.
    (d) a, b, and c are correct.

36. Increased CO_2 levels in tissues would promote
    (a) constriction of precapillary sphincters.
    (b) an increase in the pH of the blood.
    (c) dilation of precapillary sphincters.
    (d) a decrease of blood flow to tissues.

37. Elevated levels of the hormones ADH and angiotensin II will produce
    (a) increased peripheral vasodilation.
    (b) increased peripheral vasoconstriction.
    (c) increased peripheral blood flow.
    (d) increased venous return.

38. Relate the anatomical differences between arteries and veins to their functions.

39. Why do capillaries permit the diffusion of materials, whereas arteries and veins do not?

40. Why is blood flow to the brain relatively continuous and constant?

41. An accident victim displays the following signs and symptoms: hypotension; pale, cool, moist skin; confusion and disorientation. Identify her condition, and explain why each of these signs and symptoms occurs. If you took her pulse, what would you find?

Level 3 • Critical Thinking and Clinical Applications

42. Bob is sitting outside on a warm day and is sweating profusely. His friend Mary wants to practice taking blood pressures, and he agrees to play patient. Mary finds that Bob's blood pressure is elevated, even though he is resting and has lost fluid from sweating. (She reasons that fluid loss should lower blood volume and, thus, blood pressure.) Mary asks you why Bob's blood pressure is high instead of low. What should you tell her?

43. People with allergies frequently take antihistamines and decongestants to relieve their symptoms. The medications' labels warn that such medications should not be taken by individuals being treated for high blood pressure. Why?

44. Gina awakens suddenly to the sound of her alarm clock. Realizing she is late for class, she jumps to her feet, feels lightheaded, and falls back on her bed. What probably caused this to happen? Why doesn't it always happen?

The Cardiovascular System in Perspective

Functional Relationships Between the Cardiovascular System and Other Systems

The Integumentary System

- The Integumentary System's stimulated mast cells produce localized changes in bloodflow and capillary permeability
- The Cardiovascular System delivers immune system cells to injury sites; clotting response seals breaks in skin surface; carries away toxins from sites of infection; provides heat

The Skeletal System

- The Skeletal System provides calcium needed for normal cardiac muscle contraction; protects blood cells developing in bone marrow
- The Cardiovascular System provides calcium and phosphate for bone deposition; delivers EPO to bone marrow, parathyroid hormone and calcitonin to osteoblasts and osteoclasts

The Muscular System

- The Muscular System assists in moving blood through veins; protects superficial blood vessels, especially in neck and limbs
- The Cardiovascular System delivers oxygen and nutrients, removes carbon dioxide, lactic acid, and heat during skeletal muscle activity

The Nervous System

- The Nervous System controls patterns of circulation in peripheral tissues; modifies heart rate and regulates blood pressure; releases ADH
- The Cardiovascular System's endothelial cells maintain blood-brain barrier; help generate CSF

The Endocrine System

- The Endocrine System's hormone EPO regulates production of RBCs; several hormones elevate blood pressure; epinephrine stimulates cardiac muscle, elevating heart rate and contractile force
- The Cardiovascular System distributes hormones throughout the body; heart secretes ANP

For All Systems
The Cardiovascular System delivers oxygen, hormones, nutrients, and WBCs; removes carbon dioxide and metabolic wastes; transfers heat

The Lymphoid System

- The Lymphoid System defends against pathogens or toxins in blood; fights infections of cardiovascular organs; returns tissue fluid to circulation
- The Cardiovascular System distributes WBCs; carries pathogen-attacking antibodies; restricts spread of pathogens with clotting response

The Respiratory System

- The Respiratory System provides oxygen to cardiovascular organs and removes carbon dioxide
- The Cardiovascular System's RBCs transport oxygen and carbon dioxide between lungs and peripheral tissues

The Digestive System

- The Digestive System provides nutrients to cardiovascular organs; absorbs water and ions to maintain normal blood volume
- The Cardiovascular System distributes digestive tract hormones; carries absorbed nutrients, water, and ions away; delivers nutrients and toxins to liver

The Urinary System

- The Urinary System releases renin to elevate blood pressure and EPO to accelerate red blood cell production
- The Cardiovascular System delivers blood to kidneys, where filtration occurs; accepts fluids and solutes reabsorbed during urine production

The Reproductive System

- The Reproductive System maintains healthy vessels and slows development of atherosclerosis with age by estrogens
- The Cardiovascular System distributes reproductive hormones; provides nutrients, oxygen, and waste removal for developing fetus; local blood pressure changes responsible for physical changes during sexual arousal

Professional Profile

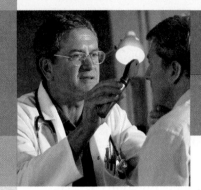

PHYSICIAN ASSISTANT
Rick Markson

> " Anywhere a doctor works, a PA can work. There are jobs in orthopedics, pediatrics, the emergency room, surgery—you name it. "

Rick Markson is a physician assistant working in the mental health program of the VA Medical Center in Phoenix, Arizona. Rick treats veterans with mental health disorders and substance abuse problems. Often his patients have physical, mental, and substance abuse problems at the same time.

Because the VA is an urgent care walk-in facility, most of the patients that Rick sees come in without a scheduled appointment. "We take them as they come," says Rick. A typical day for Rick includes mental health evaluations, treatment, follow-up with returning patients, medication management, and counseling. "At the VA, we see people returning from combat with posttraumatic stress disorder and depression, things like that. We see a lot of chronic mental illness and do crisis intervention. A lot of the day is doing assessments."

TREATING THE WHOLE PERSON

Rick finds the contact with his patients very gratifying. "One of the frustrations many people have with medicine is how fragmented it is. We treat individual symptoms and illnesses—sometimes it seems like no one in medicine is looking at the patient as a whole person. A physician assistant spends more time with patients and helps people cope in a healthier way. We do a lot of education, we intervene when people are not well, and we hope to help people live more healthy and productive lives."

Although many of Rick's patients have a mental illness that tends to get worse over time, he says that his job is to keep working with people and being there for them so that they are encouraged to improve. This can take months or years. "It's very satisfying when you see people start to take care of themselves and get better. You see people make the decision to get sober, to get their problems addressed, and to deal with their health problems."

Physician assistants, or PAs, work under the supervision of a physician, but they have a lot of authority for making decisions. They can write prescriptions, diagnose patients, and order lab tests. PAs work in many different areas of medicine. Rick has worked in hospitals, in mental health clinics, and in a county jail. "Anywhere a doctor works, a PA can work. There are jobs in orthopedics, pediatrics, the emergency room, surgery—you name it. Follow your interests."

TWO YEARS OF TRAINING

To become a physician assistant, you must complete a 24-month program of study. Some students get their bachelor's degree and PA certificate simultaneously. Others, like Rick, enroll in PA school after obtaining an A.A. or B.A. elsewhere. Rick studied social sciences as an undergraduate and did not have much science background before entering PA school. "Physician assistants need a strong background in anatomy and physiology in order to understand what's happening in the patients' bodies. Taking A & P before entering the PA program is a good idea. It will give you a boost on your studies."

Having some practical experience in medicine is often a requirement to get into PA school. Rick recommends working as a volunteer or in a paid job in some aspect of the medical field, whether as a technician, an aide, or a paramedic. Rick used his own background working in special education with disabled children as medical experience for PA school.

PAs must also pass a national exam in order to be licensed in most states. They must recertify every six years and must present evidence of the completion of continuing education credits every two years. For more information about training and career opportunities for physician assistants, contact the American Academy of Physician Assistants.

14 The Lymphoid System and Immunity

During childhood, all we notice is the sting of a vaccination. As adults, we realize that the pain of the shot is brief whereas the disease that it prevents can cripple or kill. In this chapter, we will examine the mechanisms by which the body defends itself from general assaults and specific invaders.

VOCABULARY DEVELOPMENT

anamnesis a memory; *anamnestic response*
apo- away; *apoptosis*
chemo- chemistry; *chemotaxis*
dia- through; *diapedesis*
-gen to produce; *pyrogen*

humor a liquid; *humoral immunity*
immunis safe; *immune*
inflammare to set on fire; *inflammation*
lympha water; *lymph*
nodulus little knot; *nodule*

pathos disease; *pathogen*
pedesis a leaping; *diapedesis*
ptosis a falling; *apoptosis*
pyr fire; *pyrogen*
taxis arrangement; *chemotaxis*

An Introduction to the Lymphoid System and Immunity

We do not live in a completely safe world. The external environment contains a variety of physical hazards—poisonous chemicals, extreme heat, radiation, heavy and/or sharp objects, to name but a few—that can inflict a broad range of injuries, including bumps, cuts, broken bones, and burns. Additionally, the world is full of many types of microorganisms that, if allowed entry into the body, cause some of the most important human diseases. Still other internal processes, such as cancer, can pose extreme, even lethal, danger to the human body.

Many different organs and systems work together to keep us alive and healthy. In this ongoing struggle to maintain health, the **lymphoid system** plays a central role. This chapter discusses the components of the lymphoid system and their interactions.

14-1 Anatomical barriers and defense mechanisms constitute nonspecific defense, and lymphocytes provide specific defense

The various microorganisms that cause diseases in humans—including an assortment of viruses, bacteria, fungi, and parasites—are called **pathogens** (*pathos*, disease + *-gen*, to produce). Each pathogen has a different mode of life and interacts with the body in a characteristic way. For example, most of the time viruses exist within cells, which they often eventually destroy. (Viruses lack a cellular structure, consisting only of nucleic acid and protein, and can replicate themselves only within a living cell.) Many bacteria multiply in the interstitial fluids, and some of the largest parasites, such as roundworms, burrow through internal organs. And as if that were not enough, we

are constantly at risk from renegade cells that have the potential to produce lethal cancers. ∞ p. 86

The **lymphoid system** includes the cells, tissues, and organs responsible for defending the body. The primary cells of the lymphoid system are *lymphocytes*. ∞ p. 395 These cells are vital to the body's ability to resist or overcome infection and disease.

The body has several anatomical barriers and defense mechanisms that either prevent or slow the entry of infectious organisms, or attack them if they do succeed in gaining entry. These mechanisms are called *nonspecific defenses*, because they do not distinguish one potential threat from another. In contrast, lymphocytes respond specifically: If a bacterial pathogen invades peripheral tissues, lymphocytes organize a defense against that particular type of bacterium. For this reason, lymphocytes are said to provide a *specific defense*, known as the **immune response.** The ability to resist infection and disease through the activation of specific defenses is called **immunity.**

All the cells and tissues involved in the production of immunity are sometimes considered part of an *immune system*—a physiological system that includes not only the lymphoid system, but also components of the integumentary, cardiovascular, respiratory, digestive, and other systems.

Next we examine the organization of the lymphoid system. Then we will consider the body's nonspecific defenses. Finally, we will see how the lymphoid system interacts with cells and tissues of other systems to defend the body against infection and disease.

CHECKPOINT

1. Define pathogen.
2. Explain the difference between nonspecific defense and specific defense.

See the blue Answers tab at the back of the book.

14-2 Lymphatic vessels, lymphocytes, lymphoid tissues, and lymphoid organs function in body defenses

One of the least familiar organ systems, the lymphoid system includes the following four components:

1. *Vessels.* A network of **lymphatic vessels,** often called **lymphatics,** begins in peripheral tissues and ends at connections to veins.

2. *Fluid.* A fluid called **lymph** flows through the lymphatic vessels. Lymph resembles plasma but contains a much lower concentration of suspended proteins.

3. *Lymphocytes.* Lymphocytes are specialized cells that perform an array of specific functions in defending the body.

4. *Lymphoid tissues and organs.* **Lymphoid tissues** are collections of loose connective tissue and lymphocytes in structures called *lymphoid nodules;* an example is the tonsils. **Lymphoid organs** are more complex structures that contain large numbers of lymphocytes and are connected to lymphatic vessels; examples include the lymph nodes, spleen, and thymus.

Figure 14-1 provides an overview of the components of the lymphoid system.

FUNCTIONS OF THE LYMPHOID SYSTEM

The lymphoid system has the following primary functions:

- *Production, maintenance, and distribution of lymphocytes.* Lymphocytes are produced and stored within lymphoid organs, such as the spleen, thymus, and bone marrow. Lymphocytes respond to the presence of (1) invading pathogens, such as bacteria or viruses; (2) abnormal body cells, such as virus-infected cells or cancer cells; and (3) foreign proteins, such as the toxins produced by some bacteria. Lymphocytes attempt to eliminate these threats or render them harmless through a combination of physical and chemical actions.

- *Return of fluid and solutes from peripheral tissues to the blood.* The return of tissue fluids through the lymphoid system maintains normal blood volume and eliminates local variations in the composition of the interstitial fluid. The volume of flow is considerable—roughly 3.6 liters per

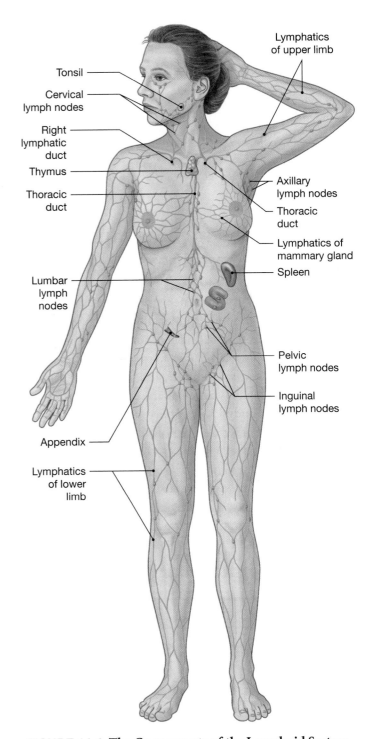

FIGURE 14-1 The Components of the Lymphoid System.

day—and a break in a major lymphatic vessel can cause a rapid and potentially fatal decline in blood volume.

- *Distribution of hormones, nutrients, and waste products from their tissues of origin to the general circulation.* Substances unable to enter the bloodstream directly may do so by way of lymphatic vessels. For example, lipids absorbed by the digestive tract do not often enter the bloodstream through capillaries. They reach the bloodstream only after they have traveled along lymphatic vessels (a process described further in Chapter 16).

LYMPHATIC VESSELS

Lymphatic vessels, or lymphatics, carry lymph from peripheral tissues to the venous system. The smallest lymphatic vessels—called **lymphatic capillaries**—begin as blind pockets in peripheral tissues (Figure 14-2a). Lymphatic capillaries are lined

(b) LM × 43

FIGURE 14-2 Lymphatic Capillaries. (a) This drawing provides a three-dimensional representation of the association of blood capillaries, tissue, interstitial fluid, and lymphatic capillaries. Arrows indicate the directions of interstitial fluid and lymph movement. **(b)** Like some veins, some lymphatic vessels contain valves.

by an endothelium (simple squamous epithelium). The lack of a basement membrane around the endothelium permits fluids and solutes, as well as viruses, bacteria, and cell debris, to flow into a lymphatic capillary. The overlapping arrangement of the endothelial cells acts as a one-way valve to prevent backflow of fluid into the intercellular spaces.

From lymphatic capillaries, lymph flows into larger lymphatic vessels that lead toward the trunk of the body. The walls of these lymphatics contain layers comparable to those of veins and, like veins, such lymphatic vessels contain valves (Figure 14-2b). Pressures within the lymphoid system are extremely low, so the valves are essential to maintaining normal lymph flow.

The lymphatic vessels ultimately empty into two large collecting structures called lymphatic ducts (Figure 14-3). The **thoracic duct** collects lymph from the lower abdomen, pelvis, and lower limbs, and from the left half of the head, neck, and chest. It empties its collected lymph into the venous system near the junction between the left internal jugular vein and the left subclavian vein. The smaller **right lymphatic duct,** which ends at a comparable location on the right side, delivers lymph from the right side of the body above the diaphragm. It empties into the right subclavian vein. Blockage of lymphatic drainage from a limb can cause the limb to swell due to the accumulation of interstitial fluid. This condition is called *lymphedema.*

LYMPHOCYTES

As noted in Chapter 11, lymphocytes account for roughly 25 percent of the circulating white blood cell population. ∞ p. 395 But circulating lymphocytes constitute only a small fraction of the total lymphocyte population. At any given moment, most of the approximately 1 trillion (10^{12}) lymphocytes—with a combined weight of over a kilogram (2.2 lbs)—are found within lymphoid organs or other tissues. The bloodstream provides a rapid transport system for lymphocytes moving from one site to another.

Types of Circulating Lymphocytes

The blood contains three classes of lymphocytes: *T cells, B cells,* and *NK cells.* Each lymphocyte class has distinctive functions.

T CELLS. Approximately 80 percent of circulating lymphocytes are **T** (thymus-dependent) **cells.** *Cytotoxic T cells* directly attack foreign cells or virus-infected body cells. These lymphocytes are the primary providers of *cell-mediated immunity,* or *cellular immunity. Helper T cells* stimulate the activities of both T cells and B cells. *Suppressor T cells* inhibit both T cells and B cells. Helper T cells and suppressor T cells are also called **regulatory T cells.**

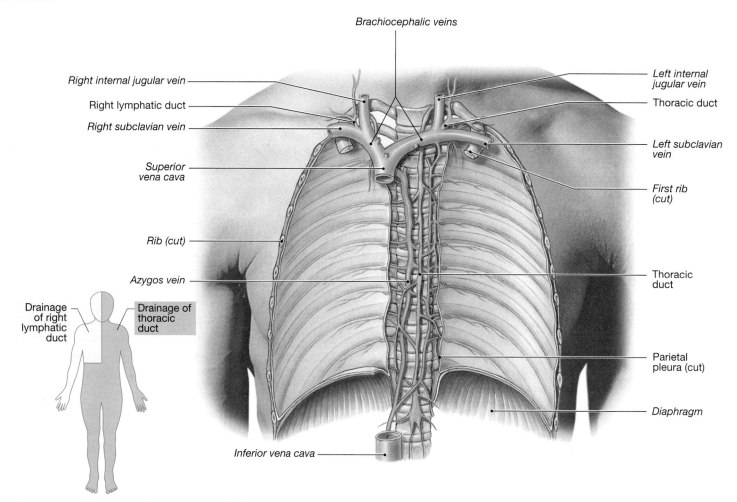

Brachiocephalic veins

Right internal jugular vein

Right lymphatic duct

Right subclavian vein

Superior vena cava

Rib (cut)

Azygos vein

Drainage of right lymphatic duct

Drainage of thoracic duct

Inferior vena cava

Left internal jugular vein

Thoracic duct

Left subclavian vein

First rib (cut)

Thoracic duct

Parietal pleura (cut)

Diaphragm

FIGURE 14-3 **The Lymphatic Ducts and the Venous System.** The thoracic duct carries lymph originating in tissues inferior to the diaphragm and from the left side of the upper body. The right lymphatic duct drains the right half of the body superior to the diaphragm.

B CELLS. B (**b**one marrow–derived) **cells** make up 10–15 percent of circulating lymphocytes. B cells can differentiate into **plasma cells,** which produce and secrete **antibodies**—soluble proteins that are also called **immunoglobulins.** ∞ p. 384 Antibodies bind to specific chemical targets called **antigens,** which are usually pathogens, parts or products of pathogens, or other foreign compounds. Formation of an antigen–antibody complex starts a chain of events leading to the destruction of the target compound or organism. B cells are said to be responsible for *antibody-mediated immunity,* which is also known as *humoral* ("liquid") *immunity* because antibodies function in body fluids.

NK CELLS. The remaining 5–10 percent of circulating lymphocytes are **NK** (**n**atural **k**iller) **cells.** These lymphocytes attack foreign cells, normal cells infected with viruses, and cancer cells that appear in normal tissues. Their continual monitoring of peripheral tissues is known as *immunological surveillance.*

The Origin and Circulation of Lymphocytes

Lymphocytes in the blood, bone marrow, spleen, thymus, and peripheral lymphoid tissues are visitors, not residents. Lymphocytes move throughout the body; after they enter a tissue, they wander through it and then enter a blood vessel or lymphatic vessel for transport to another site. In general, lymphocytes have relatively long life spans. Roughly 80 percent survive for 4 years, and some last 20 years or more. Throughout life, normal lymphocyte populations are maintained through the divisions of stem cells in the bone marrow and lymphoid tissues.

Lymphocyte production and development, or **lymphopoiesis** (lim-fō-poy-Ē-sis), involves the bone marrow and thymus (**Figure 14-4**). As each B cell and T cell develop, they gain the ability to respond to the presence of a specific antigen; similarly, NK cells gain the ability to recognize abnormal cells.

Hemocytoblasts in the bone marrow produce lymphoid stem cells with two distinct fates. One group remains in the bone

FIGURE 14-4 The Origins of Lymphocytes.

(a) Hemocytoblast divisions produce lymphoid stem cells with two fates. One group remains in the bone marrow and produces daughter cells that mature into B cells and NK cells. **(b)** The second group migrates to the thymus, where subsequent divisions produce daughter cells that mature into T cells. **(c)** Mature B cells, NK cells, and mature T cells are transported in the bloodstream to temporary sites within peripheral tissues.

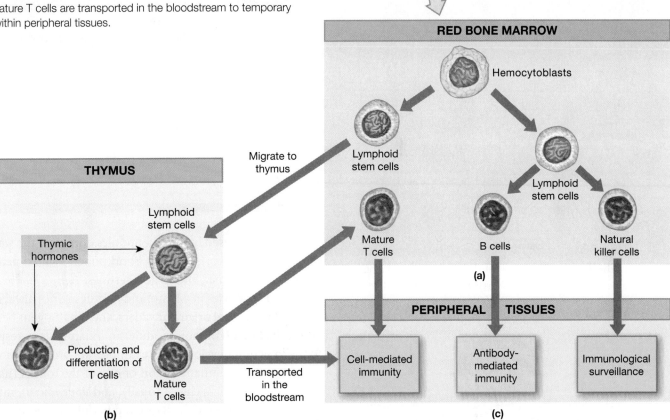

marrow and generates B cells and functional NK cells (Figure 14-4a). The second group of lymphoid stem cells migrates to the thymus. Under the influence of thymic hormones (collectively known as *thymosins*), these cells divide repeatedly, producing large numbers of T cells (Figure 14-4b). As they mature, all three types of lymphocytes enter the bloodstream and migrate to peripheral tissues (Figure 14-4c), including lymphoid tissues and organs, such as the spleen. As these lymphocyte populations migrate through peripheral tissues, they retain the ability to divide and produce daughter cells of the same type. A dividing B cell, for example, produces other B cells, not T cells or NK cells. As we will see, the ability of a specific type of lymphocyte to increase in number is important to the success of the immune response.

LYMPHOID NODULES

Lymphoid tissues are composed of loose connective tissue and lymphocytes. **Lymphoid nodules** are masses of lymphoid tissue that are not surrounded by a fibrous capsule. As a result, their size can increase or decrease, depending on the number of lymphocytes present at any given moment. Large lymphoid nodules often contain a pale central region, called a *germinal center,* where lymphocytes are actively dividing.

Lymphoid nodules are found beneath the epithelia lining various organs of the respiratory, digestive, and urinary systems. All these systems are open to the external environment and, therefore, provide a route of entry into the body for potentially harmful organisms and toxins.

Because our food usually contains foreign proteins and often contains bacteria, lymphoid tissue and nodules associated with the digestive tract play a particularly important role in the defense of the body. The **tonsils,** large lymphoid nodules in the walls of the pharynx, guard the entrance to the digestive and respiratory tracts (Figure 14-5). Five tonsils are usually present: a single *pharyngeal tonsil,* or *adenoid;* a pair of *palatine tonsils;* and a pair of *lingual tonsils.* Clusters of lymphoid nodules, or *Peyer patches,* also lie beneath the epithelial lining of the

FIGURE 14-5 **The Tonsils.** The tonsils are lymphoid nodules in the wall of the pharynx. A single pharyngeal tonsil (the adenoids) lies above the paired palatine and lingual tonsils. Each tonsil contains germinal centers where lymphocytes divide.

"Swollen Glands"

Lymph nodes are often called *lymph glands,* and "swollen glands" usually accompany tissue inflammation or infection. Chronic or excessive enlargement of lymph nodes, a sign called *lymphadenopathy* (lim-fad-e-NOP-a-thē), may occur in response to bacterial or viral infections, endocrine disorders, or cancer.

Because lymphatic capillaries offer little resistance to the passage of cancer cells, cancer cells often spread along the lymphatics and become trapped in lymph nodes. Thus, an analysis of swollen lymph nodes can provide information on the nature and distribution of cancer cells, aiding in the selection of appropriate therapies. **Lymphomas**—cancers arising from lymphocytes or lymphoid stem cells—are an important group of lymphoid system cancers.

intestines, and fused lymphoid nodules dominate the walls of the *appendix,* a worm-shaped blind pouch located near the junction of the small and large intestines.

The lymphocytes in a lymphoid nodule are not always able to destroy bacterial or viral invaders, and if pathogens become established in a lymphoid nodule, an inflammatory response to the infection develops. Two examples are probably familiar to you: *tonsillitis,* inflammation of one of the tonsils (usually the pharyngeal tonsil), and *appendicitis,* inflammation of the lymphoid nodules in the appendix.

LYMPHOID ORGANS

Lymphoid organs are separated from surrounding tissues by a fibrous connective-tissue capsule. Important lymphoid organs include the *lymph nodes,* the *thymus,* and the *spleen.*

Lymph Nodes

Lymph nodes are small, oval lymphoid organs covered by a fibrous capsule and are 1–25 mm (up to 1 in.) in diameter (Figure 14-6). *Afferent lymphatics* deliver lymph to a lymph node, and *efferent lymphatics* carry the lymph onward, toward the venous system. Lymph nodes filter and purify the lymph before it reaches the venous system. As lymph flows through the sinuses of a lymph node, at least 99 percent of the antigens present in the arriving lymph are removed by fixed macrophages. As the antigens are detected and removed, T cells and B cells are

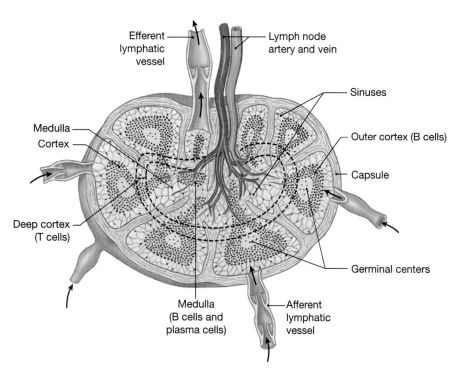

FIGURE 14-6 **The Structure of a Lymph Node.** The arrows indicate the direction of lymph flow. Mature B cells and T cells located in different regions of the cortex and medulla remove antigens from the lymph and initiate immune responses.

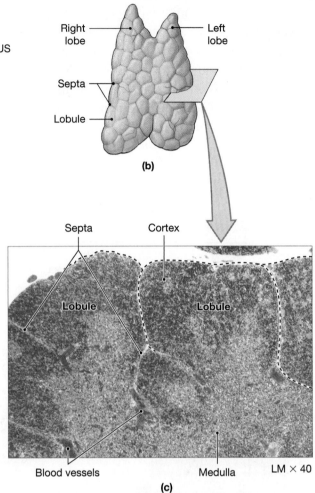

FIGURE 14-7 The Thymus. (a) This drawing indicates the position of the thymus; notice its relationship to other organs in the chest. **(b)** Each of the two lobes of the thymus contains numerous lobules. **(c)** This micrograph shows several thymic lobules.

stimulated, initiating an immune response. Lymph nodes are located in regions where they can detect and eliminate harmful "intruders" before they reach vital organs of the body (Figure 14-1).

The Thymus

The **thymus** is a pink gland that lies in the mediastinum posterior to the sternum (Figure 14-7a). It is the site of T cell production and maturation. The thymus reaches its greatest size (relative to body size) in the first year or two after birth and its maximum absolute size during puberty, when it weighs between 30 and 40 g (1.06 to 1.41 oz.). Thereafter, the thymus gradually decreases in size.

The thymus has two lobes, each divided into *lobules* by fibrous partitions, or *septa* (singular, *septum;* a wall) (Figure 14-7b). Each lobule consists of a densely packed outer cortex and a paler, central *medulla* (Figure 14-7c). The cortex contains clusters of lymphocytes surrounded by other cells that secrete the hormones collectively known as *thymosins.* Thymosins stimulate lymphocyte stem-cell divisions and T cell maturation. After the T cells migrate into the medulla, they leave the thymus in one of the blood vessels in that region.

The Spleen

The adult **spleen** contains the largest collection of lymphoid tissue in the body. It is about 12 cm (5 in.) long and can weigh about 160 g (5.6 oz.). A major function of the spleen parallels that of the lymph nodes, except that it filters blood instead of

Clinical Note

Injury to the Spleen

An impact to the left side of the abdomen can distort or damage the spleen. Such injuries are known risks of contact sports, such as football or hockey, and other athletic activities, such as skiing or sledding. However, because even a seemingly minor blow to the side may rupture the capsule, the results can be serious internal bleeding and eventual circulatory shock. The spleen can also be damaged by infection, inflammation, or invasion by cancer cells.

Because the spleen is relatively fragile, it is very difficult to repair surgically. (Sutures usually tear out before they have been tensed enough to stop the bleeding.) Treatment for a severely ruptured spleen involves its complete removal, a process called a *splenectomy* (sple-NEK-to-mē). A person without a spleen survives without difficulty but has a greater risk for bacterial infections than do individuals with a functional spleen.

lymph: It removes abnormal blood cells and components, and it initiates the responses of B cells and T cells to antigens in the circulating blood. In addition, the spleen stores iron from recycled red blood cells. ∞ p. 387

As indicated in Figure 14-8a, the spleen is wedged between the stomach, the left kidney, and the muscular diaphragm. The spleen normally has a deep red color because of the blood it contains (Figure 14-8b). The cellular components of the spleen are arranged into areas of *red pulp*, which contain large quantities of red blood cells, and areas of *white pulp* resembling lymphoid nodules (Figure 14-8c).

After the splenic artery enters the spleen, it branches outward toward the capsule into many smaller arteries that are surrounded by white pulp. Capillaries then discharge the blood into a network of reticular fibers that makes up the red pulp. Blood from the red pulp enters *venous sinusoids* (small vessels lined by macrophages) and then flows into small veins and the splenic vein. As blood passes through the spleen, macrophages identify and engulf any damaged or infected cells. The presence of lymphocytes nearby ensures that any microorganisms or other abnormal antigens stimulate an immune response.

FIGURE 14-8 The Spleen. (a) This transverse section through the trunk shows the typical position of the spleen within the abdominopelvic cavity. The shape of the spleen roughly conforms to the shapes of adjacent structures. **(b)** This external view of the intact spleen includes some important anatomical landmarks. **(c)** This photomicrograph shows the internal structure of the spleen. The white pulp appears blue because the nuclei of lymphocytes stain very darkly. Red pulp contains an abundance of red blood cells.

Roles of the Lymphoid System in Body Defenses

The human body has many defense mechanisms, but they can be sorted into two categories:

1. **Nonspecific defenses** do not distinguish between one threat and another. These defenses, which are present at birth, include *physical barriers, phagocytic cells, immunological surveillance, interferons, complement, inflammation,* and *fever*—all of which are discussed shortly. They provide the body with a defensive capability known as **nonspecific resistance.**

2. **Specific defenses** protect against particular threats. For example, a specific defense may oppose infection by one type of bacterium but ignore other bacteria and all viruses. Many specific defenses develop after birth as a result of exposure to environmental hazards or infectious agents. Specific defenses are dependent on the activities of lymphocytes. The body's specific defenses produce a state of protection known as immunity, or **specific resistance.**

Nonspecific and specific resistance does not function in an either–or fashion; both are necessary to provide adequate resistance to infection and disease.

CHECKPOINT

3. List the components of the lymphoid system.
4. How would blockage of the thoracic duct affect the circulation of lymph?
5. If the thymus gland failed to produce thymic hormones, which population of lymphocytes would be affected in what way?
6. Why do lymph nodes enlarge during some infections?

See the blue Answers tab at the back of the book.

14-3 Each nonspecific defense responds in a characteristic way regardless of the potential threat

Nonspecific defenses deny the entry, or limit the spread within the body, of microorganisms or other environmental agents. Seven categories of nonspecific defenses are summarized in Figure 14-9.

PHYSICAL BARRIERS

Physical barriers keep hazardous organisms and materials outside the body. To cause infection or disease, a foreign (antigenic) compound or pathogen must enter body tissues, which requires crossing an epithelium. The epithelial covering of the skin has a keratin coating, multiple layers, and a network of desmosomes that locks adjacent cells together. ∞ p. 123 These barriers provide very effective protection for underlying tissues.

The exterior surface of the body has several other defenses. The hairs found in most areas provide some protection against mechanical abrasion (especially on the scalp), and they often prevent hazardous materials or insects from contacting the skin's surface. The epidermal surface also receives the secretions of sebaceous glands and sweat glands. These secretions flush the surface, washing away microorganisms and chemical agents. The secretions also contain microbe-killing chemicals, destructive enzymes (*lysozymes*), and antibodies.

The epithelia lining the digestive, respiratory, urinary, and reproductive tracts are more delicate, but they are equally well defended. Mucus bathes most surfaces of the digestive tract, and the stomach contains a powerful acid that can destroy many potential pathogens. Mucus is swept across the lining of the respiratory tract, urine flushes the urinary passageways, and glandular secretions flush structures in the reproductive tract. Special enzymes, antibodies, and an acidic pH add to the effectiveness of these secretions.

PHAGOCYTES

Phagocytes in peripheral tissues remove cellular debris and respond to invasion by foreign compounds or pathogens. These cells represent the "first line of cellular defense," often attacking and removing microorganisms before lymphocytes become aware of their presence. Two general classes of phagocytic cells are found in the body: *microphages* and *macrophages.*

Microphages are the neutrophils and eosinophils that normally circulate in the blood. These phagocytic cells leave the bloodstream and enter peripheral tissues subjected to injury or infection. As noted in Chapter 11, neutrophils are abundant, mobile, and quick to phagocytize cellular debris or invading bacteria. ∞ p. 395 The less abundant eosinophils target foreign compounds or pathogens that have been coated with antibodies.

The body also contains several types of **macrophages**—large, actively phagocytic cells derived from circulating monocytes. Almost every tissue in the body shelters resident (fixed) or visiting (free) macrophages. The relatively diffuse collection of phagocytic cells throughout the body is called the

PHYSICAL BARRIERS	
Prevent approach of and deny access to pathogens	Duct of eccrine sweat gland — Hair — Secretions — Epithelium
PHAGOCYTES	
Remove debris and pathogens	Fixed macrophage Neutrophil Free macrophage Eosinophil Monocyte
IMMUNOLOGICAL SURVEILLANCE	
Destroys abnormal cells	Natural killer cell — Lysed abnormal cell
INTERFERONS	
Increase resistance of cells to viral infection; slow the spread of disease	Interferons released by activated lymphocytes, macrophages, or virus-infected cells
COMPLEMENT SYSTEM	
Attacks and breaks down cell walls; attracts phagocytes; stimulates inflammation	Complement — Lysed pathogen
INFLAMMATION RESPONSE	
Has multiple effects	Mast cell 1. Blood flow increased 2. Phagocytes activated 3. Capillary permeability increased 4. Complement activated 5. Clotting reaction walls off region 6. Regional temperature increased 7. Specific defenses activated
FEVER	
Mobilizes defenses; accelerates repairs; inhibits pathogens	Body temperature rises above 37.2°C in response to pyrogens

FIGURE 14-9 The Body's Nonspecific Defenses. Nonspecific defenses deny pathogens access to the body or destroy them without distinguishing among specific types.

monocyte–macrophage system, or the *reticuloendothelial system.* In some organs, fixed macrophages have special names. For example, *microglia* are macrophages in the central nervous system, and *Kupffer* (KOOP-fer) *cells* are macrophages found in and around blood channels in the liver.

All phagocytic cells function in much the same way, although the targets of phagocytosis may differ from one cell type to another. Mobile macrophages and microphages also share a number of other functional characteristics in addition to phagocytosis. All can move through capillary walls by squeezing between adjacent endothelial cells, a process known as *diapedesis* (*dia,* through + *pedesis,* a leaping). They may also be attracted to or repelled by chemicals in the surrounding fluids, a phenomenon called **chemotaxis** (*chemo-,* chemistry + *taxis,* arrangement). They are particularly sensitive to chemicals released by other body cells or by pathogens.

IMMUNOLOGICAL SURVEILLANCE

Our immune defenses generally ignore normal cells in the body's tissues, but abnormal cells are attacked and destroyed. The constant monitoring of normal tissues is called **immunological surveillance,** and it primarily involves the lymphocytes known as NK (natural killer) cells. The plasma membrane of an abnormal cell generally contains antigens that are not found on the membranes of normal cells. NK cells recognize an abnormal cell by detecting the presence of those antigens. NK cells are much less selective about their targets than are other lymphocytes. When they encounter such antigens on a bacterium, a cancer cell, or a cell infected with viruses, NK cells secrete proteins called *perforins,* which kill the abnormal cell by creating large pores in its plasma membrane.

NK cells respond much more rapidly than T cells or B cells upon contact with an abnormal cell. Killing the abnormal cells can slow the spread of a bacterial or viral infection, and it may eliminate cancer cells before they spread to other tissues. Unfortunately, some cancer cells avoid detection, a process called *immunological escape.* Once immunological escape has occurred, cancer cells can multiply and spread without interference by NK cells.

INTERFERONS

Interferons (in-ter-FĒR-onz) are small proteins released by activated lymphocytes, macrophages, and tissue cells infected with viruses. Normal cells exposed to interferon molecules respond by producing *antiviral proteins* that interfere with viral replication inside the cell. In addition to slowing the spread of viral infections, interferons stimulate the activities of macrophages and NK cells. Interferons are examples of **cytokines** (SĪ-tō-kīnz), chemical messengers that are released by tissue cells and coordinate local activities. Most cytokines act only within one tissue, but those released by cellular defenders also act as hormones; they affect the activities of cells and tissues throughout the body. Their role in the regulation of specific defenses will be discussed later in the chapter.

THE COMPLEMENT SYSTEM

Plasma contains 11 special *complement proteins* that constitute the **complement system.** The term *complement* refers to the fact that this system complements the actions of antibodies. Complement proteins interact with one another in chain reactions similar to those of the clotting system. The reaction begins when a particular complement protein binds either to an antibody molecule attached to a bacterial cell wall or directly to bacterial cell walls. The bound complement protein then interacts with a series of other complement proteins. Complement activation is known to (1) attract phagocytes, (2) stimulate phagocytosis, (3) destroy plasma membranes, and (4) promote inflammation.

INFLAMMATION

Inflammation, or the *inflammatory response,* is a localized tissue response to injury. ∞ p. 115 Inflammation produces local swelling, redness, heat, and pain. Inflammation can be produced by any stimulus that kills cells or damages loose connective tissue. *Mast cells* within the affected tissue play a pivotal role in this process. ∞ p. 104

The purposes of inflammation include the following:

- To perform a temporary repair at an injury site and prevent the access of additional pathogens.

- To slow the spread of pathogens from an injury site.

- To mobilize a wide range of defenses that can overcome pathogens and aid permanent tissue repair. The repair process is called *regeneration.*

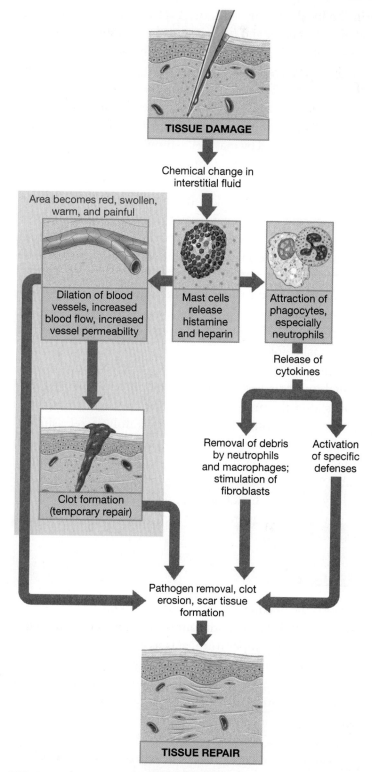

FIGURE 14-10 **Events in Inflammation.**

Figure 14-10 summarizes the events that occur during inflammation of the skin. (Comparable events will occur in almost any tissue subjected to physical damage or to infection.) When stimulated by mechanical stress or chemical changes in the local environment, mast cells release chemicals, including *histamine* and *heparin,* into the interstitial fluid. These chemicals initiate the process of inflammation. Released histamine increases capillary permeability and accelerates blood flow through the area. Increased vessel permeability allows clotting factors and complement proteins to leave the bloodstream. The combination of abnormal tissue conditions and chemicals released by mast cells stimulates local sensory neurons, producing sensations of pain. The increased blood flow reddens the area and elevates local temperature, increasing the rate of enzymatic reactions and accelerating the activity of phagocytes. Clotting does not occur at the actual site of injury, due to the presence of heparin. However, a clot soon forms around the damaged area. Additionally, the release of histamine stimulates other series of events that activate specific defenses and further pave the way for the repair of the injured tissue.

After an injury, tissue conditions generally become more abnormal before they begin to improve. The tissue destruction that occurs after cells have been injured or destroyed is called **necrosis** (ne-KRŌ-sis). The process begins several hours after the original injury and is caused by lysosomal enzymes. Lysosomes break down by autolysis, releasing digestive enzymes that first destroy the injured cells and then attack surrounding tissues. ∞ p. 76 As local inflammation continues, debris and dead and dying cells accumulate at the injury site. This thick fluid mixture is known as **pus.** An accumulation of pus in an enclosed tissue space is called an *abscess.*

FEVER

Fever is the maintenance of a body temperature greater than 37.2°C (99°F). The hypothalamus, which contains nuclei that regulate body temperature, acts as the body's thermostat. ∞ p. 276 Circulating proteins called **pyrogens** (PĪ-rō-jenz; *pyr,* fire + *-gen,* to produce) can reset this thermostat and raise body temperature. Pathogens, bacterial toxins, and antigen–antibody complexes may act as pyrogens or stimulate the release of pyrogens by macrophages.

Within limits, a fever may be beneficial. A rise in body temperature increases the rate of metabolism; cells move faster (enhancing phagocytosis), and enzymatic reactions proceed more quickly. However, high fevers (over 40°C, or 104°F) can damage many physiological systems. Such high fevers can cause CNS problems, including nausea, disorientation, hallucinations, or convulsions.

CHECKPOINT

7. List the body's nonspecific defenses.

8. What types of cells would be affected by a decrease in the number of monocyte-forming cells in the bone marrow?

9. A rise in the level of interferon in the body indicates what kind of infection?

10. What effects do pyrogens have in the body?

See the blue Answers tab at the back of the book.

14-4 Immunity (specific defenses) responds to specific threats and is either cell mediated or antibody mediated

Specific resistance, or immunity, is provided by the coordinated activities of T cells and B cells, which respond to the presence of *specific* antigens. *T cells* provide a defense against abnormal cells and pathogens inside living cells; this process is called **cell-mediated immunity,** or *cellular immunity. B cells* provide a defense against antigens and pathogens in body fluids. This process is called **antibody-mediated immunity,** or *humoral immunity.* Regardless of whether T cells or B cells are involved, immunity can be categorized into several types according to when and how it arises in the body (Figure 14-11).

TYPES OF IMMUNITY

Immunity is either innate or acquired. **Innate immunity** is genetically determined; it is present at birth and is independent of previous exposure to the antigen involved. For example, people do not get the same diseases as goldfish. By contrast, **acquired immunity** is not present at birth but instead arises by active or passive means.

Active immunity appears as a consequence of the immune response—that is, after exposure to an antigen. Even though the immune system is capable of defending against an enormous number of antigens, the appropriate defenses are mobilized only after an individual's lymphocytes encounter a particular antigen. Active immunity may develop as a result of natural exposure to an antigen in the environment (naturally acquired active immunity) or from deliberate exposure to an antigen (induced active immunity).

Naturally acquired active immunity normally begins to develop after birth, and it is continually enhanced as an individ-

FIGURE 14-11 **Types of Immunity.**

ual encounters "new" pathogens or other antigens. This process might be likened to vocabulary development—a child begins with a few basic common words and learns new ones as needed.

In *induced active immunity,* antibody production is stimulated under controlled conditions so that the individual will be able to overcome natural exposure to the same type of pathogen some time in the future. This is the basic principle behind *immunization,* or *vaccination,* to prevent disease. A **vaccine** is a preparation designed to induce an immune response. It contains either a dead or an inactive pathogen or antigens derived from that pathogen. Vaccines are given orally or by intramuscular or subcutaneous injection.

Passive immunity is produced by the transfer of antibodies to an individual from some other source. *Naturally acquired passive immunity* results when antibodies produced by a mother protect her baby against infections during gestation (by crossing the placenta) or in early infancy (through breast milk). In *induced passive immunity,* antibodies are administered to fight infection or prevent disease after exposure to the pathogen. For example, antibodies that attack the rabies virus are injected into a person recently bitten by a rabid animal.

PROPERTIES OF IMMUNITY

Immunity has four general properties:

1. *Specificity.* A specific defense mechanism is activated by a specific antigen, and the immune response targets only

that particular antigen. This process is known as **antigen recognition. Specificity** occurs because the plasma membrane of each T cell and B cell has receptors that will bind only one specific antigen, ignoring all other antigens. Each lymphocyte will inactivate or destroy that specific antigen only, without affecting other antigens or normal tissues.

2. *Versatility.* In the course of a normal lifetime, an individual encounters an enormous number of antigens—perhaps tens of thousands. Your immune system cannot anticipate which antigens it will encounter, so it must be ready to confront *any* antigen at *any* time. The immune system achieves **versatility** by producing millions of different lymphocyte populations, each with different antigen receptors, and through variability in the structure of synthesized antibodies. In this way, the immune system can produce appropriate and specific responses to each antigen when exposure occurs.

3. *Memory.* The immune system "remembers" antigens that it encounters. As a result of immunologic **memory,** the immune response to a second exposure to an antigen

is stronger and lasts longer than the response to the first exposure. During the initial response to an antigen, lymphocytes sensitive to its presence undergo repeated cell divisions. Two kinds of cells are produced: some that attack the antigen, and others that remain inactive unless they are exposed to the same antigen at a later date. These latter cells—**memory cells**—enable the immune system to "remember" previously encountered antigens and launch a faster, stronger response if one of them ever appears again.

4. *Tolerance.* Although the immune response targets foreign cells and compounds, it generally ignores normal tissues and their antigens. **Tolerance** is said to exist when the immune system does not respond to such antigens. Any B cells or T cells undergoing differentiation (in the bone marrow and thymus, respectively) that react to normal body antigens are destroyed. As a result, normal B cells and T cells will ignore normal (or *self*) antigens and will attack foreign (or *nonself*) antigens.

AN OVERVIEW OF THE IMMUNE RESPONSE

The purpose of the **immune response** is to inactivate or destroy pathogens, abnormal cells, and foreign molecules (such as toxins). It is based on the activation of lymphocytes by specific antigens through the process of *antigen recognition.* Figure 14-12 presents an overview of the immune response. When an anti-

gen triggers an immune response, it usually activates T cells first and then B cells. T cells are typically activated by phagocytes that have engulfed the antigen. (Sometimes T cells are activated by abnormal body cells.) Once activated, the T cells both attack the antigen and stimulate the activation of B cells. The activated B cells mature into cells that produce antibodies. The circulating antibodies bind to and attack the antigen.

14-5 T cells play a role in the initiation and control of the immune response

Before an immune response can begin, T cells must be activated by exposure to an antigen. However, this activation seldom results from direct lymphocyte–antigen interaction, and the mere presence of foreign compounds or pathogens in a tissue rarely stimulates an immediate response.

ANTIGEN PRESENTATION

T cells recognize antigens when those antigens are bound to membrane receptors of other cells. The structure of these antigen-binding membrane receptors is genetically determined and differs among individuals. The membrane receptors are called *major histocompatibility complex* (*MHC*) *proteins* and are grouped into two classes. An antigen bound to a Class I MHC protein acts like a red flag that in effect tells the immune system "Hey, I'm an abnormal cell—kill me!" An antigen bound to a Class II MHC protein tells the immune system "Hey, this antigen is dangerous—get rid of it!"

Class I MHC proteins are in the plasma membranes of all nucleated cells. These MHC proteins bind and display small pep-

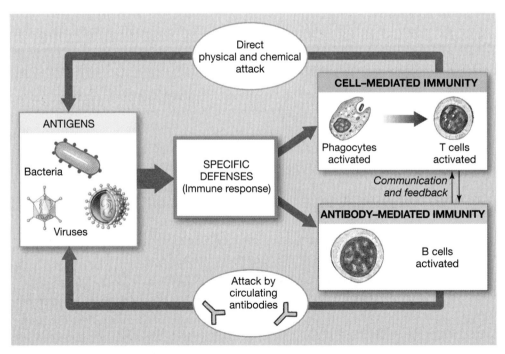

FIGURE 14-12 **An Overview of the Immune Response.**

tide molecules (chains of amino acids) that are continuously produced in the cell and exported to the plasma membrane. If the cell is healthy and the peptides are normal, T cells ignore them. If the cell contains abnormal (nonself), viral, or bacterial peptides, their appearance in the plasma membrane will activate T cells, leading to destruction of the abnormal cell. The recognition of nonself peptides in transplanted tissue is the primary reason why donated organs are commonly rejected by the recipient. In the case of viruses or bacteria, T cells can be activated by contact with viral or bacterial antigens bound to Class I MHC proteins on the surface of infected cells. The activation of T cells by these antigens results in the destruction of the infected cells.

Class II MHC proteins are found in the membranes of lymphocytes and *antigen-presenting cells* (*APCs*). APCs are specialized for activating T cells to attack foreign cells (including bacteria) and foreign proteins. Examples of antigen-presenting cells include the monocyte–macrophage group (such as the free and fixed macrophages in connective tissues) and macrophages in the liver (Kupffer cells) and central nervous system (microglia). After APCs engulf and break down pathogens or foreign antigens, fragments of the foreign antigens are displayed on their cell surfaces, bound to Class II MHC proteins. T cells that contact this APC's membrane become activated, initiating an immune response.

T CELL ACTIVATION

Inactive T cells have receptors that recognize either Class I or Class II MHC proteins. The receptors also have binding sites that detect specific bound antigens. T cell activation occurs when the MHC protein contains the specific antigen the T cell is programmed to detect. On activation, T cells divide and differentiate into cells with specific functions in the immune response. The major cell types are *cytotoxic T cells, helper T cells, memory T cells,* and *suppressor T cells.*

Cytotoxic T Cells

Cytotoxic T cells, or *killer T cells,* are responsible for cell-mediated immunity. They are activated by exposure to antigens bound to Class I MHC proteins (**Figure 14-13**). The activated cells undergo cell divisions that produce more active cytotoxic cells and memory cells. The activated cytotoxic T cells track down and attack the bacteria, fungi, protozoa, or foreign transplanted tissues that contain the target antigen.

A cytotoxic T cell may destroy its target in several ways (**Figure 14-13**):

- By secreting a *lymphotoxin* (lim-fō-TOK-sin), which kills the target cell by disrupting its metabolism.

FIGURE 14-13 The Activation of Cytotoxic T Cells. For activation to occur, an inactive cytotoxic T cell must encounter an appropriate antigen bound to MHC proteins. Once activated, the T cell undergoes divisions that produce memory T cells and active cytotoxic T cells. When one of these active cytotoxic T cells encounters a cell membrane displaying the target antigen, the T cell will use one of several methods to destroy the cell.

- By secreting *cytokines* that activate target cell genes that tell the cell to die. This process of genetically programmed cell death is called *apoptosis.* ∞ p. 84

- By releasing *perforin*, which ruptures the target cell's membrane. ∞ p. 480

Helper T Cells

Activated **helper T cells** perform two functions, achieved by releasing various cytokines: They coordinate specific and nonspecific defenses, and they stimulate both cell-mediated immunity and antibody-mediated immunity. Helper T cells are activated by exposure to antigens bound to Class II MHC proteins on antigen-presenting cells. Upon activation, they divide to produce memory cells and more active helper T cells. We will learn more about the functions of activated helper T cells in the upcoming section on B cell activation.

Memory T Cells

As previously noted, some of the cells produced following the activation of cytotoxic T cells and helper T cells develop into **memory T cells.** Memory T cells remain "in reserve." If the same antigen appears a second time, these cells will immediately differentiate into cytotoxic T cells and helper T cells, enhancing the speed and effectiveness of the immune response.

Suppressor T Cells

Activated **suppressor T cells** dampen the responses of other T cells and of B cells by secreting cytokines called *suppression factors.* Suppression does not occur immediately, because suppressor T cells are activated more slowly than other types of T cells. As a result, suppressor T cells act *after* the initial immune response. In effect, these cells "put on the brakes," limiting the degree of the immune response to a single stimulus.

The Big Picture

Cell-mediated immunity involves close physical contact between activated cytotoxic T cells and foreign, abnormal, or infected cells. T cell activation usually involves antigen presentation by a phagocytic cell. Cytotoxic T cells may destroy target cells by the local release of cytokines, lymphotoxins, or perforin.

CHECKPOINT

14. Identify the four types of T cells.

15. How can the presence of an abnormal peptide within a cell initiate an immune response?

16. A decrease in the number of cytotoxic T cells would affect what type of immunity?

17. How would a lack of helper T cells affect the antibody-mediated immune response?

See the blue Answers tab at the back of the book.

14-6 B cells respond to antigens by producing specific antibodies

B cells launch a chemical attack on antigens by participating in a series of events that results in the production of appropriate antibodies. Three events occur in the B cell response to antigen exposure: sensitization, activation, and division and differentiation into antibody-producing cells (Figure 14-14).

B CELL SENSITIZATION AND ACTIVATION

The body has millions of populations of B cells. Each B cell carries its own particular antibody molecules in its cell membrane. If corresponding antigens appear in the interstitial fluid, they will be bound by those antibodies. The antigens enter the B cell by endocytosis and become displayed on Class II MHC proteins on its surface. The B cell is now *sensitized.* Once a helper T cell has become activated to the same antigen and has attached to the MHC protein–antigen complex of the sensitized B cell, the helper T cell secretes cytokines. The cytokines have several effects, including promoting B cell activation, stimulating B cell division, and accelerating B cell development into plasma cells.

As Figure 14-14 shows, the activated B cell divides repeatedly, producing daughter cells that differentiate into **plasma cells** and **memory B cells.** Plasma cells begin synthesizing and secreting large quantities of antibodies that have the same target as the antibodies on the surface of the sensitized B cell. Memory B cells, like memory T cells, remain in reserve to respond to subsequent exposure to the same antigen. At that time, they respond by differentiating into antibody-secreting plasma cells.

ANTIBODY STRUCTURE

An antibody molecule consists of two parallel pairs of polypeptide chains: one pair of long *heavy chains* and one pair of shorter *light chains* (Figure 14-15a). Each chain contains *constant* and *variable segments.* The constant segments of the heavy chains form the base of the antibody molecule. B cells produce only five types of constant segments. (These form the basis of the antibody classification scheme described in the following section.)

The specificity of an antibody molecule depends on the structure of the variable segments of the light and heavy chains. The free tips of the two variable segments form the **antigen**

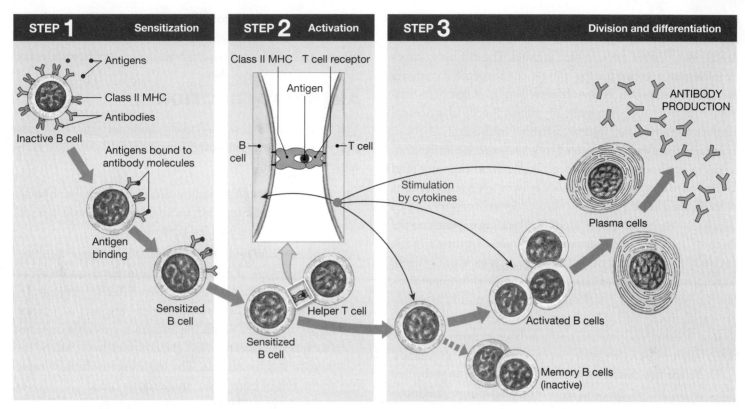

FIGURE 14-14 The B Cell Response to Antigen Exposure. A B cell is sensitized by exposure to antigens (step 1). Once antigens are bound to antibodies in the B cell membrane, the B cell displays those antigens in its plasma membrane. Activated helper T cells encountering the antigens on the sensitized B cell then release cytokines that trigger the activation of the B cell (step 2). The activated B cell then divides, producing memory B cells and plasma cells that secrete antibodies (step 3).

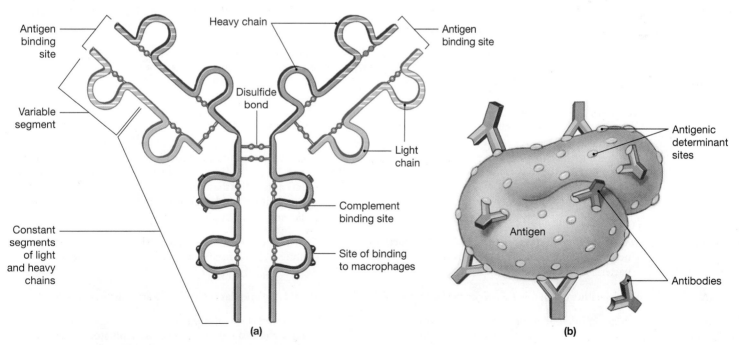

FIGURE 14-15 Antibody Structure. (a) This diagram depicts the structural features of an antibody molecule. **(b)** Antigen–antibody binding occurs between the antigen binding sites on the antibody and antigenic determinant sites on the antigen.

binding sites of the antibody molecule. Small differences in the amino acid sequence of the variable segments affect the precise shape of the antigen binding sites. The different shapes of these sites account for the differences in specificity among the antibodies produced by different B cells. It has been estimated that the approximately 10 trillion B cells of a normal adult can produce 100 million different antibodies.

When an antibody molecule binds to its specific antigen, an **antigen–antibody complex** is formed. Antibodies do not bind to the entire antigen as a whole. They bind to certain portions of its exposed surface, regions called *antigenic determinant sites* (Figure 14-15b). The specificity of that binding depends on the three-dimensional "fit" between the variable segments of the antibody molecule and the corresponding sites of the antigen. A *complete antigen* has at least two antigenic determinant sites, one for each arm of the antibody molecule. Exposure to a complete antigen can lead to B cell sensitization and an immune response. Most environmental antigens have multiple antigenic determinant sites; entire microorganisms may have thousands.

There are five classes of antibodies, or **immunoglobulins (Igs)**: *IgG, IgM, IgA, IgE,* and *IgD* (Table 14-1). Immunoglobulin G, or IgG, is the largest and most diverse class of antibodies. IgG antibodies are responsible for resistance against many viruses, bacteria, and bacterial toxins. They can also cross the placenta and provide passive immunity to the fetus. Circulating *IgM* antibodies attack bacteria and are responsible for the cross-reactions between incompatible blood types, described in Chapter 11. ∞ p. 392 IgA occurs in exocrine secretions, such as mucus, tears, and saliva, and attacks pathogens before they enter

the body. IgE that has bound to antigens stimulates basophils and mast cells to release chemicals that stimulate inflammation. IgD is attached to B cells and can be involved in their activation.

ANTIBODY FUNCTION

The function of antibodies is to eliminate antigens. The formation of an antigen–antibody complex may cause their elimination in several ways:

1. *Neutralization.* Antibodies can bind to viruses or bacterial toxins, making them incapable of attaching to a cell. This mechanism is called **neutralization.**

2. *Agglutination and precipitation.* When a large number of antigens are close together, one antibody molecule can bind to antigenic sites on two different antigens. In this way, antibodies can tie antigens together and create large complexes. When the antigen is a soluble molecule (such as a bacterial toxin), the complex may then be too large to stay in solution. The resulting insoluble complex settles out of body fluids in a process called **precipitation.** The formation of large complexes is called **agglutination.** The clumping of red blood cells that occurs when incompatible blood types are mixed is an agglutination reaction. ∞ p. 392

3. *Activation of complement.* Upon binding to an antigen, portions of the antibody molecule change shape, exposing areas of the constant segments that bind complement proteins (Figure 14-15a). The bound complement

TABLE 14-1 Classes of Antibodies

CLASS	FUNCTION	REMARKS
IgG	Responsible for defense against many viruses, bacteria, and bacterial toxins	Largest class (80%) of antibodies, with several subtypes; also cross the placenta and provide passive immunity to fetus; anti-Rh antibodies produced by Rh-negative mothers are IgG antibodies that can cross the placenta and attack fetal Rh-positive red blood cells, producing *hemolytic disease of the newborn.* ∞ p. 394
IgM	Anti-A and anti-B forms responsible for cross-reactions between incompatible blood types; other forms attack bacteria insensitive to IgG	First antibody type secreted following initial exposure to antigen; levels decline as IgG production accelerates
IgA	Attacks pathogens before they enter the body tissues	Found in glandular secretions (tears, mucus, and saliva)
IgE	Accelerates inflammation on exposure to antigen	Bound to surfaces of mast cells and basophils and stimulates release of histamine and other inflammatory chemicals; also important in allergic response
IgD	Binds antigens in the extracellular fluid to B cells	Binding can play a role in activation of B cells

molecules then activate the complement system, destroying the antigen.

4. *Attraction of phagocytes.* Antigens covered with antibodies attract eosinophils, neutrophils, and macrophages—cells that phagocytize pathogens and destroy cells with foreign or abnormal cell membranes.

5. *Enhancement of phagocytosis.* A coating of antibodies and complement proteins makes some pathogens easier to phagocytize. The antibodies involved are called *opsonins,* and the effect is known as *opsonization.*

6. *Stimulation of inflammation.* Antibodies may promote inflammation by stimulating basophils and mast cells. This action can help mobilize nonspecific defenses and slow the spread of the infection to other tissues.

The Big Picture

Antibody-mediated immunity involves the production of specific antibodies by plasma cells derived from activated B cells. B cell activation usually involves (1) antigen recognition, through binding to surface antibodies, and (2) stimulation by a helper T cell activated by the same antigen. The antibodies produced by active plasma cells bind to the target antigen and either inhibit its activity, destroy it, remove it from solution, or promote its phagocytosis by other defense cells.

PRIMARY AND SECONDARY RESPONSES TO ANTIGEN EXPOSURE

The body's initial response to antigen exposure is called the **primary response.** When an antigen appears a second time, it

Clinical Note

AIDS

Acquired immune deficiency syndrome (AIDS), or late-stage HIV disease, is caused by the **human immunodeficiency virus (HIV).**
HIV is a *retrovirus,* a virus that carries its genetic information in RNA rather than DNA. The virus enters human leukocytes by receptor-mediated endocytosis. ∞ p. 70 In the human body, the virus binds to CD4, a membrane protein characteristic of helper T cells. Several types of antigen-presenting cells, including those of the monocyte–macrophage line, are also infected by HIV, but it is the infection of helper T cells that leads to clinical problems.

Cells infected with HIV ultimately die from the infection. The gradual destruction of helper T cells impairs the immune response because these cells play a central role in coordinating cell-mediated and antibody-mediated responses to antigens. To make matters worse, suppressor T cells are relatively unaffected by the virus, and over time the excess of suppressing factors "turns off" the normal immune response. Circulating antibody levels decline, cell-mediated immunity is reduced, and the body is left without defenses against a wide variety of microbial invaders. With immune function so reduced, ordinarily harmless microorganisms can initiate lethal *opportunistic infections.* Because immunological surveillance is also depressed, the risk of cancer increases.

HIV infection occurs through intimate contact with the body fluids of infected individuals. Although all body fluids may contain the virus, the major routes of transmission involve contact with blood, semen, or vaginal secretions. Most AIDS patients become infected through sexual contact with an HIV-infected person (who may not necessarily be showing the clinical signs of AIDS). The next largest group of patients consists of intravenous drug users who shared contaminated needles. Relatively few individuals have become infected with HIV after receiving a transfusion of contaminated blood or blood products.

Finally, an increasing number of infants are born with the disease, having acquired it from their infected mothers.

AIDS is a public health problem of massive proportions. Over half a million people have already died of AIDS in the United States alone. Estimates of the total number of individuals infected with HIV in the United States range up to 1 million. The numbers worldwide are even more frightening. The World Health Organization (WHO) estimates that, as of 2007, 33 million individuals were infected. *Every 6 seconds, another person becomes infected with HIV.* The total death toll for 2007 was estimated to be more than 2 million people, including 330,000 children under age 15.

The best defense against AIDS is to abstain from sexual contact or the sharing of needles. All forms of sexual intercourse carry the risk of viral transmission. The use of natural latex (rubber) condoms and synthetic (polyurethane) condoms provide protection from HIV (and other viral STDs). Although natural lambskin condoms are effective in preventing pregnancy, they do not block the passage of viruses.

Clinical signs of AIDS may not appear for 5–10 years or more following infection. When they do appear, they are often mild, consisting of lymphadenopathy and chronic but nonfatal infections. So far as is known, however, AIDS is almost always fatal, and most people infected with the virus will eventually die of the disease. (A handful of infected individuals have been able to tolerate the virus without apparent illness for many years.)

Despite intensive efforts, a vaccine has yet to be developed that prevents HIV infection in an uninfected person exposed to the virus. The survival rate for AIDS patients has been steadily increasing because new drugs and drug combinations that slow the progression of the disease are available, and improved antibiotic therapies help combat secondary infections. This combination is extending the life span of patients while the search for more effective treatment continues.

triggers a more extensive **secondary response.** The secondary response reflects the presence of large numbers of memory cells that are already "primed" for the arrival of the antigen.

Because the antigen must activate the appropriate B cells, and the B cells must then respond by differentiating into plasma cells, the primary response takes time to develop (Figure 14-16). As plasma cells begin secreting antibodies, the concentration of circulating antibodies undergoes a gradual, sustained rise, and the antibody levels in the blood do not peak until one to two weeks after the initial exposure. IgM molecules are the first to appear in the bloodstream, followed by a slow rise in IgG. Thereafter, antibody concentrations decline (assuming that the individual is no longer being exposed to the antigen).

Memory B cells do not differentiate into plasma cells unless they are exposed to the same antigen a second time. If and when that exposure occurs, memory B cells respond immediately, dividing and differentiating into plasma cells that secrete antibodies in massive quantities. This antibody secretion is the secondary response to antigen exposure.

The secondary response produces an immediate rise in IgG concentrations to levels many times higher than those of the primary response. This response is much faster and stronger than the primary response because the numerous memory cells are activated by relatively low levels of antigen, and they give rise to plasma cells that secrete massive quantities of antibodies. The secondary response appears even if the second exposure occurs years after the first because memory cells may survive for 20 years or more.

The relatively slow primary response is much less effective at preventing disease than the more rapid and intense secondary response. Immunization is effective because it stimulates

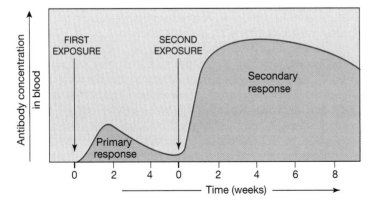

FIGURE 14-16 The Primary and Secondary Immune Responses. The primary response takes about two weeks to develop peak antibody levels, and antibody concentrations do not remain elevated. In the secondary response, antibody concentrations increase very rapidly to levels much higher than those of the primary response and remain elevated for an extended period.

the production of memory B cells under controlled conditions; it is the secondary response that prevents disease.

The Big Picture — Immunization produces a primary response to a specific antigen under controlled conditions. If the same antigen is encountered at a later date, it triggers a powerful secondary response that is usually sufficient to prevent infection and disease.

HORMONES OF THE IMMUNE SYSTEM

The body's specific and nonspecific defenses are coordinated by physical interaction and by the release of chemical messengers. An example of physical interaction is the displaying of antigens by antigen-presenting macrophages. An example of chemical messenger release is the secretion of cytokines by activated helper T cells and other cells involved in the immune response. Cytokines of the immune response are often classified according to their sources: *lymphokines,* secreted by lymphocytes, and *monokines,* released by active macrophages and other antigen-presenting cells. (These terms are misleading, however, because lymphocytes and macrophages may secrete the same chemical messenger, as may cells involved with nonspecific defenses and tissue repair.) Table 14-2 contains examples of some of the cytokines identified to date.

Interleukins (IL) may be the most diverse and important chemical messengers in the immune system. Interleukins have widespread effects that include increasing T cell sensitivity to antigens presented on macrophage membranes, stimulating B cell activity and antibody production, and enhancing nonspecific defenses, such as inflammation or fever. Some interleukins help suppress immune function and shorten the duration of an immune response.

Interferons make the cell synthesizing them and its neighbors resistant to viral infection, thereby slowing the spread of the virus. In addition to their antiviral activity, interferons attract and stimulate NK cells and macrophages. Interferons are used to treat some cancers.

Tumor necrosis factors (TNFs) slow tumor growth and kill sensitive tumor cells. In addition to these effects, TNFs stimulate the production of neutrophils, eosinophils, and basophils; promote eosinophil activity; cause fever; and increase T cell sensitivity to interleukins.

Phagocytic regulators include several cytokines that coordinate the specific and nonspecific defenses by adjusting the activities of phagocytic cells. These cytokines include factors that attract free macrophages and microphages to the area and prevent their premature departure.

TABLE 14-2 **Examples of Cytokines of the Immune Response**

COMPOUND	FUNCTIONS
INTERLEUKINS	
IL-1	Stimulates T cells to produce IL-2, promotes inflammation, causes fever; stimulates the secreting cell in a positive feedback loop that recruits more immune cells
IL-2, -12	Stimulate T cells and NK cells; stimulate the secreting cell in a positive feedback loop that recruits more immune cells
IL-3	Stimulates production of mast cells and other blood cells
IL-4, -5, -6, -7, -10, -11	Promote differentiation and growth of B cells, and stimulate plasma cell formation and antibody production
IL-8	Stimulates blood vessel formation
IL-13	Suppresses production of several cytokines (IL-1, IL-8, TNF)
INTERFERONS	Activate other cells to prevent viral entry and replication, stimulate NK cells and macrophages
TUMOR NECROSIS FACTORS (TNFs)	Kill tumor cells, slow tumor growth; stimulate activities of T cells and eosinophils, inhibit parasites and viruses
PHAGOCYTIC REGULATORS	
Monocyte-chemotactic factor (MCF)	Attracts monocytes, transforms them into macrophages
Migration-inhibitory factor (MIF)	Prevents macrophage migration from the area
COLONY-STIMULATING FACTORS (CSFs)	Stimulate RBC and WBC production
M-CSF	Stimulates production of monocytes
GM-CSF	Stimulates production of both granulocytes (neutrophils, eosinophils, and basophils) and monocytes
Multi-CSF	Stimulates production of granulocytes, monocytes, and RBCs

Colony-stimulating factors (CSFs) are produced by a wide variety of cells, including active T cells, cells of the monocyte–macrophage group, endothelial cells, and fibroblasts. CSFs stimulate the production of blood cells in the bone marrow and of lymphocytes in lymphoid tissues and organs.

The Big Picture

Viruses replicate inside of cells, whereas bacteria may live independently. Because antibodies and administered antibiotics work outside of cells, they are effective against bacteria, but not against viruses. (That's why antibiotics can't fight the common cold or flu.) T cells, NK cells, and interferons are the primary defenses against viral infection.

CHECKPOINT

18. Define sensitization.

19. Describe the structure of an antibody.

20. A sample of lymph contains an elevated number of plasma cells. Would you expect the number of antibodies in the blood to be increasing or decreasing? Why?

21. Would the primary response or the secondary response be more affected by a lack of memory B cells for a particular antigen?

See the blue Answers tab at the back of the book.

14-7 Abnormal immune responses result in immune disorders

The ability to produce a normal immune response after exposure to an antigen is called *immunological competence.* A

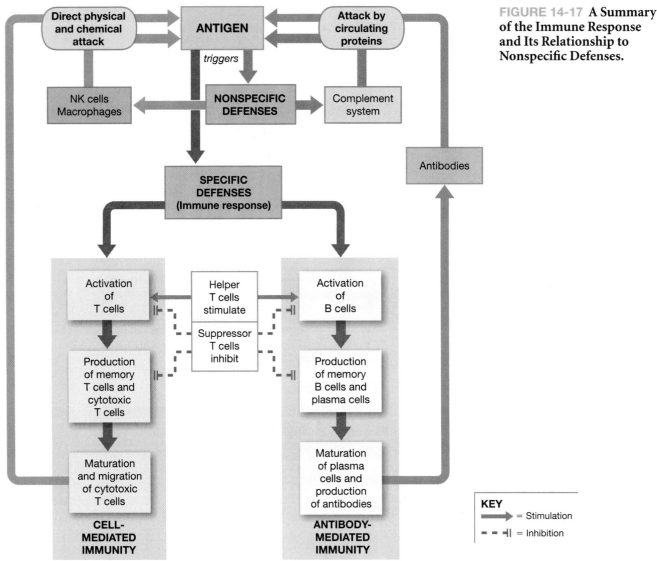

FIGURE 14-17 **A Summary of the Immune Response and Its Relationship to Nonspecific Defenses.**

summary of the events in the normal immune response, and its relationship to nonspecific defenses, is presented in Figure 14-17. Next we consider some of the disorders that result when the immune response does not respond as it should.

Because the immune response is so complex, there are many opportunities for things to go wrong. A variety of clinical conditions result from disorders of immune function. General classes of such disorders include *autoimmune disorders, immunodeficiency diseases,* and *allergies.* Immunodeficiency diseases and autoimmune disorders are relatively rare conditions—clear evidence of the effectiveness of the immune system's control mechanisms. Allergies constitute a far more common (and usually a far less dangerous) class of immune disorders.

AUTOIMMUNE DISORDERS

Autoimmune disorders develop when the immune response mistakenly targets normal body cells and tissues. The immune system usually recognizes and ignores self antigens—antigens normally found in the body. When the recognition system malfunctions, however, activated B cells begin to manufacture antibodies against normal body cells and tissues. These "misguided" antibodies are called *autoantibodies.* The resulting condition depends on the identity of the antigen attacked. For example, *rheumatoid arthritis* occurs when autoantibodies attack connective tissues around the joints, and *insulin-dependent diabetes mellitus* (*IDDM*) is caused by autoantibodies that attack cells in the pancreatic islets.

Many autoimmune disorders appear to be cases of mistaken identity. In one example, proteins associated with several viruses (including the measles and influenza viruses) contain amino acid sequences resembling those of the nervous system protein myelin. When antibodies that target these viruses mistakenly attack myelin sheaths, neurological complications sometimes associated with a vaccination or viral infection can result. This is also the mechanism that is likely responsible for *multiple sclerosis.*

For unknown reasons, the risk of autoimmune problems increases for individuals with unusual types of MHC proteins. At least 50 clinical conditions have been linked to specific variations in MHC structure. Examples of such conditions include psoriasis, rheumatoid arthritis, myasthenia gravis, narcolepsy, Graves disease, Addison disease, pernicious anemia, systemic lupus erythematosus, and chronic hepatitis.

IMMUNODEFICIENCY DISEASES

In an **immunodeficiency disease,** either the immune system fails to develop normally or the immune response is blocked in some way. Individuals born with **severe combined immunodeficiency disease (SCID)** fail to develop either cell- or antibody-mediated immunity. Such infants cannot produce an immune response, so even a mild infection can prove fatal. Total isolation offers protection at great cost, with severe restrictions on lifestyle. Bone marrow transplants and gene-splicing techniques have been used to treat some types of SCID.

AIDS, an immunodeficiency disease (p. 489), is the result of a viral infection that targets primarily helper T cells. As the number of T cells falls, the normal immune response breaks down.

ALLERGIES

Allergies are inappropriate or excessive immune responses to antigens. The sudden increase in leukocyte activity or antibody levels can have several unpleasant side effects. Neutrophils or cytotoxic T cells may destroy normal cells while attacking the antigen, or antigen–antibody complexes may trigger a massive inflammatory response. Antigens that trigger allergic reactions are often called **allergens.**

Four categories of allergies are recognized: *immediate hypersensitivity* (*Type I*), *cytotoxic reactions* (*Type II*), *immune complex disorders* (*Type III*), and *delayed hypersensitivity* (*Type IV*). Immediate hypersensitivity (discussed shortly) is probably the most common type; it includes "hay fever" and environmental allergies that may affect 15 percent of the U.S. population. The cross-reactions that occur following the transfusion of an incompatible blood type are an example of Type II (cytotoxic) hypersensitivity. ∞ p. 392 Type III allergies result if phagocytes are not able to rapidly remove circulating antigen–antibody complexes. The presence of these complexes leads to inflammation and tissue damage, especially within blood vessels and the kidneys. Type IV (delayed) hypersensitivity is an inflammatory response that occurs 2–3 days after exposure to an antigen, as in the itchy rash that may follow contact with poison ivy or poison oak.

Immediate hypersensitivity is a rapid and especially severe response to the presence of an antigen. Sensitization to an allergen during the initial exposure leads to the production of large quantities of IgE antibodies. Due to the lag time needed to activate B cells, produce plasma cells, and make antibodies, the first exposure to an allergen does not produce an allergic reaction. However, the IgE antibodies produced at this time become attached to the cell membranes of basophils and mast cells throughout the body. When exposed to the same allergen later, these cells are stimulated to release histamine, heparin, several cytokines, prostaglandins, and other chemicals into the surrounding tissues. The result is sudden inflammation of the affected tissues.

The severity of an immediate hypersensitivity allergic reaction depends on the person's sensitivity and the location involved. If allergen exposure occurs at the body surface, the response is usually restricted to that area. If the allergen enters the bloodstream, the response could be lethal.

In **anaphylaxis** (an-a-fi-LAK-sis; *ana-,* again + *phylaxis,* protection), another Type I allergy, a circulating allergen affects mast cells throughout the body. A wide range of signs and symptoms can develop within minutes. Changes in capillary permeability produces swelling and edema in the dermis, and raised welts, or *hives,* appear on the surface of the skin. Smooth muscles along the respiratory passageways contract; the narrowed passages make breathing extremely difficult. In severe cases, extensive peripheral vasodilation occurs, producing a fall in blood pressure that can lead to a circulatory collapse. This response is **anaphylactic shock.** Many of the signs and symptoms of immediate hypersensitivity can be prevented by

---

Clinical Note

Stress and the Immune Response

Interleukin-1 is one of the first cytokines produced as part of the immune response. In addition to promoting inflammation, it also stimulates production of adrenocorticotropic hormone (ACTH) by the anterior pituitary gland. This, in turn, leads to the secretion of glucocorticoids by the suprarenal cortex. ∞ p. 361 The anti-inflammatory effects of the glucocorticoids may help control the intensity of the immune response. However, the long-term secretion of glucocorticoids, as occurs in chronic stress, can depress the immune response and lower resistance to disease. ∞ p. 369 Glucocorticoids reduce inflammation, lower phagocyte numbers and activity, and inhibit interleukin production, weakening the response of lymphocytes. The mechanisms involved are still under investigation. It is well known, however, that immune system depression due to chronic stress represents a serious threat to health.

the prompt administration of **antihistamines** (an-tē-HIS-ta-mēnz)—drugs that block the action of histamine.

CHECKPOINT

22. Under what circumstances is an autoimmune disorder produced?

23. How does increased stress reduce the effectiveness of the immune response?

See the blue Answers tab at the back of the book.

14-8 The immune response diminishes with advancing age

With advancing age, the immune system becomes less effective at combating disease. T cells become less responsive to antigens, so fewer cytotoxic T cells respond to an infection. This effect may, at least in part, be associated with the gradual shrinkage of the thymus and reduced levels of circulating thymic hormones. Because the number of helper T cells is also reduced, B cells are less responsive, and antibody levels rise more slowly after antigen exposure. The net result is an increased susceptibility to viral and bacterial infections. For this reason, vaccinations for acute viral diseases, such as the flu (influenza), are strongly recommended for elderly people. The increased incidence of cancer in the elderly reflects the fact that immunological surveillance declines, so that tumor cells are not eliminated as effectively.

CHECKPOINT

24. Why are the elderly more susceptible to viral and bacterial infections?

25. What may account for the increased incidence of cancer among the elderly?

See the blue Answers tab at the back of the book.

14-9 For all body systems, the lymphoid system provides defenses against infection and returns tissue fluid to the circulation

The Lymphoid System in Perspective (p. 500) summarizes the interactions between the lymphoid system and other organ systems. Two sets of particularly close relationships—between cells involved in the immune response and the endocrine system, and

Clinical Note

Manipulating the Immune Response

With advances in our understanding of the immune system come a variety of innovative therapies. One such therapy involves *monoclonal* (mo-nō-KLŌ-nal) *antibodies,* identical antibodies produced in large quantities from genetically identical cells under laboratory conditions. The goal of one therapeutic use of monoclonal antibodies is to confer passive immunity to patients having a variety of diseases. Because monoclonal antibodies are free of impurities, the administration of these antibodies does not cause the unpleasant side effects that antibodies from other sources do. Monoclonal antibodies to which chemotherapy drugs are attached are also being used to deliver those drugs to target cancer cells.

In another treatment procedure, cytotoxic T cells were removed from patients with *malignant melanoma,* a particularly dangerous type of skin cancer. These lymphocytes could recognize tumor cells and had migrated to the tumor, but for some reason they seemed unable to kill the tumor cells. After the collected lymphocytes were grown in the laboratory, viruses were used to insert multiple copies of the genes responsible for the production of tumor necrosis factor. The patients were then given periodic infusions of these "supercharged" T cells. To enhance T cell activity further, the researchers also administered doses of interleukin-2. Initial results are promising. It is clear that the ability to manipulate the immune response will revolutionize the treatment of many serious diseases.

between those cells and the nervous system—are now the focus of intense research. In the first case, thymic hormones and cytokines stimulate TRH production by the hypothalamus, leading to the release of TSH by the pituitary gland. As a result, circulating thyroid hormone levels increase and stimulate cell and tissue metabolism when an immune response is under way. But the nervous system can also adjust the level of the immune response. For example, some antigen-presenting cells are innervated, and neurotransmitter release heightens the local immune response. It is also known that the immune response can decline suddenly after a brief period of emotional distress.

CHECKPOINT

26. Identify the role of the lymphoid system for all body systems.

27. How does the cardiovascular system aid the body's defense mechanisms?

See the blue Answers tab at the back of the book.

RELATED CLINICAL TERMS

allergy: An inappropriate or excessive immune response to antigens.

anaphylactic shock: A drop in blood pressure that may lead to circulatory collapse, resulting from a severe case of anaphylaxis.

anaphylaxis (an-a-fi-LAK-sis): An allergic reaction in which a circulating allergen (antigen) affects mast cells throughout the body, producing numerous signs and symptoms very quickly.

appendicitis: Inflammation of the lymphoid nodules in the appendix, often in response to an infection.

bone marrow transplantation: The infusion of bone marrow from a compatible donor after the destruction of the host's marrow by radiation or chemotherapy; a treatment option for acute, late-stage lymphoma.

graft-versus-host disease (GVH): A condition that results when T cells in donor tissues, such as bone marrow, attack the tissues of the recipient.

immunodeficiency disease: A disease in which either the immune system fails to develop normally or the immune response is blocked.

immunology: The study of the functions and disorders of the body's defense mechanisms.

immunosuppression: A reduction in the sensitivity of the immune system.

lymphadenopathy (lim-fad-e-NOP-a-thē): An excessive enlargement of lymph nodes.

lymphedema: A painless accumulation of lymph in a region in which lymphatic drainage has been blocked.

lymphomas: Cancers consisting of abnormal lymphocytes or lymphoid stem cells; examples include *Hodgkin disease* and *non-Hodgkin lymphoma*.

mononucleosis: A condition resulting from chronic infection by the *Epstein–Barr virus* (*EBV*); signs and symptoms include enlargement of the spleen, fever, sore throat, widespread swelling of lymph nodes, increased numbers of circulating lymphocytes, and the presence of circulating antibodies to the virus.

splenomegaly (splen-ō-MEG-a-lē): Enlargement of the spleen.

systemic lupus erythematosus (LOO-pus e-rith-ē-ma-TŌ-sis) (**SLE**): An autoimmune disorder resulting from a breakdown in the antigen recognition mechanism, leading to the production of antibodies that destroy healthy cells and tissues.

tonsillectomy: The removal of an inflamed tonsil.

tonsillitis: Inflammation of one or more tonsils, typically in response to an infection; signs and symptoms include a sore throat, high fever, and leukocytosis (an elevated white blood cell count).

vaccine (vak-SĒN): A preparation of antigens derived from a specific pathogen; administered during *immunization,* or *vaccination.*

viruses: Noncellular pathogens that replicate only within living tissue cells by directing the cells to synthesize virus-specific proteins and nucleic acids.

Chapter **14** Review

KEY TERMS

SUMMARY OUTLINE

iP Use *Interactive Physiology*® (**IP**)—available on the IP CD packaged with your new textbook—to help you understand difficult physiological concepts. Follow these navigation paths on IP for concepts in this chapter:

- Immune System/Orientation
- Immune System/Anatomy Review
- Immune System/Innate Host Defenses
- Immune System/Common Characteristics of B and T Lymphocytes
- Immune System/Humoral Immunity
- Immune System/Cellular Immunity

14-1 Anatomical barriers and defense mechanisms constitute nonspecific defense, and lymphocytes provide specific defense *p. 471*

1. The cells, tissues, and organs of the **lymphoid system** play a central role in the body's defenses against a variety of **pathogens,** or disease-causing organisms.

14-2 Lymphatic vessels, lymphocytes, lymphoid tissues, and lymphoid organs function in body defenses *p. 472*

2. The lymphoid system includes a network of **lymphatic vessels** called **lymphatics,** which carry **lymph** (a fluid similar to plasma but with a lower concentration of proteins). A series of **lymphoid organs** is connected to the lymphatic vessels. (*Figure 14-1*)

3. The lymphoid system produces, maintains, and distributes lymphocytes (cells that attack invading organisms, abnormal

cells, and foreign proteins). The system also helps maintain blood volume and eliminate local variations in the composition of the interstitial fluid.

4. Lymph flows along a network of lymphatics that originates in the **lymphatic capillaries.** The lymphatic vessels empty into the **thoracic duct** and the **right lymphatic duct.** *(Figures 14-1 to 14-3)*

5. The three classes of lymphocytes are **T cells** (*t*hymus-dependent), **B cells** (*b*one marrow–derived), and **natural killer (NK) cells.**

6. *Cytotoxic T cells* attack foreign cells or body cells infected by viruses; they provide cell-mediated immunity. **Regulatory T cells** (*helper T cells* and *suppressor T cells*) regulate and coordinate the immune response.

7. B cells can differentiate into **plasma cells,** which produce and secrete antibodies that react with specific chemical targets, or **antigens.** Antibodies in body fluids are also called **immunoglobulins.** B cells are responsible for *antibody-mediated immunity,* or *humoral immunity.*

8. NK cells attack foreign cells, normal cells infected with viruses, and cancer cells. They provide a monitoring service called *immunological surveillance.*

9. Lymphocytes continuously migrate in and out of the blood through the lymphoid tissues and organs. *Lymphopoiesis* (lymphocyte production and development) involves the bone marrow, thymus, and peripheral lymphoid tissues. *(Figure 14-4)*

10. A **lymphoid nodule** consists of loose connective tissue containing densely packed lymphocytes. **Tonsils** are lymphoid nodules in the pharynx wall. *(Figure 14-5)*

11. Important lymphoid organs include the *lymph nodes,* the *thymus,* and the *spleen.* Lymphoid tissues and organs are distributed in areas especially vulnerable to invasion by pathogens.

12. **Lymph nodes** are encapsulated masses of lymphoid tissue containing lymphocytes. Lymph nodes monitor and filter the lymph before it drains into the venous system, removing antigens and initiating appropriate immune responses. *(Figure 14-6)*

13. The **thymus** lies behind the sternum. T cells become mature in the thymus. *(Figure 14-7)*

14. The adult **spleen** contains the largest mass of lymphoid tissue in the body. *Red pulp* contains large numbers of red blood cells, and areas of *white pulp* resemble lymphoid nodules. The spleen removes antigens and damaged blood cells from the circulation, initiates appropriate immune responses, and stores iron obtained from recycled red blood cells. *(Figure 14-8)*

15. The lymphoid system is a major component of the body's defenses, which fall into two categories: (1) **nonspecific defenses,** which do not discriminate between one threat and another, and (2) **specific defenses,** which protect against particular threats.

14-3 Each nonspecific defense responds in a characteristic way regardless of the potential threat *p. 479*

16. Nonspecific defenses prevent the approach, deny the entrance, or limit the spread of living or nonliving hazards. *(Figure 14-9)*

17. Physical barriers include the skin (including hair and secretions of dermal glands) and the epithelia and various secretions of the digestive system.

18. **Phagocytes** include **microphages** (neutrophils and eosinophils) and **macrophages** (cells of the *monocyte–macrophage system*).

19. Phagocytes move between cells through *diapedesis,* and they show *chemotaxis* (sensitivity and orientation to chemical stimuli).

20. **Immunological surveillance** involves constant monitoring of normal tissues by NK cells sensitive to abnormal antigens on the surfaces of otherwise normal cells. NK cells kill both cancer cells displaying tumor-specific surface antigens and virus-infected cells.

21. **Interferons,** small proteins released by virus-infected cells, trigger the production of antiviral proteins that interfere with viral replication inside other cells. Interferons are *cytokines,* chemical messengers released by tissue cells to coordinate local activities.

22. The 11 *complement proteins* of the **complement system** interact with each other in chain reactions to destroy target cell membranes, stimulate inflammation, attract phagocytes, and enhance phagocytosis.

23. **Inflammation** represents a coordinated nonspecific response to tissue injury. *(Figure 14-10)*

24. A **fever** (body temperature greater than 37.2°C or 99°F) can inhibit pathogens and accelerate metabolic processes.

14-4 Immunity (specific defenses) responds to specific threats and is either cell mediated or antibody mediated *p. 482*

25. Specific defenses are provided by T cells and B cells. T cells provide cell-mediated immunity; B cells provide antibody-mediated immunity.

26. Specific immunity may involve **innate immunity** (genetically determined and present at birth) or **acquired immunity.** The two types of acquired immunity are **active immunity** (which appears following exposure to an antigen) and **passive immunity** (produced by the transfer of antibodies from another source). *(Figure 14-11)*

27. Lymphocytes provide specific immunity, which has four general characteristics: specificity, versatility, memory, and tolerance. **Specificity** occurs because receptors on T cell and B cell membranes can bind only to specific antigens. The immune

system has **versatility** in that it can respond to any of the tens of thousands of antigens it encounters. **Memory cells** enable the immune system to "remember" previously encountered antigens. **Tolerance** refers to the ability of the immune system to ignore some antigens, such as those of normal body cells.

28. The purpose of the **immune response** is to inactivate or destroy pathogens, abnormal cells, and foreign molecules. It is based on the activation of lymphocytes by specific antigens through the process of *antigen recognition*. *(Figure 14-12)*

14-5 T cells play a role in the initiation and control of the immune response   p. 484

29. T cells recognize antigens bound to Class I and Class II MHC proteins. Foreign antigens must usually be processed by macrophages and incorporated into their plasma membranes bound to *MHC proteins* before they can activate T cells. T cells can also be activated by viral antigens displayed on the surfaces of virus-infected cells.

30. Activated T cells may differentiate into *cytotoxic T cells, memory T cells, suppressor T cells,* or *helper T cells.*

31. Cell-mediated immunity results from the activation of **cytotoxic** (or *killer*) **T cells.** Activated **memory T cells** remain on reserve to respond to future exposures to the specific antigen involved. *(Figure 14-13)*

32. **Suppressor T cells** depress the responses of B cells and other T cells.

33. **Helper T cells** secrete cytokines that help coordinate specific and nonspecific defenses and regulate cellular and humoral immunity.

14-6 B cells respond to antigens by producing specific antibodies   p. 486

34. B cells, responsible for antibody-mediated immunity, undergo sensitization by a specific antigen before they become activated by helper T cells sensitive to the same antigen.

35. An activated B cell divides and produces plasma cells and **memory B cells.** Antibodies are produced by plasma cells. *(Figure 14-14)*

36. An antibody molecule consists of two parallel pairs of polypeptide chains containing *fixed segments* and *variable segments.* *(Figure 14-15)*

37. The binding of an antibody molecule and an antigen forms an **antigen–antibody complex.** Antibodies bind to specific *antigenic determinant sites.*

38. Five classes of antibodies exist in body fluids: (1) **immunoglobulin G (IgG),** responsible for resistance against many viruses, bacteria, and bacterial toxins; (2) **IgM,** the first antibody class secreted in response to an antigen; (3) **IgA,** found in glandular secretions; (4) **IgE,** which stimulates the release of chemicals that accelerate local inflammation; and (5) **IgD,** found on the surfaces of B cells. *(Table 14-1)*

39. Antibodies can eliminate antigens through **neutralization, precipitation, agglutination,** activation of complement, attraction of phagocytes, enhancement of phagocytosis, and stimulation of inflammation.

40. The antibodies produced by plasma cells upon first exposure to an antigen are the agents of the **primary response.** Maximum antibody levels appear during the **secondary response,** which follows subsequent exposure to the same antigen. *(Figure 14-16)*

41. **Interleukins** (IL) increase T cell sensitivity to antigens; stimulate B cell activity, plasma cell formation, and antibody production; and enhance nonspecific defenses.

42. Interferons slow the spread of a virus by making the synthesizing cell's neighbors resistant to viral infections.

43. **Tumor necrosis factors** (TNFs) slow tumor growth and kill tumor cells.

44. Several **phagocytic regulators** adjust the activities of phagocytic cells to coordinate specific and nonspecific defenses. *(Table 14-2)*

45. The body's specific and nonspecific defenses cooperate in an integrated way to eliminate foreign antigens. *(Figure 14-17)*

14-7 Abnormal immune responses result in immune disorders   p. 491

46. **Autoimmune disorders** develop when the immune response mistakenly targets normal body cells and tissues.

47. In an **immunodeficiency disease,** either the immune system does not develop normally or the immune response is somehow blocked.

48. **Allergies** are inappropriate or excessive immune responses to **allergens** (antigens that trigger allergic reactions). The four types of allergies are *immediate hypersensitivity* (*Type I*), *cytotoxic reactions* (*Type II*), *immune complex disorders* (*Type III*), and *delayed hypersensitivity* (*Type IV*).

14-8 The immune response diminishes with advancing age   p. 494

49. As individuals age, the immune system becomes less effective at combating disease.

14-9 For all body systems, the lymphoid system provides defenses against infection and returns tissue fluid to the circulation   p. 494

50. The lymphoid system has extensive interactions with the nervous and endocrine systems.

REVIEW QUESTIONS

Level 1 • Reviewing Facts and Terms

Match each item in column A with the most closely related item in column B. Place letters for answers in the spaces provided.

COLUMN A

_____ 1. humoral immunity
_____ 2. lymphoma
_____ 3. complement
_____ 4. microphages
_____ 5. macrophages
_____ 6. microglia
_____ 7. interferon
_____ 8. pyrogens
_____ 9. innate immunity
_____ 10. active immunity
_____ 11. passive immunity
_____ 12. apoptosis

COLUMN B

a. induce fever
b. system of circulating proteins
c. CNS macrophages
d. monocytes
e. genetically programmed cell death
f. transfers of antibodies
g. neutrophils, eosinophils
h. secretion of antibodies
i. present at birth
j. cytokine
k. lymphoid system cancer
l. exposure to antigen

13. Identify the structures of the lymphoid system in the following diagram.

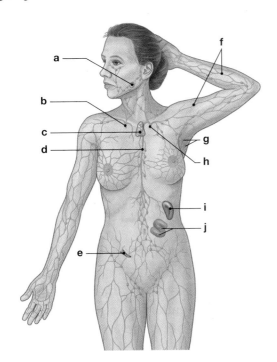

(a) _____
(b) _____
(c) _____
(d) _____
(e) _____
(f) _____
(g) _____
(h) _____
(i) _____
(j) _____

14. Lymph collected from the lower abdomen, pelvis, and lower limbs is carried by the
   (a) right lymphatic duct.
   (b) inguinal duct.
   (c) thoracic duct.
   (d) aorta.

15. Lymphocytes responsible for providing cell-mediated immunity are called
   (a) macrophages.
   (b) B cells.
   (c) plasma cells.
   (d) cytotoxic T cells.

16. B cells are responsible for
   (a) cellular immunity.
   (b) immunological surveillance.
   (c) antibody-mediated immunity.
   (d) a, b, and c are correct

17. Lymphoid stem cells that can form all types of lymphocytes occur in the
   (a) bloodstream.
   (b) thymus.
   (c) bone marrow.
   (d) spleen.

18. Lymphatic vessels are found in all portions of the body except the
   (a) lower limbs.
   (b) central nervous system.
   (c) head and neck region.
   (d) hands and feet.

19. The largest collection of lymphoid tissue in the body is contained in the
   (a) adult spleen.
   (b) adult thymus.
   (c) bone marrow.
   (d) tonsils.

20. Red blood cells that are damaged or defective are removed from the circulation by the
   (a) thymus.
   (b) lymph nodes.
   (c) spleen.
   (d) tonsils.

21. Phagocytes move through capillary walls by squeezing between adjacent endothelial cells, a process known as
    (a) diapedesis.   (b) chemotaxis.
    (c) adhesion.   (d) perforation.

22. Perforins are destructive proteins associated with the activity of
    (a) T cells.   (b) B cells.
    (c) macrophages.   (d) plasma cells.

23. Complement activation
    (a) stimulates inflammation.
    (b) attracts phagocytes.
    (c) enhances phagocytosis.
    (d) a, b, and c are correct.

24. Inflammation
    (a) aids in temporary repair at an injury site.
    (b) slows the spread of pathogens.
    (c) facilitates permanent repair.
    (d) a, b, and c are correct.

25. Memory B cells
    (a) respond to an initial threat.
    (b) secrete large numbers of antibodies into the interstitial fluid.
    (c) respond to subsequent infections that involve the same antigen.
    (d) contain binding sites that can activate the complement system.

26. Which two large collecting vessels are responsible for returning lymph to the veins of the circulatory system? What areas of the body does each serve?

27. Give a function for each of the following:
    (a) cytotoxic T cells
    (b) helper T cells
    (c) suppressor (regulatory) T cells
    (d) plasma cells
    (e) NK cells
    (f) interferons
    (g) T cells
    (h) B cells
    (i) interleukins

Level 2 • Reviewing Concepts

28. Compared with nonspecific defenses, specific defenses
    (a) do not discriminate between one threat and another.
    (b) are always present at birth.
    (c) provide protection against threats on an individual basis.
    (d) deny entry of pathogens to the body.

29. T cells and B cells can be activated only by
    (a) pathogenic microorganisms.
    (b) interleukins, interferons, and colony-stimulating factors.
    (c) cells infected with viruses, bacterial cells, or cancer cells.
    (d) exposure to a specific antigen at a specific site on a cell membrane.

30. List and explain the four general properties of immunity.

31. In what ways can the formation of an antibody–antigen complex cause elimination of an antigen?

32. What are the effects of complement system activation?

Level 3 • Critical Thinking and Clinical Applications

33. Sylvia's grandfather is diagnosed as having lung cancer. When his physician takes biopsies of several lymph nodes from neighboring regions of the body, Sylvia wonders why, since his cancer is in his lungs. What would you tell her?

34. Ted finds out that he has been exposed to the measles and is concerned that he might have contracted the disease. His physician takes a blood sample and sends it to a lab to measure antibody levels. The results show an elevated level of IgM antibodies to rubella (measles) virus but very few IgG antibodies to the virus. Did Ted contract the disease?

The Lymphoid System in Perspective

Functional Relationships Between the Lymphoid System and Other Systems

The Integumentary System

- The Integumentary System provides physical barriers to pathogen entry; macrophages in dermis resist infection and present antigens to trigger immune response; mast cells trigger inflammation, mobilize cells of lymphoid system
- The Lymphoid System provides IgA antibodies for secretion onto integumentary surfaces

The Skeletal System

- The Skeletal System's bone marrow produces and stores lymphocytes and other cells involved in the immune response
- The Lymphoid System assists in repair of bone after injuries; macrophages fuse to become osteoclasts

The Muscular System

- The Muscular System protects superficial lymph nodes and lymphatic vessels in the abdominopelvic cavity; muscle contractions help propel lymph along lymphatic vessels
- The Lymphoid System assists in repair after injuries

The Nervous System

- The Nervous System's microglia present antigens that stimulate specific defenses; glial cells secrete cytokines; innervation stimulates antigen-presenting cells
- The Lymphoid System's cytokines affect hypothalamic production of CRH and TRH

The Endocrine System

- The Endocrine System's gluco-corticoids have anti-inflammatory effects; thymosins stimulate development and maturation of lymphocytes; many hormones affect immune function
- The Lymphoid System's thymus secretes thymosins; cytokines affect cells throughout the body

The Cardiovascular System

- The Cardiovascular System distributes WBCs; carries antibodies that attack pathogens; clotting response helps restrict spread of pathogens; hemocytoblasts give rise to stem cells that produce WBCs
- The Lymphoid System fights infections of cardiovascular organs; returns tissue fluid to bloodstream

The Respiratory System

- The Respiratory System's alveolar phagocytes present antigens and trigger specific defenses; provides oxygen and eliminates carbon dioxide for the lymphoid system
- The Lymphoid System's tonsils protect against infection at entrance to respiratory tract

The Digestive System

- The Digestive System provides nutrients required by lymphatic tissues; digestive acids and enzymes provide nonspecific defense against pathogens
- The Lymphoid System's tonsils and intestinal lymphoid nodules defend against infection and toxins absorbed from the digestive tract; lymphatics carry absorbed lipids to venous system

The Urinary System

- The Urinary System eliminates metabolic wastes generated by cellular activity; acid pH of urine provides nonspecific defense against urinary tract infection
- The Lymphoid System provides specific defenses against urinary tract infections

The Reproductive System

- The Reproductive System's secretions contain lysozymes and bactericides that provide nonspecific defense against reproductive tract infections
- The Lymphoid System provides IgA antibodies for secretion by epithelial glands

For All Systems

The Lymphoid System provides specific defenses against infection; immune surveillance eliminates cancer cells; returns tissue fluid to circulation

Professional Profile

NURSE PRACTITIONER
Robin Andersen

> **"Every symptom we hear about or find in a patient has a basis in physiology."**

Robin Andersen, a nurse practitioner (NP), always knew that she would pursue a career in health care. "I became interested in nursing while I was in junior high school," she says. "Later I became aware of the role of nurse practitioner, which seemed interesting and challenging. I wanted to choose a career that would make a difference in a tangible way. So I decided during high school to become an NP."

Robin works in acute care on a general surgery service in a major academic hospital. Her day begins at 7 A.M., checking in with the residents on her team for "sign-out" on each of the patients in their care. These are patients either being evaluated for an operation or in the post-operative recovery phase.

A PIVOTAL ROLE

As a nurse practitioner, Robin formulates a diagnosis and then initiates whatever treatment the patient may need. "I address cases of hemodynamic instability, fevers, nausea, pus, and pain—anything that may indicate that a patient is having greater problems that may need a further work-up." Robin is first call for the surgical wards. "That means that when nurses have questions or concerns about the patients, they page me. I handle that throughout the day."

On top of that, Robin also takes phone calls from outpatients—usually postoperative patients who call in about problems such as fevers. She works with those patients over the phone and sees the ones that she feels should come to the clinic for examination. At the end of Robin's nine- to eleven-hour day, she updates the team of residents on all of the patients so that they can continue with the care of the patients.

A nurse practitioner must have completed a bachelor's program in nursing and preferably have worked as a registered nurse for a year or more before applying to a master's level program. Robin recommends that NP candidates make sure they've completed all of the prerequisites they will need for the program, including biology, chemistry, and statistics. A good background in anatomy and physiology is also essential, both for obtaining the MSN (master of science in nursing) and succeeding as a nurse practitioner.

According to Robin, "Every symptom we hear about or find in a patient has a basis in physiology. Physiology helps us understand why we are seeing certain lab results, hearing reports of pain, or finding changes in heart rate or blood pressure. Of course, anatomy goes hand in hand with that. If a patient complains of pain in a certain area, I have to know what is in that area, what might be the source of the pain."

UNIQUE REWARDS

The job of nurse practitioner is uniquely rewarding. "One of the great things that being an NP offers over some of the other health provider roles is the two-piece combination of actual nursing experience with education in science and internal medicine. As a result, I'm able to interact with many different people in various states of health and effect a positive change on their lives. I help keep them safe, get them on an appropriate treatment plan, educate them about their illness, and help them take care of themselves."

Nurse practitioners work in primary care offices, including pediatrics, internal medicine, and obstetrics and gynecology. Some, like Robin, work in an inpatient setting. An entry-level nurse practitioner who has passed the national accreditation exam is qualified to work in any of these settings.

15 The Respiratory System

The respiratory and cardiovascular systems are closely linked. In this chapter we will see how they cooperate to supply our tissues with vital oxygen and protect them from the carbon dioxide they generate. We will also examine the homeostatic regulation of respiratory activities as levels of physical activity change.

VOCABULARY DEVELOPMENT

alveolus a hollow cavity; *alveolus,*
  alveolar duct
ateles imperfect; *atelectasis*
bronchus windpipe, airway; *bronchus*
cricoid ring-shaped; *cricoid cartilage*

ektasis expansion; *atelectasis*
-ia condition; *pneumonia*
kentesis puncture; *thoracentesis*
oris mouth; *oropharynx*
pneuma air; *pneumothorax*

pneumon lung; *pneumonia*
stoma mouth; *tracheostomy*
thorac- chest; *thoracentesis*
thyroid shield-shaped; *thyroid*
  cartilage

An Introduction to the Respiratory System

When we think of the respiratory system, we generally think of the mechanics of breathing—moving air into and out of our bodies. However, the requirements for an efficient respiratory system go beyond merely moving air. Cells need energy for maintenance, growth, defense, and reproduction. Our cells obtain that energy through an aerobic process that requires oxygen and produces carbon dioxide. ∞ p. 77 The respiratory system provides the body's cells with the means for obtaining oxygen and eliminating carbon dioxide. This exchange takes place within the lungs at air-filled pockets called **alveoli** (al-VĒ-ō-lī; singular, *alveolus*). The gas-exchange surfaces of the alveoli are relatively delicate—they must be very thin to enable rapid diffusion between the air and the blood. The cardiovascular system provides the link between the interstitial fluids and the exchange surfaces of the lungs. Circulating blood carries oxygen from the lungs to peripheral tissues; it also accepts and then delivers to the lungs the carbon dioxide generated by those tissues.

Our discussion of the respiratory system begins by following air as it travels from outside the body to the alveoli of the lungs. Next we consider the mechanics of breathing—how air enters the lungs as a result of the actions of respiratory muscles. Then we examine the physiology of respiration, which includes the process of breathing and the processes of gas exchange and gas transport, both between the air and blood and between the blood and tissues.

15-1 The respiratory system, composed of conducting and respiratory portions, has several basic functions

The **respiratory system** is composed of structures involved in the physical movement of air into and out of the lungs and in gas exchange. In this section we consider this body system's functions and structural organization.

FUNCTIONS OF THE RESPIRATORY SYSTEM

The respiratory system has five basic functions:

1. Providing a large area for gas exchange between air and circulating blood.

2. Moving air to and from the gas-exchange surfaces of the lungs.

3. Protecting the respiratory surfaces from dehydration and temperature changes, and defending against invading pathogens.

4. Producing sounds permitting speech, singing, and nonverbal auditory communication.

5. Aiding the sense of smell by the olfactory receptors in the nasal cavity.

COMPONENTS OF THE RESPIRATORY SYSTEM

The major anatomical structures of the respiratory system are the nose (including the nasal cavity and paranasal sinuses), pharynx (throat), larynx (voice box), trachea (windpipe), bronchi, and lungs, which contain the bronchioles (air-conducting passageways) and the alveoli (exchange surfaces) (**Figure 15-1**).

The term **respiratory tract** refers to the passageways that carry air to and from the exchange surfaces of the lungs. The respiratory tract can be divided into an upper *conducting portion* and a lower *respiratory portion*. The conducting portion begins at the entrance to the nasal cavity and continues through the pharynx, larynx, trachea, bronchi, and the larger bronchioles. The respiratory portion includes the smallest and most delicate bronchioles and the alveoli within the lungs.

In addition to delivering air to the lungs, the conducting passageways filter, warm, and humidify the air, thereby protecting

FIGURE 15-1 **The Components of the Respiratory System.**

Nasal cavity

Sphenoidal sinus

Internal nares

Pharynx

Esophagus

Frontal sinus

Nasal conchae

Nose

Tongue

Hyoid bone

Larynx

Trachea

Bronchus

Bronchioles

RIGHT LUNG

LEFT LUNG

Diaphragm

Vein

Artery

Capillary network   Alveolus

the alveoli from debris, pathogens, and environmental extremes. By the time inhaled air reaches the alveoli, most foreign particles and pathogens have been removed, and the humidity and temperature are within acceptable limits.

The **respiratory mucosa** (mu-KŌ-suh) lines the conducting portion of the respiratory system. A *mucosa* is a mucous membrane, one of four types of membranes introduced in Chapter 4. ∞p. 110 The respiratory mucosa is made up of the *respiratory epithelium*, which is a ciliated columnar epithelium containing many *mucous (goblet) cells*, and an underlying loose connective tissue layer (the *lamina propria*) containing mucous glands which secrete onto the epithelial surface (**Figure 15-2**).

The exchange surfaces of the respiratory system can be severely damaged if inhaled air is contaminated with debris or pathogens. Such contamination is prevented by the mucous cells and mucous glands that produce mucus, which bathes the exposed surfaces of the *nasal cavity* and lower respiratory tract. Cilia sweep that mucus and any trapped debris or microorganisms toward the *pharynx,* where they can be swallowed and exposed to the acids and enzymes of the stomach.

CHECKPOINT

1. Identify the five functions of the respiratory system.

2. What membrane lines the conducting portion of the respiratory system?

See the blue Answers tab at the back of the book.

15-2 The nose, pharynx, larynx, trachea, bronchi, and larger bronchioles conduct air into the lungs

The conducting portion of the respiratory tract begins at the entrance to the nasal cavity and continues through the pharynx, larynx, trachea, bronchi, and the larger bronchioles.

FIGURE 15-2 The Respiratory Mucosa. (a) The appearance of the respiratory epithelium and its role in mucus transport are depicted in this sectional drawing. **(b)** The cilia of the epithelial cells form a dense layer that resembles a shag carpet. The movement of these cilia propels mucus across the epithelial surface.

THE NOSE

Air normally enters the respiratory system through the paired **external nares** (NĀ-rēz), or nostrils, which open into the **nasal cavity** (Figure 15-3). The **nasal vestibule** (VES-ti-būl) is the space enclosed within the flexible tissues of the nose. Here coarse hairs extend across the nostrils and guard the nasal cavity from large airborne particles such as sand, dust, and even insects.

The maxillary, nasal, frontal, ethmoid, and sphenoid bones form the lateral and superior walls of the nasal cavity (see Figure 6-12b, c, p. 159). The *nasal septum* divides the nasal cavity into left and right sides. The anterior portion of the nasal

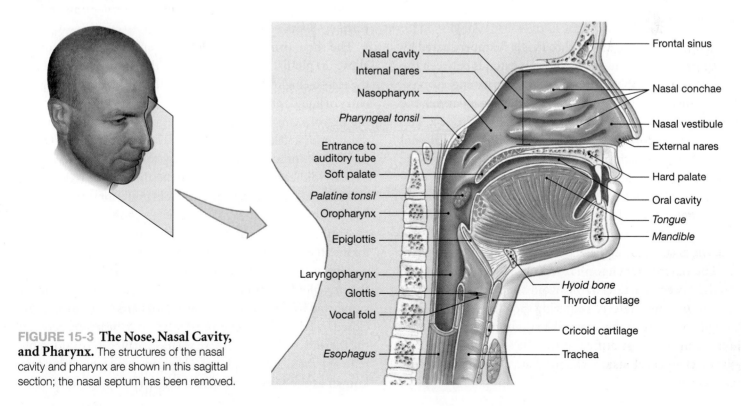

FIGURE 15-3 The Nose, Nasal Cavity, and Pharynx. The structures of the nasal cavity and pharynx are shown in this sagittal section; the nasal septum has been removed.

septum is formed of hyaline cartilage. The bony posterior septum includes portions of the vomer and the ethmoid bone (see Figure 6-11a, p. 157). A bony **hard palate,** formed by the palatine and maxillary bones, forms the floor of the nasal cavity and separates the oral and nasal cavities (Figure 15-3). A fleshy **soft palate** extends behind the hard palate and underlies the **nasopharynx** (nā-zō-FAR-inks). The nasal cavity opens into the nasopharynx at the **internal nares.**

The superior, middle, and inferior *nasal conchae* project toward the nasal septum from the lateral walls of the nasal cavity (Figure 15-3). To pass from the nasal vestibule to the internal nares, air tends to flow in narrow grooves between adjacent conchae. As the air eddies and swirls like water flowing over rapids, small airborne particles come in contact with the mucus that coats the lining of the nasal cavity. In addition to promoting filtration, the turbulent flow allows extra time for warming and humidifying the incoming air.

As noted earlier, the nasal cavity is flushed by mucus produced by the *respiratory mucosa.* The respiratory surfaces of the nasal cavity are also cleared by mucus produced in the *paranasal sinuses* (the *frontal, sphenoid, ethmoid,* and *maxillary sinuses*) (see Figure 6-13, p. 160), and by tears flowing through the nasolacrimal duct (see Figure 9-8b, p. 316). Exposure to noxious vapors, large quantities of dust and debris, allergens, or pathogens usually causes a rapid increase in the rate of mucus production, and a "runny nose" develops.

THE PHARYNX

The **pharynx** (FAR-ingks), or throat, is a chamber shared by the digestive and respiratory systems. It extends between the internal nares and the entrances to the larynx and esophagus and consists of three subdivisions: the nasopharynx, the oropharynx, and the laryngopharynx (Figure 15-3). The **nasopharynx** is connected to the nasal cavity by the internal nares and extends to the posterior edge of the soft palate. The nasopharynx, lined by a typical respiratory epithelium, contains the *pharyngeal tonsil* on its posterior wall and entrances to the *auditory tubes.* The **oropharynx** extends between the soft palate and the base of the tongue at the level of the hyoid bone. The palatine tonsils lie in the lateral walls of the oropharynx. The narrow **laryngopharynx** (la-rin-gō-FAR-ingks) extends between the level of the hyoid bone and the entrance to the esophagus. Materials entering the digestive tract pass through both the oropharynx and laryngopharynx. These regions are lined by a stratified squamous epithelium that can resist mechanical abrasion, chemical attack, and pathogenic invasion.

Clinical Note

Cystic Fibrosis

Cystic fibrosis (CF) is an inherited disease involving a defect of the respiratory mucosa. Mucous cells in the respiratory mucosa of affected individuals produce dense, viscous mucus that cannot be transported by the cilia of the respiratory tract. Mucus transport stops, and mucus blocks the smaller respiratory passageways. The clogged airways make breathing difficult, and the inactivation of the normal respiratory defenses leads to frequent bacterial infections. Individuals with CF seldom survive past age 30; death usually results from a massive bacterial infection of the lungs and associated heart failure.

CF is the most common lethal inherited disease affecting individuals of northern European descent, occurring at a frequency of 1 birth in 2500. It occurs with less frequency in those of southern European ancestry, in the Ashkenazic Jewish population, and in African Americans. The condition results from a defective gene on chromosome 7.

THE LARYNX

Inhaled air leaves the pharynx and enters the larynx through a narrow opening called the **glottis** (GLOT-is) (Figure 15-3). The **larynx** (LAR-ingks), or *voice box,* consists of nine cartilages stabilized by ligaments, skeletal muscles, or both. The three largest cartilages are the *epiglottis, thyroid cartilage,* and *cricoid cartilage* (Figure 15-4).

The shoehorn-shaped **epiglottis** (ep-i-GLOT-is) projects above the glottis. During swallowing, the larynx is elevated and the elastic epiglottis folds back over the glottis, preventing the entry of liquids or solid food into the respiratory tract. The curving **thyroid** (*thyroid;* shield-shaped) **cartilage** forms much of the anterior and lateral surfaces of the larynx. A prominent ridge on the anterior surface of this cartilage forms the "Adam's apple." The thyroid cartilage sits superior to the **cricoid** (KRĪ-koyd; ring-shaped) **cartilage,** which provides posterior support to the larynx. The thyroid and cricoid cartilages protect the glottis and the entrance to the trachea, and their broad surfaces provide sites for the attachment of important laryngeal muscles and ligaments.

The larynx also contains three pairs of smaller cartilages— the *arytenoid, corniculate,* and *cuneiform cartilages*—that are supported by the cricoid cartilage. Two pairs of ligaments, enclosed by folds of epithelium, extend across the larynx between the thyroid cartilage and these smaller cartilages, considerably reducing the size of the glottis. The ligaments of the upper pair, known as the **false vocal cords,** are relatively inelastic. They

FIGURE 15-4 The Anatomy of the Larynx and Vocal Cords. Many of the laryngeal cartilages are visible in **(a)** an anterior view of the larynx and **(b)** a posterior view of the larynx. Two superior views show the larynx with **(c)** the glottis open and **(d)** the glottis closed. **(e)** In this fiber-optic view of the larynx, the glottis is almost completely closed.

help prevent foreign objects from entering the glottis, and they protect a more delicate pair of folds. These lower folds, the **true vocal cords,** contain elastic ligaments that extend between the thyroid cartilage and the arytenoid cartilages. Small muscles that insert on these cartilages change their position and alter the tension in these ligaments.

Food or liquids that touch the vocal cords trigger the *coughing reflex.* In a cough, the glottis is kept closed while the chest and abdominal muscles contract, compressing the lungs. When the glottis is opened suddenly, the resulting blast of air through the trachea ejects material blocking the entrance to the glottis.

The Vocal Cords and Sound Production

Air passing through the glottis vibrates the vocal cords, producing sound waves. The pitch of the sound produced, like the pitch of a vibrating harp string, depends on the diameter, length, and tension of the vibrating vocal cords. Short, thin strings vibrate rapidly, producing a high-pitched sound; long, thick strings vibrate more slowly, producing a low-pitched tone. The diameter and length of the vocal cords are directly related to larynx size. Children have small larynxes with slender, short vocal cords, so their voices tend to be high-pitched. At puberty, the larynx of males enlarges more than that of females; because the vocal cords of adult males are thicker and longer, they produce lower tones than those of adult females. The amount of tension in the vocal cords is controlled by skeletal muscles that change the position of the arytenoid cartilages. Increased tension in the vocal cords raises the pitch; decreased tension lowers the pitch.

The distinctive sound of your voice does not depend solely on the sounds produced by the larynx. Further amplification and resonance occur in the pharynx, the oral cavity, the nasal cavity, and the paranasal sinuses. The final production of distinct words further depends on voluntary movements of the tongue, lips, and cheeks.

THE TRACHEA

The **trachea** (TRĀ-kē-uh), or *windpipe*, is a tough, flexible tube that is about 2.5 cm (1 in.) in diameter and approximately 11 cm (4.25 in.) long (Figure 15-5). The trachea begins at the level of the sixth cervical vertebra, where it attaches to the cricoid cartilage of the larynx. It ends in the mediastinum, at the level of the fifth thoracic vertebra, where it branches to form the right and left primary bronchi.

The walls of the trachea are supported by 15–20 **tracheal cartilages.** These C-shaped cartilages protect the airway; by stiffening the tracheal walls, they prevent the trachea's collapse or overexpansion as pressures change in the respiratory system. The open portions of the C-shaped tracheal cartilages face posteriorly, toward the esophagus, so the posterior tracheal wall can easily distort, allowing large masses of food to pass along the esophagus. The ends of each tracheal cartilage are connected by an elastic ligament and the *trachealis muscle*, a band of smooth muscle. The diameter of the trachea is adjusted by the contractions of these muscles, which are under autonomic control. Sympathetic stimulation increases the diameter of the trachea, making it easier to move large volumes of air along the respiratory passageways.

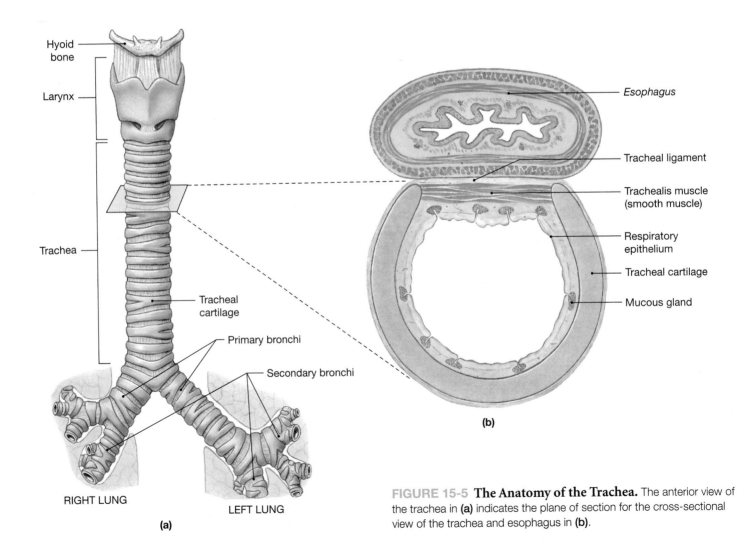

FIGURE 15-5 The Anatomy of the Trachea. The anterior view of the trachea in **(a)** indicates the plane of section for the cross-sectional view of the trachea and esophagus in **(b)**.

Clinical Note

Tracheal Blockage

We sometimes breathe in foreign objects in a process called *aspiration.* Foreign objects that become lodged in the larynx or trachea are usually expelled by coughing. If the individual can speak or make a sound, the airway is still open, and no emergency measures should be taken. If the victim can neither breathe nor speak, an immediate threat to life exists. Unfortunately, many victims become acutely embarrassed by this situation, and rather than seek assistance, they run to the nearest rest room, where they die.

In the *Heimlich* (HĪM-lik) *maneuver,* or *abdominal thrust,* a rescuer applies compression to the abdomen just beneath the diaphragm. This action elevates the diaphragm forcefully and may generate enough pressure to remove the blockage. The maneuver must be performed properly to avoid damage to internal organs. Organizations such as the American Red Cross, local fire departments, and other charitable groups periodically hold brief training sessions in the proper performance of the Heimlich maneuver.

If blockage results from a swelling of the epiglottis or tissues surrounding the glottis, a professionally qualified rescuer may insert a curved tube through the pharynx and glottis to permit airflow. This procedure is called *intubation.* If a tracheal blockage remains, a *tracheostomy* (trā-kē-OS-to-mē; *stoma,* mouth) may be performed. In this procedure, an incision is made through the anterior tracheal wall and a tube is inserted. The tube bypasses the larynx and permits air to flow directly into the trachea.

THE BRONCHI

Within the mediastinum the trachea branches into the **right** and **left primary bronchi** (BRONG-kī) (Figure 15-5). The walls of the primary bronchi resemble that of the trachea, including a ciliated epithelium and C-shaped cartilaginous rings. The right primary bronchus supplies the right lung, and the left supplies the left lung. Because the right primary bronchus is larger in diameter and descends toward the lung at a steeper angle, most foreign objects that enter the trachea find their way into the right primary bronchus rather than the left.

In each lung, the primary bronchi branch into smaller and smaller airways that form the **bronchial tree** (Figure 15-6a). As each primary bronchus enters the lung, it gives rise to **secondary bronchi,** which enter the lobes of that lung. The secondary bronchi divide to form 9–10 **tertiary bronchi** in each lung. Each tertiary bronchus branches repeatedly into smaller bronchi.

The cartilages of the secondary bronchi are relatively massive, but farther along the branches of the bronchial tree they become smaller and smaller. When the diameter of the passageway has narrowed to about 1 mm (.04 in.), cartilages disappear completely. This narrow passage is a **bronchiole.**

The walls of bronchioles are dominated by smooth muscle tissue, whose activity is regulated by the autonomic nervous system. Bronchioles are to the respiratory system what arterioles are to the circulatory system. Just as adjustments to the diameter of arterioles regulate blood flow into capillary beds, adjustments to the diameter of bronchioles control the amount of resistance to airflow and the distribution of air in the lungs. Sympathetic activation leads to a relaxation of smooth muscles in the walls of bronchioles, causing *bronchodilation,* the enlargement of airway diameter. Parasympathetic stimulation leads to contraction of these smooth muscles and *bronchoconstriction,* a reduction in the diameter of the airway. Extreme bronchoconstriction can almost completely block the passageways, making breathing difficult or impossible. This can occur during an *asthma* (AZ-muh) attack or during allergic reactions in response to inflammation of the bronchioles.

CHECKPOINT

3. The surfaces of the nasal cavity are flushed by what materials or fluids?

4. The pharynx is a passageway for which two body systems?

5. When tension in the vocal cords increases, what happens to the pitch of the voice?

6. In the trachea, why are C-shaped cartilages functionally better than completely circular cartilages would be?

See the blue Answers tab at the back of the book.

15-3 The smallest bronchioles and the alveoli within the lungs make up the respiratory portion of the respiratory tract

THE BRONCHIOLES

Bronchioles branch further into the finest conducting passageways, the *terminal bronchioles,* with internal diameters of 0.3–0.5 mm. Each terminal bronchiole supplies air to a lobule of the lung. A **lobule** (LOB-ūl) is a segment of lung tissue that is

FIGURE 15-6 **The Bronchial Tree and Lobules of the Lung.** (a) This illustration shows a simplified version of the branching pattern of the airways in the left lung. (b) This drawing of a pulmonary lobule shows the lung tissue supplied by a single respiratory bronchiole. Note that a capillary bed surrounds each alveolus.

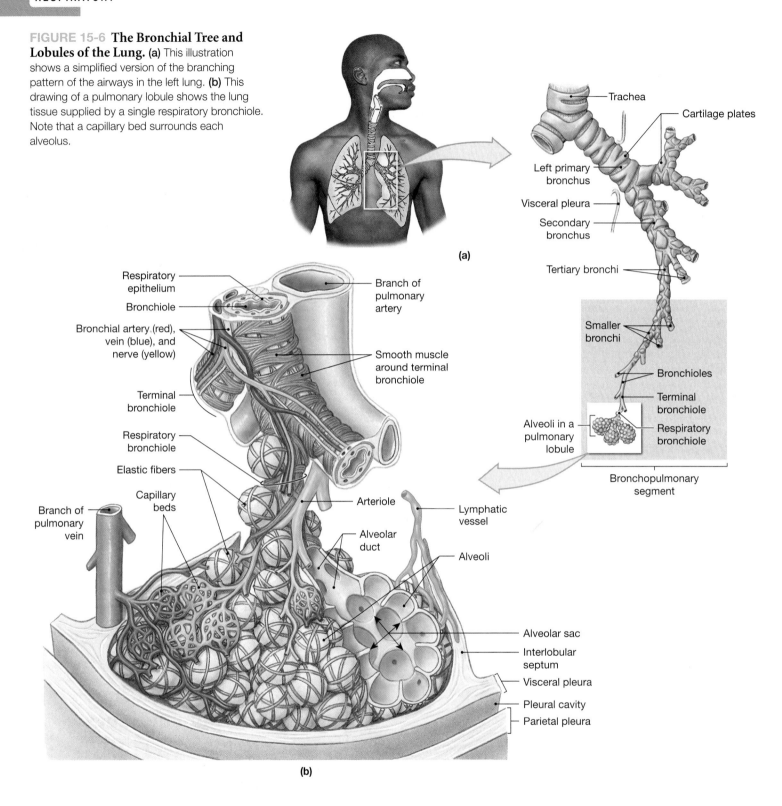

(a)

(b)

bounded by connective tissue partitions and supplied by a single bronchiole, accompanied by branches of the pulmonary arteries and pulmonary veins (Figure 15-6b). Within a lobule, a terminal bronchiole divides to form several *respiratory bronchioles.* These passages, the thinnest branches of the bronchial tree, deliver air to the gas-exchange surfaces of the lungs.

THE ALVEOLAR DUCTS AND ALVEOLI

Respiratory bronchioles open into passageways called **alveolar ducts** (Figure 15-7a). The ducts end at **alveolar sacs,** common chambers connected to multiple individual alveoli—the exchange surfaces of the lungs. Each lung contains about

(a) Alveolar organization

Respiratory bronchiole
Alveolar duct
Alveolus
Alveolar sac
Smooth muscle
Elastic fibers
Capillaries

(b) Alveolar ducts and alveoli   SEM × 270

Alveoli
Alveolar sac
Alveolar duct

(c) Alveolar structure

Septal cell (secretes surfactant)
Alveolar epithelial cell
Alveolar macrophage
Elastic fibers
Alveolar macrophage
Capillary
Endothelial cell of capillary

(d) The respiratory membrane

Red blood cell
Capillary lumen
Nucleus of endothelial cell
Endothelium
0.5 µm
Fused basement membranes
Alveolar epithelium
Surfactant
Alveolar air space

FIGURE 15-7 Alveolar Organization. (a) Several alveoli open off of a single alveolar duct. **(b)** This SEM reveals the open, spongy texture of lung tissue. **(c)** This diagram provides some details of alveolar structure. **(d)** The respiratory membrane is made up of an alveolar epithelial cell, a capillary endothelial cell, and their fused basement membranes.

150 million alveoli, and their abundance gives the lung an open, spongy appearance (Figure 15-7b).

To meet our metabolic requirements, the alveolar exchange surfaces of the lungs must be very large, equal to approximately 140 square meters—roughly one-half of a tennis court. The alveolar epithelium primarily consists of an unusually thin simple squamous epithelium (Figure 15-7c). Roaming **alveolar macrophages** (*dust cells*) patrol the epithelium, phagocytizing dust or debris that has reached the alveolar surfaces.

Scattered among the squamous cells are larger **septal cells,** which secrete onto the alveolar surfaces an oily secretion called **surfactant** (sur-FAK-tant). Surfactant is important because by forming a superficial coating over the thin layer of water coating the alveolar surface, it reduces surface tension, which results from the attraction between water molecules at an air–water boundary. Without surfactant, the surface tension would collapse the delicate alveolar walls. When surfactant levels are inadequate (as a result of injury or genetic abnormalities), each inhalation must be forceful enough to pop open the alveoli. An individual with this condition—called **respiratory distress syndrome**—is soon exhausted by the effort required to keep inflating the deflated lungs.

THE RESPIRATORY MEMBRANE

Gas exchange occurs across the **respiratory membrane** of the alveoli. The respiratory membrane (**Figure 15-7d**) is a composite structure made up of three layers:

1. The squamous epithelial cells lining the alveoli.

2. The endothelial cells lining an adjacent capillary.

3. The fused basement membranes that lie between the alveolar and endothelial cells.

At the respiratory membrane, the distance separating alveolar air from blood can be as little as 0.1 μm. Diffusion across the respiratory membrane proceeds very rapidly because the distance is small and because both oxygen and carbon dioxide are lipid soluble. Thus the membranes of the epithelial and endothelial cells do not pose a barrier to the movement of oxygen and carbon dioxide between blood and the alveolar air spaces.

The respiratory exchange surfaces receive blood from arteries of the *pulmonary circuit.* ∞ p. 446 The pulmonary arteries

enter the lungs and branch, following the bronchi and their branches to the lobules. Each lobule receives an arteriole, and a network of capillaries surrounds each alveolus directly beneath the alveolar epithelium. After passing through the capillaries and into pulmonary venules, blood enters the pulmonary veins, which deliver it to the left atrium.

Blood pressure in the pulmonary circuit is usually relatively low, with pulmonary artery systolic pressures of 30 mm Hg or less. With pressures that low, pulmonary arteries can easily become blocked by small blood clots, fat masses, or air bubbles. Because the lungs receive the entire cardiac output, any drifting masses in the blood are likely to cause problems almost at once. The blockage of a branch of a pulmonary artery will stop blood flow to a group of lobules or alveoli, a condition called **pulmonary embolism.**

THE LUNGS

Each of the two **lungs** has distinct **lobes** that are separated by deep fissures (**Figure 15-8**). The right lung has three lobes (*superior, middle,* and *inferior*), and the left lung has two (*superior* and *inferior*). The bluntly rounded *apex* of each lung extends into the base of the neck above the first rib, and the concave base rests on the superior surface of the diaphragm, the muscular sheet that separates the thoracic and abdominopelvic cavities. The curving *costal surface* follows the inner contours of the rib cage. The *mediastinal surfaces* of both lungs bear grooves that mark the passage of large blood vessels and indentations of the pericardium. In anterior view, the medial edge of the right lung forms a vertical line, whereas the medial margin of the left lung is indented at the *cardiac notch.*

The lungs have a light and spongy consistency because most of the actual volume of each lung consists of air-filled passageways and alveoli. An abundance of elastic fibers gives the lungs the ability to tolerate large changes in volume.

THE PLEURAL CAVITIES

The thoracic cavity has the shape of a broad cone. Its walls are the rib cage, and its floor is the muscular diaphragm. Within the thoracic cavity, each lung occupies a single pleural cavity, lined by a serous membrane called the **pleura** (PLOOR-uh). ∞ p. 111 The *parietal pleura* covers the inner surface of the body wall and extends over the diaphragm and mediastinum, whereas the *visceral pleura* covers the outer surfaces of the lungs, extending into the fissures between the lobes (**Figure 15-9**). The two pleural cavities are separated by the mediastinum.

Clinical Note

Pneumonia

Pneumonia (noo-MŌ-nē-uh; *pneumon,* lung + *-ia,* condition) is inflammation of the pulmonary lobules that typically results from an infection. The inflammation reduces respiratory function as swelling of the respiratory bronchioles constricts the airway, and fluids leak into the alveoli. When bacteria are involved, they are usually normal residents of the mouth and pharynx that have somehow managed to evade the respiratory defenses. Pneumonia becomes more likely when the respiratory defenses have been compromised by other factors, such as epithelial damage from smoking or the breakdown of the immune system (as in AIDS). The most common pneumonia that develops in individuals with AIDS is caused by the fungus *Pneumocystis carinii.* This fungus is normally found in the alveoli, but in healthy individuals the respiratory defenses are able to prevent invasion and tissue damage.

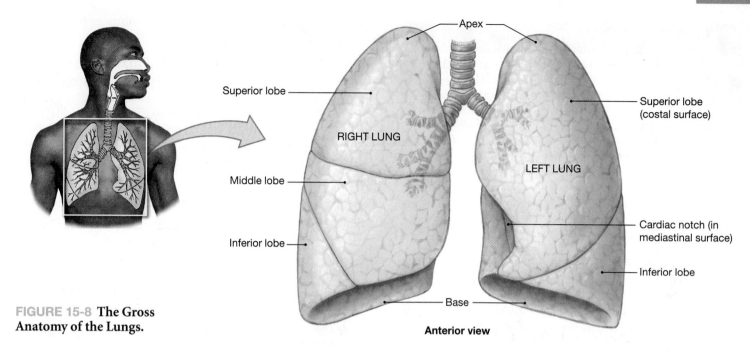

FIGURE 15-8 The Gross Anatomy of the Lungs.

Labels: Apex · Superior lobe · RIGHT LUNG · Middle lobe · Inferior lobe · Base · Superior lobe (costal surface) · LEFT LUNG · Cardiac notch (in mediastinal surface) · Inferior lobe · **Anterior view**

Each pleural cavity actually represents a potential space rather than an open chamber because the parietal and visceral layers are usually in close contact. During breathing, friction between the pleural surfaces is reduced through the lubricating action of *pleural fluid,* which is secreted by both pleural layers. Pleural fluid is sometimes obtained for diagnostic purposes using a long needle inserted between the ribs. This procedure is called *thoracentesis* (thōr-a-sen-TĒ-sis; *thorac-,* chest + *kentesis,* puncture). The fluid is examined for the presence of bacteria, blood cells, and other abnormal components.

An injury to the chest wall that penetrates the parietal pleura or damages the alveoli and the visceral pleura can allow air into the pleural cavity. This condition—**pneumothorax** (noo-mō-THŌ-raks; *pneuma,* air)—breaks the fluid bond between the pleurae and allows the elastic fibers to contract. The result is a collapsed lung, or *atelectasis* (at-e-LEK-ta-sis; *ateles,* imperfect + *ektasis,* expansion). Treatment involves removing as much of the air as possible before sealing the opening. This procedure restores the fluid bond and reinflates the lung. Lung volume can also be reduced by the accumulation of blood in the pleural cavity. This condition is called **hemothorax.**

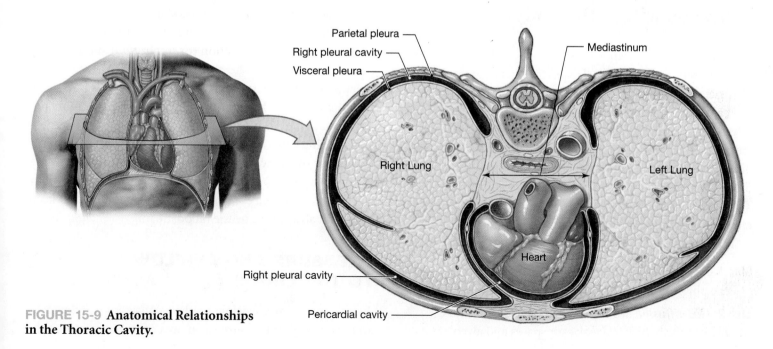

Labels: Parietal pleura · Right pleural cavity · Visceral pleura · Mediastinum · Right Lung · Left Lung · Heart · Right pleural cavity · Pericardial cavity

FIGURE 15-9 Anatomical Relationships in the Thoracic Cavity.

Clinical Note

Tuberculosis

Tuberculosis (too-ber-kū-LŌ-sis), or **TB**, results from a bacterial infection of the lungs, although other organs may be invaded as well. The bacterium, *Mycobacterium tuberculosis,* may colonize respiratory passageways, interstitial spaces, or alveoli, or a combination of all three. Signs and symptoms are variable but generally include coughing and chest pain with fever, night sweats, fatigue, and weight loss.

Tuberculosis is a major worldwide health problem. With roughly 3 million deaths each year from TB, it is the leading cause of death among infectious diseases. An estimated *2 billion* people are currently infected, and 8 million new cases are diagnosed each year. Unlike other deadly infectious diseases, such as AIDS, TB is transmitted through casual contact. By coughing, sneezing, or speaking, an infected individual can send the bacterium into the air in tiny droplets that can be inhaled by other people.

CHECKPOINT

7. Trace the path of airflow from the glottis to the respiratory membrane.

8. What would happen to the alveoli if surfactant were not produced?

9. What are the functions of the pleural surfaces?

See the blue Answers tab at the back of the book.

15-4 External respiration and internal respiration allow gas exchange within the body

The general term *respiration* refers to two integrated processes: *external respiration* and *internal respiration.* **External respiration** includes all the processes involved in the exchange of oxygen and carbon dioxide between the body's interstitial fluids and the external environment. The purpose of external respiration, and the primary function of the respiratory system, is meeting the respiratory demands of cells. **Internal respiration** is the absorption of oxygen and the release of carbon dioxide by those cells. The cellular pathways involving oxygen use and carbon dioxide release are discussed in Chapter 17.

Three integrated steps are involved in external respiration:

Step 1 *Pulmonary ventilation,* or breathing, which involves the physical movement of air into and out of the lungs.

Step 2 *Gas diffusion* at two sites: across the respiratory membrane between alveolar air spaces and alveolar capillaries, and across capillary cell membranes between blood and other tissues.

Step 3 *Transport of oxygen and carbon dioxide* between the alveolar capillaries and the capillary beds in other tissues.

Abnormalities affecting any of these processes will ultimately affect the gas concentrations of the interstitial fluids and, thus, cellular activities as well. If oxygen concentrations decline, the affected tissues will become oxygen starved. **Hypoxia** (hī-POK-sē-uh), or *low tissue oxygen levels,* places severe limits on the metabolic activities of the affected area. If the supply of oxygen gets cut off completely, **anoxia** (an-OK-sē-uh) results, and cells die very quickly. Much of the damage caused by strokes and heart attacks is the result of localized anoxia.

CHECKPOINT

10. Define external respiration and internal respiration.

11. Name the integrated steps involved in external respiration.

See the blue Answers tab at the end of the book.

15-5 Pulmonary ventilation— the exchange of air between the atmosphere and the lungs— involves pressure changes and muscle movement

Pulmonary ventilation is the physical movement of air into and out of the respiratory tract. A single breath, or **respiratory cycle,** consists of an inhalation (or *inspiration*) and an exhalation (or *expiration*). The **respiratory rate** is the number of breaths per minute. In normal adults at rest, this rate ranges from 12 to 18 breaths per minute. Children breathe more rapidly, about 18 to 20 breaths per minute.

Breathing functions to maintain adequate **alveolar ventilation,** the movement of air into and out of the alveoli. Alveolar ventilation prevents the buildup of carbon dioxide in the alveoli and ensures a continuous supply of oxygen that keeps pace with absorption by the bloodstream.

PRESSURE AND AIRFLOW TO THE LUNGS

As we know from television weather reports, air will flow from an area of higher pressure to an area of lower pressure. This difference between the high and low pressures is called a *pressure gradient,* and it applies both to the movement of atmospheric winds and to the movement of air into and out of the lungs (pulmonary ventilation). In a closed, flexible container (such as a lung), the pressure on a gas (such as air) can be changed by increasing or decreasing the container's volume: As the volume of the container (the lungs) increases, the pressure of the gas (air) decreases; as volume decreases, pressure increases.

The volume of the lungs depends on the volume of the pleural cavities. As we have seen, only a thin film of pleural fluid separates the parietal and pleural membranes, and although the two membranes can slide across each other, they are held together by that fluid film. (You encounter the same principle when you set a wet glass on a smooth surface. You can slide the glass easily, but when you try to lift it, you encounter considerable resistance from this fluid bond.) Because a fluid bond exists between the parietal pleura and the visceral pleura covering the lungs, the surface of each lung sticks to the inner wall of the chest and to the superior surface of the diaphragm. Thus, any expansion or contraction of the thoracic cavity directly affects the volume of the lungs.

Changes in the volume of the thoracic cavity result from movements of the diaphragm and rib cage, as shown in Figure 15-10a:

● *Diaphragm.* The diaphragm forms the floor of the thoracic cavity. When relaxed, the diaphragm is dome shaped and projects upward into the thoracic cavity, compressing the lungs. When the diaphragm contracts,

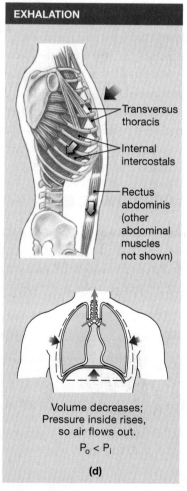

FIGURE 15-10 Pressure and Volume Relationships in the Lungs. (a) Just as raising the handle of a bucket increases the amount of space between it and the bucket, the volume of the thoracic cavity increases when the ribs are elevated and when the diaphragm is depressed during contraction. **(b)** When the rib cage and diaphragm are at rest, the pressures inside and outside are equal, and no air movement occurs. **(c)** During inhalation, elevation of the rib cage and depression of the diaphragm increase the volume of the thoracic cavity. Pressure in the lungs decreases, and air flows into the lungs. **(d)** During exhalation, the rib cage returns to its original position or the diaphragm relaxes, reducing the volume of the thoracic cavity. Pressure in the lungs rises, and air flows out of the lungs. During both inhalation and exhalation, contraction of accessory muscles may assist movements of the rib cage to increase the depth and rate of respiration.

it flattens, increasing the volume of the thoracic cavity and expanding the lungs. When the diaphragm relaxes, it returns to its original position, which decreases the volume of the thoracic cavity.

- *Rib cage.* Because of the way the ribs and the vertebrae articulate, elevation of the rib cage increases the volume of the thoracic cavity, whereas lowering of the rib cage decreases the volume of the thoracic cavity. The external intercostal muscles and accessory muscles (such as the sternocleidomastoid) elevate the rib cage. The internal intercostal muscles and accessory muscles (such as the rectus abdominis and other abdominal muscles) lower the rib cage.

At the start of a breath, pressures inside and outside the lungs are identical, and there is no movement of air (Figure 15-10b). When the diaphragm contracts and the movement of respiratory muscles enlarges the thoracic cavity, the pleural cavities and lungs expand to fill the additional space, so the pressure inside the lungs decreases. Air now enters the respiratory passageways because the pressure inside the lungs (P_i) is lower than atmospheric pressure (pressure outside, or P_o) (Figure 15-10c). Downward movement of the rib cage and upward movement of the diaphragm during exhalation reverse the process and reduce the volume of the lungs. Pressure inside the lungs now exceeds atmospheric pressure, and air moves out of the lungs (Figure 15-10d).

COMPLIANCE

The **compliance** of the lungs is an indication of their resilience and ability to expand. The lower the compliance, the greater is the force required to fill and empty the lungs; the greater the compliance, the easier it is to fill and empty the lungs. Various

Clinical Note — Artificial Respiration

Artificial respiration is a technique to provide air to an individual whose respiratory muscles are no longer functioning. In *mouth-to-mouth resuscitation,* a rescuer provides ventilation by exhaling into the victim's mouth (or mouth and nose). After each breath, contact is broken to permit passive exhalation by the victim. Air provided in this way contains adequate oxygen to meet the victim's needs. Trained rescuers may supply air through an endotracheal tube, which is inserted into the trachea through the glottis. Mechanical ventilators, if available, can be attached to the endotracheal tube. If the victim's cardiovascular system is nonfunctional as well, a technique called *cardiopulmonary resuscitation* (CPR) is required to maintain adequate blood flow and tissue oxygenation.

disorders affect compliance. For example, the loss of supporting tissues due to alveolar damage, as occurs in *emphysema*, increases compliance (see p. 520). Compliance is reduced if surfactant production is insufficient to prevent the alveoli from collapsing on exhalation, as occurs in *respiratory distress syndrome* (see p. 512). Arthritis or other skeletal disorders that affect the joints of the ribs or spinal column also reduce compliance.

When you are at rest, the muscular activity involved in pulmonary ventilation accounts for 3–5 percent of your resting energy demand. If compliance is reduced, the energy demand increases dramatically, and you can become exhausted simply trying to continue breathing.

MODES OF BREATHING

The respiratory muscles are used in various combinations, depending on the volume of air that must be moved into and out of the system. Respiratory movements are classified as quiet breathing or forced breathing.

In *quiet breathing*, inhalation involves muscular contractions, but exhalation is passive. Inhalation involves the contraction of the diaphragm and the external intercostal muscles. Diaphragm contraction normally accounts for around 75 percent of the air movement in normal quiet breathing, and the external intercostal muscles account for the remaining 25 percent. These percentages can change, however. For example, pregnant women increasingly rely on movements of the rib cage as expansion of the uterus forces abdominal organs against the diaphragm.

In *forced breathing*, both inhalation and exhalation are active. Forced breathing involves the accessory muscles during inhalation and the internal intercostal muscles and abdominal muscles during exhalation.

LUNG VOLUMES AND CAPACITIES

As noted earlier, a respiratory cycle is a single cycle of inhalation and exhalation. The amount of air moved into or out of the lungs during a single respiratory cycle is the **tidal volume.** Only a small proportion of the air in the lungs is exchanged during a single quiet respiratory cycle; the tidal volume can be increased by inhaling more vigorously and exhaling more completely.

The amounts of air in the lungs can be expressed as various *volumes* and *capacities* (Figure 15-11):

- *Expiratory reserve volume.* During a normal, quiet respiratory cycle under resting conditions, the *resting tidal volume* (V_T) averages about 500 mL. The amount of air that could be voluntarily expelled at the end of such a respiratory cycle—about 1000 mL—is the **expiratory reserve volume (ERV).**

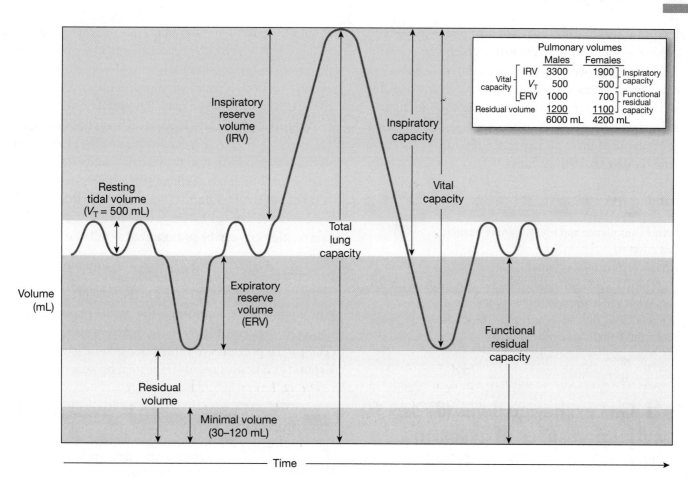

Pulmonary volumes			
		Males	Females
Vital capacity	IRV	3300	1900] Inspiratory capacity
	V_T	500	500
	ERV	1000	700] Functional residual capacity
Residual volume		1200	1100
		6000 mL	4200 mL

FIGURE 15-11 Respiratory Volumes and Capacities. This graph diagrams the relationships between the respiratory volumes and capacities of an average male. The table compares the values for males and females. The red line indicates the volume of air within the lungs as respiratory movements are performed.

- *Inspiratory reserve volume.* The **inspiratory reserve volume (IRV)** is the amount of air that can be taken in over and above the resting tidal volume. Because the lungs of males are larger than those of females, the IRV of males averages 3300 mL versus 1900 mL in females.

- *Vital capacity.* The sum of the inspiratory reserve volume, the expiratory reserve volume, and the tidal volume is the **vital capacity**—the maximum amount of air that can be moved into and out of the respiratory system in a single respiratory cycle.

- *Residual volume.* The **residual volume** is the amount of air that remains in your lungs even after a maximal exhalation—typically about 1200 mL in males and 1100 mL in females. Most of this residual volume exists because the lungs are held against the thoracic wall, preventing their elastic fibers from contracting further.

- *Minimal volume.* When the chest cavity has been penetrated, as in a pneumothorax, the lungs collapse, and the amount of air in the respiratory system is reduced to the **minimal volume.** Some air remains in the lungs, even at

minimal volume, because the surfactant coating the alveolar surfaces prevents their collapse.

Clinical Note

Pulmonary Function Tests

Pulmonary function tests monitor various aspects of respiratory function. A *spirometer* (spī-ROM-e-ter) measures parameters such as vital capacity, expiratory reserve volume, and inspiratory reserve volume. A *pneumotachometer* determines the rate of air movement. A *peak flow meter* records the maximum rate of forced expiration. These tests are relatively simple to perform and have considerable diagnostic significance. For example, in people with asthma the constricted airways tend to close before an exhalation is completed. As a result, pulmonary function tests show a reduction in vital capacity, ERV, and peak flow rate. The amount of air remaining in the lungs after the completion of a quiet respiratory cycle declines, and the narrow respiratory passageways reduce the flow rate as well. Air whistling through the constricted airways produces the characteristic "wheezing" that accompanies an asthma attack.

Not all of the inspired air reaches the alveolar exchange surfaces within the lungs. A typical inhalation pulls around 500 mL of air into the respiratory system. The first 350 mL travels along the conducting passageways and enters the alveolar spaces, but the last 150 mL never gets farther than the conducting passageways and does not take part in gas exchange with the blood. The total volume of these passageways (150 mL) is known as the *anatomic dead space* of the lungs.

CHECKPOINT

12. Define compliance and identify some factors that affect it.

13. What is resting tidal volume?

14. Mark breaks a rib and it punctures the chest wall on his left side. What will happen to his left lung?

15. In pneumonia, fluid accumulates in the alveoli of the lungs. How would vital capacity be affected?

See the blue Answers tab at the end of the book.

15-6 Gas exchange depends on the partial pressures of gases and the diffusion of molecules

During pulmonary ventilation, the alveoli are supplied with oxygen, and carbon dioxide is removed from the bloodstream. The actual process of gas exchange with the external environment occurs between the blood and alveolar air across the respiratory membrane. This process depends on (1) the partial pressures of the gases involved and (2) the diffusion of molecules between a gas and a liquid. ⚬ p. 65

MIXED GASES AND PARTIAL PRESSURES

The air we breathe is not a single gas but a mixture of gases. Nitrogen molecules (N_2) are the most abundant, accounting for about 78.6 percent of atmospheric gas molecules. Oxygen molecules (O_2), the second most abundant, make up roughly 20.9 percent of the atmospheric content. Most of the remaining 0.5 percent consists of water vapor molecules, with carbon dioxide (CO_2) contributing a mere 0.04 percent.

Atmospheric pressure at sea level is approximately 760 mm Hg. Each of the gases in air contributes to the total atmospheric pressure in proportion to its relative abundance. The pressure contributed by a single gas is the **partial pressure** of that gas, abbreviated as P. All the partial pressures added together equal the total pressure exerted by the gas mixture. For the atmosphere, this relationship can be summarized as follows:

$$P_{N_2} + P_{O_2} + P_{H_2O} + P_{CO_2} = 760\text{mm Hg}$$

Because each gas contributes to the total pressure in proportion to its relative abundance, the partial pressure of oxygen, P_{O_2}, is 20.9 percent of 760 mm Hg, or approximately 159 mm Hg. The partial pressures of other atmospheric gases are listed in Table 15-1. These values are important because the partial pres-

Clinical Note

Decompression Sickness

Decompression sickness is a painful condition that develops when a person is exposed to a sudden drop in atmospheric pressure. Nitrogen is the gas responsible for the problems experienced because of its high partial pressure in air. When the pressure drops, nitrogen comes out of solution and forms bubbles, just as bubbles form when a shaken can of soda is opened. The bubbles may form in joint cavities, in the bloodstream, and in the cerebrospinal fluid. Individuals with decompression sickness typically curl up because of the pain in affected joints; this reaction accounts for the condition's common name: *the bends*. Decompression sickness most often affects scuba divers who return to the surface too quickly after breathing air under greater than normal pressures while submerged. It can also develop in airline passengers subjected to sudden losses of cabin pressure.

TABLE 15-1 **Partial Pressures (mm Hg) and Normal Gas Concentrations (%) in Air**

SOURCE OF SAMPLE	NITROGEN (N_2)	OXYGEN (O_2)	WATER VAPOR (H_2O)	CARBON DIOXIDE (CO_2)
INHALED AIR (DRY)	597 (78.6%)	159 (20.9%)	3.7 (0.5%)	0.3 (0.04%)
ALVEOLAR AIR (SATURATED)	573 (75.4%)	100 (13.2%)	47 (6.2%)	40 (5.2%)
EXHALED AIR (SATURATED)	569 (74.8%)	116 (15.3%)	47 (6.2%)	28 (3.7%)

sure of each gas determines its rate of diffusion between alveolar air and the bloodstream. Note that whereas the partial pressure of oxygen determines how much oxygen enters solution, it has no effect on the diffusion rates of nitrogen or carbon dioxide.

ALVEOLAR AIR VERSUS ATMOSPHERIC AIR

As soon as air enters the respiratory tract, its characteristics begin to change. For example, in passing through the nasal cavity, the air becomes warmer and the amount of water vapor increases. On reaching the alveoli, the incoming air mixes with air that remained in the alveoli after the previous respiratory cycle. The resulting alveolar gas mixture, thus, contains more carbon dioxide and less oxygen than does atmospheric air. As noted earlier, the last 150 mL of inhaled air (about 30% of the tidal volume) never gets farther than the conducting passageways, the anatomic dead space of the lungs. During expiration, the departing alveolar air mixes with air in the dead space to produce yet another mixture that differs from both atmospheric and alveolar samples. The differences in composition between atmospheric (inhaled) and alveolar air can be seen in Table 15-1.

PARTIAL PRESSURES IN THE PULMONARY AND SYSTEMIC CIRCUITS

Figure 15-12 indicates the partial pressures of oxygen and carbon dioxide in alveolar air and capillaries, and in the arteries and veins of the pulmonary and systemic circuits. The deoxygenated blood delivered by the pulmonary arteries has a lower P_{O_2} and a higher P_{CO_2} than does alveolar air (**Figure 15-12a**). Diffusion between the alveolar air and the pulmonary capillaries, thus, elevates the P_{O_2} of the blood while lowering its P_{CO_2}. By the time it enters the pulmonary venules, the oxygenated blood has reached equilibrium with the alveolar air, so it departs the alveoli with a P_{O_2} of about 100 mm Hg and a P_{CO_2} of roughly 40 mm Hg.

Normal interstitial fluid has a P_{O_2} of 40 mm Hg and a P_{CO_2} of 45 mm Hg. As a result, oxygen diffuses out of the capillaries, and carbon dioxide diffuses in, until the capillary partial pressures are the same as those in the adjacent tissues (**Figure 15-12b**). When the blood returns to the alveolar capillaries, external respiration will replace the oxygen released into the tissues at the same time that the excess CO_2 is lost.

CHECKPOINT

16. True or false: Each gas in a mixture exerts a partial pressure equal to its relative abundance.

17. What happens to air as it passes through the nasal cavity?

18. Compare the oxygen and carbon dioxide content of alveolar air and atmospheric air.

See the blue Answers tab at the end of the book.

15-7 Most O₂ is transported bound to hemoglobin (Hb), whereas CO₂ is transported as carbonic acid, bound to Hb, or dissolved in plasma

Oxygen and carbon dioxide have limited solubilities in blood plasma. The limited extent to which these gases dissolve in plasma is a problem because peripheral tissues need more oxygen and generate more carbon dioxide than the plasma can absorb and transport. The problem is solved by red blood cells (RBCs), which take up dissolved oxygen and carbon dioxide molecules from plasma and either bind them (in the case of oxygen) or use them to manufacture soluble compounds (in the case of carbon dioxide). Because these reactions remove dissolved gases from the blood plasma, gases continue to diffuse into the blood and never reach equilibrium. These reactions are also *temporary* and *completely reversible.* When plasma oxygen or carbon dioxide concentrations are high, the excess molecules are removed by RBCs; when the plasma concentrations are low, the RBCs release their stored reserves.

OXYGEN TRANSPORT

Only about 1.5 percent of the oxygen content of arterial blood consists of oxygen molecules in solution. The rest of the

Clinical Note

Emphysema

Emphysema (em-fi-ZĒ-ma) is a chronic, progressive condition in which certain factors—possibly including the inhalation of fine particulate matter or toxic vapors, such as those in cigarette smoke—destroy alveolar surfaces, resulting in an inadequate surface area for oxygen and carbon dioxide exchange. The alveoli gradually expand, their walls become incomplete, and adjacent alveoli merge to form larger, nonfunctional air spaces, resulting in shortness of breath and an inability to tolerate physical exertion. Genetic factors also predispose individuals to this condition. Some degree of emphysema is a normal consequence of aging; an estimated 66 percent of adult males and 25 percent of adult females have detectable emphysematous areas in their lungs.

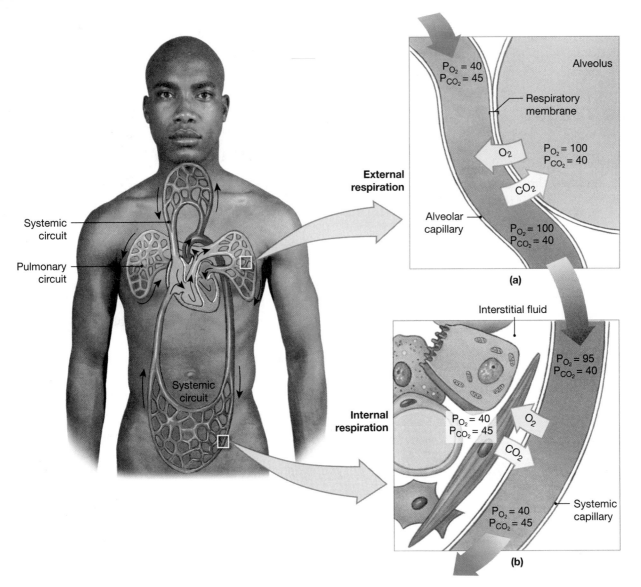

FIGURE 15-12 **An Overview of Respiration and Respiratory Processes. (a)** External respiration is the diffusion of gases between the blood and alveolar air across the respiratory membrane. Diffusion between the alveolar air and the pulmonary capillaries elevates the P_{O_2} of the blood and lowers its P_{CO_2}. **(b)** Internal respiration is the diffusion of gases between blood and interstitial fluid across capillary cell membranes. Diffusion between the systemic capillaries and interstitial fluid lowers the P_{O_2} of the blood and increases its P_{CO_2}.

oxygen molecules are bound to hemoglobin (Hb) molecules—specifically, to the iron ions in the center of heme units. ∞ p. 385 This process occurs through a reversible reaction that can be summarized as follows:

$$Hb + O_2 \rightleftharpoons HbO_2$$

The amount of oxygen bound (or released) by hemoglobin depends primarily on the P_{O_2} of its surroundings. The lower the oxygen content of a tissue, the more oxygen is released by hemoglobin molecules passing through local capillaries. For example, inactive tissues have little demand for oxygen, and the

local P_{O_2} is about 40 mm Hg. Under these conditions, hemoglobin releases about 25 percent of its stored oxygen. In contrast, if the local P_{O_2} of active tissues declines to 15–20 mm Hg (about one-half of the P_{O_2} of normal tissue), hemoglobin then releases up to 80 percent of its stored oxygen. In practical terms, this means that active tissues will receive roughly three times as much oxygen as will inactive tissues.

In addition to the effect of P_{O_2} the amount of oxygen released by hemoglobin is influenced by pH and temperature. Active tissues generate acids that lower the pH of the interstitial fluids. When the pH declines, hemoglobin molecules re-

Carbon Monoxide Poisoning

Murder victims who die in their cars inside a locked garage are popular characters for mystery writers. In real life, entire families are killed each winter by leaky furnaces or space heaters. The cause of death is **carbon monoxide poisoning.** The exhaust of automobiles and other petroleum-burning engines, of oil lamps, and of fuel-fired space heaters contains carbon monoxide (CO) gas. CO competes with O_2 molecules for the binding sites on heme units. Unfortunately, the carbon monoxide usually wins because at very low partial pressures it has a much stronger affinity for hemoglobin. The bond is extremely strong, and the attachment of a CO molecule essentially makes that heme unit unavailable for respiratory purposes. If CO molecules make up just 0.1 percent of inhaled air, enough hemoglobin will be affected that survival is impossible without medical assistance. Treatment may include (1) the administration of pure oxygen, because at sufficiently high partial pressures the O_2 molecules "bump" the CO from the hemoglobin; and, if necessary, (2) the transfusion of compatible red blood cells.

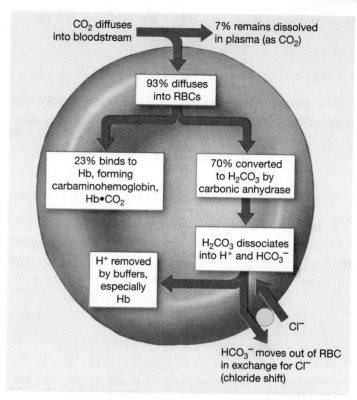

FIGURE 15-13 **Carbon Dioxide Transport in the Blood.**

lease their bound oxygen molecules more readily. Hemoglobin also releases more oxygen when body temperature rises.

All three of these factors (P_{O_2}, pH, and temperature) are important during periods of maximal exertion. When a skeletal muscle works hard, its temperature rises and the local pH and P_{O_2} decline. The combination makes the hemoglobin entering the area release much more oxygen that can be used by active muscle fibers. Without this automatic adjustment, tissue P_{O_2} would fall to very low levels almost immediately, and the exertion would come to a premature halt.

CARBON DIOXIDE TRANSPORT

Carbon dioxide is generated by aerobic metabolism in peripheral tissues. After entering the bloodstream, a CO_2 molecule may (1) dissolve in the plasma, (2) bind to hemoglobin within red blood cells, or (3) be converted to a molecule of carbonic acid (H_2CO_3) (Figure 15-13). All three processes are completely reversible.

The Big Picture

Hemoglobin within RBCs carries most of the oxygen in the bloodstream, and it releases it in response to changes in the oxygen partial pressure in the surrounding plasma. If the P_{O_2} increases, hemoglobin binds oxygen; if the P_{O_2} decreases, hemoglobin releases oxygen. At a given P_{O_2}, hemoglobin will release additional oxygen if the pH decreases or the temperature increases.

Transport in Plasma

Plasma becomes saturated with carbon dioxide quite rapidly, and only about 7 percent of the carbon dioxide absorbed by peripheral capillaries is transported as dissolved gas molecules. The rest diffuses into RBCs.

Hemoglobin Binding

Once in red blood cells, some of the carbon dioxide molecules are bound to the protein "globin" portions of hemoglobin molecules, forming **carbaminohemoglobin** (kar-bām-i-nō-hē-mō-GLŌ-bin). Such binding does not interfere with the binding of oxygen to heme units, so hemoglobin can transport both oxygen and carbon dioxide simultaneously. Normally, about 23 percent of the carbon dioxide entering the blood in peripheral tissues is transported as carbaminohemoglobin.

Carbonic Acid Formation

About 70 percent of all carbon dioxide molecules in the body are ultimately transported in the plasma as bicarbonate ions. First, carbon dioxide in RBCs is converted to carbonic acid by the enzyme carbonic anhydrase. However, the carbonic acid molecules do not remain intact; almost immediately, each of these molecules dissociates into a hydrogen ion and a bicarbonate ion. The reactions can be summarized as follows:

$$CO_2 + H_2O \overset{\text{carbonic anhydrase}}{\rightleftharpoons} H_2CO_3 \rightleftharpoons H^+ + HCO_3^-$$

The reactions occur very rapidly and are completely reversible. Because most of the carbonic acid formed immediately dissociates into bicarbonate and hydrogen ions, we can ignore the intermediary step and summarize the reaction as follows:

$$CO_2 + H_2O \overset{\text{carbonic anhydrase}}{\rightleftharpoons} H^+ + HCO_3^-$$

In peripheral capillaries, this reaction rapidly ties up large numbers of carbon dioxide molecules. The reaction is driven from left to right because carbon dioxide continues to arrive, diffusing out of the interstitial fluids, and the hydrogen ions and bicarbonate ions are being removed continuously. Most of the hydrogen ions bind to hemoglobin molecules, preventing both their release from the RBCs and a lowering of plasma pH. The bicarbonate ions diffuse into the surrounding plasma. The exit of the bicarbonate ions is matched by the entry of chloride ions from the plasma, thus trading one anion for another. This mass movement of chloride ions into RBCs is known as the *chloride shift*.

When venous blood reaches the alveoli, carbon dioxide diffuses out of the plasma, and the P_{CO_2} declines. Because all of the carbon dioxide transport mechanisms are reversible, when carbon dioxide diffuses out of the red blood cells, the processes shown in **Figure 15-13** proceed in the opposite direction: Hydrogen ions leave the hemoglobin molecules, and bicarbonate ions diffuse into the cytoplasm of the RBCs and are converted to water and CO_2.

Figure 15-14 summarizes the events by which oxygen and carbon dioxide are transported and exchanged between the respiratory and cardiovascular systems.

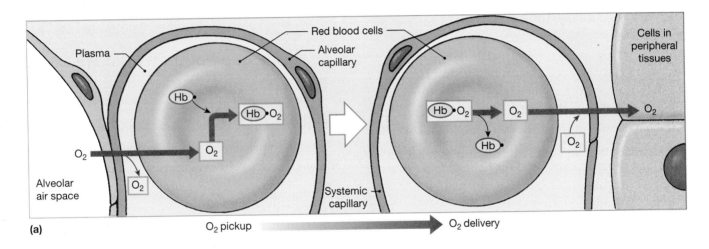

(a) O_2 pickup ⟶ O_2 delivery

(b) CO_2 delivery ⟵ CO_2 pickup

FIGURE 15-14 A Summary of Gas Transport and Exchange. Shown here are the events that occur in **(a)** oxygen pickup from the alveoli and delivery to peripheral tissues and **(b)** carbon dioxide pickup from peripheral tissues and delivery to the alveoli.

The Big Picture

Carbon dioxide travels in the bloodstream primarily as bicarbonate ions, which form through dissociation of the carbonic acid produced by carbonic anhydrase inside RBCs. Lesser amounts of CO_2 are bound to hemoglobin or dissolved in plasma.

CHECKPOINT

19. Identify the three ways that carbon dioxide is transported in the bloodstream.

20. As you exercise, hemoglobin releases more oxygen to active skeletal muscles than it does when the muscles are at rest. Why?

21. How would blockage of the trachea affect blood pH?

See the blue Answers tab at the end of the book.

15-8 Neurons in the medulla oblongata and pons, along with respiratory reflexes, control respiration

Cells continuously absorb oxygen from the interstitial fluids and generate carbon dioxide. Under normal conditions, cellular rates of absorption and generation are matched by the rates of delivery and removal at the capillaries. Moreover, those rates are identical to those of oxygen absorption and carbon dioxide excretion at the lungs. If these rates become unbalanced, the activities of the cardiovascular and respiratory systems must be adjusted. Equilibrium is restored through homeostatic mechanisms that involve (1) changes in blood flow and oxygen delivery under local control and (2) changes in the depth and rate of respiration under the control of the brain's respiratory centers.

THE LOCAL CONTROL OF RESPIRATION

Both the rate of oxygen delivery at each tissue and the efficiency of oxygen pickup at the lungs are regulated at the local level. If a peripheral tissue becomes more active, the interstitial P_{O_2} falls and the P_{CO_2} rises. These changes increase the difference between partial pressures in the tissues and arriving blood, so more oxygen is delivered and more carbon dioxide is carried away. In addition, rising P_{CO_2} levels cause the relaxation of smooth muscles in the walls of arterioles in the area, increasing blood flow.

Local adjustments in blood flow, or of the flow of air into alveoli, also improve the efficiency of gas transport. For example, as blood flows to alveolar capillaries, it is directed to pulmonary lobules in which P_{O_2} is relatively high. This occurs because precapillary sphincters in alveolar capillary beds constrict when the local P_{O_2} is low. (This response is the opposite of that seen in peripheral tissues. ∞ p. 433) Smooth muscles in the walls of bronchioles are sensitive to the P_{CO_2} of the air they contain. When the P_{CO_2} increases, the bronchioles dilate; when the P_{CO_2} declines, the bronchioles constrict. Airflow is, therefore, directed to lobules in which the P_{CO_2} is high.

CONTROL BY THE RESPIRATORY CENTERS OF THE BRAIN

Respiratory control has both involuntary and voluntary components. The brain's involuntary respiratory centers (in the medulla oblongata and pons) regulate the respiratory muscles and control the frequency (respiratory rate) and the depth of breathing. They do so in response to sensory information arriving from the lungs and other portions of the respiratory tract, as well as from a variety of other sites. The voluntary control of respiration reflects activity in the cerebral cortex that affects the output of the respiratory centers or of motor neurons that control respiratory muscles.

The **respiratory centers** are three pairs of nuclei in the reticular formation of the pons and medulla oblongata. The **respiratory rhythmicity centers** of the medulla oblongata set the pace for respiration. Each center can be subdivided into a *dorsal respiratory group (DRG)*, which contains an *inspiratory center,* and a *ventral respiratory group (VRG)*, which contains an *expiratory center.* Their output is adjusted by the two pairs of nuclei making up the respiratory centers of the pons. The centers in the pons adjust the respiratory rate and the depth of respiration in response to sensory stimuli, emotional states, or speech patterns.

The Activities of the Respiratory Rhythmicity Centers

The DRG's inspiratory center functions in every respiratory cycle. It contains neurons that control the external intercostal muscles and the diaphragm (inspiratory muscles). During quiet breathing, the neurons of the inspiratory center gradually increase stimulation of the inspiratory muscles for 2 seconds, and then the inspiratory center becomes silent for the next 3 seconds. During that period of inactivity, the inspiratory muscles relax and passive exhalation occurs. The inspiratory center will maintain this basic rhythm even in the absence of sensory or regulatory stimuli. The VRG functions only during forced breathing when it activates the accessory muscles involved in inhalation and exhalation. The relationships between the inspiratory and expiratory centers during quiet breathing and forced breathing are diagrammed in Figure 15-15.

The performance of these respiratory centers can be affected by any factor that alters the metabolic or chemical activities of neural tissues. For example, elevated body temperature or CNS stimulants (such as amphetamines or caffeine) increase the respiratory rate. Conversely, decreased body temperature or CNS depressants (such as barbiturates or opiates) reduce the respiratory rate. Respiratory activities are also strongly influenced by reflexes that are triggered by mechanical or chemical stimuli.

THE REFLEX CONTROL OF RESPIRATION

Normal breathing occurs automatically without conscious control. The activities of the respiratory centers are modified by sensory information from mechanoreceptors (such as stretch and pressure receptors) and chemoreceptors. Information from these receptors alters the pattern of respiration. The induced changes are called *respiratory reflexes.*

Mechanoreceptor Reflexes

Mechanoreceptors respond to changes in lung volume or to changes in arterial blood pressure. Several populations of baroreceptors that are involved in respiratory function are described in Chapter 9. ∞ p. 311

The **inflation reflex** prevents the lungs from overexpanding during forced breathing. The mechanoreceptors involved are stretch receptors that are stimulated when the lungs expand. Sensory fibers leaving the lungs reach the respiratory rhythmicity centers through the vagus nerves. As the volume of the lungs increases, the DRG inspiratory center is gradually inhibited, and the VRG expiratory center is stimulated. Thus, inhalation stops as the lungs near maximum volume, and active exhalation then begins. In contrast, the **deflation reflex** inhibits the expiratory center and stimulates the inspiratory center when the lungs are collapsing. The smaller the volume of the lungs, the greater the inhibition of the expiratory center.

Although neither the inflation reflex nor the deflation reflex is involved in normal quiet breathing, both are important in regulating the forced inhalations and exhalations that accompany strenuous exercise. Together, the inflation and deflation reflexes are known as the *Hering-Breuer reflexes,* after the physiologists who described them in 1865.

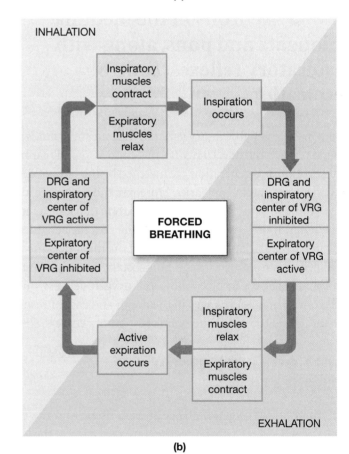

FIGURE 15-15 Basic Regulatory Patterns of Respiration.
This figure depicts the events occurring during **(a)** quiet breathing and **(b)** forced breathing.

The effects of the carotid and aortic baroreceptors on systemic blood pressure were described in Chapter 13. ∞ p. 441

The output from these baroreceptors also affects the respiratory centers. When blood pressure falls, the respiratory rate increases; when blood pressure rises, the respiratory rate declines. This adjustment results from the stimulation or inhibition of the respiratory centers by sensory fibers in the glossopharyngeal (N IX) and vagus (N X) nerves.

Chemoreceptor Reflexes

Chemoreceptors respond to chemical changes in the blood and cerebrospinal fluid. ∞ p. 312 Their stimulation leads to an increase in the depth and rate of respiration. Centers in the carotid bodies (adjacent to the carotid sinus) and the aortic bodies (near the aortic arch) are sensitive to the pH, P_{CO_2}, and P_{O_2} in arterial blood. Receptors in the medulla oblongata respond to the pH and P_{CO_2} in cerebrospinal fluid.

Carbon dioxide levels have a much more powerful effect on respiratory activity than do oxygen levels. The reason is that a relatively small increase in arterial P_{CO_2} stimulates CO_2 receptors, but arterial P_{O_2} does not usually decline enough to activate oxygen receptors. Carbon dioxide levels are, therefore, responsible for regulating respiratory activity under normal conditions. However, when arterial P_{O_2} does fall, the two types of receptors cooperate. Carbon dioxide is generated during oxygen consumption, so when oxygen concentrations are falling rapidly, carbon dioxide levels are usually increasing. As a result, you cannot hold your breath "until you turn blue." Once the P_{CO_2} rises to critical levels, you will be forced to take a breath.

The cooperation between the carbon dioxide and oxygen receptors breaks down only under unusual circumstances. For example, an individual can hold his or her breath longer than normal by taking deep, full breaths, but the practice is very

---

Clinical Note   Lung Cancer, Smoking, and Diet

Lung cancer, or *bronchopulmonary carcinoma,* is an aggressive class of malignancies originating in the bronchial passageways or alveoli. These cancers affect the epithelial cells that line conducting passageways, mucous glands, or alveoli. Signs and symptoms usually do not appear until the condition has progressed to the point that the tumor masses are restricting airflow or compressing adjacent structures. Chest pain, shortness of breath, a cough or a wheeze, and weight loss commonly occur. Treatments vary with the cellular organization of the tumor and whether metastasis (cancer cell migration) has occurred, but surgery, radiation exposure, or chemotherapy may be involved.

Deaths from lung cancer were rare at the beginning of the twentieth century, but 29,000 such deaths occurred in the United States in 1956; 105,000 in 1978; and an estimated 161,840 in 2008. The rise coincided with the increased rate of smoking in the population. From 2007 to 2008, about 15 percent of new cancers detected were lung cancers; in the United States in 2008, an estimated 114,690 men and 100,330 women were diagnosed with this condition. Compared to rates in 1989, these numbers reflect a marked decrease among men (fewer men are smoking) and an increase among women (more women are smoking). Lung cancers now account for about 29 percent of all cancer deaths, making this condition the primary cause of cancer death in the U.S. population.

Despite advances in the treatment of other forms of cancer, the survival statistics for lung cancer have not changed significantly. Even with early detection, five-year survival rates are only 30 percent for men and 50 percent for women, and most lung cancer patients die within a year of diagnosis. Detailed statistical and experimental evidence has shown that 85–90 percent of all lung cancers are the direct result of cigarette smoking. Claims to the contrary are simply unjustified and insupportable. The data are far too extensive to detail here, but the incidence of lung cancer for nonsmokers is 3.4 per 100,000 population, whereas the incidence for smokers ranges from 59.3 per 100,000 for those who smoke between a half-pack and a pack of cigarettes a day, to 217.3 per 100,000 for those smoking one to two packs a day.

Smoking changes the quality of the inspired air, making it drier and contaminated with several carcinogenic compounds and particulate matter. The combination damages epithelial cells throughout the respiratory system, which overloads the respiratory defenses. Whether lung cancer develops appears to be related to the total cumulative exposure to the carcinogens. The more cigarettes smoked, the greater the risk, whether those cigarettes are smoked over a period of weeks or years. Up to the point at which tumors form, the histological changes induced by smoking are reversible; a normal epithelium will return if the carcinogens are removed. At the same time, the statistical risks decline to significantly lower levels. Ten years after quitting, an ex-smoker stands only a 10 percent greater chance of developing lung cancer than a nonsmoker.

The fact that cigarette smoking often causes cancer is not surprising in view of the toxic chemicals in the smoke. What is surprising is that more smokers do not develop lung cancer. Evidence indicates that some smokers have a genetic predisposition for developing one form of lung cancer. Dietary factors may play a role in preventing lung cancer, although the details are controversial. In terms of the influence of such factors on the risk of lung cancer, there is general agreement that (1) vitamin A has no effect; (2) vegetables containing beta-carotene reduce the risk, but pills containing beta-carotene may increase the risk; and (3) a high-cholesterol, high-fat diet increases the risk.

dangerous. The danger lies in the fact that the increased ability is due not to extra oxygen but to the loss of carbon dioxide. If the P_{CO_2} is reduced enough, breath-holding ability may increase to the point that an individual becomes unconscious from oxygen starvation in the brain without ever feeling the urge to breathe.

The chemoreceptors monitoring CO_2 levels are also sensitive to pH, and any condition affecting the pH of blood or CSF will affect respiratory performance. For example, the rise in lactic acid levels after exercise causes a drop in pH that helps stimulate respiratory activity.

Clinical Note

Hypercapnia

The term **hypercapnia** (hī-per-KAP-nē-uh) refers to an increase in the P_{CO_2} of arterial blood. Such a change stimulates the chemoreceptors in the carotid and aortic bodies and, because carbon dioxide crosses the blood-brain barrier quite rapidly, the chemoreceptive neurons of the medulla oblongata as well. These receptors stimulate the respiratory centers to produce **hyperventilation** (hī-per-ven-ti-LĀ-shun), an increase in the rate and depth of respiration. Breathing becomes more rapid, and more air moves into and out of the lungs with each breath. Because more air moves into and out of the alveoli each minute, alveolar concentrations of carbon dioxide decline, accelerating the diffusion of carbon dioxide from the alveolar capillaries. If the arterial P_{CO_2} drops below normal levels, chemoreceptor activity declines and the respiratory rate falls. This **hypoventilation** continues until the P_{CO_2} returns to normal.

CONTROL BY HIGHER CENTERS

Higher centers influence respiration through their effects on the respiratory centers of the pons and by the direct control of respiratory muscles. For example, the contractions of respiratory muscles can be voluntarily suppressed or exaggerated; this control is necessary during talking or singing. The depth and rate of respiration also change following the activation of centers involved with rage, eating, or sexual arousal. These changes, directed by the limbic system, occur at an involuntary level. Figure 15-16 summarizes the factors involved in the regulation of respiration.

RESPIRATORY CHANGES AT BIRTH

Several important differences exist between the respiratory systems of a fetus and a newborn. Before delivery, the pulmonary

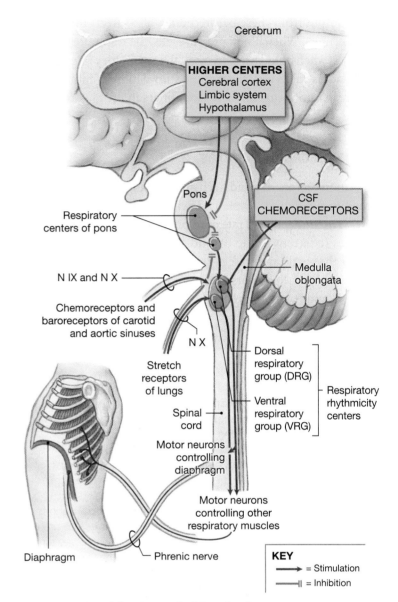

FIGURE 15-16 The Control of Respiration.

vessels are collapsed, so pulmonary arterial resistance is high. The rib cage is compressed, and the lungs and conducting passageways contain only small amounts of fluid and no air.

At birth, the newborn takes a truly heroic first breath through powerful contractions of the diaphragm and the external intercostal muscles. The inhaled air enters the passageways with enough force to push the contained fluids out of the way and to inflate the entire bronchial tree and most of the alveoli. The same drop in pressure that pulls air into the lungs pulls blood into the pulmonary circulation. The exhalation that follows fails to empty the lungs completely, because the rib cage does not return to its former, fully compressed state. Cartilages and connective tissues keep the conducting passageways open, and

Clinical Note

SIDS

Sudden infant death syndrome (SIDS), also known as *crib death,* kills an estimated 2500 infants each year in the United States. Most crib deaths occur between midnight and 9:00 A.M., in the late fall or winter, and involve infants 2 to 4 months old. Eyewitness accounts indicate that the sleeping infant suddenly stops breathing, turns blue, and relaxes. Various risk factors likely to cause a SIDS death have been suggested; sleeping on the stomach is at the top of the list. Genetic factors appear to be involved, but controversy remains as to the relative importance of other factors. The age at the time of death corresponds with a period when the respiratory centers are establishing connections with other portions of the brain. It has been proposed that SIDS results from a problem in the interconnection process that disrupts the reflexive respiratory pattern.

the surfactant covering the alveolar surfaces prevents their collapse. Subsequent breaths complete the inflation of the alveoli.

Pathologists sometimes use these physical changes to determine whether a newborn died before delivery or shortly thereafter. Before the first breath, the lungs are completely filled with fluid, and they will sink if placed in water. After an infant's first breath, even the collapsed lungs contain enough air to keep them afloat.

The Big Picture

A basic pace of respiration is established by the interplay between respiratory centers in the pons and medulla oblongata. That pace is modified in response to input from chemoreceptors, baroreceptors, and stretch receptors. In general, carbon dioxide levels, rather than oxygen levels, are the primary drivers for respiratory activity. Respiratory activity can also be interrupted by protective reflexes and adjusted by the conscious control of respiratory muscles.

CHECKPOINT

22. Are peripheral chemoreceptors more sensitive to carbon dioxide levels or to oxygen levels?

23. Strenuous exercise stimulates which set of respiratory reflexes?

24. Little Johnny tells his mother he will hold his breath until he turns blue and dies. Should she worry?

See the blue Answers tab at the end of the book.

15-9 Respiratory performance declines with age

Of the many factors that interact to reduce the efficiency of the respiratory system in elderly individuals, two are noteworthy:

1. Chest movements are restricted by arthritic changes in rib articulations, decreased flexibility at the costal cartilages, and age-related muscular weakness. (These skeletal and muscular restrictions counterbalance an increase in compliance of the lungs that occurs with the deterioration of elastic tissue with age.) Together, the stiffening and reduction in chest movement limit pulmonary ventilation and vital capacity, and contribute to the reduction in exercise performance and capabilities with increasing age.

2. Some degree of emphysema is normal in individuals over age 50. However, the extent varies widely with lifetime exposure to cigarette smoke and other respiratory irritants. Comparative studies of nonsmokers and those who have smoked for various lengths of time clearly show the negative effects of smoking on respiratory performance.

CHECKPOINT

25. Describe two age-related changes that combine to reduce the efficiency of the respiratory system.

See the blue Answers tab at the end of the book.

15-10 The respiratory system provides oxygen to, and removes carbon dioxide from, other organ systems

The respiratory system has extensive structural and functional connections to the cardiovascular system. Its many functional links to other organ systems are depicted in the Respiratory System in Perspective (p. 532).

CHECKPOINT

26. Describe the functional relationship between the respiratory system and all other organ systems.

27. What homeostatic functions of the nervous system support the functional role of the respiratory system?

See the blue Answers tab at the end of the book.

RELATED CLINICAL TERMS

anoxia (an-ok-SĒ-uh): A lack of oxygen in a tissue.

apnea (AP-nē-uh): The cessation of breathing.

asthma (AZ-muh): An acute respiratory disorder characterized by unusually sensitive, irritated conducting airways.

atelectasis (at-e-LEK-ta-sis): A collapsed lung.

bronchitis (brong-KĪ-tis): Inflammation of the bronchial lining.

bronchoscope: A fiber-optic bundle small enough to be inserted into the trachea and finer airways; the procedure is called *bronchoscopy*.

chronic obstructive pulmonary disease (COPD): A condition characterized by chronic bronchitis and chronic airway obstruction.

cystic fibrosis (CF): A relatively common lethal inherited disease; respiratory mucosa secretions become too thick to be transported easily, leading to respiratory problems.

dyspnea (DISP-nē-uh): Difficult or labored breathing.

emphysema (em-fi-ZĒ-ma): A chronic, progressive condition characterized by shortness of breath and an inability to tolerate physical exertion due to enlarged air spaces in the lungs.

epistaxis (ep-i-STAK-sis): A nosebleed.

hypercapnia (hī-per-KAP-nē-uh): An abnormally high level of carbon dioxide in the blood.

hypocapnia: An abnormally low level of carbon dioxide in the blood.

hypoxia (hī-POKS-ē-uh): A low oxygen concentration in a tissue.

influenza: A viral infection of the respiratory tract; "the flu."

pleurisy: Inflammation of the pleurae and secretion of excess amounts of pleural fluid.

pneumonia (noo-MŌ-nē-uh): A respiratory disorder characterized by fluid leakage into the alveoli and/or swelling and constriction of the respiratory bronchioles.

pneumothorax (noo-mō-THŌ-raks): The entry of air into the pleural cavity.

pulmonary embolism: Blockage of a branch of a pulmonary artery, typically by a blood clot (thrombus), producing an interruption of blood flow to a group of lobules and/or alveoli.

respiratory distress syndrome: A condition resulting from inadequate surfactant production and associated alveolar collapse.

tracheostomy (trā-kē-OS-to-mē): The insertion of a tube directly into the trachea to bypass a blocked or damaged larynx.

Chapter 15 Review

KEY TERMS

alveolus/alveoli *503*
bronchial tree *509*
bronchiole *509*
bronchus/bronchi *509*
larynx *506*
lungs *512*
nasal cavity *505*
partial pressure *518*

pharynx *506*
respiratory membrane *512*
respiratory mucosa *504*
respiratory rhythmicity
  centers *523*
surfactant *511*
trachea *508*
vital capacity *517*

SUMMARY OUTLINE

iP Use *Interactive Physiology*® (IP)—available on the IP CD packaged with your new textbook—to help you understand difficult physiological concepts. Follow these navigation paths on IP for concepts in this chapter:

- Respiratory System/Pulmonary Ventilation.
- Respiratory System/Gas Transport.
- Respiratory System/Gas Exchange.
- Respiratory System/Control of Respiration.

An Introduction to the Respiratory System *p. 503*

1. To continue functioning, body cells must obtain oxygen and eliminate carbon dioxide. These processes take place in **alveoli**, air-filled pockets in the lungs.

15-1 The respiratory system, composed of conducting and respiratory portions, has several basic functions *p. 503*

2. The functions of the **respiratory system** include (1) providing an area for gas exchange between air and circulating blood; (2) moving air to and from exchange surfaces; (3) protecting exchange surfaces from environmental fluctuations and defending the respiratory system and other tissues from pathogens; (4) producing sound; and (5) facilitating the stimulation of olfactory (smell) receptors.

3. The respiratory system includes the nose (including the nasal cavity and paranasal sinuses), pharynx, larynx, trachea, and various conducting passageways leading to the surfaces of the lungs. (*Figure 15-1*)

4. The **respiratory tract** consists of the conducting passageways that carry air to and from the alveoli.

5. The **respiratory mucosa** (respiratory epithelium and underlying connective tissue) lines the conducting portion of the respiratory system (*Figure 15-2*).

15-2 The nose, pharynx, larynx, trachea, bronchi, and larger bronchioles conduct air into the lungs *p. 504*

6. Air normally enters the respiratory system through the **external nares,** which open into the **nasal cavity.** The **nasal vestibule** (entrance) is guarded by hairs that screen out large particles. *(Figure 15-3)*

7. The **hard palate** separates the oral and nasal cavities. The **soft palate** separates the superior nasopharynx from the rest of the pharynx. The **internal nares** connect the nasal cavity and nasopharynx. *(Figure 15-3)*

8. The **pharynx** (throat) is a chamber shared by the digestive and respiratory systems.

9. Inhaled air passes through the **glottis** en route to the lungs; the **larynx** surrounds and protects the glottis. The **epiglottis** projects into the pharynx. Exhaled air passing through the glottis vibrates the **true vocal cords** and produces sound. *(Figure 15-4)*

10. The wall of the **trachea** ("windpipe") contains C-shaped tracheal cartilages, which protect the airway. The posterior tracheal wall can distort to permit large masses of food to pass. *(Figure 15-5)*

11. The trachea branches within the mediastinum to form the **right** and **left primary bronchi.** *(Figure 15-5)*

12. The primary bronchi, **secondary bronchi,** and their branches form the *bronchial tree.* As the **tertiary bronchi** branch within the lung, the amount of cartilage in their walls decreases, and the amount of smooth muscle increases. *(Figure 15-6a)*

15-3 The smallest bronchioles and the alveoli within the lungs make up the respiratory portion of the respiratory tract *p. 509*

13. Each terminal **bronchiole** delivers air to a single pulmonary **lobule.** Within the lobule, the terminal bronchiole branches into *respiratory bronchioles. (Figure 15-6b)*

14. The respiratory bronchioles open into **alveolar ducts,** which end at **alveolar sacs.** Many alveoli are interconnected at each alveolar sac. *(Figure 15-7a,b)*

15. The **respiratory membrane** consists of (1) a simple squamous alveolar epithelium, (2) a capillary endothelium, and (3) their fused basement membranes. **Septal cells** produce **surfactant,** an oily secretion that keeps the alveoli from collapsing. **Alveolar macrophages** engulf foreign particles. *(Figure 15-7c,d)*

16. The **lungs** are made up of five **lobes:** three in the right lung and two in the left lung. *(Figure 15-8)*

17. Each lung occupies a single pleural cavity lined by a **pleura** (serous membrane). *(Figure 15-9)*

15-4 External respiration and internal respiration allow gas exchange within the body *p. 514*

18. *Respiration* involves two integrated processes: **external respiration** (the exchange of oxygen and carbon dioxide between interstitial fluid and the external environment) and **internal respiration** (the exchange of oxygen and carbon dioxide between interstitial fluid and cells). If the oxygen content declines, the affected tissues suffer from **hypoxia;** if the oxygen supply is completely shut off, **anoxia** and tissue death result.

19. External respiration includes *pulmonary ventilation,* or breathing (movement of air into and out of the lungs); *gas diffusion* between the alveoli and circulating blood, and between the blood and interstitial fluids; and *transport of oxygen and carbon dioxide* between the blood and interstitial fluids.

15-5 Pulmonary ventilation—the exchange of air between the atmosphere and the lungs—involves pressure changes and muscle movement *p. 514*

20. A single breath, or **respiratory cycle,** consists of an inhalation (*inspiration*) and an exhalation (*expiration*).

21. The relationship between the pressure inside the respiratory tract and atmospheric pressure determines the direction of airflow. *(Figure 15-10)*

22. The diaphragm and the external intercostal muscles are involved in *quiet breathing,* in which exhalation is passive. Accessory muscles become active during the active inspiratory and expiratory movements of *forced breathing,* in which exhalation is active. *(Figure 15-10)*

23. The **vital capacity** includes the **tidal volume** plus the **expiratory reserve volume** and the **inspiratory reserve volume.** The air left in the lungs at the end of maximum expiration is the **residual volume.** *(Figure 15-11)*

15-6 Gas exchange depends on the partial pressures of gases and the diffusion of molecules *p. 518*

24. In a mixed gas, the individual gases exert a pressure proportional to their abundance in the mixture. The pressure contributed by a single gas is its **partial pressure.**

25. Alveolar air and atmospheric air differ in composition. Gas exchange occurs efficiently across the respiratory membrane. *(Figure 15-12; Table 15-1)*

15-7 Most O_2 is transported bound to hemoglobin (Hb), whereas CO_2 is transported as carbonic acid, bound to Hb, or dissolved in plasma *p. 519*

26. Blood entering peripheral capillaries delivers oxygen and takes up carbon dioxide. The transport of oxygen and carbon dioxide in the blood involves reactions that are completely reversible.

27. Over the range of oxygen pressures normally present in the body, a small change in plasma P_{O_2} will result in a large change in the amount of oxygen bound or released by hemoglobin.

28. Aerobic metabolism in peripheral tissues generates carbon dioxide. Roughly 7 percent of the CO_2 transported in the blood is dissolved in the plasma; another 23 percent is bound as **carbaminohemoglobin** in RBCs; and 70 percent is converted to carbonic acid, which dissociates into a hydrogen ion and a bicarbonate ion. The bicarbonate ion exits the RBC and enters the plasma. *(Figures 15-13, 15-14)*

15-8 Neurons in the medulla oblongata and pons, along with respiratory reflexes, control respiration *p. 523*

29. Large-scale changes in oxygen demand require the integration of cardiovascular and respiratory responses.

30. Arterioles leading to alveolar capillaries constrict when oxygen is low, and bronchioles dilate when carbon dioxide is high.

31. The **respiratory centers** include three pairs of nuclei in the reticular formation of the pons and medulla oblongata. These nuclei regulate the respiratory muscles and control the respiratory rate and the depth of breathing. The paired **respiratory rhythmicity centers** in the medulla oblongata set the basic pace for respiration. *(Figure 15-15)*

32. The **inflation reflex** prevents overexpansion of the lungs during forced breathing; the **deflation reflex** stimulates inspiration when the lungs are collapsing. Chemoreceptor reflexes respond to changes in the pH, P_{O_2}, and P_{CO_2} of the blood and cerebrospinal fluid.

33. Conscious and unconscious thought processes can affect respiration by affecting the respiratory centers or the motor neurons controlling respiratory muscles. *(Figure 15-16)*

34. Before delivery, the fetal lungs are fluid filled and collapsed. After the first breath, the alveoli normally remain inflated for the life of the individual.

15-9 Respiratory performance declines with age *p. 527*

35. The respiratory system is generally less efficient in the elderly because (1) movements of the thoracic cage are restricted by arthritic changes, decreased flexibility of costal cartilages, and age-related muscle weakness interact to lower pulmonary ventilation and vital capacity of the lungs and (2) some degree of emphysema is normal in the elderly.

15-10 The respiratory system provides oxygen to, and removes carbon dioxide from, other organ systems *p. 527*

36. The respiratory system has extensive anatomical connections to the cardiovascular system. *(Figure 15-17)*

REVIEW QUESTIONS

WWW Access more review material online at The Anatomy & Physiology Place (www.anatomyandphysiology.com). There, you'll find Chapter Guides, Chapter Quizzes, Chapter Practice Tests, Interactive Flashcards, a Glossary with Pronunciations, and more to help you succeed in the course.

Level 1 • Reviewing Facts and Terms

Match each item in column A with the most closely related item in column B. Place letters for answers in the spaces provided.

COLUMN A	COLUMN B
_____ 1. nasopharynx	a. no O_2 supply to tissues
_____ 2. laryngopharynx	b. alveolar macrophages
_____ 3. thyroid cartilage	c. produce oily secretion
_____ 4. septal cells	d. covers inner surface of thoracic wall
_____ 5. dust cells	e. low O_2 content in tissue fluids
_____ 6. parietal pleura	f. inferior portion of pharynx
_____ 7. visceral pleura	g. inspiration
_____ 8. hypoxia	h. superior portion of pharynx
_____ 9. anoxia	i. Adam's apple
_____ 10. collapsed lung	j. covers outer surface of lungs
_____ 11. inhalation	k. expiration
_____ 12. exhalation	l. atelectasis

13. Identify the structures of the respiratory system in the following figure:

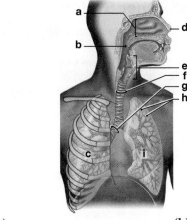

(a) _____ (b) _____
(c) _____ (d) _____
(e) _____ (f) _____
(g) _____ (h) _____
(i) _____

14. Identify the structures in the following figure:

(a) _____ (b) _____
(c) _____ (d) _____
(e) _____

Then label the pink and light blue arrows in the upper and lower portions of the figure to indicate the directions of the diffusion of oxygen and carbon dioxide.

15. The structure that prevents the entry of liquids or solid food into the respiratory passageways during swallowing is the
(**a**) glottis. (**b**) arytenoid cartilage.
(**c**) epiglottis. (**d**) thyroid cartilage.

16. The amount of air moved into or out of the lungs during a single respiratory cycle is the
(**a**) respiratory rate. (**b**) tidal volume.
(**c**) residual volume. (**d**) inspiratory capacity.

Level 2 • Reviewing Concepts

17. When the diaphragm contracts, it tenses and moves inferiorly, causing
(**a**) an increase in the volume of the thoracic cavity.
(**b**) a decrease in the volume of the thoracic cavity.
(**c**) decreased pressure on the contents of the abdominopelvic cavity.
(**d**) increased pressure in the thoracic cavity.

18. Gas exchange at the respiratory membrane is efficient because
(**a**) the differences in partial pressure are substantial.
(**b**) the gases are lipid soluble.
(**c**) the total surface area is large.
(**d**) a, b, and c are correct.

19. What is the functional significance of the decreased amount of cartilage and the increased amount of smooth muscle in the lower respiratory passageways?

20. Why is breathing through the nasal cavity more desirable than breathing through the mouth?

21. Justify the following statement: "The bronchioles are to the respiratory system what the arterioles are to the cardiovascular system."

Level 3 • Critical Thinking and Clinical Applications

22. A decrease in blood pressure will trigger a baroreceptor reflex that leads to increased ventilation. What is the possible advantage of this reflex?

23. You spend a winter night at a friend's house. Your friend's home is quite old, and the hot-air furnace lacks a humidifier. When you wake up in the morning, you have a fair amount of nasal congestion and decide you might be coming down with a cold. After you take a steamy shower and drink some juice for breakfast, the nasal congestion disappears. Explain.

The Respiratory System in Perspective

Functional Relationships Between the Respiratory System and Other Systems

The Integumentary System

- The Integumentary System protects portions of upper respiratory tract; hairs guard entry to external nares

The Skeletal System

- The Skeletal System's rib movements by respiratory muscles assist breathing; axial skeleton surrounds and protects lungs

The Muscular System

- The Muscular System's activity generates carbon dioxide; respiratory muscles fill and empty lungs; other muscles control entrances to respiratory tract; intrinsic laryngeal muscles control airflow through larynx and produce sounds

The Nervous System

- The Nervous System monitors respiratory volume and blood gas levels; controls pace and depth of respiration

The Endocrine System

- The Endocrine System hormones epinephrine and norepinephrine stimulate respiratory activity and dilate respiratory passageways

The Cardiovascular System

- The Cardiovascular System's red blood cells transport oxygen and carbon dioxide between lungs and peripheral tissues
- The Respiratory System's transport of carbon dioxide as bicarbonate ions contributes to the buffering capability of blood

The Lymphoid System

- The Lymphoid System's tonsils protect against infection at entrance to respiratory tract; lymphatic vessels monitor lymph drainage from lungs and mobilize specific defenses when infection occurs
- The Respiratory System's alveolar phagocytes present antigens to trigger specific defenses; mucous membrane lining the nasal cavity and upper pharynx traps pathogens, protects deeper tissues

The Digestive System

- The Digestive System provides substrates, vitamins, water, and ions that are necessary to all cells of the respiratory system
- The Respiratory System can assist in defecation by increased thoracic and abdominal pressure through contraction of respiratory muscles

The Urinary System

- The Urinary System eliminates organic wastes generated by cells of the respiratory system; maintains normal fluid and ion balance in the blood
- The Respiratory System assists in the regulation of pH by eliminating carbon dioxide

The Reproductive System

- The Respiratory System changes respiratory rate and volume during sexual arousal

For All Systems
The Respiratory System provides oxygen
and eliminates carbon dioxide

Professional Profile

RESPIRATORY THERAPIST
Stephen Lowenstein

> **Because the cardio and pulmonary systems are so interdependent, it is very important to know the global physiology of the body.**

Stephen Lowenstein is a respiratory therapist and technical director of the Pulmonary Physiology Laboratory at Lenox Hill Hospital in New York City. Respiratory therapy is a part of the diagnosis, surgical treatment, and postoperative care of patients. Although a typical day for a respiratory therapist can include a lot of variety, one constant for Stephen is that he is always treating or evaluating patients sent to him by their doctors.

"Physicians request preoperative testing for patients who are headed for surgery as well as diagnostic tests for patients with shortness of breath, asthma, and occupation-related diseases," says Stephen. "We also manage mechanical ventilation for patients on respirators, draw blood gases, perform pulmonary tests, and distribute medications to postoperative patients." There are many types of tests in respiratory therapy, including cardiopulmonary stress tests (during which the patient exercises on a stationary bicycle), gas analysis, and lung volume tests.

In addition, respiratory therapists are an integral part of the cardiopulmonary surgery team. "In surgery, we do endotracheal intubations, we open the airways of emergency patients, and we do life support, putting patients who have had open heart procedures on a mechanical ventilator."

In all of these roles, a thorough understanding of anatomy and physiology is crucial. Stephen says, "In respiratory therapy, it's important to know the physiology of how the body works. When you give medications to a patient, you have to monitor how the person reacts to them. When you do physiological stress testing, you have to know how blood pressure, heart rate, and the lungs react to different levels of exercise. When we put patients on a mechanical ventilator, we are pushing in a certain volume of air at a certain frequency and oxygen concentration. Changing the pressure will change cardiac output and venous return,

as well as other aspects. Because these systems are so interdependent, it is very important to know the global physiology of the body."

A two-year degree and completion of an oral and written certification exam are required in this field. A certified respiratory therapist (CRT) is qualified to administer diagnostic tests, maintain and monitor mechanical ventilation, draw blood gases, intubate patients, and do chest therapy. CRTs can perform hospital duties, pulmonary rehabilitation, or home care therapy. In this allied health field, there are additional opportunities for therapists who continue their education at the four-year undergraduate, master's, and doctorate levels, and for those who acquire the status of a state-registered or nationally registered respiratory therapist.

According to Stephen, respiratory therapists perform a vital role in "evaluating a patient's pulmonary status and making recommendations to the physician."

Stephen points out that it can be challenging to do the job well. "It seems like more of an art than a science sometimes. Doing a complete and accurate test on a patient, who may not be able to fully participate, can be difficult. Results may vary depending on how and when you perform the test. You want the test results to reflect the true situation." However, he says, "giving an accurate understanding of the problem to the physician is very rewarding."

Stephen advises those interested in respiratory therapy to visit a local two- or four-year training program and to arrange to observe therapists at work at a hospital. He also recommends contacting national organizations. The National Board for Respiratory Care certifies respiratory therapists and sets standards for care. The American Respiratory Care Foundation supports research and education, and offers awards at both student and professional levels.

16 The Digestive System

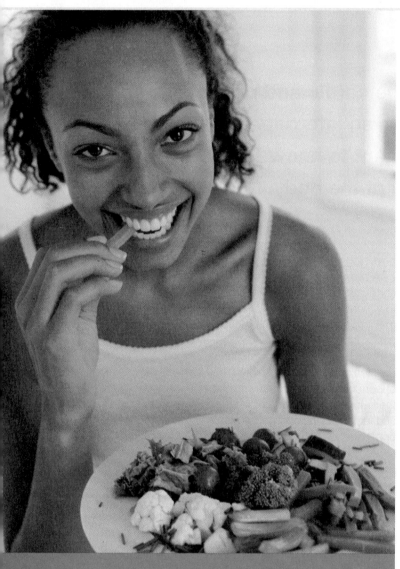

Releasing the various nutrients contained in our foods, such as the carrots and other fresh vegetables displayed on this plate, depends on the proper functioning of the digestive system. This chapter introduces the organs of the digestive system and discusses how they process foods for use by body cells.

LEARNING OUTCOMES

After completing this chapter, you should be able to do the following:

16-1 Identify the organs of the digestive system, list their major functions, and describe the four layers of the wall of the digestive tract.

16-2 Discuss the anatomy of the oral cavity, and list the functions of its major structures.

16-3 Describe the structures and functions of the pharynx and esophagus, and the key events of the swallowing process.

16-4 Describe the anatomy of the stomach, including its histological features, and discuss its roles in digestion and absorption.

16-5 Describe the anatomy of the small intestine, including its histological features, and explain the functions and regulation of intestinal secretions.

16-6 Describe the structure and functions of the pancreas, liver, and gallbladder, and explain how their activities are regulated.

16-7 Describe the structure of the large intestine, including its regional specializations, and list its absorptive functions.

16-8 List the nutrients required by the body, describe the chemical digestion of organic nutrients, and discuss the absorption of organic and inorganic nutrients.

16-9 Describe the effects of aging on the digestive system.

16-10 Give examples of interactions between the digestive system and each of the other organ systems.

VOCABULARY DEVELOPMENT

chymos juice; *chyme*
deciduus falling off; *deciduous*
enteron intestine; *myenteric plexus*
frenulum small bridle; *lingual frenulum*
gaster stomach; *gastric juice*
hepaticus liver; *hepatocyte*

hiatus gap or opening; *esophageal hiatus*
lacteus milky; *lacteal*
nutrients nourishing; *nutrient*
odonto- tooth; *periodontal ligament*
omentum fat skin; *greater omentum*
pyle gate; *pyloric sphincter*

rugae wrinkles; *rugae*
sigmoides Greek letter *S*; *sigmoid colon*
stalsis constriction; *peristalsis*
vermis worm; *vermiform appendix*
villus shaggy hair; *intestinal villus*

An Introduction to the Digestive System

Few people give any serious thought to the digestive system unless it malfunctions. Still, we spend hours of conscious effort filling and emptying it. References to this system are part of our everyday language. We "have a gut feeling," "want to chew on" something, or find someone's opinions "hard to swallow." When something does go wrong with the digestive system, even something minor, most people seek relief immediately. For this reason, every hour of television programming contains advertisements that promote toothpaste and mouthwash, dietary supplements, antacids, and laxatives.

All living organisms must obtain nutrients from their environment to sustain life. These substances are used as raw materials for synthesizing essential compounds (anabolism) or are decomposed to provide the energy that cells need to continue functioning (catabolism). ∞ pp. 35–37, 209–210

This chapter discusses the structure and function of the digestive tract and several digestive glands (notably the liver and pancreas), how the process of digestion breaks down large and complex organic molecules to smaller fragments that can be absorbed by the digestive epithelium, and how a few organic wastes are removed from the body.

16-1 The digestive system— the digestive tract and accessory organs—performs various food-processing functions

In our bodies, the respiratory system works with the cardiovascular system to supply the oxygen needed to "burn" metabolic fuels. The digestive system provides the fuel that keeps all the body's cells functioning, plus the building blocks needed for cell growth and repair. The digestive system consists of a muscular tube—the **digestive tract**—and **accessory organs,** such as the teeth, tongue, salivary glands, gallbladder, liver, and pancreas.

The major components of the digestive system are shown in Figure 16-1. The digestive tract, also called the *gastrointestinal* (*GI*) *tract* or *alimentary canal,* begins with the oral cavity (mouth) and continues through the pharynx, esophagus, stomach, small intestine, and large intestine before ending at the rectum and anus. Although these subdivisions of the digestive tract have overlapping functions, each region has certain areas of specialization and shows distinctive histological specializations.

FUNCTIONS OF THE DIGESTIVE SYSTEM

Digestive functions involve six related processes:

1. **Ingestion** occurs when foods enter the digestive tract through the mouth.

2. **Mechanical processing** is the physical manipulation of solid foods, first by the tongue and the teeth in the oral cavity and then by swirling and mixing motions of the digestive tract. Mechanical processing makes food materials easier to propel along the digestive tract and increases their surface area, making them more susceptible to attack by enzymes.

3. **Digestion** refers to the chemical breakdown of food into small organic fragments that can be absorbed by the digestive epithelium.

4. **Secretion** is the release of water, acids, enzymes, and buffers by the digestive tract and by glandular accessory organs.

5. **Absorption** is the movement of small organic molecules, electrolytes (inorganic ions), vitamins, and water across the digestive epithelium and into the interstitial fluid of the digestive tract.

FIGURE 16-1 **The Components of the Digestive System and Their Functions.**

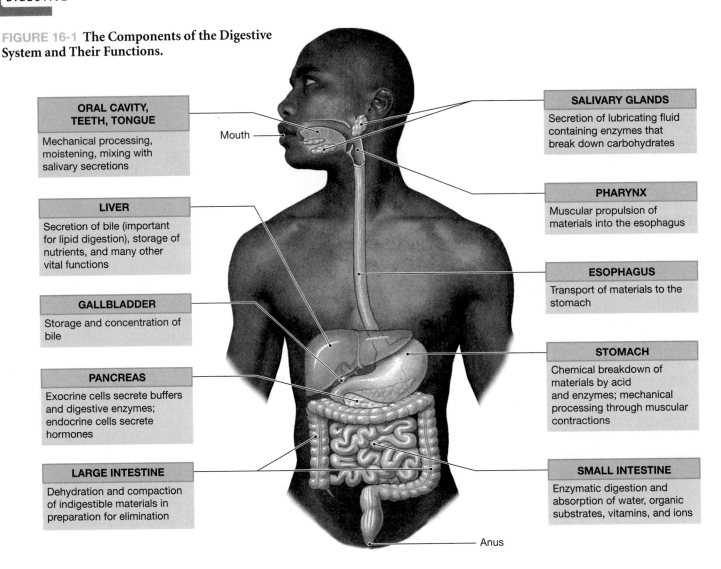

ORAL CAVITY, TEETH, TONGUE
Mechanical processing, moistening, mixing with salivary secretions

LIVER
Secretion of bile (important for lipid digestion), storage of nutrients, and many other vital functions

GALLBLADDER
Storage and concentration of bile

PANCREAS
Exocrine cells secrete buffers and digestive enzymes; endocrine cells secrete hormones

LARGE INTESTINE
Dehydration and compaction of indigestible materials in preparation for elimination

Mouth

SALIVARY GLANDS
Secretion of lubricating fluid containing enzymes that break down carbohydrates

PHARYNX
Muscular propulsion of materials into the esophagus

ESOPHAGUS
Transport of materials to the stomach

STOMACH
Chemical breakdown of materials by acid and enzymes; mechanical processing through muscular contractions

SMALL INTESTINE
Enzymatic digestion and absorption of water, organic substrates, vitamins, and ions

Anus

6. **Excretion** is the removal of waste products from body fluids. Within the digestive tract, these waste products are compacted and discharged as *feces* through the process of *defecation* (def-e-KĀ-shun).

The lining of the digestive tract also plays defensive roles: It protects surrounding tissues from the corrosive effects of digestive acids and enzymes, and it protects against bacteria that either are swallowed with food or reside in the digestive tract. The digestive epithelium and its secretions provide a nonspecific defense against these bacteria; any bacteria reaching the underlying tissues are attacked by macrophages and other cells of the immune system.

HISTOLOGICAL ORGANIZATION OF THE DIGESTIVE TRACT

The digestive tract has four major layers (**Figure 16-2**): the *mucosa*, the *submucosa*, the *muscularis externa*, and the *serosa*.

The Mucosa

The **mucosa,** or inner lining of the digestive tract, is an example of a *mucous membrane.* ⊂⊃ p. 110 It consists of a mucosal epithelium (an epithelial surface moistened by glandular secretions) and an underlying layer of loose connective tissue, the *lamina propria.* Along most of the length of the digestive tract, the mucosa is thrown into folds that both increase the surface area available for absorption and permit expansion after a large meal. In the small intestine, the mucosa forms fingerlike projections, called *villi* (*villus,* shaggy hair), that further increase the area for absorption.

The oral cavity, pharynx, esophagus, and anus (where mechanical stresses are most severe) are lined by a stratified squamous epithelium. The remainder of the digestive tract is lined by a simple columnar epithelium, often containing various types of secretory cells. Ducts opening onto the epithelial surfaces carry the secretions of glands located in the lamina propria, in the surrounding submucosa, or within accessory

FIGURE 16-2 The Structure of the Digestive Tract. Illustrated here is a representative portion of the digestive tract: the small intestine. The wall of the digestive tract is made up of four layers: the mucosa, submucosa, muscularis externa, and serosa.

glandular organs. In most regions of the digestive tract, the outer portion of the mucosa contains a narrow band of smooth muscle and elastic fibers. Contractions of this layer, the *muscularis* (mus-kū-LĀ-ris) *mucosae* (mū-KŌ-sē) (Figure 16-2), move the mucosal folds and villi.

The Submucosa

The **submucosa** is a second layer of loose connective tissue that is immediately deep to the muscularis mucosae. It contains large blood vessels and lymphatic vessels, as well as a network of nerve fibers, sensory neurons, and parasympathetic motor neurons. This neural tissue—the *submucosal plexus*—is involved in controlling and coordinating contractions of the smooth muscle layers and in regulating the secretion of digestive glands.

The Muscularis Externa

The **muscularis externa** is a band of smooth muscle cells arranged in an inner circular layer and an outer longitudinal layer (Figure 16-2). Contractions of these layers in various combinations both agitate materials and propel them along the digestive tract. Both actions are autonomic reflex movements controlled primarily by another network of nerves—the

myenteric plexus (*mys*, muscle + *enteron*, intestine)—sandwiched between the circular and longitudinal smooth muscle layers. Parasympathetic stimulation increases muscular tone and activity, whereas sympathetic stimulation promotes muscular inhibition and relaxation.

The Serosa

The **serosa,** a serous membrane, covers the muscularis externa along most portions of the digestive tract within the peritoneal cavity. This *visceral peritoneum* is continuous with the *parietal peritoneum*, which lines the inner surfaces of the body wall. ∞ p. 111 In some areas within the peritoneal cavity, portions of the digestive tract are suspended by **mesenteries** (MEZ-en-ter-ēz)—double sheets of serous membrane composed of the parietal peritoneum and visceral peritoneum. The loose connective tissue sandwiched between the epithelial surfaces of the mesenteries provides a pathway for the blood vessels, nerves, and lymphatic vessels servicing the digestive tract. The mesenteries also stabilize the positions of the attached organs and prevent the intestines from becoming entangled during digestive movements or sudden changes in body position.

There is no serosa covering the muscularis externa of the oral cavity, pharynx, esophagus, and rectum. Instead, the muscularis externa is surrounded by a dense network of collagen fibers that

p. 213

FIGURE 16-3 **Peristalsis.** Peristalsis is the process that propels materials along the length of the digestive tract.

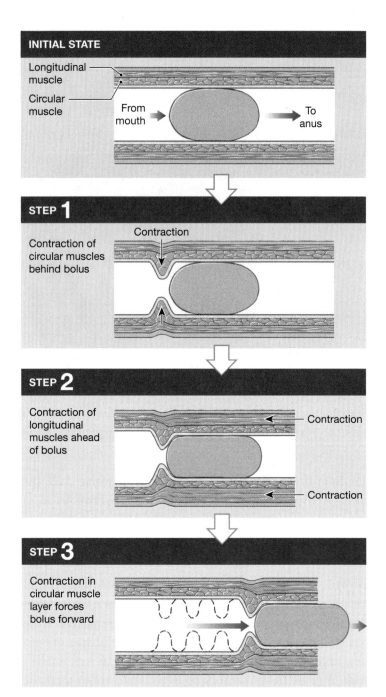

INITIAL STATE

Longitudinal muscle
Circular muscle
From mouth → To anus

STEP 1
Contraction of circular muscles behind bolus
Contraction

STEP 2
Contraction of longitudinal muscles ahead of bolus
Contraction
Contraction

STEP 3
Contraction in circular muscle layer forces bolus forward

firmly attaches these regions of the digestive tract to adjacent structures. This fibrous wrapping is called an *adventitia* (ad-ven-TISH-ē-uh).

THE MOVEMENT OF DIGESTIVE MATERIALS

As previously noted, the muscular layers of the digestive tract consist of smooth muscle tissue. *Pacesetter cells* in the smooth muscle of the digestive tract trigger waves of contraction, resulting in rhythmic cycles of activity. The coordinated contractions in the walls of the digestive tract play a vital role in two processes: *peristalsis* (peri-, around + stalsis, constriction), the movement of material along the tract, and *segmentation*, the mechanical mixing of the material.

The muscularis externa propels materials from one part of the digestive tract to another by means of **peristalsis** (per-i-STAL-sis), waves of muscular contractions that move along the length of the digestive tract (Figure 16-3). During a peristaltic movement, the circular muscles first contract behind the digestive contents. Then longitudinal muscles contract, shortening adjacent segments of the tract. A wave of contraction in the circular muscles then forces the materials in the desired direction.

Regions of the small intestine also undergo **segmentation,** movements that churn and fragment digestive materials. Over time, this action results in a thorough mixing of the contents with intestinal secretions. Because they do not follow a set pattern, segmentation movements do not propel materials in any particular direction.

Clinical Note

Ascites

The peritoneal lining continuously produces peritoneal fluid, which lubricates the opposing parietal and visceral surfaces. Even though about 7 liters of fluid is secreted and reabsorbed each day, the volume within the cavity at any moment is very small. Several conditions, including liver disease, kidney disease, and heart failure, can cause an increase in the rate of fluid movement into the peritoneal cavity. The resulting accumulation of fluid creates a characteristic abdominal swelling called **ascites** (a-SĪ-tēz). The distortion of internal organs by the accumulated fluid can result in symptoms such as heartburn, indigestion, and low back pain.

CHECKPOINT

1. Identify the organs of the digestive system.
2. List and define the six primary functions of the digestive system.
3. Describe the functions of the mesenteries.
4. Name the layers of the digestive tract beginning with the outermost layer.
5. Which process is more efficient in propelling intestinal contents from one place to another—peristalsis or segmentation?

See the blue Answers tab at the back of the book.

16-2 The oral cavity contains the tongue, salivary glands, and teeth, each with specific functions

The mouth opens into the **oral cavity,** the part of the digestive tract that receives food. The oral cavity is lined by a mucous membrane that has a stratified squamous epithelium. The oral cavity (1) senses and analyzes material before swallowing; (2) mechanically processes material through the actions of the teeth, tongue, and surfaces of the palate; (3) lubricates material by mixing it with mucus and salivary secretions; and (4) begins the digestion of carbohydrates and lipids with salivary enzymes.

Figure 16-4 shows the boundaries of the oral cavity, also known as the **buccal** (BUK-ul) **cavity.** The *cheeks* form the lateral walls of this chamber; anteriorly they are continuous with the lips, or **labia** (LĀ-bē-uh; singular, *labium*). The **vestibule** is the space between the cheeks or lips and the teeth. A pink ridge—the gums or **gingivae** (JIN-ji-vē; singular, *gingiva*)—surrounds the bases of the teeth. The gums cover the tooth-bearing surfaces of the upper and lower jaws.

The **hard palate** and **soft palate** form a roof for the oral cavity; the tongue dominates its floor. The free anterior portion of the tongue is connected to the underlying epithelium by a thin fold of mucous membrane, the **lingual frenulum** (FREN-ū-lum; *frenulum,* a small bridle). The imaginary dividing line between the oral cavity and the oropharynx extends between the base of the tongue and the dangling *uvula* (Ū-vū-luh).

THE TONGUE

The muscular **tongue** manipulates materials inside the mouth and is occasionally used to bring foods (such as ice cream) into the oral cavity. The primary functions of the tongue are (1) mechanical processing by compression, abrasion, and distortion; (2) manipulation to assist in chewing and to prepare the material for swallowing; and (3) sensory analysis by touch, temperature, and taste receptors. Most of the tongue lies within the oral cavity, but the base of the tongue extends into the oropharynx. A pair of prominent lateral swellings at the base of the tongue marks the location of the *lingual tonsils,* lymphoid nodules that help resist infections. ∞ p. 475

SALIVARY GLANDS

Three pairs of salivary glands secrete into the oral cavity (Figure 16-5). On each side, a large **parotid salivary gland** lies under the skin covering the lateral and posterior surface of the mandible. ∞ p. 160 The **parotid duct** empties into the vestibule at the level of the second upper molar. The **sublingual salivary glands** are located beneath the mucous membrane of the floor of the mouth, and numerous sublingual ducts open along either side of the lingual frenulum. The **submandibular salivary glands** are in the floor of the mouth along the inner

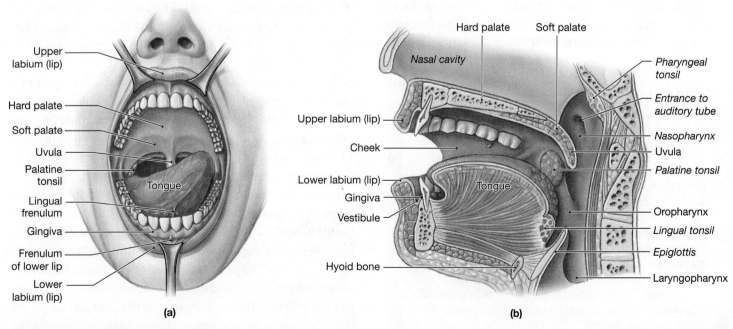

(a)

(b)

FIGURE 16-4 The Oral Cavity. These drawings show the structures of the oral cavity in **(a)** an anterior view, as seen through the open mouth, and **(b)** a sagittal section.

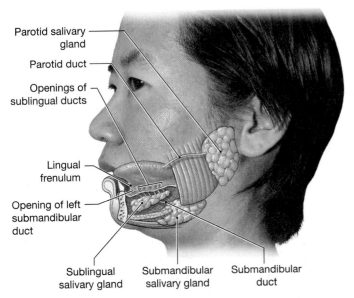

Parotid salivary gland

Parotid duct

Openings of sublingual ducts

Lingual frenulum

Opening of left submandibular duct

Sublingual salivary gland

Submandibular salivary gland

Submandibular duct

FIGURE 16-5 The Salivary Glands. This lateral view shows the relative positions of the salivary glands and ducts on the left side of the head. The left half of the mandible has been removed to show deeper structures.

surfaces of the mandible; their ducts open into the mouth behind the teeth on either side of the lingual frenulum.

These salivary glands produce 1.0–1.5 liters of saliva each day. Saliva is 99.4 percent water, plus *mucins* and an assortment of ions, buffers, waste products, metabolites, and enzymes. Mucins absorb water and form mucus. At mealtimes, large quantities of saliva lubricate the mouth and dissolve chemicals that stimulate the taste buds. Coating the food with slippery mucus reduces friction and makes swallowing possible. A continuous background level of secretion flushes and cleans the oral surfaces, and salivary antibodies (IgA) and *lysozyme* help control populations of oral bacteria. When salivary secretions

Clinical Note

Mumps

The *mumps virus* most often targets the salivary glands, especially the parotid salivary glands, although other organs can also become infected. Infection typically occurs at 5–9 years of age. The first exposure stimulates antibody production and usually confers permanent immunity; active immunity can be induced by immunization. In postadolescent males, the mumps virus may also infect the testes and cause sterility. Infection of the pancreas by the mumps virus may produce temporary or permanent diabetes; other organ systems, including the central nervous system, may be affected in severe cases. Widespread distribution of an effective mumps vaccine has reduced the incidence of the disease in the United States.

are reduced, such as by radiation exposure, emotional distress, or other factors, the bacterial population in the oral cavity explodes. This bacterial increase soon leads to recurring infections and the progressive erosion of the teeth and gums.

Each of the salivary glands produces a slightly different kind of saliva. The parotid glands produce a secretion rich in **salivary amylase,** an enzyme that breaks down starches (complex carbohydrates) into smaller molecules that can be absorbed by the digestive tract. Saliva originating in the submandibular and sublingual salivary glands contains fewer enzymes but more buffers and mucus. During eating, all three salivary glands increase their rates of secretion, and salivary production may reach 7 mL per minute, with about 70 percent of that volume provided by the submandibular glands. The pH of the saliva also rises, shifting from slightly acidic (pH 6.7) to slightly basic (pH 7.5). Salivary secretions are normally controlled by the autonomic nervous system.

TEETH

Movements of the tongue are important in passing food across the opposing surfaces of the **teeth.** These surfaces perform chewing, or **mastication** (mas-ti-KĀ-shun), of food. Mastication breaks down tough connective tissues in meat and the plant fibers in vegetable matter, and it helps saturate the materials with salivary secretions.

Figure 16-6a shows the parts of a tooth. The **neck** of the tooth marks the boundary between the **root** and the **crown.** The crown is covered by a layer of **enamel,** which contains a crystalline form of calcium phosphate, the hardest biologically manufactured substance. Adequate amounts of calcium, phosphates, and vitamin D_3 during childhood are essential if the enamel coating is to be complete and resistant to decay.

The bulk of each tooth consists of **dentin** (DEN-tin), a mineralized matrix similar to that of bone. Dentin differs from bone in that it does not contain cells. Instead, cytoplasmic processes extend into the dentin from cells within the central **pulp cavity.** The pulp cavity receives blood vessels and nerves through a narrow **root canal** at the root (base) of the tooth. The root sits within a bony socket, or *alveolus* (a hollow cavity). Collagen fibers of the **periodontal ligament** (*peri-*, around + *odonto-*, tooth) extend from the dentin of the root to the surrounding bone. A layer of **cementum** (se-MEN-tum) covers the dentin of the root, providing protection and firmly anchoring the periodontal ligament. Cementum is similar in structure to bone, but softer. Where the tooth penetrates the gum surface, epithelial cells form tight attachments to the tooth and prevent bacterial access to the easily eroded cementum of the root.

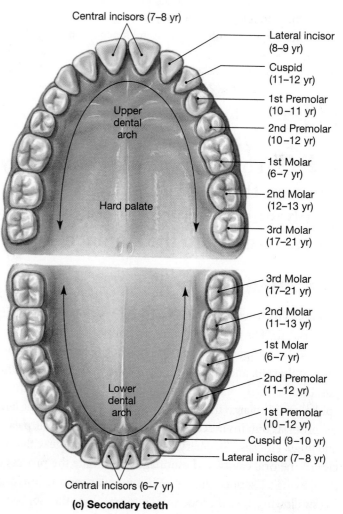

FIGURE 16-6 **Teeth: Structural Components and Dental Succession.** **(a)** The structures of a typical adult tooth are labeled in this diagrammatic section. Humans have two sets of teeth: **(b)** primary (deciduous) teeth and **(c)** adult teeth. The ages at eruption are indicated for the teeth in each set.

Types of Teeth

A set of adult teeth is shown in Figure 16-6c. Each of the four types of teeth has a specific function. **Incisors** (in-SĪ-zerz), blade-shaped teeth found at the front of the mouth, are useful for clipping or cutting, as when you nip off the tip of a carrot stick. **Cuspids** (KUS-pidz), or *canines,* are conical, with a sharp ridgeline and a pointed tip. They are used for tearing or slashing. You might weaken a tough piece of celery by the clipping action of the incisors and then take advantage of the shearing action provided by the cuspids. **Bicuspids** (bi-KUS-pidz), or *premolars,* and **molars** have flattened crowns with prominent ridges. They are used for crushing, mashing, and grinding. You might shift a tough nut or piece of meat to the premolars and molars for crushing.

Dental Succession

During development, two sets of teeth begin to form. The first to appear are the **deciduous teeth** (de-SID-ū-us; *deciduus,* falling off), also known as *primary teeth, milk teeth,* or *baby teeth.* Most children have 20 deciduous teeth (Figure 16-6b).

These teeth are later replaced by the **secondary dentition,** or *permanent dentition* (Figure 16-6c), which permits the processing of a wider variety of foods. As replacement proceeds, the periodontal ligaments and roots of the deciduous teeth erode until these teeth either fall out or are pushed aside by the **eruption** (emergence) of the secondary teeth. Adult jaws are larger and can accommodate more than 20 teeth. As a person ages, three additional teeth appear on each side of the upper and lower jaws, bringing the permanent tooth count to 32. The last teeth to appear are the *third molars,* or *wisdom teeth.* Wisdom teeth (or any other teeth) that develop in locations that do not permit their eruption are called *impacted teeth.* Impacted teeth can be surgically removed to prevent the formation of abscesses.

CHECKPOINT

6. Name the structures associated with the oral cavity.

7. The oral cavity is lined by which type of epithelium?

8. The digestion of which nutrient would be affected by damage to the parotid salivary glands?

9. Which type of tooth is most useful for chopping off bits of raw vegetables?

See the blue Answers tab at the end of the book.

16-3 The pharynx is a passageway between the oral cavity and the esophagus, which conducts solids and liquids on to the stomach

THE PHARYNX

The **pharynx** serves as a common passageway for solid food, liquids, and air. The three major subdivisions of the pharynx were discussed in Chapter 15. p. 506 Food normally passes through the oropharynx and laryngopharynx on its way to the esophagus. Both of these pharyngeal regions have a stratified squamous epithelium similar to that of the oral cavity. The underlying lamina propria contains mucous glands plus the pharyngeal, palatal, and lingual tonsils. The pharyngeal muscles cooperate with muscles of the oral cavity and esophagus to initiate the process of swallowing (described shortly). The muscular contractions during swallowing force the food mass into and along the esophagus.

THE ESOPHAGUS

The **esophagus** (Figure 16-1) is a muscular tube, about 25 cm (10 in.) long and about 2 cm (0.75 in.) in diameter, that conveys solid food and liquids to the stomach. It begins at the pharynx, runs posterior to the trachea in the neck, passes through the mediastinum in the thoracic cavity, and enters the peritoneal cavity through an opening in the diaphragm—the *esophageal hiatus* (hī-Ā-tus; a gap or opening)—before emptying into the stomach.

The esophagus is lined with a stratified squamous epithelium that resists abrasion, hot or cold temperatures, and chemical attack. The secretions of esophageal mucous glands lubricate this epithelial surface and prevent materials from sticking to it during swallowing. The upper third of the muscularis externa contains skeletal muscle, the lower third contains smooth muscle, and a mixture of each makes up the middle third. Regions of circular muscle in the superior and inferior ends of the esophagus make up the *upper esophageal sphincter* and the *lower esophageal sphincter.* The lower sphincter is normally in active contraction, a condition that prevents the backflow of materials from the stomach into the esophagus.

SWALLOWING

Swallowing, or **deglutition** (de-gloo-TISH-un), is a complex process that can be initiated voluntarily but proceeds automatically once it begins. Although you take conscious control over swallowing when you eat or drink, swallowing is also controlled at the subconscious level. Before food can be swallowed, it must have the proper texture and consistency. Once the material has been shredded or torn by the teeth, moistened with salivary secretions, and "approved" by the taste receptors, the tongue begins compacting the debris into a small mass, or **bolus.**

The process of swallowing occurs in a series of steps, or phases (Figure 16-7). Swallowing begins in the **oral phase,** with the compression of the bolus against the hard palate. The tongue retracts, forcing the bolus into the pharynx and helping to elevate the soft palate, so that the bolus does not enter the nasopharynx. The oral phase is the only phase of swallowing that can be consciously controlled.

In the **pharyngeal phase,** the bolus comes in contact with sensory receptors around the pharynx and the posterior pharyngeal wall, initiating the involuntary *swallowing reflex.* The larynx elevates, and the epiglottis folds to direct the bolus past the closed glottis. In less than a second, the contraction of pharyngeal muscles forces the bolus through the entrance to the esophagus, which is guarded by the upper esophageal sphincter.

STEP 1   BUCCAL PHASE

- Soft palate
- Bolus
- Epiglottis
- Esophagus
- Trachea

STEP 2   PHARYNGEAL PHASE

- Tongue
- Bolus

STEP 3   ESOPHAGEAL PHASE

- Peristalsis
- Trachea

STEP 4   BOLUS ENTERS STOMACH

- Thoracic cavity
- Lower esophageal sphincter
- Diaphragm
- Stomach

FIGURE 16-7 The Swallowing Process. This sequence, based on a series of x-rays, shows the phases of swallowing and the movement of materials from the mouth to the stomach.

The **esophageal phase** begins as the bolus enters the esophagus. During this phase, the bolus is pushed toward the stomach by a peristaltic contraction. The approach of the bolus triggers the opening of the lower esophageal sphincter (Step 4, Figure 16-7), and the bolus enters the stomach.

For a typical bolus, the entire trip from oral cavity to esophagus takes about 9 seconds. Liquids may make the journey in a few seconds, flowing ahead of the peristaltic contractions; a relatively dry or bulky bolus travels much more slowly, and repeated peristaltic waves may be required to drive it into the stomach. A completely dry bolus cannot be swallowed at all, for friction with the walls of the esophagus will make peristalsis ineffective.

Clinical Note

Esophagitis and Diaphragmatic (Hiatal) Hernias

A weakened or permanently relaxed lower esophageal sphincter can cause inflammation of the esophagus, or **esophagitis** (ē-sof-a-JĪ-tis), as strong gastric acids enter the lower esophagus. The esophageal epithelium has few defenses against acids and enzymes, and inflammation, epithelial erosion, and intense discomfort result. Occasional incidents of reflux, or backflow, from the stomach are responsible for the symptoms of "heartburn." This relatively common problem supports a multimillion-dollar industry devoted to producing and promoting antacids.

The esophagus and major blood vessels pass from the thoracic cavity to the abdominopelvic cavity through an opening in the diaphragm called the *esophageal hiatus.* In a **diaphragmatic hernia,** or **hiatal** (hī-Ā-tal) **hernia,** abdominal organs slide up into the thoracic cavity through the esophageal hiatus. The severity of the condition depends on the location and size of the herniated organ or organs. Hiatal hernias are actually very common, and most go unnoticed. When clinical problems develop, they usually occur because the intruding abdominal organs are exerting pressure on structures or organs in the thoracic cavity.

CHECKPOINT

10. Describe the function of the pharynx.

11. Which structure connects the pharynx to the stomach?

12. What process is occurring when the soft palate and larynx elevate and the glottis closes?

See the blue Answers tab at the end of the book.

16-4 The J-shaped stomach receives the bolus from the esophagus and aids in chemical and mechanical digestion

The **stomach,** located within the left upper quadrant of the abdominopelvic cavity (see Figure 1-7c, p. 17), receives food from the esophagus. The stomach has four primary functions: (1) temporary storage of ingested food, (2) mechanical breakdown of ingested food, (3) breakdown of chemical bonds in food items through the action of acids and enzymes, and (4) production of *intrinsic factor,* a compound necessary for the absorption of vitamin B_{12}. Ingested materials mix with secretions of the stomach glands, producing a viscous, highly acidic, soupy mixture of partially digested food called **chyme** (kīm).

The stomach is a muscular, J-shaped organ with four main regions (Figure 16-8a). The esophagus connects to the smallest part of the stomach, the **cardia** (KAR-dē-uh). The bulge of the stomach superior to the cardia is the **fundus** (FUN-dus) of the stomach, and the large area between the fundus and the curve of the J is the **body.** The distal part of the J, the **pylorus** (pī-LOR-us; *pyle,* gate + *ouros,* guard), connects the stomach with the small intestine. A muscular **pyloric sphincter** regulates the flow of chyme between the stomach and small intestine.

The stomach's volume increases when food enters it, then decreases as chyme enters the small intestine. When the stomach is relaxed, or empty, its mucosa contains a number of prominent ridges and folds, called **rugae** (ROO-gē; wrinkles). As the stomach expands, the rugae gradually flatten out until, at maximum distension, they almost disappear. When empty, the stomach resembles a muscular tube with a narrow and constricted lumen. When fully expanded, it can contain 1–1.5 liters of material.

Unlike the two-layered muscularis externa of other portions of the digestive tract, that of the stomach contains a longitudinal layer, a circular layer, and an inner oblique layer. This extra layer of smooth muscle adds strength and assists in the mixing and churning essential to forming chyme.

The visceral peritoneum covering the outer surface of the stomach is continuous with a pair of mesenteries. The **greater omentum** (ō-MEN-tum; *omentum,* a fatty skin) extends below the *greater curvature* and forms an enormous pouch that hangs over and protects the abdominal viscera (Figure 16-8b). The much smaller **lesser omentum** extends from the *lesser curvature* to the liver.

THE GASTRIC WALL

The stomach is lined by a simple columnar epithelium dominated by mucous cells. The alkaline mucus secreted by this *mucous epithelium* covers and protects epithelial cells from acids, enzymes, and abrasive materials. Shallow depressions, called **gastric pits,** open onto the gastric surface (Figure 16-8c). The mucous cells at the base, or *neck,* of each gastric pit actively divide and replace superficial cells of the mucous epithelium shed into the chyme.

In the fundus and body of the stomach, each gastric pit communicates with **gastric glands** that extend deep into the underlying lamina propria (Figure 16-8c). Each day the cells in these gastric glands secrete about 1500 mL of **gastric juice.** The cells that produce the components of gastric juice are *parietal cells* and *chief cells* (Figure 16-8d).

Gastric glands within the lower stomach (the *pylorus*) also contain endocrine cells that are involved in regulating gastric activity. Their role in the regulation of gastric activity will be discussed shortly.

Parietal Cells

Parietal cells secrete intrinsic factor and hydrochloric acid (HCl). **Intrinsic factor** facilitates the absorption of vitamin B_{12} across the intestinal lining. Hydrochloric acid lowers the pH of the gastric juice, keeping the stomach contents at a pH of 1.5–2.0. The acidity of gastric juice kills microorganisms, breaks down plant cell walls and connective tissues in meat, and activates the enzyme secretions of chief cells.

Chief Cells

Chief cells secrete a protein called **pepsinogen** (pep-SIN-ō-jen) into the stomach lumen. When it contacts the hydrochloric acid released by the parietal cells, pepsinogen is converted to **pepsin,** a *proteolytic* (protein-digesting) *enzyme.* In newborns (but not adults), the stomach produces *rennin* and *gastric lipase,* enzymes important for the digestion of milk. Rennin coagulates milk, thus slowing its passage through the stomach and allowing more time for its digestion. Gastric lipase initiates the digestion of milk fats.

THE REGULATION OF GASTRIC ACTIVITY

The production of acid and enzymes by the stomach mucosa is regulated by the central nervous system, by reflexes within

(a) This anterior view of the stomach shows important superficial landmarks.

Esophagus
Body
Lesser curvature (medial surface)
Lesser omentum
Pylorus

Cardia
Diaphragm
Fundus
Greater curvature (lateral surface)
Greater omentum
Rugae

(a)

(b)

Diaphragm
Liver
Pancreas
Duodenum
Mesentery
Rectum

Lesser omentum
Stomach
Mesentery
Transverse colon
Greater omentum
Parietal peritoneum
Small intestine
Uterus
Bladder

Gastric pit (opening to gastric gland)
Mucous epithelium
Lymphatic vessel
Lamina propria
Muscularis mucosae
Submucosa
Oblique muscle
Circular muscle
Longitudinal muscle
Serosa

Myenteric plexus
Artery and vein

(c)

Gastric pit
Gastric gland

Mucous cells
Neck
Parietal cells
Smooth muscle cell
Chief cells
Endocrine cell

(d)

FIGURE 16-8 The Anatomy of the Stomach.
(a) This anterior view of the stomach shows important superficial landmarks. **(b)** The stomach's position in the peritoneal cavity is maintained by the greater and lesser omenta. **(c)** The organization of the stomach wall is shown in this diagrammatic section. **(d)** This diagram of a gastric gland reveals the sites of parietal cells and chief cells, which are present in all gastric glands. Note that endocrine cells are also present in glands lining the lower portion (pylorus) of the stomach.

545

the walls of the digestive tract, and by hormones of the digestive tract. Regulation of gastric secretion proceeds in three overlapping phases (Figure 16-9), named according to the location of the control center:

1. *Cephalic phase.* The sight, smell, taste, or thought of food initiates the **cephalic phase** of gastric secretion. This stage, which is directed by the CNS, prepares the stomach to receive food. Under the control of the vagus nerves, parasympathetic fibers of the submucosal plexus innervate mucous cells, parietal cells, chief cells, and endocrine cells of the stomach. In response to stimulation, the production of gastric juice accelerates, reaching rates of about 500 mL per hour. This phase usually lasts only minutes before the gastric phase commences.

2. *Gastric phase.* The **gastric phase** begins with the arrival of food in the stomach. The stimulation of stretch receptors in the stomach wall and of chemoreceptors in the mucosa triggers local reflexes controlled by the submucosal and myenteric plexuses. The myenteric plexus stimulates mixing waves in the stomach wall. The submucosal plexus stimulates the parietal cells and chief cells, as well as stimulating endocrine cells in gastric glands within the pylorus to release the hormone **gastrin** into the circulatory system. Proteins, alcohol in small doses, and caffeine are potent stimulators of gas-

Clinical Note — Gastritis and Peptic Ulcers

Inflammation of the gastric mucosa is called **gastritis** (gas-TRĪ-tis). This condition can result from bacterial infection of the gastric wall or from the ingestion of irritating substances (including strongly acidic or alkaline chemicals, or drugs such as alcohol and aspirin); it can also appear after severe emotional or physical stress.

A **peptic ulcer** develops when the digestive acids and enzymes erode the lining of the stomach or proximal portions of the small intestine. The specific locations are indicated by the terms **gastric ulcer** (in the stomach) or **duodenal ulcer** (in the duodenum of the small intestine). Peptic ulcers result from the excessive production of acid or the inadequate production of the alkaline mucus that defends the epithelium against that acid. Since the late 1970s, drugs such as *cimetidine* (*Tagamet*) have been used to inhibit acid production by parietal cells. Because at least 80 percent of peptic ulcers result from infections by the bacterium *Helicobacter pylori,* current treatment commonly involves the administration of antibiotics.

FIGURE 16-9 **The Phases of Gastric Secretion.**

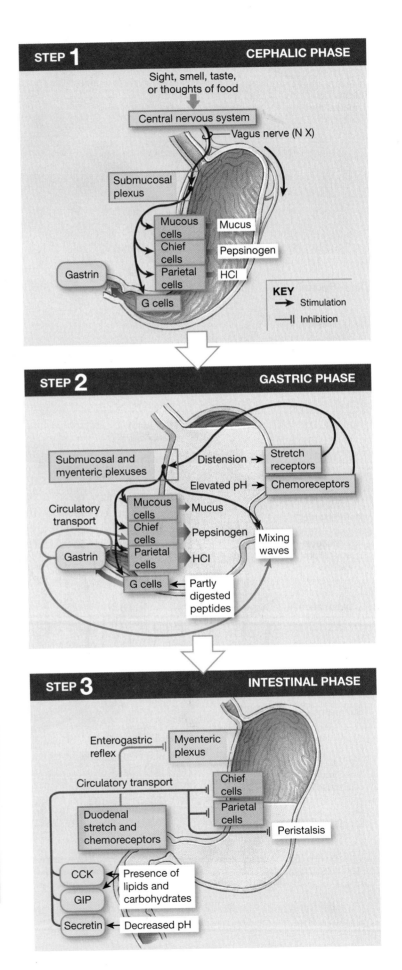

tric secretion because they excite the chemoreceptors in the gastric lining. Both parietal and chief cells respond to the presence of gastrin by accelerating their secretory activities. The effect on the parietal cells is the most pronounced, and the pH of the gastric juice drops sharply. This phase may continue for several hours while the acids and enzymes process the ingested materials.

During this period, gastrin stimulates stomach contractions, which begin to swirl and churn the gastric contents, mixing the ingested materials with the gastric secretions to form chyme. As mixing proceeds, the contractions begin sweeping down the length of the stomach, and each time the pylorus contracts, a small quantity of chyme squirts through the pyloric sphincter.

3. *Intestinal phase.* The **intestinal phase** begins when chyme first enters the small intestine. Most of the regulatory controls for this phase (whether neural or endocrine) are inhibitory; by controlling the rate of gastric emptying, they ensure that the secretory, digestive, and absorptive functions of the small intestine can proceed efficiently. For example, the movement of chyme temporarily reduces the stimulation of stretch receptors in the stomach wall and increases their stimulation in the wall of the small intestine. This produces the *enterogastric reflex,* which temporarily inhibits neural stimulation of gastrin production and gastric motility,

and further movement of chyme. At the same time, the entry of chyme stimulates the release of the intestinal hormones *secretin, cholecystokinin (CCK),* and *gastric inhibitory peptide (GIP);* the resulting reduced gastric activity gives the small intestine time to adjust to the arriving acids.

Inhibitory reflexes that depress gastric activity are stimulated when the proximal portion of the small intestine becomes too full, too acidic, unduly irritated by chyme, or filled with partially digested proteins, carbohydrates, or fats.

In general, the rate of movement of chyme into the small intestine is highest when the stomach is greatly distended and the meal contains relatively little protein. A large meal containing small amounts of protein, large amounts of carbohydrates (such as rice or pasta), wine (alcohol), and after-dinner coffee (caffeine) will leave your stomach extremely quickly because both alcohol and caffeine stimulate gastric secretion and motility.

DIGESTION IN THE STOMACH

Within the stomach, pepsin performs the preliminary digestion of proteins, and for a variable time salivary amylase continues the digestion of carbohydrates. Salivary amylase remains active until the pH of the stomach contents falls below 4.5, usually within 1–2 hours after a meal.

As the stomach contents become more fluid and the pH approaches 2.0, pepsin activity increases and protein disassembly begins. Protein digestion is not completed in the stomach, but pepsin typically breaks down complex proteins into smaller peptide and polypeptide chains before chyme enters the small intestine.

Although digestion occurs in the stomach, nutrients are not absorbed there because (1) the epithelial cells are covered by a blanket of alkaline mucus and are not directly exposed to chyme, (2) the epithelial cells lack the specialized transport mechanisms found in cells lining the small intestine, (3) the gastric lining is impermeable to water, and (4) digestion has not proceeded to completion by the time chyme leaves the stomach. At this stage, most carbohydrates, lipids, and proteins are only partially broken down.

Clinical Note: Stomach Cancer

Stomach (or *gastric*) **cancer** is one of the most common lethal cancers, responsible for roughly 12,000 deaths in the United States each year. The incidence is higher in Japan and Korea, where the typical diet includes large quantities of pickled foods. Because the signs and symptoms can resemble those of gastric ulcers, the condition may not be reported in its early stages. Diagnosis usually involves x-rays of the stomach at various degrees of distension. The gastric mucosa can also be visually inspected using a flexible instrument called a *gastroscope.* Attachments permit the collection of tissue samples for histological analysis.

The treatment of stomach cancer involves a *gastrectomy* (gas-TREK-to-mē), the surgical removal of part or all of the stomach. People can survive even a total gastrectomy because the loss of such functions as food storage and acid production is not life threatening. Protein breakdown can still be performed by the small intestine, although at reduced efficiency, and the lack of intrinsic factor (produced by the stomach) can be overcome by supplementing the diet with high daily doses of vitamin B$_{12}$.

The Big Picture

Food is stored in the stomach while it is physically broken down in preparation for chemical digestion. Protein digestion begins in the acid environment of the stomach through the action of pepsin. Carbohydrate digestion begins in the mouth with the release of salivary amylase by the salivary glands before swallowing, and continues after substances arrive in the stomach.

13. Name the four main regions of the stomach.

14. Discuss the significance of the low pH in the stomach.

15. When a person suffers from chronic gastric ulcers, the branches of the vagus nerves that serve the stomach are sometimes cut in an attempt to provide relief. Why might this be an effective treatment?

See the blue Answers tab at the end of the book.

16-5 The small intestine digests and absorbs nutrients

The **small intestine** plays a key role in the digestion and absorption of nutrients. Ninety percent of nutrient absorption occurs in the small intestine. (Most of the rest occurs in the large intestine.) The small intestine is about 6 m (20 ft) long and has a diameter ranging from 4 cm (1.6 in.) at the stomach to about 2.5 cm (1 in.) at the junction with the large intestine. It has three segments: the *duodenum*, the *jejunum*, and the *ileum* (Figure 16-10):

1. The **duodenum** (doo-AH-de-num) is 25 cm (10 in.) in length and is the segment closest to the stomach. From its

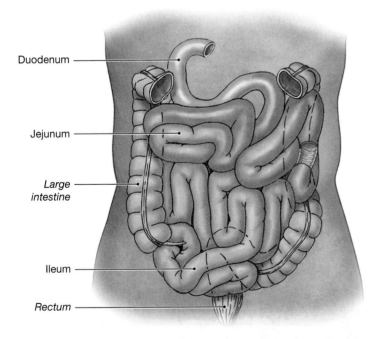

Duodenum ——

Jejunum ——

Large intestine ——

Ileum ——

Rectum ——

FIGURE 16-10 The Segments of the Small Intestine. In this diagram, the three segments of the small intestine—the duodenum, jejunum, and ileum—are shown in different colors.

connection with the stomach, the duodenum curves in a C that encloses the pancreas. This segment is a "mixing bowl" that receives chyme from the stomach and digestive secretions from the pancreas and liver. Unlike the stomach and its proximal 2.5 cm (1 in.), the duodenum lies outside the peritoneal cavity (Figure 16-8b, p. 545). Organs that lie posterior to (instead of within) the peritoneal cavity are called *retroperitoneal* (*retro*, behind).

2. An abrupt bend marks the boundary between the duodenum and the **jejunum** (je-JOO-num) and the site at which the duodenum reenters the peritoneal cavity. The jejunum, which is supported by a sheet of mesentery, is about 2.5 m (8 ft) long. The bulk of chemical digestion and nutrient absorption occurs in the jejunum. One rather drastic approach to weight control involves the surgical removal of a significant portion of the jejunum.

3. The jejunum leads to the third segment, the **ileum** (IL-ē-um). It is also the longest, averaging 3.5 m (12 ft) in length. The ileum ends at the *ileocecal valve*, a sphincter that controls the flow of material from the ileum into the *cecum*, the first portion of the large intestine.

The small intestine fills much of the peritoneal cavity. Its position is stabilized by a mesentery attached to the dorsal body wall (Figure 16-8b, p. 545). Blood vessels, lymphatic vessels, and nerves run to and from the segments of the small intestine within the connective tissue of the mesentery.

THE INTESTINAL WALL

The intestinal lining bears a series of transverse folds called **plicae circulares** (PLĪ-sē sir-kū-lar-ēs) (Figure 16-11a). The lining of the intestine is composed of a multitude of fingerlike projections called **villi** (Figure 16-11b). These structures are covered by a simple columnar epithelium carpeted with microvilli (Figure 16-11c). Because the microvilli project from the epithelium like the bristles on a brush, these cells are said to have a *brush border* (Figure 16-11d).

If the small intestine were a simple tube with smooth walls, it would have a total absorptive area of about 3300 cm^2 (3.6 ft^2). Instead, the epithelium contains plicae circulares; each plica circulares supports a forest of villi, and each villus is covered by epithelial cells blanketed in microvilli. This arrangement increases the total area for absorption to approximately 2 million cm^2, or more than 2200 ft^2.

Each villus contains a network of capillaries (Figure 16-11c) that transports respiratory gases and carries absorbed nutrients

FIGURE 16-11 **The Intestinal Wall.** **(a)** This view of the intestinal lining features one plica and multiple villi. **(b)** A cross section of the intestinal wall reveals its histological structure. **(c)** Each villus contains nerve endings, a capillary network, and a lymphatic capillary (lacteal).

to the hepatic portal circulation for delivery to the liver. ∞ p. 458 In addition to capillaries, each villus contains nerve endings and a lymphatic capillary called a **lacteal** (LAK-tē-ul; *lacteus*, milky). Lacteals transport materials that cannot enter blood capillaries. For example, absorbed fatty acids are assembled into protein-lipid packages that are too large to diffuse into the bloodstream. These packets, called *chylomicrons* (*chylos,* juice), reach the venous circulation by way of the thoracic duct of the lymphoid system. The name *lacteal* refers to the pale, milky appearance of lymph that contains large quantities of lipids.

At the bases of the villi are entrances to *intestinal glands* (**Figure 16-11b**). Stem cells within the bases of the intestinal

glands divide continuously to replenish the intestinal epithelium. Other cells secrete a watery *intestinal juice*. In addition to the intestinal glands, the duodenum contains large *duodenal glands,* or *submucosal glands,* which secrete an alkaline mucus that helps buffer the acids in chyme. Intestinal glands also contain endocrine cells responsible for the production of intestinal hormones discussed in a later section.

INTESTINAL MOVEMENTS

Once the chyme has entered the small intestine, segmentation contractions mix it with mucous secretions and enzymes. As absorption subsequently occurs, weak peristaltic contractions slowly move the remaining materials along the length of the small intestine. These contractions are local reflexes not under CNS control, and the effects are limited to within a few centimeters of the site of the original stimulus.

More elaborate reflexes coordinate activities along the entire length of the small intestine. Distension of the stomach initiates the *gastroenteric* (gas-trō-en-TER-ik) *reflex,* which immediately accelerates glandular secretion and peristaltic activity in all intestinal segments. The increased peristalsis moves materials along the length of the small intestine and empties the duodenum. The *gastroileal* (gas-trō-IL-ē-al) *reflex* is a response to circulating levels of the hormone gastrin. The entry of food into the stomach triggers the release of gastrin, which relaxes the ileocecal valve at the entrance to the large intestine. Because the valve is relaxed, peristalsis pushes materials from the ileum into the large intestine. On average, it takes about 5 hours for ingested food to pass from the duodenum to the end of the ileum, so the first of the materials to enter the duodenum after breakfast may leave the small intestine during lunch.

INTESTINAL SECRETIONS

Roughly 1.8 liters of watery **intestinal juice** enters the intestinal lumen each day. Much of this fluid arrives by osmosis (as water flows out of the mucosa), and the rest is secreted by intestinal glands stimulated by the activation of touch and stretch receptors in the intestinal walls. Intestinal juice moistens the intestinal contents, helps buffer acids, and keeps both the digestive enzymes and the products of digestion in solution.

Hormonal and CNS controls are important in regulating the secretions of the digestive tract and accessory organs. Because the duodenum is the first segment of the intestine to receive chyme, it is the focus of these regulatory mechanisms. Here the acid content of the chyme must be neutralized and the appropriate enzymes added. The duodenal glands protect the duodenal epithelium from gastric acids and enzymes. They increase their secretions in response to local reflexes and also to parasympathetic stimulation carried by the vagus nerves. As a result of parasympathetic stimulation, the duodenal glands begin secreting during the cephalic phase of gastric secretion, long before chyme reaches the pyloric sphincter. Sympathetic stimulation inhibits their activation, leaving the duodenal lining relatively unprepared for the arrival of the acid chyme. This is probably why duodenal ulcers can be caused by chronic stress or by other factors that promote sympathetic activation.

Clinical Note

Vomiting

The responses of the digestive tract to chemical or mechanical irritation are rather predictable: Fluid secretion accelerates all along the digestive tract, and the intestinal contents are eliminated as quickly as possible. The *vomiting reflex* occurs in response to irritation of the soft palate, pharynx, esophagus, stomach, or proximal portions of the small intestine. The sensations of irritation are relayed to the vomiting center of the medulla oblongata, which coordinates the motor responses. In preparation, the pylorus relaxes, and the contents of the duodenum and proximal jejunum are discharged into the stomach by strong peristaltic waves that travel toward the stomach rather than toward the ileum. Vomiting, or *emesis* (EM-ē-sis), then occurs as the stomach regurgitates its contents through the esophagus and pharynx. As regurgitation occurs, the uvula and soft palate block the entrance to the nasopharynx. Increased salivary secretion assists in buffering the stomach acids, thereby preventing erosion of the teeth. In conditions marked by repeated vomiting, severe tooth damage can occur; this is one sign of the eating disorder *bulimia.* Most of the force of vomiting comes from a powerful expiratory movement that elevates intra-abdominal pressures and presses the stomach against the tensed diaphragm.

INTESTINAL HORMONES

Duodenal endocrine cells produce various peptide hormones that coordinate the secretory activities of the stomach, duodenum, pancreas, and liver. These hormones were introduced in the discussion on the regulation of gastric activity, and Figure 16-9 indicates the factors that stimulate their secretion.

Gastrin is secreted by duodenal cells in response to large quantities of incompletely digested proteins. Gastrin promotes increased stomach motility and stimulates the production of acids and enzymes. (As previously noted, gastrin is also secreted by endocrine cells in the distal portion of the stomach.)

Secretin (sē-KRĒ-tin) is released when the pH in the duodenum falls as acidic chyme arrives from the stomach. The primary effect of secretin is to increase the secretion of bile and buffers by the liver and pancreas.

Cholecystokinin (kō-lē-sis-tō-KĪ-nin), or **CCK,** is secreted when chyme arrives in the duodenum, especially when the chyme contains lipids and partially digested proteins. CCK also targets the pancreas and gallbladder. In the pancreas, CCK accelerates the production and secretion of all types of digestive enzymes. At the gallbladder, it causes the ejection of *bile* into the duodenum. The presence of either secretin or CCK in high concentrations also reduces gastric motility and secretory rates.

Gastric inhibitory peptide (GIP) is released when fats and carbohydrates (especially glucose) enter the small intestine. GIP inhibits gastric activity and causes the release of insulin from the pancreatic islets.

The functions of the major gastrointestinal hormones are summarized in Table 16-1, and their interactions are diagrammed in Figure 16-12.

DIGESTION IN THE SMALL INTESTINE

In the stomach, food becomes saturated with gastric juices and exposed to the digestive effects of a strong acid (HCl) and a

proteolytic enzyme (pepsin). Most of the important digestive processes are completed in the small intestine, where the final products of digestion—simple sugars, fatty acids, and amino acids—are absorbed, along with most of the water content. However, the small intestine produces only a few of the enzymes needed to break down the complex materials found in the diet. Most of the enzymes and buffers are contributed by the liver and pancreas, which are discussed in the next section.

The Big Picture

The small intestine receives and raises the pH of materials arriving from the stomach. It then absorbs water, ions, vitamins, and the chemical products released by the action of digestive enzymes secreted by intestinal glands and exocrine glands of the pancreas.

TABLE 16-1 **Important Gastrointestinal Hormones and Their Primary Effects**

HORMONE	STIMULUS	ORIGIN	TARGET	EFFECTS
Gastrin	Vagus nerve stimulation or arrival of food in the stomach	Stomach	Stomach	Stimulates production of acids and enzymes, increases motility
	Arrival of chyme containing large quantities of undigested proteins	Duodenum	Stomach	As above
Secretin	Arrival of chyme in the duodenum	Duodenum	Pancreas	Stimulates production of alkaline buffers
			Stomach	Inhibits gastric secretion and motility
			Liver	Increases rate of bile secretion
Cholecystokinin (CCK)	Arrival of chyme containing lipids and partially digested proteins	Duodenum	Pancreas	Stimulates production of pancreatic enzymes
			Gallbladder	Stimulates contraction of gallbladder
			Duodenum	Causes relaxation of sphincter at base of bile duct
			Stomach	Inhibits gastric secretion and motility
			CNS	May reduce hunger
Gastric inhibitory peptide (GIP)	Arrival of chyme containing large quantities of fats and glucose	Duodenum	Pancreas	Stimulates release of insulin by pancreatic islets
		Stomach		Inhibits gastric secretion and motility

FIGURE 16-12 The Activities of Major Digestive Tract Hormones. Depicted are the primary actions of gastrin, GIP, secretin, and CCK.

CHECKPOINT

16. Which ring of muscle regulates the flow of chyme from the stomach to the small intestine?

17. Name the three segments of the small intestine from proximal to distal.

18. How is the small intestine adapted for the absorption of nutrients?

See the blue Answers tab at the end of the book.

16-6 The pancreas, liver, and gallbladder are accessory glands that assist with the digestive process in the small intestine

The pancreas provides digestive enzymes, as well as buffers that help neutralize chyme. The liver secretes *bile,* a solution stored in the gallbladder for subsequent discharge into the small intestine. Bile contains buffers and *bile salts,* compounds that facilitate the digestion and absorption of lipids.

THE PANCREAS

The **pancreas,** shown in Figure 16-13a, lies behind the stomach, extending laterally from the duodenum toward the spleen. It is an elongate, pinkish-gray organ with a length of about 15 cm (6 in.) and a weight of around 80 g (3 oz.). The surface of the pancreas has a lumpy texture, and its tissue is soft and easily torn. Like the duodenum, the pancreas is retroperitoneal (lies outside the peritoneal cavity); only its anterior surface is covered by peritoneum (Figure 16-8b).

Histological Organization of the Pancreas

In Chapter 10 we learned that collections of endocrine cells called **pancreatic islets** secrete the hormones insulin and glucagon, but these cells account for only about 1 percent of the cell population of the pancreas. ∞ p. 364 Exocrine cells and

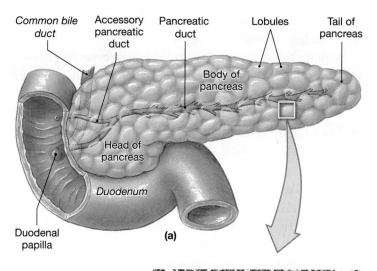

Common bile duct   Accessory pancreatic duct   Pancreatic duct   Lobules   Tail of pancreas

Body of pancreas

Head of pancreas

Duodenum

Duodenal papilla

(a)

Duct

Pancreatic acini (exocrine)

Pancreatic islet (endocrine)

(b)   LM × 75

FIGURE 16-13 **The Pancreas. (a)** The head of the pancreas is tucked into a curve of the duodenum that begins at the pylorus of the stomach. **(b)** Pancreatic acini and their ducts constitute the vast majority of all pancreatic cells.

their associated ducts account for the rest, as the pancreas is primarily an exocrine organ that produces **pancreatic juice,** a mixture of digestive enzymes and buffers. The numerous ducts that branch throughout the pancreas end at saclike pouches called **pancreatic acini** (AS-i-nī; singular *acinus,* grape) (Figure 16-13b). Enzymes and buffers are secreted by the *acinar cells* of these pouches and by the epithelial cells that line the ducts. The smaller ducts converge to form larger ducts that ultimately fuse to form the **pancreatic duct,** which carries these secretions to the duodenum. The pancreatic duct penetrates the duodenal wall with the *common bile duct* from the liver and gallbladder.

Pancreatic enzymes do most of the digestive work in the small intestine. Pancreatic enzymes are broadly classified according to their intended targets. **Carbohydrases** (kar-bō-HĪ-drā-sez) digest sugars and starches, **lipases** (LĪ-pā-sez) break down lipids, **nucleases** break down nucleic acids, and **proteases** (prō-tē-ā-sez) (proteolytic enzymes) break proteins apart.

The Control of Pancreatic Secretion

Each day the pancreas secretes about 1000 mL (1 qt) of pancreatic juice. The secretions are controlled primarily by hormones from the duodenum.

When acidic chyme arrives in the duodenum, secretin is released, triggering the pancreas to secrete a watery, alkaline fluid with a pH between 7.5 and 8.8. Among its other components, this secretion contains buffers, primarily *sodium bicarbonate,* that increase the pH of the chyme.

A different intestinal hormone, CCK, controls the production and secretion of pancreatic enzymes. The specific enzymes involved are **pancreatic amylase,** which like salivary amylase breaks down carbohydrates; **pancreatic lipase,** a group of nucleases; and several proteases.

Proteases account for about 70 percent of total pancreatic enzyme production. The most abundant proteases are **trypsin** (TRIP-sin), **chymotrypsin** (kī-mō-TRIP-sin), and **carboxypeptidase** (kar-bok-sē-PEP-ti-dās). Together they break down complex proteins into a mixture of short peptide chains and amino acids. Pancreatic enzymes are quite powerful, and the pancreatic cells protect themselves by secreting their products as inactive *proenzymes,* which are activated by other enzymes within the intestinal tract.

Clinical Note

Pancreatitis

Pancreatitis (pan-krē-a-TĪ-tis) is inflammation of the pancreas. Blockage of the excretory ducts, bacterial or viral infections, ischemia (circulatory blockage), and drug reactions (especially those involving alcohol) are among the factors that may produce this painful condition. These stimuli provoke a crisis by injuring exocrine cells in at least a portion of the organ. Lysosomes within the damaged cells then activate the pancreatic enzymes, which digest the surrounding undamaged cells, activating their enzymes as well. The result is a chain reaction of destructive autodigestion. In most cases, only a portion of the pancreas is affected, and the condition subsides in a few days. However, in 10–15 percent of pancreatitis cases the process does not subside, and the enzymes may ultimately destroy the organ. Loss of the entire pancreas results in two disease conditions: *diabetes mellitus* (which requires the administration of insulin) and *nutrient malabsorption* (which requires oral administration of pancreatic enzymes).

The Big Picture

The exocrine pancreas produces essential digestive buffers and enzymes in response to the release of regulatory hormones (secretin and CCK) by the duodenum.

THE LIVER

The firm, reddish-brown **liver** is the largest visceral organ, weighing about 1.5 kg (3.3 lb) and accounting for roughly 2.5 percent of total body weight. Most of the liver lies in the right hypochondriac and epigastric abdominopelvic regions. ⚬⚬ p. 17

Anatomy of the Liver

The liver is wrapped in a tough fibrous capsule and covered by a layer of visceral peritoneum. The liver is divided into four unequal lobes: the large **left** and **right lobes** and the smaller **caudate** and **quadrate lobes** (Figure 16-14). A tough connective tissue fold, the *falciform ligament,* marks the division between the left and right lobes. The thickened posterior margin of the falciform ligament is the *round ligament,* a fibrous remnant of the fetal umbilical vein.

Lodged within a recess under the right lobe of the liver is the *gallbladder,* a muscular sac that stores and concentrates bile before it is excreted into the small intestine. The gallbladder and associated structures will be described in a later section.

Histological Organization of the Liver

The lobes of the liver are divided by connective tissue into about 100,000 **liver lobules,** the basic functional unit of the liver. The histological organization and structure of a typical liver lobule is shown in Figure 16-15.

Within a lobule, liver cells—called **hepatocytes** (HEP-a-tō-sīts)—are arranged into a series of irregular plates like the spokes of a wheel. The plates are only one cell thick and, where they are exposed, covered with microvilli. *Sinusoids,* specialized and highly permeable capillaries, form passageways between the adjacent plates that empty into the *central vein.* The sinusoidal lining includes a large number of phagocytic *Kupffer* (KOOP-fer) *cells.* These cells, part of the monocyte–macrophage system, engulf pathogens, cell debris, and damaged blood cells.

The circulation of blood to the liver was discussed in Chapter 13 (p. 458) and illustrated in Figure 13-24 (p. 459). Blood enters the sinusoids from branches of the hepatic portal vein and hepatic artery. These two branches, plus a small branch of the bile duct, form a *portal area,* or *hepatic triad,* at each of the six corners of a lobule (Figure 16-15a). As blood flows through the sinusoids, the hepatocytes absorb solutes from the plasma and secrete materials such as plasma proteins. Blood then leaves the sinusoids and enters the **central vein** of the lobule. The central veins of all of the lobules ultimately merge to form the *hepatic veins,* which empty into the inferior vena cava. Liver diseases (including the various forms of *hepatitis*) and conditions such as alcoholism can lead to degenerative changes in liver tissue and reduction of the blood supply.

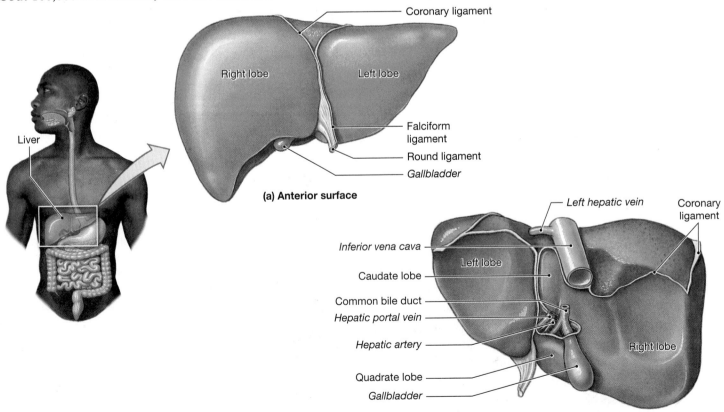

FIGURE 16-14 The Surface Anatomy of the Liver.

(a) Anterior surface

Coronary ligament

Right lobe

Left lobe

Falciform ligament

Round ligament

Gallbladder

Liver

(b) Posterior surface

Left hepatic vein

Coronary ligament

Inferior vena cava

Left lobe

Caudate lobe

Common bile duct

Hepatic portal vein

Hepatic artery

Quadrate lobe

Gallbladder

Right lobe

(a)

Bile duct

Branch of hepatic portal vein

Portal area

Sinusoid

Hepatocytes

Branch of hepatic portal vein (containing blood)

Branch of hepatic artery

Bile duct

(c) LM × 35

Central vein

Kupffer cells

Bile canaliculi

Branch of hepatic portal vein

(b)

The hepatocytes also secrete a fluid called **bile.** Bile is released into a network of narrow channels, called **bile canaliculi,** between adjacent liver cells (Figure 16-15b). These canaliculi extend outward from the central vein, carrying bile toward a network of ever-larger bile ducts within the liver until it eventually leaves the liver through the **common hepatic duct** (Figure 16-16a). Bile in the common hepatic duct may either flow into the **common bile duct,** which empties into the duodenum, or enter the **cystic duct,** which leads to the gallbladder.

Liver Functions

The liver has three general functional roles: (1) *metabolic regulation,* (2) *hematological regulation,* and (3) *bile production.* Because the liver has over 200 known functions, only a general overview is provided here.

METABOLIC REGULATION. The liver is the primary organ involved in regulating the composition of circulating blood. All blood leaving the absorptive areas of the digestive tract flows through the liver before reaching the general circulation. Thus, hepatocytes can (1) extract absorbed nutrients or toxins from the blood before they reach the rest of the body and (2) monitor and adjust the circulating levels of organic nutrients. Excesses are removed and stored, and deficiencies are corrected by mobilizing stored reserves or synthesizing the necessary compounds. When blood glucose levels rise, for example, the liver removes glucose and synthesizes the storage compound glycogen. When blood glucose levels fall, the liver breaks down stored glycogen and releases glucose into the circulation. Circulating toxins and metabolic wastes are also removed for later inactivation or excretion. Additionally, fat-soluble vitamins (A, D, K, and E) are absorbed and stored.

HEMATOLOGICAL REGULATION. The liver, the largest blood reservoir in the body, receives about 25 percent of cardiac output. As blood passes through the liver, phagocytic Kupffer cells remove aged or damaged red blood cells, debris, and pathogens from the circulation. Kupffer cells are antigen-presenting cells that can stimulate an immune response. ∞ p. 485 Equally important, hepatocytes synthesize the plasma proteins that determine the osmotic concentration of the blood, transport nutrients, and make up the clotting and complement systems. ∞ p. 384

THE PRODUCTION AND ROLE OF BILE. As previously noted, bile is synthesized in the liver and excreted into the lumen of the duodenum. Bile consists mostly of water, ions, *bilirubin* (a pigment derived from hemoglobin), cholesterol, and an assortment of lipids collectively known as **bile salts.** The water and ions in bile help dilute and buffer acids in chyme as it enters the small

intestine. Bile salts are synthesized from cholesterol in the liver and are required for the normal digestion and absorption of fats.

Most dietary lipids are not water soluble. Mechanical processing in the stomach creates large droplets containing various lipids. Pancreatic lipase is not lipid soluble and can interact with lipids only at the surface of the droplet. The larger the droplet, the more lipids are inside it, isolated and protected from these digestive enzymes. Bile salts break the droplets apart through a process called **emulsification** (ē-mul-si-fi-KĀ-shun), which creates tiny droplets with a superficial coating of bile salts. The formation of tiny droplets increases the surface area available for enzymatic attack. In addition, the layer of bile salts facilitates interaction between lipids and the lipid-digesting enzymes from the pancreas. (We will return to the mechanism of lipid digestion later.)

Table 16-2 provides a summary of the liver's major functions.

THE GALLBLADDER

The **gallbladder** is a hollow, muscular, pear-shaped organ that stores and concentrates bile prior to its excretion into the small intestine (Figure 16-16a). The cystic duct extends from the gallbladder to the point where its union with the common hepatic

---

Clinical Note

Liver Disease

Any condition that severely damages the liver represents a serious threat to life. The liver has a limited ability to regenerate itself after injury, but liver function cannot be fully recovered unless a normal circulatory pattern is reestablished. Examples of important types of liver disease include *cirrhosis,* which is characterized by the replacement of lobules by fibrous tissue, and various forms of *hepatitis* resulting from viral infections. In some cases, liver transplants are used to treat liver failure, but the supply of suitable donor organs is limited, and the success rate is highest in young, otherwise healthy recipients. Clinical trials are now under way to test an artificial liver known as *ELAD* (extracorporeal *liver assist device*), which may prove suitable for the long-term support of individuals with chronic liver disease.

TABLE 16-2 Major Functions of the Liver

DIGESTIVE AND METABOLIC FUNCTIONS
Synthesis and secretion of bile
Storage of glycogen and lipid reserves
Maintenance of normal blood levels of glucose, amino acids, and fatty acids
Synthesis and interconversion of nutrient types (e.g., transamination of amino acids or conversion of carbohydrates to lipids)
Synthesis and release of cholesterol bound to transport proteins
Inactivation of toxins
Storage of iron reserves
Storage of fat-soluble vitamins

OTHER MAJOR FUNCTIONS
Synthesis of plasma proteins
Synthesis of clotting factors
Synthesis of the inactive hormone angiotensinogen
Phagocytosis of damaged red blood cells (by Kupffer cells)
Blood storage (major contributor to venous reserve)
Absorption and breakdown of circulating hormones (insulin, epinephrine) and immunoglobulins
Absorption and inactivation of lipid-soluble drugs

FIGURE 16-16 The Gallbladder. (a) A view of the inferior surface of the liver reveals the position of the gallbladder and the ducts that transport bile from the liver to the gallbladder and duodenum. **(b)** This interior view of the duodenum shows the opening at the duodenal papilla and the location of the hepatopancreatic sphincter.

duct forms the common bile duct. The common bile duct and the pancreatic duct join and share a passageway that enters the duodenum at the *duodenal papilla* (Figure 16-16b). The muscular **hepatopancreatic sphincter** surrounds their shared passageway.

A major function of the gallbladder is *bile storage.* Bile is secreted continuously—roughly 1 liter each day—but it is released into the duodenum only under the stimulation of the intestinal hormone cholecystokinin (CCK). In the absence of CCK, the hepatopancreatic sphincter remains closed, so bile leaving the liver in the common hepatic duct cannot flow through the common bile duct and enter the duodenum. Instead, it enters the cystic duct and is stored within the expandable gallbladder. Whenever chyme enters the duodenum, CCK is released, relaxing the hepatopancreatic sphincter and stimulating contractions within the walls of the gallbladder that push bile into the small intestine. The amount of CCK secreted increases if the chyme contains large amounts of fat.

Another function of the gallbladder is *bile modification.* When filled to capacity, the gallbladder contains 40–70 mL of bile. The composition of bile gradually changes as it remains in the gallbladder. Water is absorbed, and the bile salts and other components of bile become increasingly concentrated. If the bile salts become too concentrated, they may precipitate, forming *gallstones* that can cause a variety of clinical problems.

The Big Picture

The liver is the center for metabolic regulation in the body. It also produces bile that is stored in the gallbladder and ejected into the duodenum under stimulation of the hormone CCK. Bile is needed for the efficient digestion of lipids because it breaks down large lipid droplets so that individual lipid molecules can be attacked by digestive enzymes.

CHECKPOINT

19. How would a meal that is high in fat affect the level of cholecystokinin (CCK) in the blood?

20. Damage to the exocrine pancreas would most impair the digestion of which nutrient?

21. What effect would a decrease in the amount of bile salts in bile have on the digestion and absorption of fats?

See the blue Answers tab at the end of the book

16-7 The large intestine is divided into three parts with regional specialization

The horseshoe-shaped **large intestine** begins at the end of the ileum and ends at the anus (Figure 16-17). The large intestine lies below the stomach and liver and almost completely frames the small intestine. The main functions of the large intestine include (1) reabsorption of water and compaction of the intestinal contents into feces, (2) absorption of important vitamins freed by bacterial action, and (3) storage of fecal material prior to defecation.

The large intestine, also called the *large bowel*, has an average length of approximately 1.5 m (5 ft) and a width of 7.5 cm (3 in.). It can be divided into three parts: (1) the pouchlike *cecum*, the first portion; (2) the *colon*, the largest portion; and (3) the *rectum*, the last 15 cm (6 in.) of the large intestine and the end of the digestive tract.

THE CECUM

Material arriving from the ileum first enters an expanded pouch, the **cecum** (SĒ-kum), where compaction begins. A muscular sphincter, the **ileocecal** (il-ē-ō-SĒ-kal) **valve,** guards the connection between the ileum and the cecum. The slender, hollow **appendix,** or *vermiform* (*vermis,* worm) *appendix,* attaches to the cecum along its posteromedial surface. The appendix is generally about 9 cm (3.5 in.) long, but its size and shape are quite variable. The walls of the appendix are dominated by lymphoid nodules, and it functions primarily as an organ of the lymphoid system. Inflammation of the appendix is known as *appendicitis.*

THE COLON

The **colon** is roughly three times larger in diameter than the small intestine, but it has a thinner wall. Major characteristics of the colon are a lack of villi and an abundance of mucous cells. The most striking external feature of the colon is the presence of pouches, or **haustra** (HAWS-truh; singular, *haustrum*), that permit considerable distension and elongation (Figure 16-17a). Three longitudinal bands of smooth muscle—the **taeniae coli** (TĒ-nē-ē-KŌ-lē)—run along the outer surface of the colon just beneath the serosa. Muscle tone within these bands creates the haustra.

The colon can be divided into four segments. The **ascending colon** begins at the ileocecal valve. It ascends along the right side of the peritoneal cavity until it reaches the inferior mar-

gin of the liver. It then turns horizontally, becoming the **transverse colon.** The transverse colon continues toward the left side, passing below the stomach and following the curve of the body wall. Near the spleen, it turns inferiorly to form the **descending colon.** The descending colon continues along the left side until it curves and forms the S-shaped **sigmoid** (SIG-moyd; *sigmeidos,* the Greek letter *S*) **colon.** The sigmoid colon empties into the rectum.

THE RECTUM

The **rectum** (REK-tum) forms the end of the digestive tract and is an expandable organ for the temporary storage of feces (Figure 16-17b). The last portion of the rectum, the **anal canal,** contains small longitudinal folds called *anal columns.* The distal margins of these columns are joined by transverse folds that mark the boundary between the columnar epithelium of the rectum and a stratified squamous epithelium like that found in the oral cavity. Very close to the **anus,** which is the exit of the anal canal, the epidermis becomes keratinized and identical to that on the skin surface.

The circular muscle layer of the muscularis externa in this region forms the **internal anal sphincter,** the smooth muscle cells of which are not under voluntary control. The **external anal sphincter,** which encircles the anus, consists of skeletal muscle fibers and is under voluntary control.

THE FUNCTIONS OF THE LARGE INTESTINE

The major functions of the large intestine are absorbing a variety of substances and preparing the fecal material for elimination.

Clinical Note

Colorectal Cancer

Colorectal cancer is relatively common in both men and women. Approximately 108,070 new colon cancer cases and 40,740 new rectal cancer cases were expected in the United States in 2008. Although colorectal cancer is the second leading cause of cancer-related deaths—an estimated 49,960 colorectal cancer deaths were expected in 2008—the death rate has declined over the past 20 years. The best defense appears to be early detection and prompt treatment. The standard screening test—checking the feces for blood—is a simple procedure that can easily be performed on a stool (fecal) sample as part of a routine physical examination.

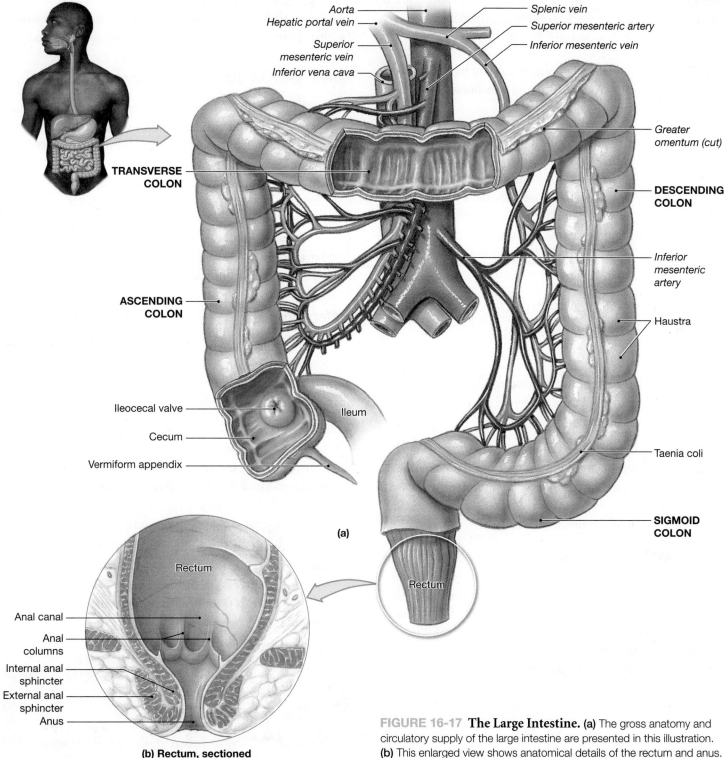

TRANSVERSE
COLON

Aorta
Hepatic portal vein
Superior
mesenteric vein
Inferior vena cava

Splenic vein
Superior mesenteric artery
Inferior mesenteric vein

Greater
omentum (cut)

DESCENDING
COLON

ASCENDING
COLON

Inferior
mesenteric
artery

Haustra

Ileocecal valve
Cecum
Vermiform appendix

Ileum

Taenia coli

(a)

SIGMOID
COLON

Rectum

Rectum

Anal canal
Anal
columns
Internal anal
sphincter
External anal
sphincter
Anus

(b) Rectum, sectioned

FIGURE 16-17 The Large Intestine. (a) The gross anatomy and circulatory supply of the large intestine are presented in this illustration. **(b)** This enlarged view shows anatomical details of the rectum and anus.

Absorption in the Large Intestine

The reabsorption of water is an important function of the large intestine. Although roughly 1500 mL of watery material enters the colon each day, only about 200 mL of feces is ejected. The remarkable efficiency of digestion can best be appreciated by considering the average composition of feces: 75 percent water, 5 percent bacteria, and the rest a mixture of indigestible materials, small quantities of inorganic matter, and the remains of intestinal epithelial cells.

In addition to reabsorbing water, the large intestine absorbs a variety of other substances. Examples include useful compounds (including bile salts and vitamins), organic waste products (such as bilirubin, derived from the breakdown of hemoglobin), and various toxins generated by bacterial action.

BILE SALTS. Most of the bile salts remaining in the material reaching the cecum are reabsorbed and transported to the liver for secretion in bile.

VITAMINS. **Vitamins** are organic molecules related to lipids and carbohydrates that are essential to many metabolic reactions. Many enzymes require the binding of an additional ion or molecule, called a *cofactor,* before substrates can also bind. *Coenzymes* are nonprotein molecules that function as cofactors, and many vitamins are essential coenzymes.

Bacteria residing within the colon generate three vitamins that supplement our dietary supply:

- *Vitamin K,* a fat-soluble vitamin needed by the liver to synthesize four clotting factors, including *prothrombin.*

- *Biotin,* a water-soluble vitamin important in glucose metabolism.

- *Vitamin B_5* (pantothenic acid), a water-soluble vitamin required in the manufacture of steroid hormones and some neurotransmitters.

Vitamin K deficiencies lead to impaired blood clotting. Intestinal bacteria produce roughly half of our daily vitamin K requirements. Deficiencies of biotin or vitamin B_5 are extremely rare after infancy because the intestinal bacteria produce enough to make up for any shortage in the diet.

ORGANIC WASTES. The breakdown of heme and its release as bilirubin in the bile was discussed in Chapter 11. ∞ p. 388 Within the large intestine, bacteria convert bilirubin into other products, some of which are absorbed into the bloodstream and excreted in the urine, producing its yellow color. Others remain in the colon and, upon exposure to oxygen, are further modified into the pigments that give feces a brown color.

TOXINS. Bacterial action breaks down peptides remaining in the feces and generates (1) ammonia, (2) nitrogen-containing compounds that are responsible for the odor of feces, and (3) hydrogen sulfide (H_2S), a gas that produces a "rotten egg" odor. Much of the ammonia and other toxins are absorbed into the hepatic portal circulation and removed by the liver. The liver processes them into relatively nontoxic compounds that are excreted at the kidneys.

Indigestible carbohydrates are not altered by intestinal enzymes and arrive in the colon intact. These molecules provide a nutrient source for resident bacteria, whose metabolic activities are responsible for intestinal gas, or *flatus,* in the large intestine. Meals containing large amounts of indigestible carbohydrates (such as beans) stimulate the production of gas by bacteria.

Movements of the Large Intestine

The gastroileal and gastroenteric reflexes move material into the cecum while you eat. Movement from the cecum to the transverse colon is very slow, allowing hours for the reabsorption of water. Movement from the transverse colon through the rest of the large intestine results from powerful peristaltic contractions called *mass movements,* which occur a few times a day. The normal stimulus for mass movements is distension of the stomach and duodenum. In response to commands relayed over the intestinal nerve plexuses, contractions force fecal material into the rectum, causing the urge to defecate.

Defecation

The rectum is usually empty until a powerful peristaltic contraction forces fecal material out of the sigmoid colon. Distension of the rectal wall then triggers the **defecation reflex,** which involves two positive feedback loops:

1. In the shorter feedback loop, stretch receptors in the rectal walls stimulate a series of increased local peristaltic contractions in the sigmoid colon and rectum. The contractions move feces toward the anus and increase distension of the rectum.

2. The stretch receptors in the rectal walls also stimulate parasympathetic motor neurons in the sacral spinal cord. These neurons stimulate increased peristalsis (mass movements) in the descending colon and sigmoid colon that push feces toward the rectum, further increasing distension there.

Clinical Note

Diverticulosis

In the condition termed **diverticulosis** (dī-ver-tik-ū-LŌ-sis), pockets (*diverticula*) form in the intestinal mucosa, generally in the sigmoid colon. These pockets get forced outward, probably by the pressures generated during defecation. If the pockets push through weak points in the muscularis externa, they form semi-isolated chambers that are subject to recurrent infection and inflammation. The inflammation of diverticula causes pain and occasional bleeding, a condition known as *diverticulitis* (dī-ver-tik-ū-LĪ-tis). Inflammation of other portions of the colon is called *colitis* (ko-LĪ-tis).

Clinical Note

Diarrhea and Constipation

Diarrhea (dī-a-RĒ-uh) exists when an individual has frequent, watery bowel movements. Diarrhea results when the mucosa of the colon becomes unable to maintain normal levels of absorption, or when the rate of fluid entry into the colon exceeds the colon's maximum reabsorptive capacity. Bacterial, viral, or protozoan infection of the colon or small intestine can cause acute bouts of diarrhea lasting several days. Severe diarrhea is life threatening due to cumulative fluid and ion losses. In *cholera* (KOL-e-ruh), bacteria bound to the intestinal lining release a toxin that stimulates a massive secretion of fluid across the intestinal epithelium. Without treatment, a person with cholera can die of acute dehydration in a matter of hours.

Constipation is infrequent defecation, generally involving dry, hard feces. Constipation occurs when fecal material is moving through the colon so slowly that excessive water reabsorption occurs. The feces then become extremely compact, difficult to move, and highly abrasive. Inadequate dietary fiber and fluids, coupled with a lack of exercise, are common causes. Constipation can usually be treated by oral administration of stool softeners such as Colace, laxatives, or *cathartics* (ka-THAR-tiks), which promote defecation. These compounds either promote water movement into the feces, increase fecal mass, or irritate the lining of the colon to stimulate peristalsis. The promotion of peristalsis is one benefit of "high-fiber" cereals. Indigestible fiber adds bulk to the feces, aiding moisture retention and stimulating stretch receptors that promote peristalsis. Active movement during exercise also assists in the movement of fecal material through the colon.

The passage of feces through the anal canal requires relaxation of the internal anal sphincter, but when it relaxes, the external sphincter automatically closes. Thus, the actual release of feces requires conscious effort to open the external sphincter voluntarily. If the conscious commands do not arrive, peristaltic contractions cease until additional rectal expansion triggers the defecation reflex a second time.

In addition to opening the external sphincter, consciously directed activities, such as tensing the abdominal muscles or exhaling while closing the glottis (called the *Valsalva maneuver*), elevate intra-abdominal pressures and help to force fecal material out of the rectum. Such pressures also force blood into the network of veins in the lamina propria and submucosa of the anal canal, causing them to stretch. Repeated incidents of straining to force defecation can cause the veins to be permanently distended, producing *hemorrhoids*.

The Big Picture

The large intestine stores digestive wastes and reabsorbs water. Bacterial residents of the large intestine are an important source of vitamins, especially vitamin K, biotin, and vitamin B_5.

CHECKPOINT

22. Identify the four segments of the large intestine.

23. What are some structural differences between the large intestine and the small intestine?

24. A narrowing of the ileocecal valve would hamper movement of chyme between what two organs?

See the blue Answers tab at the end of the book.

16-8 Digestion is the mechanical and chemical alteration of food that allows the absorption and use of nutrients

A typical meal contains a mixture of carbohydrates, proteins, lipids, water, electrolytes (minerals), and vitamins. The digestive system handles each component differently. Large organic molecules must be broken down through digestion before absorption can occur. Water, electrolytes, and vitamins can be absorbed without preliminary processing, but special transport mechanisms may be involved.

THE PROCESSING AND ABSORPTION OF NUTRIENTS

Food contains large organic molecules, many of them insoluble. The digestive system first breaks down the physical structure of the ingested material and then disassembles the component molecules into smaller fragments. This disassembly produces small organic molecules that can be released into the bloodstream. Once absorbed by cells, they are used to generate ATP or to synthesize complex carbohydrates, proteins, and lipids. This section will focus on the mechanics of digestion and absorption; the fates of the compounds inside cells will be considered in Chapter 17.

Foods are usually complex chains of simpler molecules. In a typical dietary carbohydrate, the basic molecules are simple sugars. In a protein, the building blocks are amino acids, and in lipids they are usually fatty acids. Digestive enzymes break the bonds between the component molecules in a process called *hydrolysis*. The hydrolysis of carbohydrates, lipids, and proteins was detailed in Chapter 2. ∞ pp. 41, 43, 46

Digestive enzymes differ in their specific targets. Carbohydrases break the bonds between sugars; lipases separate fatty acids from glycerides; and proteases split the linkages between amino acids. Specific enzymes in each class may be even more selective, breaking bonds between specific molecular participants. For example, a given carbohydrase might ignore all bonds except those connecting two glucose molecules. Figure 16-18 summarizes the chemical events in the digestion of carbohydrates, lipids, and proteins. Table 16-3 reviews the major digestive enzymes and their functions.

Carbohydrate Digestion and Absorption

Carbohydrate digestion begins in the mouth through the action of salivary amylase (Figure 16-18a). Amylase breaks down complex carbohydrates into smaller fragments, producing a mixture primarily composed of disaccharides (two simple sugars) and trisaccharides (three simple sugars). Salivary amylase continues to digest the starches and glycogen in the meal for an hour or two before stomach acids render it inactive. In the duodenum, the remaining complex carbohydrates are broken down through the action of pancreatic amylase.

Before disaccharides and trisaccharides are absorbed, they are fragmented into simple sugars (monosaccharides) by brush border enzymes found on the surfaces of the intestinal microvilli. ∞ p. 548 The intestinal epithelium then absorbs the resulting simple sugars through carrier-mediated transport mechanisms, such as facilitated diffusion or cotransport. ∞ p. 68 Glucose uptake, for example, occurs through cotransport with sodium ions. (The sodium ions are then ejected by the sodium–potassium exchange pump.)

Simple sugars entering an intestinal cell diffuse through the cytoplasm and cross the basement membrane by facilitated diffusion to enter the interstitial fluid. They then enter intestinal capillaries for delivery to the hepatic portal vein and liver.

Lipid Digestion and Absorption

The structure of fats, or triglycerides, the most abundant dietary lipids, was introduced in Chapter 2. ∞ p. 44 A triglyceride

Clinical Note

Lactose Intolerance

Lactose is the primary carbohydrate in milk. By breaking down lactose, the enzyme lactase performs an essential service throughout infancy and early childhood. If the intestinal mucosa stops producing lactase by the time of adolescence, the individual becomes lactose intolerant. Individuals who are lactose intolerant can have a variety of unpleasant digestive problems after eating a meal containing milk and other dairy products.

TABLE 16-3 **Digestive Enzymes and Their Functions**

ENZYME	SOURCE	OPTIMAL pH	TARGET	PRODUCTS
CARBOHYDRASES				
Amylase	Salivary glands, pancreas	6.7–7.5	Complex carbohydrates	Disaccharides and trisaccharides
Maltase, sucrase, lactase	Small intestine	7–8	Maltose, sucrose, lactose	Monosaccharides
LIPASES				
Pancreatic lipase	Pancreas	7–8	Triglycerides	Fatty acids and monoglycerides
PROTEASES				
Pepsin	Stomach	1.5–2.0	Proteins, polypeptides	Short polypeptides
Trypsin, chymotrypsin, carboxypeptidase	Pancreas	7–8	Proteins, polypeptides	Short peptide chains
Peptidases	Small intestine	7–8	Dipeptides, tripeptides	Amino acids
NUCLEASES	Pancreas	7–8	Nucleic acids	Nitrogenous bases and simple sugars

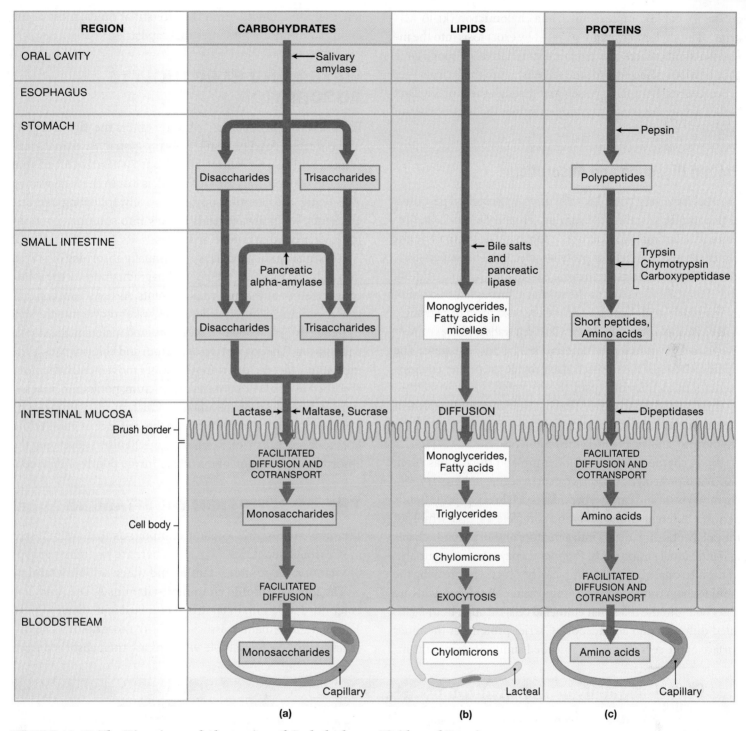

REGION	CARBOHYDRATES	LIPIDS	PROTEINS
ORAL CAVITY	← Salivary amylase		
ESOPHAGUS			
STOMACH	Disaccharides Trisaccharides		← Pepsin Polypeptides
SMALL INTESTINE	Pancreatic alpha-amylase Disaccharides Trisaccharides	← Bile salts and pancreatic lipase Monoglycerides, Fatty acids in micelles	Trypsin Chymotrypsin Carboxypeptidase Short peptides, Amino acids
INTESTINAL MUCOSA Brush border Cell body	Lactase → ← Maltase, Sucrase FACILITATED DIFFUSION AND COTRANSPORT Monosaccharides FACILITATED DIFFUSION	DIFFUSION Monoglycerides, Fatty acids Triglycerides Chylomicrons EXOCYTOSIS	← Dipeptidases FACILITATED DIFFUSION AND COTRANSPORT Amino acids FACILITATED DIFFUSION AND COTRANSPORT
BLOODSTREAM	Monosaccharides Capillary	Chylomicrons Lacteal	Amino acids Capillary
	(a)	(b)	(c)

FIGURE 16-18 **The Digestion and Absorption of Carbohydrates, Lipids, and Proteins.**

molecule consists of three fatty acids attached to a single molecule of glycerol. Triglycerides and other dietary fats are relatively unaffected by conditions in the stomach and enter the duodenum in the form of large lipid droplets.

As noted previously, in the duodenum bile salts emulsify these drops into tiny droplets that can be attacked by pancreatic lipase (**Figure 16-18b**). This enzyme breaks the triglycerides

apart, and the resulting mixture of fatty acids and monoglycerides interacts with bile salts to form small lipid-bile salt complexes called **micelles** (mī-SELZ). When a micelle contacts the intestinal epithelium, the enclosed triglyceride products diffuse across the cell membrane and enter the cytoplasm. The intestinal cells use the arriving fatty acids and monoglycerides to manufacture new triglycerides that are then coated with proteins. This step

563

creates a soluble complex known as a **chylomicron** (kī-lō-MĪ-kron). The chylomicrons are secreted by exocytosis into the interstitial fluids, where they enter intestinal lacteals through large gaps between adjacent endothelial cells. From the lacteals they proceed along lymphatic vessels and through the thoracic duct before finally entering the bloodstream at the left subclavian vein.

Protein Digestion and Absorption

Proteins have very complex structures, so protein digestion is both complex and time consuming. Protein digestion first requires disrupting the structure of food so that proteolytic enzymes can attack individual protein molecules. This step involves mechanical processing in the oral cavity, through mastication, and chemical processing in the stomach, through the action of hydrochloric acid. Exposure of the ingested food to a strongly acid environment breaks down plant cell walls and the connective tissues in animal products and kills most pathogens. The acidic contents of the stomach also provide the proper environment for the activity of pepsin, the proteolytic enzyme secreted by chief cells of the stomach. Pepsin does not complete protein digestion, but it does reduce the relatively huge proteins of the chyme into smaller polypeptide fragments (Figure 16-18c).

When chyme enters the duodenum and the pH has risen, pancreatic proteolytic enzymes can now begin working. Trypsin, chymotrypsin, and carboxypeptidase each break peptide bonds between different amino acids and complete the disassembly of the polypeptide fragments into a mixture of short peptide chains and individual amino acids. *Peptidases,* enzymes on the surfaces of the intestinal microvilli, complete the process by breaking the peptide chains into individual amino acids. The amino acids are absorbed into the intestinal epithelial cells through both facilitated diffusion and cotransport. Carrier proteins at the inner surface of the cells release the absorbed amino acids into the interstitial fluid. Once within the interstitial fluids, most of the amino acids diffuse into intestinal capillaries.

WATER AND ELECTROLYTE ABSORPTION

Each day, roughly 2000 mL of water enters the digestive tract in the form of food or drink. Salivary, gastric, intestinal, pancreatic, and bile secretions add about 7000 mL. Out of that total of 9000 mL, only about 150 mL is lost in the fecal wastes. This water conservation occurs passively, following osmotic gradients; water always tends to flow into solutions containing higher concentrations of solutes.

Intestinal epithelial cells are continually absorbing dissolved nutrients and ions, and these activities gradually lower the solute concentration of the intestinal contents. As the solute concentration within the intestine decreases, water moves into the surrounding tissues, "following" the solutes and maintaining osmotic equilibrium. The absorption of sodium and chloride ions is the most important factor promoting water movement. Other ions absorbed in smaller quantities are calcium, potassium, magnesium, iodine, bicarbonate, and iron. Calcium absorption occurs under hormonal control, requiring the presence of parathyroid hormone and calcitriol. Regulatory mechanisms governing the absorption or excretion of the other ions are poorly understood.

THE ABSORPTION OF VITAMINS

Vitamins are essential organic compounds that are required in very small quantities. p. 560 There are two major groups of vitamins: fat-soluble vitamins and water-soluble vitamins.

The four **fat-soluble vitamins**—vitamins A, D, E, and K—enter the duodenum in fat droplets, mixed with dietary lipids. The vitamins remain in association with those lipids when micelles form. The fat-soluble vitamins are then absorbed from

---

Clinical Note — Malabsorption Syndromes

Malabsorption is imperfect, inadequate, or otherwise flawed absorption of nutrients. This disorder may affect the absorption of only one nutrient or many.

Several factors can cause malabsorption. Certain genetic inabilities to manufacture specific enzymes can result in discrete patterns of malabsorption; *lactose intolerance* is a good example.

Damage to accessory glands or the intestinal mucosa can cause malabsorption of all types of nutrients. In other cases—when the accessory organs are functioning normally but their secretions cannot reach the duodenum—the cause of malabsorption is either *biliary obstruction* (bile duct blockage) or *pancreatic obstruction* (pancreatic duct blockage). Alternatively, malabsorption may result when the ducts remain open but the glandular cells are damaged and unable to continue normal secretory activities. *Pancreatitis* and *cirrhosis,* noted earlier in the chapter, are two causes of such damage.

Even when fully functional enzymes are present in the lumen, effective absorption cannot occur if the mucosa cannot function properly. Thus mucosal damage due to ischemia (interruption of the blood supply), radiation exposure (such as from radiation therapy or contaminated food), toxic compounds, or infection can also hinder absorption and deplete nutrient and fluid reserves.

the micelles along with the products of lipid digestion. Vitamin K is also produced by the action of resident bacteria in the colon. ⚬⚬ p. 560

The nine **water-soluble vitamins** include the B vitamins, common in milk and meats, and vitamin C, found in citrus fruits. All but one, vitamin B_{12}, are easily absorbed by the digestive epithelium. Vitamin B_{12} cannot be absorbed by the intestinal mucosa unless it has been bound to intrinsic factor, a protein secreted by the parietal cells of the stomach. ⚬⚬ p. 544 Bacteria residing in the intestinal tract are an important source of several water-soluble vitamins. In Chapter 17 we will further consider the functions of vitamins (see Tables 17-3 and 17-4, pp. 591–592), and those of minerals as well.

CHECKPOINT

25. An increase in which component of a meal would increase the number of chylomicrons in the lacteals?

26. Removal of the stomach would impair the absorption of which vitamin?

27. Why is diarrhea potentially life threatening but constipation is not?

See the blue Answers tab at the end of the book

16-9 Many age-related changes affect digestion and absorption

Essentially normal digestion and absorption occur in elderly individuals. However, many changes in the digestive system parallel age-related changes already described for other systems:

- *The division rate of epithelial stem cells declines.* Because the digestive epithelium becomes more susceptible to damage by abrasion, acids, or enzymes, peptic ulcers become more likely. In the mouth, esophagus, and anus, the stratified epithelium becomes thinner and more fragile.

- *Smooth muscle tone decreases.* General gastrointestinal motility decreases, and peristaltic contractions are weaker. This change slows the rate of intestinal movement and promotes constipation. Sagging and inflammation of the pouches (haustra) in the walls of the colon can occur. Straining to eliminate compacted fecal material can stress the less resilient walls of blood vessels, producing hemorrhoids. Problems are not restricted to the lower digestive tract. For example, weakening of muscular sphincters can lead to esophageal reflux and frequent bouts of "heartburn."

- *The effects of cumulative damage become apparent.* One example is the gradual loss of teeth due to *dental caries* ("cavities") or *gingivitis* (inflammation of the gums). Cumulative damage can involve internal organs as well. Toxins such as alcohol and other injurious chemicals absorbed by the digestive tract are transported to the liver for processing, but liver cells are not immune to these compounds. Chronic exposure can lead to cirrhosis or other types of liver disease.

- *Cancer rates increase.* Cancers are most common in organs in which stem cells divide to maintain epithelial cell populations. Rates of colon cancer and stomach cancer rise in the elderly; oral and pharyngeal cancers are particularly common in elderly smokers.

- *Dehydration is common among the elderly.* Because osmoreceptor sensitivity declines with age, dehydration is common among the elderly.

- *Changes in other systems have direct or indirect effects on the digestive system.* For example, a reduction in bone mass and calcium content in the skeleton is associated with erosion of the tooth sockets and eventual tooth loss. The decline in smell and taste sensitivity with age can lead to dietary changes that affect the entire body.

CHECKPOINT

28. Identify general digestive system changes that occur with aging.

See the blue Answers tab at the end of the book

16-10 The digestive system is extensively integrated with other body systems

The digestive system is functionally linked to all other systems, and it has extensive anatomical connections to the nervous, cardiovascular, endocrine, and lymphoid systems. The Digestive System in Perspective (p. 572) summarizes the functional relationships between the digestive system and other organ systems.

CHECKPOINT

29. Identify the functional relationships between the digestive system and other body systems.

30. List the digestive system functions that are related to the cardiovascular system.

See the blue Answers tab at the end of the book

RELATED CLINICAL TERMS

achalasia (ak-a-LĀ-zē-uh): A condition that results when a bolus cannot reach the stomach due to constriction of the lower esophageal sphincter.

ascites (a-SĪ-tēz): The accumulation of fluid in the peritoneal cavity following its leakage across the serous membranes of the liver and viscera.

cholecystitis (kō-lē-sis-TĪ-tis): Inflammation of the gallbladder due to a blockage of the cystic duct or common bile duct by gallstones.

cholelithiasis (ko-lē-li-THĪ-a-sis): The presence of gallstones in the gallbladder.

cirrhosis (sir-Ō-sis): A disease characterized by the widespread destruction of hepatocytes resulting from drug usage (especially alcohol), viral infection, ischemia, or blockage of the hepatic ducts.

colectomy (ko-LEK-to-mē): The removal of all or a portion of the colon.

colonoscope (ko-LON-o-skōp): A fiber-optic device for examining the interior of the colon.

colostomy (ko-LOS-to-mē): The attachment of the cut end of the colon to an opening in the body wall after a colectomy.

esophagitis (ē-sof-a-JĪ-tis): Inflammation of the esophagus.

gallstones: Deposits of minerals, bile salts, and cholesterol that form when bile becomes too concentrated.

gastrectomy (gas-TREK-to-mē): The surgical removal of the stomach, generally to treat advanced stomach cancer.

gastroenteritis (gas-trō-en-ter-Ī-tis): Inflammation of the lining of the stomach and intestine, characterized by vomiting and diarrhea and resulting from bacterial toxins, viral infections, or various poisons.

gastroenterology (gas-trō-en-ter-OL-o-jē): The study of the digestive system and its diseases and disorders.

hepatitis (hep-a-TĪ-tis): Inflammation of the liver, most commonly virally induced; the most common forms include *hepatitis A, B,* and *C.*

inflammatory bowel disease (ulcerative colitis): A chronic inflammation of the digestive tract, most commonly affecting the colon.

irritable bowel syndrome: A disorder characterized by diarrhea, constipation, or both alternately. When constipation is the primary problem, this condition may be called a *spastic colon or spastic colitis.*

laparoscopy (lap-a-ROS-ko-pē): The use of a flexible fiber-optic instrument introduced through the abdominal wall to permit direct visualization of the viscera, tissue sampling, and limited surgical procedures.

liver biopsy: A sample of liver tissue, generally taken by inserting a long needle through the anterior abdominal wall.

perforated ulcer: A particularly dangerous ulcer in which gastric acids erode through the wall of the digestive tract, allowing its contents to enter the peritoneal cavity.

periodontal disease: A loosening of the teeth within the bony sockets (alveolar sockets) caused by erosion of the periodontal ligaments by acids produced through bacterial action.

peritonitis (per-i-tō-NĪ-tis): Inflammation of the peritoneal membrane.

polyps (POL-ips): Small masses of tissue that project beyond the normal surface level, such as from the intestinal wall; some polyps are tumors.

Chapter 16 Review

KEY TERMS

bile *555*
chylomicrons *564*
chyme *544*
defecation reflex *560*
digestion *535*
duodenum *548*
esophagus *542*
gallbladder *556*
gastric glands *544*
lacteal *549*

liver *553*
mesentery *537*
mucosa *536*
pancreas *552*
pancreatic juice *553*
peristalsis *538*
stomach *544*
teeth *540*
villus/villi *548*

SUMMARY OUTLINE

IP Use *Interactive Physiology*® (**IP**)—available on the IP CD packaged with your new textbook—to help you understand difficult physiological concepts. Follow these navigation paths on IP for concepts in this chapter:

- Digestive System/Orientation.
- Digestive System/Motility.
- Digestive System/Anatomy Review.
- Digestive System/Digestion and Absorption.

16-1 The digestive system—the digestive tract and accessory organs—performs various food-processing functions *p. 535*

1. The digestive system consists of the muscular **digestive tract** and various **accessory organs.**

2. Digestive functions include **ingestion, mechanical processing, digestion, secretion, absorption,** and **excretion.**

3. The digestive tract includes the oral cavity, pharynx, esophagus, stomach, small intestine, large intestine, rectum, and anus. *(Figure 16-1)*

4. The epithelium and underlying connective tissue, the *lamina propria,* form the **mucosa** (mucous membrane) of the digestive tract. Next, moving outward, are the **submucosa,** the **muscularis externa,** and the *adventitia,* a layer of loose connective tissue. In the peritoneal cavity, the muscularis externa is covered by the **serosa,** a serous membrane. *(Figure 16-2)*

5. Double sheets of peritoneal membrane called **mesenteries** suspend portions of the digestive tract.

6. The neurons that innervate the smooth muscle of the muscularis externa are not under voluntary control.

7. The muscularis externa propels materials through the digestive tract by means of the contractions of **peristalsis. Segmentation** movements in areas of the small intestine churn digestive materials. *(Figure 16-3)*

16-2 The oral cavity contains the tongue, salivary glands, and teeth, each with specific functions   *p. 539*

8. The functions of the **oral cavity** are (1) sensory analysis of potential foods; (2) mechanical processing using the teeth, tongue, and palatal surfaces; (3) lubrication of food by mixing with mucus and salivary secretions; and (4) digestion by salivary enzymes.

9. The oral cavity, or **buccal cavity,** is lined by oral mucosa. The **hard palate** and **soft palate** form its roof, and the tongue forms its floor. *(Figure 16-4)*

10. The primary functions of the **tongue** include (1) mechanical processing, (2) manipulation to assist in chewing and swallowing, and (3) sensory analysis.

11. The **parotid, sublingual,** and **submandibular salivary glands** discharge their secretions into the oral cavity. Saliva lubricates the mouth, dissolves chemicals, flushes the oral surfaces, and helps control bacteria. Salivation is usually controlled by the ANS. *(Figure 16-5)*

12. **Mastication** (chewing) occurs through the contact of the opposing surfaces of the **teeth.** The **periodontal ligament** anchors each tooth in a bony socket. **Dentin** forms the basic structure of a tooth. The **crown** is coated with **enamel,** and the **root** is covered with **cementum.** *(Figure 16-6a)*

13. The 20 primary teeth, or **deciduous teeth,** are replaced by the 32 teeth of the **secondary dentition** during development. *(Figure 16-6b,c)*

16-3 The pharynx is a passageway between the oral cavity and the esophagus, which conducts solids and liquids on to the stomach   *p. 542*

14. The **pharynx** serves as a common passageway for solid food, liquids, and air. Pharyngeal muscle contractions during swallowing propel the food mass along the esophagus and into the stomach.

15. The **esophagus** carries solids and liquids from the pharynx to the stomach through an opening in the diaphragm, the *esophageal hiatus.*

16. **Deglutition** (swallowing) can be divided into **oral, pharyngeal,** and **esophageal phases.** Swallowing begins with the compaction of a **bolus** and its movement into the pharynx, followed by the elevation of the larynx, reflection of the epiglottis, and closure of the glottis. After opening of the *upper esophageal sphincter,* peristalsis moves the bolus down the esophagus to the *lower esophageal sphincter. (Figure 16-7)*

16-4 The j-shaped stomach receives the bolus from the esophagus and aids in chemical and mechanical digestion   *p. 544*

17. The **stomach** has four major functions: (1) temporary storage of ingested food, (2) mechanical breakdown of food, (3) breakage of chemical bonds by acids and enzymes, and (4) production of intrinsic factor. **Chyme** forms in the stomach as gastric and salivary secretions are mixed with food.

18. The four regions of the stomach are the **cardia, fundus, body, and pylorus.** The **pyloric sphincter** guards the exit out of the stomach. In a relaxed state the stomach lining contains numerous **rugae** (ridges and folds). *(Figure 16-8)*

19. Within the **gastric glands, parietal cells** secrete **intrinsic factor** and hydrochloric acid. **Chief cells** secrete **pepsinogen,** which acids in the gastric lumen convert to the enzyme **pepsin.** Gastric gland endocrine cells secrete the hormone **gastrin.**

20. Gastric secretion includes (1) the **cephalic phase,** which prepares the stomach to receive ingested materials; (2) the **gastric phase,** which begins with the arrival of food in the stomach; and (3) the **intestinal phase,** which controls the rate of gastric emptying. *(Figure 16-9)*

16-5 The small intestine digests and absorbs nutrients   *p. 548*

21. The **small intestine** includes the **duodenum,** the **jejunum,** and the **ileum.** The *ileocecal valve,* a sphincter, marks the junction between the small and large intestines. *(Figure 16-10)*

22. The intestinal mucosa bears transverse folds called **plicae circulares** and small projections called intestinal **villi.** Both structures increase the surface area for absorption. Each villus contains a lymphatic capillary called a **lacteal.** *(Figure 16-11)*

23. Some of the smooth muscle cells in the musularis externa of the small intestine contract periodically, without stimulation, to produce brief localized peristaltic contractions that slowly move materials along the tract. More extensive peristaltic activities are coordinated by the *gastroenteric* and the *gastroileal reflexes.*

24. Intestinal glands secrete **intestinal juice,** mucus, and hormones. Intestinal juice moistens the chyme, helps buffer acids, and dissolves digestive enzymes and the products of digestion.

25. Intestinal hormones include **gastrin, secretin, cholecystokinin (CCK),** and **gastric inhibitory peptide (GIP).** *(Figure 16-12; Table 16-1)*

26. Most of the important digestive and absorptive functions occur in the small intestine. Digestive enzymes and buffers are produced by the pancreas, liver, and gallbladder.

16-6 The pancreas, liver, and gallbladder are accessory glands that assist with the digestive process in the small intestine   *p. 552*

27. The **pancreatic duct** penetrates the wall of the duodenum, where it delivers the secretions of the **pancreas.** *(Figure 16-13a)*

28. Exocrine gland ducts branch repeatedly before ending in the **pancreatic acini** (blind pockets). *(Figure 16-13b)*

29. The pancreas has both an endocrine function (secreting insulin and glucagon into the blood) and an exocrine function (secreting water, ions, and digestive enzymes into the small intestine). Pancreatic enzymes include **carbohydrases, lipases, nucleases,** and **proteases.**

30. Pancreatic exocrine cells produce a watery **pancreatic juice** in response to hormonal instructions from the duodenum. When chyme arrives in the small intestine, secretin and CCK are released.

31. The release of secretin triggers the pancreatic production of a fluid containing buffers (primarily sodium bicarbonate) that increases the pH of the chyme. CCK stimulates the pancreas to produce and secrete **pancreatic amylase, pancreatic lipase,** nucleases, and several proteolytic enzymes—notably, **trypsin, chymotrypsin,** and **carboxypeptidase.**

32. The **liver,** the largest visceral organ in the body, performs over 200 known functions.

33. The liver is made up of four unequally sized lobes: the **left, right, caudate,** and **quadrate lobes.** *(Figure 16-14)*

34. The **liver lobule** is the organ's basic functional unit. Blood is supplied to the lobules by branches of the hepatic artery and hepatic portal vein. Within the lobules, blood flows past *hepatocytes* through *sinusoids* to the **central vein. Bile canaliculi** carry bile away from the central vein and toward bile ducts. *(Figure 16-15)*

35. The bile ducts from each lobule unite to form the **common hepatic duct,** which meets the **cystic duct** to form the **common bile duct,** which empties into the duodenum. *(Figure 16-16a)*

36. The liver performs several major functions, including metabolic regulation, hematological regulation, and the production of **bile.** *(Table 16-2)*

37. The **gallbladder** stores and concentrates bile for release into the duodenum. Relaxation of the **hepatopancreatic sphincter** by cholecystokinin (CCK) permits bile to enter the duodenum. *(Figure 16-16b)*

16-7 The large intestine is divided into three parts with regional specialization   *p. 558*

38. The main functions of the **large intestine** are to (1) reabsorb water and compact the feces, (2) absorb vitamins made by bacteria, and (3) store fecal material prior to defecation. The large intestine has three parts: the cecum, the colon, and the rectum. *(Figure 16-17a)*

39. The **cecum** collects and stores material from the ileum and begins the process of compaction. The **appendix** is attached to the cecum.

40. The **colon** has a larger diameter and a thinner wall than the small intestine. It bears **haustra** (pouches) and **taeniae coli** (longitudinal bands of muscle).

41. The **rectum** terminates in the **anal canal,** leading to the **anus.** *(Figure 16-17b)*

42. The large intestine reabsorbs water and other substances, such as *vitamins, bile salts, organic wastes,* and *toxins.* Bacteria residing in the large intestine are responsible for intestinal gas, or *flatus.*

43. Distension of the stomach and duodenum stimulates peristalsis, or *mass movements,* of feces from the colon into the rectum. Muscular sphincters control the passage of fecal material to the anus. Distension of the rectal wall triggers the *defecation reflex.* Under normal circumstances, the release of feces cannot occur unless the **external anal sphincter** is voluntarily relaxed.

16-8 Digestion is the mechanical and chemical alteration of food that allows the absorption and use of nutrients   *p. 561*

44. The digestive system first breaks down the physical structure of ingested materials, and then digestive enzymes break the component molecules into smaller fragments through a process called *hydrolysis.* *(Table 16-3)*

45. Amylases break down complex carbohydrates into *disaccharides* and *trisaccharides.* Enzymes at the epithelial surface break these molecules into *monosaccharides* that are absorbed by the intestinal epithelium through facilitated diffusion or cotransport. *(Figure 16-18a)*

46. *Triglycerides* are emulsified into large lipid droplets. The resulting fatty acids and other lipids interact with bile salts to form **micelles** from which they diffuse across the intestinal epithelium. The intestinal cells absorb fatty acids and synthesize new triglycerides. These are packaged in **chylomicrons,** which are released into the interstitial fluid and transported to the venous system by lymphatics. *(Figure 16-18b)*

47. Protein digestion involves low pH and the enzyme pepsin in the stomach, and various pancreatic proteases in the small intestine. Peptidases liberate amino acids that are absorbed by the intestinal epithelium and released into the interstitial fluids. *(Figure 16-18c)*

48. About 2 liters of water are ingested each day, and digestive secretions provide another 7 liters. All but about 150 mL of water is reabsorbed through osmosis.

49. Various processes are responsible for the movement of ions (such as sodium, calcium, chloride, and bicarbonate).

50. The **fat-soluble vitamins** are enclosed within fat droplets and are absorbed with the products of lipid digestion. The **water-soluble vitamins** (except B_{12}) diffuse easily across the digestive epithelium.

16-9 Many age-related changes affect digestion and absorption   *p. 565*

51. Age-related digestive system changes include a thinner and more fragile epithelium due to a reduction in epithelial stem cell divisions, weaker peristaltic contractions as smooth muscle tone decreases, the effects of cumulative damage, increased cancer rates, and increased dehydration.

16-10 The digestive system is extensively integrated with other body systems   *p. 565*

52. The digestive system has extensive structural and functional connections to the nervous, cardiovascular, endocrine, and lymphoid systems.

REVIEW QUESTIONS

WWW   Access more review material online at The Anatomy & Physiology Place (**www.anatomyandphysiology.com**). There, you'll find Chapter Guides, Chapter Quizzes, Chapter Practice Tests, Interactive Flashcards, a Glossary with Pronunciations, and more to help you succeed in the course.

Level 1 • Reviewing Facts and Terms

Match each item in column A with the most closely related item in column B. Place letters for answers in the spaces provided.

COLUMN A

_____ **1.** pyloric sphincter
_____ **2.** liver cells
_____ **3.** mucosa
_____ **4.** mesentery
_____ **4.** chief cells
_____ **6.** palate
_____ **7.** parietal cells
_____ **8.** parasympathetic stimulation
_____ **9.** sympathetic stimulation
_____ **10.** peristalsis
_____ **11.** bile salts
_____ **12.** salivary amylase

COLUMN B

a. serous membrane sheet
b. moves materials along digestive tract
c. regulates flow of chyme
d. increases muscular activity of digestive tract
e. starch digestion
f. inhibits muscular activity of digestive tract
g. inner lining of digestive tract
h. roof of oral cavity
i. pepsinogen
j. hydrochloric acid
k. hepatocytes
l. emulsification of fats

13. The enzymatic breakdown of large molecules into their basic building blocks is called
(a) absorption.
(b) secretion.
(c) mechanical digestion.
(d) chemical digestion.

14. The activities of the digestive system are regulated by
(a) hormonal mechanisms.
(b) local mechanisms.
(c) neural mechanisms.
(d) a, b, and c are correct.

15. The layer of the peritoneum that lines the inner surfaces of the body wall is the
(a) visceral peritoneum.
(b) parietal peritoneum.
(c) greater omentum.
(d) lesser omentum.

16. Protein digestion in the stomach results primarily from secretions released by
(a) hepatocytes.
(b) parietal cells.
(c) chief cells.
(d) goblet cells.

17. Label the digestive system structures in the following figure.

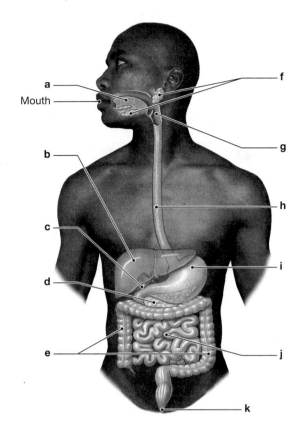

(a) _____
(b) _____
(c) _____
(d) _____
(e) _____
(f) _____
(g) _____
(h) _____
(i) _____
(j) _____
(k) _____

18. The part of the gastrointestinal tract that plays the primary role in the digestion and absorption of nutrients is the
  (a) large intestine.
  (b) small intestine.
  (c) stomach.
  (d) cecum and colon.

19. The duodenal hormone that stimulates the production and secretion of pancreatic enzymes is
  (a) pepsinogen.
  (b) gastrin.
  (c) secretin.
  (d) cholecystokinin.

20. The essential physiological service(s) provided by the liver is (are)
  (a) metabolic regulation.
  (b) hematological regulation.
  (c) bile production.
  (d) a, b, and c are correct.

21. Label the four layers of the digestive tract in the following figure.

(a) _____ (b) _____
(c) _____ (d) _____

22. Bile release from the gallbladder into the duodenum occurs only under the stimulation of
  (a) cholecystokinin.
  (b) secretin.
  (c) gastrin.
  (d) pepsinogen.

23. The major function(s) of the large intestine is (are)
  (a) reabsorption of water and compaction of feces.
  (b) absorption of vitamins produced by bacterial action.
  (c) storage of fecal material prior to defecation.
  (d) a, b, and c are correct.

24. The part of the colon that empties into the rectum is the
  (a) ascending colon.
  (b) descending colon.
  (c) transverse colon.
  (d) sigmoid colon.

25. What are the primary digestive functions?

26. What is the purpose of the transverse or longitudinal folds in the mucosa of the digestive tract?

27. Name and describe the layers of the digestive tract, proceeding from the innermost layer to the outermost layer.

28. What are the four primary functions of the oral (buccal) cavity?

29. What specific function does each of the four types of teeth perform in the oral cavity?

30. What three segments of the small intestine are involved in the digestion and absorption of food?

31. What are the primary digestive functions of the pancreas, liver, and gallbladder?

32. What are the three major functions of the large intestine?

33. What six age-related changes occur in the digestive system?

Level 2 • Reviewing Concepts

34. If the lingual frenulum is too restrictive, an individual
  (a) has difficulty tasting food.
  (b) cannot swallow properly.
  (c) cannot control movements of the tongue.
  (d) cannot eat or speak normally.

35. The gastric phase of secretion is initiated by
  (a) distension of the stomach.
  (b) an increase in the pH of the gastric contents.
  (c) the presence of undigested materials in the stomach.
  (d) a, b, and c are correct.

36. A drop in pH to 4.0 in the duodenum stimulates the secretion of
  (a) secretin.
  (b) cholecystokinin.
  (c) gastrin.
  (d) a, b, and c are correct.

37. Describe how the action and outcome of peristalsis differ from those of segmentation.

38. How does the stomach promote and assist in the digestive process?

39. Describe the events that occur during the three phases of gastric secretion.

Level 3 • Critical Thinking and Clinical Applications

40. Explain why some patients with gallstones develop pancreatitis.

41. Barb suffers from Crohn's disease, a regional inflammation of the intestine that is thought to have some genetic basis, although the actual cause remains unknown. When the disease flares up, she experiences abdominal pain, weight loss, and anemia. Which part(s) of the intestine is (are) probably involved, and what are the causes of her signs and symptoms?

The Digestive System in Perspective

Functional Relationships Between the Digestive System and Other Systems

The Integumentary System

- The Integumentary System provides vitamin D_3 needed for the absorption of calcium and phosphorus
- The Digestive System provides lipids for storage by adipocytes in subcutaneous layer

The Skeletal System

- The Skeletal System's axial division and pelvic girdle support and protect parts of digestive tract; teeth important in mechanical processing of food
- The Digestive System absorbs calcium and phosphate ions for incorporation into bone matrix; provides lipids for storage in yellow marrow

The Muscular System

- The Muscular System protects and supports digestive organs in abdominal cavity; controls entrances and exits of digestive tract
- The Digestive System's liver regulates blood glucose and fatty acid levels, metabolizes lactic acid from active muscles

The Nervous System

- The Nervous System's ANS regulates movement and secretion; reflexes coordinate passage of materials along tract; control over skeletal muscles regulates ingestion and defecation; hypothalamic centers control hunger, satiation and feeding behaviors
- The Digestive System provides substrates essential for neuro-transmitter synthesis

The Endocrine System

- The Endocrine System's hormones epinephrine and norepinephrine stimulate constriction of sphincters and depress digestive activity; hormones coordinate activity along tract
- The Digestive System provides nutrients and substrates to endocrine cells; endocrine cells of pancreas secrete insulin and glucagon; liver produces angiotensinogen

The Cardiovascular System

- The Cardiovascular System distributes the hormones of the digestive tract; carries nutrients, water, and ions from sites of absorption; delivers nutrients and toxins to liver
- The Digestive System absorbs fluid to maintain normal blood volume; absorbs vitamin K; liver excretes heme (as bilirubin), synthesizes blood clotting proteins

The Lymphoid System

- The Lymphoid System's tonsils and other lymphoid nodules along digestive tract defend against infection and toxins absorbed from the tract; lymphatic vessels carry absorbed lipids to venous system
- The Digestive System's secretions (acids and enzymes) provide non-specific defense against pathogens

The Respiratory System

- The Respiratory System can assist in defecation by increased thoracic and abdominal pressure through contraction of respiratory muscles
- The Digestive System's organs may press against the diaphragm to assist in exhalation and limit inhalation

The Urinary System

- The Urinary System excretes toxins absorbed by the digestive epithelium; excretes some bilirubin produced by liver
- The Digestive System absorbs water needed to excrete waste products at the kidneys; absorbs ions needed to maintain normal body fluid concentrations

The Reproductive System

- The Digestive System provides additional nutrients required to support gamete production and (in pregnant women) embryonic and fetal development

For All Systems
The Digestive System absorbs organic substrates, vitamins, ions, and water required by all cells

Professional Profile

DENTAL ASSISTANT
Jurlene "Mickey" Washington

> " Meeting new people every day and helping them is the best part of my job. "

Jurlene "Mickey" Washington is a dental assistant working for a periodontal dental practice in New York City. Periodontics is the treatment of diseases of the gums that surround the teeth. Treatment may include scaling and root planing to remove plaque, surgery to reduce the depth of pockets around the teeth, soft tissue grafts, and dental implants. Dental assistants assist in all of these procedures and ensure that the treatment area is clean and safe.

Mickey sees 25 to 30 patients a day. Her work includes dental cleanings and taking x-rays, digital x-rays, and CT scans. She assists the dentist in surgery, which may include bone grafts, implants, and other work.

EMPATHY FOR PATIENTS

Mickey always reviews patients' medical history before she begins the clinical work. "I have to check to see if something has changed. If their health has changed or they are taking a new medication, we need to know that." Her schooling in anatomy and physiology is important when she takes medical histories because it helps her understand the information patients give her. It also helps her read x-rays and answer patients' questions. "Patients ask a lot of questions about procedures and their health. I have to answer them as best I can."

Mickey has a lot of empathy for her patients, who often have to undergo painful or lengthy procedures. She's experienced many of the procedures personally. "When I was 17 years old I was diagnosed with juvenile periodontal disease. I was treated at New York University's dental school, and my treatment included surgery, dental caps, and implants. I'm familiar with what patients go through. I understand it, and I know what some of the aftereffects can be."

Being a periodontal patient actually launched Mickey's career. While undergoing treatment at NYU, one of the dentists hired her to work as his part-time assistant. She went on to work for that dentist full-time and has been a dental assistant ever since.

Because many patients are uncomfortable or even fearful about dental care, a dental assistant must work well with people, be personable, keep a good sense of humor, and be prepared to deal with whatever physical and mental symptoms occur. It's possible that a patient will exhibit erratic behavior because of nervousness or a phobia. Even so, she says, "Meeting new people every day and helping them is the best part of my job."

CONSTANT CHALLENGES

Dental assistants train at dental schools for their certification. They must have up-to-date certification in CPR. In addition, they must continue to take refresher courses throughout their careers. After completing their training, most dental assistants work in private practice, although some work in clinics or in hospitals.

Being a dental assistant is always interesting. "I'm always learning new technologies and new dental techniques, because dentistry is constantly evolving."

According to Mickey, assisting with surgery is a challenging aspect of the job. Problems can arise when a patient does not fully disclose information about his or her health. "You may have a patient who hasn't told you that he's taking blood thinners, and he starts bleeding profusely. Or your patient's heart rate or blood pressure may rise. You never know what you're going to run into during surgery."

A dental assistant can't be squeamish or afraid of the sight of blood. "The first time I saw blood I almost fainted. The dentist told me to leave the room and come back in 10 minutes. I needed time to get over the fainting feeling, but it was important to come in and finish the job. That's how you get used to it."

17 Nutrition and Metabolism

This outdoor market table holds a colorful selection of grains and vegetables, two of the basic food groups in a balanced and healthy diet. Grains and vegetables provide the body's cells with some of the important organic compounds (vitamins and carbohydrates) needed to maintain homeostasis. This chapter examines several aspects of metabolism, including nutrition, energy use, heat production, and the regulation of body temperature under normal and abnormal conditions.

LEARNING OUTCOMES

After completing this chapter, you should be able to do the following:

17-1 Define metabolism, and explain why cells need to synthesize new organic molecules.

17-2 Describe the basic steps involved in glycolysis, the TCA cycle, and the electron transport system, and summarize the energy yields of glycolysis and cellular respiration.

17-3 Describe the pathways involved in lipid metabolism, and summarize mechanisms of lipid transport and distribution.

17-4 Discuss protein metabolism and the use of proteins as an energy source.

17-5 Discuss nucleic acid metabolism and the limited use of nucleic acids as an energy source.

17-6 Explain what constitutes a balanced diet, and why such a diet is important.

17-7 Define metabolic rate, describe the factors involved in determining an individual's metabolic rate, and discuss the homeostatic mechanisms that maintain a constant body temperature.

17-8 Describe the age-related changes in dietary requirements.

VOCABULARY DEVELOPMENT

anabole a building up; *anabolism*
genesis an origin; *thermogenesis*
glykus sweet; *glycolysis*

katabole a throwing down; *catabolism*
lipos fat; *lipogenesis*
lysis a loosening; *glycolysis*

neo- new; *gluconeogenesis*
therme heat; *thermogenesis*
vita life; *vitamin*

An Introduction to Nutrition and Metabolism

The amount and type of nutrients you obtain in meals can vary widely. Your body stores energy reserves when nutrients, such as carbohydrates or lipids, are abundant, and mobilizes them when nutrients are in short supply. The endocrine system, with the assistance of the nervous system, adjusts and coordinates the metabolic activities of the body's tissues and controls the storage and mobilization of these energy reserves. This chapter considers what happens to nutrients once they are inside the body, how energy is obtained by the breakdown of organic molecules, and how energy is used to support intracellular operations such as the construction of new organic molecules.

17-1 Metabolism refers to all the chemical reactions that occur in the body

Cells are chemical factories that break down organic molecules to obtain energy, which can then be used to generate ATP. Chemical reactions within mitochondria provide most of the energy a typical cell needs. ∞ p. 77 To carry out their energy-generating processes, cells in the human body must also obtain oxygen and nutrients. Whereas oxygen is absorbed at the lungs, **nutrients**—essential substances such as water, vitamins, mineral ions, carbohydrates, lipids, and proteins—are normally obtained from the diet by absorption at the digestive tract. The cardiovascular system distributes oxygen and nutrients to cells throughout the body.

The energy a cell produces in the form of ATP supports cell growth, cell division, contraction, secretion, and all the other special functions that vary from cell to cell and tissue to tissue. Because each tissue type contains different populations of cells, the energy and nutrient requirements of any two tissues (such as loose connective tissue and cardiac muscle) are typically quite different. When cells, tissues, and organs change their patterns or levels of activity, the body's metabolic needs change. Thus, our nutrient requirements can vary from moment to moment (resting versus active), hour to hour (asleep versus awake), and year to year (child versus adult).

The term **metabolism** refers to all the chemical reactions that occur in the body. ∞ p. 35 *Cellular metabolism*—chemical reactions within cells—provides the energy needed to maintain homeostasis and to perform essential functions. Figure 17-1 provides an overview of the processes involved in cellular metabolism. Amino acids, lipids, and simple sugars cross the plasma membrane and join the other nutrients already in the cytoplasm. All of the cell's metabolic operations rely on this *nutrient pool.*

The breakdown of organic molecules is called *catabolism,* a process that releases energy for synthesizing ATP or other high-energy compounds. ∞ p. 36 Catabolism proceeds in a series of steps. In general, the first steps occur in the cytosol, where enzymes break down large organic molecules into smaller fragments. Carbohydrates are broken down into short carbon chains, triglycerides are split into fatty acids and glycerol, and proteins are broken down to individual amino acids.

Relatively little ATP is formed during these preparatory steps. However, the simple molecules produced can be absorbed and processed by mitochondria, and the mitochondrial reactions release significant amounts of energy. As mitochondrial enzymes break the covalent bonds that hold these molecules together, they capture roughly 40 percent of the energy released. The captured energy is used to convert ADP to ATP, and the rest escapes as heat that warms the interior of the cell and the surrounding tissues.

Anabolism, the synthesis of new organic molecules, involves the formation of new chemical bonds. ∞ p. 36 The ATP produced by mitochondria provides energy to support anabolism and other cell functions. Those additional functions, such as ciliary or cell movement, contraction, active transport, and cell division, vary from one cell to another. For example, muscle fibers need ATP to provide energy for contraction, whereas gland cells need ATP to synthesize and transport their secretions.

Cells synthesize new organic components for four basic reasons:

1. *To perform structural maintenance and repairs.* All cells must expend energy for ongoing maintenance and repairs because most structures in the cell are temporary, not permanent. The continuous removal

FIGURE 17-1 Cellular Metabolism. Cells obtain organic molecules from the interstitial fluid and catabolize them (break them down) in mitochondria to produce ATP. Only about 40 percent of the energy released through catabolism is captured in ATP; the rest is radiated as heat. The ATP generated by catabolism provides energy for all vital cellular activities, including anabolism.

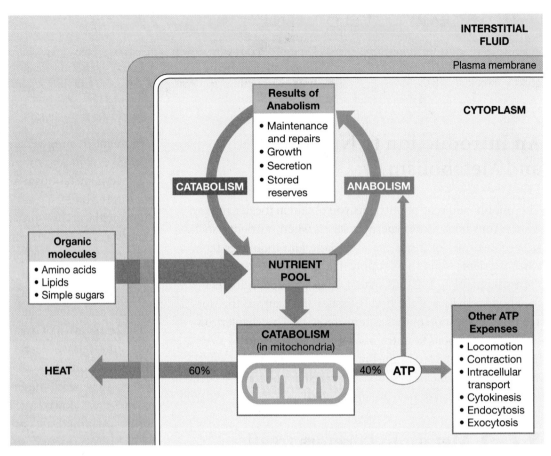

and replacement of these structures are part of the process of **metabolic turnover.**

2. *To support growth.* Cells preparing to divide enlarge and synthesize extra proteins and organelles.

3. *To produce secretions.* Secretory cells must synthesize their products and deliver them to the interstitial fluid.

4. *To build nutrient reserves.* Most cells "prepare for a rainy day"—some emergency, an interval of extreme activity, or a time when the nutrient supply in the bloodstream is inadequate—by storing nutrients in a form that can be mobilized as needed. For example, muscle cells store glucose in the form of glycogen, fat cells (adipocytes) store triglycerides, and liver cells store both molecules.

The nutrient pool is the source of organic molecules for both catabolism and anabolism (Figure 17-1). As you might expect, cells tend to conserve materials needed to build new compounds and tend to break down the rest. Cells continuously replace membranes, organelles, enzymes, and structural proteins. These anabolic activities require more amino acids than lipids, and few carbohydrates. Energy-releasing catabolic activities, however, tend to process these organic molecules in the reverse order. In general, when a cell with excess carbohydrates, lipids, and amino

acids needs energy, it will break down carbohydrates first. Lipids are the second choice as an energy source, and amino acids are seldom broken down if other energy sources are available.

Mitochondria provide the energy that supports cellular operations. In effect, the cell feeds its mitochondria from its nutrient pool, and in return the cell gets the ATP it needs. However, mitochondria are picky eaters: They will accept only specific organic molecules for processing and energy production. Thus, chemical reactions in the cytoplasm take whichever organic nutrients are available and break them into smaller fragments that the mitochondria can use (Figure 17-2). The mitochondria then break down the fragments further, generating carbon dioxide, water, and ATP. This mitochondrial activity involves two pathways: the TCA cycle and the electron transport system. In the next section we examine the important catabolic and anabolic reactions that occur in our cells.

The Big Picture

There is an energy cost to staying alive, even at rest. All cells must expend ATP to perform routine maintenance, such as removing and replacing intracellular and extracellular structures and components. Cells must also expend additional energy doing other vital functions, such as growth, secretion, and contraction.

FIGURE 17-2 Nutrient Use in Cellular Metabolism. Cells use molecules in the nutrient pool to build up reserves and to manufacture cellular structures. Catabolism within mitochondria provides the ATP needed to sustain cell functions. Mitochondria absorb small carbon chains produced by the breakdown of fatty acids, glucose, and amino acids from the nutrient pool. The small carbon chains are broken down further by means of the tricarboxylic acid (TCA) cycle and the electron transport system.

CHECKPOINT

1. Define metabolism.

2. Define catabolism.

3. Define anabolism.

See the blue Answers tab at the back of the book.

17-2 Carbohydrate metabolism involves glycolysis, ATP production, and gluconeogenesis

Carbohydrates, most familiar to us as sugars and starches, are important sources of energy. Most cells generate ATP and other high-energy compounds by breaking down carbohydrates, especially glucose. The complete reaction sequence can be summarized as:

$$\underset{\text{glucose}}{C_6H_{12}O_6} + \underset{\text{oxygen}}{6O_2} \longrightarrow \underset{\text{carbon dioxide}}{6CO_2} + \underset{\text{water}}{6H_2O}$$

The breakdown occurs in a series of small steps, several of which release enough energy to support the conversion of ADP to ATP. During the complete catabolism of glucose, a typical cell gains 36 ATP molecules.

Although most ATP production occurs inside mitochondria, the first steps take place in the cytosol as a sequence of reactions called *glycolysis*. The steps were outlined in Chapter 7; because those steps do not require oxygen, they are said to be *anaerobic*. ∞ p. 209 The subsequent reactions, which occur within mitochondria, consume oxygen and are thus *aerobic*. The mitochondrial activity responsible for ATP production is called **aerobic metabolism,** or *cellular respiration.*

GLYCOLYSIS

Glycolysis (glī-KOL-i-sis; *glykus,* sweet + *lysis,* a loosening) is the breakdown of glucose to *pyruvic acid.* In this process, a series of enzymatic steps breaks the six-carbon glucose molecule ($C_6H_{12}O_6$) into two three-carbon molecules of pyruvic acid (CH_3—CO—$COOH$). Glycolysis requires (1) glucose molecules, (2) appropriate cytoplasmic enzymes, (3) ATP and ADP, and (4) **NAD** (**n**icotinamide **a**denine **d**inucleotide), a coenzyme that removes hydrogen atoms. *Coenzymes* are organic molecules, usually derived from vitamins, that must be present for an enzymatic reaction to occur. If any of these four participants are missing, glycolysis cannot occur.

The basic steps of glycolysis are summarized in Figure 17-3. This reaction sequence yields a net gain of two ATP molecules for each glucose molecule converted to two pyruvic acid molecules. A few highly specialized cells, such as red blood cells, lack mitochondria and derive all of their ATP by glycolysis. Skeletal muscle fibers rely on glycolysis for energy production during periods of active contraction, and most cells can survive brief periods of hypoxia (low oxygen levels) by using the ATP provided by glycolysis alone. When oxygen is readily available, however, mitochondrial activity provides most of the ATP cells require.

ENERGY PRODUCTION WITHIN MITOCHONDRIA

Even though glycolysis yields an immediate net gain of two ATP molecules for the cell, a great deal of additional energy is still stored in the chemical bonds of pyruvic acid. The cell's ability to capture that energy depends on the availability of oxygen. If oxygen supplies are adequate, mitochondria will absorb the pyruvic acid molecules and break them down completely. The hydrogen atoms of pyruvic acid are removed by coenzymes and are ultimately the source of most of the cell's energy gain. The carbon and oxygen atoms are removed and released as carbon dioxide.

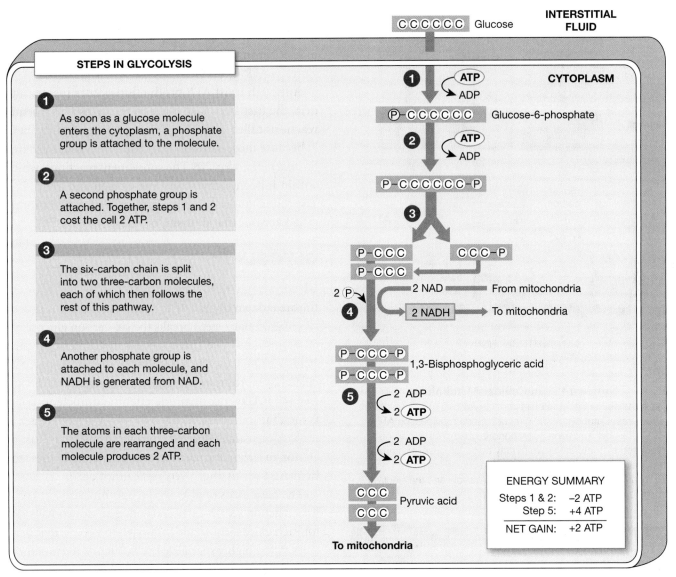

FIGURE 17-3 Glycolysis. Within a cell's cytoplasm, glycolysis involves a series of enzymatic steps that break down a six-carbon glucose molecule into two three-carbon pyruvic acid molecules. Each glucose molecule converted to pyruvic acid yields a net gain of two ATPs.

Two membranes surround each mitochondrion. ∞ p. 77 The outer membrane is permeable to pyruvic acid, and a carrier protein in the inner membrane transports the pyruvic acid into the mitochondrial matrix. Once inside the mitochondrion, each pyruvic acid molecule participates in a reaction leading to a sequence of enzymatic reactions called the **tricarboxylic** (trī-kar-bok-SIL-ik) **acid (TCA) cycle** (Figure 17-4). The function of the TCA cycle is to remove hydrogen atoms from organic molecules and transfer them to coenzymes in the electron transport system.

The TCA Cycle

In the mitochondrion, a complex reaction involving pyruvic acid, NAD, and another coenzyme called *coenzyme A* (or *CoA*)

yields one molecule of carbon dioxide, one molecule of NADH, and one molecule of **acetyl-CoA** (AS-e-til-KŌ -ā). Acetyl-CoA consists of a two-carbon *acetyl group* (CH_3CO) bound to coenzyme A. When the acetyl group is transferred from CoA to a four-carbon molecule, a six-carbon molecule called *citric acid* is produced. The formation of citric acid is the basis for another name for these reactions: the *citric acid cycle*. (This sequence is also known as the *Krebs cycle* in honor of Hans Krebs, the biochemist who described these reactions in 1937.)

As citric acid is produced, CoA is released intact to bind with another acetyl group. A complete revolution of the TCA cycle removes the two added carbon atoms, regenerating the initial four-carbon molecule. (This is why this reaction sequence is called a *cycle.*) The two removed carbon atoms generate two molecules

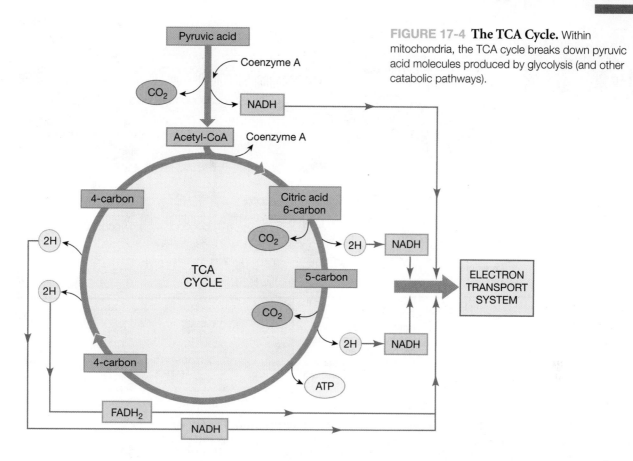

FIGURE 17-4 The TCA Cycle. Within mitochondria, the TCA cycle breaks down pyruvic acid molecules produced by glycolysis (and other catabolic pathways).

of carbon dioxide (CO_2), a metabolic waste product. The hydrogen atoms of the acetyl group are removed by coenzymes.

The only immediate energy benefit of one revolution of the TCA cycle is the formation of a single molecule of *GTP* (*guanosine triphosphate*), a high-energy compound readily converted into ATP. The real value of the TCA cycle can be seen by following the fate of the hydrogen atoms that are removed by the coenzymes NAD and **FAD** (**f**lavine **a**denine **d**inucleotide). The two coenzymes form NADH and $FADH_2$, and transfer the hydrogen atoms to the *electron transport system* (Figure 17-4).

The Electron Transport System

The **electron transport system (ETS)** is embedded in the inner mitochondrial membrane (Figure 17-5). The ETS consists of an electron transport chain made up of a series of protein-pigment complexes called *cytochromes*. The ETS does not produce ATP directly. Instead, it creates the conditions necessary for ATP production.

The hydrogen atoms from the TCA cycle do not enter the ETS intact. Only the electrons (which carry the energy) enter the ETS; the protons that accompany them are released into the mitochondrial matrix. The red lines in Figure 17-5 indicate that the path of the electrons from NADH involves the *coenzyme FMN*,

whereas the path from $FADH_2$ (labeled "FAD") moves directly to *coenzyme Q*. The electrons from both paths are passed from coenzyme Q to the first cytochrome (cytochrome *b*) and then from cytochrome to cytochrome, losing energy in each of a series of small steps. At several steps along the way, this energy is used to drive hydrogen ion pumps that move hydrogen ions from the mitochondrial matrix into the intermembrane space between the two mitochondrial membranes. This creates a large concentration gradient of hydrogen ions across the inner membrane, so the hydrogen ions then diffuse back into the matrix through a membrane enzyme called *ATP synthase*. The kinetic energy of the passing hydrogen ions is used to attach a phosphate group to ADP, forming ATP. This process is called *chemiosmosis* (kem-ē-oz-MŌ-sis), a term that links the chemical formation of ATP with transport across a membrane. At the end of the electron transport system, an oxygen atom accepts the electrons and combines with two hydrogen ions to form a molecule of water.

The electron transport system is the most important mechanism for the generation of ATP; in fact, it provides roughly 95 percent of the ATP needed to keep our cells alive. Halting or significantly slowing the rate of mitochondrial activity will usually kill a cell. If many cells are affected, the individual may die. If, for example, the cell's supply of oxygen is cut off, mitochondrial

FIGURE 17-5 **The Electron Transport System (ETS) and ATP Formation.** This diagrammatic view shows the locations of the coenzymes and the electron transport system in the inner mitochondrial membrane. The electrons of hydrogen atoms from the TCA cycle are transferred by coenzyme Q to the ETS (a series of cytochrome molecules), and the hydrogen ions (H^+) remain in the matrix. The energy-carrying electrons are passed from one cytochrome to another. Energy released by the passed electrons is used to pump H^+ from the matrix into the intermembrane space. This creates a difference in the concentration of H^+ across the inner membrane. The hydrogen ions then diffuse through ATP synthase in the inner membrane, and their kinetic energy is used to generate ATP.

ATP production will cease because the ETS will be unable to pass along its electrons. With the last reaction in the chain stopped, the entire ETS comes to a halt, like a line of cars at a washed-out bridge. The affected cell quickly dies of energy deprivation.

ENERGY YIELD OF GLYCOLYSIS AND CELLULAR RESPIRATION

For most cells, the series of chemical reactions that begins with glucose and ends with carbon dioxide and water is the main method of generating ATP. A cell gains ATP at several steps along the way:

- During glycolysis in the cytoplasm, the cell gains two molecules of ATP for each glucose molecule broken down to pyruvic acid.

- Inside the mitochondria, the two pyruvic acid molecules derived from each glucose molecule are fully broken down in the TCA cycle. Two revolutions of the TCA cycle,

each yielding a molecule of ATP, provide a net gain of two additional molecules of ATP.

- For each molecule of glucose broken down, activity at the electron transport chain in the inner mitochondrial membrane provides 32 molecules of ATP.

Summing up, for each glucose molecule processed, a typical cell gains 36 molecules of ATP. *All but two of them are produced within mitochondria.*

ALTERNATE CATABOLIC PATHWAYS

Aerobic metabolism is relatively efficient and capable of generating large amounts of ATP. It is the cornerstone of normal cellular metabolism, but it has one obvious limitation—cells must have adequate supplies of both oxygen and glucose. Cells can survive only for brief periods without oxygen. Low glucose concentrations have a much smaller effect on most cells, because cells can break down other nutrients to provide organic molecules for the TCA cycle, as shown in Figure 17-6. Many cells can switch from one nutrient source to another as the need arises. For example, many cells can shift from glucose-based ATP production to lipid-based ATP production when necessary. When actively contracting, skeletal muscles catabolize glucose, but at rest they rely on fatty acids.

Cells break down proteins for energy only when lipids or carbohydrates are unavailable; this makes sense because the enzymes and organelles that cells need to survive are composed of proteins. Nucleic acids are present only in small amounts, and they are seldom catabolized for energy, even when the cell is dying of acute starvation. This constraint makes sense, too, as the DNA in the nucleus determines all of the structural and functional characteristics of the cell. We will consider the catabolism of other compounds in later sections as we discuss the metabolism of lipids and proteins.

GLUCONEOGENESIS (GLUCOSE SYNTHESIS)

Because some of the steps in glycolysis are not reversible, cells cannot generate glucose by performing glycolysis in reverse,

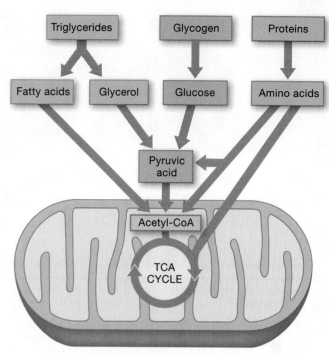

FIGURE 17-6 **Alternate Catabolic Pathways.**

Carbohydrate Loading

Although other nutrients can be broken down to provide raw materials (substrates) for the TCA cycle, carbohydrates require the least processing and preparation. Thus, it is not surprising that athletes have tried to devise ways of exploiting these compounds as ready sources of energy.

Eating carbohydrates just before exercising does not improve performance and can actually decrease endurance by slowing the mobilization of the body's existing energy reserves. Runners or swimmers preparing for lengthy endurance events, such as a marathon or 5-km swim, do not eat immediately before participating, and for 2 hours before the event they limit their intake to drinking water.

Performance in endurance sports improves if muscles have large stores of carbohydrate reserves (glycogen). Endurance athletes try to achieve this by eating carbohydrate-rich meals for 3 days before competing, a practice called **carbohydrate loading.** Studies in Sweden, Australia, and South Africa have shown that attempts to deplete carbohydrate stores by exercising to exhaustion before carbohydrate loading—a practice called *carbohydrate depletion/loading*—are less effective than 3 days of rest or minimal exercise during carbohydrate loading. This less intense approach improves mood and reduces the risks of muscle and kidney damage.

using the same enzymes. Therefore, glycolysis and the production of glucose require different sets of regulatory enzymes, and the two processes are independently regulated. Because some three-carbon molecules other than pyruvic acid can be used to synthesize glucose, a cell can create glucose molecules from other carbohydrates, lactic acid, glycerol, or some amino acids (Figure 17-7). However, acetyl-CoA cannot be used to make glucose because the reaction that removes the carbon dioxide molecule (a *decarboxylation*) between pyruvic acid and acetyl-CoA cannot be reversed. The synthesis of glucose from noncarbohydrate precursor molecules, such as lactic acid, glycerol (from lipids), or some amino acids (from proteins), is called **gluconeogenesis** (gloo-kō-nē-ō-JEN-e-sis; *glykus,* sweet + *neo-,* new + *genesis,* an origin). Fatty acids and many amino acids cannot be used for gluconeogenesis because their breakdown produces acetyl-CoA.

Glucose molecules synthesized during gluconeogenesis can be used to manufacture other simple sugars, complex carbohydrates, or nucleic acids. In the liver and in skeletal muscle, glucose molecules are stored as **glycogen.** Glycogen is an important energy reserve that can be broken down when the cell cannot obtain enough glucose from the interstitial fluid. Although glycogen molecules are large, glycogen reserves take up very little space because they form compact, insoluble granules.

FIGURE 17-7 Carbohydrate Metabolism. This flow chart presents the major pathways of glycolysis and gluconeogenesis. Carbohydrates (including lactic acid), glycerol, and some amino acids can be converted to glucose.

CHECKPOINT

4. What is the primary role of the TCA cycle in the production of ATP?

5. Hydrogen cyanide gas is a poison that produces its lethal effect by binding to the last cytochrome molecule in the electron transport system. What effect would this have at the cellular level?

6. Define gluconeogenesis.

See the blue Answers tab at the back of the book.

17-3 Lipid metabolism involves lipolysis, beta-oxidation, and the transport and distribution of lipids as lipoproteins and free fatty acids

Like carbohydrates, lipid molecules contain carbon, hydrogen, and oxygen but in different proportions. Because triglyc-erides (fats) are the most abundant lipid in the body, our discussion will focus on pathways of triglyceride breakdown and synthesis. ∞ p. 44

LIPID CATABOLISM

During lipid catabolism, or **lipolysis** (lip-OL-i-sis), lipids are broken down into pieces that can be converted to pyruvic acid or channeled directly into the TCA cycle (Figure 17-6). A triglyceride is first split into its component parts by hydrolysis, yielding one molecule of glycerol and three fatty acid molecules. Glycerol enters the TCA cycle after cytoplasmic enzymes convert it to pyruvic acid. The catabolism of fatty acids, known as **beta-oxidation,** involves a different set of enzymes that breaks the fatty acids down into two-carbon fragments. Beta-oxidation occurs inside mitochondria, so the two-carbon fragments can enter the TCA cycle immediately as acetyl-CoA. (Some of the two-carbon fragments may combine to form *ketone bodies,* short carbon chains discussed on p. 585). A cell generates 144 ATP molecules from the breakdown of one 18-carbon fatty acid molecule—almost 1.5 times the energy obtained from the breakdown of three six-carbon glucose molecules.

LIPIDS AND ENERGY PRODUCTION

Lipids are important energy reserves because their breakdown provides large amounts of ATP. Because they are insoluble in water, lipids are stored in compact droplets in the cytosol. However, if the droplets are large, it is difficult for water-soluble enzymes to get at them. This makes lipid reserves more difficult to access than carbohydrate reserves. In addition, most lipids are processed inside mitochondria, and mitochondrial activity is limited by the availability of oxygen. The net result is that lipids cannot provide large amounts of ATP quickly. However, cells with modest energy demands can shift to lipid-based energy production when glucose supplies are limited. Skeletal muscle fibers normally cycle between lipid metabolism and carbohydrate metabolism. At rest (when energy demands are low), these cells break down fatty acids. During activity (when energy demands are high and immediate), skeletal muscle fibers shift to glucose metabolism.

LIPID SYNTHESIS

The synthesis of lipids is known as **lipogenesis** (lip-ō-JEN-e-sis; *lipos,* fat). Glycerol is synthesized from an intermediate three-carbon product of glycolysis. The synthesis of most other types of lipids, including steroids and almost all fatty acids, begins with acetyl-CoA. Lipogenesis can use almost any organic molecule because lipids, amino acids, and carbohydrates

Clinical Note

Dietary Fats and Cholesterol

Elevated cholesterol levels are associated with the development of *atherosclerosis* and *coronary artery disease* (CAD). ∞ pp. 432, 415 Nutritionists currently recommend that you limit cholesterol intake to under 300 mg per day. This amount represents a 40 percent reduction for the average American adult. As a result of rising concerns about cholesterol, such phrases as "low in cholesterol," "contains no cholesterol," and "cholesterol free" are widely used in the advertising and packaging of foods. Cholesterol content alone, however, does not tell the entire story; consider the following basic information about cholesterol and about lipid metabolism in general:

- *Cholesterol has many vital functions in the human body.* It serves as a waterproofing agent in the epidermis, a lipid component of all plasma membranes, a key constituent of bile, and the precursor of several steroid hormones and vitamin D_3. Because cholesterol is so important, the goal of dietary restrictions is *not* to eliminate cholesterol from the diet or from the circulating blood but instead to keep cholesterol levels within acceptable limits.

- *The cholesterol content of the diet is not the only source of circulating cholesterol.* The human body can manufacture cholesterol from acetyl-CoA produced during glycolysis or by the breakdown (beta-oxidation) of other lipids. If the diet contains an abundance of saturated fats, blood cholesterol levels will rise because excess lipids are broken down to acetyl-CoA, which can be used to make cholesterol. This means that a person trying to lower serum cholesterol by dietary control must also restrict other lipids—especially saturated fats.

- *Genetic factors affect each individual's cholesterol level.* If you reduce your dietary intake of cholesterol, your body will synthesize more to maintain "acceptable" concentrations in the blood. What is an "acceptable" level depends on your genetic makeup. Because individuals have different genes, their cholesterol levels can vary, even on similar diets. In virtually all instances, however, dietary restrictions can lower blood cholesterol significantly.

- *Cholesterol levels vary with age and physical condition.* At age 19, three out of four males have cholesterol levels below 170 mg/dL. Cholesterol levels in females of this age are slightly higher, typically at or below 175 mg/dL. As age increases, cholesterol values gradually climb; over age 70,

typical values are 230 mg/dL (males) and 250 mg/dL (females). A cholesterol level is considered unhealthy if it is higher than those of 90 percent of the population in a given age group. For males, this "cutoff" value increases from 185 mg/dL at age 19 to 250 mg/dL at age 70. For females, the comparable values are 190 mg/dL and 275 mg/dL.

To determine whether you need to reduce your cholesterol level, remember three simple rules:

1. Individuals of any age with total cholesterol values below 200 mg/dL probably need not change their lifestyle unless they have a family history of coronary artery disease and atherosclerosis.

2. Those with cholesterol levels between 200 and 239 mg/dL should modify their diet, lose weight (if overweight), and have annual checkups.

3. Cholesterol levels over 240 mg/dL warrant drastic changes in dietary lipid consumption, perhaps coupled with drug treatment. Drug therapies are always recommended when serum cholesterol levels exceed 350 mg/dL. Examples of drugs used to lower cholesterol levels are *cholestyramine, colestipol,* and *lovastatin.*

When most physicians order a blood test for cholesterol, they also request information on circulating triglycerides. When cholesterol levels are high, or when an individual has a family history of atherosclerosis or CAD, the HDL level may be measured, and the LDL may be calculated from an equation relating the levels of cholesterol, HDL, and triglycerides. A high total cholesterol value linked to a high LDL spells trouble. In effect, an unusually large amount of cholesterol is being exported to peripheral tissues. Problems can also exist if the individual has high total cholesterol—or even normal total cholesterol—and HDL levels below 35 mg/dL. In this case, excess cholesterol delivered to the tissues cannot easily be returned to the liver for excretion. In either event, the amount of cholesterol in peripheral tissues, and especially in arterial walls, is likely to increase.

For years, LDL/HDL ratios were used to predict the risk of developing atherosclerosis. Risk-factor analysis and LDL levels are now thought to be more accurate indicators. Many clinicians recommend dietary restrictions and drug therapy for males with more than one risk factor and LDL levels exceeding 130 mg/dL, regardless of total cholesterol or HDL levels.

can be converted to acetyl-CoA (**Figure 17-8**). Body cells cannot *build* every fatty acid they can break down. For example, neither *linoleic acid* nor *linolenic acid,* both 18-carbon unsaturated fatty acids, can be synthesized. Because they must be included in your diet, they are called **essential fatty acids.** (They are synthesized by plants.) These fatty acids are also needed to synthesize prostaglandins and phospholipids for plasma membranes throughout the body.

LIPID TRANSPORT AND DISTRIBUTION

All cells need lipids to maintain their plasma membranes, and steroid hormones must reach their target cells in many different tissues. Because most lipids are not soluble in water, special mechanisms are required to transport them around the body. Most lipids circulate in the bloodstream as

FIGURE 17-8 Lipid Synthesis.
Pathways of lipid synthesis begin with acetyl-CoA. Molecules of acetyl-CoA can be strung together in the cytoplasm, yielding fatty acids that can be used to synthesize glycerides or other lipid molecules. Lipids can also be synthesized from amino acids or carbohydrates by using acetyl-CoA as an intermediate.

lipoproteins—lipid–protein complexes that contain triglycerides and cholesterol within an outer coating of phospholipids and proteins. The proteins and phospholipids make the entire complex soluble. The exposed proteins, which bind to specific membrane receptors, determine which cells absorb the associated lipids.

Lipoproteins are classified by size and by their relative proportions of lipid and protein. One group, the *chylomicrons,* is produced by intestinal epithelial cells from the fats in food. ∞ p. 564 Chylomicrons are the largest lipoproteins, and some 95 percent of their weight consists of triglycerides. Chylomicrons transport triglycerides absorbed from the intestinal tract to the bloodstream, from which they are absorbed by skeletal muscle, cardiac muscle, adipose tissue, and the liver.

Two other major groups of lipoproteins are the **low-density lipoproteins (LDLs)** and **high-density lipoproteins (HDLs).** These lipoproteins are formed in the liver and contain few triglycerides. Their main roles are to shuttle cholesterol between the liver and other tissues. LDLs deliver cholesterol to peripheral tissues. Because LDL cholesterol may end up in arterial plaques, it is often called "bad cholesterol." HDLs transport excess cholesterol from peripheral tissues to the liver for storage or excretion in the bile. Because HDL cholesterol does not cause circulatory problems, it is called "good cholesterol."

Free fatty acids (FFA) are lipids that can diffuse easily across plasma membranes. A major source of these fatty acids is the breakdown of fat stored in adipose tissue. When released into the blood, the fatty acids bind to albumin, the most abundant plasma protein. Liver cells, cardiac muscle cells, skeletal muscle fibers, and many other body cells can metabolize free fatty acids. They are an important energy source during periods of starvation, when glucose supplies are limited.

CHECKPOINT

7. Define lipolysis.

8. Define beta-oxidation.

9. Why are high-density lipoproteins (HDLs) considered beneficial?

See the blue Answers tab at the back of the book.

17-4 Protein catabolism involves transamination and deamination, whereas protein synthesis involves amination and transamination

Even though the body can synthesize at least 100,000 different proteins, each with varied forms, functions, and structures, all proteins are composed of some combination of only 20 amino acids. Under normal conditions, a continuous recycling of cellular proteins occurs in the cytoplasm. Peptide bonds are broken, and the resulting free amino acids are used to manufacture new proteins. If other energy sources are inadequate, mitochondria can break down amino acids in the TCA cycle to generate ATP. Not all amino acids enter the TCA cycle at the same point, so the ATP benefits vary. However, the average ATP yield is comparable to that of carbohydrate catabolism.

AMINO ACID CATABOLISM

The first step in amino acid catabolism is the removal of the amino group, which requires a coenzyme derived from **vitamin B₆** (*pyridoxine*). The amino group is removed by either transamination or deamination.

Transamination (trans-am-i-NĀ-shun) attaches the amino group of an amino acid to another carbon chain, creating a "new" amino acid. Transaminations enable a cell to synthesize many of the amino acids needed for protein synthesis. Cells of the liver, skeletal muscles, heart, lung, kidney, and brain, which are particularly active in protein synthesis, perform many transaminations.

Deamination (dē-am-i-NĀ-shun) prepares an amino acid for breakdown in the TCA cycle. Deamination is the removal of an amino group in a reaction that generates an ammonia molecule (NH_3). Ammonia is highly toxic, even in low concentrations. The liver, the primary site of deamination, has the enzymes needed to deal with the problem of ammonia generation. Liver cells combine carbon dioxide with ammonia to produce **urea,** a relatively harmless, water-soluble compound that is excreted in the urine.

The fate of the carbon chain remaining after deamination in the liver depends on its structure. The carbon chains of some amino acids can be converted to pyruvic acid and then used in gluconeogenesis. Other carbon chains are converted to acetyl-CoA and broken down in the TCA cycle. Still others are converted to **ketone bodies,** organic acids that are also produced during lipid catabolism. One example of a ketone body generated in the body is *acetone,* a small molecule that can diffuse into the alveoli of the lungs, giving the breath a distinctive odor.

Ketone bodies diffuse into the general circulation, but they are not metabolized by the liver. Instead, other body cells reconvert them into acetyl-CoA for breakdown in the TCA cycle and the production of ATP. The increased production of ketone bodies that occurs during protein and lipid catabolism by the liver results in high ketone body concentrations in body fluids, a condition called **ketosis** (kē-TŌ-sis).

Three factors make protein catabolism an impractical source of quick energy:

1. Proteins are more difficult to break apart than are complex carbohydrates or lipids.

2. One of the by-products, ammonia, is toxic to cells.

3. Because proteins form the most important structural and functional components of any cell, extensive protein catabolism threatens homeostasis at the cellular and systems levels.

AMINO ACIDS AND PROTEIN SYNTHESIS

The basic mechanism of protein synthesis was detailed in Chapter 3. ∞ p. 80–83 Your body can synthesize roughly half of the different amino acids needed to build proteins. Of the 10 **essential amino acids,** eight (*isoleucine, leucine, lysine, threonine, tryptophan, phenylalanine, valine,* and *methionine*) cannot be synthesized; the other two (*arginine* and *histidine*) can be synthesized but in amounts that are insufficient for growing children. The other amino acids, which can be synthesized on demand, are called **nonessential amino acids.** Your body cells can readily synthesize the carbon frameworks of the nonessential amino acids, and a nitrogen group can be added by **amination**—the attachment of an amino group—or by transamination.

Protein deficiency diseases develop when an individual does not consume adequate amounts of all essential amino acids. All amino acids must be available if protein synthesis is to occur. If every transfer RNA molecule does not appear at the active ribosome at the proper time bearing its individual amino acid, the entire process comes to a halt. Regardless of the diet's energy content, if it is deficient in essential amino acids, the individual will be malnourished to some degree. Examples of protein

Clinical Note

Ketoacidosis

A ketone body is also called a *keto acid* because it dissociates in solution, releasing a hydrogen ion. As a result, the appearance of ketone bodies represents a threat to blood plasma pH that must be controlled. During prolonged starvation, ketone levels continue to rise. Eventually, the pH-buffering capacities of the blood are exceeded, and a dangerous drop in pH occurs. This acidification of the blood and body tissues is called **ketoacidosis** (kē-tō-as-i-DŌ-sis). In severe ketoacidosis, pH may fall below 7.05, low enough to disrupt normal tissue activities and cause coma, cardiac arrhythmias, and death.

In *diabetes mellitus,* most peripheral tissues cannot utilize glucose because of a lack of insulin. ∞ p. 366 Under these circumstances, cells survive by catabolizing lipids and proteins. The result is the production of large numbers of ketone bodies. This condition leads to *diabetic ketoacidosis,* the most common and life-threatening form of ketoacidosis.

deficiency diseases include *marasmus* and *kwashiorkor*. More than 100 million children worldwide are affected by these disorders, although neither condition is common in the United States today.

Several inherited metabolic disorders result from an inability to produce specific enzymes involved in amino acid metabolism. Individuals with **phenylketonuria** (fen-il-kē-to-NOO-rē-uh), or **PKU,** cannot convert the amino acid phenylalanine to the amino acid tyrosine, because of a defect in the enzyme phenylalanine hydroxylase. This reaction is an essential step in the synthesis of norepinephrine, epinephrine, and melanin. If PKU is not detected in infancy, central nervous system development is inhibited, and severe brain damage results.

Figure 17-9 summarizes the major pathways of cellular metabolism for lipids, carbohydrates and proteins. Although this diagram presents the reactions in a "typical" cell, no one cell can perform all of the anabolic and catabolic operations required by the body as a whole. As differentiation proceeds, each cell type develops its own complement of enzymes that determines its metabolic capabilities. In the presence of such cellular diversity, homeostasis can be preserved only when the metabolic activities of tissues, organs, and organ systems are coordinated.

CHECKPOINT

10. Define transamination.
11. Define deamination.
12. How would a diet deficient in vitamin B_6 affect protein metabolism?

See the blue Answers tab at the back of the book.

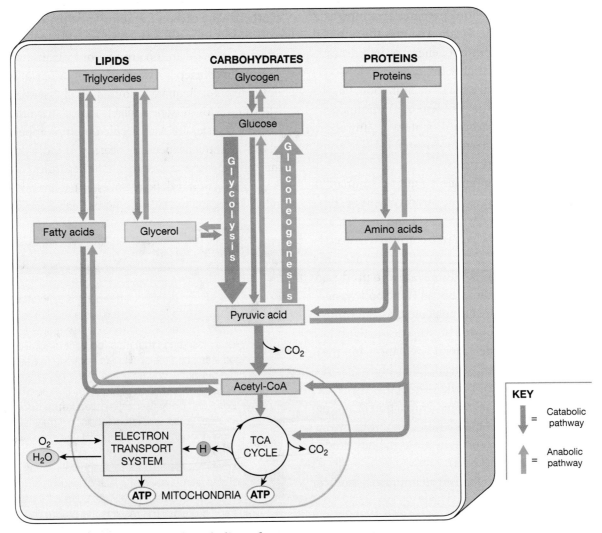

FIGURE 17-9 **A Summary of Catabolic and Anabolic Pathways.** This figure provides a diagrammatic overview of the major catabolic (red) and anabolic (blue) pathways for lipids, carbohydrates, and proteins.

17-5 Nucleic acid catabolism involves RNA, but not DNA

Living cells contain both DNA and RNA. The genetic information contained in nuclear DNA is absolutely essential to the long-term survival of a cell. As a result, DNA is never catabolized for energy, even if the cell is dying of starvation. By contrast, the RNA molecules involved in protein synthesis are broken down and replaced regularly.

RNA CATABOLISM

In the breakdown of RNA, the molecule is disassembled into individual nucleotides. Although most nucleotides are recycled into new nucleic acids, they can be broken down to simple sugars and nitrogen bases. When nucleotides are broken down, only the sugars, cytosines, and uracils can enter the TCA cycle and be used to generate ATP. Adenine and guanine cannot be catabolized; instead, they undergo deamination and are excreted as **uric acid.** Like urea, uric acid is a relatively nontoxic waste product, but it is far less soluble than urea. Urea and uric acid are called *nitrogenous wastes,* because they contain nitrogen atoms.

An elevated level of uric acid in the blood is called *hyperuricemia* (hī-per-ū-ri-SĒ-mē-uh). Uric acid saturates body fluids and, although symptoms may not appear immediately, uric acid crystals may begin to form. The condition that then develops is called *gout.* Most cases of hyperuricemia and gout are linked to problems with the excretion of uric acid by the kidneys.

NUCLEIC ACID SYNTHESIS

Most cells synthesize RNA, but DNA synthesis occurs only in cells preparing for mitosis (cell division) or meiosis (gamete production). The process of DNA replication was described in Chapter 3. ∞ p. 84

Messenger RNA (mRNA), transfer RNA (tRNA), and ribosomal RNA (rRNA) are transcribed by different forms of the enzyme RNA polymerase. Messenger RNA is manufactured as needed, when specific genes are activated. A strand of mRNA has a life span measured in minutes or hours. Ribosomal RNA and tRNA are more durable than mRNA. For example, the average strand of rRNA lasts just over 5 days. However, because a typical cell contains roughly 100,000 ribosomes and many times that number of tRNA molecules, their replacement involves a considerable amount of synthetic activity.

CHECKPOINT

13. Why do cells not use DNA as an energy source?

14. What are nitrogenous wastes?

15. Elevated levels of uric acid in the blood could indicate an increased catabolic rate for which type of macromolecule?

See the blue Answers tab at the back of the book.

17-6 Adequate nutrition is necessary to prevent deficiency disorders and maintain homeostasis

Homeostasis can be maintained indefinitely only if the digestive tract absorbs fluids, organic substrates, minerals, and vitamins at a rate that keeps pace with cellular demands. The absorption of essential nutrients from food is called **nutrition.**

The body's requirement for each nutrient varies from day to day and from person to person. *Nutritionists* attempt to analyze a diet in terms of its ability to prevent and treat illnesses for specific individuals and population groups. A **balanced diet** contains all the nutrients needed to maintain homeostasis, including adequate substrates for generating energy, essential amino acids and fatty acids, minerals, and vitamins. In addition, the diet must include enough water to replace losses in urine, feces, and evaporation. A balanced diet prevents **malnutrition,** an unhealthy state resulting from the inadequate or excessive intake of one or more nutrients.

FOOD GROUPS AND THE MYPYRAMID PLAN

One way of maintaining good health and preventing malnutrition is to consume a diet based on the updated food pyramid, called the MyPyramid Plan (**Figure 17-10**). After twelve years, the United States Department of Agriculture updated its food pyramid to reflect the balance between food consumption and physical activity. The widths of the color-coded vertical food group bands running from top to bottom indicate the proportions of food we should consume from each of the **five basic food groups:** grains (orange), vegetables (green), fruits (plum), milk products (blue), and meat and beans (purple). Oils (yellow) are to be eaten sparingly in addition to the five basic food groups. Twelve different pyramids have been developed based on level of physical activity and general health; all aim to increase healthful eating habits. Visit www.mypyramid.gov for more information. Table 17-1 summarizes what each of these

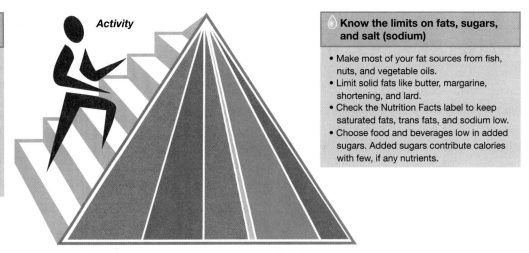

Find your balance between food and physical activity

- Be sure to stay within your daily calorie needs.
- Be physically active for at least 30 minutes most days of the week.
- About 60 minutes a day of physical activity may be needed to prevent weight gain.
- For sustaining weight loss, at least 60 to 90 minutes a day of physical activity may be required.
- Children and teenagers should be physically active for 60 minutes most days.

Activity

Know the limits on fats, sugars, and salt (sodium)

- Make most of your fat sources from fish, nuts, and vegetable oils.
- Limit solid fats like butter, margarine, shortening, and lard.
- Check the Nutrition Facts label to keep saturated fats, trans fats, and sodium low.
- Choose food and beverages low in added sugars. Added sugars contribute calories with few, if any, nutrients.

GRAINS	VEGETABLES	FRUITS	OILS	MILK	MEAT & BEANS
Make half your grains whole	Vary your veggies	Focus on fruits		Get your calcium-rich foods	Go lean with proteins

FIGURE 17-10 The MyPyramid Plan. The proportion of each food group is indicated by the widths of the color-coded bands. Foods should be consumed in proportions based on both the food group and the individual's level of activity.

TABLE 17-1 Basic Food Groups of the 2005 Dietary Guidelines and Their General Effects on Health

NUTRIENT GROUP	PROVIDES	HEALTH EFFECTS
Grains (recommended: at least half of the total eaten as whole grains)	Carbohydrates; vitamins E, thiamine, niacin, folate; calcium; phosphorus; iron; sodium; dietary fiber	Whole grains prevent rapid rise in blood glucose levels, and consequent rapid rise in insulin levels
Vegetables (recommended: especially dark-green and orange vegetables)	Carbohydrates; vitamins A, C, E, folate; dietary fiber; potassium	Reduce risk of cardiovascular disease; protect against colon cancer (folate) and prostate cancer (lycopene in tomatoes)
Fruits (recommended: a variety of fruit each day)	Carbohydrates; vitamins A, C, E, folate; dietary fiber; potassium	Reduce risk of cardiovascular disease; protect against colon cancer (folate)
Milk (recommended: low-fat or fat-free milk, yogurt, and cheese)	Complete proteins; fats; carbohydrates; calcium; potassium; magnesium; sodium; phosphorus; vitamins A, B_{12}, pantothenic acid, thiamine, riboflavin	Whole milk: High in calories, may cause weight gain; saturated fats correlated with heart disease
Meat and Beans (recommended: lean meats, fish, poultry, eggs, dry beans, nuts, legumes)	Complete proteins; fats; calcium; potassium; phosphorus; iron; zinc; vitamins E, thiamine, B_6	Fish and poultry lower risk of heart disease and colon cancer (compared to red meat); consumption of up to one egg per day does not appear to increase incidence of heart disease; nuts and legumes improve blood cholesterol ratios, lower risk of heart disease and diabetes

The Big Picture

A balanced diet contains all the ingredients needed to maintain homeostasis, including adequate substrates for energy generation, essential amino acids and fatty acids, minerals, vitamins, and water.

nutrient groups provides in the diet, as well as recommended choices from the dietary guidelines and their general effects on health.

Such groupings can help in planning a balanced and healthful diet. It is important to obtain nutrients not only in sufficient *quantity* (to meet energy needs) but also in adequate *quality* (including essential amino acids, fatty acids, vitamins, and minerals). There is nothing magical about five groups—since 1940, the U.S. government has at various times advocated 11, 7, 4, or 6 food groups. The key is to make intelligent choices about what you eat. Poor choices can lead to malnutrition even if all five groups are represented.

Consider, for example, the essential amino acids. The liver cannot synthesize any of these amino acids, so you must obtain them from your diet. Some members of the milk and meat and beans groups—specifically, beef, fish, poultry, eggs, and milk—provide all the essential amino acids in sufficient quantities. They are said to contain **complete proteins,** because they contain all of the essential amino acids in sufficient quantities. Many plants contain adequate *amounts* of protein, but these are **incomplete proteins** because they are deficient in one or more essential amino acids. Vegetarians who largely restrict themselves to the grains, fruits, and vegetables groups (with or without the milk group) must become adept at varying their food choices to include a combination of ingredients that meets all of their amino acid requirements. Even if their diets contain a proper balance of amino acids, vegetarians who avoid all animal products face a significant problem because vitamin B_{12} can be obtained only from animal products, or from fortified cereals or tofu.

MINERALS, VITAMINS, AND WATER

Minerals, vitamins, and water are essential components of the diet. The body cannot synthesize minerals, and our cells can generate only a small quantity of water and very few vitamins.

Minerals

Minerals are inorganic ions released through the dissociation of electrolytes, such as sodium chloride. Minerals are important for the following reasons:

1. *Ions such as sodium and chloride determine the osmotic concentration of body fluids.* Potassium is important in maintaining the osmotic concentration inside body cells.

2. *Ions in various combinations play major roles in important physiological processes.* As we have seen, these processes include the maintenance of membrane potentials, the construction and maintenance of the skeleton, muscle contraction, action potential generation, neurotransmitter release, blood clotting, the transport of respiratory gases, buffer systems, fluid absorption, and waste removal.

3. *Ions are essential cofactors in a variety of enzymatic reactions.* For example, the enzyme that breaks down ATP in a contracting skeletal muscle requires the presence of calcium and magnesium ions, and an enzyme required for the conversion of glucose to pyruvic acid needs both potassium and magnesium ions.

The most important minerals and a summary of their functions are presented in Table 17-2. Your body contains significant reserves of several important minerals that help reduce the effects of variations in dietary supply. These reserves are often relatively small, however, and chronic dietary deficiencies can lead to various clinical problems. Alternatively, because storage capabilities are limited, a dietary excess of mineral ions can prove equally dangerous.

Vitamins

Vitamins (*vita,* life) are essential organic nutrients related to lipids and carbohydrates. They are of two types: fat-soluble vitamins and water-soluble vitamins.

FAT-SOLUBLE VITAMINS. Vitamins A, D, E, and K are **fat-soluble vitamins,** as they are absorbed primarily from the digestive tract along with the lipid contents of micelles.

The term *vitamin D* refers to a group of steroid-like molecules, including vitamin D_3, or cholecalciferol. ∞ p. 45 Unlike the other fat-soluble vitamins, which must be obtained by absorption across the digestive tract, vitamin D_3 can usually be synthesized in adequate amounts by skin exposed to sunlight. Current information concerning the fat-soluble vitamins is summarized in Table 17-3.

Because fat-soluble vitamins dissolve in lipids, they normally diffuse into plasma membranes, including the lipid inclusions in the liver and adipose tissue. Your body, therefore,

TABLE 17-2 Minerals and Mineral Reserves

MINERAL	SIGNIFICANCE	TOTAL BODY CONTENT	PRIMARY ROUTE OF EXCRETION	RECOMMENDED DAILY INTAKE
BULK MINERALS				
Sodium	Major cation in body fluids; essential for normal membrane function	110 g, primarily in body fluids	Urine, sweat, feces	1.5 g
Potassium	Major cation in cytoplasm; essential for normal membrane function	140 g, primarily in cytoplasm	Urine	4.7 g
Chloride	Major anion in body fluids	89 g, primarily in body fluids	Urine, sweat	2.3 g
Calcium	Essential for normal muscle and neuron function, and for normal bone structure	1.36 kg, primarily in skeleton	Urine, feces	1000–1200 mg
Phosphorus	As phosphate in high-energy compounds, nucleic acids, and bone matrix	744 g, primarily in skeleton	Urine, feces	700 mg
Magnesium	Cofactor of enzymes, required for normal membrane functions	29 g (skeleton, 17 g; cytoplasm and body fluids, 12 g)	Urine	310–400 mg
TRACE MINERALS				
Iron	Component of hemoglobin, myoglobin, cytochromes	3.9 g (1.6 g stored as ferritin or hemosiderin)	Urine (traces)	8–18 mg
Zinc	Cofactor of enzyme systems, notably carbonic anhydrase	2 g	Urine, hair (traces)	8–11 mg
Copper	Required as cofactor for hemoglobin synthesis	127 mg	Urine, feces (traces)	900 μg
Manganese	Cofactor for some enzymes	11 mg	Feces, urine (traces)	1.8–2.3 mg

contains a significant reserve of these vitamins, and normal metabolic operations can continue for several months after dietary sources have been cut off. For this reason, symptoms of **avitaminosis** (ā-vī-ta-min-Ō-sis), or *vitamin deficiency disease*, rarely result from dietary insufficiency of fat-soluble vitamins. However, avitaminosis involving either fat-soluble or water-soluble vitamins can result from factors other than dietary deficiencies, including an inability to absorb a vitamin from the digestive tract, inadequate storage, or excessive demand.

Table 17-3 also points out that *too much* of a vitamin can produce effects just as unpleasant as *too little*. **Hypervitaminosis** (hī-per-vī-ta-min-Ō-sis) occurs when dietary intake exceeds the ability to store, utilize, or excrete a particular vitamin. This condition most often involves one of the fat-soluble vitamins because the excess vitamins are retained and stored in body lipids.

WATER-SOLUBLE VITAMINS. Most of the water-soluble vitamins are components of coenzymes (Table 17-4). For example, NAD is derived from niacin, and coenzyme A from vitamin B_5 (pantothenic acid). Water-soluble vitamins are rapidly exchanged between the digestive tract and the circulating blood, and excess amounts are readily excreted in the urine. For this reason, hypervitaminosis involving water-soluble vitamins is relatively uncommon, except among individuals taking large doses of vitamin supplements.

The bacteria that reside in the intestines help prevent deficiency diseases by producing five of the nine water-soluble vitamins, in addition to fat-soluble vitamin K. The intestinal epithelium can easily absorb all of the water-soluble vitamins except B_{12}. The B_{12} molecule is large, and it must be bound to intrinsic factor, secreted by the gastric mucosa, before absorption can occur. ⁐p. 544

TABLE 17-3 The Fat-Soluble Vitamins

VITAMIN	SIGNIFICANCE	SOURCES	RECOMMENDED DAILY INTAKE	EFFECTS OF DEFICIENCY	EFFECTS OF EXCESS
A	Maintains epithelia; required for synthesis of visual pigments; supports immune system; promotes growth and bone remodeling	Leafy green and yellow vegetables	700–900 µg	Retarded growth, night blindness, deterioration of epithelial membranes	Liver damage, skin peeling, CNS effects (nausea, anorexia)
D (steroid-like compounds, including cholecalciferol or D_3)	Required for normal bone growth, calcium and phosphorus absorption at gut and retention at kidneys	Synthesized in skin exposed to sunlight	5–15 µg*	Rickets, skeletal deterioration	Calcium deposits in many tissues, disrupting functions
E (tocopherols)	Prevents breakdown of vitamin A and fatty acids	Meat, milk, vegetables	15 mg	Anemia, other problems suspected	Nausea, stomach cramps, blurred vision, fatigue
K	Essential for liver synthesis of prothrombin and other clotting factors	Vegetables; production by intestinal bacteria	90–120 µg	Bleeding disorders	Liver dysfunction, jaundice

*Recommended intakes are higher if sunlight exposure is inadequate for extended periods and alternative sources (fortified milk products) are unavailable.

Water

Daily water requirements average 2500 mL (10 cups), or roughly 40 mL/kg body weight. The specific requirement varies with environmental conditions and metabolic activities. For example, exercise increases metabolic energy requirements and accelerates water losses due to evaporation and perspiration. The temperature rise accompanying a fever has a similar effect; for each degree (°C) temperature rises above normal, daily water loss increases by 200 mL. Thus, the advice "Drink plenty of fluids" when you are sick has a solid physiological basis.

Most of your daily water ration is obtained by eating or drinking. The food you consume provides roughly 48 percent, and another 40 percent is obtained by drinking fluids. But a small amount of water—called *metabolic water*—is produced in mitochondria during the operation of the electron transport system. ∞p. 579 The actual amount produced per day varies with the composition of the diet. A typical mixed diet in the United States contains 46 percent carbohydrates, 40 percent lipids, and 14 percent protein. This diet would produce roughly 300 mL of water per day (slightly more than 1 cup), about 12 percent of the average daily water requirement.

DIET AND DISEASE

Diet has a profound influence on general health. We have already considered the effects of too many and too few nutrients, above-normal or below-normal concentrations of minerals, and hypervitaminosis and avitaminosis. More subtle long-term problems can occur when the diet includes the wrong proportions or combinations of nutrients. The average diet in the United States contains too much sodium and too many calories, and lipids—particularly saturated fats—provide too great a proportion of those calories. Such a diet increases the incidence of obesity, heart disease, atherosclerosis, hypertension, and diabetes in the U.S. population.

TABLE 17-4 **The Water-Soluble Vitamins**

VITAMIN	SIGNIFICANCE	SOURCES	RECOMMENDED DAILY INTAKE	EFFECTS OF DEFICIENCY	EFFECTS OF EXCESS
B_1 (thiamine)	Coenzyme in decarboxylation reactions (removal of a carbon dioxide molecule)	Milk, meat, bread	1.1–1.2 mg	Muscle weakness, CNS and cardiovascular problems including heart disease; called *beriberi*	Hypotension
B_2 (riboflavin)	Part of FAD	Milk, meat	1.1–1.3 mg	Epithelial and mucosal deterioration	Itching, tingling
Niacin (nicotinic acid)	Part of NAD	Meat, bread, potatoes	14–16 mg	CNS, GI, epithelial, and mucosal deterioration; called *pellagra*	Itching, burning; vasodilation, death after large dose
B_5 (pantothenic acid)	Part of acetyl-CoA	Milk, meat	5 mg	Retarded growth, CNS disturbances	None reported
B_6 (pyridoxine)	Coenzyme in amino acid and lipid metabolism	Meat	1.3–1.7 mg	Retarded growth, anemia, convulsions, epithelial changes	CNS alterations, perhaps fatal
Folate (folic acid)	Coenzyme in amino acid and nucleic acid metabolisms	Vegetables, cereal, bread	400 µg	Retarded growth, anemia, gastrointestinal disorders, developmental abnormalities	Few noted except at massive doses
B_{12} (cobalamin)	Coenzyme in nucleic acid metabolism	Milk, meat	2.4 µg	Impaired RBC production causes *pernicious anemia*	Polycythemia (elevated hematocrit)
Biotin	Coenzyme in decarboxylation reactions	Eggs, meat, vegetables	30 µg	Fatigue, muscular pain, nausea, dermatitis	None reported
C (ascorbic acid)	Coenzyme; delivers hydrogen ions, antioxidant	Citrus fruits	75–90 mg Smokers: add 35mg	Epithelial and mucosal deterioration; called *scurvy*	Kidney stones

16. Identify the two types of vitamins.

17. What is the difference between foods described as containing complete proteins and those described as containing incomplete proteins?

18. How would a decrease in the amount of bile salts in the bile affect the amount of vitamin A in the body?

See the blue Answers tab at the end of the book.

17-7 Metabolic rate is the average caloric expenditure, and thermoregulation involves balancing heat-producing and heat-losing mechanisms

In this section we consider topics that relate to energy measurement, energy intake and expenditure, and thermoregulation.

UNITS OF ENERGY

When chemical bonds are broken, energy is released. Inside cells, some of that energy may be captured as ATP, but much of it is lost to the environment as heat. The unit of energy measurement is the **calorie (cal)** (KAL-o-rē), the amount of energy required to raise the temperature of 1 g of water 1 degree Celsius. One gram of water is not a very practical measure when you are interested in the metabolic operations that keep a 70-kg human alive, however, so the **kilocalorie (kcal)** (KIL-ō-kal-o-rē), or **Calorie (Cal),** is used instead. One Calorie is the amount of energy needed to raise the temperature of 1 *kilo*gram of water 1 degree Celsius. Calorie-counting guides that give the caloric value of various foods list Calories, not calories.

THE ENERGY CONTENT OF FOOD

In cells, organic molecules combine with oxygen and are broken down to carbon dioxide and water. Oxygen is also consumed when something burns, and this process of combustion can be experimentally observed and measured. A known amount of food is placed in a chamber, called a **calorimeter** (kal-o-RIM-e-ter), which is filled with oxygen and surrounded by a known volume of water. Once the food is inside, the chamber is sealed and the contents are electrically ignited. When the food is completely burned and only ash remains in the cham-

ber, the number of Calories released can be determined by comparing the water temperatures before and after the test. Such measurements show that the burning, or catabolism, of lipids releases a considerable amount of energy—roughly 9.46 Calories per gram (Cal/g). In contrast, the catabolism of carbohydrates releases 4.18 Cal/g, and the catabolism of protein releases 4.32 Cal/g. Most foods are mixtures of fats, proteins, and carbohydrates, so the values in a "Calorie counter" vary as a result.

ENERGY EXPENDITURE: METABOLIC RATE

Clinicians can assess your metabolic state to learn how many Calories your body uses. The result can be expressed as Calories per hour, Calories per day, or Calories per unit of body weight per day. What is actually measured is the sum of all the various anabolic and catabolic processes occurring in your body—its **metabolic rate** at that time. Metabolic rate varies with the activity under way; for instance, measurements of someone sprinting and someone sleeping are quite different. To reduce such variations, the testing conditions are standardized so as to determine the **basal metabolic rate (BMR).** Ideally, the BMR reflects the minimum, resting energy expenditures of an awake, alert person. An average individual has a BMR of 70 Cal per hour, or about 1680 Cal per day. Although the test conditions are standardized, other uncontrollable factors influence the BMR, including age, sex, physical condition, body weight, and genetic differences.

Daily energy expenditures for a given individual vary widely with activity. For example, a person leading a sedentary life may have near-basal energy demands, but one hour of swimming can increase the daily caloric requirements by 500 Cal or more. If daily energy intake exceeds the body's total energy demands, the excess energy will be stored, primarily as triglycerides in adipose tissue. If daily caloric expenditures exceed dietary intake, a net reduction in the body's energy reserves will occur, with a corresponding loss in weight. This relationship explains the importance of both Calorie counting and daily exercise in a weight-control program.

THERMOREGULATION

The BMR (basal metabolic rate) provides only an estimate of the rate of energy use. Body cells capture only a part of that energy as ATP, and the rest is "lost" as heat. This heat loss serves an important homeostatic purpose. Humans are subject to vast changes in environmental temperatures, but our complex biochemical systems have a major limitation: Enzymes operate over only a relatively narrow range of temperatures. Fortunately, certain anatomical and physiological mechanisms keep body temperatures within acceptable limits, regardless of environmental conditions. This homeostatic process is called **thermoregulation** (*therme*, heat). ∞p. 13 Failure to control body temperature can result in serious physiological effects (**Figure 17-11**). For example, a body temperature below 36°C (97°F) or above 40°C (104°F) can cause disorientation, and a temperature above 42°C (108°F) can cause convulsions and permanent cell damage.

Mechanisms of Heat Transfer

Heat exchange with the environment involves four basic processes—*radiation, conduction, convection,* and *evaporation.*

1. *Radiation.* Warm objects lose heat energy as infrared radiation. When we feel the sun's heat, we are experiencing radiant heat. Your body loses heat the same way. More than half of the heat you lose occurs by radiation.

2. *Conduction.* Conduction is the direct transfer of energy through physical contact. When you sit on a cold plastic chair in an air-conditioned room, you are immediately

aware of this process. Conduction is generally not an effective mechanism of gaining or losing heat.

3. *Convection.* Convection is the result of conductive heat loss to the air that overlies the surface of an object. Warm air rises because it is lighter than cool air. As your body conducts heat to the air next to your skin, that air warms and rises, moving away from your skin surface. Cooler air replaces it, and as this air in turn warms, the pattern repeats.

4. *Evaporation.* When water evaporates, it changes from a liquid to a vapor. This process absorbs energy—roughly 580 calories (0.58 Cal) per gram of water evaporated—thereby cooling any surface on which it occurs. The rate of evaporation and heat loss occurring at your skin is highly variable. Each hour, 20–25 mL of water cross epithelia and evaporate from the alveolar surfaces of the lungs and the surface of the skin. This *insensible perspiration* remains relatively constant; it accounts for roughly one-fifth of the average heat loss from a body at rest. The sweat glands responsible for *sensible perspiration* have a tremendous scope of activity, ranging from virtual inactivity to secretory rates of 2–4 liters (or 2–4 kg) per hour. This is equivalent to an entire day's resting water loss in under an hour.

To maintain a constant body temperature, an individual must lose heat as fast as it is generated by metabolic operations. Altering the rates of heat loss and heat gain requires the coordinated activity of many different systems. That activity is coordinated by the **heat-loss center** and **heat-gain center** of the hypothalamus. The heat-loss center adjusts activity through the parasympathetic division of the autonomic nervous system, whereas the heat-gain center directs its responses through the sympathetic division. The overall effect is to control temperature fluctuations by influencing two events: the rate of heat production and the rate of heat loss to the environment. These events may be further supported by behavioral changes or modifications, such as moving into the shade or sunlight, or the addition or removal of clothing.

PROMOTING HEAT LOSS. When the temperature at the heat-loss center exceeds its set point, three responses occur:

1. Peripheral blood vessels dilate, sending warm blood flowing to the surface of the body. The skin takes on a reddish color and rises in temperature; heat loss through radiation and convection increases.

2. Sweat glands are stimulated, and as perspiration flows across the skin, heat loss through evaporation accelerates.

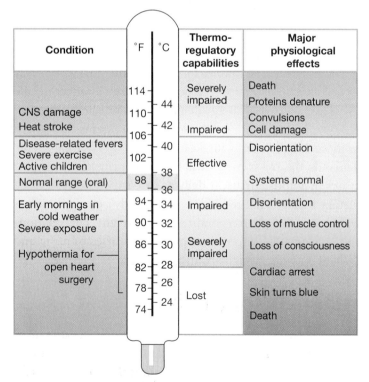

FIGURE 17-11 **Normal and Abnormal Variations in Body Temperature.**

3. The respiratory centers are stimulated, and the depth of respiration increases. The individual often begins respiring through the mouth, enhancing heat loss through increased evaporation from the lungs.

The efficiency of heat loss by evaporation varies with environmental conditions, especially the "relative humidity" of the air. At 100 percent humidity, the air is saturated; it is holding as much water vapor as it can at that temperature. Under these conditions, evaporation is ineffective as a cooling mechanism. This is why humid, tropical conditions can be so uncomfortable—people perspire continuously but remain warm and wet.

PROMOTING HEAT GAIN: HEAT CONSERVATION AND GENERATION.
The function of the heat-gain center of the brain is to prevent **hypothermia** (hī-pō-THER-mē-uh), or below-normal body temperature. When body temperature falls below acceptable levels, the heat-loss center is inhibited and the heat-gain center is activated. Its activation results in responses that conserve body heat and promote heat generation.

Heat is conserved by decreasing blood flow to the skin, thereby reducing losses by radiation, convection, and conduction. The skin cools, and with blood flow restricted, it may take on a bluish or pale coloration. In addition, blood returning from the limbs is shunted into a network of deep veins that lies beneath an insulating layer of subcutaneous fat. ∞ p. 454 (Under warm conditions, blood flows through a superficial venous network, through which heat can be lost.)

In addition to conserving heat, the heat-gain center stimulates two mechanisms that generate heat. In *shivering thermogenesis* (ther-mō-JEN-e-sis), muscle tone is gradually increased until stretch receptors stimulate brief, oscillatory contractions of antagonistic skeletal muscles. The resulting shivering stimulates energy consumption by skeletal muscles, and the generated heat warms the deep vessels to which the blood has been diverted. Shivering can increase the rate of heat generation by as much as 400 percent.

The release of hormones that increase the metabolic activity of cells in all tissues produces *nonshivering thermogenesis.* Epinephrine from the suprarenal glands immediately increases both the breakdown of glycogen and glycolysis in the liver and in skeletal muscles, and increases the metabolic rate in most tissues. The heat-gain center also stimulates the release of thyroxine by the thyroid gland, accelerating carbohydrate use and the breakdown of all other nutrients. These effects develop gradually over a period of days to weeks.

CHECKPOINT

19. Compare a pregnant woman's BMR (basal metabolic rate) to her BMR when she is not pregnant.

20. Under what conditions would evaporative cooling of the body be ineffective?

21. What effect would vasoconstriction of peripheral blood vessels have on body temperature on a hot day?

See the blue Answers tab at the end of the book.

17-8 Caloric needs decline with advancing age

Nutritional requirements do not change drastically with age. However, changes in lifestyle, eating habits, and income that often accompany aging can directly affect nutrition and health. The recommended proportions of calories provided by different foods do not change with advancing age; current guidelines indicate that for individuals of all ages, proteins should provide 11–12% of daily caloric intake, carbohydrates 55–60%, and fats less than 30%. Caloric *requirements,* however, do change with aging. For each decade after age 50, caloric requirements decrease by 10 percent. These decreases are associated with reductions in metabolic rates, body mass, activity levels, and exercise tolerance.

With age, several factors combine to result in an increased need for calcium. Some degree of osteoporosis is a normal consequence of aging; a sedentary lifestyle contributes to the problem. The rate of bone loss decreases if calcium levels are kept elevated. The elderly are also likely to require supplemental vitamin D_3 if they are to absorb the calcium they need. Many elderly people spend most of their time indoors and avoid the sun when outdoors. Although this behavior slows sun damage to their skin, which is thinner than that of younger people, it also eliminates vitamin D_3 production by the skin. ∞ p. 126 This vitamin is converted to the hormone calcitriol, which stimulates calcium absorption by the small intestine.

Maintaining a healthy diet becomes more difficult with age as a result of changes in the senses of smell and taste and in the structure of the digestive system. With age, the number and sensitivity of olfactory and gustatory receptors decrease. ∞ p. 339 As a result, food becomes less appetizing, so less food is eaten. Making matters worse, the mucosal lining of the digestive tract becomes thinner with age, so nutrient absorption becomes less efficient. Thus, what food the elderly do eat is not utilized very efficiently. Elderly people on fixed budgets may reduce their consumption of animal protein, which is the primary source of dietary iron. The combination of small quantities plus inefficient absorption makes them prone to iron deficiency, which causes anemia.

RELATED CLINICAL TERMS

antipyretic drugs: Drugs administered to control or reduce fever.

avitaminosis (ā-vī-ta-min-Ō-sis)**:** A vitamin deficiency disease.

eating disorders: Psychological problems that result in inadequate or excessive food consumption. Examples include anorexia nervosa and bulimia.

gout: A metabolic disorder characterized by the precipitation of uric acid crystals within joint cavities.

heat exhaustion: A malfunction of thermoregulatory mechanisms caused by excessive fluid loss in perspiration.

heat stroke: A condition in which the thermoregulatory center stops functioning and body temperature rises uncontrollably.

hyperuricemia (hī-per-ū-ri-SĒ-mē-uh)**:** Elevated uric acid levels in blood; values above 7.4 mg/dL can result in the condition called *gout*.

hypervitaminosis (hī-per-vī-ta-mi-NŌ-sis)**:** A disorder caused by the ingestion of excessive quantities of one or more vitamins.

hypothermia (hī-pō-THER-mē-uh)**:** Below-normal body temperature.

ketoacidosis (kē-tō-as-i-DŌ-sis)**:** Reduced blood pH due to the presence of ketone bodies.

ketonemia (kē-tō-NĒ-mē-uh)**:** Elevated levels of ketone bodies in blood.

ketonuria (kē-tō-NOO-rē-uh)**:** The presence of ketone bodies in urine.

ketosis (kē-TŌ-sis)**:** A condition characterized by the abnormally high production of ketone bodies.

liposuction: The removal of adipose tissue by suction through an inserted tube.

obesity: Body weight more than 20 percent above the ideal weight for a given individual.

phenylketonuria (fen-il-kē-to-NOO-rē-uh)**:** An inherited metabolic disorder characterized by an inability to convert phenylalanine to tyrosine.

protein deficiency diseases: Nutritional disorders resulting from a lack of essential amino acids.

pyrexia (pī-REK-sē-uh)**:** A fever; that is, a body temperature greater than 99°F (37.2°C).

CHECKPOINT

22. Which changes with aging: nutritional requirements or caloric requirements?

See the blue Answers tab at the end of the book.

Chapter 17 Review

KEY TERMS

aerobic metabolism *577*

basal metabolic rate (BMR) *593*

Calorie *593*

electron transport system (ETS) *579*

glycogen *581*

glycolysis *577*

metabolic turnover *576*

metabolism *575*

nutrient *575*

nutrition *587*

thermoregulation *594*

tricarboxylic (TCA, citric acid, or Krebs) cycle *578*

vitamin *589*

SUMMARY OUTLINE

17-1 Metabolism refers to all the chemical reactions that occur in the body *p. 575*

1. Body cells are chemical factories that break down organic molecules and their building blocks to obtain energy for growth, cell division, and other tissue specific activities.

2. In general, during *cellular metabolism,* cells break down excess carbohydrates first, then lipids, while conserving amino acids.

Only about 40 percent of the energy released through *catabolism* is captured in ATP; the rest is released as heat. *(Figure 17-1)*

3. Cells synthesize new compounds (*anabolism*) to (1) perform structural maintenance and repair, (2) support growth, (3) produce secretions, and (4) build nutrient reserves.

4. Cells "feed" small organic molecules to their mitochondria; in return, the cells get the ATP they need to perform cellular functions. *(Figure 17-2)*

17-2 Carbohydrate metabolism involves glycolysis, ATP production, and gluconeogenesis *p. 577*

5. Most cells generate ATP and other high-energy compounds through the breakdown of carbohydrates.

6. **Glycolysis** and **aerobic metabolism** provide most of the ATP used by typical cells. In glycolysis, each molecule of glucose yields two molecules of pyruvic acid and two molecules of ATP. *(Figure 17-3)*

7. In the presence of oxygen, the pyruvic acid molecules enter the mitochondria, where they are broken down completely in the

tricarboxylic acid (TCA) cycle. The carbon and oxygen atoms are lost as carbon dioxide, and the hydrogen atoms are passed by *coenzymes* to the *electron transport system*. *(Figure 17-4)*

8. *Cytochromes* of the **electron transport system (ETS)** pass along electrons to oxygen to form water and generate ATP. *(Figure 17-5)*

9. For each glucose molecule completely broken down by aerobic pathways, a typical cell gains 36 ATP molecules.

10. When supplies of glucose are limited, cells can break down other nutrients to provide molecules for the TCA cycle. *(Figure 17-6)*

11. **Gluconeogenesis,** the synthesis of glucose, enables a cell to manufacture glucose molecules from other carbohydrates, glycerol, or some amino acids. *Glycogen* is an important energy reserve when extracellular glucose is low. *(Figure 17-7)*

17-3 Lipid metabolism involves lipolysis, beta-oxidation, and the transport and distribution of lipids as lipoproteins and free fatty acids *p. 582*

12. During **lipolysis** (lipid catabolism), lipids are broken down into pieces that can be converted into pyruvic acid or channeled into the TCA cycle.

13. Triglycerides, the most abundant lipids in the body, are split into glycerol and fatty acids. Glycerol enters glycolytic pathways, and fatty acids enter mitochondria.

14. *Beta-oxidation* is the breakdown of fatty acid molecules into two-carbon fragments that can enter the TCA cycle or be converted to ketone bodies.

15. Lipids cannot provide large amounts of ATP in a short amount of time. However, cells can shift to lipid-based energy production when glucose reserves are limited.

16. In **lipogenesis,** the synthesis of lipids, almost any organic molecule can be used to form glycerol. **Essential fatty acids** cannot be synthesized and must be included in the diet. *(Figure 17-8)*

17. Lipids circulate as **lipoproteins** (lipid–protein complexes that contain triglycerides and cholesterol) or as **free fatty acids (FFA)** (lipids associated with albumin that can diffuse easily across plasma membranes).

17-4 Protein catabolism involves transamination and deamination, whereas protein synthesis involves amination and transamination *p. 584*

18. If other energy sources are inadequate, mitochondria can break down amino acids. In the mitochondria, the amino group may be removed by *transamination* or *deamination*. The resulting carbon skeleton may enter the TCA cycle to generate ATP or be converted to ketone bodies.

19. Protein catabolism is impractical as a source of quick energy.

20. The body can synthesize roughly half of the amino acids needed to build proteins. The 10 *essential amino acids* must be acquired through the diet.

21. No one cell can perform all of the anabolic and catabolic operations necessary to support life. Homeostasis can be preserved only when the metabolic activities of different tissues are coordinated. *(Figure 17-9)*

17-5 Nucleic acid catabolism involves RNA, but not DNA *p. 587*

22. DNA in the nucleus is never catabolized for energy. RNA molecules are broken down and replaced regularly; usually they are recycled as new nucleic acids.

17-6 Adequate nutrition is necessary to prevent deficiency disorders and maintain homeostasis *p. 587*

23. **Nutrition** is the absorption of essential nutrients from food. A *balanced diet* contains all of the ingredients needed to maintain homeostasis; it prevents **malnutrition**.

24. The five **basic food groups** are grains, vegetables, fruits, milk, and meat and beans. These are arranged in a *food pyramid* to reflect a recommended daily food consumption, which should be balanced with daily physical activity. *(Figure 17-10, Table 17-1)*

25. **Minerals** act as cofactors in various enzymatic reactions. They also contribute to the osmotic concentration of body fluids, and they play a role in transmembrane potentials, action potentials, neurotransmitter release, muscle contraction, skeletal construction and maintenance, gas transport, buffer systems, fluid absorption, and waste removal. *(Table 17-2)*

26. **Vitamins** are needed in very small amounts. Vitamins A, D, E, and K are **fat-soluble vitamins;** taken in excess, they can lead to **hypervitaminosis. Water-soluble vitamins** are not stored in the body; a lack of adequate dietary supplies can lead to **avitaminosis** (*deficiency disease*). *(Tables 17-3, 17-4)*

27. Daily water requirements average about 40 mL/kg body weight. Water is obtained from food, drink, and metabolic generation.

28. A balanced diet can improve one's general health.

17-7 Metabolic rate is the average caloric expenditure, and thermoregulation involves balancing heat-producing and heat-losing mechanisms *p. 593*

29. The energy content of food is usually expressed as **Calories** per gram (Cal/g). Less than half of the energy content of glucose or any other organic nutrient can be captured by body cells.

30. The catabolism of each gram of lipid releases 9.46 C, about twice the Calories released by the breakdown of the same amount of carbohydrate or protein.

31. The total of all the body's anabolic and catabolic processes over a given period of time is an individual's **metabolic rate.** The **basal metabolic rate (BMR)** is the rate of energy utilization at rest.

32. The homeostatic regulation of body temperature is **thermoregulation.** Heat exchange with the environment involves four processes: **radiation, conduction, convection,** and **evaporation.** *(Figure 17-11)*

33. The hypothalamus acts as the body's thermostat, containing the **heat-loss center** and the **heat-gain center.**

34. Mechanisms for increasing heat loss include both physiological mechanisms (superficial blood vessel dilation, increased perspiration, and accelerated respiration) and behavioral adaptations.

35. Body heat may be conserved by reducing blood flow to the skin. Heat can be generated by *shivering thermogenesis* and *nonshivering thermogenesis.*

17-8 Caloric needs decline with advancing age   *p. 595*

36. Caloric requirements drop by 10 percent each decade after age 50. Changes in the senses of smell and taste dull appetite, and changes to the digestive system decrease the efficiency of nutrient absorption from the digestive tract.

REVIEW QUESTIONS

WWW   Access more review material online at The Anatomy & Physiology Place (**www.anatomyandphysiology.com**). There, you'll find Chapter Guides, Chapter Quizzes, Chapter Practice Tests, Interactive Flashcards, a Glossary with Pronunciations, and more to help you succeed in the course.

Level 1 • Reviewing Facts and Terms

Match each item in column A with the most closely related item in column B. Place letters for answers in the spaces provided.

COLUMN A

_____ **1.** glucose formation
_____ **2.** lipid catabolism
_____ **3.** synthesis of lipids
_____ **4.** linoleic acid
_____ **5.** deamination
_____ **6.** phenylalanine
_____ **7.** ketoacidosis
_____ **8.** A, D, E, K
_____ **9.** B complex and vitamin C
_____ **10.** calorie
_____ **11.** uric acid
_____ **12.** hypothermia

COLUMN B

a. gluconeogenesis
b. essential amino acid
c. below-normal body temperature
d. unit of energy
e. fat-soluble vitamins
f. water-soluble vitamins
g. lipolysis
h. nitrogenous waste
i. essential fatty acid
j. removal of an amino group
k. decrease in pH
l. lipogenesis

13. Cells synthesize new organic components to
(a) perform structural maintenance and repairs.
(b) support growth.
(c) produce secretions.
(d) a, b, and c are correct.

14. During the complete catabolism of one molecule of glucose, a typical cell gains
(a) 4 ATP.   (b) 18 ATP.
(c) 36 ATP.   (d) 144 ATP.

15. The breakdown of glucose to pyruvic acid is
(a) glycolysis.   (b) gluconeogenesis.
(c) cellular respiration.   (d) beta-oxidation.

16. Glycolysis yields an immediate net gain of _____ molecules for the cell.
(a) 1 ATP   (b) 2 ATP
(c) 4 ATP   (d) 36 ATP

17. The electron transport chain yields a total of _____ molecules of ATP in the complete catabolism of one glucose molecule.
(a) 2   (b) 4
(c) 32   (d) 36

18. The synthesis of glucose from simpler molecules is called
(a) glycolysis.   (b) lipolysis.
(c) gluconeogenesis.   (d) beta-oxidation.

19. Choose from the word bank to label the missing terms in the following diagram of nutrient use in cellular metabolism.

Word Bank: TCA cycle, amino acids, glucose, electron transport system, fatty acids, ATP, CO_2, small carbon chains, H_2O.

(a) _____   (b) _____
(c) _____   (d) _____
(e) _____   (f) _____
(g) _____   (h) _____
(i) _____

20. The lipoproteins that transport excess cholesterol from peripheral tissues back to the liver for storage or excretion in the bile are the
    (a) chylomicrons.   (b) FFA.
    (c) LDLs.   (d) HDLs.

21. The removal of an amino group in a reaction that generates an ammonia molecule is called
    (a) ketoacidosis.   (b) transamination.
    (c) deamination.   (d) denaturation.

22. A complete protein contains
    (a) the proper balance of amino acids.
    (b) all the essential amino acids in sufficient quantities.
    (c) a combination of nutrients selected from the food pyramid.
    (d) N compounds produced by the body.

23. All minerals and most vitamins
    (a) are fat soluble.
    (b) cannot be stored by the body.
    (c) cannot be synthesized by the body.
    (d) must be synthesized by the body because they are not present in adequate amounts in the diet.

24. The basal metabolic rate represents the
    (a) maximum energy expenditure when exercising.
    (b) minimum, resting energy expenditure of an awake, alert person.
    (c) minimum amount of energy expenditure during light exercise.
    (d) muscular energy expenditure added to the resting energy expenditure.

25. Over half of the heat loss from our bodies is attributable to
    (a) radiation.   (b) conduction.
    (c) convection.   (d) evaporation.

26. Define the terms metabolism, anabolism, and catabolism.

27. What is a lipoprotein? What are the major groups of lipoproteins, and how do they differ?

28. Why are vitamins and minerals essential components of the diet?

29. What are the energy yields (in Calories per gram) of the catabolism of carbohydrates, lipids, and proteins?

30. What is the basal metabolic rate (BMR)?

31. What four processes are involved in heat transfer?

Level 2 • Reviewing Concepts

32. The function of the TCA cycle is to
    (a) produce energy during periods of active muscle contraction.
    (b) break six-carbon chains into three-carbon fragments.
    (c) prepare the glucose molecule for further reactions.
    (d) remove hydrogen atoms from organic molecules and transfer them to coenzymes.

33. During periods of fasting or starvation, the presence of ketone bodies in the circulation causes
    (a) an increase in blood pH.
    (b) a decrease in blood pH.
    (c) a neutral blood pH.
    (d) diabetes insipidus.

34. Define glycolysis. What substances are required for this process?

35. What substances enter the TCA cycle, and what substances leave it? Why is it called a cycle?

36. How does beta-oxidation function in lipid (triglyceride) catabolism?

37. How can the MyPyramid Plan be used as a tool for developing a healthy lifestyle?

38. How is the brain involved in the regulation of body temperature?

39. Articles in popular media sometimes refer to "good cholesterol" and "bad cholesterol." To what types of cholesterol do these terms refer, and what are their functions?

Level 3 • Critical Thinking and Clinical Applications

40. Why is a starving individual more susceptible to infectious disease than a well-nourished individual?

41. Charlie has a blood test that shows a normal level of LDLs but an elevated level of HDLs in his blood. Given that his family has a history of cardiovascular disease, he wonders if he should modify his lifestyle. What would you tell him?

18 The Urinary System

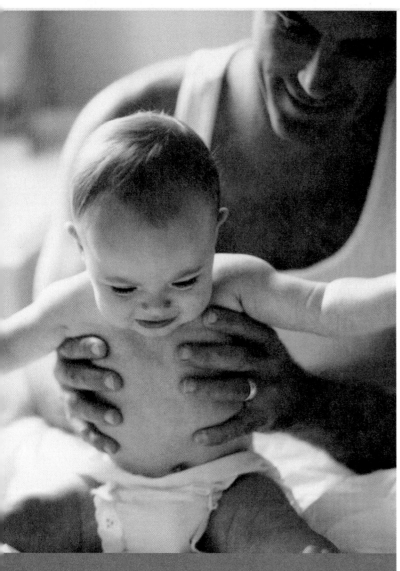

Infants involuntarily urinate when their bladder is full, a process that sometimes seems nonstop to their parents. Urine contains waste products that form after the digestive system assimilates a meal and the body uses the nutrients it needs. The urinary system performs this service while efficiently conserving water and other valuable substances. As we will see it also carries out a variety of other vital, but less obvious functions.

VOCABULARY DEVELOPMENT

calyx a cup of flowers; *minor calyx*
detrudere to push down; *detrusor muscle*
fenestra a window; *fenestrated capillaries*
glomus a ball; *glomerulus*

gonion angle; *trigone*
juxta near; *juxtaglomerular complex*
micturire to urinate; *micturition*
nephros kidney; *nephron*
papillae small, nipple-shaped projections; *renal papillae*

podon foot; *podocyte*
rectus straight; *vasa recta*
ren kidney; *renal artery*
retro- behind; *retroperitoneal*
vasa vessels; *vasa recta*

An Introduction to the Urinary System

The human body contains trillions of cells bathed in extracellular fluid. In previous chapters we compared these cells to factories that burn nutrients to obtain energy. Imagine what would happen if real factories were as close together as cells in the body. Each factory would generate significant quantities of solid wastes and noxious gases, creating a serious pollution problem.

Comparable problems do not develop within the body as long as the activities of the digestive, cardiovascular, respiratory, and urinary systems are coordinated. The digestive tract absorbs nutrients from food and excretes solid wastes, and the liver adjusts the nutrient concentration of the circulating blood. The cardiovascular system delivers these nutrients, plus oxygen from the respiratory system, to peripheral tissues. As blood leaves these tissues, it carries the waste gas carbon dioxide and organic waste products to sites of excretion. The carbon dioxide is eliminated at the lungs, as described in Chapter 15. Most of the organic waste products in the blood are removed by the urinary system.

This chapter examines the organization of the urinary system, describes the major regulatory mechanisms that control urine production and concentration, and examines the roles of fluid balance, electrolyte balance, and acid-base balance in homeostasis.

18-1 The urinary system, consisting of the kidneys, ureters, urinary bladder, and urethra, has three primary functions

The **urinary system** (Figure 18-1) has three major functions: (1) *excretion*, the removal of organic waste products from body fluids; (2) *elimination*, the discharge of these waste products into the environment; and (3) homeostatic regulation of the volume and solute concentration of blood plasma. The excretory functions of the urinary system are performed by the two **kidneys**—organs that produce **urine**, a fluid containing water, ions, and small soluble compounds. Urine leaving the kidneys flows along the **urinary tract**, which consists of paired tubes called **ureters** (ū-RĒ-terz), to the **urinary bladder**, a muscular sac for temporary storage of urine. On leaving the urinary bladder, urine passes through the **urethra** (ū-RĒ-thra), which conducts the urine to the exterior. The urinary bladder and the urethra are responsible for the elimination of urine, a process called **urination** or **micturition** (mik-choo-RISH-un). In this process, contraction of the muscular urinary bladder forces urine through the urethra and out of the body.

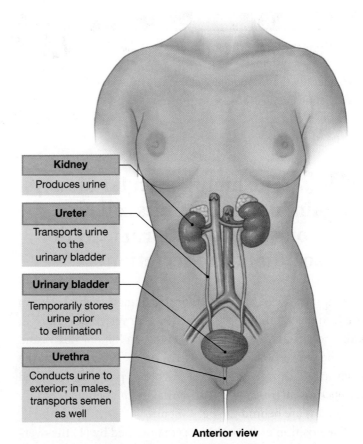

Kidney
Produces urine

Ureter
Transports urine to the urinary bladder

Urinary bladder
Temporarily stores urine prior to elimination

Urethra
Conducts urine to exterior; in males, transports semen as well

Anterior view

FIGURE 18-1 **The Components of the Urinary System.**

In addition to removing organic wastes generated by the body's cells, the urinary system's other essential homeostatic functions include the following:

- *Regulating blood volume and blood pressure,* by (1) adjusting the volume of water lost in the urine, (2) releasing erythropoietin, and (3) releasing renin. ∞ p. 366

- *Regulating plasma concentrations of sodium, potassium, chloride,* and *other ions,* by controlling the quantities lost in the urine, and by controlling the concentration of calcium ions through the synthesis of calcitriol. ∞ p. 366

- *Helping to stabilize blood pH,* by controlling the loss of hydrogen ions (H^+) and bicarbonate ions (HCO_3^-) in the urine.

- *Conserving valuable nutrients,* such as glucose and amino acids, by preventing their excretion in the urine, while excreting organic waste products (especially the nitrogenous wastes *urea* and *uric acid*).

These activities are carefully regulated to keep the composition of the blood within acceptable limits. A disruption of any of these functions has immediate and potentially fatal consequences.

CHECKPOINT

1. Name the three primary functions of the urinary system.
2. Identify the components of the urinary system.
3. Define micturition.

See the blue Answers tab at the back of the book.

18-2 The highly vascular kidneys contain functional units called nephrons, which perform filtration, reabsorption, and secretion

The **kidneys** are located on either side of the vertebral column between the last thoracic and third lumbar vertebrae. The right kidney often sits slightly lower than the left (Figure 18-2a), and both lie between the muscles of the dorsal body wall and the peritoneal lining (Figure 18-2b). This position is called *retroperitoneal* (re-trō-per-i-tō-NĒ-al; *retro-,* behind) because the organs are behind the peritoneum.

The position of the kidneys is maintained by (1) the overlying peritoneum, (2) contact with adjacent organs, and (3) sup-

(a) Posterior view

(b) Superior view

FIGURE 18-2 **An Overview of Kidney Anatomy. (a)** This posterior view of the trunk shows the positions of the kidneys and other components of the urinary system. **(b)** A superior view of a section at the level indicated in part (a) reveals the kidney's retroperitoneal position.

porting connective tissues. Each kidney is covered by a *fibrous capsule* and is packed in a soft cushion of adipose tissue. These connective tissues, along with suspensory collagen fibers, help prevent the jolts and shocks of day-to-day existence from disturbing normal kidney function. Damage to the suspensory fibers may cause the kidney to be displaced. This condition, called a *floating kidney,* is dangerous because the ureters or renal blood vessels may become twisted or kinked during movement.

SUPERFICIAL AND SECTIONAL ANATOMY OF THE KIDNEYS

A typical kidney is reddish-brown and about 10 cm (4 in.) long, 5.5 cm (2.2 in.) wide, and 3 cm (1.2 in.) thick in adults. Each kidney weighs about 150 g (5.25 oz). An indentation called the **hilum** is the site of exit for the ureter (Figure 18-2b), as well as the site at which the renal artery and renal nerve enter, and the renal vein exits. (The adjective *renal* is derived from *ren,* which means "kidney" in Latin.) The **fibrous capsule** covers the surface of the kidney and lines the *renal sinus,* an internal cavity.

The kidney is divided into an outer **renal cortex** and an inner **renal medulla** (Figure 18-3a,b). The medulla contains 6 to 18 conical **renal pyramids.** The tip of each pyramid, known as the **renal papilla,** projects into the renal sinus. Bands of cortical tissue called *renal columns* extend toward the renal sinus between adjacent renal pyramids.

Urine production occurs in the renal pyramids and overlying areas of renal cortex. Ducts within each renal papilla discharge urine into a cup-shaped drain, called a **minor calyx** (KĀ-liks; *calyx,* a cup of flowers; plural *calyces*). Four or five minor calyces (KAL-i-sēz) merge to form the **major calyces,** both of which combine to form a large, funnel-shaped chamber, the **renal pelvis.** The renal pelvis is connected to the ureter, through which urine drains out of the kidney.

Urine production begins in the renal cortex, in microscopic tubular structures called **nephrons** (NEF-ronz) (Figure 18-3c). Each kidney has roughly 1.25 million nephrons, with a combined length of about 145 kilometers (85 miles).

FIGURE 18-3 The Structure of the Kidney. Two frontal sections through the left kidney—(a) a diagrammatic view and (b) a photograph—reveal the internal anatomy of the kidney. (c) This enlarged view shows the location and general structure of a nephron.

THE BLOOD SUPPLY TO THE KIDNEYS

Because the kidneys function to filter out wastes in the blood and excrete them in the urine, it's not surprising that the kidneys are well supplied with blood. In healthy individuals, about 1200 mL of blood flows through the kidneys each minute, or some 20–25 percent of cardiac output—a phenomenal amount of blood for organs with a combined weight of less than 300 g (10.5 oz)!

Figure 18-4a diagrams the path of blood flow to, within, and out of the kidney. Each kidney receives blood from a **renal**

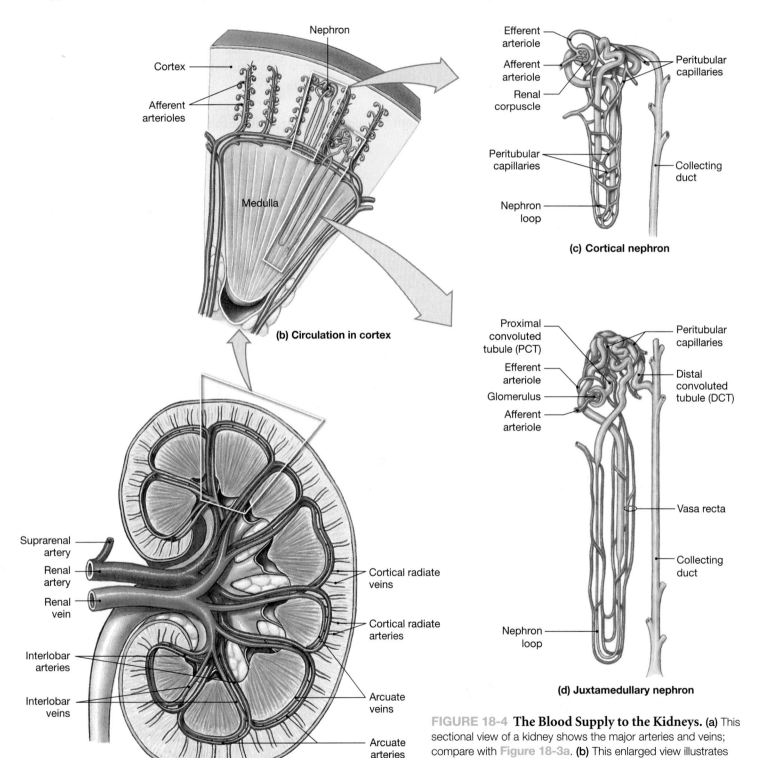

(b) Circulation in cortex

(c) Cortical nephron

(d) Juxtamedullary nephron

(a) Arteries and veins of kidney

FIGURE 18-4 **The Blood Supply to the Kidneys. (a)** This sectional view of a kidney shows the major arteries and veins; compare with **Figure 18-3a**. **(b)** This enlarged view illustrates the circulation in the cortex. Further enlargements show the circulation to **(c)** a cortical nephron and **(d)** a juxtamedullary nephron.

artery that originates from the abdominal aorta. As the renal artery enters the renal sinus, it divides into branches that supply a series of **interlobar arteries** that radiate outward between the renal pyramids. They then turn, arching along the boundary lines between the cortex and medulla as the **arcuate** (AR-kū-āt) **arteries.** Each arcuate artery gives rise to a number of **cortical radiate arteries,** or *interlobular arteries,* supplying the cortex. **Afferent arterioles** branching from each cortical radiate artery deliver blood to the capillaries supplying individual nephrons (Figure 18-4b).

Blood reaches each nephron through an afferent arteriole and leaves in an **efferent arteriole** (Figure 18-4c). It then travels to the **peritubular capillaries** surrounding the proximal and distal convoluted tubules. The peritubular capillaries provide a route for the pickup or delivery of substances that are reabsorbed or secreted by these portions of the nephron.

The path of blood from the peritubular capillaries differs in **cortical nephrons,** which are located mostly within the cortex (Figure 18-4c), and in **juxtamedullary** (juks-ta-MED-ū-lar-ē) **nephrons** (*juxta,* near), which are located near the renal medulla. In juxtamedullary nephrons, the peritubular capillaries are connected to the **vasa recta** (*rectus,* straight)—long, straight capillaries that parallel the nephron loop deep into the medulla (Figure 18-4d). As we will see later, it is the juxtamedullary nephrons that enable the kidneys to produce concentrated urine.

Blood from the peritubular capillaries and vasa recta enters a network of venules and small veins that converge on the **cortical radiate veins,** or *interlobular veins.* In a mirror image of the arterial distribution, blood continues to converge and empty into the **arcuate, interlobar,** and **renal veins** (Figure 18-4a).

THE NEPHRON

The nephron is the basic functional unit in the kidney. Each nephron consists of two main parts: (1) a *renal corpuscle,* and (2) a 50-mm-long (2-inch-long) **renal tubule** composed of two *convoluted* (coiled or twisted) segments separated by a simple U-shaped tube (Figure 18-3c). The convoluted segments are in the cortex, and the U-shaped tube extends partially or completely into the medulla.

An Overview of the Nephron

A schematic diagram of a representative nephron is shown in Figure 18-5. The nephron begins at the **renal corpuscle** (KOR-pus-ul), a round structure consisting of the *glomerular* (Bowman) *capsule,* a cup-shaped chamber that contains a

The Big Picture

The kidneys remove waste products from the blood; they also assist in regulating blood volume and blood pressure, ion levels, and blood pH. Nephrons are the functional units of the kidneys.

capillary network, or *glomerulus* (glo-MER-ū-lus; *glomus,* a ball). As previously described, blood arrives at the glomerulus by way of an *afferent arteriole* and departs in an *efferent arteriole.* In the renal corpuscle, blood pressure forces fluid and dissolved solutes out of the glomerular capillaries and into the surrounding *capsular space.* This process is called *filtration.* ∞ p. 68 Filtration produces a protein-free solution known as a **filtrate.**

From the renal corpuscle, the filtrate enters the renal tubule. The major segments of the renal tubule are the *proximal convoluted tubule* (PCT), the *nephron loop,* also called the *loop of Henle* (HEN-lē), and the *distal convoluted tubule* (DCT). As the filtrate travels along the tubule, its composition gradually changes, and it is then called **tubular fluid.** The changes that occur and the urine that results depend on the specialized activities under way in each segment of the nephron.

Each nephron empties into a *collecting duct,* the start of the **collecting system.** The collecting duct leaves the cortex and descends into the medulla, carrying tubular fluid from many nephrons toward a *papillary duct* that delivers the fluid, now called *urine,* into the calyces and on to the renal pelvis.

Functions of the Nephron

Urine has a very different composition from the filtrate produced at the renal corpuscle. The role(s) of each segment of the nephron in converting filtrate to urine is indicated in Figure 18-5. The renal corpuscle is the site of filtration. The functional advantage of filtration is that it is passive; it does not require an expenditure of energy. The disadvantage of filtration is that any filter with pores large enough to permit the passage of organic waste products cannot *prevent* the passage of water, ions, and nutrients such as glucose, fatty acids, and amino acids. These substances, along with most of the water, must be reclaimed or they are lost in the urine.

Filtrate leaves the renal corpuscle and enters the renal tubule, which is responsible for the following functions:

- Reabsorbing all of the useful organic molecules from the filtrate.

- Reabsorbing over 90 percent of the water in the filtrate.

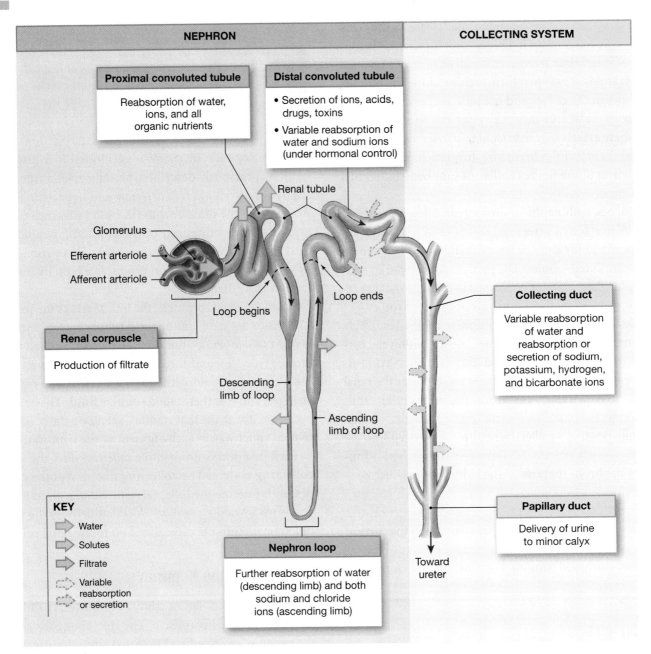

FIGURE 18-5 **A Representative Nephron and the Collecting System.** This schematic drawing highlights the major structures and functions of each segment of the nephron (purple) and the collecting system (tan).

- Secreting into the tubular fluid any waste products that were missed by the filtration process.

Additional water and salts will be removed in the collecting system before the urine is released into the renal sinus.

The Renal Corpuscle

The **renal corpuscle** (Figure 18-6) consists of (1) the capillary network of the **glomerulus** and (2) the **glomerular capsule,** formerly called *Bowman's capsule*. The glomerular capsule forms the outer wall of the renal corpuscle and encloses the glomeru-

lar capillaries. The glomerulus projects into the glomerular capsule much as the heart projects into the pericardial cavity (Figure 18-6a). A *capsular epithelium* makes up the wall of the capsule and is continuous with a specialized *visceral epithelium* covering the glomerular capillaries. The two epithelia are separated by the **capsular space,** which receives the filtrate and empties into the renal tubule.

The epithelium covering the capillaries consists of cells called **podocytes** (PŌ-dō-sīts, *podon,* foot) (Figure 18-6b). Podocytes have long cellular processes, or "feet"—called *pedicels*—that wrap around individual capillaries. A thick

FIGURE 18-6 The Renal Corpuscle. (a) This sectional view of a renal corpuscle illustrates its important structural features. **(b)** A cross section through a segment of the glomerulus reveals the components of the filtration membrane. **(c)** This colorized photomicrograph shows the glomerular surface, including individual podocytes and their processes.

basement membrane separates the endothelial cells of the capillaries from the podocytes. The glomerular capillaries are said to be *fenestrated* (FEN-e-strā-ted; *fenestra,* a window) because their endothelial cells contain pores (Figure 18-6b). To enter the capsular space, a solute must be small enough to pass through (1) the pores of the endothelial cells, (2) the fibers of the basement membrane, and (3) the *filtration slits* between the slender processes of the podocytes. The fenestrated capillary, basement membrane, and filtration slits form a **filtration membrane** that prevents the passage of blood cells and most plasma proteins but permits the movement of water, metabolic wastes, ions, glucose, fatty acids, amino acids, vitamins, and other solutes into the capsular space. Most of the valuable solutes will be reabsorbed by the proximal convoluted tubule.

The Proximal Convoluted Tubule

The filtrate next moves into the first segment of the renal tubule, the **proximal convoluted tubule (PCT)** (Figure 18-5). The cells lining the PCT absorb organic nutrients, plasma proteins, and ions from the tubular fluid and release them into the interstitial fluid surrounding the renal tubule. As a result of this transport, the solute concentration of the interstitial fluid increases while that of the tubular fluid decreases. Water then moves out of the tubular fluid by osmosis, reducing the volume of tubular fluid.

The Nephron Loop

The last portion of the PCT bends sharply toward the renal medulla and connects to the **nephron loop,** or *loop of Henle* (Figure 18-5). This loop is composed of a *descending limb* that travels toward the renal pelvis, and an *ascending limb* that returns to the cortex. The ascending limb, which is not permeable to water and solutes, actively transports sodium and chloride ions out of the tubular fluid. As a result, the interstitial fluid of the medulla contains an unusually high solute concentration. The descending limb is permeable to water, and as it descends into the medulla, water moves out of the tubular fluid by osmosis.

The Distal Convoluted Tubule

The ascending limb of the nephron loop ends where it bends and comes in close contact with the glomerulus and its vessels (Figure 18-3c). At this point, the **distal convoluted tubule (DCT)** begins, and it passes immediately adjacent to the afferent and efferent arterioles (Figure 18-6a).

The distal convoluted tubule is an important site for (1) the active secretion of ions, acids, drugs, and toxins and (2) the selective reabsorption of sodium ions from the tubular fluid. In the final portions of the DCT, an osmotic flow of water may assist in concentrating the tubular fluid.

The epithelial cells of the DCT closest to the glomerulus are unusually tall, and their nuclei are clustered together. This region of the DCT is called the *macula densa* (MAK-ū-la DEN-sa) (Figure 18-6a). The cells of the macula densa are closely associated with unusual smooth muscle fibers—the *juxtaglomerular* (*juxta,* near) *cells*—in the wall of the afferent arteriole. Together, the macula densa and juxtaglomerular cells form the **juxtaglomerular complex,** or *juxtaglomerular apparatus,* an endocrine structure that secretes the hormone erythropoietin and the enzyme renin, introduced in Chapter 10. ∞ p. 366

The Collecting System

The distal convoluted tubule, the last segment of the nephron, opens into the collecting system, which consists of collecting ducts and papillary ducts (Figure 18-5). Each **collecting duct** receives tubular fluid from many nephrons, and several collecting ducts merge to form a **papillary duct,** which delivers urine to a minor calyx. In addition to transporting tubular fluid from the nephron to the renal pelvis, the collecting system can make final adjustments to the composition of the urine by reabsorbing water and by reabsorbing or secreting sodium, potassium, hydrogen, and bicarbonate ions.

Table 18-1 summarizes the functions of the different regions of the nephron and collecting system.

TABLE 18-1 The Functions of the Nephron and Collecting System in the Kidney

REGION	PRIMARY FUNCTION
Renal corpuscle	Filtration of plasma to initiate urine formation
Proximal convoluted tubule (PCT)	Reabsorption of ions, organic molecules, vitamins, water
Nephron loop	Descending limb: reabsorption of water from tubular fluid
	Ascending limb: reabsorption of ions; creates the concentration gradient in the medulla, enabling the kidney to produce concentrated urine
Distal convoluted tubule (DCT)	Reabsorption of sodium ions; secretion of acids, ammonia, and drugs
Collecting duct	Reabsorption of water and of sodium and bicarbonate ions
Papillary duct	Conduction of urine to minor calyx

4. How does the position of the kidneys differ from that of most other organs in the abdominal region?

5. Why don't plasma proteins pass into the capsular space under normal circumstances?

6. Damage to which part of the nephron would interfere with the hormonal control of blood pressure?

See the blue Answers tab at the back of the book.

18-3 Different portions of the nephron form urine by filtration, reabsorption, and secretion

The primary purpose of **urine** production is to maintain homeostasis by regulating the volume and composition of the blood. This process involves the excretion of dissolved solutes, especially the following three metabolic waste products:

1. *Urea.* Urea is the most abundant organic waste. Your body generates about 21 grams of urea each day, most of it during the breakdown of amino acids.

2. *Creatinine.* Creatinine is generated in skeletal muscle tissue through the breakdown of creatine phosphate, a high-energy compound that plays an important role in muscle contraction. Your body generates roughly 1.8 g of creatinine each day.

3. *Uric acid.* As a product of the breakdown and recycling of RNA, your body generates about 480 mg of uric acid each day.

These waste products must be excreted in solution, and their elimination is accompanied by an unavoidable water loss. The kidneys can minimize this water loss by producing urine that is four to five times more concentrated than normal body fluids. If the kidneys could not concentrate the filtrate produced by glomerular filtration, water losses would lead to fatal dehydration within hours. At the same time, the kidneys ensure that the excreted urine does not contain potentially useful organic substrates present in blood plasma, such as sugars or amino acids.

BASIC PROCESSES OF URINE FORMATION

To accomplish its functions, the kidneys perform three distinct processes:

1. *Filtration.* In filtration, blood pressure forces water across the filtration membrane in the renal corpuscle. Solute molecules small enough to pass through the membrane are carried into the filtrate by the surrounding water molecules.

2. *Reabsorption.* Reabsorption is the removal of water and solute molecules from the filtrate and their reentry into the circulation at the peritubular capillaries. Reabsorption occurs after the filtrate enters the renal tubule. Whereas solute filtration occurs solely on the basis of size, reabsorption of solutes is a selective process involving simple diffusion or the activity of carrier proteins in the tubular epithelium. Water reabsorption occurs passively through osmosis.

3. *Secretion.* Secretion is the transport of solutes from the peritubular capillaries, across the tubular epithelium, and into the filtrate. This process is necessary because filtration does not force all of the dissolved materials out of the blood. Secretion can further lower the plasma concentration of undesirable materials, including many drugs.

Together, these three processes produce a fluid that is very different from other body fluids. Table 18-2 indicates the efficiency of the renal system by comparing the solute compositions of

TABLE 18-2 **Significant Differences in Solute Concentrations Between Urine and Plasma**

COMPONENT	URINE	PLASMA
IONS (meq/L)		
Sodium (Na⁺)	90	140
Potassium (K⁺)	47.5	4.6
Chloride (Cl⁻)	153.3	99
Bicarbonate (HCO₃⁻)	1.9	24.8
METABOLITES AND NUTRIENTS (mg/dL)		
Glucose	0	100
Lipids	0.002	600
Amino acids	100	4.2
Proteins	62	7.5 g/dL
NITROGENOUS WASTES (mg/dL)		
Urea	900	10–20
Creatinine	150	1–1.5
Ammonia	60	< 0.1
Uric acid	40	3

urine and plasma. The kidneys can continue to work efficiently only so long as filtration, reabsorption, and secretion proceed in proper balance. Any disruption in this balance has immediate and potentially disastrous effects on the composition of the circulating blood. If both kidneys fail to perform their assigned roles, death will occur within a few days unless medical assistance is provided.

As we have seen, all segments of the nephron and collecting system participate in the process of urine formation. Most regions perform a combination of reabsorption and secretion, but the balance between these two processes varies from one region to another. As indicated in Table 18-1:

- Filtration occurs exclusively in the renal corpuscle, across the glomerular capillary walls.

- Reabsorption of nutrients occurs primarily at the proximal convoluted tubule.

- Active secretion occurs primarily at the distal convoluted tubule.

- Regulation of the amounts of water, sodium ions, and potassium ions lost in the urine results from interactions between the nephron loop and the collecting system.

Next we will take a closer look at events in each of the segments of the nephron and collecting system.

FILTRATION AT THE GLOMERULUS

Filtration Pressure

The forces acting across capillary walls were introduced in Chapter 13. (You may find it helpful to review Figure 13-7 before you proceed.) ∞ p. 436 Blood pressure at the glomerulus tends to force water and solutes out of the bloodstream and into the capsular space. For filtration to occur, this outward force must exceed any opposing pressures, such as the osmotic pressure of the blood. The net force promoting filtration is called the **filtration pressure.** Filtration pressure at the glomerulus is higher than capillary blood pressure elsewhere in the body because of the slight difference in the diameters of afferent and efferent arterioles (**Figure 18-6a**). The diameter of the efferent arteriole is slightly smaller, so it offers more resistance to blood flow than does the afferent arteriole. As a result, blood "backs up" in the afferent arteriole, increasing the blood pressure in the glomerular capillaries.

Filtration pressure is very low (around 10 mm Hg), and kidney filtration will stop if glomerular blood pressure falls significantly. Reflexive changes in the diameters of the afferent

arterioles, the efferent arterioles, and/or the glomerular capillaries can compensate for minor variations in blood pressure. These changes can occur automatically or in response to sympathetic stimulation. More serious declines in systemic blood pressure can reduce or even stop glomerular filtration. As a result, hemorrhaging, shock, or dehydration can cause a dangerous or even fatal reduction in kidney function. Because the kidneys are more sensitive to blood pressure than are other organs, it is not surprising to find that they control many of the homeostatic mechanisms responsible for regulating blood pressure and blood volume. One example of such a mechanism—the renin-angiotensin system—is considered later in this chapter.

The Glomerular Filtration Rate

The process of filtrate production at the glomerulus is called *glomerular filtration.* The **glomerular filtration rate (GFR)** is the amount of filtrate produced in the kidneys each minute. Because each kidney contains about 6 square meters—some 64 square feet—of filtration surface, the GFR averages an astounding *125 mL per minute.* This means that almost 20 percent of the fluid delivered to the kidneys by the renal arteries leaves the bloodstream and enters the capsular spaces. In the course of a single day, the glomeruli generate about 180 liters (48 gal) of filtrate, roughly 70 times the total plasma volume. But as the filtrate passes through the renal tubules, over 99 percent of it is reabsorbed.

Tubular reabsorption is obviously an extremely important process. An inability to reclaim the water entering the filtrate, as in *diabetes insipidus,* can quickly cause death by dehydration. (This condition, caused by inadequate ADH secretion, was discussed in Chapter 10.) ∞ p. 355

Glomerular filtration is the vital first step essential to all kidney functions. If filtration does not occur, waste products are not excreted, pH control is jeopardized, and an important mechanism for blood volume regulation is eliminated. Filtration depends on the maintenance of adequate blood flow to the glomerulus and of normal filtration pressures. The regulatory factors involved in maintaining a stable GFR are discussed later in the section on the control of kidney function.

The Big Picture

Roughly 180 L (about 48 gal) of filtrate is produced at the glomeruli each day, which represents 70 times the total plasma volume. Almost all of that fluid volume must be reabsorbed to avoid fatal dehydration.

REABSORPTION AND SECRETION ALONG THE RENAL TUBULE

Reabsorption and secretion in the kidney involve a combination of diffusion, osmosis, and carrier-mediated transport. Recall that in carrier-mediated transport, a specific substrate binds to a carrier protein that facilitates its movement across the plasma membrane. ∞ p. 68 This movement may or may not require energy from ATP molecules.

Events at the Proximal Convoluted Tubule

The cells of the PCT actively reabsorb organic nutrients, plasma proteins, and ions from the filtrate and then transport them into the interstitial fluid surrounding the renal tubule. Osmotic forces pull water across the wall of the PCT and into the surrounding interstitial fluid. The reabsorbed materials and water diffuse into peritubular capillaries.

The PCT usually reclaims 60–70 percent of the volume of filtrate produced at the glomerulus, along with virtually all of the glucose, amino acids, and other organic nutrients. The PCT also actively reabsorbs ions, including sodium, potassium, calcium, magnesium, bicarbonate, phosphate, and sulfate ions. The ion pumps involved are individually regulated and may be influenced by circulating ion or hormone levels. For example, the presence of parathyroid hormone stimulates calcium ion reabsorption. ∞ p. 360

Although reabsorption represents the primary function of the PCT, a few substances (such as hydrogen ions) can be actively secreted into the tubular fluid. Such active secretion can play an important role in the regulation of blood pH, a topic considered in a later section. A few compounds in the tubular fluid, including urea and uric acid, are ignored by the PCT and by other segments of the renal tubule. As water and other nutrients are removed, the concentrations of these waste products gradually rise in the tubular fluid.

Events at the Nephron Loop

Roughly 60–70 percent of the volume of the filtrate produced at the glomerulus has been reabsorbed before the tubular fluid reaches the nephron loop. In the process, useful organic molecules and many mineral ions have been reclaimed. The nephron loop reabsorbs more than half of the remaining water, as well as two-thirds of the sodium and chloride ions remaining in the tubular fluid.

The descending and ascending limbs of the nephron loop have different permeability characteristics. Because the descending limb is permeable to water but not to solutes, water can flow in or out by osmosis, but solutes cannot cross the tubular epithelium. The ascending limb is impermeable both to water and to solutes. However, the ascending limb actively pumps sodium and chloride ions out of the tubular fluid and into the surrounding interstitial fluid of the renal medulla. Over time, a *concentration gradient* is created in the medulla; the highest concentration of solutes (roughly four times that of plasma) occurs near the bend in the nephron loop. Because the descending limb is freely permeable to water, water continually flows out of the tubular fluid and into the interstitial fluid by osmosis. From there, the sodium ions, chloride ions, and water diffuse into the peritubular capillaries and vasa recta and back into circulation.

Roughly half the volume of filtrate that enters the nephron loop is reabsorbed in the descending limb, and most of the sodium and chloride ions are removed in the ascending limb. With the loss of the sodium and chloride ions, the solute concentration of the filtrate declines to around one-third that of plasma. However, waste products such as urea now make up a significant percentage of the remaining solutes. In essence, most of the water and solutes have been removed, leaving relatively highly concentrated waste products behind.

Events at the Distal Convoluted Tubule and the Collecting System

By the time the filtrate reaches the distal convoluted tubule, roughly 80 percent of the water and 85 percent of the solutes have already been reabsorbed. The DCT is connected to a collecting duct that drains into the renal pelvis.

As filtrate passes through the DCT and collecting duct, final adjustments are made in its composition and concentration. Its composition depends on the types of solutes present; its concentration depends on the volume of water in which the solutes are dissolved. Because the DCT and collecting duct are impermeable to solutes, changes in filtrate composition can occur only through active reabsorption or secretion. The primary function of the DCT is active secretion.

Throughout most of the DCT, the tubular cells actively transport sodium ions out of the tubular fluid in exchange for potassium ions or hydrogen ions. The DCT and collecting ducts contain ion pumps that respond to the hormone **aldosterone** produced by the suprarenal cortex. Aldosterone secretion occurs in response to lowered sodium ion concentrations or elevated potassium ion concentrations in the blood. The higher the aldosterone levels, the more sodium ions are reclaimed, and the more potassium ions are lost.

The amount of water reabsorbed along the DCT and collecting duct is controlled by circulating levels of *antidiuretic hormone (ADH)*. In the absence of ADH, the distal convoluted tubule and collecting duct are impermeable to water. The higher the level of circulating ADH, the greater the water permeability and the more concentrated the urine. Water moves out of the DCT and collecting duct because in each case the tubular fluid contains fewer solutes than the surrounding interstitial fluid. As previously noted, the fluid arriving at the DCT has a solute concentration only about one-third that of the interstitial fluid in the surrounding cortex because the ascending limb of the nephron loop has removed most of the sodium and chloride ions. The fluid passing along the collecting duct travels into the medulla, where it passes through the concentration gradient established by the nephron loop.

If circulating ADH levels are low, little water reabsorption will occur, and virtually all of the water reaching the DCT will be lost in the urine (**Figure 18-7a**). If circulating ADH levels

The Big Picture

Reabsorption involves a combination of diffusion, osmosis, and active transport. Many of these processes are independently regulated by local or hormonal mechanisms. Water reabsorption occurs because "water follows salt." Secretion is a selective, carrier-mediated process.

are high, the DCT and collecting duct will be very permeable to water (**Figure 18-7b**). In this case, the individual will produce a small quantity of urine with a solute concentration four to five times that of extracellular fluids.

THE PROPERTIES OF NORMAL URINE

The general characteristics of normal urine are listed in Table 18-3. Note, however, that the composition of the 1200 mL of urine excreted each day depends on the metabolic and hormonal

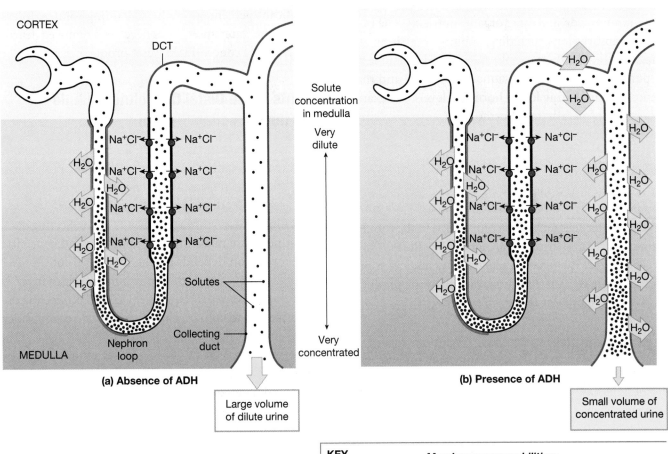

FIGURE 18-7 The Effects of ADH on the DCT and Collecting Duct. These diagrams indicate the permeabilities of the DCT and collecting duct and the resulting urine production **(a)** in the absence of ADH and **(b)** in the presence of ADH.

TABLE 18-3 General Characteristics of Normal Urine

CHARACTERISTIC	NORMAL RANGE
pH	4.5–8 (average: 6.0)
Specific gravity (density of urine/density of pure water)	1.003–1.030
Osmotic concentration (Osmolarity) (number of solute particles per liter; for comparison, fresh water ≈ 5 mOsm/L, body fluids ≈ 300 mOsm/L and sea water ≈1000 mOsm/L)	855–1335 mOsm/L
Water content	93–97%
Volume	700–2000 mL/day
Color	Clear yellow
Odor	Varies with composition
Bacterial content	None (sterile)

events under way. Because the *composition* and *concentration* of the urine vary independently, an individual can produce either a small quantity of concentrated urine or a large quantity of dilute urine and still excrete the same amount of dissolved materials. For this reason, physicians often analyze the urine produced over a 24-hour period rather than testing a single sample. This enables them to assess both quantity and composition accurately.

A SUMMARY OF KIDNEY FUNCTION AND URINE FORMATION

Figure 18-8 provides a functional overview of the major steps involved in the reabsorption of water and the production of concentrated urine.

Step 1 Glomerular filtration produces a filtrate resembling blood plasma but containing few plasma proteins. This filtrate has the same osmotic, or solute, concentration as plasma or interstitial fluid.

Step 2 In the PCT, 60–70 percent of the water and almost all of the dissolved nutrients are reabsorbed. The osmotic concentration of the tubular fluid remains unchanged.

Step 3 In the PCT and descending limb of the nephron loop, water moves into the surrounding interstitial fluid and then into the peritubular capillaries, leaving a small fluid volume (roughly 20 percent of the original filtrate) of highly concentrated tubular fluid.

Step 4 The ascending limb is impermeable to water and solutes. The tubular cells actively pump sodium and

chloride ions out of the tubular fluid. Because only sodium and chloride ions are removed, urea now accounts for a greater proportion of the solutes in the tubular fluid.

Step 5 The final composition and concentration of the tubular fluid are determined by events under way in the DCT and the collecting ducts. These segments are impermeable to solutes, but ions may be actively transported into or out of the filtrate under the control of hormones such as aldosterone.

Step 6 The concentration of urine is controlled by variations in the water permeability of the DCT and the collecting ducts. These segments are impermeable to water unless exposed to antidiuretic hormone (ADH). In the absence of ADH, no water reabsorption occurs, and the individual produces a large volume of dilute urine. At high concentrations of ADH, the collecting ducts become freely permeable to water, and the individual produces a small volume of highly concentrated urine.

Step 7 The vasa recta absorbs solutes and water reabsorbed by the nephron loop and the collecting ducts, thereby maintaining the concentration gradient in the medulla.

CHECKPOINT

7. A decrease in blood pressure would have what effect on the GFR?

8. If nephrons lacked a nephron loop, what would be the effect on the volume and solute (osmotic) concentration of the urine produced?

9. What affect would low circulating levels of antidiuretic hormone (ADH) have on urine production?

See the blue Answers tab at the back of the book.

18-4 Normal kidney function depends on a stable GFR

Normal kidney function depends on adequate blood flow to maintain filtration pressures and a stable glomerular filtration rate (GFR). The GFR is regulated in three ways: (1) by local, automatic adjustments in glomerular pressures; (2) through activities of the sympathetic division of the autonomic nervous system (ANS); and (3) through the effects of various hormones. The hormonal mechanisms result in long-term adjustments in blood pressure and blood volume that stabilize the GFR.

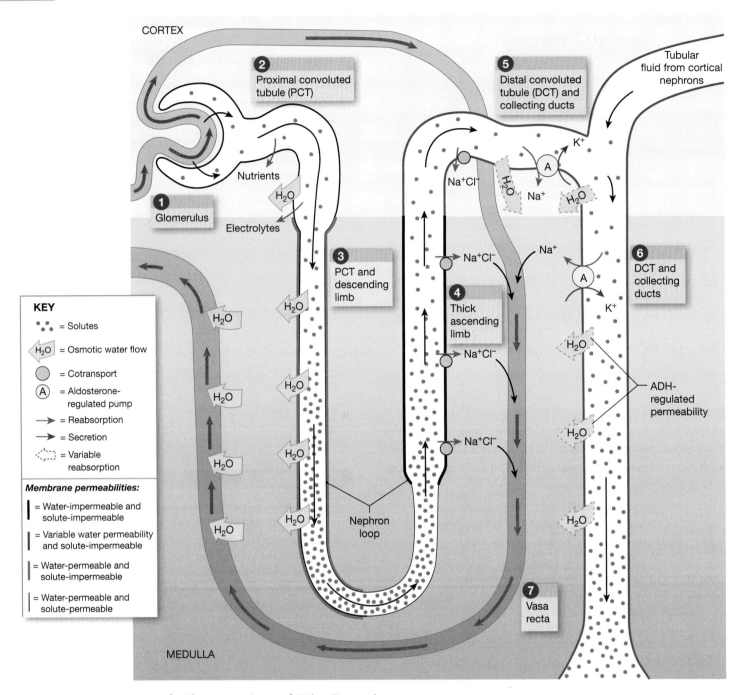

FIGURE 18-8 A Summary of Kidney Function and Urine Formation.

THE LOCAL REGULATION OF KIDNEY FUNCTION

Local, automatic changes in the diameters of afferent arterioles, efferent arterioles, and glomerular capillaries can compensate for minor variations in blood pressure. For example, a reduction in blood flow and a decline in glomerular filtration pressure trigger dilation of the afferent arteriole and glomerular capillaries, and constriction of the efferent arteriole. This combination keeps glomerular blood pressure and blood flow within normal limits. As a result, glomerular filtration rates remain relatively constant. If blood pressure rises, the afferent arteriole walls become stretched, and smooth muscle cells respond by contracting. The resulting reduction in afferent arteriolar diameter decreases glomerular blood flow and keeps the GFR within normal limits.

SYMPATHETIC ACTIVATION AND KIDNEY FUNCTION

Autonomic regulation of kidney function occurs primarily through the sympathetic division of the ANS. Sympathetic activity primarily serves to shift blood flow away from the kidneys, which lowers the glomerular filtration rate. Sympathetic activation has both direct and indirect effects on kidney function. The direct effect of sympathetic activation is a powerful constriction of the afferent arterioles, decreasing the GFR and slowing production of filtrate. Triggered by a sudden crisis, such as an acute reduction in blood pressure or a heart attack, sympathetic activation can override the local regulatory mechanisms that act to stabilize the GFR. As the crisis passes and sympathetic activity decreases, the GFR returns to normal.

When the sympathetic division changes the regional pattern of blood circulation, blood flow to the kidneys is often affected. This change can further reduce the GFR. For example, the dilation of superficial vessels in warm weather shunts blood away from the kidneys, and glomerular filtration declines temporarily. The effect becomes especially pronounced during periods of strenuous exercise. As blood flow increases to the skin and skeletal muscles, it decreases to the kidneys. At maximal levels of exertion, renal blood flow may be less than one-quarter of normal resting levels.

Such a reduction can create problems for distance swimmers and marathon runners, whose glomerular cells may be damaged by low oxygen levels and the buildup of metabolic wastes over the course of a long event. After such events, protein is commonly lost in the urine, and in some cases, blood appears in the urine. Such problems generally disappear within 48 hours, although a small number of runners experience kidney failure (renal failure) and permanent impairment of kidney function.

THE HORMONAL CONTROL OF KIDNEY FUNCTION

The major hormones involved in regulating kidney function are angiotensin II, ADH, aldosterone, and ANP. These hormones have been discussed in earlier chapters, so only a brief overview will be provided here. ∞ p. 441 The secretion of angiotensin II, aldosterone, and ADH is integrated by the *renin-angiotensin system*.

The Renin-Angiotensin System

When glomerular pressures remain low because of a decrease in blood volume, a fall in systemic pressures, or a blockage in the renal artery or its tributaries, the juxtaglomerular complex releases the enzyme renin into the circulation. **Renin** converts inactive *angiotensinogen* to *angiotensin I*, which a *converting enzyme* activates to **angiotensin II.** Figure 18-9 diagrams the primary effects of this potent hormone in regulating GFR.

Angiotensin II has the following effects:

● *In peripheral capillary beds,* it causes a brief but powerful vasoconstriction, elevating blood pressure in the renal arteries.

Clinical Note | The Treatment of Kidney Failure

Kidney failure, or **renal failure,** occurs when the kidneys become unable to perform the excretory functions needed to maintain homeostasis. Renal failure is of two general types. *Acute renal failure* occurs when exposure to toxic drugs, renal ischemia, urinary obstruction, or trauma causes a sudden reduction or stoppage of filtration. In *chronic renal failure,* kidney function deteriorates gradually, and the associated problems accumulate over time. The condition generally cannot be reversed, only prolonged, and symptoms of acute renal failure eventually develop.

Management of chronic kidney failure typically involves restricting dietary protein, water, and salt intake and reducing caloric intake to a minimum. This combination reduces strain on the urinary system by (1) minimizing the volume of urine produced and (2) preventing the generation of large quantities of nitrogenous wastes. Acidosis—blood plasma pH below 7.35—is a common problem in patients with kidney failure; it can be countered with infusions of bicarbonate ions. If drugs, infusions, and dietary controls cannot stabilize the composition of the blood, more drastic measures are taken, such as dialysis or kidney transplantation.

In *dialysis,* the functions of damaged kidneys are performed by a machine that facilitates diffusion between the patient's blood and a *dialysis fluid* whose composition is carefully regulated. The process, which takes several hours, must be repeated two or three times each week.

In a *kidney transplant,* the kidney of a healthy compatible donor is surgically inserted into the patient's body and connected to the recipient's urinary bladder. If the surgical procedure is successful, the transplanted kidney(s) can take over all normal kidney functions.

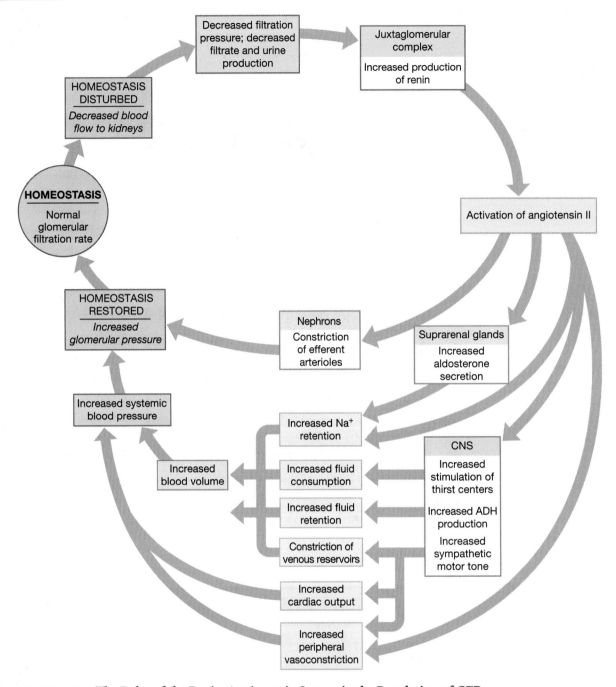

FIGURE 18-9 The Roles of the Renin-Angiotensin System in the Regulation of GFR.

- *At the nephron,* it triggers constriction of the efferent arterioles, elevating glomerular pressures and filtration rates.
- *In the CNS,* it triggers the release of ADH, which in turn stimulates the reabsorption of water and sodium ions and induces the sensation of thirst.

- *At the suprarenal gland,* it stimulates the secretion of aldosterone by the suprarenal cortex and of epinephrine (E) and norepinephrine (NE) by the suprarenal medullae. The result is a sudden, dramatic increase in systemic blood pressure. At the kidneys, aldosterone stimulates sodium reabsorption along the DCT and collecting system.

Antidiuretic Hormone (ADH)

Antidiuretic hormone (1) increases the water permeability of the DCT and collecting duct, stimulating the reabsorption of water from the tubular fluid, and (2) induces the sensation of thirst, leading to the consumption of additional water. ADH release occurs under angiotensin II stimulation; it also occurs independently, when hypothalamic neurons are stimulated by a reduction in blood pressure or an increase in the solute concentration of the circulating blood. The nature of the receptors involved has not been determined, but these specialized hypothalamic neurons are called *osmoreceptors*.

Aldosterone

Aldosterone secretion stimulates the reabsorption of sodium ions and the secretion of potassium ions along the DCT and collecting duct. Aldosterone secretion primarily occurs (1) under angiotensin II stimulation and (2) in response to a rise in the potassium ion concentration of the blood. ∞ p. 361

Atrial Natriuretic Peptide (ANP)

The actions of ANP oppose those of the renin-angiotensin system (see Figure 13-12b, ∞ p. 443). This hormone is released by atrial cardiac muscle cells when blood volume and blood pressure are too high. The actions of ANP that affect the kidneys include (1) a decrease in the rate of sodium ion reabsorption in the DCT, leading to increased sodium ion loss in the urine; (2) dilation of glomerular capillaries, which results in increased glomerular filtration and urinary water loss; and (3) inactivation of the renin-angiotensin system through the inhibition of renin, aldosterone, and ADH secretion. The net result is an accelerated loss of sodium ions and an increase in the volume of urine produced. This combination lowers blood volume and blood pressure.

CHECKPOINT

10. List the factors that affect the glomerular filtration rate (GFR).

11. What is the effect of sympathetic activation on kidney function?

12. What effect would increased amounts of aldosterone have on the K⁺ concentration in urine?

See the blue Answers tab at the back of the book.

18-5 Urine is transported by the ureters, stored in the bladder, and eliminated through the urethra, aided by the micturition reflex

Filtrate modification and urine production end when the fluid enters the renal pelvis. The structures responsible for the transport, storage, and elimination of urine constitute the *urinary tract:* the ureters, urinary bladder, and urethra (Figure 18-10).

THE URETERS

The **ureters** (ū-RĒ-terz) are a pair of muscular tubes that conduct urine from the kidneys to the urinary bladder, a distance of about 30 cm (12 in.) (Figure 18-1). Each ureter begins at the funnel-shaped renal pelvis and ends at the posterior wall of the bladder; the ureters never enter the peritoneal cavity. Their **ureteral openings** within the urinary bladder are slitlike, a shape that prevents the backflow of urine into the ureters or kidneys when the urinary bladder contracts.

The wall of each ureter contains an inner expandable transitional epithelium, a middle layer of longitudinal and circular bands of smooth muscle, and an outer connective tissue layer continuous with the renal capsule. About every 30 seconds, a peristaltic contraction begins at the renal pelvis and sweeps along the ureter, forcing urine toward the urinary bladder.

Occasionally, solids composed of calcium deposits, magnesium salts, or crystals of uric acid form within the kidney, ureters, or urinary bladder. These solids are called *calculi* (KAL-kū-lī), or *kidney stones*, and their presence results in a painful condition known as *nephrolithiasis* (nef-rō-li-THĪ-a-sis). Kidney stones not only obstruct the flow of urine but may also reduce or prevent filtration in the affected kidney.

THE URINARY BLADDER

The **urinary bladder** is a hollow, muscular organ that stores urine prior to urination. Its dimensions vary depending on its state of distension, but a full urinary bladder can contain up to a liter of urine. The urinary bladder lies in the pelvic cavity, and only its superior surface is covered by a layer of peritoneum. It is held in position by peritoneal folds (*umbilical ligaments*) that

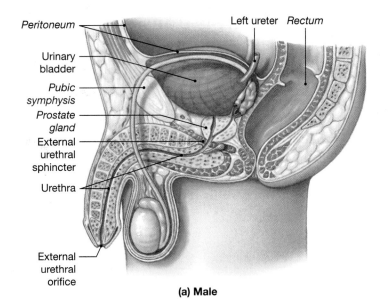

Peritoneum
Left ureter   Rectum
Urinary bladder
Pubic symphysis
Prostate gland
External urethral sphincter
Urethra
External urethral orifice

(a) Male

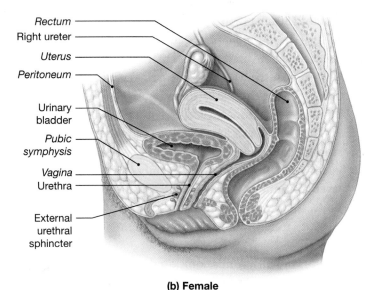

Rectum
Right ureter
Uterus
Peritoneum
Urinary bladder
Pubic symphysis
Vagina
Urethra
External urethral sphincter

(b) Female

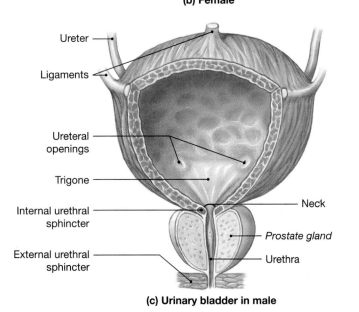

Ureter
Ligaments
Ureteral openings
Trigone
Internal urethral sphincter
External urethral sphincter
Neck
Prostate gland
Urethra

(c) Urinary bladder in male

FIGURE 18-10 Organs for the Conduction and Storage of Urine. The organs of urinary transport and storage are shown in lateral views of **(a)** a male and **(b)** a female. **(c)** The urinary bladder of a male is shown in a frontal view.

extend to the umbilicus (navel), and by bands of connective tissue attached to the pelvic and pubic bones. In males, the base of the urinary bladder lies between the rectum and the pubic symphysis (Figure 18-10a). In females, the urinary bladder sits inferior to the uterus and anterior to the vagina (Figure 18-10b).

The triangular area within the urinary bladder that is bounded by the ureteral openings and the entrance to the urethra forms the *trigone* (TRĪ-gōn) of the bladder (Figure 18-10c). The urethral entrance lies at the apex of this triangle at the lowest point in the bladder. The area surrounding the urethral entrance, called the *neck* of the urinary bladder, contains a muscular **internal urethral sphincter.** The smooth muscle of this sphincter provides involuntary control over the discharge of urine from the bladder.

A *transitional epithelium* continuous with the renal pelvis and the ureters also lines the urinary bladder. This stratified epithelium can tolerate a considerable amount of stretching, as indicated in Figure 4-5c. ∞ p. 100 The middle layer of the bladder wall consists of inner and outer layers of longitudinal smooth muscle with a circular layer in between. These three layers of smooth muscle form the powerful *detrusor* (de-TROO-sor) *muscle* of the bladder. Contraction of this muscle compresses the urinary bladder and expels its contents into the urethra.

THE URETHRA

The urethra extends from the neck of the urinary bladder to the exterior of the body. In males, the urethra extends from the neck of the urinary bladder to the external opening, or **external urethral orifice**, at the tip of the penis, a distance of about 18–20 cm (7–8 in.). In females, the **urethra** is very short, extending 2.5–3.0 cm (about 1 in.) from the bladder to the external urethral orifice in the vestibule anterior to the vagina. In both sexes, as the urethra passes through the muscular floor of the pelvic cavity, a circular band of skeletal muscle forms the **external urethral sphincter** (Figure 18-10). This sphincter consists of skeletal muscle fibers, and its contractions are under voluntary control.

Clinical Note

Urinary Tract Infections

Urinary tract infections (UTIs) result from the colonization of the urinary tract by bacteria or yeasts (fungi). The intestinal bacterium *Escherichia coli* is most commonly involved. Women are particularly susceptible to UTIs because the external urethral orifice is so close to the anus. Sexual intercourse can push bacteria into the urethra; because the urethra is relatively short in females, the urinary bladder can also become infected.

The condition may produce no symptoms, but it can be detected by the presence of bacteria and blood cells in urine. If inflammation of the urethral wall occurs, the condition is termed *urethritis;* inflammation of the lining of the bladder is called *cystitis.* Many infections, including sexually transmitted diseases (STDs) such as *gonorrhea,* cause a combination of urethritis and cystitis. These conditions cause painful urination, a symptom known as *dysuria* (dis-Ū-rē-uh), and the urinary bladder becomes tender and sensitive to pressure. Despite the discomfort that urination produces, the individual feels the urge to urinate frequently. UTIs generally respond to antibiotic therapies, although reinfections can occur.

In untreated cases, the bacteria may proceed along the ureters to the renal pelvis. The resulting inflammation of the walls of the renal pelvis produces *pyelitis* (pī-e-LĪ-tis). If the bacteria invade the renal cortex and medulla as well, *pyelonephritis* (pī-e-lō-nef-RĪ-tis) results. Signs and symptoms of pyelonephritis include a high fever, intense pain on the affected side, vomiting, diarrhea, and the presence of blood cells and pus in the urine.

THE MICTURITION REFLEX AND URINATION

Peristaltic contractions of the ureters move the urine into the urinary bladder. The process of urination, or micturition, is coordinated by the **micturition reflex** (Figure 18-11). Stretch receptors in the wall of the urinary bladder are stimulated as the bladder fills with urine. Afferent sensory fibers in the pelvic nerves carry the resulting impulses to the sacral spinal cord. The increased level of activity in the fibers (1) brings parasympathetic motor neurons in the sacral spinal cord close to threshold and (2) stimulates interneurons that relay sensations to the cerebral cortex. As a result, we become consciously aware of the fluid pressure within the urinary bladder.

The urge to urinate usually occurs when the bladder contains about 200 mL of urine. The micturition reflex begins to function when the stretch receptors have provided adequate stimulation to the parasympathetic motor neurons. At this time, the motor neurons stimulate the detrusor muscle in the bladder wall. These commands travel over the pelvic nerves and produce a sustained contraction of the urinary bladder.

This contraction elevates fluid pressures inside the bladder, but urine ejection cannot occur unless both the internal and external sphincters are relaxed. The relaxation of the external sphincter occurs under voluntary control. Once the external sphincter relaxes, so does the internal sphincter. If the external sphincter does not relax, the internal sphincter remains closed, and the bladder gradually relaxes. A further increase in bladder volume begins the cycle again, usually within an hour. Each increase in urinary volume leads to an increase in stretch receptor stimulation that makes the sensation more

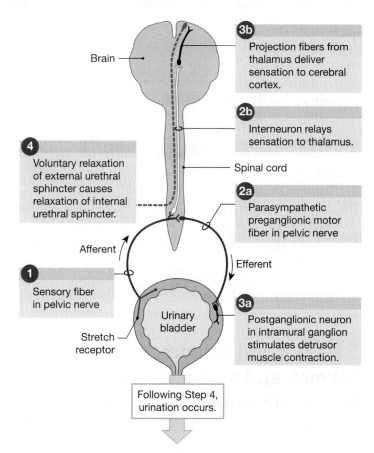

FIGURE 18-11 The Micturition Reflex. This diagram illustrates the components of the reflex arc that stimulates smooth muscle contractions in the urinary bladder. Micturition occurs after voluntary relaxation of the external urethral sphincter.

acute. Once the volume of the urinary bladder exceeds 500 mL, the micturition reflex may generate enough pressure to force open the internal sphincter. A reflexive relaxation of the external sphincter follows, and urination occurs despite voluntary

Clinical Note

Incontinence

Incontinence (in-KON-ti-nens) is the inability to control urination voluntarily. Infants lack voluntary control over urination because the necessary corticospinal connections have yet to be established. Accordingly, "toilet training" before age 2 often involves training the parent to anticipate the timing of the micturition reflex rather than training the child to exert conscious control.

Trauma to the internal or external urethral sphincter can contribute to incontinence in otherwise normal adults. Some new mothers, for example, develop *stress incontinence* after childbirth has stretched and damaged the sphincter muscles. In this condition, elevated intra-abdominal pressures, caused simply by a cough or sneeze, can overwhelm the sphincter muscles, causing urine to leak out. Incontinence may also develop in older individuals because of a general loss of muscle tone.

Damage to the CNS, the spinal cord, or the nerve supply to the bladder or external sphincter may also produce incontinence. For example, incontinence often accompanies Alzheimer disease or spinal cord injury. In most cases, the affected individual develops an *automatic bladder*. The micturition reflex remains intact, but voluntary control of the external sphincter is lost, and the person cannot prevent the reflexive emptying of the bladder. Damage to the pelvic nerves can eliminate the micturition reflex entirely because these nerves carry both afferent and efferent fibers controlling this reflex. The urinary bladder becomes greatly distended with urine and remains filled to capacity while excess urine flows into the urethra in an uncontrolled stream. The insertion of a catheter is commonly required to facilitate the discharge of urine.

---

opposition or potential inconvenience. At the end of normal micturition, less than 10 mL of urine remains in the bladder.

CHECKPOINT

13. What is responsible for the movement of urine from the kidneys to the urinary bladder?

14. An obstruction of a ureter by a kidney stone would interfere with the flow of urine between what two structures?

15. Control of the micturition reflex depends on the ability to control which muscle?

See the blue Answers tab at the back of the book.

18-6 Fluid balance, electrolyte balance, and acid-base balance are interrelated and essential to homeostasis

This section provides an overview that integrates earlier discussions involving fluid, electrolyte, and acid-base balance in the body. Few other topics have such wide-ranging clinical importance: *Treatment of any serious illness affecting the nervous, cardiovascular, respiratory, urinary, or digestive system must always include steps to restore normal fluid, electrolyte, and acid-base balance.*

Most of your body weight is water. Water accounts for up to 99 percent of the volume of the fluid outside cells, and it is an essential ingredient of cytoplasm. All of a cell's operations rely on water as a diffusion medium for the distribution of gases, nutrients, and waste products. If the water content of the body declines too far, cellular activities are jeopardized: Proteins denature, enzymes cease functioning, and cells ultimately die. To survive, the body must maintain a normal volume and composition in both the **extracellular fluid** or **ECF** (the interstitial fluid, plasma, and other body fluids) and the **intracellular fluid** or **ICF** (the cytosol).

The concentrations of various ions and the pH of the body's water are as important as their absolute quantities. If concentrations of calcium or potassium ions in the ECF become too high, cardiac arrhythmias develop, placing the individual's life in jeopardy. A pH outside the normal range can lead to a variety of dangerous conditions. Low pH is especially dangerous because hydrogen ions break chemical bonds, change the shapes of complex molecules, disrupt cell membranes, and impair tissue functions.

In this section we consider the dynamics of exchange between the various body fluids, such as blood plasma and interstitial fluid, and between the body and the external environment. Homeostasis of fluid volumes, solute concentrations, and pH involves three interrelated factors:

- *Fluid balance.* You are in **fluid balance** when the amount of water you gain each day is equal to the amount you lose to the environment. Maintaining normal fluid balance involves regulating the content and distribution of water in the ECF and ICF. Because your cells and tissues cannot transport water, fluid balance primarily reflects the creation of ion concentration gradients that are then eliminated by osmosis.

- *Electrolyte balance.* **Electrolytes** are ions released through the dissociation of inorganic compounds; they are so named because when in solution they can conduct an electrical current. ∞ p. 40 Each day, your body fluids gain electrolytes from the food and drink you consume, and they lose electrolytes in urine, sweat, and feces. **Electrolyte balance** exists when there is neither a net gain nor a net loss of any ion in body fluids. Electrolyte balance primarily involves balancing the rates of absorption across the digestive tract with rates of loss at the kidneys.

- *Acid-base balance.* You are in **acid-base balance** when the production of hydrogen ions is equal to their loss. When acid-base balance exists, the pH of body fluids remains within normal limits. Preventing a reduction in pH is a primary problem because normal metabolic operations generate a variety of acids. The kidneys and lungs play key roles in maintaining the acid-base balance of body fluids.

THE ECF AND THE ICF

Water accounts for roughly 60 percent of the total body weight of an adult male, and for 50 percent of that of an adult female. This sex-related difference primarily reflects the relatively larger mass of adipose tissue in adult females and the greater average muscle mass in adult males. (Adipose tissue is 10 percent water, whereas skeletal muscle is 75 percent water.) In both sexes, intracellular fluid contains more of the total body water than does extracellular fluid.

Figure 18-12 illustrates the distribution of water in the body. Nearly two-thirds of the total body water content is found inside living cells, as the intracellular fluid or ICF (the cytosol), ∞ p. 72 The extracellular fluid or ECF contains the rest of the body's water. The largest subdivisions of the ECF are the interstitial fluid in peripheral tissues, the plasma of the circulating blood, and water in the ground substance of bone and dense connective tissue. Minor components of the ECF include lymph, cerebrospinal fluid (CSF), synovial fluid, serous fluids (pleural, pericardial, and peritoneal fluids), aqueous humor, and the fluids of the inner ear (perilymph and endolymph). Exchange between the ICF and ECF occurs across plasma membranes by osmosis, diffusion, and carrier-mediated processes (see Table 3-3, p. 72).

Exchange among the subdivisions of the ECF occurs primarily across the endothelial lining of capillaries. Fluid may also travel from the interstitial spaces to the plasma through

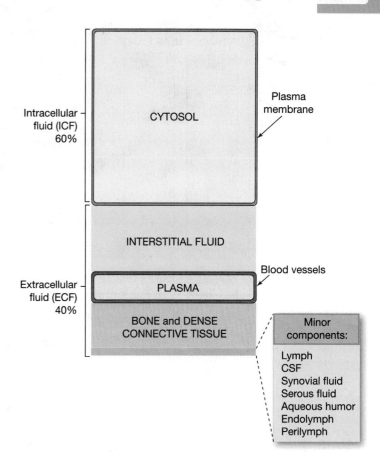

FIGURE 18-12 Body Fluid Compartments The rectangles in this diagram represent the major body fluid compartments (and their relative proportions) in a healthy adult.

lymphatic vessels that drain into the venous system. The kinds and amounts of dissolved electrolytes, proteins, nutrients, and waste products within each ECF subdivision or component are not the same. However, these variations are relatively minor compared with the major differences *between* the ECF and the ICF.

The ICF and ECF are called **fluid compartments** because they commonly behave as distinct entities. As noted in earlier chapters, the principal ions in the ECF are sodium, chloride, and bicarbonate. The ICF contains an abundance of potassium, magnesium, and phosphate ions, plus large numbers of negatively charged proteins. Figure 18-13 compares the ions in the ICF with those in plasma and interstitial fluid, the two main subdivisions of the ECF.

Despite these differences in the concentrations of specific substances, the osmotic concentrations of the ICF and ECF are identical. Osmosis eliminates minor differences in concentration almost at once because most plasma membranes are freely permeable to water. Because changes in solute concentrations lead to immediate changes in water distribution, the regulation of water balance and electrolyte balance is tightly intertwined.

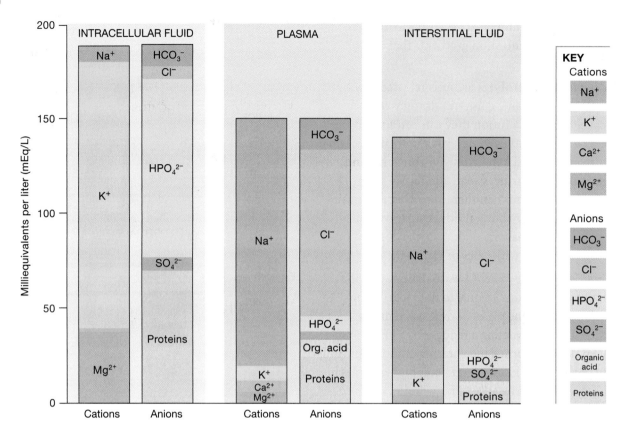

FIGURE 18-13 **Ions in Body Fluids** Note the differences in the ion concentrations between the plasma and interstitial fluid of the ECF and those in the ICF. For information concerning the chemical composition of other body fluids, see Appendix.

CHECKPOINT

16. Identify the three interrelated processes essential to stabilizing body fluid volumes.

17. List the major component(s) of the intracellular fluid (ICF) and the extracellular fluid (ECF).

See the blue Answers tab at the back of the book.

18-7 Blood pressure and osmosis are involved in maintaining fluid and electrolyte balance

FLUID BALANCE

Water circulates freely within the ECF compartment. At capillary beds throughout the body, capillary blood pressure forces water out of the plasma and into the interstitial spaces. Some of that water is reabsorbed due to higher blood osmotic pressure along the distal portion of the capillary bed, and the rest circulates into lymphatic vessels for transport to the venous circulation (see Figure 13-7, p. 436).

Water also moves back and forth across the epithelial surfaces lining the peritoneal, pleural, and pericardial cavities and through the synovial membranes lining joint capsules. The flow rate is significant; for example, roughly 7 liters (1.8 gal) of peritoneal fluid is produced and reabsorbed each day. Small volumes of water move between the blood and the cerebrospinal fluid, the aqueous and vitreous humors of the eye, and the perilymph and endolymph of the inner ear.

Roughly 2500 mL of water is lost each day in urine, feces, and perspiration (Table 18-4). The water lost in perspiration varies with the level of activity; in vigorously exercising individuals, the additional losses can be considerable, reaching well over 4 liters an hour. p. 131 Water losses are normally balanced by the gain of fluids through eating (40 percent), drinking (48 percent), and metabolic generation (12 percent). *Metabolic generation* of water occurs primarily as a result of mitochondrial ATP production. p. 591

FLUID SHIFTS

Water movement between the ECF and ICF is called a **fluid shift.** Fluid shifts occur relatively rapidly, reaching equilibrium

TABLE 18-4 **Water Balance**

SOURCE	DAILY INPUT (mL)
Water content of food	1000
Water consumed as liquid	1200
Metabolic water produced during catabolism	300
Total	2500

METHOD OF ELIMINATION	DAILY OUTPUT (ML)
Urination	1200
Evaporation at skin	750
Evaporation at lungs	400
Loss in feces	150
Total	2500

within a period of minutes to hours. These shifts occur in response to changes in the osmotic concentration, or *osmolarity*, of the extracellular fluid.

- If the ECF becomes more concentrated (hypertonic) with respect to the ICF, water will move from the cells into the ECF until equilibrium is restored.
- If the ECF becomes more dilute (hypotonic) with respect to the ICF, water will move from the ECF into the cells, and the volume of the ICF will increase accordingly.

In summary, if the osmolarity of the ECF changes, a fluid shift between the ICF and ECF will tend to oppose the change. Because the volume of the ICF is much greater than that of the ECF, the ICF acts as a "water reserve." In effect, instead of a large change in the osmotic concentration of the ECF, smaller changes occur in both the ECF and the ICF.

ELECTROLYTE BALANCE

As previously noted, you are in electrolyte balance when the rates of gain and loss are equal for each electrolyte in your body. Electrolyte balance is important because:

- *A gain or loss of electrolytes can cause a gain or loss in water.*
- *The concentrations of individual electrolytes affect a variety of cell functions.* Many examples of the effects of ions on cell function were described in earlier chapters. For example, the effects of high or low calcium and potassium ion concentrations on cardiac muscle tissue were noted in Chapter 12. ∞ p. 423

Two cations, Na^+ and K^+, deserve attention because (1) they are major contributors to the osmotic concentrations of the ECF and ICF, and (2) they directly affect the normal functioning of all cells. Sodium is the dominant cation within the extracellular fluid. More than 90 percent of the osmotic concentration of the ECF results from the presence of sodium salts—principally, sodium chloride (NaCl) and sodium bicarbonate ($NaHCO_3$)—so changes in the osmotic concentration of extracellular fluids usually reflect changes in the concentration of sodium ions. Potassium is the dominant cation in the intracellular fluid; extracellular potassium concentrations are normally low. In general:

- *The most common problems involving electrolyte balance are caused by an imbalance between sodium gains and losses.*
- *Problems with potassium balance are less common but significantly more dangerous than those related to sodium balance.*

Sodium Balance

The amount of sodium in the ECF represents a balance between sodium ion absorption at the digestive tract and sodium ion excretion at the kidneys and other sites. The rate of uptake varies directly with the amount included in the diet. Sodium losses occur primarily by excretion in urine and through perspiration. The kidneys are the most important sites for regulating sodium ion losses. In response to circulating aldosterone, the kidneys reabsorb sodium ions (which decreases sodium loss), and in response to atrial natriuretic peptide, the kidneys increase the loss of sodium ions. ∞ p. 617

Whenever the rate of sodium intake or output changes, a corresponding gain or loss of water tends to keep the Na^+ concentration constant. For example, eating a heavily salted meal will not raise the sodium ion concentration of body fluids because as sodium chloride crosses the digestive epithelium, osmosis brings additional water into the ECF. This is why individuals with high blood pressure are told to restrict their salt intake; dietary salt is absorbed, and because "water follows salt," blood volume—and, thus, blood pressure—increases.

Potassium Balance

Roughly 98 percent of the potassium content of the body lies within the ICF. Cells expend energy to recover potassium ions as the ions diffuse out of the cytoplasm and into the ECF. The K^+ concentration of the ECF is relatively low and represents a balance between (1) the rate of gain across the digestive epithelium and (2) the rate of loss in urine. The rate of gain is proportional

The Big Picture

Fluid balance and electrolyte balance are interrelated. Small water gains or losses affect electrolyte concentrations only temporarily. The impacts are reduced by fluid shifts between the ECF and ICF, and by hormonal responses that adjust the rates of water intake and excretion. Similarly, electrolyte gains or losses produce only temporary changes in solute concentration. These changes are opposed by fluid shifts, adjustments in the rates of ion absorption and secretion, and adjustments to the rates of water gain and loss.

to the amount of potassium in the diet. The rate of loss is strongly affected by aldosterone. Urinary potassium losses are controlled through adjustments in the rate of active secretion along the distal convoluted tubules of the kidneys. The ion pumps sensitive to aldosterone reabsorb sodium ions from the filtrate in exchange for potassium ions from the interstitial fluid. High plasma concentrations of potassium ions also stimulate aldosterone secretion directly. When potassium levels rise in the ECF, aldosterone levels climb, and additional potassium ions are lost in the urine. When potassium levels fall in the ECF, aldosterone levels decline, and potassium ions are conserved.

CHECKPOINT

18. Define a fluid shift.

19. How would eating a meal high in salt content affect the amount of fluid in the intracellular fluid compartment (ICF)?

20. What effect would being in the desert without water for a day have on your blood osmotic concentration?

See the blue Answers tab at the back of the book.

18-8 In acid-base balance, buffer systems and respiratory and renal compensation mechanisms regulate hydrogen ions in body fluids

The pH of your body fluids represents a balance among the acids, bases, and salts in solution. The pH of the ECF normally remains within relatively narrow limits, usually 7.35–7.45. Any deviation from the normal range is extremely dangerous because changes in hydrogen ion concentrations disrupt the stability of cell membranes, alter protein structure, and change the activities of important enzymes. You could not survive for long with a pH below 6.8 or above 7.7.

When the pH of blood falls below 7.35, the physiological state called **acidosis** exists. **Alkalosis** exists if the pH exceeds 7.45. These conditions affect virtually all systems, but the nervous and cardiovascular systems are particularly sensitive to pH fluctuations. Severe acidosis (pH below 7.0) can be deadly because (1) CNS function deteriorates, and the individual becomes comatose; (2) cardiac contractions grow weak and irregular, and signs of heart failure develop; and (3) peripheral vasodilation produces a dramatic drop in blood pressure, and circulatory collapse can occur.

Acidosis and alkalosis are both dangerous, but in practice, problems with acidosis are much more common because several acids (including carbonic acid) are generated by normal cellular activities.

ACIDS IN THE BODY

Carbonic acid (H_2CO_3) is an important acid in body fluids. At the lungs, carbonic acid breaks down into carbon dioxide and water; the carbon dioxide diffuses into the alveoli. In peripheral tissues, carbon dioxide in solution interacts with water to form carbonic acid. As noted in Chapter 15, the carbonic acid molecules then dissociate to produce hydrogen ions and bicarbonate ions. p. 521 The complete reaction sequence is

$$\underset{\text{carbon dioxide}}{CO_2} + \underset{\text{water}}{H_2O} \rightleftharpoons \underset{\text{carbonic acid}}{H_2CO_3} \rightleftharpoons \underset{\text{hydrogen ion}}{H^+} + \underset{\text{bicarbonate ion}}{HCO_3^-}$$

This reaction occurs spontaneously in body fluids, but it occurs very rapidly in the presence of *carbonic anhydrase,* an enzyme found in many cell types, including red blood cells, liver and kidney cells, and parietal cells of the stomach.

Because most of the carbon dioxide in solution is converted to carbonic acid, and most of the carbonic acid dissociates, the partial pressure of carbon dioxide (P_{CO_2}) and pH are inversely related (Figure 18-14). When carbon dioxide concentrations rise, additional hydrogen ions and bicarbonate ions are released, and pH goes down. (Recall that the greater the concentration of hydrogen ions, the lower the pH value.) The P_{CO_2} is the most important factor affecting pH in body tissues.

At the alveoli, carbon dioxide diffuses into the atmosphere, the number of hydrogen ions and bicarbonate ions drops, and the pH rises. This process, which effectively removes hydrogen ions from solution, will be considered in more detail in the next section.

Organic acids, or metabolic acids, are generated during normal metabolism. Some are generated during the catabolism of amino acids, carbohydrates, or lipids. Examples are lactic acid produced during anaerobic metabolism of pyruvic acid, and ke-

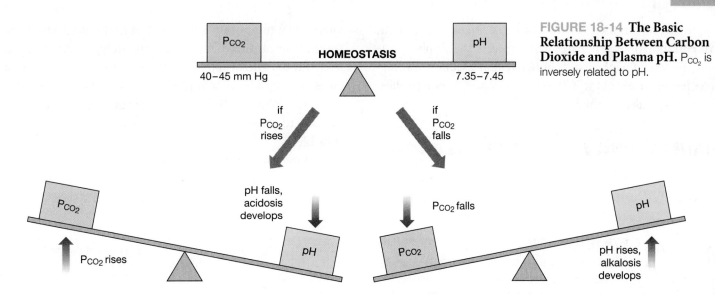

FIGURE 18-14 **The Basic Relationship Between Carbon Dioxide and Plasma pH.** P_{CO_2} is inversely related to pH.

tone bodies produced in the breakdown of fatty acids. Under normal conditions, metabolic acids are recycled or excreted rapidly, and significant accumulations do not occur.

BUFFERS AND BUFFER SYSTEMS

The acids produced in the course of normal metabolic operations are temporarily neutralized by buffers and buffer systems in body fluids. *Buffers,* introduced in Chapter 2, are dissolved compounds that can provide or remove hydrogen ions (H^+), thereby stabilizing the pH of a solution. ∞ p. 41 Buffers include *weak acids* that can donate H^+, and *weak bases* that can absorb H^+. A **buffer system** consists of a combination of a weak acid and its dissociation products: a hydrogen ion and an anion. The body has three major buffer systems, each with slightly different characteristics and distributions: *protein buffer systems,* the *carbonic acid–bicarbonate buffer system,* and the *phosphate buffer system.*

Protein buffer systems contribute to the regulation of pH in the ECF and ICF. Protein buffer systems depend on amino acid side groups of proteins and the side group and structural groups of free amino acids to respond to changes in pH by accepting or releasing hydrogen ions. If pH climbs, the carboxyl group (—COOH) of the amino acid can dissociate, releasing a hydrogen ion. If pH drops, the amino group (—NH_2) can accept an additional hydrogen ion, forming an amino ion (—NH_3^+).

The plasma proteins and hemoglobin in red blood cells contribute to the buffering capabilities of the blood. Interstitial fluids contain extracellular protein fibers and dissolved amino acids that also help regulate pH. In the ICF of active cells, structural and other proteins provide an extensive buffering capability that prevents destructive pH changes when organic acids, such as lactic acid, are produced by cellular metabolism.

The **carbonic acid–bicarbonate buffer system** is an important buffer system in the ECF. With the exception of red blood cells, your cells generate carbon dioxide 24 hours a day. As noted earlier, most of the carbon dioxide is converted to carbonic acid, which then dissociates into a hydrogen ion and a bicarbonate ion. The carbonic acid and its dissociation products constitute the carbonic acid–bicarbonate buffer system; the carbonic acid acts as a weak acid, and the bicarbonate ion acts as a weak base. The net effect of this buffer system is that $CO_2 + H_2O \rightleftharpoons H^+ + HCO_3^-$. If hydrogen ions are removed, they will be replaced through the combining of water with carbon dioxide; if hydrogen ions are added, most will be removed through the formation of carbon dioxide and water.

The primary role of the carbonic acid–bicarbonate buffer system is to prevent pH changes caused by organic (metabolic) acids. The hydrogen ions released through the dissociation of these acids combine with bicarbonate ions, producing water and carbon dioxide. The carbon dioxide can then be excreted at the lungs. This buffering system can cope with large amounts of acid because body fluids contain an abundance of bicarbonate ions, known as the *bicarbonate reserve.* When hydrogen ions enter the ECF, the bicarbonate ions that combine with them are replaced by the bicarbonate reserve.

The **phosphate buffer system** consists of an anion, *dihydrogen phosphate* ($H_2PO_4^-$), which is a weak acid. The dihydrogen phosphate ion and its dissociation products constitute the phosphate buffer system:

$$\underset{\text{dihydrogen phosphate}}{H_2PO_4^-} \rightleftharpoons \underset{\text{hydrogen ion}}{H^+} + \underset{\text{monohydrogen phosphate}}{HPO_4^{2-}}$$

In solution, dihydrogen phosphate ($H_2PO_4^-$) reversibly dissociates into a hydrogen ion and monohydrogen phosphate (HPO_4^{2-}). In the ECF, the phosphate buffer system plays only a supporting role in the regulation of pH, primarily because the concentration of bicarbonate ions far exceeds that of phosphate ions. However, the phosphate buffer system is quite important in buffering the pH of the ICF, where the concentration of phosphate ions is relatively high.

MAINTAINING ACID-BASE BALANCE

Buffer systems can tie up excess hydrogen ions (H^+), but because the H^+ have not been eliminated, buffer systems pro-

vide only a temporary solution. For homeostasis to be preserved, the captured H^+ must ultimately be removed from body fluids. The problem is that the supply of buffer molecules is limited; once a buffer binds a H^+, it cannot bind any more H^+. With the buffer molecules tied up, the capacity of the ECF to absorb more H^+ is reduced, and pH control is impossible.

The maintenance of acid-base balance involves balancing hydrogen ion losses and gains. In this "balancing act," respiratory and renal mechanisms support the buffer systems by (1) se-

Clinical Note — Disturbances of Acid-Base Balance

The terms used to describe disturbances of acid-base balance usually indicate the primary source of the disturbance. *Respiratory acid-base disorders* result from a mismatch between carbon dioxide generation in peripheral tissues and carbon dioxide excretion at the lungs. When a respiratory acid-base disorder is present, the carbon dioxide level of the ECF is abnormal. *Metabolic acid-base disorders* are caused by the generation of organic acids or by conditions affecting the concentration of bicarbonate ions in the ECF.

Respiratory compensation alone can often restore normal acid-base balance in individuals suffering from respiratory disorders. In contrast, compensation mechanisms for metabolic disorders may be able to stabilize pH, but other aspects of acid-base balance (buffer system function, bicarbonate levels, and P_{CO_2}) remain abnormal until the underlying metabolic problem is corrected.

Respiratory Acidosis

Respiratory acidosis develops when the respiratory system is unable to eliminate all of the CO_2 generated by peripheral tissues. The primary indication is low plasma pH due to *hypercapnia,* an elevated plasma P_{CO_2}. As carbon dioxide levels climb, hydrogen and bicarbonate ion concentrations rise as well. Other buffer systems can tie up some of the hydrogen ions, but once the combined buffering capacity has been exceeded, pH begins to fall rapidly.

Respiratory acidosis represents the most frequent challenge to acid-base balance. The usual cause is *hypoventilation,* an abnormally low respiratory rate. Because tissues generate carbon dioxide at a rapid rate, even a few minutes of hypoventilation can cause acidosis, reducing the pH of the ECF to as low as 7.0. Under normal circumstances, chemoreceptors monitoring the P_{CO_2} of the plasma and CSF will eliminate the problem by stimulating increases in breathing rate.

Respiratory Alkalosis

Problems with **respiratory alkalosis** are relatively uncommon. This condition develops when respiratory activity reduces plasma P_{CO_2} to below-normal levels, a condition called *hypocapnia.* Temporary hypocapnia can be produced by

hyperventilation, when increased respiratory activity leads to a reduction in arterial P_{CO_2}. Continued hyperventilation can elevate pH to levels as high as 8. This condition usually corrects itself, for the reduction in P_{CO_2} removes the stimulation for the chemoreceptors, and the urge to breathe fades until carbon dioxide levels have returned to normal. Respiratory alkalosis caused by hyperventilation seldom persists long enough to cause a clinical emergency.

Metabolic Acidosis

Metabolic acidosis is the second most common type of acid-base imbalance. The most frequent cause is the production of large quantities of metabolic acids such as lactic acid or ketone bodies. Metabolic acidosis can also be caused by an impaired ability to excrete hydrogen ions at the kidneys, and any condition accompanied by severe kidney damage can result in metabolic acidosis. Compensation for metabolic acidosis usually involves a combination of respiratory and renal mechanisms. Hydrogen ions interacting with bicarbonate ions form carbon dioxide molecules that are eliminated at the lungs, while the kidneys excrete additional hydrogen ions into the urine and generate bicarbonate ions that are released into the ECF.

Metabolic Alkalosis

Metabolic alkalosis occurs when bicarbonate ion concentrations become elevated. The bicarbonate ions then interact with hydrogen ions in solution, forming carbonic acid; the reduction in H^+ concentrations produces alkalosis. Cases of severe metabolic alkalosis are relatively rare. A temporary metabolic alkalosis occurs during meals, when large numbers of bicarbonate ions are released into the ECF during the secretion of HCl by the parietal cells of the stomach. (Hydrogen ions and bicarbonate ions are formed from CO_2 and H_2O within the parietal cells, and the bicarbonate ions are released into the blood in exchange for chloride ions.) Serious metabolic alkalosis may result from bouts of repeated vomiting, because the stomach continues to generate stomach acids to replace those that are lost. As a result, the HCO_3^- concentration of the ECF continues to rise. Compensation for metabolic alkalosis involves a reduction in pulmonary ventilation, coupled with the increased loss of bicarbonates in the urine.

creting or absorbing hydrogen ions; (2) controlling the excretion of acids and bases; and (3) generating additional buffers. It is the *combination* of buffer systems and these respiratory and renal mechanisms that maintain body pH within narrow limits.

Respiratory Contributions to pH Regulation

Respiratory compensation is a change in the respiratory rate that helps stabilize the pH of the ECF. Respiratory compensation occurs whenever pH exceeds normal limits. Respiratory activity has a direct effect on the carbonic acid–bicarbonate buffer system. Increasing or decreasing the rate of respiration alters pH by lowering or raising the partial pressure of CO_2 (P_{CO_2}). Changes in P_{CO_2} have a direct effect on the concentration of hydrogen ions in the plasma. When the P_{CO_2} rises, the pH declines, and when the P_{CO_2} decreases, the pH increases (Figure 18-14).

Mechanisms responsible for controlling the respiratory rate were discussed in Chapter 15, p. 523 and only a brief summary will be presented here. A rise in P_{CO_2} stimulates chemoreceptors in the carotid and aortic bodies and within the CNS; a fall in P_{CO_2} inhibits them. Stimulation of the chemoreceptors leads to an increase in the respiratory rate. As the rate of respiration increases, more CO_2 is lost at the lungs, so the P_{CO_2} returns to normal levels. When the P_{CO_2} of the blood or CSF declines, respiratory activity becomes depressed, the breathing rate falls, and the P_{CO_2} in the extracellular fluids rises.

Renal Contributions to pH Regulation

Renal compensation is a change in the rates of hydrogen ion and bicarbonate ion secretion or absorption by the kidneys in response to changes in plasma pH. Under normal conditions, the body generates H^+ through the production of metabolic acids. The H^+ these acids release must be excreted in the urine to maintain acid-base balance. Glomerular filtration puts hydrogen ions, carbon dioxide, and the other components of the carbonic acid–bicarbonate and phosphate buffer systems into the filtrate. The kidney tubules then modify the pH of the filtrate by secreting hydrogen ions or reabsorbing bicarbonate ions.

ACID-BASE DISORDERS

Together, buffer systems, respiratory compensation, and renal compensation maintain normal acid-base balance. These mechanisms are usually able to control pH very precisely, so that the pH of extracellular fluids seldom varies more than 0.1 pH units, from 7.35 to 7.45. When buffering mechanisms are severely stressed, however, pH wanders outside these limits, producing symptoms of alkalosis or acidosis.

Respiratory acid-base disorders result when abnormal respiratory function causes an extreme rise or fall in CO_2 levels in the ECF. Metabolic acid-base disorders result from the generation of organic acids or by conditions affecting the concentration of bicarbonate ions in the ECF. Table 18-5 summarizes the general causes and treatments of acid-base disorders.

The Big Picture

The most common and acute acid-base disorder is respiratory acidosis, which develops when respiratory activity cannot keep pace with the rate of carbon dioxide generation in peripheral tissues.

TABLE 18-5 Acid-Base Disorders

DISORDER	PH (NORMAL = 7.35–7.45)	GENERAL CAUSES	TREATMENT
Respiratory acidosis	Decreased (below 7.35)	Generally caused by hypoventilation and CO_2 buildup in tissues and blood	Improve ventilation—in some cases, with bronchodilation and mechanical assistance
Metabolic acidosis	Decreased (below 7.35)	Caused by buildup of metabolic acid, impaired H^+ excretion at kidneys, or bicarbonate loss in urine or feces	Administration of bicarbonate (gradual) with other steps as needed to correct primary cause
Respiratory alkalosis	Increased (above 7.45)	Generally caused by hyperventilation and reduction in plasma CO_2 levels	Reduce respiratory rate, allow rise in P_{CO_2}
Metabolic alkalosis	Increased (above 7.45)	Usually caused by prolonged vomiting and associated acid loss	For pH below 7.55, no treatment; pH above 7.55 may require administration of ammonium chloride

18-9 Age-related changes affect kidney function and the micturition reflex

In general, aging is associated with an increased incidence of kidney problems. Age-related changes in the urinary system, and in aspects of fluid, electrolyte, and acid-base balance, include the following:

1. *A decline in the number of functional nephrons.* The total number of nephrons in the kidneys drops by 30–40 percent between ages 25 and 85.

2. *A reduction in the GFR.* This results from fewer glomeruli, cumulative damage to the filtration apparatus in the remaining glomeruli, and reductions in renal blood flow. Fewer nephrons and a reduced GFR also reduce the body's ability to regulate pH through renal compensation.

3. *Reduced sensitivity to ADH and aldosterone.* With age, the distal portions of the nephron and collecting system become less responsive to ADH and aldosterone. Reabsorption of water and sodium ions is reduced, and more potassium ions are lost in the urine.

4. *Problems with the micturition reflex.* Several factors are involved in such problems:

   - The sphincter muscles lose tone and become less effective at voluntarily retaining urine. Loss of muscle tone leads to incontinence, often involving a slow leakage of urine.

   - The ability to control micturition is often lost after a stroke, Alzheimer disease, or other CNS problems affecting the cerebral cortex or hypothalamus.

   - In males, **urinary retention** may develop secondary to enlargement of the prostate gland. In this condition, swelling and distortion of surrounding prostatic tissues compress the urethra, restricting or preventing the flow of urine.

5. *A gradual decrease of total body water content with age.* Between ages 40 and 60, total body water content averages 60 percent for males and 50 percent for females. After age 60, the values decline to roughly 50 percent for males and 45 percent for females. Among other effects, such decreases result in less dilution of waste products, toxins, and administered drugs.

6. *A net loss in body mineral content in many people over age 60 as muscle mass and skeletal mass decrease.* This loss can be prevented, at least in part, by a combination of exercise and increased dietary mineral intake.

7. *Increased incidence of disorders affecting major systems with increasing age.* Most of these disorders have some impact on fluid, electrolyte, and/or acid-base balance.

18-10 The urinary system is one of several body systems involved in waste excretion

The urinary system is not the only organ system involved in excretion. Along with the urinary system, the integumentary, respiratory, and digestive systems are considered to form an anatomically diverse *excretory system.* Each of these body systems has specialized excretory activities:

1. *Integumentary system.* Water and electrolyte losses in perspiration affect plasma volume and composition. The effects are most apparent when losses are extreme, as occurs during maximum sweat production. Small amounts of metabolic wastes, including urea, are also excreted in perspiration.

2. *Respiratory system.* The lungs remove the carbon dioxide generated by cells. Small amounts of other compounds, such as acetone and water, evaporate into the alveoli and are eliminated during exhalation.

3. *Digestive system.* The liver excretes metabolic waste products in bile, and a variable amount of water is lost in feces.

All these nonurinary excretory activities affect the composition of body fluids. However, the excretory functions of these systems are not as closely regulated as are those of the kidneys, and the effects of integumentary and digestive excretory activities normally are minor compared with those of the urinary system.

The Urinary System in Perspective (p. 636) summarizes the functional interactions between the urinary system and other organ systems.

CHECKPOINT

26. What organ systems constitute the body's excretory system?

See the blue Answers tab at the back of the book.

RELATED CLINICAL TERMS

calculi (KAL-kū-lī): Insoluble deposits within the urinary tract formed from calcium salts, magnesium salts, or uric acid.

cystitis: Inflammation of the lining of the urinary bladder.

diuretics (dī-ū-RET-iks): Substances that promote fluid loss in urine.

dysuria (dis-Ū-rē-uh): Painful urination.

glomerulonephritis (glo-mer-ū-lō-nef-RĪ-tis): Inflammation of the glomeruli (the filtration units of the nephron).

glycosuria (glī-kō-SOO-rē-uh): The presence of glucose in urine.

hematuria: The presence of blood in urine.

hypernatremia: A condition characterized by excess sodium in the blood.

hyponatremia: A condition characterized by lower-than-normal sodium in the blood.

incontinence (in-KON-ti-nens): An inability to control urination voluntarily.

nephritis: Inflammation of the kidneys.

nephrology (ne-FROL-o-jē): The medical specialty concerned with the kidneys and their disorders.

proteinuria: The presence of protein in urine.

pyelogram (PĪ-el-ō-gram): An x-ray image of the kidneys taken after a radiopaque compound has been administered.

pyelonephritis (pī-e-lō-nef-RĪ-tis): Inflammation of kidney tissues.

renal failure: An inability of the kidneys to excrete wastes in sufficient quantities to maintain homeostasis.

urethritis: Inflammation of the urethra.

urinalysis: A physical and chemical assessment of urine.

urinary tract infection (UTI): An infection of the urinary tract by bacteria or fungi (yeast).

urology (u-ROL-o-jē): Branch of medicine concerned with the urinary system and its disorders, and with the male reproductive tract and its disorders.

Chapter **18** Review

KEY TERMS

acidosis *624*

aldosterone *611*

alkalosis *624*

angiotensin II *615*

buffer system *625*

filtrate *605*

glomerular filtration rate *610*

glomerulus *606*

juxtaglomerular complex *608*

kidney *601*

micturition *601*

nephron *603*

nephron loop *608*

peritubular capillaries *605*

renin *615*

ureters *601*

urinary bladder *601*

urine *609*

SUMMARY OUTLINE

iP Use *Interactive Physiology*® (**IP**)—available on the IP CD packaged with your new textbook—to help you understand difficult physiological concepts. Follow these navigation paths on IP for concepts in this chapter:

- Urinary System/Glomerular Filtration
- Urinary System/Early Filtrate Processing
- Urinary System/Late Filtrate Processing
- Fluids and Electrolytes/Water Homeostasis
- Fluids and Electrolytes/Electrolyte Homeostasis
- Fluids and Electrolytes/Acid-Base Homeostasis

18-1 The urinary system, consisting of the kidneys, ureters, urinary bladder, and urethra, has three primary functions   *p. 601*

1. The three major functions of the **urinary system** are *excretion,* the removal of organic waste products from body fluids; *elimination,* the discharge of these waste products into the environment; and homeostatic regulation of the volume and solute concentration of blood plasma. Other homeostatic functions include regulating blood volume and pressure by adjusting the volume of water lost and the release of hormones; regulating plasma concentrations of ions; helping to stabilize blood pH; and conserving nutrients.

2. The urinary system includes the **kidneys,** the **ureters,** the **urinary bladder,** and the **urethra.** The kidneys produce **urine,** a fluid containing water, ions, and soluble compounds. During **urination (micturition),** urine is forced out of the body. *(Figure 18-1)*

18-2 The highly vascular kidneys contain functional units called nephrons, which perform filtration, reabsorption, and secretion   *p. 602*

3. The left **kidney** extends superiorly slightly more than the right kidney. Both kidneys lie in a *retroperitoneal* position. *(Figure 18-2)*

4. A fibrous capsule surrounds each kidney. The **hilum** provides entry for the *renal artery* and *renal nerve,* and exit for the *renal vein* and *ureter.*

5. The ureter is continuous with the **renal pelvis.** This chamber branches into two **major calyces,** each connected to four or five **minor calyces,** which enclose the **renal papillae.** Urine production begins in **nephrons.** *(Figure 18-3)*

6. The blood vessels of the kidneys include the **interlobar, arcuate,** and **cortical radiate arteries** and the **interlobar, arcuate,** and **cortical radiate veins.** Blood travels from the **afferent** and **efferent arterioles** to the **peritubular capillaries** and the **vasa recta.** Diffusion occurs between the capillaries of the vasa recta and the tubular cells through the interstitial fluid that surrounds the nephron. *(Figure 18-4)*

7. The **nephron** (the basic functional unit in the kidney) includes the *renal corpuscle* and a **renal tubule,** which empties into the **collecting system** through a *collecting duct.* From the renal corpuscle, filtrate travels through the *proximal convoluted* tubule, the *nephron loop,* and the *distal convoluted tubule.* *(Figures 18-3c, 18-5)*

8. Nephrons are responsible for (1) the production of **filtrate,** (2) the reabsorption of nutrients, and (3) the reabsorption of water and ions.

9. The **renal corpuscle** consists of a knot of intertwined capillaries, called the **glomerulus,** surrounded by the **glomerular** *(Bowman)* **capsule.** Blood arrives from the *afferent arteriole* and departs in the *efferent arteriole. (Figure 18-6)*

10. At the glomerulus, **podocytes** cover the basement membrane of the capillaries that project into the **capsular space.** The processes of the podocytes are separated by narrow slits. *(Figure 18-6)*

11. The **proximal convoluted tubule (PCT)** actively reabsorbs nutrients, plasma proteins, and electrolytes from the filtrate. These substances are then released into the surrounding interstitial fluid. *(Figure 18-5)*

12. The **nephron loop,** or *loop of Henle,* includes a *descending limb* and an *ascending limb.* The ascending limb is impermeable to water and solutes; the descending limb is permeable to water. *(Figure 18-5)*

13. The ascending limb delivers fluid to the **distal convoluted tubule (DCT),** which actively secretes ions and reabsorbs sodium ions from the urine. The **juxtaglomerular complex,** which releases renin and erythropoietin, is located at the start of the DCT. *(Figure 18-6a)*

14. The **collecting ducts** receive urine from nephrons and merge into a **papillary duct,** which delivers urine to a minor calyx. The collecting system makes final adjustments to the urine by reabsorbing water or reabsorbing or secreting various ions.

18-3 Different portions of the nephron form urine by filtration, reabsorption, and secretion   *p. 609*

15. The primary purpose in **urine** production is the excretion and elimination of dissolved solutes, principally metabolic waste products such as **urea, creatinine,** and **uric acid.**

16. Urine formation involves **filtration, reabsorption,** and **secretion.** *(Tables 18-1, 18-2)*

17. Glomerular filtration occurs as fluids move across the wall of the glomerular capillaries into the capsular space in response to blood pressure in those capillaries. The **glomerular filtration rate (GFR)** is the amount of filtrate produced in the kidneys each minute. Any factor that alters the **filtration** (blood) **pressure** will change the GFR and affect kidney function.

18. Declining filtration pressures stimulate the juxtaglomerular complex to release *renin.* Renin release results in increases in blood volume and blood pressure.

19. The cells of the PCT normally reabsorb 60–70 percent of the volume of the filtrate produced in the renal corpuscle. The PCT reabsorbs nutrients, sodium and other ions, and water from the filtrate and transports them into the interstitial fluid. It also secretes various substances into the tubular fluid.

20. Water and ions are reclaimed from the filtrate by the nephron loop. The ascending limb pumps out sodium and chloride ions, and the descending limb reabsorbs water. A concentration gradient in the medulla encourages the osmotic flow of water out of the tubular fluid and into the interstitial fluid. As water is lost by osmosis and the volume of tubular fluid decreases, the urea concentration rises.

21. The DCT performs final adjustments by actively secreting or absorbing materials. Sodium ions are actively absorbed in exchange for potassium and hydrogen ions discharged into the tubular fluid. **Aldosterone** secretion increases the rate of sodium reabsorption and potassium loss.

22. The amount of water in the urine in the collecting ducts is regulated by the secretion of *antidiuretic hormone* (*ADH*). In the absence of ADH, the DCT, collecting tubule, and collecting duct are impermeable to water. The higher the ADH level in circulation, the more water is absorbed and the more concentrated the urine. (*Figure 18-7*)

23. More than 99 percent of the filtrate produced each day is reabsorbed before reaching the renal pelvis. Still, normal urine is 93–97 percent water. (*Table 18-3*)

24. Each segment of the nephron and collecting system contributes to the production of hypertonic urine. (*Figure 18-8*)

18-4 Normal kidney function depends on a stable GFR *p. 613*

25. Renal function may be regulated by automatic adjustments in glomerular filtration pressures through changes in the diameters of afferent and efferent arterioles.

26. Sympathetic activation produces powerful vasoconstriction of afferent arterioles, decreasing the GFR and slowing filtrate production. Sympathetic activation also alters the GFR by changing the regional blood circulation pattern.

27. Hormones that regulate kidney function include angiotensin II, aldosterone, ADH, and atrial natriuretic peptide (ANP). (*Figure 18-9*)

18-5 Urine is transported by the ureters, stored in the bladder, and eliminated through the urethra, aided by the micturition reflex *p. 617*

28. Filtrate modification and urine production end when the fluid enters the renal pelvis. The rest of the urinary system is responsible for transporting, storing, and eliminating the urine.

29. The **ureters** extend from the renal pelvis to the urinary bladder. Peristaltic contractions by smooth muscles in the walls of the ureters move the urine. (*Figures 18-1, 18-10*)

30. Internal features of the **urinary bladder**, a distensible sac for urine storage, include the *trigone*, the neck, and the **internal urethral sphincter.** Contraction of the *detrusor muscle* compresses the bladder and expels the urine into the urethra. (*Figure 18-10*)

31. In both sexes, as the urethra passes through the muscular pelvic floor, a circular band of skeletal muscles forms the **external urethral sphincter**, which is under voluntary control. (*Figure 18-10*)

32. The process of **urination** is coordinated by the **micturition reflex,** which is initiated by stretch receptors in the bladder wall. Voluntary urination involves coupling this reflex with the voluntary relaxation of the external urethral sphincter, which allows the opening of the internal urethral sphincter. (*Figure 18-11*)

18-6 Fluid balance, electrolyte balance, and acid-base balance are interrelated and essential to homeostasis *p. 620*

33. The maintenance of normal volume and composition in the extracellular and intracellular fluids is vital to life. Three types of homeostasis are involved: *fluid balance, electrolyte balance,* and *acid-base balance.*

34. The **intracellular fluid** (**ICF**) contains about 60 percent of the total body water; the **extracellular fluid** (**ECF**) contains the rest. Exchange occurs between the ICF and ECF, but the two **fluid compartments** retain their distinctive characteristics. (*Figures 18-12, 18-13*)

35. Water circulates freely within the ECF compartment.

36. Water losses are normally balanced by gains through eating, drinking, and metabolic generation. (*Table 18-4*)

18-7 Blood pressure and osmosis are involved in maintaining fluid and electrolyte balance *p. 622*

37. Water movement between the ECF and ICF is called a **fluid shift**. If the ECF becomes hypertonic relative to the ICF, water will move from the ICF into the ECF until osmotic equilibrium has been restored. If the ECF becomes hypotonic relative to the ICF, water will move from the ECF into the cells, and the volume of the ICF will increase accordingly.

38. Electrolyte balance is important because total electrolyte concentrations affect water balance, and because the levels of individual electrolytes can affect a variety of cell functions. Problems with electrolyte balance generally result from an imbalance between sodium gains and losses. Problems with potassium balance are less common but more dangerous.

39. The rate of sodium uptake across the digestive epithelium is directly related to the amount of sodium in the diet. Sodium losses occur mainly in the urine and through perspiration. The rate of sodium reabsorption along the DCT is regulated by aldosterone levels; aldosterone stimulates sodium ion reabsorption.

40. Potassium ion concentrations in the ECF are very low. Potassium excretion increases (1) when sodium ion concentrations decline and (2) as ECF potassium concentrations rise. The rate of potassium excretion is regulated by aldosterone; aldosterone stimulates potassium ion excretion.

18-8 In acid-base balance, buffer systems and respiratory and renal compensation mechanisms regulate hydrogen ions in body fluids *p. 624*

41. The pH of normal body fluids ranges from 7.35 to 7.45; variations outside this range produce **acidosis** or **alkalosis.**

42. Carbonic acid is the most important substance affecting the pH of the ECF. In solution, CO_2 reacts with water to form carbonic acid; the dissociation of carbonic acid releases hydrogen ions. An inverse relationship exists between the concentration of CO_2 and pH. *(Figure 18-14)*

43. Organic acids (metabolic acids) include products of metabolism such as lactic acid and ketone bodies.

44. A buffer system consists of a weak acid and its anion dissociation product, which acts as a weak base. The three major buffer systems are *protein buffer systems* in the ECF and ICF; the *carbonic acid–bicarbonate buffer system,* most important in the ECF; and the *phosphate buffer system* in the intracellular fluids.

45. In **protein buffer systems,** the component amino acids respond to changes in H^+ concentrations. Blood plasma proteins and hemoglobin in red blood cells help prevent drastic changes in pH.

46. The **carbonic acid–bicarbonate buffer system** prevents pH changes due to organic acids in the ECF.

47. The **phosphate buffer system** is important in preventing pH changes in the intracellular fluid.

48. In **respiratory compensation,** the lungs help regulate pH by affecting the carbonic acid–bicarbonate buffer system; changing the respiratory rate can raise or lower the P_{CO_2} of body fluids, affecting the buffering capacity.

49. In **renal compensation,** the kidneys vary their rates of hydrogen ion secretion and bicarbonate ion reabsorption depending on the pH of extracellular fluids.

50. Respiratory acid-base disorders result when abnormal respiratory function causes an extreme rise or a fall in CO_2 levels. Metabolic acid-base disorders are caused by the formation of organic acids or conditions affecting the levels of bicarbonate ions. *(Table 18-5)*

18-9 Age-related changes affect kidney function and the micturition reflex *p. 628*

51. Aging is usually associated with increased kidney problems. Age-related changes in the urinary system include (1) loss of functional nephrons, (2) reduced GFR, (3) reduced sensitivity to ADH, (4) problems with the micturition reflex (urinary retention may develop in men whose prostate gland is inflamed), (5) declining body water content, (6) a loss of mineral content, and (7) disorders affecting either fluid, electrolyte, or acid-base balance.

18-10 The urinary system is one of several body systems involved in waste excretion *p. 628*

52. The urinary, integumentary, respiratory, and digestive systems are sometimes considered an anatomically diverse *excretory system.* The systems' components work together to perform all of the excretory functions that affect the composition of body fluids.

REVIEW QUESTIONS

Level 1 • Reviewing Facts and Terms

Match each item in column A with the most closely related item in column B. Place letters for answers in the spaces provided.

COLUMN A

_____ 1. urination
_____ 2. fibrous capsule
_____ 3. hilum
_____ 4. medulla
_____ 5. nephrons
_____ 6. renal corpuscle
_____ 7. external urethral sphincter
_____ 8. internal urethral sphincter
_____ 9. aldosterone
_____ 10. podocytes
_____ 11. efferent arteriole
_____ 12. afferent arteriole
_____ 13. vasa recta
_____ 14. ADH
_____ 15. ECF
_____ 16. sodium
_____ 17. potassium

COLUMN B

a. site of urine production
b. capillaries around nephron loop
c. causes sensation of thirst
d. accelerated sodium reabsorption
e. voluntary control
f. filtration slits
g. covers kidney
h. blood leaves glomerulus
i. dominant cation in ICF
j. renal pyramids
k. blood to glomerulus
l. interstitial fluid
m. contains glomerulus
n. exit for ureter
o. dominant cation in ECF
p. involuntary control
q. micturition

18. Identify the different regions of a nephron and the structure into which it empties in the following diagram.

(a) _____ (b) _____
(c) _____ (d) _____
(e) _____

19. The filtrate leaving the glomerular capsule empties into the
   (a) distal convoluted tubule.
   (b) nephron loop.
   (c) proximal convoluted tubule.
   (d) collecting duct.

20. The distal convoluted tubule is an important site for
   (a) active secretion of ions.
   (b) active secretion of acids and other materials.
   (c) selective reabsorption of sodium ions from the tubular fluid.
   (d) a, b, and c are correct.

21. The endocrine structure that secretes renin and erythropoietin is the
   (a) juxtaglomerular complex.
   (b) vasa recta.
   (c) glomerular capsule.
   (d) suprarenal gland.

22. The primary purpose of the collecting system is to
   (a) transport urine from the bladder to the urethra.
   (b) selectively reabsorb sodium ions from tubular fluid.
   (c) transport urine from the renal pelvis to the ureters.
   (d) make final adjustments to the osmotic concentration and volume of urine.

23. Identify the structures of the kidney in the following diagram.

(a) _____ (b) _____
(c) _____ (d) _____
(e) _____ (f) _____
(g) _____ (h) _____
(i) _____ (j) _____
(k) _____ (l) _____
(m) _____

24. A person is in fluid balance when
  (a) the ECF and ICF are isotonic.
  (b) no fluid movement occurs between compartments.
  (c) the amount of water gained each day is equal to the amount lost to the environment.
  (d) a, b, and c are correct.

25. The primary components of the extracellular fluid are
  (a) lymph and cerebrospinal fluid.
  (b) blood plasma and serous fluids.
  (c) interstitial fluid and plasma.
  (d) a, b, and c are correct.

26. All the homeostatic mechanisms that monitor and adjust the composition of body fluids respond to changes
  (a) in the ICF.
  (b) in the ECF.
  (c) inside the cell.
  (d) a, b, and c are correct.

27. The most common problems with electrolyte balance are caused by an imbalance between gains and losses of
  (a) calcium ions.
  (b) chloride ions.
  (c) potassium ions.
  (d) sodium ions.

28. What is the primary function of the urinary system?

29. What are the structural components of the urinary system?

30. What are fluid shifts? What is their function, and what factors can cause them?

31. What three major hormones mediate major physiological adjustments that affect fluid and electrolyte balance? What are the primary effects of each hormone?

Level 2 • Reviewing Concepts

32. The urinary system regulates blood volume and pressure by
  (a) adjusting the volume of water lost in the urine.
  (b) releasing erythropoietin.
  (c) releasing renin.
  (d) a, b, and c are correct.

33. The balance of solute and water reabsorption in the renal medulla is maintained by the
  (a) segmental arterioles and veins.
  (b) interlobar arteries and veins.
  (c) vasa recta.
  (d) arcuate arteries.

34. The higher the plasma concentration of aldosterone, the more efficiently the kidney will
  (a) conserve sodium ions.
  (b) retain potassium ions.
  (c) stimulate urinary water loss.
  (d) secrete greater amounts of ADH.

35. When pure water is consumed,
  (a) the ECF becomes hypertonic with respect to the ICF.
  (b) the ECF becomes hypotonic with respect to the ICF.
  (c) the ICF becomes hypotonic with respect to the plasma.
  (d) water moves from the ICF into the ECF.

36. Increasing or decreasing the rate of respiration alters pH by
  (a) lowering or raising the partial pressure of carbon dioxide.
  (b) lowering or raising the partial pressure of oxygen.
  (c) lowering or raising the partial pressure of nitrogen.
  (d) a, b, and c are correct.

37. What interacting controls stabilize the glomerular filtration rate (GFR)?

38. Describe the micturition reflex.

39. Differentiate among fluid balance, electrolyte balance, and acid-base balance, and explain why they are important to homeostasis.

40. Why should a person with a fever drink plenty of fluids?

41. Exercise physiologists recommend that adequate amounts of fluid be ingested before, during, and after exercise. Why is adequate fluid replacement during extensive sweating important?

Level 3 • Critical Thinking and Clinical Applications

42. Long-haul truck drivers are on the road for long periods of time between restroom stops. Why might that lead to kidney problems?

43. For the past week, Susan has felt a burning sensation in the area of her urethra when she urinates. She checks her temperature and finds that she has a low-grade fever. What is likely occurring, and what unusual substances are likely to be in her urine?

44. *Mannitol* is a sugar that is filtered but not reabsorbed by the kidneys. What effect would drinking a solution of mannitol have on the volume of urine produced?

The Urinary System in Perspective

Functional Relationships Between the Urinary System and Other Systems

The Integumentary System

- The Integumentary System assists in elimination of water and solutes, especially sodium and chloride ions, with sweat glands; keratinized epidermis prevents excessive fluid loss through skin surface; epidermis produces vitamin D_3, important for the renal production of calcitriol

The Skeletal System

- The Skeletal System provides some protection for kidneys and ureters; pelvis protects urinary bladder and proximal portion of urethra
- The Urinary System conserves calcium and phosphate needed for bone growth

The Muscular System

- The Muscular System provides some protection for urinary organs with muscle layers of the trunk; sphincter muscles close the urethral opening
- The Urinary System removes waste products of protein metabolism; assists in regulation of calcium and phosphate

The Nervous System

- The Nervous System adjusts renal blood pressure; monitors distension of urinary bladder and controls urination

The Endocrine System

- The Endocrine System's hormones aldosterone and ADH adjust rates of fluid and electrolyte reabsorption in kidneys
- The Urinary System releases renin when local blood pressure declines, and erythropoietin (EPO) when renal oxygen levels decline

The Cardiovascular System

- The Cardiovascular System delivers blood to capillaries, where filtration occurs; accepts fluids and solutes reabsorbed during urine production
- The Urinary System releases renin to elevate blood pressure and erythropoietin (EPO) to accelerate red blood cell production

The Lymphoid System

- The Lymphoid System provides specific defenses against urinary tract infections
- The Urinary System eliminates toxins and wastes generated by cellular activities; acid pH of urine provides nonspecific defense against urinary tract infections

The Respiratory System

- The Respiratory System assists in the regulation of pH by eliminating carbon dioxide
- The Urinary System assists in the elimination of carbon dioxide; provides bicarbonate buffers that assist in pH regulation

The Digestive System

- The Digestive System absorbs water needed to excrete wastes at kidneys; absorbs ions needed to maintain normal body fluid concentrations; liver removes bilirubin
- The Urinary System excretes toxins absorbed by the digestive tract; excretes bilirubin and nitrogenous wastes produced by the liver; calcitrol production by kidneys aids calcium and phosphate absorption along digestive tract

The Reproductive System

- The Reproductive System's secretions by male accessory organs may have antibacterial action that prevents urethral infections
- The Urinary System carries semen in the male urethra

For All Systems
The Urinary System excretes waste products; maintains normal body fluid pH and ion composition

Professional Profile

HEALTH EDUCATOR
Kim Lambertson

> **"** One of the great things about a nursing degree is that you can take it anywhere and apply it to something you're interested in.**"**

"A nursing degree opens up a lot of career opportunities, not just as a nurse but in other roles as well," says Kim Lambertson. As a registered nurse, Kim worked in a hospital setting for 12 years but then changed careers to become a health educator for a private company.

As a health educator, Kim instructs nurses in the procedures of peritoneal dialysis (PD), the process of cleaning the blood by filling and draining the abdominal cavity with a cleaning solution through a catheter. PD replaces kidney function for people with kidney failure. Kim teaches nurses how to recognize which patients are candidates for PD therapy, how to train patients, and how to follow up and treat complications.

EVERY DAY IS DIFFERENT

Based in Denver, Colorado, Kim travels part of the week throughout the western states, visiting hospitals and clinics in Idaho, Wyoming, New Mexico, and Utah. She trains nurses one-on-one and also teaches classes. Every day is different and she is constantly meeting new people. In many cases, she works with nurses and doctors in rural areas. "Because these people are more isolated, they really depend on what I offer as an educator," she says.

Kim enjoyed patient care as a nurse but realized that teaching was her real interest. "As a health educator, I work with nurses to improve patient care and outcomes. I get to see the results of what I do, helping a nurse blossom and become successful."

EARLY TRAINING AS A NURSE

Before becoming an educator, Kim worked as a dialysis nurse. She became interested in the field while she was in nursing school. "Although I originally thought I would work in oncology or some other area, I chose dialysis because it was a very interesting way to help people."

Kim was also fascinated by the integral role the kidneys play in physiology. "We tend to think that if something is wrong with one part of the body, it doesn't affect anything else. In fact, when your kidneys fail, it increases your risk of heart disease, which in turn worsens kidney function. We are complex machines."

This integration makes the study of anatomy and physiology crucial. "It's important to know how disease processes such as diabetes, hypertension, and autoimmune diseases like lupus can alter many systems of the body. When kidney disease overcomes a person, it has a cascade of physiological effects. It alters metabolism and the cardiovascular system, for example."

Like Kim, most health educators have a master's degree in nursing. She recommends spending some time interning with an educator while getting your undergraduate training. "By doing so, you'll discover if you have the qualities a health educator needs: an interest in teaching, enthusiasm for keeping up with current practices, a sense of humor, and the ability to explain concepts at an applied, relevant level."

Kim also recommends keeping your options open while you're in school. "Get a lot of varied experience. Be flexible. One of the great things about a nursing degree is that you can take it anywhere and apply it to something you're interested in. You can work in corporate nursing education, like I do, or in case management, taking care of the needs of particular patients. You will find your niche by exploring a lot of possibilities."

19 The Reproductive System

Of all our organ systems, only the reproductive system is not needed for an individual's survival. In a sense, our reproductive system does not exist for us at all—it exists for the human species. In this chapter, we'll study the system that has enabled humans to exist for a very long time—and with luck, to stick around for at least a while longer.

VOCABULARY DEVELOPMENT

andro- male; *androgen*
crypto hidden; *cryptorchidism*
diplo double; *diploid*
follis a leather bag; *follicle*
genesis generation; *oogenesis*
gyne woman; *gynecologist*
haplo single; *haploid*

labium lip; *labium minus*
lutea yellow; *corpus luteum*
meioun to make smaller; *meiosis*
men month; *menopause*
metra uterus; *endometrium*
myo- muscle; *myometrium*
oon an egg; *oocyte*

orchis testis; *cryptorchidism*
pausis cessation; *menopause*
pellucidus translucent; *zona pellucida*
rete a net; *rete testis*
tetras four; *tetrad*

An Introduction to the Reproductive System

Although an individual life span lasts but decades, the human species has perpetuated itself for hundreds of thousands of years through the activities of the reproductive system. The entire process of reproduction seems almost magical; many aboriginal societies failed to discover even the basic link between sexual activity and childbirth and assumed that supernatural forces were responsible for producing new individuals. Our society has a much clearer understanding of the reproductive process, but the events of procreation—the fusion of two reproductive cells, one produced by a man, the other by a woman, which starts a chain of events leading to the birth of an infant—still produces a sense of wonder. This chapter and the next will consider the mechanisms involved in this remarkable process.

19-1 Basic reproductive system structures are gonads, ducts, accessory glands and organs, and external genitalia

This chapter begins by examining the anatomy and physiology of the **reproductive system.** This system ensures the continued existence of the human species—by producing, storing, nourishing, and transporting functional male and female reproductive cells, or **gametes** (GAM-ēts).

The reproductive system includes the following basic components:

- **Gonads** (GŌ-nadz; *gone,* seed, generation), or reproductive organs that produce gametes and hormones.
- Ducts that receive and transport the gametes.
- Accessory glands and organs that secrete fluids into reproductive system ducts or into other excretory ducts.

- Perineal structures that are collectively known as the **external genitalia** (jen-i-TĀ-lē-uh).

In both males and females, the ducts are connected to chambers and passageways that open to the exterior of the body. The structures involved make up the *reproductive tract.* The male and female reproductive systems are functionally quite different, however. In adult males, the **testes** (TES-tēz; singular, *testis*), or male gonads, secrete sex hormones called *androgens* (principally *testosterone*). The testes also produce the male gametes, called **spermatozoa** (sper-ma-tō-ZŌ-uh; singular, *spermatozoon*), or *sperm*—one-half billion each day. During *emission,* mature spermatozoa travel along a lengthy duct system, where they are mixed with the secretions of accessory glands. The mixture created is known as **semen** (SĒ-men). During *ejaculation,* semen is expelled from the body.

In adult females, the **ovaries,** or female gonads, typically release only one immature gamete, an **oocyte,** per month. This immature gamete travels along one of two short *uterine tubes,* which end in the muscular organ called the *uterus* (Ū-ter-us). If a sperm reaches the oocyte and initiates the process of *fertilization,* the oocyte matures into an **ovum** (plural, *ova*). A short passageway, the *vagina* (va-JĪ-nuh), connects the uterus with the exterior. Ejaculation introduces semen into the vagina during *sexual intercourse,* and the spermatozoa then ascend the female reproductive tract. If fertilization occurs, the uterus will enclose and support a developing *embryo* as it grows into a *fetus* and prepares for birth.

Next we will examine further the anatomy of the male and female reproductive systems and will consider the physiological and hormonal mechanisms responsible for the regulation of reproductive function.

CHECKPOINT

1. Define gamete.
2. List the basic components of the human reproductive system.
3. Define gonads.

See the blue Answers tab at the end of the book.

19-2 Sperm formation (spermatogenesis) occurs in the testes, and hormones from the hypothalamus, pituitary gland, and testes control male reproductive functions

The principal structures of the male reproductive system are shown in Figure 19-1. Proceeding from each testis, spermatozoa travel within structures composing the *male reproductive tract*—the *epididymis* (ep-i-DID-i-mus), the *ductus deferens* (DUK-tus DEF-e-renz), the *ejaculatory* (ē-JAK-ū-la-tō-rē) *duct*, and the *urethra*—before leaving the body. Accessory organs including the *seminal* (SEM-i-nal) *glands*, the *prostate* (PROS-tāt) *gland*, and the *bulbo-urethral* (bul-bō-ū-RĒ-thral) *glands* secrete their products into the ejaculatory ducts and urethra. The external genitalia of the male include the *scrotum* (SKRŌ-tum), which encloses the testes, and the *penis* (PĒ-nis), an erectile organ through which the distal portion of the urethra passes.

THE TESTES

The *primary sex organs* of the male system, the testes, hang within the **scrotum,** a fleshy pouch suspended from the perineum posterior to the base of the penis. The scrotum is subdivided into two chambers, or *scrotal cavities,* each containing a testis. Each testis has the shape of a flattened egg roughly 5 cm (2 in.) long, 3 cm (1.2 in.) wide, and 2.5 cm (1 in.) thick and weighs 10–15 g (0.35–0.53 oz). A serous membrane lines the scrotal cavity, reducing friction between the inner surface of the scrotum and the outer surface of the testis.

The scrotum consists of a thin layer of skin containing smooth muscle (Figure 19-2a). Sustained contractions of the smooth muscle layer, the *dartos* (DAR-tōs), cause the characteristic wrin-

Clinical Note

Cryptorchidism

During normal development of a male fetus, the testes descend from inside the body cavity and pass through the inguinal canal of the abdominal wall into the scrotum. In **cryptorchidism** (krip-TOR-ki-dizm; *crypto,* hidden + *orchis,* testis), one or both of the testes have not completed this process (*descent of the testes*) by the time of birth. This condition occurs in about 3 percent of full-term deliveries and in roughly 30 percent of premature births. In most instances, normal descent occurs a few weeks later, but the condition can be surgically corrected if it persists. Corrective measures should be taken before *puberty* (sexual maturation) because cryptorchid (abdominal) testes will not produce sperm, and the individual will be *sterile* (*infertile*) and unable to father children. If the testes cannot be moved into the scrotum, they are usually removed, because about 10 percent of men with uncorrected cryptorchid testes eventually develop testicular cancer. This surgical procedure is called a *bilateral orchiectomy* (or-kē-EK-to-mē; *ectomy,* excision).

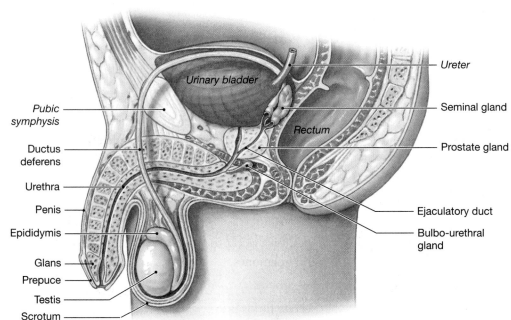

Pubic symphysis
Ductus deferens
Urethra
Penis
Epididymis
Glans
Prepuce
Testis
Scrotum

Urinary bladder
Ureter
Seminal gland
Rectum
Prostate gland
Ejaculatory duct
Bulbo-urethral gland

FIGURE 19-1 The Male Reproductive System. This diagrammatic sagittal section provides a view of the reproductive organs of males.

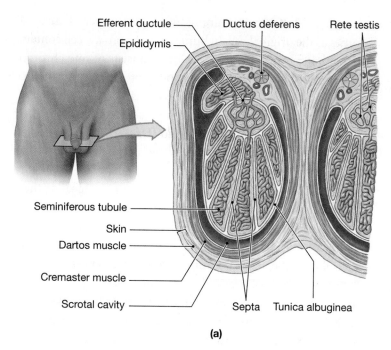

Efferent ductule
Ductus deferens
Rete testis
Epididymis

Seminiferous tubule
Skin
Dartos muscle
Cremaster muscle
Scrotal cavity
Septa   Tunica albuginea

(a)

Seminiferous tubules containing nearly mature
spermatozoa about to be released into the lumen

Seminiferous tubules
containing late spermatids
Seminiferous tubules
containing early spermatids

(b)

kling of the scrotal surface. Beneath the dermis is a layer of skeletal muscle, the **cremaster** (krē-MAS-ter) **muscle,** which can contract to pull the testes closer to the body. Normal sperm development in the testes requires temperatures about 1.1°C (2°F) lower than those elsewhere in the body. When air or body temperatures rise, the cremaster relaxes, and the testes move away from the body. Sudden cooling of the scrotum, as occurs during entry into a cold swimming pool, results in contractions of the cremaster muscle that pull the testes closer to the body and keep testicular temperatures from falling.

Each testis is wrapped in a dense fibrous capsule, the **tunica albuginea** (TŪ-ni-ka al-bū-JIN-ē-uh). Collagen fibers from this wrapping extend into the testis, forming partitions, or *septa,* that subdivide the testis into roughly 250 *lobules.* Distributed among the lobules are approximately 800 slender, tightly coiled **seminiferous** (sem-i-NIF-er-us) **tubules** (Figure 19-2b). Each tubule averages about 80 cm (32 in.) in length, and a typical testis contains nearly half a mile of seminiferous tubules. Sperm produced within the seminiferous tubules (by a process discussed shortly) leave the tubules and pass through a maze of passageways—the **rete** (RĒ-tē; *rete,* a net) **testis** and *efferent ductules*—before entering the epididymis, the beginning of the male reproductive tract (Figure 19-2a).

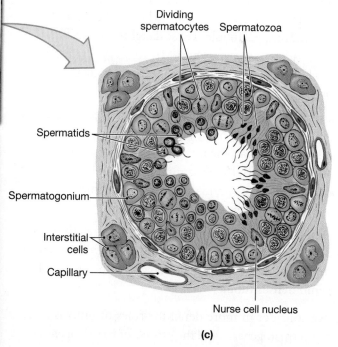

Dividing
spermatocytes   Spermatozoa

Spermatids

Spermatogonium

Interstitial
cells

Capillary

Nurse cell nucleus

(c)

FIGURE 19-2 The Scrotum, Testes, and Seminiferous Tubules. (a) This horizontal section reveals the anatomical relationships of the testes within the scrotum. **(b)** This photomicrograph shows a section through a coiled seminiferous tubule. **(c)** This diagrammatic view details the cellular organization of a seminiferous tubule.

The spaces between the tubules are filled with loose connective tissue, numerous blood vessels, and large **interstitial cells** (Figure 19-2c) that produce male sex hormones, or *androgens*. The steroid **testosterone** is the most important androgen. ∞ p. 367

Each seminiferous tubule contains numerous cells. Among them are large **nurse cells,** or *sustentacular* (sus-ten-TAK-ū-lar) (or *Sertoli*) *cells,* that extend from the perimeter of the tubule to the lumen (Figure 19-2c). Nurse cells nourish the developing sperm cells. Between and adjacent to the nurse cells are the various cells involved in **spermatogenesis** (sper-ma-tō-JEN-e-sis), a series of cell divisions that ultimately produces sperm cells (spermatozoa). With each successive division, the daughter cells move closer to the lumen.

Spermatogenesis

Spermatogenesis involves three processes:

1. *Mitosis.* Spermatogenesis begins with the mitotic divisions of stem cells called **spermatogonia** (sper-ma-tō-GŌ-nē-uh; singular, *spermatogonium*), located in the outermost layer of cells in the seminiferous tubules (Figure 19-2c). (See Chapter 3 for a review of mitosis and cell division.) ∞ p. 83 Spermatogonia undergo mitosis throughout the individual's adult life. One daughter cell from each mitotic division is pushed toward the lumen of the seminiferous tubule. These daughter cells differentiate into *spermatocytes* (sper-MA-tō-sīts), which prepare to begin the second process in spermatogenesis—meiosis.

2. *Meiosis.* The special form of cell division called *meiosis* (mī-Ō-sis; *meioun,* to make smaller) produces gametes, cells that contain half the number of chromosomes found in other cells. In the seminiferous tubules, the meiotic divisions of spermatocytes produce immature gametes called *spermatids* (Figure 19-2c).

3. *Spermiogenesis.* In *spermiogenesis,* the small, relatively unspecialized spermatids develop into physically mature spermatozoa, which enter the fluid within the lumen of the seminiferous tubule.

Next we consider in more detail the roles of mitosis and meiosis in spermatogenesis, and the process of spermiogenesis.

MITOSIS AND MEIOSIS. In both males and females, mitosis and meiosis differ significantly in terms of the events occurring in the nucleus. **Mitosis** is part of the process of *somatic* (nonreproductive) cell division, which involves one division that produces two daughter cells, each containing the same number of chromosomes as the original cell. In humans, each somatic cell contains 23 pairs of chromosomes. Each pair consists of one chromosome provided by the father, and another provided by the mother, at the time of fertilization. Because each cell contains both members of each chromosome pair, these cells, and each of their daughter cells, are said to be **diploid** (DIP-loyd; *diplo,* double).

By contrast, **meiosis** involves two cycles of cell division (*meiosis I* and *meiosis II*) and produces four cells, or gametes, each containing 23 individual chromosomes. Because these gametes contain only one member of each chromosome pair, gametes are said to be **haploid** (HAP-loyd; *haplo,* single). Thus, the fusion of a haploid sperm and a haploid egg yields a single cell with the normal number of chromosomes.

Figure 19-3 illustrates the role of meiosis in spermatogenesis. (To make the chromosomal events easier to follow, only 3 of the 23 pairs of chromosomes present in each spermatogonium are shown.) Each mitotic division of spermatogonia produces two primary spermatocytes. Like spermatogonia, primary spermatocytes are diploid cells, but they divide by meiosis rather than mitosis. As a primary spermatocyte prepares to begin meiosis, DNA replication occurs within the nucleus, just as it does in a cell preparing to undergo mitosis. As prophase of the first meiotic division (meiosis I) occurs, the chromosomes condense and become visible. As in mitosis, each chromosome consists of two duplicate *chromatids* (KRŌ-ma-tidz).

At this point, the close similarities between meiosis and mitosis end. As prophase of meiosis I unfolds, the corresponding maternal and paternal chromosomes come together. This event, known as **synapsis** (si-NAP-sis), produces 23 pairs of chromosomes, each member of the pair consisting of two identical chromatids. A matched set of four chromatids is called a **tetrad** (TET-rad; *tetras,* four). An exchange of genetic material can occur between the chromatids of a chromosome pair at this time. This exchange, called *crossing-over,* increases genetic variation among offspring. Prophase ends with the disappearance of the nuclear envelope.

During metaphase of meiosis I, the tetrads line up along the metaphase plate. As anaphase begins, the tetrads break up, and the maternal and paternal chromosomes separate. This is a major difference between mitosis and meiosis: In mitosis, each daughter cell receives one of the two copies of *every* chromosome, maternal and paternal, whereas in meiosis, each daughter cell receives both copies of *either* the maternal chromosome or the paternal chromosome from each tetrad.

As anaphase proceeds, the maternal and paternal components are randomly distributed. For example, most of the maternal chromosomes may go to one daughter cell, and most of the paternal chromosomes to the other. As a result, telophase I ends with the formation of two daughter cells containing unique combinations of maternal and paternal chromosomes. In the testes, the daughter cells produced by the first meiotic division (meiosis I) are called **secondary spermatocytes.**

Every secondary spermatocyte contains 23 chromosomes, each of which consists of two duplicate chromatids. The duplicate chromatids separate during **meiosis II.** The interphase separating meiosis I and meiosis II is very brief, and the secondary spermatocyte soon enters meiosis II. The completion of meiosis II produces four immature gametes, or **spermatids** (SPER-ma-tidz), identical in size and each with 23 chromosomes.

In summary, for every diploid primary spermatocyte that enters meiosis, four haploid spermatids are produced (Figure 19-3). (Meiosis in females produces one huge ovum and three tiny, nonfunctional cells that disintegrate. We will consider ovum production in a later section.)

SPERMIOGENESIS. In **spermiogenesis,** each spermatid matures into a single **spermatozoon** (sper-ma-tō-ZŌ-on), or sperm cell. The entire process of spermatogenesis, from spermatogonial division to the release of a physically mature spermatozoon, takes approximately 9 weeks.

As previously noted, nurse cells play a key role in spermatogenesis and spermiogenesis. Neither spermatocytes undergoing meiosis nor spermatids are free in the seminiferous tubules. Instead, they are surrounded by the cytoplasm of nurse cells. Because there are no blood vessels inside the seminiferous tubules, all nutrients must enter by diffusion from the surrounding interstitial fluids. The large nurse cells control the chemical environment inside the seminiferous tubules and provide nutrients and chemical stimuli that promote the production and differentiation of spermatozoa. They also help regulate spermatogenesis by producing *inhibin,* a hormone introduced in Chapter 10. ∞ p. 367

Anatomy of a Spermatozoon

A sperm cell, or spermatozoon, has three distinct regions: the head, the middle piece, and the tail (Figure 19-4). The **head** contains a nucleus filled with densely packed chromosomes.

The Big Picture

Meiosis produces gametes that contain half the number of chromosomes found in somatic cells. For each cell entering meiosis, the testes produce four spermatozoa, whereas the ovaries produce a single ovum.

FIGURE 19-3 **Spermatogenesis.** In this process, which occurs within the seminiferous tubules, each diploid primary spermatocyte that undergoes meiosis produces four haploid spermatids. Each spermatid then develops into a spermatozoon.

At the tip of the head is the **acrosomal** (ak-rō-SŌ-mal) **cap,** which contains enzymes essential for fertilization. A short **neck** attaches the head to the **middle piece,** which contains mitochondria arranged in a spiral that provide the energy (in the form of ATP) for moving the tail. The **tail** is the only example of a *flagellum* in the human body. It moves the sperm cell from one place to another. ∞ p. 74

Unlike most other cells, a mature spermatozoon lacks an endoplasmic reticulum, a Golgi apparatus, lysosomes, peroxisomes, and many other intracellular structures. Because the cell does not contain glycogen or other energy reserves, it must absorb nutrients (primarily fructose) from the surrounding fluid.

Acrosomal cap

Head

Neck

Middle piece

Nucleus

Mitochondrial spiral

Tail (flagellum)

Cell membrane of flagellum

FIGURE 19-4 Spermatozoon Structure. A spermatozoon measures only 60 μm (0.06 mm) in total length.

The Big Picture

Spermatogenesis begins at puberty (sexual maturation) and continues until relatively late in life (after age 70). It is a continuous process, and all stages of meiosis can be observed within the seminiferous tubules.

THE MALE REPRODUCTIVE TRACT

The testes produce physically mature spermatozoa that are not yet capable of fertilizing an ovum. The other portions of the male reproductive system are responsible for the functional maturation, nourishment, storage, and transport of spermatozoa.

The Epididymis

Late in their development, spermatozoa detach from nurse cells and lie within the lumen of the seminiferous tubule. Although they have most of the physical characteristics of mature sperm cells, they are still functionally immature and incapable of coordinated locomotion or fertilization. At this point, cilia-driven fluid currents within the efferent ducts transport them into the **epididymis** (Figure 19-1). The epididymides (ep-i-DID-i-mi-dēz) can be felt through the skin of the scrotum. Each tubule, almost 7 meters (23 ft) long, is twisted and coiled so as to take up very little space.

The functions of the epididymis include adjusting the composition of the fluid from the seminiferous tubules, acting as a recycling center for damaged spermatozoa, and storing maturing spermatozoa. Cells lining the epididymis absorb cellular debris from damaged or abnormal spermatozoa and release it for pickup by surrounding blood vessels; the cells also absorb organic nutrients. Spermatozoa complete their physical maturation during the two weeks it takes for them to travel through the epididymis and arrive at the ductus deferens.

Although spermatozoa leaving the epididymis are physically mature, they remain immobile. To become motile (actively swimming) and fully functional, they must undergo **capacitation.** Capacitation occurs after spermatozoa (1) mix with secretions of the seminal glands and (2) are exposed to conditions inside the female reproductive tract. The epididymis secretes a substance that prevents premature capacitation.

The Ductus Deferens

Each **ductus deferens,** or *vas deferens,* is 40–45 cm (16–18 in.) long (Figure 19-1). It ascends into the abdominal cavity within the *spermatic cord,* a sheath of connective tissue and muscle that also encloses the blood vessels, nerves, and lymphatics serving the testis. (The passageway through the abdominal musculature is called the *inguinal canal.*)

Once within the abdominal cavity, each ductus deferens passes lateral to the urinary bladder (Figure 19-1); then each curves downward past the ureter on its way toward the prostate gland (Figure 19-5a). Peristaltic contractions in the muscular walls of the ductus deferens propel spermatozoa and fluid along the length of the duct. The ductus deferens can also store spermatozoa for up to several months. During this period spermatozoa are inactive and have low metabolic rates.

The junction of the ductus deferens with the duct of the seminal vesicle creates the *ejaculatory duct,* a relatively short (2 cm, or less than 1 in.) passageway (Figure 19-5a). This duct penetrates the muscular wall of the prostate gland and empties into the urethra near the opening of the ejaculatory duct from the other side.

The Urethra

In males, the urethra extends 18–20 cm (7–8 in.) from the urinary bladder to the tip of the penis (Figure 19-1). The male

Ureter

Urinary bladder

Ductus deferens

Seminal gland

Ejaculatory duct

Prostate gland

Urethra

Bulbo-urethral gland

Smooth muscle

Lumen of ductus deferens

(a)

(b)

FIGURE 19-5 **The Ductus Deferens.** **(a)** This posterior view shows the segments of the ductus deferens in relation to nearby structures. **(b)** These micrographs show extensive layering with smooth muscle around the lumen of the ductus deferens. (Reproduced from R. G. Kessel and R. H. Kardon, *Tissues and Organs: A Text-Atlas of Scanning Electron Microscopy,* W. H. Freeman & Co., 1979. All Rights Reserved.) (LM × 34; SEM × 42)

urethra is a passageway that functions in both the urinary and reproductive systems.

THE ACCESSORY GLANDS

The fluids contributed by the seminiferous tubules and the epididymis account for only about 5 percent of the volume of *semen,* the fluid that transports and nourishes sperm. The majority of seminal fluid is composed of secretions from the *seminal glands,* the *prostate gland,* and the *bulbo-urethral glands* (Figure 19-5a). Primary functions of these glands include (1) activating spermatozoa, (2) providing nutrients spermatozoa need for motility, (3) generating peristaltic contractions that propel spermatozoa and fluids along the reproductive tract, and (4) producing buffers that counteract the acidity of the urethral and vaginal environments.

The Seminal Glands (Seminal Vesicles)

Each **seminal gland,** also called a **seminal vesicle,** is a tubular gland about 15 cm (6 in.) long (Figures 19-1 and 19-5a). The body of the gland is coiled and folded into a compact, tapered mass roughly 5 cm by 2.5 cm (2 in. by 1 in.).

The seminal glands are extremely active secretory glands that contribute about 60 percent of the volume of semen. Their secretions contain (1) fructose, a six-carbon sugar easily metabolized by spermatozoa; (2) prostaglandins, which can stimulate smooth muscle contractions along the male and female reproductive tracts; and (3) fibrinogen, which after ejaculation forms a temporary clot within the vagina. The slight alkalinity of the secretions helps neutralize acids in prostate gland secretions and within the vagina. When mixed with seminal gland secretions, mature but previously inactive spermatozoa begin beating their flagella and become highly motile.

The Prostate Gland

The **prostate gland** is a small, muscular, rounded organ, about 4 cm (1.6 in.) in diameter, that surrounds the urethra as it leaves the urinary bladder (Figure 19-5a). The *prostatic fluid* produced by the prostate gland is a slightly acidic secretion that contributes 20–30 percent of the volume of semen. In addition to several other compounds of uncertain significance, prostatic fluid contains **seminalplasmin** (sem-i-nal-PLAZ-min), an antibiotic that may help prevent

Clinical Note

Prostatitis

Prostatic inflammation, or **prostatitis** (pros-ta-TĪ-tis), can occur in males of any age but most often afflicts older men. Prostatitis can result from bacterial infections, but it also occurs in the apparent absence of pathogens. Signs and symptoms can resemble those of prostate cancer. Individuals with prostatitis may complain of pain in the lower back, perineum, or rectum, sometimes accompanied by painful urination and the discharge of mucous secretions from the urethral opening. Antibiotic therapy is usually effective in treating most cases resulting from bacterial infection.

urinary tract infections in males. These secretions are ejected into the urethra by peristaltic contractions of the muscular prostate wall.

The Bulbo-urethral Glands

The paired **bulbo-urethral glands,** or *Cowper glands,* are spherical structures almost 10 mm (less than 0.5 in.) in diameter (Figure 19-5a). These glands secrete a thick, sticky, alkaline mucus that helps neutralize urinary acids in the urethra and has lubricating properties.

Semen

Semen (SĒ-men) is the fluid that contains sperm and the secretions of the accessory glands of the male reproductive tract. In a typical *ejaculation* (ē-jak-ū-LĀ-shun), 2–5 mL of semen is expelled from the body. This volume of fluid, called an **ejaculate,** contains three major components:

- *Spermatozoa.* A normal **sperm count** ranges from 20 million to 100 million spermatozoa per milliliter of semen.

- *Seminal fluid.* **Seminal fluid,** the fluid component of semen, is a mixture of glandular secretions with a distinct ionic and nutrient composition. Of the total volume of seminal fluid, the seminal glands contribute about 60 percent; the prostate, 30 percent; the nurse cells and epididymis, 5 percent; and the bulbo-urethral glands, less than 5 percent.

- *Enzymes.* Several important enzymes are present in seminal fluid, including (1) a protease that helps dissolve mucous secretions in the vagina; (2) *seminalplasmin,* a prostatic antibiotic enzyme that kills a variety of bacteria;

(3) a prostatic enzyme that causes the semen to clot in the vagina; and (4) an enzyme that subsequently liquefies the clotted semen.

THE EXTERNAL GENITALIA

The male external genitalia consist of the scrotum (described earlier on p. 640) and penis. The **penis** is a tubular organ that both introduces semen into the female's vagina during sexual intercourse and conducts urine to the exterior through the urethra (Figure 19-1). As shown in Figure 19-6a, the penis is composed of three regions: (1) the **root,** the fixed portion that attaches the penis to the body wall; (2) the **body (shaft),** the tubular portion that contains masses of erectile tissue; and (3) the **glans,** the expanded distal portion surrounding the external urethral opening, or *external urethral orifice.*

The skin overlying the penis resembles that of the scrotum. A fold of skin, the **prepuce** (PRĒ-pūs), or *foreskin,* surrounds the tip of the penis (Figure 19-6b). The prepuce attaches to the relatively narrow neck of the penis and continues over the glans. *Preputial glands* in the skin of the neck and inner surface of the prepuce secrete a waxy material called *smegma* (SMEG-ma). Unfortunately, smegma can be an excellent nutrient source for bacteria. Mild inflammation and infections in this region are common, especially if the area is not washed frequently. One way to avoid these conditions is *circumcision* (ser-kum-SIZH-un), the surgical removal of the prepuce. In Western societies (especially the United States), this procedure is generally performed shortly after birth.

Most of the body, or shaft, of the penis consists of three columns of **erectile tissue** (Figure 19-6c). Erectile tissue consists of a maze of vascular channels incompletely separated by partitions of elastic connective tissue and smooth muscle. The anterior surface of the penis covers two cylindrical **corpora cavernosa** (KOR-por-a ka-ver-NŌ-suh). Their bases are bound to the pubis and ischium of the pelvis (Figure 19-6a). The corpora cavernosa extend along as far as the glans of the penis. The relatively slender **corpus spongiosum** (spon-jē-Ō-sum) surrounds the urethra and extends all the way to the tip of the penis, where it forms the glans.

In the resting state, little blood flows into the erectile tissue because the arterial branches are constricted and the muscular partitions are tense. Parasympathetic innervation of the penile arteries involves neurons that release nitric oxide (NO) at their synaptic knobs. In response to the NO, the smooth muscle in the arterial walls relaxes and the vessels dilate, resulting in increased blood flow and **erection** of the penis.

FIGURE 19-6 **The Penis.** **(a)** This anterolateral view of a penis shows the positions of the erectile tissues. **(b)** A frontal section through the penis and associated organs provides another view of the erectile tissues. **(c)** This sectional view through the penis reveals the texture of the erectile tissues.

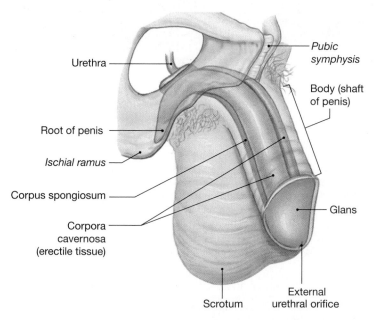

(a) Anterior and lateral view of penis

(b) Frontal section

(c) Section through shaft of penis

HORMONES AND MALE REPRODUCTIVE FUNCTION

The major reproductive hormones were introduced in Chapter 10. ∞ pp. 367–368 The interactions among the reproductive hormones in males are diagrammed in Figure 19-7. In the presence of **gonadotropin-releasing hormone (GnRH)**—a peptide synthesized in the hypothalamus and carried to the anterior pituitary by the hypophyseal portal system—the anterior pituitary gland releases two hormones: **follicle-stimulating hormone (FSH)** and **luteinizing hormone (LH)**.

FSH and Spermatogenesis

In males, FSH targets primarily nurse cells of the seminiferous tubules. Under FSH stimulation, and in the presence of testosterone from the interstitial cells, nurse cells promote spermatogenesis and spermiogenesis.

The rate of spermatogenesis is regulated by a negative-feedback mechanism involving GnRH, FSH, testosterone, and inhibin. Under GnRH stimulation, FSH promotes spermatogenesis along the seminiferous tubules. As spermatogenesis accelerates, however, so does the rate of inhibin secretion by the nurse cells of the testes. Inhibin inhibits FSH production in the anterior pituitary and may also inhibit secretion of GnRH at the hypothalamus. Rising levels of testosterone also reduce GnRH secretion and pituitary gland responsiveness to GnRH, thereby inhibiting FSH (and LH) secretion.

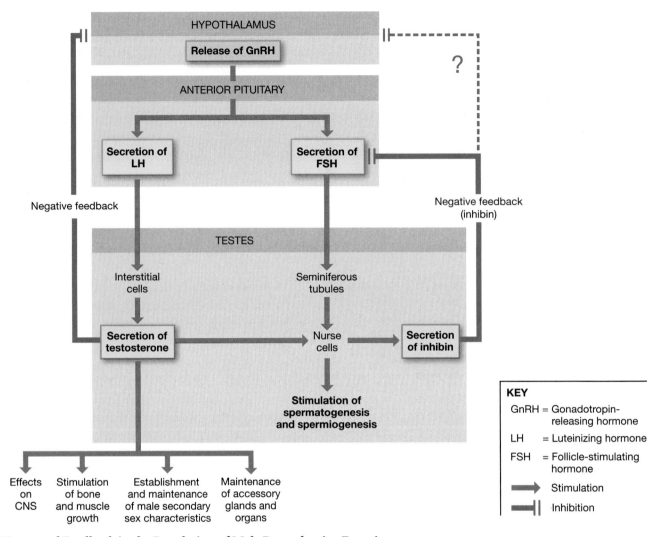

FIGURE 19-7 Hormonal Feedback in the Regulation of Male Reproductive Function.

The net effect is that when FSH levels become elevated, inhibin production increases until FSH levels return to normal. If FSH levels decline, inhibin production falls, so the rate of FSH production accelerates.

LH and Androgen Production

LH in males—which was once called *interstitial cell-stimulating hormone, ICSH,* before it was found to be identical to the hormone in females—causes the secretion of testosterone and other androgens by the interstitial cells of the testes. Testosterone, the most important androgen, has numerous functions, including (1) stimulating spermatogenesis and promoting the functional maturation of spermatozoa; (2) affecting central nervous system (CNS) function, including the influence of sexual drive (libido) and related behaviors; (3) stimulating metabolism throughout the body, especially pathways concerned with protein synthesis and muscle and bone growth; (4) determining and maintaining secondary sex characteristics, such as facial hair, increased muscle mass and body size, and the quantity and location of adipose tissue; (5) maintaining the accessory glands and organs of the male reproductive tract; and (6) regulating LH and FSH secretion at the hypothalamus.

Testosterone production begins around the seventh week of development and reaches a peak after roughly 6 months of development. The early surge in testosterone levels stimulates the differentiation of the male duct system and accessory organs and affects CNS development. Testosterone secretion accelerates markedly at puberty, initiating sexual maturation and the appearance of secondary sex characteristics. In adult males, negative-feedback mechanisms control the level of testosterone production. Above-normal testosterone levels inhibit the release of GnRH by the hypothalamus. This inhibition causes a reduction in LH (and FSH) secretion and lowers testosterone levels.

CHECKPOINT

4. List the male reproductive structures.

5. On a warm day, would the cremaster muscle be contracted or relaxed? Why?

6. What happens when arteries within the penis dilate?

7. What effect would low FSH levels have on sperm production?

See the blue Answers tab at the back of the book.

19-3 Ovum production (oogenesis) occurs in the ovaries, and hormones from the pituitary gland and ovaries control female reproductive functions

A woman's reproductive system produces sex hormones and gametes, and it must also be able to protect and support a developing embryo and nourish a newborn infant. The principal organs of the female reproductive system are the *ovaries,* the *uterine tubes,* the *uterus* (womb), the *vagina,* and the components of the external genitalia (Figure 19-8a). The female reproductive system also includes the mammary glands and a variety of accessory glands that secrete their products into the reproductive tract.

THE OVARIES

The paired ovaries are small, lumpy, almond-shaped organs near the lateral walls of the pelvic cavity (Figure 19-8b). The ovaries are responsible for (1) the production of female gametes, or **ova** (singular *ovum*); (2) the secretion of female sex hormones, including *estrogens* and *progestins;* and (3) the secretion of inhibin, involved in the negative-feedback control of pituitary FSH production.

A typical **ovary** is a flattened oval that measures approximately 5 cm long, 2.5 cm wide, and 8 mm thick (2 in. × 1 in. × 0.33 in.). It has a pale white or yellowish coloration and a consistency that resembles cottage cheese or lumpy oatmeal.

The position of each ovary is stabilized by a mesentery known as the *broad ligament* and by a pair of supporting ligaments. The mesentery also encloses the uterine tubes and uterus. The ligaments attached to each ovary extend to the uterus and pelvic wall. The latter contain the major blood vessels of each ovary: the *ovarian artery* and *ovarian vein.*

Oogenesis

Ovum production, or **oogenesis** (ō-ō-JEN-e-sis; *oon,* egg), is a process in females that begins before birth, accelerates at puberty, and ends at *menopause* (*men,* month + *pausis,* cessation). Between puberty and menopause, oogenesis occurs in the ovaries each month, as part of the *ovarian cycle* (discussed shortly). The events in oogenesis are summarized in Figure 19-9.

In the ovaries, the **oogonia** (ō-ō-GŌ-nē-uh), or stem cells, complete their mitotic divisions before birth (Figure 19-9). Between the third and seventh months of fetal development, the daughter cells, or **primary oocytes** (Ō-ō-sīts), begin to undergo meiosis. They proceed as far as prophase of meiosis I, but then the process stops. The primary oocytes remain in a state of suspended development for years—until the individual reaches puberty—awaiting the hormonal signal to complete meiosis. Not all of the primary oocytes survive; of the roughly 2 million in the ovaries at birth, about 400,000 remain at the start of puberty. The rest of the primary oocytes degenerate in a process called *atresia* (a-TRĒ-zē-uh).

Although the nuclear events under way during meiosis in the ovary are the same as those in the testis, the process differs in two important ways:

1. The cytoplasm of the original oocyte is not evenly distributed during the meiotic divisions. Oogenesis produces one functional ovum, containing most of that cytoplasm, and up to three nonfunctional **polar bodies** that later disintegrate.

2. The ovary does not release a mature gamete; instead of a mature ovum, a *secondary oocyte* is released. Moreover, the second meiotic division is not completed until *after* fertilization.

Follicle Development

Specialized structures called **ovarian follicles** (ō-VAR-ē-an FOL-i-klz) are the sites of both oocyte growth and meiosis I of oogenesis. In the outer portion of each ovary are clusters of primary oocytes, each surrounded by a single layer of *follicle cells.* The combination is known as a **primordial** (prī-MOR-dē-al) **follicle** (Figure 19-10). Beginning at puberty, primordial follicles are continuously activated to join other follicles already in development. The activating mechanism is unknown, although local hormones or growth factors within the ovary may be involved. The activated primordial follicle will either mature and be released as a secondary oocyte or degenerate (atresia).

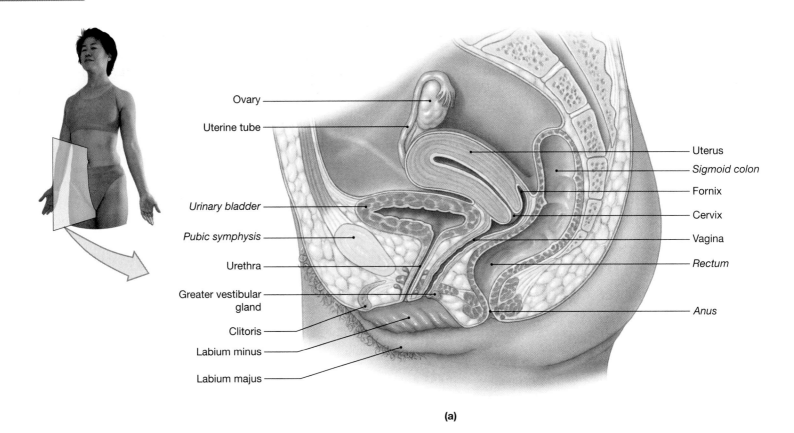

Ovary

Uterine tube

Uterus

Sigmoid colon

Fornix

Cervix

Urinary bladder

Vagina

Pubic symphysis

Rectum

Urethra

*Greater vestibular
gland*

Anus

Clitoris

Labium minus

Labium majus

(a)

Uterine tube   Ovarian
ligament

Fimbriae

Ovarian artery
and vein

Suspensory
ligament

Uterus

Ovary

Broad ligament

Broad ligament

Infundibulum

Ureter

External os

Cervix

Vaginal rugae

Vaginal wall

(b)

FIGURE 19-8 **The Female Reproductive System.** **(a)** This sagittal section shows the female
reproductive organs. **(b)** The locations of the uterus, uterine tubes, and ovaries are apparent in this
posterior view.

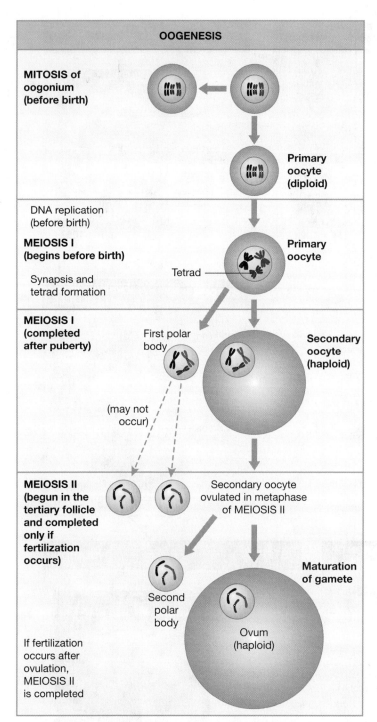

OOGENESIS

MITOSIS of oogonium (before birth)

Primary oocyte (diploid)

DNA replication (before birth)

MEIOSIS I (begins before birth)

Synapsis and tetrad formation

Tetrad

Primary oocyte

MEIOSIS I (completed after puberty)

First polar body

Secondary oocyte (haploid)

(may not occur)

MEIOSIS II (begun in the tertiary follicle and completed only if fertilization occurs)

Secondary oocyte ovulated in metaphase of MEIOSIS II

If fertilization occurs after ovulation, MEIOSIS II is completed

Second polar body

Ovum (haploid)

Maturation of gamete

FIGURE 19-9 Oogenesis. In oogenesis, each diploid primary oocyte that undergoes meiosis produces a haploid ovum plus two or three nonfunctional polar bodies. Most of the events depicted here occur in the ovary as part of the ovarian cycle, shown in Figure 19-10.

The preliminary steps in follicle development are of variable length, but may take almost a year to complete. Follicle development begins with the activation of primordial follicles into **primary follicles** (Step 1 of Figure 19-10). The follicular

cells enlarge, divide, and form several layers of cells around the growing primary oocyte. Microvilli from the surrounding follicular cells intermingle with microvilli originating at the surface of the oocyte. This region is called the **zona pellucida** (ZŌ-na pe-LOO-sid-uh; *pellucidus,* translucent). The microvilli increase the surface area available for the transfer of materials from the follicular cells to the growing oocyte.

Although many primordial follicles develop into primary follicles, only a few of the primary follicles mature further. This process is apparently under the control of a growth factor produced by the oocyte. The transformation begins as the wall of the follicle thickens and the deeper follicular cells begin secreting small amounts of fluid. This *follicular fluid* accumulates in small pockets that gradually expand and separate the inner and outer layers of the follicle. At this stage, the complex is known as a **secondary follicle** (Step 2). Although the primary oocyte continues to grow slowly, the follicle as a whole enlarges rapidly because follicular fluid accumulates.

The Ovarian Cycle

The follicles are then ready to complete their maturation as part of the **ovarian cycle,** a 28-day cycle that includes follicle maturation (the *follicular phase*), ovulation, and the subsequent release of hormones by the remaining follicle cells (the *luteal phase*). Each of these phases lasts approximately 14 days, and the changes in follicle structure that occur as part of the ovarian cycle are shown in Steps 3 through 5 in Figure 19-10.

THE FOLLICULAR PHASE. At the start of each ovarian cycle, an ovary contains only a few secondary follicles destined for further development; by day 5 of the cycle, usually only one remains. Stimulated by FSH, that follicle forms a **tertiary follicle,** or mature *Graafian* (GRAF-ē-an) *follicle,* roughly 15–20 mm in diameter (Step 3). The tertiary follicle is formed by days 10–14 of the ovarian cycle. Its large size creates a prominent bulge in the surface of the ovary. The oocyte and its covering of follicular cells projects into the expanded central chamber of the follicle, the **antrum** (AN-trum).

Until this time, the primary oocyte has been suspended in prophase of meiosis I. As the development of the tertiary follicle ends, rising LH levels prompt the primary oocyte to complete meiosis I. The completion of the first meiotic division produces a secondary oocyte (and also a nonfunctional polar body; Figure 19-9). The secondary oocyte begins meiosis II but stops short of dividing. Meiosis II will not be completed unless fertilization occurs.

FIGURE 19-10 Follicle Development and the Ovarian Cycle. The photomicrographs show the changes in a follicle as it develops and enters the ovarian cycle. The drawing of the ovary illustrates the sequence and relative sizes of the various stages in the development, ovulation, and degeneration of an ovarian follicle; follicles do not physically move around the periphery of the ovary.

Generally, on day 14 of a 28-day ovarian cycle, the secondary oocyte and its surrounding follicular cells lose their connections with the follicular wall and float within the antrum. The follicular cells surrounding the oocyte are now known as the *corona radiata* (ko-RŌ-nuh rā-dē-A-tuh).

OVULATION. At **ovulation** (ōv-ū-LĀ-shun), the tertiary follicle releases the secondary oocyte (an immature gamete) (Step 4). The distended follicular wall then ruptures, releasing the follicular contents, including the secondary oocyte, into the pelvic cavity. The sticky follicular fluid keeps the corona radiata

Oogenesis begins during embryonic development, and primary oocyte production is completed before birth. After puberty, the ovarian cycle produces one or more secondary oocytes each month from the pre-existing population of primary oocytes. The number of viable and responsive primary oocytes declines markedly over time, until ovarian cycles end at age 45–55.

attached to the surface of the ovary near the ruptured wall of the follicle. Contact with projections of the uterine tube or with fluid currents established by its ciliated epithelium then sweeps the secondary oocyte into the uterine tube.

THE LUTEAL PHASE. The 14-day luteal phase of the ovarian cycle begins at ovulation. The empty follicle collapses, and the remaining follicular cells invade the resulting cavity and multiply to create an endocrine structure known as the **corpus luteum** (LOO-tē-um; *lutea*, yellow) (Step 5). Unless fertilization occurs, the corpus luteum begins to degenerate roughly 12 days after ovulation. The disintegration of the corpus luteum marks the end of an ovarian cycle. A new ovarian cycle begins with the selection of another secondary follicle and its formation into a tertiary follicle under the stimulation of FSH.

THE UTERINE TUBES

Each **uterine tube** (*Fallopian tube*, or *oviduct*) measures roughly 13 cm (5 in.) in length. The end closest to the ovary forms an expanded funnel, or **infundibulum** (in-fun-DIB-ū-lum; *infundibulum*, a funnel), with numerous fingerlike projections that extend into the pelvic cavity (Figure 19-8b). Both the projections, called **fimbriae** (FIM-brē-ē), and the inner surfaces of the infundibulum are carpeted with cilia that beat toward the broad entrance to the uterine tube.

Oocyte transport involves a combination of ciliary movement and peristaltic contractions by smooth muscles in the walls of the uterine tubes. It normally takes 3–4 days for the oocyte to travel from the infundibulum to the uterine cavity. *If fertilization is to occur, the secondary oocyte must encounter spermatozoa during the first 12–24 hours of its passage.* Unfertilized oocytes will degenerate in the uterine tubes or uterus without completing meiosis.

In addition to ciliated cells, the epithelium lining the uterine tubes contains *peg cells* and scattered mucin-secreting cells. The peg cells project into the lumen of the uterine tube and secrete a fluid that both completes the capacitation of spermatozoa and supplies nutrients to spermatozoa and the developing *pre-embryo* (the cluster of cells produced by initial mitotic divisions following fertilization).

THE UTERUS

The **uterus** (Ū-ter-us) is a muscular chamber that provides mechanical protection and nutritional support for the developing *embryo* (weeks 1–8) and *fetus* (week 9 to delivery). In addition, contractions in the muscular wall of the uterus are important in ejecting the fetus at birth.

A typical uterus is a small, pear-shaped organ that is about 7.5 cm (3 in.) long and 5 cm (2 in.) in diameter (Figure 19-8b). It weighs 30–40 g (1–1.4 oz.) and is stabilized by various ligaments. In its normal position, the uterus bends anteriorly near its base (Figure 19-8a).

The uterus consists of two regions: the body and the cervix (Figure 19-11). The **body** is the largest division of the uterus. The *fundus* is the rounded portion of the body superior to the attachment of the uterine tubes. Laterally, the body ends at a

Clinical Note

Pelvic Inflammatory Disease (PID)

Pelvic inflammatory disease (PID) is a term used for an infection of the uterus, uterine tubes, and ovaries. The infection starts with invasion of the cervix by bacteria and then spreads to the uterus and uterine tubes. PID is a major cause of female sterility (infertility), affecting an estimated 1 million women each year in the United States.

Signs and symptoms of pelvic inflammatory disease include fever, lower abdominal pain, and elevated white blood cell counts. In severe cases, the infection can spread to other visceral organs or produce a generalized peritonitis. Most cases are thought to be caused by sexually transmitted diseases (STDs), most often **gonorrhea** (gon-ō-RĒ-a) and **chlamydia** (kla-MID-ē-a). PID may also result from invasion of the region by bacteria normally found within the vagina.

Sexually active women ages 15–24 have the highest incidence of PID. Whereas the use of an oral contraceptive or condom decreases the risk of infection, the presence of an intrauterine device (IUD) may increase the risk. Treatment with antibiotics may control the condition, but chronic abdominal pain may persist. In addition, damage and scarring of the uterine tubes can cause infertility by preventing the passage of sperm to the egg or of a zygote to the uterus. Despite the fact that women with *Chlamydia* infection may experience few, if any, symptoms, scarring of the uterine tubes can still occur.

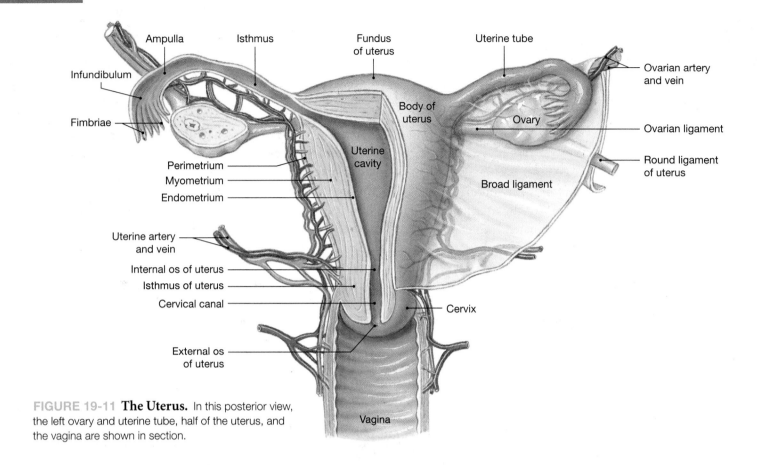

FIGURE 19-11 **The Uterus.** In this posterior view, the left ovary and uterine tube, half of the uterus, and the vagina are shown in section.

constriction known as the **isthmus.** The tubular **cervix** (SER-viks), the inferior portion of the uterus, projects a short distance into the vagina, where its surface surrounds the **external os** (*os*, an opening or mouth), or *external orifice*, of the uterus. The cervical canal opens into the **uterine cavity** at the **internal os,** or *internal orifice.*

The uterine wall is made up of an inner **endometrium** (en-dō-MĒ-trē-um) and a muscular **myometrium** (mī-ō-MĒ-trē-um; *myo-*, muscle + *metra*, uterus), covered by the **perimetrium,** a layer of visceral peritoneum (Figure 19-11). The endometrium includes the epithelium lining the uterine cavity and the underlying connective tissues. *Uterine glands,* also called *endometrial glands,* open onto the endometrial surface and extend deep into the connective tissue layer almost to the myometrium. The myometrium consists of a thick mass of interwoven smooth muscle cells. In adult women of reproductive age who have not given birth, the uterine wall is about 1.5 cm (0.5 in.) thick.

The endometrium consists of a superficial *functional zone* and a deeper *basilar zone* that is adjacent to the myometrium. The structure of the basilar layer remains relatively constant over time, but that of the functional zone undergoes cyclical changes in response to sex hormone levels. These alterations produce the characteristic features of the monthly uterine cycle.

The Uterine Cycle

The **uterine cycle,** or *menstrual* (MEN-stroo-al) *cycle,* is a repeating series of changes in the structure of the endometrium. The first uterine cycle occurs with the **menarche** (me-NAR-kē), or first menstrual period at puberty, typically age 11–12. The cycles continue until age 45–55, when **menopause** (MEN-ō-pawz), the last menstrual cycle, occurs. In the interim, the regular appearance of menstrual cycles is interrupted only by circumstances such as illness, stress, starvation, or pregnancy.

The uterine cycle averages 28 days in length, but it can range from 21 to 35 days in normal individuals. It consists of three stages: *menses,* the *proliferative phase,* and the *secretory phase.*

MENSES. The menstrual cycle begins with the onset of **menses** (MEN-sēz), a period marked by the degeneration of the superficial *functional zone* of the endometrium. The process is triggered by a decline in progesterone and estrogen levels as the corpus luteum disintegrates. Endometrial arteries constrict, reducing blood flow to this region, and the secretory glands, epithelial cells, and other tissues of the functional zone die of oxygen and nutrient deprivation. Eventually the weakened arterial walls rupture, and blood pours into the connective tissues of the functional zone. Blood cells and degenerating tissues break away and enter the uterine cavity to be lost by passage through the vagina. This sloughing of tissue, which continues until the entire functional zone has been lost, is called **menstruation** (men-stroo-Ā-shun). Menstruation usually lasts 1 to 7 days, and roughly 35–50 mL (1.2 to 1.7 oz.) of blood is lost. Painful menstruation, or *dysmenorrhea,* can result from uterine inflammation, myometrial contractions ("cramps"), or conditions involving adjacent pelvic structures.

THE PROLIFERATIVE PHASE. The **proliferative phase** begins in the days following the completion of menses as the surviving epithelial cells multiply and spread across the surface of the endometrium. This repair process is stimulated by rising estrogen levels that accompany the growth of another set of ovarian follicles. By the time ovulation occurs, the functional zone is several millimeters thick, and its new set of uterine glands is secreting a mucus rich in glycogen. In addition, the entire functional zone is filled with small arteries that branch from larger trunks in the myometrium.

THE SECRETORY PHASE. During the **secretory phase** of the uterine cycle, uterine glands enlarge, increasing their rates of secretion as the endometrium prepares for the arrival of a developing embryo. This activity is stimulated by progestins and estrogens from the corpus luteum. This phase begins at ovulation and persists as long as the corpus luteum remains intact. Secretory activities peak about 12 days after ovulation. Over the next day or two glandular activity declines, and the uterine cycle ends. A new cycle then begins with the onset of menses and the disintegration of the functional zone.

THE VAGINA

The **vagina** (va-JĪ-nuh) is an elastic, muscular tube extending between the uterus and the vestibule, a space bounded by the external genitalia (Figure 19-8a). The vagina is typically 7.5–9 cm (3–3.5 in.) long, but its diameter varies because it is highly distensible. The cervix of the uterus projects into the vagina (Figure 19-11). The shallow recess surrounding the cervical protrusion is known as the **fornix** (FOR-niks) (Figure 19-8a). The vagina lies parallel to the rectum, and the two are in close contact posteriorly. The urethra extends along the superior wall of the vagina from the urinary bladder to the urethral opening, or external urethral orifice.

Clinical Note

Amenorrhea

If menarche does not occur by age 16, or if a woman's normal menstrual cycle becomes interrupted for 6 months or more, the condition of **amenorrhea** (ā-men-ō-RĔ-uh) exists. *Primary amenorrhea*—the failure to begin menses—may indicate developmental abnormalities, such as nonfunctional ovaries, the absence of a uterus, or some endocrine or genetic disorder. It can also result from malnutrition; puberty is delayed if leptin levels are too low. ∞ p. 367 *Transient secondary amenorrhea* may be caused by severe physical or emotional stresses. In effect, the reproductive system gets "switched off." Factors that cause either type of amenorrhea include drastic weight reduction programs, anorexia nervosa, and severe depression or grief. Amenorrhea has also been observed in marathon runners and other women engaged in training programs that require sustained high levels of exertion and thus severely reduce body lipid reserves.

The vaginal walls contain a network of blood vessels and layers of smooth muscle. The lining is moistened by the mucous secretions of the cervical glands and by the movement of water across the permeable epithelium. The vagina and vestibule are separated by an elastic epithelial fold, the **hymen** (HĪ-men) (Figure 19-12), which partially or completely blocks the entrance

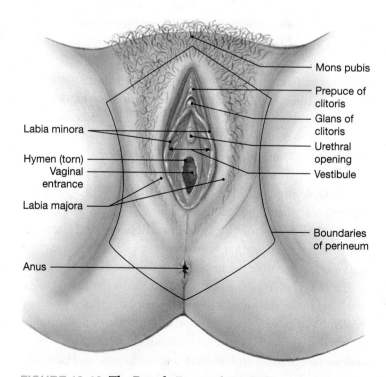

FIGURE 19-12 **The Female External Genitalia.**

to the vagina before the first occasion of sexual intercourse or tampon usage. A bulbospongiosus muscle lies on either side of the vaginal entrance (see Figure 7-16a, p. 225), which is constricted by their contractions.

The vagina has three major functions: It (1) serves as a passageway for the elimination of menstrual fluids; (2) receives the penis during sexual intercourse and holds spermatozoa prior to their passage into the uterus; and (3) forms the lower portion of the birth canal, through which the fetus passes during delivery.

The vagina normally contains resident bacteria supported by nutrients in the cervical mucus. The metabolic activity of these bacteria creates an acidic environment, which restricts the growth of many pathogens. Inflammation of the vaginal canal, known as *vaginitis* (vaj-i-NĪ-tis), is typically caused by fungi, bacteria, or parasites. In addition to any discomfort that may result, the condition may lower the survival of sperm and thereby reduce fertility.

THE EXTERNAL GENITALIA

The **perineum,** the muscular floor of the pelvic cavity ∞ p. 223, includes the anus and reproductive system structures called the **external genitalia** (Figure 19-12). The perineal region enclosing the female external genitalia is the **vulva** (VUL-vuh), or *pudendum.* The vagina opens into the **vestibule,** a central space bounded by the **labia minora** (LĀ-bē-uh mi-NOR-uh; *labia,* lips; singular *labium minus*). The labia minora are covered with smooth, hairless skin. The urethra opens into the vestibule just anterior to the vaginal entrance. Anterior to the urethral opening, the **clitoris** (KLIT-ō-ris) projects into the vestibule. The clitoris is derived from the same embryonic structures as the penis in males. Internally it contains erectile tissue comparable to the corpora cavernosa of the penis. The clitoris engorges with blood during sexual arousal. A small erectile *glans* sits atop the organ, and extensions of the labia minora encircle the body of the clitoris, forming the *prepuce.*

A variable number of small **lesser vestibular glands** discharge secretions onto the exposed surface of the vestibule, keeping it moist. During sexual arousal, a pair of ducts discharges the secretions of the **greater vestibular glands** into the vestibule near the vaginal entrance (Figure 19-8). These mucous glands resemble the bulbo-urethral glands of males.

The outer limits of the vulva are formed by the mons pubis and labia majora. The prominent bulge of the **mons pubis** is created by adipose tissue beneath the skin anterior to the pubic symphysis. Adipose tissue also accumulates in the fleshy **labia majora** (singular *labium majus*), which encircle and partially conceal the labia minora and vestibular structures.

THE MAMMARY GLANDS

A newborn cannot fend for itself, as several of its key organ systems have not yet developed fully. During its adjustment to an independent existence, the infant gains nourishment from the milk secreted by the **mammary glands** of the breasts (Figure 19-13). Milk production, or **lactation** (lak-TĀ-shun), occurs in these glands. In females, the mammary glands are specialized organs of the integumentary system that are controlled by hormones of the reproductive system and of the *placenta,* a temporary structure that provides the embryo and fetus with nutrients.

Each breast contains a mammary gland within the subcutaneous tissue of the *pectoral fat pad* beneath the skin. The ducts of the underlying mammary gland open onto the body surface at a small conical projection—the **nipple.** The reddish-brown skin surrounding each nipple is the **areola** (a-RĒ-ō-luh). Large sebaceous glands beneath the areolar surface give it a grainy texture.

The glandular tissue of a mammary gland consists of separate lobes, each made up of several lobules containing milk glands. Within each lobe, the ducts leaving the lobules converge, giving rise to a single **lactiferous** (lak-TIF-er-us) **duct.** Near the

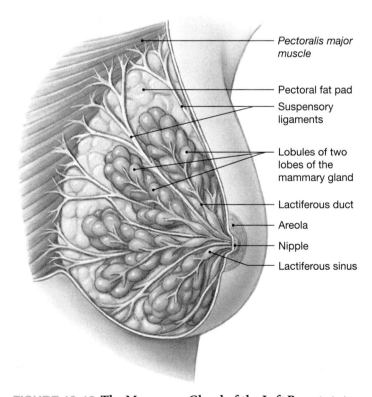

Pectoralis major muscle

Pectoral fat pad

Suspensory ligaments

Lobules of two lobes of the mammary gland

Lactiferous duct

Areola

Nipple

Lactiferous sinus

FIGURE 19-13 The Mammary Gland of the Left Breast. Lobes of glandular tissue within each mammary gland are responsible for the production of breast milk.

Clinical Note

Breast Cancer

Breast cancer is a malignant, metastasizing tumor of the mammary gland. Almost 90 percent of breast cancers begin in the ducts and lobes of the mammary glands and are called *ductal carcinomas* and *lobular carcinomas,* respectively. If the tumor cells have spread outside of a duct or lobule and into the surrounding tissue, the cancer is called an *invasive ductal* or *lobular carcinoma.* Cancers that have not spread are called *in situ,* which means "in place," and are known as *ductal carcinoma in situ* (*DCIS*) and *lobular carcinoma in situ* (*LCIS*).

Breast cancer is the leading cause of death in women between the ages of 35 and 45, but it is most common in women over age 50. Estimates made in 2008 predicted 40,480 female deaths and approximately 182,460 new cases of breast cancer in the United States in that year. An estimated 12 percent of U.S. women will develop breast cancer at some point in their lifetime, and the rate is steadily rising. The incidence is highest among Caucasian Americans, somewhat lower in African Americans, and lowest in Asian Americans and American Indians. Notable risk factors include (1) a family history of breast cancer, (2) a first pregnancy after age 30, and (3) early menarche (first menstrual period) or late menopause (last menstrual period). Breast cancers in males are very rare, but about 400 men die from the disease each year in the United States.

nipple, that lactiferous duct expands, forming an expanded chamber called a **lactiferous sinus.** Some 15–20 lactiferous sinuses open onto the surface of each nipple. Dense connective tissue surrounds the duct system and forms partitions that extend between the lobes and lobules. These bands of connective tissue, the *suspensory ligaments of the breast,* originate in the dermis of the overlying skin. A layer of loose connective tissue separates the mammary gland complex from the underlying muscles, and the two can move relatively independently.

HORMONES AND THE FEMALE REPRODUCTIVE CYCLE

As is the case for males, activity of the reproductive system in females is under hormonal control by both pituitary and gonadal secretions. However, the regulatory pattern in females is much more complicated than in males because circulating hormones must coordinate the ovarian and uterine cycles to ensure that the **female reproductive cycle** results in the proper functioning of all reproductive activities. If the ovarian and uterine cycles are not coordinated normally, infertility results. A woman who fails to ovulate will be unable to conceive, even if her uterus is perfectly normal. A woman who ovulates normally but whose uterus is not ready to support an embryo will be just as infertile.

Hormones and the Follicular Phase

The **follicular phase** (or *preovulatory phase*) of the ovarian cycle begins each month when FSH from the anterior pituitary stimulates some of the secondary follicles to begin their development into tertiary (Graafian) follicles (Figure 19-10, p. 652). As the follicular cells enlarge and multiply, they release steroid hormones collectively known as **estrogens.** The most important estrogen is **estradiol** (es-tra-DĪ-ol). Estrogens have multiple functions, including (1) affecting central nervous system (CNS) activity (especially in the hypothalamus, where estrogens increase sexual drive); (2) stimulating bone and muscle growth; (3) establishing and maintaining female secondary sex characteristics, such as the distributions of body hair and adipose tissue deposits; (4) maintaining functional accessory reproductive glands and organs; and (5) initiating the repair and growth of the endometrium. Figure 19-14 diagrams the hormonal regulation of ovarian activity, and includes an overview of the effects of estrogens on various aspects of reproductive function.

Figure 19-15 shows the changes in circulating hormonal levels that accompany the ovarian cycle. Early in the follicular phase, estrogen and inhibin levels are low (Figure 19-15c). The estrogens and inhibin have complementary effects on the secretion of FSH and LH: Low levels of estrogen inhibit LH and FSH secretion (Figure 19-14). As follicular development proceeds, the concentrations of circulating estrogens and inhibin rise (Figure 19-15c) because the follicular cells are increasing in number and in secretory activity. As secondary follicles develop, FSH levels decline due to the negative-feedback effects of inhibin, and estrogen levels continue to rise. Despite the slow decline in FSH concentrations, the combination of estrogens, FSH, and LH continues to support follicular development and maturation.

Estrogen concentrations take a sharp upturn in the second week of the ovarian cycle, with the development of a tertiary follicle as it enlarges in preparation for ovulation (Figure 19-15b). The rapid increase in estrogens leads to the secretion of FSH and LH by acting on the hypothalamus and stimulating the production of GnRH. The pituitary gland also becomes more sensitive to GnRH and contributes to the rise in FSH and LH. At roughly day 10 of the cycle, the effect of estrogen on LH secretion also changes from inhibition to stimulation (Figure 19-14). At about day 14, estrogen levels peak, accompanying the maturation of the tertiary follicle. The high estrogen concentration then triggers a massive outpouring, or

FIGURE 19-14 Hormonal Regulation of Ovarian Activity.

surge, of LH from the anterior pituitary, which triggers the rupture of the follicular wall and ovulation.

Hormones and the Luteal Phase

The **luteal phase,** or *postovulatory phase,* of the ovarian cycle begins as the high LH levels that triggered ovulation also stimulate the remaining follicular cells to form a corpus luteum (Figure 19-15a–c). The yellow color of the corpus luteum results from its lipid reserves, which are used to manufacture steroid hormones known as **progestins** (prō-JES-tinz), predominantly the steroid **progesterone** (prō-JES-ter-ōn). Progesterone, the principal hormone of the luteal phase, prepares the uterus for pregnancy by stimulating the growth and development of the blood supply and secretory glands of the endometrium (Figure 19-15d). Progesterone also stimulates metabolic activity and elevates basal body temperature (Figure 19-15e).

Luteinizing hormone (LH) levels remain elevated for only 2 days, but that is long enough to stimulate the formation of a functional corpus luteum. Progesterone secretion continues at relatively high levels for the next week. Unless pregnancy occurs, however, the corpus luteum begins to degenerate. Roughly 12 days after ovulation, the corpus luteum becomes nonfunctional, and progesterone and estrogen levels fall markedly. With this decline, hypothalamic production of GnRH is no longer inhibited and GnRH production increases (Figure 19-14). The increased secretion of GnRH, in turn, leads to increased FSH production in the anterior pituitary gland, and the ovarian cycle begins again.

Hormones and the Uterine Cycle

The declines in progesterone and estrogen levels that accompany the breakdown of the corpus luteum result in

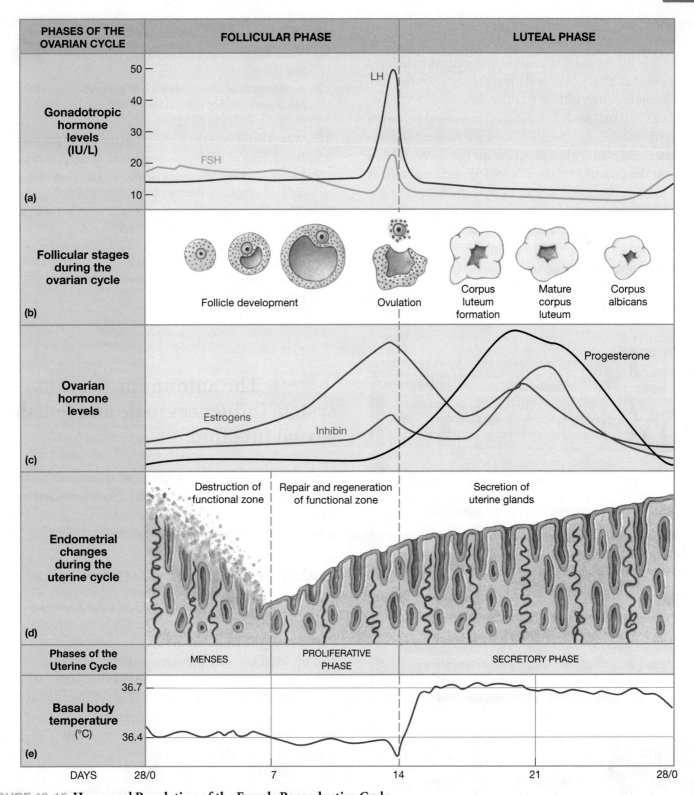

PHASES OF THE OVARIAN CYCLE	FOLLICULAR PHASE	LUTEAL PHASE

(a) Gonadotropic hormone levels (IU/L) — LH, FSH

(b) Follicular stages during the ovarian cycle — Follicle development, Ovulation, Corpus luteum formation, Mature corpus luteum, Corpus albicans

(c) Ovarian hormone levels — Estrogens, Inhibin, Progesterone

(d) Endometrial changes during the uterine cycle — Destruction of functional zone, Repair and regeneration of functional zone, Secretion of uterine glands

Phases of the Uterine Cycle — MENSES, PROLIFERATIVE PHASE, SECRETORY PHASE

(e) Basal body temperature (°C)

DAYS 28/0   7   14   21   28/0

FIGURE 19-15 **Hormonal Regulation of the Female Reproductive Cycle.**

menses (Figure 19-15d). The loss of endometrial tissue continues for several days, until rising estrogen levels stimulate the regeneration of the functional zone of the endometrium.

The proliferative phase continues until rising progesterone levels mark the arrival of the secretory phase. The combination of estrogen and progesterone then causes the enlargement of uterine glands as well as an increase in their secretions.

Hormones and Body Temperature

The monthly hormonal fluctuations also cause physiological changes that affect core body temperature. During the follicular phase, when estrogen is the dominant hormone, the resting (or basal) body temperature measured on awakening in the morning is about 0.3°C (0.5°F) lower than it is during the luteal phase, when progesterone dominates (Figure 19-15e). At the time of ovulation, basal temperature declines sharply, making the temperature rise over the following day even more noticeable. By keeping records of body temperature over a few menstrual cycles, a woman can often determine the precise day of ovulation. This information can be very important for those wishing to avoid or promote a pregnancy because fertilization leading to pregnancy typically occurs within a day of ovulation.

Clinical Note

Infertility

Infertility (*sterility*) is usually defined as an inability to achieve pregnancy after 1 year of appropriately timed sexual intercourse. Problems with infertility are relatively common. An estimated 10–15 percent of married couples in the United States are infertile, and another 10 percent are unable to have as many children as they desire. It is, thus, not surprising that reproductive physiology has become a popular field of medicine and that the treatment of infertility has become a major medical industry. Recent advances in our understanding of reproductive physiology are providing new solutions to fertility problems as varied as low sperm count, abnormal spermatozoa, inadequate maternal hormone levels, problems with oocyte production or oocyte transport from ovary to uterine tube, blocked uterine tubes, abnormal oocytes, and an abnormal uterine environment. Procedures meant to resolve these reproductive difficulties are known as *assisted reproductive technologies* (*ART*).

The Big Picture

Cyclic changes in FSH and LH levels are responsible for the maintenance of the ovarian cycle; the hormones produced by the ovaries in turn regulate the uterine cycle. Inadequate hormone levels, inappropriate or inadequate responses to circulating hormones, or poor coordination and timing of hormone production or secondary oocyte release will reduce or eliminate the chances of pregnancy.

19-4 The autonomic nervous system influences male and female sexual function

Sexual intercourse, also known as **coitus** (KŌ-i-tus) or *copulation,* introduces semen into the female reproductive tract. The following sections consider the physiological bases for the sexual responses of males and females.

MALE SEXUAL FUNCTION

Male sexual function is coordinated by reflex pathways involving both divisions of the ANS. During sexual **arousal,** erotic thoughts or the stimulation of sensory nerves in the genital region increase the parasympathetic outflow over the pelvic nerves. This outflow leads to erection of the penis (discussed on p. 646). The skin of the glans of the penis contains numerous sensory receptors, and erection tenses the skin and increases their sensitivity. Subsequent stimulation may initiate the secretion of the bulbo-urethral glands, lubricating the urethra and the surface of the glans.

During intercourse, the sensory receptors in the penis are rhythmically stimulated, eventually resulting in emission and ejaculation. **Emission** occurs under sympathetic stimulation. The process begins with peristaltic contractions of the ductus deferens, which push fluid and spermatozoa through the ejaculatory ducts and into the urethra. The seminal glands then contract, followed by waves of contraction in the prostate gland. While these contractions are proceeding, sympathetic commands close the sphincter at the entrance to the urinary bladder, preventing the passage of semen into the bladder.

Ejaculation occurs as powerful, rhythmic contractions appear in the *ischiocavernosus* and *bulbospongiosus* muscles, two superficial skeletal muscles of the pelvic floor. (The positions of these muscles can be seen in Figure 7-16b, p. 225.) Ejaculation is associated with intensely pleasurable sensations, an experience known as male **orgasm** (OR-gazm). Several other physiological changes also occur at this time, including temporary increases in heart rate and blood pressure. After ejaculation, blood begins to leave the erectile tissue, and the erection begins to subside. This subsidence, called *detumescence* (dē-tū-MES-ens), is mediated by the sympathetic nervous system. An inability to achieve or maintain an erection is called **impotence.**

FEMALE SEXUAL FUNCTION

The events in female sexual function are largely comparable to those that occur in males. During sexual arousal, parasympathetic activation leads to an engorgement of the erectile tissues of the clitoris and increased secretion of cervical mucous glands and the greater vestibular glands. Clitoral erection increases the receptors' sensitivity to stimulation, and the cervical and vestibular glands provide lubrication for the vaginal walls. A network of blood vessels in the vaginal walls becomes filled with blood at this time, and the vaginal surfaces are also moistened by fluid from underlying connective tissues. Parasympathetic stimulation also causes engorgement of blood vessels at the nipples, making them more sensitive to touch and pressure.

During intercourse, rhythmic contact of the penis with the clitoris and vaginal walls, reinforced by touch sensations from the breasts and other stimuli (visual, olfactory, and auditory), provides stimulation that can lead to orgasm. Female orgasm is accompanied by peristaltic contractions of the uterine and vaginal walls and by rhythmic contractions of the bulbospongiosus and ischiocavernosus muscles. The latter contractions give rise to the sensations of orgasm.

CHECKPOINT

16. List the physiological events of sexual intercourse in both sexes, and indicate those that occur in males but not in females.

17. An inability to contract the ischiocavernosus and bulbospongiosus muscles would interfere with which part of the sexual response in males?

18. What changes occur in females during sexual arousal as the result of increased parasympathetic stimulation?

See the blue Answers tab at the back of the book.

19-5 With age, decreasing levels of reproductive hormones cause functional changes

Aging affects all body systems, including the reproductive systems of men and women alike. After puberty, when these systems become fully functional in both sexes, the most striking age-related changes in the female reproductive system occur at menopause. Comparative changes in the male reproductive system occur more gradually and over a longer period of time.

MENOPAUSE

Menopause is usually defined as the time that ovulation and menstruation cease. It typically occurs at age 45–55, but in the years preceding it, the ovarian and menstrual cycles become irregular. The transition period from normal menstrual cycles to none at all is called *perimenopause,* and it normally begins at age 40. A shortage of follicles is the underlying cause of cycle irregularities. Of an estimated 2 million potential oocytes present at birth, only a few hundred thousand remain at puberty. By age

Clinical Note — Sexually Transmitted Diseases

Sexual activity carries with it the risk of infection by a variety of microorganisms. Some such infections can be merely inconvenient, whereas others can be lethal. **Sexually transmitted diseases (STDs)** are transferred from individual to individual during sexual activity, primarily or exclusively by the exchange of body fluids containing the pathogen. At least two dozen bacterial, viral, and fungal infections are currently recognized as STDs. The bacterium *Chlamydia* can cause PID and infertility; AIDS, caused by a virus, is deadly. The incidence of STDs has been increasing in the United States since 1984; an estimated 19 million cases are diagnosed each year. Poverty, prostitution, intravenous drug use (needle sharing exchanges body fluids), and the appearance of drug-resistant pathogens all contribute to the problem.

50, there are often no secondary follicles left to respond to FSH. In *premature menopause,* this depletion occurs before age 40.

Menopause is accompanied by a decline in circulating concentrations of estrogens and progesterone and a sharp and sustained rise in the production of GnRH, FSH, and LH. The decline in estrogen levels leads to reductions in the sizes of the uterus and breasts, accompanied by a thinning of the urethral and vaginal walls. The reduced estrogen concentrations have also been linked to the development of osteoporosis, presumably because bone deposition proceeds at a slower rate. A variety of neural effects are also reported, including "hot flashes," anxiety, and depression. Hot flashes typically begin while estrogen levels are declining and cease when estrogen levels become minimal. These intervals of elevated body temperature are associated with surges in LH production. The hormonal mechanisms involved in other CNS effects of menopause are not well understood. In addition, the risks of atherosclerosis and other forms of cardiovascular disease increase after menopause.

The majority of women experience only mild symptoms, but some individuals experience unpleasant symptoms in perimenopause or during or after menopause. For most of those individuals, hormone replacement therapy (HRT) involving a combination of estrogens and progestins can control the neural and vascular changes associated with menopause. However, recent studies suggest that taking estrogen-replacement therapy for more than 5 years increases the risk of heart disease, breast cancer, Alzheimer disease, blood clots, and strokes.

THE MALE CLIMACTERIC

Changes in the male reproductive system occur more gradually than do those in the female reproductive system. The period of declining reproductive function, which corresponds to perimenopause in women, is known as the **male climacteric,** or *andropause.* Levels of circulating testosterone begin to decline between ages 50 and 60, and levels of FSH and LH increase. Although sperm production continues (men well into their eighties can father children), older men experience a gradual reduction in sexual activity. This decrease may be linked to declining testosterone levels, and some clinicians suggest the use of testosterone replacement therapy to enhance libido

(sexual drive) in elderly men, but this may increase the risk of prostate disease.

The Big Picture

Sex hormones have widespread effects on the body. They affect brain development and behavioral drives, muscle mass, bone mass and density, body proportions, and the patterns of hair and body fat distribution. As aging occurs, reduction in sexual hormone levels affect appearance, strength, and a variety of physiological functions.

CHECKPOINT

19. Define menopause.

20. Why do FSH levels rise and remain high during menopause?

21. What is the male climacteric?

See the blue Answers tab at the back of the book.

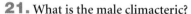

19-6 The reproductive system secretes hormones affecting growth and metabolism of all body systems

Normal human reproduction is a complex process that requires the participation of multiple systems. The hormones discussed in this chapter (Table 19-1) play major roles in coordinating reproductive events. Reproduction depends on various physical, physiological, and psychological factors. For example, the male's sperm count must be adequate, the semen must have the correct pH and nutrients, and erection and ejaculation must occur in the proper sequence; the woman's ovarian and uterine cycles must be properly coordinated, ovulation and oocyte transport must occur normally, and her reproductive tract must be suitable for sperm survival, movement, and fertilization. Many of these events require the participation and normal functioning of the digestive, endocrine, nervous, cardiovascular, and urinary systems. The Reproductive System in Perspective (p. 670) summarizes the interactions between these organ systems and the reproductive system.

TABLE 19-1 **Hormones of the Reproductive System**

HORMONE	SOURCE	REGULATION OF SECRETION	PRIMARY EFFECTS
Gonadotropin-Releasing Hormone (GNRH)	Hypothalamus	*Males:* inhibited by testosterone *Females:* inhibited by estrogens and/or progestins	Stimulates FSH secretion and LH synthesis in males and females
Follicle-Stimulating Hormone (FSH)	Anterior pituitary gland	*Males:* stimulated by GnRH, inhibited by inhibin and testosterone *Females:* stimulated by GnRH, inhibited by estrogens and/or progestins	*Males:* stimulates spermatogenesis and spermiogenesis through effects on nurse cells *Females:* stimulates follicle development, estrogen production, and oocyte maturation
Luteinizing Hormone (LH)	Anterior pituitary gland	*Males:* stimulated by GnRH *Females:* production stimulated by GnRH and secretion by estrogens	*Males:* stimulates interstitial cells to secrete testosterone *Females:* stimulates ovulation, formation of corpus luteum, and progestin secretion
Androgens (primarily testosterone)	Interstitial cells of testes	Stimulated by LH	Establishes and maintains secondary sex characteristics and sexual behavior, promotes maturation of spermatozoa, inhibits GnRH secretion
Estrogens (primarily estradiol)	Follicular cells of ovaries; corpus luteum	Stimulated by FSH	Stimulates LH secretion (at high levels), establishes and maintains secondary sex characteristics and behavior, stimulates repair and growth of endometrium, inhibits secretion of GnRH
Progestins (primarily progesterone)	Corpus luteum	Stimulated by LH	Stimulates endometrial growth and glandular secretion, inhibits GnRH secretion
Inhibin	Nurse cells of testes and follicle cells of ovaries	Stimulated by factors released by developing sperm (*male*) or developing follicles (*female*)	Inhibits secretion of FSH (and possibly GnRH)

Even when all is normal, and fertilization occurs at the proper time and place, a healthy infant will still not be produced unless the zygote—a single cell the size of a pinhead—manages to develop into a full-term fetus that typically weighs about 3 kg (6.6 lb). Chapter 20 considers the process of development and the mechanisms that determine both body structure and the distinctive characteristics of individuals.

CHECKPOINT

22. Describe the interactions between the integumentary system and the reproductive system.

23. Describe the interactions between the reproductive system and the skeletal system.

See the blue Answers tab at the back of the book.

Clinical Note

Birth Control Strategies

For diverse reasons, most adults practice some form of conception control during their reproductive years. Two out of three U.S. women ages 15–44 employ some method of contraception. When the simplest and most obvious method—sexual abstinence—is unsatisfactory, another method of contraception must be used to avoid unwanted pregnancies. Many methods are available, and because each has specific strengths and weaknesses, the potential risks and benefits must be carefully analyzed on an individual basis.

Hormonal contraceptives manipulate the female hormonal cycle so that ovulation does not occur. The contraceptive pills produced in the 1950s contained combined estrogen and progestins sufficient to suppress pituitary GnRH production, so FSH was not released and ovulation did not occur. Most of the oral contraceptives developed subsequently contain much smaller amounts of estrogen, or only progesterone. Current *combination* hormone contraceptives are administered cyclically, using medication for 3 weeks followed by no medication during week 4. For user convenience, monthly injections, weekly skin patches, and insertable vaginal rings containing combined estrogen/progesterone products are available.

An estimated 200 million women use combination oral contraceptives worldwide. In the United States, 33 percent of women under age 45 use the combination pill to prevent conception. The failure rate for combination oral contraceptives, when used as prescribed, is 0.24 percent over a 2-year period. (*Failure* for a birth control method is defined as a pregnancy.) Birth control pills are not risk free: Combination pills can worsen problems associated with severe hypertension, diabetes mellitus, epilepsy, gallbladder disease, heart trouble, and acne. Women taking oral contraceptives are also at increased risk for venous thrombosis, strokes, pulmonary embolism, and (for women over 35) heart disease. However, pregnancy has similar or higher risks.

Hormonal post-coital contraception, or the emergency "morning after" pill, involves taking either combination estrogen/progesterone birth control pills or progesterone-only pills in two large doses 12 hours apart within 72 hours of unprotected sexual intercourse. Particularly useful when barrier methods malfunction or coerced intercourse occurs, it reduces expected pregnancy rates by up to 89 percent. The progesterone-only version is considered safe for nonprescription use and may become available for purchase over the counter in the future.

Progesterone-only forms of birth control—Depo-provera, the Norplant system, and the progesterone-only pill—are now available. Depo-provera is injected every 3 months. The Silastic (silicon rubber) tubes of the Norplant system are saturated with progesterone and inserted under the skin. This method provides birth control for approximately 5 years. Fertility returns immediately after the removal of a Norplant device. (Initial high cost, problems with its removal, and side effect concerns have limited its use, and its manufacturer stopped supplying it to the U.S. market in 2004.) Both can cause irregular menstruation and temporary amenorrhea, but they are extremely convenient to use. The progesterone-only pill is taken daily and may cause irregular uterine cycles. Skipping just one pill may result in pregnancy.

The **condom,** also called a *prophylactic* or "rubber," covers the glans and body of the penis during intercourse and keeps sperm from reaching the female reproductive tract. Latex condoms also reduce the spread of STDs, such as syphilis, gonorrhea, HPV, and AIDS. The reported condom failure rate varies from 6 percent to 17 percent.

Vaginal barriers such as the *diaphragm* and *cervical cap* rely on similar principles. A diaphragm, the most popular form of vaginal barrier in use today, consists of a dome of latex rubber with a small metal hoop supporting the rim. Before intercourse, the diaphragm is inserted so that it covers the external os of the uterus, and it is usually coated with a small amount of spermicidal (sperm-killing) jelly or cream, adding to the effectiveness of the barrier. The failure rate of a properly fitted diaphragm is estimated at 5–6 percent. A cervical cap is smaller and lacks the metal rim. It, too, must be fitted carefully, but unlike the diaphragm, it can be left in place for several days. Its failure rate (8 percent) is higher than that for diaphragm use.

An **intrauterine device (IUD)** consists of a small plastic loop or a T that is inserted into the uterine cavity. The mechanism of action remains uncertain, but IUDs are known to stimulate prostaglandin production in the uterus. The resulting change in the chemical composition of uterine secretions lowers the likelihood of fertilization and subsequent *implantation* of the zygote in the uterine lining. (Implantation is discussed in Chapter 20.) In the United States, IUDs are in limited use, but they remain popular in many other countries. The failure rate is estimated at 5–6 percent.

The **rhythm method** involves abstaining from sexual intercourse on the days ovulation might be occurring. The timing is estimated on the basis of previous patterns of menstruation and in some cases by monitoring changes in basal body temperature. The failure rate for the rhythm method is very high—almost 25 percent.

Sterilization is a surgical procedure that makes an individual unable to provide functional gametes for fertilization. Members of either sex may be sterilized. In a **vasectomy** (vaz-EK-to-mē) a segment of the ductus deferens is removed, making it impossible for sperm to pass from the epididymis to the distal portions of the reproductive tract. The surgery can be performed in a physician's office in a matter of minutes. The spermatic cords are located as they ascend from the scrotum on either side; after each cord is opened, the ductus deferens is severed. After a 1-cm section is removed, the cut ends are usually tied shut (Figure 19-16a). The cut ends cannot reconnect; in time, scar tissue forms a permanent seal. Alternatively, the cut ends of the ductus deferens are blocked with silicone plugs that can later be removed. This more recent vasectomy procedure may make it possible to restore fertility at a later date. After a vasectomy, men experience normal sexual function, for epididymal and testicular secretions account for only about 5 percent of the volume of the semen. Sperm continue to develop, but they remain within the

Birth Control Strategies

epididymis until they degenerate. The failure rate for this procedure is 0.08 percent.

The uterine tubes can be blocked through a surgical procedure known as a **tubal ligation** (Figure 19-16b). The failure rate for this procedure is estimated at 0.45 percent. Because the surgery involves entering the abdominopelvic cavity, complications are more likely than with a vasectomy. As in a vasectomy, attempts to restore fertility after a tubal ligation may not be possible, and both forms of contraception should be considered permanent.

Oral contraceptives, condoms, vaginal barriers, and sterilization are the primary contraception methods for individuals of all age groups. But the proportion of the population using a particular method varies by age group. Sterilization is most popular among older men and women, who may already have had children. Relative availability also plays a role. For example, a sexually active female under age 18 can buy a condom more easily than she can obtain a prescription for an oral contraceptive. But many of the differences are attributable to the relationship between risks and benefits for each age group. When considering the use and selection of contraceptives, many people simply examine the list of potential complications and make the "safest" choice. For example, media coverage of the potential risks associated with oral contraceptives made many women reconsider their use. But complex decisions should not be made on such a simplistic basis, and the risks associated with contraceptive use must be considered in terms of their relative efficiencies.

Although pregnancy is a natural phenomenon, it has risks, and the mortality rate for pregnant women in the United States averages about 8 deaths per 100,000 pregnancies. That average incorporates a broad range; the rate is 7 per 100,000 among women under 20 but 40 per 100,000 for women over 40. Although these risks are small, for pregnant women over age 35, the chances of dying from pregnancy-related complications are almost twice as great as the chances of being killed in an automobile accident, and are many times greater than the risks associated with the use of oral contraceptives. For women in developing nations, the comparison is even more striking: The mortality rate for pregnant women in parts of Africa is approximately 1 per 150 pregnancies.

Before age 35, the risks associated with contraceptive use are lower than the risks associated with pregnancy. The notable exception involves individuals who take oral contraceptives but also smoke cigarettes. Younger women are more fertile, so despite a lower mortality rate for each pregnancy, they are likely to have more pregnancies. As a result, birth control failures imply a higher risk in the younger age groups.

After age 35, the risks of complications associated with oral contraceptive use increase, but the risks of using other methods remains relatively stable. Women over age 35 (smokers) or 40 (nonsmokers) are, therefore, typically advised to seek other forms of contraception.

(a)

(b)

FIGURE 19-16 Surgical Sterilization. (a) In a vasectomy, the removal of a 1-cm section of the ductus deferens prevents the passage of sperm cells. **(b)** In a tubal ligation, the removal of a section of the uterine tube prevents the passage of sperm and the movement of an ovum or embryo into the uterus.

RELATED CLINICAL TERMS

amenorrhea: The failure of menarche to appear before age 16, or a cessation of menstruation for 6 months or more in an adult female of reproductive age.

cervical cancer: A malignant, metastazing tumor of the cervix; the most common reproductive cancer in women.

cryptorchidism (krip-TOR-ki-dizm): The failure of one or both testes to descend into the scrotum by the time of birth.

dysmenorrhea: Painful menstruation.

endometriosis (en-dō-mē-trē-Ō-sis): The growth of endometrial tissue outside the uterus.

gynecology (gī-ne-KOL-o-jē): The study of the female reproductive tract and its disorders.

mammography: The use of x-rays to examine breast tissue.

mastectomy: The surgical removal of part or all of a breast, typically as treatment for breast cancer.

oophoritis (ō-of-ō-RĪ-tis): Inflammation of the ovaries.

orchiectomy (or-kē-EK-to-mē): The surgical removal of a testis.

orchitis (or-KĪ-tis): Inflammation of the testis.

ovarian cancer: A malignancy of the ovaries; the most dangerous reproductive cancer in women.

pelvic inflammatory disease (PID): An infection of the uterine tubes.

prostate cancer: A malignant, metastazing tumor of the prostate gland; the second most common cause of cancer deaths in males.

prostatectomy (pros-ta-TEK-to-mē): The surgical removal of the prostate gland.

testicular torsion: A condition in which twisting of the spermatic cord obstructs the blood supply to a testis.

vaginitis (va-jin-ī-tis): Inflammation of the vaginal canal.

vasectomy (vaz-EK-to-mē): The surgical removal of a segment of the ductus deferens, making it impossible for spermatozoa to reach the distal portions of the male reproductive tract.

Chapter 19 Review

KEY TERMS

ductus deferens *644*

endometrium *654*

estrogens *657*

lactation *656*

meiosis *642*

menses *654*

oogenesis *649*

ovarian follicles *649*

ovary *639*

ovulation *652*

perineum *656*

prepuce *646*

progesterone *658*

seminiferous tubules *641*

spermatogenesis *642*

spermatozoa *639*

testes *639*

testosterone *642*

vulva *656*

SUMMARY OUTLINE

19-1 Basic reproductive system structures are gonads, ducts, accessory glands and organs, and external genitalia *p. 639*

1. The human **reproductive system** produces, stores, nourishes, and transports functional **gametes** (reproductive cells). **Fertilization** is the fusion of male and female gametes.

2. The reproductive system includes **gonads** (**testes** or **ovaries**), ducts, accessory glands and organs, and the **external genitalia.**

3. In males, the testes produce **spermatozoa,** which are expelled from the body in **semen** during *ejaculation.* The ovaries of a sexually mature female produce **oocytes** (immature **ova**) that travel along *uterine tubes* toward the *uterus.* The *vagina* connects the uterus with the exterior of the body.

19-2 Sperm formation (spermatogenesis) occurs in the testes, and hormones from the hypothalamus, pituitary gland, and testes control male reproductive functions *p. 640*

4. In males, the *testes* produce **sperm** cells. The **spermatozoa** travel along the *epididymis,* the *ductus deferens,* the *ejaculatory duct,* and the *urethra* before leaving the body. Accessory organs (notably, the *seminal vesicles, prostate gland,* and *bulbourethral glands*) secrete products into the ejaculatory ducts and urethra. The scrotum encloses the testes, and the penis is an erectile organ. *(Figure 19-1)*

5. The **testes,** the primary sex organ of males, hang within the **scrotum.** The *dartos* muscle layer gives the scrotum a wrinkled appearance. The **cremaster muscle** pulls the testes closer to the body. The **tunica albuginea** surrounds each testis. Septa subdivide each testis into a series of lobules. **Seminiferous tubules** within each lobule are the sites of sperm production. Between the seminiferous tubules are **interstitial cells,** which secrete sex hormones. *(Figure 19-2)*

6. Seminiferous tubules contain **spermatogonia,** stem cells involved in **spermatogenesis,** and **nurse cells,** which sustain and promote the development of spermatozoa. *(Figure 19-3)*

7. Each spermatozoon has a **head, middle piece,** and **tail.** *(Figure 19-4)*

8. From the testis, the spermatozoa enter the **epididymis,** an elongate tubule that regulates the composition of the tubular fluid and serves as a recycling center for damaged spermatozoa. Spermatozoa leaving the epididymis are functionally mature, yet immobile.

9. The **ductus deferens,** or *vas deferens,* begins at the epididymis and passes through the inguinal canal within the **spermatic cord.** The junction of the base of the seminal gland and the ductus deferens creates the **ejaculatory duct,** which penetrates the prostate gland and empties into the urethra. *(Figure 19-5)*

10. The **urethra** extends from the urinary bladder to the tip of the penis and serves as a passageway that functions in both the urinary and reproductive systems.

11. Each **seminal gland,** or **seminal vesicle,** is an active secretory gland that contributes about 60 percent of the volume of semen; its secretions contain fructose, which is easily metabolized by spermatozoa. The **prostate gland** secretes fluid that makes up about 30 percent of seminal fluid. Alkaline mucus secreted by the **bulbo-urethral glands** has lubricating properties. *(Figure 19-5)*

12. A typical **ejaculation** expels 2–5 mL of semen (an **ejaculate**), which contains 20–100 million sperm per milliliter.

13. The skin overlying the **penis** resembles that of the scrotum. Most of the body of the penis consists of three masses of **erectile tissue.** Beneath the superficial layers are two **corpora cavernosa** and a single **corpus spongiosum,** which surrounds the urethra. Dilation of the erectile tissue with blood produces an **erection.** *(Figure 19-6)*

14. Important regulatory hormones of males include **follicle stimulating hormone (FSH), luteinizing hormone (LH),** and **gonadotropin-releasing hormone (GnRH).** Testosterone is the most important *androgen. (Figure 19-7)*

19-3 Ovum production (oogenesis) occurs in the ovaries, and hormones from the pituitary gland and ovaries control female reproductive functions *p. 649*

15. Principal organs of the female reproductive system include the *ovaries, uterine tubes, uterus, vagina,* and *external genitalia.* *(Figure 19-8)*

16. The **ovaries** are the primary sex organs of females. Ovaries are the site of **ovum** production, or **oogenesis,** which occurs monthly in **ovarian follicles** as part of the **ovarian cycle.** As development proceeds, **primary, secondary,** and **tertiary follicles** form. At **ovulation,** a secondary oocyte and the surrounding follicular walls of the **corona radiata** are released through the ruptured ovarian wall. *(Figures 19-9, 19-10)*

17. Each **uterine tube** has an **infundibulum,** a funnel that opens into the pelvic cavity. For fertilization to occur, a secondary oocyte must encounter spermatozoa during the first 12–24 hours of its passage from the infundibulum to the uterine cavity. *(Figure 19-11)*

18. The **uterus** provides mechanical protection and nutritional support to the developing embryo. It is stabilized by various ligaments. Major anatomical landmarks of the uterus include the **body, cervix, external os, uterine cavity,** and **internal os.** The uterine wall consists of an inner **endometrium,** a muscular **myometrium,** and a superficial **perimetrium.** *(Figure 19-11)*

19. A typical 28-day **uterine cycle,** or *menstrual cycle,* begins with the onset of **menses** and the destruction of the *functional zone* of the endometrium. This process of menstruation continues from 1 to 7 days.

20. After menses, the **proliferative phase** begins, and the functional zone undergoes repair and thickens. During the **secretory phase,** the uterine glands are active and the uterus is prepared for the arrival of an embryo. Menstrual activity begins at **menarche** and continues until **menopause.**

21. The **vagina** is a muscular tube extending between the uterus and the external genitalia. A thin epithelial fold, the **hymen,** partially blocks the entrance to the vagina.

22. The components of the **vulva,** or perineal region enclosing the female external genitalia, include the **vestibule,** the **labia minora,** the **clitoris,** the **labia majora,** the **mons pubis,** and the **lesser** and **greater vestibular glands.** *(Figure 19-12)*

23. A newborn infant gains nourishment from milk secreted by maternal **mammary glands. Lactation** is the process of milk production. *(Figure 19-13)*

24. Regulation of the **female reproductive cycle** involves the coordination of the ovarian and uterine cycles by circulating hormones.

25. **Estradiol,** one of the estrogens, is the dominant hormone of the **follicular phase** of the ovarian cycle. Estrogens have multiple functions that affect the activities of many tissues and organs, *(Figure 19-14)*

26. The hypothalamic secretion of GnRH triggers the pituitary secretion of FSH and the synthesis of LH. FSH stimulates secondary follicle development, and activated follicles and ovarian interstitial cells produce estrogens. Ovulation occurs in response to a midcycle surge in LH secretion. **Progesterone,** one of the steroid hormones called **progestins,** is the principal hormone of the **luteal phase** of the ovarian cycle. Hormonal changes regulate the uterine, or menstrual, cycle. *(Figures 19-14, 19-15)*

19-4 The autonomic nervous system influences male and female sexual function *p. 660*

27. During **arousal** in males, erotic thoughts, sensory stimulation, or both lead to parasympathetic activity that ultimately produces erection. Stimuli accompanying **coitus** (sexual intercourse) lead to **emission** and ejaculation. Strong muscle contractions are associated with **orgasm.**

28. The phases of female sexual function resemble those of the male, with parasympathetic arousal and muscular contractions associated with orgasm.

19-5 With age, decreasing levels of reproductive hormones cause functional changes   *p. 661*

29. Menopause (the time that ovulation and menstruation cease in women) typically occurs around age 50. Production of GnRH, FSH, and LH rise while circulating concentrations of estrogen and progesterone decline.

30. During the **male climacteric,** at ages 50–60, circulating testosterone levels decline while levels of FSH and LH rise.

19-6 The reproductive system secretes hormones affecting growth and metabolism of all body systems   *p. 662*

31. Hormones play a major role in coordinating reproduction. *(Table 19-1)*

32. In addition to the endocrine and reproductive systems, reproduction requires the normal functioning of the digestive, nervous, cardiovascular, and urinary systems.

REVIEW QUESTIONS

WWW   Access more review material online at The Anatomy & Physiology Place (www. anatomyandphysiology.com). There, you'll find Chapter Guides, Chapter Quizzes, Chapter Practice Tests, Interactive Flashcards, a Glossary with Pronunciations, and more to help you succeed in the course.

Level 1 • Reviewing Facts and Terms

Match each item in column A with the most closely related item in column B. Place letters for answers in the spaces provided.

COLUMN A
_____ 1. gametes
_____ 2. gonads
_____ 3. interstitial cells
_____ 4. seminal glands
_____ 5. prostate gland
_____ 6. bulbo-urethral glands
_____ 7. prepuce
_____ 8. corpus luteum
_____ 9. endometrium
_____ 10. myometrium
_____ 11. dysmenorrhea
_____ 12. menarche
_____ 13. clitoris
_____ 14. lactation
_____ 15. coitus

COLUMN B
a. production of androgens
b. outer muscular uterine wall
c. high concentration of fructose
d. female erectile tissue
e. secretes thick, sticky, alkaline mucus
f. painful menstruation
g. sexual intercourse
h. uterine lining
i. reproductive cells
j. female puberty
k. milk production
l. secretes antibiotic
m. reproductive organs
n. foreskin of penis
o. endocrine structure

16. Perineal structures associated with the reproductive system are collectively known as
(a) gonads.
(b) sex gametes.
(c) external genitalia.
(d) accessory glands.

17. Meiosis in males produces four spermatids, each of which contains
(a) 23 chromosomes.
(b) 23 pairs of chromosomes.
(c) the diploid number of chromosomes.
(d) 46 pairs of chromosomes.

18. Erection of the penis occurs when
(a) sympathetic activation of penile arteries occurs.
(b) arterial branches are constricted and muscular partitions are tense.
(c) the vascular channels become engorged with blood.
(d) a, b, and c are correct.

19. In males, the primary target of FSH is the
(a) nurse cells of the seminiferous tubules.
(b) interstitial cells of the seminiferous tubules.
(c) prostate gland.
(d) epididymis.

20. The ovaries are responsible for
(a) the production of female gametes.
(b) the secretion of female sex hormones.
(c) the secretion of inhibin.
(d) a, b, and c are correct.

21. Ovum production, or oogenesis, begins
(a) before birth.
(b) after birth.
(c) at puberty.
(d) after puberty.

22. Identify the principal structures of the male reproductive system in the following diagram.

(a) _____	**(b)** _____
(c) _____	**(d)** _____
(e) _____	**(f)** _____
(g) _____	**(h)** _____
(i) _____	**(j)** _____

23. Identify the principal structures of the female reproductive system in the following diagram.

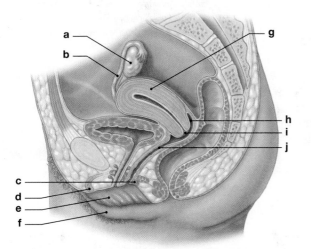

(a) _____	**(b)** _____
(c) _____	**(d)** _____
(e) _____	**(f)** _____
(g) _____	**(h)** _____
(i) _____	**(j)** _____

24. In females, meiosis is not completed
(a) until birth.
(b) until puberty.
(c) unless and until fertilization occurs.
(d) until ovulation occurs.

25. If fertilization is to occur, an ovum must encounter spermatozoa during the first _____ of its passage.
(a) 1 to 5 hours **(b)** 6 to 11 hours
(c) 12 to 24 hours **(d)** 25 to 36 hours

26. The part of the endometrium that undergoes cyclical changes in response to variations in sex hormone levels is the
(a) serosa. **(b)** basilar zone.
(c) muscular myometrium. **(d)** functional zone.

27. A sudden surge in LH concentration causes
(a) the onset of menses.
(b) the rupture of the follicular wall and ovulation.
(c) the beginning of the proliferative phase.
(d) the end of the uterine cycle.

28. At the time of ovulation, basal body temperature
(a) is not affected.
(b) increases noticeably.
(c) declines sharply.
(d) may increase or decrease a few degrees.

29. Menopause is accompanied by
(a) sustained rises in GnRH, FSH, and LH.
(b) declines in circulating levels of estrogen and progesterone.
(c) thinning of the urethral and vaginal walls.
(d) a, b, and c are correct.

30. Identify the reproductive accessory organs and glands in males, and list their functions.

31. What are the primary functions of an epididymis?

32. What are the primary functions of the ovaries?

33. What are the three major functions of the vagina?

Level 2 • Reviewing Concepts

34. How does the reproductive system differ functionally from all other organ systems in the body?

35. Define meiosis, and identify the products of this process in both males and females.

36. Using an average uterine cycle of 28 days, describe each of the three phases of the menstrual cycle.

37. Describe the hormonal events associated with the uterine cycle.

38. How does aging affect the reproductive systems of men and women?

Level 3 • Critical Thinking and Clinical Applications

39. Diane has peritonitis (inflammation of the peritoneum), which her physician says resulted from a urinary tract infection. Why could this situation occur in females but not in males?

40. Rod injures the sacral region of his spinal cord. Will he still be able to achieve an erection? Explain.

41. Female bodybuilders and women with eating disorders such as anorexia nervosa often stop having menstrual cycles, a condition known as amenorrhea. What does this relationship suggest about the role of body fat in menstruation? How might the body benefit from ceasing to menstruate under such circumstances?

The Reproductive System in Perspective

Functional Relationships Between the Reproductive System and Other Systems

The Integumentary System

- The Integumentary System covers external genitalia; provides sensations that stimulate sexual behaviors; mammary gland secretions provide nourishment for newborn
- The Reproductive System's sex hormones affect distribution of body hair and subcutaneous fat deposits

The Skeletal System

- The Skeletal System (pelvis) protects reproductive organs of females and portions of ductus deferens and accessory glands in males
- The Reproductive System's sex hormones stimulate growth and maintenance of bones; sex hormones at puberty accelerate growth and closure of epiphyseal plates

The Muscular System

- The Muscular System ejects semen from male reproductive tract; muscle contractions during sexual act produce pleasurable sensations in both sexes
- The Reproductive System's sex hormones, especially testosterone, accelerate skeletal muscle growth

The Nervous System

- The Nervous System controls sexual behaviors and sexual function
- The Reproductive System's sex hormones affect CNS development and sexual behaviors

The Endocrine System

- The Endocrine System's hypothalamic regulatory and pituitary hormones regulate sexual development and function; oxytocin stimulates smooth muscle contractions in uterus and mammary glands
- The Reproductive System's steroid sex hormones and inhibin inhibit secretions of hyopthalamus and pituitary gland

The Cardiovascular System

- The Cardiovascular System distributes reproductive hormones; provides nutrients, oxygen, and waste removal for fetus; local blood pressure changes are responsible for physical changes during sexual arousal
- The Reproductive System produces estrogen which may help maintain healthy vessels and slow development of atherosclerosis

The Lymphoid System

- The Lymphoid System provides IgA for secretions by epithelial glands; assists in repairs and defense against infection
- The Reproductive System secretes lysozymes and bactericidal chemicals for nonspecific defense against reproductive tract infections

The Respiratory System

- The Respiratory System provides oxygen and removes carbon dioxide generated by tissues of the reproductive system
- The Reproductive System produces changes in respiratory rate and depth occur during sexual arousal, under control of the nervous system

The Digestive System

- The Digestive System provides additional nutrients required to support gamete production and (in pregnant women) embryonic and fetal development

The Urinary System

- The Urinary System removes wastes generated by reproductive tissues and (in pregnant women) by a growing embryo and fetus; urethra in males carries semen
- The Reproductive System's secretions by male accessory organs may have antibacterial action that helps prevent urethral infections

For All Systems
The Reproductive System's secretion of hormones with effects on growth and metabolism

Professional Profile

MAMMOGRAPHER
Beth Feinberg

> " **A & P is extremely relevant. You must know how to image the correct body part and how to position the body for the best images.** "

Are you interested in a medical career that will allow you to see the country and work when you want to or need to? Many health care fields offer opportunities for "travelers," professionals with national licensing that allows them to work anywhere they wish. Radiologic imaging is one of those fields.

Knowing that x-ray imaging is a universal need helped Beth Feinberg make the decision to go into mammography, a specialty within the field of radiologic technology. Beth's interests in traveling, keeping a flexible schedule, and working with people are all met by her career.

Mammographers work in hospitals, clinics, and mobile units. Wherever they work, a typical day involves seeing many patients and performing the same function for each—taking diagnostic images of the breasts. Mammographers also participate in procedures such as ultrasound, biopsies, and cyst aspirations. Mammography is an important tool in breast cancer screening and assists in early detection, leading to a higher rate of successful treatment.

AN OPPORTUNITY TO TRAVEL

Like many mammographers, Beth has worked as a traveler. Travelers work at one place—usually a hospital—for a contracted length of time and then, if they wish, move on. Beth has worked in many states, including Maine, Florida, and California. For the time being, Beth is happy at her current location and intends to stay there. However, because x-ray techs are in such high demand, Beth is virtually assured of work if she decides to travel again. "I knew being a mammographer would be steady work if, when, and where I wanted it. Being able to travel was very important to me."

Performing mammography puts Beth in contact with people all day long. Although the job of a mammographer can be repetitive, each patient is different. "Although most of my day is mammography," says Beth, "I am also dealing with women's emotions and concerns."

"I am not a desk job kind of person. Helping people is very important to me. The best part of my job is giving women good news—that everything is okay. They're very nervous when they come in, whether they've been diagnosed with breast cancer or not."

Like many people in her profession, Beth studied in an accredited two-year radiologic technology training program. Half of the day was spent in the classroom and the other half took place in a hospital, where students learned procedures. As part of her training, Beth took courses in anatomy and physiology. "A & P is extremely relevant," she says. "You must know how to image the correct body part and how to position the body for the best images."

Beth then obtained her national license by passing an exam. She is certified by the American Registry of Radiologic Technicians. Some states also require that x-ray techs obtain a state license, and some require a separate test. "Because you are dealing with ionizing radiation, licensing is required." In addition to passing the national registry exam, mammographers must also have taken 100 mammograms before they can be licensed.

IMPORTANT SKILLS

What are the qualities of a successful mammographer? Beth says, "You need to be patient, care about the people you see all day, and have good interpersonal and technical skills."

At the same time, mammography and other types of radiologic technology work can be physically demanding. "X-ray technology is much more than pushing buttons," says Beth. "It takes a lot of stamina to correctly position people on a daily basis."

20 Development and Inheritance

Many physiological processes last only a fraction of a second; others may take hours at most. But some important processes of life are measured in months, years, or decades. A human being develops in the womb for 9 months, grows to maturity in 15 to 20 years, and may live the better part of a century. Conception, birth, growth, maturation, aging, and death are all parts of a single, continuous process. That process does not end with the individual because human beings can pass at least some of their characteristics on to a new generation whose individuals will repeat the same cycle.

LEARNING OUTCOMES

After completing this chapter, you should be able to do the following:

20-1 Explain the relationship between differentiation and development, and describe the various stages of development.

20-2 Describe the process of fertilization.

20-3 List the three stages of prenatal development, and describe the major events of each.

20-4 Explain how the three germ layers participate in the formation of extraembryonic membranes, and discuss the importance of the placenta as an endocrine organ.

20-5 Describe the interplay between maternal organ systems and the developing fetus, and discuss the structural and functional changes in the uterus during gestation.

20-6 List and discuss the events that occur during labor and delivery.

20-7 Identify the features and physiological changes of the postnatal stages of life.

20-8 Relate the basic principles of genetics to the inheritance of human traits.

VOCABULARY DEVELOPMENT

allanto- sausage; *allantois*
amphi two-sided; *amphimixis*
blast precursor; *trophoblast*
gestare to bear; *gestation*
heteros other; *heterozygous*
homos same; *homozygous*

karyon nucleus; *karyotyping*
koiloma hollow; *blastocoele*
meros part; *blastomere*
meso- middle; *mesoderm*
mixis mixing; *amphimixis*
morula mulberry; *morula*

phainein to display; *phenotype*
praegnans with child; *pregnant*
tropho- food; *trophoblast*
typos mark; *phenotype*
vitro glass; *in vitro*

20-1 Development is a continuous process that occurs from fertilization to maturity

Time refuses to stand still; today's infant will be tomorrow's adult. The gradual modification of anatomical structures and physiological characteristics during the period from conception to maturity is called **development.** The changes are truly remarkable—what begins as a single cell slightly larger than the period at the end of this sentence becomes an individual whose body contains trillions of cells organized into tissues, organs, and organ systems. The formation of different cell types in this process is called **differentiation.** Differentiation occurs through selective changes in genetic activity. As development proceeds, some genes are turned off and others are turned on. The kinds of genes turned off or on vary from one cell type to another.

Development involves (1) the division and differentiation of cells and (2) the changes that produce and modify anatomical structures. Development begins at **fertilization,** or **conception.** We can divide development into several periods. **Embryological development** involves events that occur in the first 2 months after fertilization. The study of these events in the developing organism, or **embryo,** is called **embryology** (em-brē-OL-ō-jē). After 2 months, the developing embryo becomes a **fetus. Fetal development** begins at the start of the ninth week and continues until birth. Together, embryological development and fetal development are referred to as **prenatal development,** the primary focus of this chapter. **Postnatal development** begins at birth and continues to **maturity,** the state of full development or completed growth.

Although all human beings go through the same developmental stages, differences in genetic makeup produce distinctive individual characteristics. **Inheritance** refers to the transfer of genetically determined characteristics from generation to generation. **Genetics** is the study of the mechanisms responsible for inheritance. This chapter considers basic genetics as it applies to inherited characteristics such as sex, hair color, and various diseases.

CHECKPOINT

1. Define differentiation.
2. What event marks the beginning of development?
3. Define inheritance.

See the blue Answers tab at the end of the book.

20-2 Fertilization—the fusion of a secondary oocyte and a spermatozoon—forms a zygote

AN OVERVIEW OF FERTILIZATION

Fertilization involves the fusion of two haploid gametes, producing a *zygote* that contains 46 chromosomes, the normal number for a *somatic* (nonreproductive) cell. The roles and contributions of the male and female gametes are very different. Whereas the spermatozoon simply delivers the paternal chromosomes to the site of fertilization, the female gamete— a secondary oocyte ∞ p. 649—must provide all of the nourishment and genetic programming needed to support development of the embryo for nearly a week after conception. At fertilization, the diameter of the secondary oocyte is more than twice the length of the spermatozoon (**Figure 20-1a**). The ratio of their volumes is even more striking—roughly 2000 to 1.

The sperm deposited in the vagina are already motile, as a result of mixing with secretions of the seminal glands—the first step of *capacitation.* ∞ p. 644 But they cannot accomplish fertilization until they have been exposed to conditions in the female reproductive tract (specifically, those within a uterine tube). Although secretions by nonciliated peg cells within the epithelial lining of a uterine tube help with capacitation, the exact mechanism responsible for capacitation remains unknown.

Fertilization typically occurs in the upper one-third of a uterine tube within a day after ovulation. It takes sperm between 30 minutes and 2 hours to pass from the vagina to the

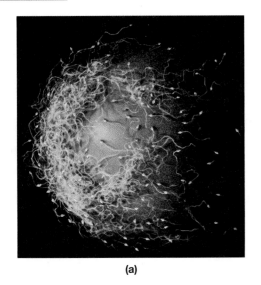

(a)

upper portion of a uterine tube. Of the 200 million spermatozoa introduced into the vagina in a typical ejaculation, only about 10,000 enter the uterine tube, and fewer than 100 actually reach the secondary oocyte. In general, a male with a sperm count below 20 million per milliliter is sterile because too few sperm survive to reach the oocyte. Dozens of sperm cells are required for successful fertilization, because, as we will see, a single sperm cannot penetrate the *corona radiata,* the layer of follicle cells that surrounds the oocyte. ∞ p. 652

FIGURE 20-1 Fertilization. (a) An oocyte and numerous sperm cells are shown at the time of fertilization. Note the difference in size between the gametes. **(b)** Fertilization and the preparations for cleavage occur in the sequence of events diagrammed here.

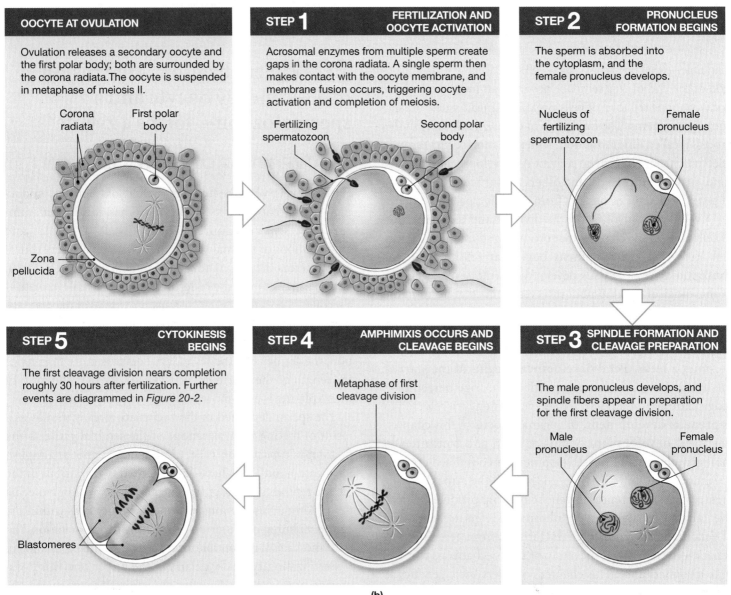

OOCYTE AT OVULATION

Ovulation releases a secondary oocyte and the first polar body; both are surrounded by the corona radiata. The oocyte is suspended in metaphase of meiosis II.

Corona radiata
First polar body
Zona pellucida

STEP 1 — FERTILIZATION AND OOCYTE ACTIVATION

Acrosomal enzymes from multiple sperm create gaps in the corona radiata. A single sperm then makes contact with the oocyte membrane, and membrane fusion occurs, triggering oocyte activation and completion of meiosis.

Fertilizing spermatozoon
Second polar body

STEP 2 — PRONUCLEUS FORMATION BEGINS

The sperm is absorbed into the cytoplasm, and the female pronucleus develops.

Nucleus of fertilizing spermatozoon
Female pronucleus

STEP 5 — CYTOKINESIS BEGINS

The first cleavage division nears completion roughly 30 hours after fertilization. Further events are diagrammed in *Figure 20-2.*

Blastomeres

STEP 4 — AMPHIMIXIS OCCURS AND CLEAVAGE BEGINS

Metaphase of first cleavage division

STEP 3 — SPINDLE FORMATION AND CLEAVAGE PREPARATION

The male pronucleus develops, and spindle fibers appear in preparation for the first cleavage division.

Male pronucleus
Female pronucleus

(b)

OVULATION AND OOCYTE ACTIVATION

Ovulation occurs before the oocyte is completely mature. The secondary oocyte leaving the follicle is in metaphase of the second meiotic division (meiosis II). The cell's metabolic operations have been discontinued, and the oocyte drifts in a sort of suspended animation, awaiting the stimulus for further development. If fertilization does not occur, the oocyte disintegrates without completing meiosis.

Fertilization and the events that follow are diagrammed in Figure 20-1b. The corona radiata protects the oocyte as it passes through the ruptured follicular wall and into the infundibulum of a uterine tube. Although the physical process of fertilization requires that only a single sperm contact the oocyte membrane, that spermatozoon must first penetrate the corona radiata (the layer of follicular cells surrounding the oocyte). The corona radiata protects the oocyte as it passes through the ruptured follicular wall and into the infundibulum of a uterine tube. The acrosomal cap of the sperm contains several enzymes, including *hyaluronidase* (hi-a-loo-RON-a-dās), which breaks down the bonds between adjacent follicle cells. Dozens of sperm cells must release hyaluronidase before an opening forms between the follicular cells.

No matter how many sperm slip through the resulting gap in the corona radiata, only a single spermatozoon accomplishes fertilization and activates the oocyte (Step 1). That sperm cell first binds to sperm receptors in the zona pellucida. ∞ p. 651 Next, its acrosomal cap ruptures, releasing hyaluronidase and another proteolytic enzyme, which digests a path through the zona pellucida to the oocyte membrane. Upon contact, the membranes of the sperm cell and oocyte begin to fuse, triggering **oocyte activation** (Figure 20-1b). As the membranes fuse, the entire sperm enters the cytoplasm of the oocyte.

Activation of the oocyte involves a series of sudden metabolic changes. For example, vesicles located just interior to the oocyte membrane undergo exocytosis, releasing enzymes that prevent an abnormal process called *polyspermy* (fertilization by more than one sperm). Polyspermy produces a zygote that is incapable of normal development. Other important changes include the completion of meiosis II and a rapid increase in the oocyte's metabolic rate.

After oocyte activation has occurred and meiosis has been completed, the nuclear material remaining within the ovum reorganizes into a *female pronucleus* (Step 2, Figure 20-1b). At the same time, the nucleus of the spermatozoon swells, becoming the *male pronucleus* (Step 3). The male pronucleus and female pronucleus then fuse in a process called **amphimixis** (am-fi-MIK-sis; Step 4). The cell is now a zygote that contains the normal complement of 46 chromosomes, and fertilization is complete. The first cleavage division yields two daughter cells (Step 5).

CHECKPOINT

4. What two important roles do the acrosomal enzymes of spermatozoa play in fertilization?

5. How many chromosomes are contained within a zygote?

See the blue Answers tab at the back of the book.

20-3 Gestation consists of three stages of prenatal development: the first, second, and third trimesters

During prenatal development, a single cell ultimately forms a 3–4 kg (6.6–8.8 lb) infant. The time spent in prenatal development is known as the period of **gestation** (jes-TĀ-shun), or *pregnancy*. Gestation occurs within the uterus over a period of 9 months. For convenience, prenatal development is usually divided into three **trimesters,** each 3 months in duration:

1. The **first trimester** is the period of embryological and early fetal development. During this period, the basic components of each of the major organ systems appear.

2. The **second trimester** is dominated by the development of organs and organ systems to near completion. The fetus's body proportions change, and by the end of the second trimester it looks distinctively human.

3. The **third trimester** is characterized by rapid fetal growth and deposition of adipose tissue. Early in the third trimester most of the major organ systems become fully functional. An infant born 1 month or even 2 months prematurely has a reasonable chance of survival.

CHECKPOINT

6. Define gestation.

7. Describe the key features of each trimester.

See the blue Answers tab at the back of the book.

20-4 Cleavage, implantation, placentation, and embryogenesis are critical events of the first trimester

At the moment of conception, a fertilized ovum is a single cell that is about 0.135 mm (0.005 in.) in diameter and weighs approximately 150 mg. By the end of the first trimester, the fetus is almost 75 mm (3 in.) long and weighs about 14 g (0.5 oz). Many complex and vital developmental events accompany this increase in size and weight. Perhaps because the events are so complex, *the first trimester is the most dangerous period in prenatal life*—only about 40 percent of conceptions produce embryos that survive this period. For that reason, pregnant women are advised to take great care to avoid drugs and other disruptive stresses during the first trimester.

In the sections that follow we will focus on four general processes that occur during the first trimester: *cleavage and blastocyst formation, implantation, placentation,* and *embryogenesis.*

CLEAVAGE AND BLASTOCYST FORMATION

Cleavage (KLĒV-ij) is a series of cell divisions that begins immediately after fertilization. This process produces an ever-increasing number of smaller and smaller daughter cells called **blastomeres** (BLAS-tō-mērz; *blast,* precursor + *meros,* part) (**Figure 20-2**). The first cleavage division produces two daughter cells, each one-half the size of the original zygote. The first division is completed roughly 30 hours after fertilization, and subsequent cleavage divisions occur at intervals of 10–12 hours.

After 3 days of cleavage, the embryo—now well on its way along a uterine tube—is a solid ball of cells resembling a mulberry (**Figure 20-2**). This stage is called the **morula** (MOR-ū-la; *morula,* mulberry). Over the next 2 days, as the embryo enters the uterine cavity, the blastomeres form a **blastocyst,** a hollow ball with an inner cavity known as the *blastocoele* (BLAS-tō-sēl; *koiloma,* cavity). At this stage, differences among the blastomeres of the blastocyst become apparent. The outer layer of cells separating the outside world from the blastocoele is called the **trophoblast** (TRŌ-fō-blast). As implied by its name—

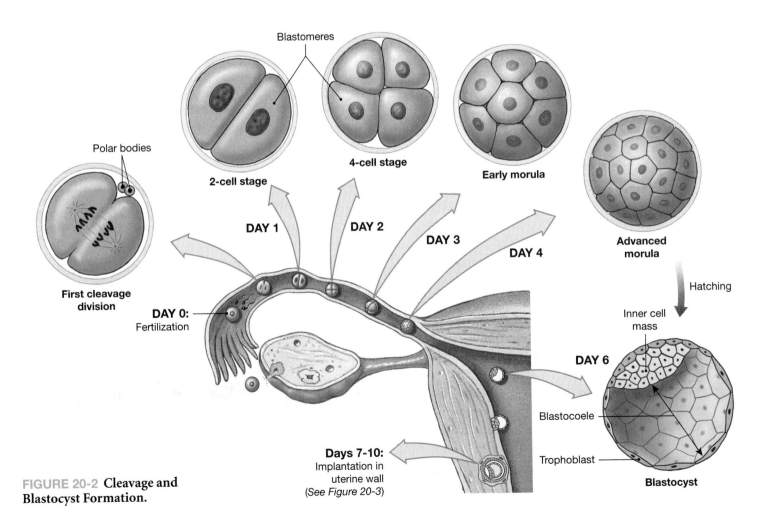

FIGURE 20-2 Cleavage and Blastocyst Formation.

tropho, food + *blast,* precursor—this layer of cells provides food to the developing embryo. A second group of cells, the **inner cell mass,** lies clustered in one portion of the blastocyst. In time, the inner cell mass will form the embryo.

During this time, the zona pellucida is shed in a process known as *hatching.* The blastocyst is now freely exposed to the fluid contents of the uterine cavity. This glycogen-rich fluid, secreted by the uterine glands of the uterus, provides nutrients to the blastocyst. When fully formed, the blastocyst contacts the endometrium; at that time, cleavage ends and implantation begins.

IMPLANTATION

Implantation (Figure 20-3) begins as the surface of the blastocyst adjacent to the inner cell mass touches and adheres to the uterine lining (see day 7, Figure 20-3). At the area of contact, the superficial cells undergo rapid divisions, making the trophoblast several layers thick. The cells closest to the interior of the blastocyst remain intact and form a layer called the *cellular trophoblast* (see day 8, Figure 20-3). Near the uterine wall, the cell membranes separating the trophoblast cells disappear, creating a layer of cytoplasm containing multiple nuclei. This outer layer, called the *syncytial* (sin-SISH-al) *trophoblast,* erodes a path through the uterine epithelium. At first, this erosion creates a gap in the uterine lining, but the division and migration of epithelial cells soon repair the surface. By day 10, repairs are complete, and the blastocyst no longer contacts the uterine cavity. Further development occurs entirely within the functional zone of the endometrium.

In most cases, implantation occurs in the fundus or elsewhere in the body of the uterus. In an **ectopic pregnancy,** implantation occurs somewhere other than within the uterus, such as in one of the uterine tubes. Approximately 0.6 percent of pregnancies are ectopic pregnancies, which do not produce a viable embryo and can be life-threatening to the mother.

As implantation proceeds, the syncytial trophoblast continues to enlarge into the surrounding endometrium (see day 9, Figure 20-3). The erosion of uterine gland cells releases nutrients that are absorbed by the trophoblast and spread by diffusion to the inner cell mass. These nutrients provide the energy needed to support the early stages of embryo formation. Extensions of the trophoblast grow around endometrial capillaries. As the capillary walls are destroyed, maternal blood begins to flow through trophoblastic channels known as *lacunae* (singular *lacuna*). Fingerlike *villi* extend away from the trophoblast into the surrounding endometrium; these extensions gradually increase in size and complexity as development proceeds.

FIGURE 20-3 Events in Implantation.

Formation of the Amniotic Cavity

By the time of implantation, the inner cell mass has separated from the trophoblast. The separation gradually enlarges, creating a fluid-filled chamber called the **amniotic** (am-nē-OT-ik) **cavity** (see day 9, Figure 20-3; details from days 10–12 are shown in Figure 20-4.) When the amniotic cavity first appears, cells of the inner cell mass are organized into an oval sheet that is two cell layers thick—a superficial layer that faces the amniotic cavity and a deeper layer that is exposed to the fluid contents of the blastocoele.

Gastrulation and Germ Layer Formation

By day 12, a third layer of cells begins forming through the process of **gastrulation** (gas-troo-LĀ-shun) (day 12, Figure 20-4). During gastrulation, some of the cells of the inner cell mass exposed to the amniotic cavity move toward a center line, called the *primitive streak,* and migrate down and in between the two existing layers. This movement creates three distinct embryonic layers of cells, or **germ layers**—each with markedly different fates. The superficial layer in contact with the amniotic cavity is called the **ectoderm,** the layer facing the blastocoele is known as the **endoderm,** and the poorly organized layer of migrating cells is the **mesoderm** (*meso-,* middle). Table 20-1 lists the contributions of each germ layer to the body systems described in previous chapters. Thus, gastrulation produces an oval, three-layered sheet known as the

embryonic disc. The embryonic disc will form the body of the embryo, whereas the rest of the blastocyst will be involved in forming the extraembryonic membranes.

The Formation of Extraembryonic Membranes

The three germ layers also participate in the formation of four **extraembryonic membranes** that support embryonic and fetal development: the *yolk sac,* the *amnion,* the *allantois,* and the *chorion* (Figure 20-5). Few traces of their existence remain in adult systems.

YOLK SAC. The first extraembryonic membrane to appear is the **yolk sac.** The yolk sac, already present 10 days after fertilization, forms a pouch within the blastocoele (Figure 20-4). As gastrulation proceeds, mesodermal cells migrate around this pouch and complete the formation of the yolk sac (see week 2, Figure 20-5). Blood vessels soon appear within the mesoderm, and the yolk sac becomes an important site of blood cell formation.

AMNION. The **amnion** (AM-nē-on) is composed of both ectoderm and mesoderm. Ectodermal cells first spread over the inner surface of the amniotic cavity and, soon after, mesodermal cells follow and create a second, outer layer. As the embryo and later the fetus enlarges, the amnion continues to expand, increasing the size of the amniotic cavity (see week 3, Figure 20-5). The amnion contains *amniotic fluid,* which surrounds and cushions the developing embryo and fetus (see week 10, Figure 20-5).

Day 10: The inner cell mass begins as two layers: a superficial layer, facing the amniotic cavity, and a deep layer, exposed to the blastocoele. Migration of cells around the amniotic cavity is the first step in the formation of the amnion. Migration of cells around the edges of the blastocoele is the first step in yolk sac formation.

FIGURE 20-4 **The Inner Cell Mass and Gastrulation.**

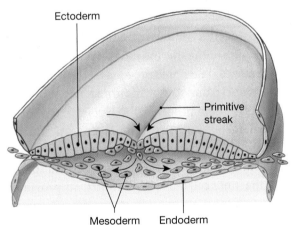

Day 12: Migration of superficial cells to the interior creates a third layer. From the time this process (gastrulation) begins, the superficial layer is called *ectoderm,* the deep layer *endoderm,* and the migrating cells *mesoderm.*

TABLE 20-1 **The Fates of the Germ Layers**

GERM LAYER	DEVELOPMENTAL CONTRIBUTIONS TO THE BODY
Ectoderm	*Integumentary system:* epidermis, hair follicles and hairs, nails, and glands communicating with the skin (sweat glands, mammary glands, and sebaceous glands) *Skeletal system:* pharyngeal cartilages of the embryo develop into portions of sphenoid and hyoid bones, auditory ossicles, and styloid processes of temporal bones *Nervous system:* all neural tissue, including brain and spinal cord *Endocrine system:* pituitary gland and the suprarenal medullae *Respiratory system:* mucous epithelium of nasal passageways *Digestive system:* mucous epithelium of mouth and anus, salivary glands
Mesoderm	*Integumentary system:* dermis (and hypodermis) *Skeletal system:* all components except some pharyngeal cartilage derivatives *Muscular system:* all components *Endocrine system:* suprarenal cortex, endocrine tissues of heart, kidneys, and gonads *Cardiovascular system:* all components *Lymphoid system:* all components *Urinary system:* the kidneys, including the nephrons and the initial portions of the collecting system *Reproductive system:* the gonads and the adjacent portions of the duct systems *Miscellaneous:* the lining of the body cavities (pleural, pericardial, and peritoneal) and the connective tissues that support all organ systems
Endoderm	*Endocrine system:* thymus, thyroid gland, and pancreas *Respiratory system:* respiratory epithelium (except nasal passageways) and associated mucous glands *Digestive system:* mucous epithelium (except mouth and anus), exocrine glands (except salivary glands), liver, and pancreas *Urinary system:* urinary bladder and distal portions of the duct system *Reproductive system:* distal portions of the duct system, stem cells that produce gametes

THE ALLANTOIS. The **allantois** (a-LAN-tō-is) is a sac of endoderm and mesoderm that extends away from the embryo (see week 3, Figure 20-5). The base of the allantois later gives rise to the urinary bladder. The allantois accumulates some of the small amount of urine produced by the kidneys during embryological development.

THE CHORION. The **chorion** (kō-rē-on) is created as migrating mesodermal cells form a layer beneath the trophoblast, separating it from the blastocoele (see weeks 2 and 3, Figure 20-5). When implantation first occurs, the nutrients absorbed by the trophoblast can easily reach the inner cell mass by diffusion. But as the embryo and trophoblast enlarge, the distance between them increases, and diffusion alone cannot keep pace with the demands of the embryo. Blood vessels now begin to develop within the mesoderm of the chorion, creating a rapid-transit system for nutrients that links the embryo with the trophoblast.

PLACENTATION

The **placenta** is a temporary structure in the uterine wall that provides a site for diffusion between the fetal and maternal circulatory systems. **Placentation** (pla-sen-TĀ-shun), or *placenta formation,* takes place when blood vessels form in the chorion around the periphery of the blastocyst (Figure 20-5). By week 3 of development, the mesoderm extends along each of the trophoblastic villi, forming *chorionic villi* in contact with maternal tissues. Embryonic blood vessels develop in each villus, and circulation through these chorionic vessels begins early in week 3, when the heart starts beating. These villi continue to enlarge and branch, forming an intricate network within the endometrium. Blood vessels continue to be eroded, and maternal blood flows slowly through the lacunae. Chorionic blood vessels pass close by, and gases and nutrients diffuse between the embryonic and maternal circulations across the trophoblast layers.

WEEK 2

Migration of mesoderm around the inner surface of the trophoblast creates the chorion. Mesodermal migration around the outside of the amniotic cavity, between the ectodermal cells and the trophoblast, forms the amnion. Mesodermal migration around the endodermal pouch creates the yolk sac.

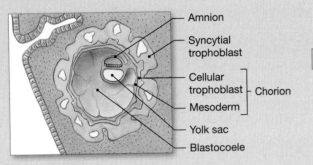

- Amnion
- Syncytial trophoblast
- Cellular trophoblast ⎤
- Mesoderm ⎦ Chorion
- Yolk sac
- Blastocoele

WEEK 3

The embryonic disc bulges into the amniotic cavity at the head fold. The allantois, an endodermal extension surrounded by mesoderm, extends toward the trophoblast.

- Amniotic cavity (containing amniotic fluid)
- Allantois
- Head fold of embryo
- Chorion
- Syncytial trophoblast
- Chorionic villi of placenta

Yolk sac

WEEK 5

The developing embryo and extraembryonic membranes bulge into the uterine cavity. The trophoblast pushing out into the uterine lumen remains covered by endometrium but no longer participates in nutrient absorption and embryo support. The embryo moves away from the placenta, and the body stalk and yolk stalk fuse to form an umbilical stalk.

- Uterus
- Myometrium
- Umbilical stalk
- Placenta
- Yolk sac
- Chorionic villi of placenta
- Chorion
- Uterine cavity

WEEK 4

The embryo now has a head fold and a tail fold. Constriction of the connections between the embryo and the surrounding trophoblast narrows the yolk stalk and body stalk.

- Tail fold
- Body stalk
- Yolk stalk
- Yolk sac
- Embryonic gut
- Embryonic head fold

WEEK 10

The amnion has expanded greatly, filling the uterine cavity. The fetus is connected to the placenta by an elongated umbilical cord that contains a portion of the allantois, blood vessels, and the remnants of the yolk stalk.

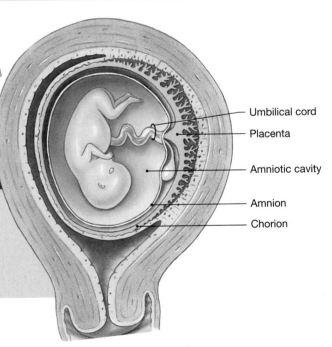

- Umbilical cord
- Placenta
- Amniotic cavity
- Amnion
- Chorion

FIGURE 20-5 **Extraembryonic Membranes and Placenta Formation.**

Initially, the entire blastocyst is surrounded by chorionic villi. The chorion continues to enlarge, expanding like a balloon within the endometrium, and by week 4 the embryo, amnion, and yolk sac are suspended within an expansive, fluid-filled chamber. The *body stalk,* the connection between the embryo and the chorion, contains the distal portions of the allantois and blood vessels that carry blood to and from the placenta. The narrow connection between the endoderm of the embryo and the yolk sac is called the *yolk stalk.* As the end of the first trimester approaches, the fetus moves farther away from the placenta.

The yolk stalk and body stalk begin to fuse, forming an *umbilical stalk* (see week 5, Figure 20-5). By week 10, the fetus floats free within the amniotic cavity. The fetus remains connected to the placenta by the elongate **umbilical cord,** which contains the allantois, placental blood vessels, and the yolk stalk.

Placental Circulation

Figure 20-6 diagrams circulation at the placenta near the end of the first trimester. Deoxygenated blood flows from the

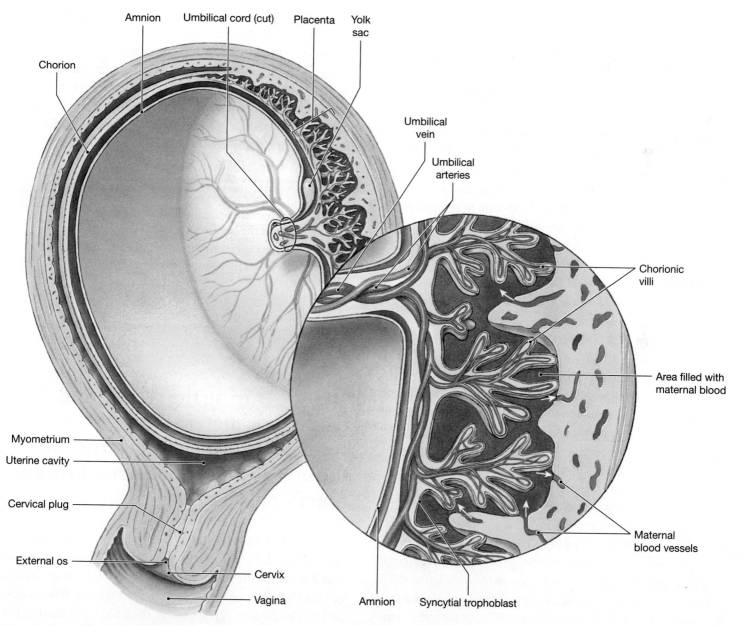

FIGURE 20-6 The Placenta and Placental Circulation. For clarity, the uterus is shown after the embryo has been removed and the umbilical cord cut. Oxygenated blood flows from the mother into the placenta through ruptured maternal arteries. It then flows around chorionic villi that contain fetal blood vessels. Deoxygenated fetal blood enters the chorionic villi in paired umbilical arteries, and oxygenated blood then leaves in a single umbilical vein. Deoxygenated maternal blood reenters the mother's venous system through the broken walls of small uterine veins. Note that no mixing of maternal and fetal blood occurs.

developing embryo or fetus to the placenta through the paired **umbilical arteries,** and oxygenated blood returns to the developing embryo or fetus in a single **umbilical vein.** ∞ p. 460 The chorionic villi provide the surface area for the active and passive exchanges of gases, nutrients, and wastes between the fetal and maternal bloodstreams.

The Endocrine Placenta

In addition to its role in the nutrition of the fetus, the placenta functions as an endocrine organ. Several placental hormones—including *human chorionic gonadotropin, progesterone, estrogens, human placental lactogen, placental prolactin,* and *relaxin*—are synthesized by the syncytial trophoblast and released into the maternal bloodstream.

Human chorionic (kō-rē-ON-ik) **gonadotropin (hCG)** appears in the maternal bloodstream soon after implantation has occurred. The presence of hCG in blood or urine samples is a reliable indication of pregnancy. Kits sold for the early detection of a pregnancy are sensitive to the presence of this hormone. Like luteinizing hormone, hCG maintains the corpus luteum and promotes the continued secretion of progesterone. As a result, the endometrial lining remains perfectly functional, and menses does not occur. In the absence of hCG, the pregnancy ends, because another uterine cycle begins and the endometrial lining disintegrates.

In the presence of hCG, the corpus luteum persists for 3–4 months before gradually shrinking. The decline of the corpus luteum does not trigger the return of menstrual periods, because by the end of the first trimester, the placenta is actively secreting both **progesterone** and **estrogens.**

After the first trimester, the placenta produces sufficient amounts of progesterone to maintain the endometrial lining and continue the pregnancy. As the end of the third trimester approaches, estrogen production accelerates. The rising estrogen levels play a role in stimulating labor and delivery.

Human placental lactogen (hPL) and **placental prolactin** help prepare the mammary glands for milk production. The conversion of the mammary glands from resting to active status requires the presence of both placental hormones (hPL, placental prolactin, estrogen, and progesterone) and maternal hormones (growth hormone, prolactin, and thyroid hormones).

Relaxin is a hormone secreted by both the placenta and the corpus luteum. Relaxin (1) increases the flexibility of the pubic symphysis, permitting the pelvis to expand during delivery; (2) causes the dilation of the cervix, making it easier for the fetus to enter the vaginal canal; and (3) delays the onset of labor contractions by suppressing the release of oxytocin by the hypothalamus.

EMBRYOGENESIS

Shortly after gastrulation begins, the body of the embryo begins to separate itself from the rest of the embryonic disc, and the embryo's internal organs start to form. The process of embryo formation is called **embryogenesis** (em-brē-ō-JEN-e-sis). Embryogenesis begins as folding and differential growth of the embryonic disc produce a bulge—the *head fold*—that projects into the amniotic cavity (see week 3, Figure 20-5). Similar movements lead to the formation of a *tail fold* (see week 4, Figure 20-5). By this time, the embryo can be seen to have dorsal and ventral surfaces and left and right sides. The changes in proportions and appearance that occur between week 2 of development and the end of the first trimester are presented in Figure 20-7.

The first trimester is a critical period for development, because events during the first 12 weeks establish the basis for **organogenesis,** the process of organ formation. Table 20-2 includes important developmental milestones, including those during the first trimester.

CHECKPOINT

8. What is the developmental fate of the inner cell mass of the blastocyst?

9. Sue's pregnancy test indicates elevated levels of the hormone hCG (human chorionic gonadotropin). Is she pregnant?

10. What are two important functions of the placenta?

See the blue Answers tab at the back of the book.

20-5 During the second and third trimesters, maternal organ systems support the developing fetus, and the uterus undergoes structural and functional changes

By the end of the first trimester (week 12), the basic elements of all the major organ systems have formed. Over the next 3 months, the fetus will grow to a weight of about 0.64 kg (1.4 lb). During this second trimester, the fetus, encircled by the amnion, grows faster than the surrounding placenta. When the outer surface of the amnion contacts the inner surface of the chorion, these layers fuse. Figure 20-8a shows a 4-month fetus; Figure 20-8b shows a 6-month fetus. The changes in body form that occur during the first

(a) Week 2

- Future head of embryo
- Thickened neural plate (will form brain)
- Axis of future spinal cord
- Somites
- Neural folds
- Cut wall of amniotic cavity
- Future tail of embryo

(b) Week 4

- Medulla
- Ear
- Forebrain
- Eye
- Heart
- Body stalk
- Tail
- Pharyngeal arches
- Somites
- Arm bud
- Leg bud

(c) Week 8

- Chorionic villi
- Amnion
- Umbilical cord
- Placenta

(d) Week 12

FIGURE 20-7 Development During the First Trimester. (a) This SEM shows the superior surface of a monkey embryo after 2 weeks of development. A human embryo at this stage would look essentially the same. (**b–d**) Fiber-optic technology provided these views of human embryos (b, c) and a human fetus (d). For actual sizes, see Figure 20-9 (p. 687).

trimester and part of the second trimester are shown in the upper portion of Figure 20-9.

During the third trimester, the basic components of all the organ systems appear, and most become ready to perform their normal functions. The rate of growth starts to decrease, but in absolute terms, the largest weight gain occurs in this trimester. In the last 3 months of gestation, the fetus gains about 2.6 kg (5.7 lb), reaching a full-term weight of about 3.2 kg (7 lb). Important events in organ system development during the second and third trimesters are summarized in Table 20-2.

The Big Picture

The basic body plan, the foundations of all of the organ systems, and the four extraembryonic membranes appear during the first trimester. These processes are complex and delicate; not every zygote starts cleavage, and fewer than half of the zygotes that do begin cleavage survive until the end of the first trimester. The second trimester is a period of rapid growth, accompanied by the development of fetal organs that will then become fully functional by the end of the third trimester.

TABLE 20-2 **An Overview of Prenatal and Early Postnatal Development***

GESTATIONAL AGE (MONTHS)	SIZE AND WEIGHT	INTEGUMENTARY SYSTEM	SKELETAL SYSTEM	MUSCULAR SYSTEM	NERVOUS SYSTEM	SPECIAL SENSE ORGANS
1	5 mm 0.02 g		(b) Somite formation	(b) Somite formation	(b) Neural tube formation	(b) Eye and ear formation
2	28 mm 2.7 g	(b) Nail beds, hair follicles, sweat glands	(b) Axial and appendicular cartilage formation	(c) Rudiments of axial musculature	(b) CNS, PNS organization, growth of cerebrum	(b) Taste buds, olfactory epithelium
3	78 mm 26 g	(b) Epidermal layers appear	(b) Ossification centers spreading	(c) Rudiments of appendicular musculature	(c) Basic spinal cord and brain structure	
4	133 mm 0.15 kg	(b) Hair, sebaceous glands formation (c) Sweat glands	(b) Articulations (c) Facial and palatal organization	Movements of fetus can be felt by the mother	(b) Rapid expansion of cerebrum	(c) Basic eye and ear structure (b) Peripheral receptor formation
5	185 mm 0.46 kg	(b) Keratin production, nail production			(b) Myelination of spinal cord	
6	230 mm 0.64 kg			(c) Perineal muscles	(b) CNS tract formation (c) Layering of cortex	
7	270 mm 1.492 kg	(b) Keratinization, nail formation, hair formation				(c) Eyelids open, retinae sensitive to light
8	310 mm 2.274 kg		(b) Epiphyseal cartilage formation			(c) Taste receptors functional
9	346 mm 3.2 kg					
Postnatal Development		Hair changes in consistency and distribution	Formation and growth of epiphyseal cartilages continue	Muscle mass and control increase	Myelination, layering, CNS tract formation continue	

*(b) = beginning to form; (c) = completed

ENDOCRINE SYSTEM	CARDIOVASCULAR AND LYMPHOID SYSTEMS	RESPIRATORY SYSTEM	DIGESTIVE SYSTEM	URINARY SYSTEM	REPRODUCTIVE SYSTEM
	(b) Heartbeat	(b) Trachea and lung formation	(b) Intestinal tract, liver, pancreas (c) Yolk sac	(c) Allantois	
(b) Thymus, thyroid, pituitary, suprarenal glands	(c) Basic heart structure, major blood vessels, lymph nodes and ducts (b) Blood formation in liver	(b) Extensive bronchial branching into mediastinum (c) Diaphragm	(b) Intestinal subdivisions, villi, salivary glands	(b) Kidney formation (adult form)	(b) Mammary glands formation
(c) Thymus, thyroid gland	(b) Tonsils, blood formation in bone marrow		(c) Gallbladder, pancreas		(b) Formation of gonads, ducts, and genitalia; oogonia in female
	(b) Migration of lymphocytes to lymphoid organs, blood formation in spleen			(b) Degeneration of embryonic kidneys	
	(c) Tonsils	(c) Nostrils open	(c) Intestinal subdivisions		
(c) Suprarenal glands	(c) Spleen, liver, bone marrow	(b) Formation of alveoli	(c) Epithelial organization, glands		
(c) Pituitary gland			(c) Intestinal plicae circulares		(b) Testes descend
		Complete pulmonary branching and alveolar formation		(c) Nephron formation	Descent of testes complete at or near time of delivery
	Cardiovascular changes at birth; immune response gradually becomes operative				

(a)   (b)

FIGURE 20-8 **The Fetus During the Second and Third Trimesters.** **(a)** This photograph of a 4-month fetus was taken through a fiber-optic endoscope. **(b)** This image of a 6-month fetus was obtained during an ultrasound procedure.

THE EFFECTS OF PREGNANCY ON MATERNAL SYSTEMS

The developing fetus is totally dependent on maternal organ systems for nourishment, respiration, and waste removal. The mother must absorb enough oxygen, nutrients, and vitamins for herself and her fetus, and she must eliminate all of the wastes generated by both of them. Although this is not a burden over the initial weeks of gestation, the demands placed on the mother become significant as the fetus grows larger. For the mother to survive under these conditions, maternal systems must make major adjustments. In practical terms, the mother must breathe, eat, and excrete for two.

The major changes that take place in maternal systems include the following:

- *Maternal respiratory rate and tidal volume increase.* As a result, the mother's lungs deliver the extra oxygen the fetus requires and remove the excess carbon dioxide the fetus generates.

- *Maternal blood volume increases.* This increase occurs because (1) blood flowing into the placenta reduces the volume in the rest of the systemic circuit, and (2) fetal activity lowers blood P_{O_2} and elevates blood P_{CO_2}. The combination stimulates the production of renin and erythropoietin (EPO) by the kidneys, leading to an increase in maternal blood volume (see Figure 13-12a, p. 443). By the end of gestation, maternal blood volume has increased by almost 50 percent.

- *Maternal requirements for nutrients climb 10–30 percent.* Because pregnant women must nourish both themselves and their fetus, they tend to have increased sensations of hunger.

- *Maternal glomerular filtration rate increases by roughly 50 percent.* This increase, which corresponds to the increase in blood volume, accelerates the excretion of metabolic wastes generated by the fetus. Because the volume of urine produced increases and the weight of the uterus presses down on the urinary bladder, pregnant women need to urinate frequently.

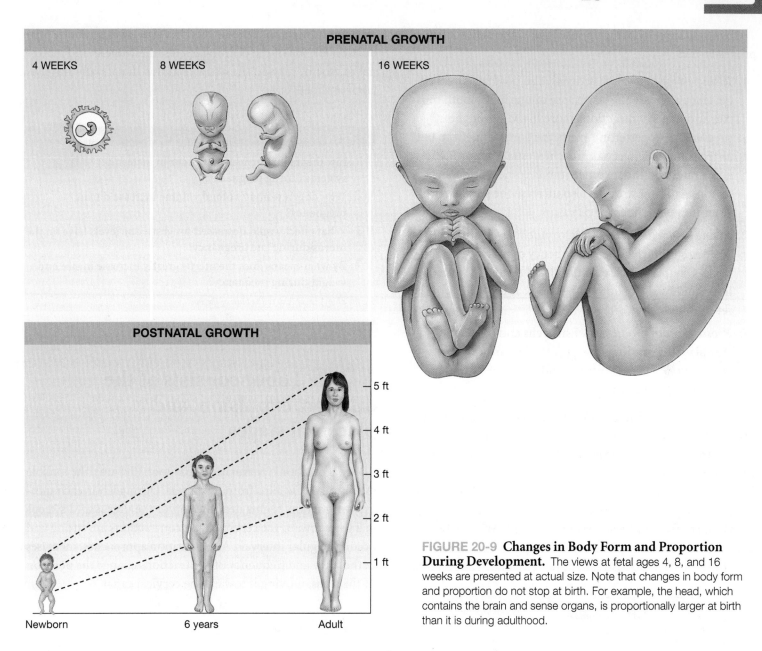

FIGURE 20-9 Changes in Body Form and Proportion During Development. The views at fetal ages 4, 8, and 16 weeks are presented at actual size. Note that changes in body form and proportion do not stop at birth. For example, the head, which contains the brain and sense organs, is proportionally larger at birth than it is during adulthood.

- *The uterus undergoes a tremendous increase in size.* Structural and functional changes in the expanding uterus are so important that we will discuss them in a separate section.

- *The mammary glands increase in size, and secretory activity begins.* By the end of the sixth month of pregnancy, the mammary glands are fully developed and begin producing secretions that are stored in the duct system of those glands.

STRUCTURAL AND FUNCTIONAL CHANGES IN THE UTERUS

At the end of gestation, a typical uterus will have grown from 7.5 cm (3 in.) long to 30 cm (12 in.) long, and from 60 g (2 oz.) to 1100 g (2.4 lb). The uterus may then contain almost 2 liters of fluid, plus fetus and placenta, for a total weight of roughly 6–7 kg (13–15.4 lb). This remarkable expansion occurs through the enlargement of existing cells (especially smooth muscle cells) rather than by an increase in the total number of cells.

The tremendous stretching of the uterus is accompanied by a gradual increase in the rates of spontaneous smooth muscle contractions in the myometrium. In the early stages of pregnancy, the contractions are weak, painless, and brief. Evidence indicates that progesterone released by the placenta has an inhibitory effect on uterine smooth muscle, preventing more extensive and powerful contractions.

Three major factors oppose the calming action of progesterone:

1. *Rising estrogen levels.* Estrogens, also produced by the placenta, increase the sensitivity of uterine smooth muscles and make contractions more likely. Throughout pregnancy, progesterone exerts the dominant effect, but as the time of delivery approaches, estrogen production accelerates and the myometrium becomes more sensitive to stimulation. Estrogens also increase the sensitivity of smooth muscle fibers to oxytocin.

2. *Rising oxytocin levels.* Rising oxytocin levels stimulate increases in the force and frequency of uterine contractions. Oxytocin release is stimulated by high estrogen levels and by distortion of the cervix as the weight of the fetus increases.

3. *Prostaglandin production.* Estrogens and oxytocin stimulate the production of prostaglandins in the endometrium. These prostaglandins further stimulate smooth muscle contractions.

After 9 months of gestation, several factors interact to produce **labor contractions** in the myometrium of the uterine wall. Once begun, positive feedback ensures that the contractions continue until delivery has been completed.

Figure 20-10 diagrams important factors that stimulate and sustain labor. The actual trigger for the onset of labor may be events in the fetus rather than in the mother. When labor begins, the fetal pituitary gland secretes oxytocin that is released into the maternal bloodstream at the placenta. The resulting

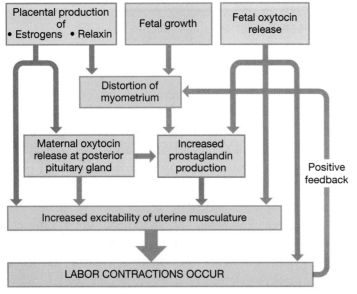

FIGURE 20-10 **Factors Involved in Initiating and Sustaining Labor and Delivery.**

increase in myometrial contractions and prostaglandin production, on top of the priming effects of estrogens and maternal oxytocin, may be the extra stimulus that finally initiates labor and delivery.

CHECKPOINT

11. List the major changes that occur in maternal systems during pregnancy.

12. Why does a woman's blood volume increase during pregnancy?

13. What effect would decreased progesterone levels have on the uterus during late pregnancy?

14. By what means does the uterus greatly increase in size and weight during pregnancy?

See the blue Answers tab at the back of the book.

20-6 Labor consists of the dilation, expulsion, and placental stages

The goal of labor is **parturition** (par-toor-ISH-un), the forcible expulsion of the fetus from the uterus. During labor, each uterine contraction begins near the top of the uterus and sweeps in a wave toward the cervix. These contractions are strong and occur at regular intervals. As parturition approaches, increases in the force and frequency of contractions change the position of the fetus, moving it toward the cervical canal.

THE STAGES OF LABOR

Labor consists of three stages: the *dilation stage*, the *expulsion stage*, and the *placental stage* (Figure 20-11).

1. The **dilation stage** begins with the onset of labor, as the cervix dilates and the fetus begins to slide down the cervical canal (Stage 1 in Figure 20-11). This stage is highly variable in length but typically lasts 8 or more hours. At the start of this stage, labor contractions occur once every 10–30 minutes; their frequency increases steadily. Late in this stage, the amnion usually ruptures, an event sometimes referred to as "having one's water break."

2. The **expulsion stage** begins as the cervix, pushed open by the approaching fetus, dilates completely (Stage 2 in Figure 20-11). Expulsion continues until the fetus has emerged from the vagina, a period that usually takes less

Placenta   Umbilical cord   Sacral promontory   Cervical canal   Pubic symphysis   Cervix   Vagina

Fully developed fetus before labor begins

FIGURE 20-11 **The Stages of Labor.**

STAGE **1**   THE DILATION STAGE

STAGE **2**   THE EXPULSION STAGE

STAGE **3**   THE PLACENTAL STAGE

Uterus   Ejection of the placenta

than 2 hours. The arrival of the newborn into the outside world is **delivery,** or birth.

If the vaginal canal is too small to permit the passage of the fetus, posing acute danger of perineal tearing, a physician may temporarily enlarge the passageway by performing an **episiotomy** (e-pēz-ē-OT-o-mē), an incision through the perineal musculature. After delivery, this smooth surgical cut can be repaired with sutures, a much simpler procedure than suturing the jagged edges associated with an extensive perineal tear. If complications arise during the dilation or expulsion stage, the infant can be surgically removed by **cesarean section,** or *"C-section,"* which involves making an incision through the abdominal wall and the uterus that is just large enough to allow passage of the infant's head. This procedure is performed during 15–25 percent of the deliveries in the United States—more often than necessary, according to some studies. Over the past decade, efforts have been made to reduce the frequency of both episiotomies and cesarean sections.

3. During the **placental stage** of labor, building muscle tension in the walls of the uterus (which still contains the placenta) gradually decreases the size of the uterus (Stage 3 in Figure 20-11). This contraction of the uterus tears connections between the endometrium and the placenta. Usually within an hour after delivery, the placental stage ends with the ejection of the placenta, or "afterbirth." The disruption of the placenta is accompanied by a loss of

blood. Because maternal blood volume has increased greatly during pregnancy, this loss can be tolerated without difficulty.

PREMATURE LABOR

Premature labor occurs when labor contractions begin before the fetus has completed normal development. The chances of a newborn's survival are directly related to its body weight at delivery. Even with massive supportive efforts, newborns weighing less than 400 g (14 oz.) at birth will not survive, primarily because their respiratory, cardiovascular, and urinary systems are unable to support life. As a result, the dividing line between spontaneous abortion and **immature delivery** is usually set at a body weight of 500 g (17.6 oz.), the normal weight near the end of the second trimester.

Most fetuses born at 25–27 weeks of gestation (birth weight under 600 g or 21.1 oz) die despite intensive neonatal care; survivors have a high risk of developmental abnormalities. **Premature delivery** usually refers to birth at 28–36 weeks (birth weight over 1 kg or 2.2 lb). Given the proper medical care, these infants have a good chance of surviving and developing normally.

MULTIPLE BIRTHS

Of all multiple births (twins, triplets, quadruplets, and so forth), twins are most common. In the U.S. population, one of every 89 births contains twins, whereas triplets occur in one of every 89^2 (or 7921) births. About 70 percent of all twins are "fraternal," or **dizygotic** (dī-zī-GOT-ik). Fraternal twins develop when two eggs are fertilized at the same time, forming two separate zygotes. Fraternal twins can be of the same or different sexes.

"Identical," or **monozygotic,** twins result from the separation of blastomeres early in cleavage or from the splitting of the inner cell mass before gastrulation. In either event, the genetic makeup and sex of the pair are identical because both twins are formed from the same pair of gametes. Identical twins occur in about 30 percent of all twin births. Triplets and larger multiple births can result from the same processes that produce twins.

If the splitting of the blastomeres or of the embryonic disc is not complete, **conjoined** (*Siamese*) **twins** may develop. These genetically identical twins typically share some skin, a portion of the liver, and perhaps other internal organs as well. When the fusion is minor, the infants can be surgically separated with some success. Most conjoined twins with more extensive fusions fail to survive delivery.

20-7 Postnatal stages are the neonatal period, infancy, childhood, adolescence, maturity, and senescence

Developmental processes do not cease at delivery. A newborn has few of the anatomical, functional, or physiological characteristics of mature adults. In postnatal development, each individual passes through a number of **life stages**—*the neonatal period, infancy, childhood, adolescence,* and *maturity*—each with a distinctive combination of characteristics and abilities.

THE NEONATAL PERIOD, INFANCY, AND CHILDHOOD

The **neonatal period** extends from the moment of birth to 1 month thereafter. **Infancy** then continues to 2 years of age, and **childhood** lasts until **adolescence,** the period of sexual and physical maturation.

During these developmental stages, the major nonreproductive organ systems become fully operational and gradually acquire the functional characteristics of adult structures. Additionally, the individual grows rapidly, and body proportions change significantly.

Pediatrics is the medical specialty that focuses on postnatal development from infancy through adolescence. Infants and young children often cannot clearly describe the problems they are experiencing, so pediatricians and parents must be skilled observers. Standardized tests are used to compare developmental progress with average values.

The Neonatal Period

Physiological and anatomical changes occur as a fetus completes the transition to the status of a newborn, or **neonate.** Before delivery, dissolved gases, nutrients, waste products, hormones, and antibodies were transferred across the placenta.

At birth, a newborn must come to rely on its own specialized organs and organ systems to perform respiration, digestion, and excretion. Neonates must make numerous adjustments to life outside the womb, including the following:

- At birth, the lungs are collapsed and filled with fluid. Filling them with air requires a powerful inhalation. ∞ p. 526

- When the lungs expand, the pattern of cardiovascular circulation changes due to alterations in blood pressure and flow rates. The circulation changes result in separation of the pulmonary and systemic circuits. ∞ p. 461

- Typical neonatal heart rates (120–140 beats per minute) are lower than fetal heart rates (averaging 150 beats per minute). Both neonatal heart rates and respiratory rates (30 breaths per minute) are considerably higher than those of adults.

- Before birth, the digestive system remains relatively inactive, although it does accumulate a mixture of bile secretions, mucus, and epithelial cells. The collected debris is excreted in the first few days of life. Over that period newborns begin to nurse.

- As waste products build up in the arterial blood, they are excreted at the kidneys. Glomerular filtration is normal, but neonates cannot concentrate urine to any significant degree. As a result, urinary water losses are high, and neonatal fluid requirements are proportionally much greater than those of adults.

- A neonate has little ability to control body temperature, particularly in the first few days after delivery. As an infant grows larger and its insulating subcutaneous fat "blanket" gets thicker, its metabolic rate also rises. Daily and even hourly shifts in body temperature continue throughout childhood.

LACTATION AND THE MAMMARY GLANDS. By the end of the sixth month of pregnancy, an expectant mother's mammary glands are fully developed, and the gland cells begin producing a secretion known as **colostrum** (kō-LOS-trum). Ingested by a newborn during the first 2 or 3 days of life, colostrum contains more proteins and far less fat than breast milk. Many of the proteins are antibodies that help the infant ward off infections until its own immune system becomes fully functional. As colostrum production declines, the mammary glands convert to milk production. Breast milk consists of water, proteins, amino acids, lipids, sugars, and salts. It also contains large quantities of *lysozymes,* enzymes with antibiotic properties.

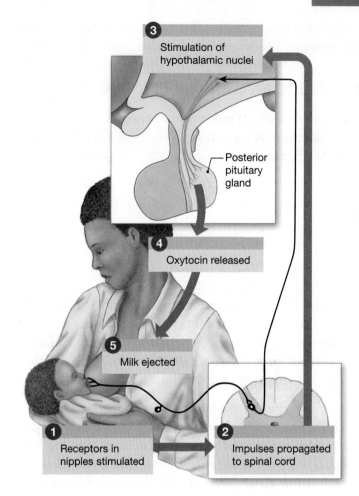

FIGURE 20-12 **The Milk Let-Down Reflex.**

Milk becomes available to infants through the **milk let-down reflex** (Figure 20-12). Mammary gland secretion is triggered when the infant begins to suck on the nipple. The stimulation of tactile receptors there leads to the release of oxytocin at the posterior pituitary gland. The arrival of circulating oxytocin at the mammary gland stimulates the contraction of contractile cells in the walls of the lactiferous ducts and sinuses, resulting in the ejection of milk. The milk let-down reflex continues to function until *weaning,* typically 1–2 years after birth. Milk production ceases soon after, and the mammary glands gradually return to a resting state.

Infancy and Childhood

The rate of growth is greatest during prenatal development and declines after delivery. Postnatal growth during infancy and childhood occurs under the direction of circulating hormones, notably pituitary growth hormone, suprarenal steroids, and thyroid hormones. These hormones affect each tissue and organ in specific ways, depending on the sensitivities of the individual cells. As a result, growth does not occur uniformly, and body proportions gradually change (Figure 20-9, p. 687).

ADOLESCENCE AND MATURITY

Adolescence begins at **puberty,** the period of sexual maturation, and ends when growth is completed. Three hormonal events interact at the onset of puberty:

1. The hypothalamus increases its production of gonadotropin-releasing hormone (GnRH).

2. The anterior pituitary gland becomes more sensitive to the presence of GnRH, and circulating levels of FSH and LH rise rapidly.

3. Ovarian or testicular cells become more sensitive to FSH and LH. These changes initiate gamete formation, turn on the production of sex hormones that stimulate the appearance of secondary sex characteristics and behaviors, and cause a sudden acceleration in the growth rate, ending in the closure of the epiphyseal cartilages.

The age at which puberty begins varies. In the United States today, puberty generally occurs at about age 12 in boys and at 11 in girls, but the normal ranges are broad (10–15 in boys, 9–14 in girls). The combination of sex hormones, growth hormone, suprarenal steroids, and thyroxine leads to a sudden acceleration in the growth rate. The timing of the growth spurt varies between the sexes, corresponding to different ages at the onset of puberty. In girls, the growth rate is maximal between ages 10 and 13; boys grow most rapidly between ages 12 and 15. Growth continues at a slower pace until ages 18 to 21. By that time, most of the epiphyseal cartilages have closed. ∞ p. 148

The boundary between adolescence and maturity is very hazy, because it has physical, emotional, and behavioral components. Adolescence is often said to be over when growth stops, typically in the late teens or early twenties. The individual is then considered physically mature. Although physical growth ends at maturity, physiological changes continue. The sex-specific differences produced at puberty are retained, but further changes occur when sex hormone levels decline at menopause or the male climacteric. ∞ p. 661 All these changes are part of the aging process, or **senescence.** As we have seen, aging reduces an individual's functional capabilities. Even in the absence of such factors as disease or injury, aging-related changes at the molecular level ultimately lead to death.

Clinical Note

Abortion

Abortion is the termination of a pregnancy. Most references distinguish among spontaneous, induced, and therapeutic abortions. **Spontaneous abortions,** or *miscarriages,* occur as a result of some developmental or physiological problem. For example, spontaneous abortions can result from chromosomal defects in the embryo or from hormonal problems, including inadequate LH production by the maternal pituitary gland or placental failure to produce adequate levels of hCG. Spontaneous abortions occur in roughly 15 percent of all pregnancies.

Induced abortions, or *elective abortions,* are performed at a woman's request. Induced abortions remain the focus of considerable controversy, largely for nonmedical reasons. Most induced abortions involve unmarried or adolescent women. The ratio of abortions to deliveries for married women averages 1:10, whereas it is nearly 2:1 for unmarried women and adolescents. In most states, induced abortions are legal during the first 3 months after conception; under certain conditions, induced abortions may be permitted until the fifth or sixth month.

Therapeutic abortions are performed when continuing a pregnancy represents a threat to the life and health of the mother.

CHECKPOINT

18. Name the postnatal stages of development.

19. What is the difference between colostrum and breast milk?

20. Increases in the blood levels of GnRH, FSH, LH, and sex hormones mark the onset of which stage of development?

See the blue Answers tab at the back of the book.

20-8 Genes and chromosomes determine patterns of inheritance

Chromosomes contain DNA, and genes are segments of DNA. Each gene carries the information needed to direct the synthesis of a specific polypeptide. Chromosome structure and the functions of genes were introduced in Chapter 3. ∞ p. 78 Every nucleated somatic cell in your body carries copies of the original 46 chromosomes present when you were a zygote. Those chromosomes and their component genes represent your **genotype** (JĒN-ō-tīp).

Through development and differentiation, the instructions contained within the genotype are expressed in many ways. No single living cell or tissue makes use of all the information contained within the genotype. For example, in muscle fibers the genes important for excitable membrane formation and contractile proteins are active, whereas a different set of genes is operating in pancreatic islet cells. Collectively, however, the instructions contained within the genotype determine the anatomical and physiological characteristics that make you a unique individual. Collectively those characteristics make up your **phenotype** (FĒ-nō-tīp; *phainein*, to display + *typos*, mark). Specific elements in your phenotype, such as your hair and eye color, skin tone, and foot size, are called phenotypic *characters,* or *traits.*

Even though your genotype is derived from the genotypes of your parents, you are neither an exact copy of either parent nor an easily identifiable mixture of their phenotypes. Our discussion of genetics will begin with an overview of the basic patterns of inheritance and their implications. We will then examine the mechanisms responsible for regulating the activities of the genotype during prenatal development.

PATTERNS OF INHERITANCE

In humans, every somatic cell contains 46 chromosomes arranged in 23 pairs. The sperm contributed one member of each pair, the ovum the other. The two members of each pair are known as **homologous** (hō-MOL-o-gus) **chromosomes.** Twenty-two of those pairs are known as **autosomal** (aw-tō-SŌ-mal) **chromosomes.** The twenty-third pair is called the *sex chromosomes* because this pair differs between the two sexes. Figure 20-13 shows the **karyotype,** or entire set of chromosomes, of a normal male.

The two chromosomes in a homologous autosomal pair have the same structure and carry genes that affect the same traits. Suppose one member of the pair contains three genes in a row, with number 1 determining hair color, number 2 eye color, and number 3 skin pigmentation. The other member of the pair contains genes that affect the same traits, and the genes are in the same positions and sequence along the chromosomes.

The two chromosomes in a pair may not carry the same *form* of each gene. The various forms of any one gene are called **alleles** (a-LĒLZ; *allelon*, of one another). If both chromosomes of one of your homologous pairs carry the same allele of a particular gene, you are **homozygous** (hō-mō-ZĪ-gus; *homos*, same) for the trait affected by that gene. That allele's trait will be expressed in your phenotype. For example, if you receive a gene for curly hair from your father and one for curly

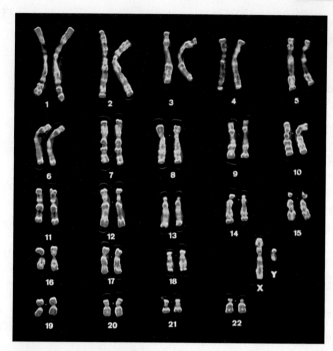

FIGURE 20-13 **Chromosomes of a Normal Male.**

hair from your mother, you will be homozygous for curly hair and will have curly hair. Because the chromosomes of a homologous pair have different origins, one paternal and the other maternal, they need not carry identical alleles. When you have two different alleles of the same gene, you are **heterozygous** (het-er-ō-ZĪ-gus; *heteros*, other) for the trait determined by that gene. In that case, your phenotype will be determined by the interactions between the corresponding alleles:

- An allele that is **dominant** will be expressed in the phenotype regardless of any conflicting instructions carried by the other allele.

- An allele that is **recessive** will be expressed in the phenotype only if it is present on both chromosomes of a homologous pair. For example, albinism is characterized by an inability to synthesize the yellow-brown pigment *melanin.* ∞ p. 125 The presence of a single dominant allele results in normal skin coloration; two recessive alleles must be present to produce albinism.

Predicting Inheritance

Not every allele can be neatly characterized as dominant or recessive. For the traits listed as dominant in Table 20-3, you can predict the characteristics of individuals on the basis of the parents' alleles.

Dominant alleles are traditionally indicated by capitalized abbreviations, and recessives are abbreviated in lower-

TABLE 20-3 The Inheritance of Selected Phenotypic Characteristics

DOMINANT TRAITS
One allele determines phenotype; the other is suppressed:
normal skin pigmentation
lack of freckles
brachydactyly (short fingers)
ability to taste phenylthiocarbamate (PTC)
free earlobes
curly hair
color vision
presence of Rh factor on red blood cell membranes
Both dominant alleles are expressed (codominance):
presence of A or B antigens on red blood cell membranes
structure of serum proteins (albumins, transferrins)
structure of hemoglobin molecule

RECESSIVE TRAITS
albinism
freckles
normal digits
attached earlobes
straight hair
blond hair
red hair (expressed only if individual is also homozygous for blond hair)
lack of A, B surface antigens (Type O blood)
inability to roll the tongue into a U-shape

SEX-LINKED TRAITS
color blindness
hemophilia

POLYGENIC TRAITS
eye color
hair colors other than pure blond or red

case letters. For a gene designated *A*, the possible genotypes are indicated by *AA* (homozygous dominant), *Aa* (heterozygous), or *aa* (homozygous recessive). Each gamete involved in fertilization contributes a single allele for a given trait. That allele must be one of the two contained in all somatic cells in the parent's body. Consider, for example, the offspring of an albino mother and a father with normal skin pigmentation. Because albinism is a recessive trait, the maternal alleles are abbreviated *aa*. No matter which of her oocytes gets fertilized, it will carry the recessive *a* allele. The father has normal pigmentation, a dominant trait. He, therefore, is either homozygous dominant or heterozygous for

this trait, because both *AA* and *Aa* will produce the same phenotype—normal skin pigmentation.

A simple box diagram known as a *Punnett square* enables us to predict the probabilities that a given child will have particular characteristics. In the Punnett squares in Figure 20-14, the two maternal alleles are displayed along the horizontal axis, and the two paternal alleles along the vertical axis. The possible combinations of alleles a child can inherit are indicated in the small boxes. Figure 20-14a shows the possible offspring of an *aa* (albino) mother and an *AA* father. Every child must have the genotype *Aa*, so every child will have normal skin pigmentation. Compare these results with those of Figure 20-14b, involving a heterozygous father (*Aa*). The heterozygous male produces two types of gametes, *A* and *a*, and either one may fertilize the oocyte. As a result, the probability is 50 percent that a child of such a father will inherit the genotype *Aa* and so have normal skin pigmentation. The probability of inheriting the genotype *aa*, and thus having the albino phenotype, is also 50 percent. A Punnett square can also be used to draw conclusions about the identity and genotype of a given child's parent. For example, a man with the genotype *AA* cannot be the father of an albino child (*aa*).

In **simple inheritance,** phenotypes are determined by interactions between a single pair of alleles. The frequency of appearance of an inherited disorder resulting from simple inheritance can be predicted using a Punnett square. Although they are rare disorders in terms of overall numbers, more than 1200 inherited conditions are known to reflect the presence of one or two abnormal alleles for a single gene. A partial listing of inherited disorders is given in Table 20-4.

Many phenotypic characters are determined by interactions among several genes. Such interactions are called **polygenic inheritance.** Because multiple alleles are involved, the presence or absence of phenotypic traits cannot easily be predicted using a simple Punnett square. The risks of developing several important adult disorders, including hypertension and coronary artery disease, fall within this category.

Many of the developmental disorders responsible for fetal deaths and congenital (present at birth) malformations result from polygenic inheritance. In these cases, the particular genetic composition of the individual does not by itself determine the onset of the disease. Instead, the conditions regulated by these genes establish a susceptibility to particular environmental influences. This means that not every individual with the genetic tendency for a certain condition will actually develop that condition. It is therefore difficult to track polygenic conditions

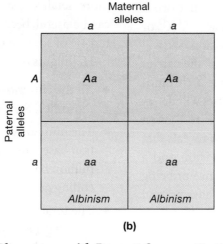

Maternal alleles

(a)

(b)

(c)

FIGURE 20-14 Predicting Genotypes and Phenotypes with Punnett Squares. The Punnett squares in parts (a) and (b) concern the inheritance of albinism. **(a)** All the offspring of a homozygous dominant (normally pigmented) father and a homozygous recessive (albino) mother will be heterozygous for that trait, and all will have normal pigmentation. **(b)** The offspring of a heterozygous father and a homozygous recessive mother will either be heterozygous or homozygous for the recessive trait. In this example, half of the offspring will have normal pigmentation and half will be albinos. **(c)** This Punnett square shows the inheritance of color blindness, a sex-linked trait. A father with normal vision ($X^C Y$) and a heterozygous mother ($X^C X^c$) will produce daughters with normal vision, but half of the sons will be color-blind.

TABLE 20-4 Fairly Common Inherited Disorders

DISORDER	PAGE IN TEXT
AUTOSOMAL DOMINANTS	
Marfan syndrome	p. 105
Huntington disease	p. 297
AUTOSOMAL RECESSIVES	
Deafness	p. 338
Albinism	p. 126
Sickle-cell anemia	p. 386
Cystic fibrosis	p. 506
Phenylketonuria	p. 586
SEX-LINKED	
Duchenne muscular dystrophy	p. 199
Hemophilia (one form)	p. 400
Color blindness	p. 325

through successive generations. However, because many inherited polygenic conditions are likely (but not guaranteed) to occur, steps can be taken to prevent a crisis. For example, you can reduce the likelihood of developing hypertension by controlling your diet and fluid intake, and you can prevent coronary artery disease by lowering your serum cholesterol levels.

Sex-Linked (X-Linked) Inheritance

The **sex chromosomes** determine an individual's biological sex. Unlike the other 22 chromosomal pairs, the sex chromosomes are not identical in appearance and gene content. There are two different sex chromosomes: an **X chromosome** and a **Y chromosome.** X chromosomes are considerably larger and have more genes than Y chromosomes. Each Y chromosome includes dominant alleles that specify that an individual with that chromosome will be male. The normal pair of sex chromosomes in males is XY. Females do not have a Y chromosome; their sex chromosome pair is XX.

All ova carry an X chromosome, because the only sex chromosomes females have are X chromosomes. But each sperm carries either an X chromosome or a Y chromosome. Thus, using a Punnett square you can show that the ratio of male to female offspring should be 1:1.

The X chromosome also carries genes that affect somatic structures. These characteristics are called **X-linked** (or *sex-linked*) because in most cases there are no corresponding alleles on the Y chromosome. The best-known X-linked traits are associated with noticeable diseases or functional deficits.

The inheritance of color blindness demonstrates the differences between sex-linked and autosomal inheritance. Normal color vision is determined by the presence of a dominant allele, *C,* on the X chromosome (designated X^C), whereas red-green color blindness results from the presence of a recessive allele c, on the X chromosome (X^c). A woman, with her two X chromosomes, can be either homozygous dominant, X^CX^C, or heterozygous, X^CX^c, and still have normal color vision. She will be unable to distinguish reds from greens only if she carries two recessive alleles, X^cX^c. But a male has only one X chromosome, so whichever allele that chromosome carries will determine whether he has normal color vision or is red-green color-blind. The Punnett square in Figure 20-14c reveals that each son produced by a father with normal vision and a heterozygous mother will have a 50 percent chance of being red-green color-blind, whereas all daughters will have normal color vision.

A number of other clinical disorders involve X-linked traits, including certain forms of hemophilia, diabetes insipidus, and muscular dystrophy. In several instances, advances in molecular genetics techniques have enabled geneticists to locate specific genes on the X chromosome. These techniques provide a relatively direct method of screening for the presence of a particular condition before signs and symptoms appear, and even before birth.

THE HUMAN GENOME PROJECT AND BEYOND

It has long been appreciated that all diseases—whether inherited or due to the body's responses to stresses, such as radiation, toxins, or pathogens—have a connection to chromosomes and genes. A much richer and fuller understanding of these relationships is now on the horizon, thanks to the biotechnological methods and techniques developed during the **Human Genome Project (HGP)**. Funded by the National Institutes of Health and the Department of Energy, the project's goal was to transcribe the entire human **genome**—that is, the full set of genetic material (DNA), nucleotide by nucleotide, found in our chromosomes. Begun in 1990, the project was completed in 2003, with 99 percent of the entire genome listed as finished, "high-quality sequence." A high-quality sequence is defined as a complete sequence of nucleotides, with no gaps or ambiguities and an error rate of no more than one base per 10,000. The final HGP papers were published in 2006.

The first step in accessing the human genome was to prepare a map of the individual chromosomes. **Karyotyping** (KAR-ē-ō-tīp-ing; *karyon*, nucleus + *typos*, mark) is the determination of an individual's complete set of chromosomes, as shown in Figure 20-13. Each chromosome has characteristic banding patterns when stained with special dyes. The banding patterns are useful as reference points for the preparation of more detailed genetic maps. The banding patterns themselves can be useful, because abnormal banding patterns are characteristic of some genetic disorders and several cancers.

Highlights of the Human Genome Project include:

- All the chromosomes (22 autosomes and both sex chromosomes, X and Y) have been completely sequenced.

- The human genome was found to consist of some 3.2 billion base pairs, or 3200 Mb (1 Mb = 1 megabase, or 1 million base pairs). Somewhat surprisingly, the protein-coding genes represent just 2 percent of the total genome.

- The total number of genes is now estimated at 25,000–30,000 genes. Almost 20,000 protein-coding genes are confirmed and, based on DNA segments, an additional 2188 more are predicted. (Defining a gene is not always straightforward. For example, small genes can easily be overlooked in a nucleotide sequence, a gene may code for more than one protein, some genes code for RNA, and two genes can overlap.)

- Although more than 99 percent of human nucleotide bases are the same in all people, there are about 1.4 million single-base differences, or single nucleotide polymorphisms (SNPs). These SNPs can be used to locate disease-associated sequences on chromosomes.

- The genes responsible for roughly 1500 disorders, including those causing 60 inherited disorders, have been identified. Examples are included in Figure 20-15. Genetic screening and diagnostic tests for abnormal genes are now performed for many of these disorders.

It was originally thought that the relationship between genes and proteins was 1:1, and as a result, investigators were anticipating the discovery of as many as 140,000 genes in the human genome. The discovery that the total number of protein-coding genes is only about 20,000 stands in stark contrast with a minimal estimate of 400,000 different proteins in the human body. The realization that one gene can carry instructions for more than one protein has revolutionized thinking about genetic diseases and potential therapies. A whole new set of questions has arisen as a result. For example, what factors and enzymes control mRNA processing? How are these factors regulated? Although we may be close to unraveling the human genome, we are still many years from the answers to these questions—and they must be answered if we are to manipulate genes effectively to treat many congenital diseases.

The Human Genome Project has determined the normal genetic composition of a "typical" human. Yet we all are vari-

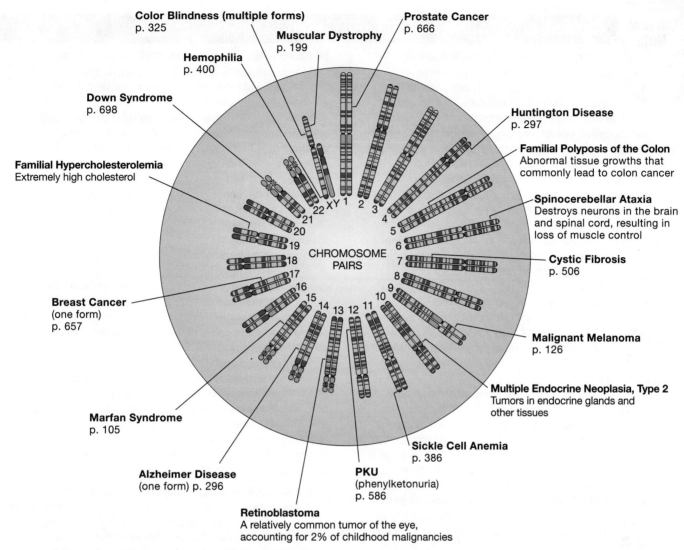

Color Blindness (multiple forms)
p. 325

Muscular Dystrophy
p. 199

Prostate Cancer
p. 666

Hemophilia
p. 400

Down Syndrome
p. 698

Huntington Disease
p. 297

Familial Polyposis of the Colon
Abnormal tissue growths that
commonly lead to colon cancer

Familial Hypercholesterolemia
Extremely high cholesterol

Spinocerebellar Ataxia
Destroys neurons in the brain
and spinal cord, resulting in
loss of muscle control

Cystic Fibrosis
p. 506

CHROMOSOME
PAIRS

Breast Cancer
(one form)
p. 657

Malignant Melanoma
p. 126

Multiple Endocrine Neoplasia, Type 2
Tumors in endocrine glands and
other tissues

Marfan Syndrome
p. 105

Sickle Cell Anemia
p. 386

Alzheimer Disease
(one form) p. 296

PKU
(phenylketonuria)
p. 586

Retinoblastoma
A relatively common tumor of the eye,
accounting for 2% of childhood malignancies

FIGURE 20-15 A Map of Human Chromosomes. This diagram of the chromosomes of a normal
male individual shows typical banding patterns and the locations of the genes responsible for specific
inherited disorders. The chromosomes are not drawn to scale.

ations on a basic theme. How do we decide what set of genes
to accept as "normal?" Moreover, as we improve our abilities
to manipulate our genome, we will face many additional trou-
bling ethical and legal decisions. For example, few people object to the insertion of a "correct" gene into somatic cells to
cure a specific disease. But what if we could insert that modified gene into a gamete and change not only that individual
but all of his or her descendants as well? And what if the goal
of manipulating the gene was not to correct or prevent any
disorder, but instead to "improve" the individual by increasing his or her intelligence, height, or vision, or by altering some
other phenotypic characteristic? Such difficult questions will
not go away. In the years to come, we will have to find answers
that are acceptable to us all.

CHECKPOINT

21. Describe the relationship between genotype
and phenotype.

22. Curly hair is an autosomal dominant trait. What would
be the phenotype of a person who is heterozygous for
this trait?

23. Joe has three daughters and complains that it's his
wife's "fault" that he has no sons. What would you
tell him?

24. The human genome consists of approximately 3200 Mb.
What is a genome, and how many nucleotide base pairs does
3200 Mb represent?

See the blue Answers tab at the back of the book.

Clinical Note

Chromosomal Abnormalities and Genetic Analysis

Embryos that have abnormal autosomal chromosomes rarely survive. However, *translocation defects* and *trisomy* are two types of autosomal chromosome abnormalities that do not invariably result in prenatal death.

In a **translocation defect,** crossing-over occurs between different chromosome pairs such that, for example, a piece of chromosome 8 may become attached to chromosome 14. The genes moved to their new position may function abnormally, becoming inactive or overactive. A translocation between chromosomes 8 and 14 is responsible for *Burkitt lymphoma,* a type of lymphoid system cancer.

In **trisomy,** something goes wrong in meiosis. One of the gametes involved in fertilization carries an extra copy of one chromosome, so the zygote then has three copies of this chromosome rather than two. (The nature of the trisomy is indicated by the number of the chromosome involved. Thus, individuals with trisomy 13 have three copies of chromosome 13.) Zygotes with extra copies of chromosomes seldom survive. Individuals with trisomy 13 and trisomy 18 may survive until delivery but rarely live longer than a year. The notable exception is trisomy 21.

Trisomy 21, or **Down syndrome,** is the most common viable chromosomal abnormality. Estimates of its frequency in the U.S. population range from 1.5 to 1.9 per 1000 births. Affected individuals exhibit mental retardation and characteristic physical malformations, including a facial appearance that gave rise to the term *mongolism,* once used to describe this condition. The degree of mental retardation ranges from moderate to severe. Few individuals with this condition lead independent lives. Anatomical problems affecting the cardiovascular system often prove fatal during childhood or early adulthood. Although some individuals survive to moderate old age, many develop Alzheimer disease while still relatively young (before age 40).

For unknown reasons, there is a direct correlation between maternal age and the risk of having a child with trisomy 21. For a maternal age below 25, the incidence of Down syndrome approaches 1 in 2000 births, or 0.05 percent. For maternal ages 30–34, the odds increase to 1 in 900, and over the next decade they go from 1 in 290 to 1 in 46, or more than 2 percent. These statistics are becoming increasingly significant because many women are delaying childbearing until their mid-thirties or later.

Abnormal numbers of sex chromosomes do not produce effects as severe as those induced by extra or missing autosomal chromosomes. In **Klinefelter syndrome,** the individual carries the sex chromosome pattern XXY. The phenotype is male, but the extra X chromosome causes reduced androgen production. As a result, the testes fail to mature so the individuals are sterile, and the breasts are slightly enlarged. The incidence of this condition among newborn males averages 1 in 750 births.

Individuals with **Turner syndrome** have only one female sex chromosome; their sex chromosome complement is abbreviated XO. This kind of chromosomal deletion is known as **monosomy.** The incidence of this condition at delivery has been estimated as 1 in 10,000 live births. At birth, the condition may not be recognized, because the phenotype is normal female. But maturational changes do not appear at puberty. The ovaries are nonfunctional, and estrogen production occurs at negligible levels.

Fragile-X syndrome causes mental retardation, abnormal facial development, and enlarged testes in affected males. The cause is an abnormal X chromosome that contains a *genetic stutter,* an abnormal repetition of a single nucleotide triplet. The presence of the stutter in some way disrupts the normal functioning of adjacent genes and so produces the signs and symptoms of the disorder.

Many of these conditions can be detected before birth through the analysis of fetal cells. In **amniocentesis,** a sample of amniotic fluid is removed and the fetal cells it contains are analyzed. This procedure permits the identification of more than 20 congenital conditions, including Down syndrome. The needle inserted to obtain a fluid sample is guided into position during an ultrasound procedure. ∞ p. 24 Unfortunately, amniocentesis has two major drawbacks:

1. Because the sampling procedure represents a potential threat to the health of fetus and mother alike, amniocentesis is performed only when known risk factors are present. Examples of risk factors are a family history of specific conditions, or in the case of Down syndrome, maternal age over 35.

2. Sampling cannot safely be performed until the volume of amniotic fluid is large enough that the fetus will not be injured during the process. The usual time for amniocentesis is at 14–15 weeks of gestation. It may take several weeks to obtain results once samples have been collected, and by the time the results are received, an induced or therapeutic abortion may no longer be a viable option.

An alternative procedure known as **chorionic villus sampling** analyzes cells collected from the chorionic villi during the first trimester. Although it can be performed at an earlier gestational age, this technique has largely been abandoned because it is associated with an increased risk of spontaneous abortion (miscarriage).

RELATED CLINICAL TERMS

abruptio placentae (ab-RUP-shē-ō pla-SEN-tē): A tearing away of the placenta from the uterine wall after the fifth gestational month.

amniocentesis: A procedure for the collection and genetic analysis of fetal cells taken from a sample of amniotic fluid.

Apgar rating: A method of evaluating newborns for developmental problems and neurological damage.

breech birth: A delivery during which the legs or buttocks of the fetus enter the vaginal canal first.

chorionic villus sampling: A procedure for the genetic analysis of cells collected from the chorionic villi during the first trimester.

congenital malformation: A severe structural abnormality, present at birth, that affects major systems.

ectopic pregnancy: A pregnancy in which implantation occurs somewhere other than the uterus.

fetal alcohol syndrome (FAS): A neonatal condition resulting from maternal alcohol consumption; characterized by developmental defects typically involving the skeletal, nervous, and/or cardiovascular systems.

geriatrics: A medical specialty concerned with aging and its medical problems.

infertility: The inability to achieve pregnancy after 1 year of appropriately timed sexual intercourse.

in vitro fertilization: Fertilization outside the body, generally in a petri dish.

pediatrics: A medical specialty focusing on postnatal development from infancy through adolescence.

placenta previa: A condition resulting from implantation in or near the cervix, in which the placenta covers the cervix and prevents normal birth.

teratogens (TER-a-tō-jenz): Agents or factors that disrupt normal development by damaging cells, altering chromosome structure, or altering the chemical environment of the embryo.

Chapter **20** Review

KEY TERMS

amnion *678*	implantation *677*
blastocyst *676*	neonate *690*
embryo *673*	parturition *683*
fetus *673*	phenotype *693*
genotype *692*	placenta *679*
gestation *675*	trimester *675*
heterozygous *693*	trophoblast *676*
homozygous *693*	

SUMMARY OUTLINE

20-1 Development is a continuous process that occurs from fertilization to maturity *p. 673*

1. **Development** is the gradual modification of physical and physiological characteristics from **conception** to physical maturity. The creation of different cell types during development is **differentiation**.

2. **Prenatal development** occurs before birth; **postnatal development** begins at birth and continues to maturity, when senescence (aging) begins. **Inheritance** is the transfer of genetically determined characteristics from generation to generation. **Genetics** is the study of the mechanisms of inheritance.

20-2 Fertilization—the fusion of a secondary oocyte and a spermatozoon—forms a zygote *p. 673*

3. **Fertilization** normally occurs in a uterine tube within a day after ovulation. Sperm cannot fertilize an egg until they have undergone **capacitation.**

4. The acrosomal caps of spermatozoa release *hyaluronidase,* an enzyme that separates cells of the *corona radiata.* Another acrosomal enzyme digests the zona pellucida and exposes the oocyte membrane. When a single spermatozoon contacts that membrane, fertilization occurs and **oocyte activation** follows.

5. During activation, the secondary oocyte completes meiosis, and the penetration of additional sperm is prevented.

6. After activation, the *female pronucleus* and *male pronucleus* fuse in a process called **amphimixis.** *(Figure 20-1)*

20-3 Gestation consists of three stages of prenatal development: the first, second, and third trimesters *p. 675*

7. The 9-month period of **gestation,** or *pregnancy,* can be divided into three **trimesters.**

8. The **first trimester** is the most dangerous period of prenatal development. The processes of *cleavage and blastocyst formation, implantation, placentation,* and *embryogenesis* take place during this critical period.

20-4 Cleavage, implantation, placentation, and embryogenesis are critical events of the first trimester   *p. 676*

9. **Cleavage** is a series of cell divisions that subdivide the cytoplasm of the zygote. The zygote becomes a hollow ball of **blastomeres** called a **blastocyst.** The blastocyst consists of an outer **trophoblast** and an **inner cell mass.** *(Figure 20-2)*

10. During **implantation,** the blastocyst burrows into the uterine endometrium. Implantation occurs about 7 days after fertilization. *(Figure 20-3)*

11. As the trophoblast enlarges and spreads, maternal blood flows through open *lacunae.* After **gastrulation,** there is an embryonic disc composed of **endoderm, ectoderm,** and **mesoderm.** It is from these three **germ layers** that the body systems differentiate. *(Figure 20-4; Table 20-1)*

12. Germ layers help form four **extraembryonic membranes:** the *yolk sac, amnion, allantois,* and *chorion. (Figure 20-5)*

13. The **yolk sac** is an important site of blood cell formation. The **amnion** encloses fluid that surrounds and cushions the developing embryo. The base of the **allantois** later gives rise to the urinary bladder. Circulation within the vessels of the **chorion** provides a "rapid-transport system" linking the embryo with the trophoblast.

14. **Placentation** occurs as blood vessels form around the blastocyst and the **placenta** develops. *Chorionic villi* extend outward into the maternal tissues, forming a branching network through which maternal blood flows. As development proceeds, the **umbilical cord** connects the fetus to the placenta. *(Figure 20-6)*

15. The trophoblast synthesizes **human chorionic gonadotropin (hCG),** estrogens, progestins, **human placental lactogen (hPL), placental prolactin,** and **relaxin.**

16. The first trimester is critical because events in the first 12 weeks establish the basis for **organogenesis** (organ formation). *(Figure 20-7; Table 20-2)*

20-5 During the second and third trimesters, maternal organ systems support the developing fetus, and the uterus undergoes structural and functional changes   *p. 682*

17. In the **second trimester,** the organ systems increase in complexity. During the **third trimester,** these organ systems become functional. *(Figures 20-8, 20-9; Table 20-2)*

18. The developing fetus is totally dependent on maternal organs for nourishment, respiration, and waste removal. Maternal adaptations include increases in blood volume, respiratory rate, tidal volume, nutrient intake, and glomerular filtration rate.

19. Progesterone produced by the placenta has an inhibitory effect on uterine muscles; its calming action is opposed by estrogens, oxytocin, and prostaglandins. At some point, multiple factors interact to produce **labor contractions** in the uterine wall. *(Figure 20-10)*

20-6 Labor consists of the dilation, expulsion, and placental stages   *p. 688*

20. The goal of labor is **parturition,** the forcible expulsion of the fetus from the uterus.

21. Labor can be divided into three stages: the **dilation stage, expulsion stage,** and **placental stage.** *(Figure 20-11)*

22. **Premature labor** results in the delivery of a newborn that has not completed normal development.

23. Twins are either **dizygotic** (fraternal) or **monozygotic** (identical).

20-7 Postnatal stages are the neonatal period, infancy, childhood, adolescence, maturity, and senescence   *p. 690*

24. Postnatal development involves a series of five **life stages:** the *neonatal period, infancy, childhood, adolescence,* and *maturity. Senescence* begins at maturity and ends in the death of the individual.

25. The **neonatal period** extends from birth to 1 month of age. **Infancy** then continues to 2 years of age, and **childhood** lasts until puberty commences. During these stages, major nonreproductive organ systems become fully operational and gradually acquire adult characteristics, and the individual grows rapidly.

26. In the transition from fetus to **neonate,** the respiratory, circulatory, digestive, and urinary systems begin functioning independently. The newborn must also begin to perform thermoregulation.

27. Mammary glands produce protein-rich **colostrum** during the neonate's first few days and then convert to milk production. These secretions are released as a result of the *milk let-down reflex. (Figure 20-12)*

28. **Adolescence** begins at **puberty:** (1) The hypothalamus increases its production of GnRH, (2) circulating levels of FSH and LH rise rapidly, and (3) ovarian or testicular cells become more sensitive to FSH and LH. These changes initiate gametogenesis, the production of sex hormones, and a sudden acceleration in growth rate. Adolescence continues until growth is completed.

29. **Maturity,** the end of growth and adolescence, occurs by the early twenties. Postmaturational changes in physiological processes are part of aging, or **senescence.**

20-8 Genes and chromosomes determine patterns of inheritance   *p. 692*

30. Every somatic cell carries copies of the zygote's original 46 chromosomes; these chromosomes and their genes make up the individual's genotype. The physical expression of the individual's **genotype** is the **phenotype.**

31. Every somatic human cell contains 23 pairs of chromosomes; each pair consists of **homologous chromosomes.** Twenty-two

pairs are **autosomal chromosomes.** The chromosomes of the twenty-third pair are the sex chromosomes, which differ between the sexes. *(Figure 20-13)*

32. Chromosomes contain DNA, and genes are functional segments of DNA. The various forms of a gene are called **alleles.** If both homologous chromosomes carry the same allele of a particular gene, the individual is **homozygous;** if they carry different alleles, the individual is **heterozygous.**

33. Alleles are either **dominant** or **recessive** depending on how their traits are expressed. *(Table 20-3)*

34. Combining maternal and paternal alleles in a *Punnett square* helps us to predict the characteristics of offspring. *(Figure 20-14)*

35. In **simple inheritance,** phenotypic traits are determined by interactions between a single pair of alleles. **Polygenic inheritance** involves interactions among alleles on several chromosomes. *(Table 20-4)*

36. The two types of **sex chromosomes** are an **X chromosome** and a **Y chromosome.** The normal sex chromosome complement of males is XY; that of females is XX. The X chromosome carries **X-linked** (sex-linked) **genes,** which affect somatic structures but have no corresponding alleles on the Y chromosome.

37. The **Human Genome Project** has mapped close to 25,000 genes, including some of those responsible for inherited disorders. *(Figure 20-15; Table 20-4)*

REVIEW QUESTIONS

WWW Access more review material online at The Anatomy & Physiology Place (www. anatomyandphysiology.com). There, you'll find Chapter Guides, Chapter Quizzes, Chapter Practice Tests, Interactive Flashcards, a Glossary with Pronunciations, and more to help you succeed in the course.

Level 1 • Reviewing Facts and Terms

Match each item in column A with the most closely related item in column B. Place letters for answers in the spaces provided.

COLUMN A

_____ 1. gestation
_____ 2. cleavage
_____ 3. gastrulation
_____ 4. chorion
_____ 5. human chorionic gonadotropin
_____ 6. birth
_____ 7. episiotomy
_____ 8. afterbirth
_____ 9. senescence
_____ 10. neonate
_____ 11. phenotype
_____ 12. homozygous recessive
_____ 13. heterozygous
_____ 14. male genotype
_____ 15. female genotype
_____ 16. trisomy 21

COLUMN B

a. blastocyst formation
b. ejection of placenta
c. germ-layer formation
d. indication of pregnancy
e. embryo-maternal circulatory exchange
f. visible characteristics
g. time of prenatal development
h. *aa*
i. Down syndrome
j. newborn infant
k. *Aa*
l. XY
m. XX
n. parturition
o. process of aging
p. perineal musculature incision

17. The gradual modification of anatomical structures during the period from conception to maturity is
    (a) development.　(b) differentiation.
    (c) embryogenesis.　(d) capacitation.

18. Human fertilization involves the fusion of two haploid gametes, producing a zygote containing
    (a) 23 chromosomes.
    (b) 46 chromosomes.
    (c) the normal haploid number of chromosomes.
    (d) 46 pairs of chromosomes.

19. The secondary oocyte leaving the follicle is in
    (a) interphase.
    (b) metaphase of the first meiotic division.
    (c) telophase of the second meiotic division.
    (d) metaphase of the second meiotic division.

20. Identify structures a–e in the following diagram of week 10 of development.

(a) _____   (b) _____
(c) _____   (d) _____
(e) _____

21. The process that establishes the foundation of all major organ systems is
(a) cleavage.   (b) implantation.
(c) placentation.   (d) embryogenesis.

22. The zygote arrives in the uterine cavity as a
(a) morula.   (b) trophoblast.
(c) lacuna.   (d) blastomere.

23. The surface that enables active and passive exchange between the fetal and maternal bloodstreams is the
(a) yolk stalk.   (b) chorionic villi.
(c) umbilical veins.   (d) umbilical arteries.

24. Milk let-down is associated with
(a) events occurring in the uterus.
(b) placental hormonal influences.
(c) circadian rhythms.
(d) reflex action triggered by suckling.

25. If an allele must be present on both the maternal and paternal chromosomes to affect the phenotype, the allele is said to be
(a) dominant.   (b) recessive.
(c) complementary.   (d) heterozygous.

26. Name the four extraembryonic membranes.

27. Identify the three stages of labor, and describe the events that characterize each stage.

28. Identify the three life stages that occur between birth and approximately age 10. Describe the timing and characteristics of each stage.

Level 2 • Reviewing Concepts

29. Relaxin is a peptide hormone that
(a) increases the flexibility of the symphysis pubis.
(b) causes dilation of the cervix.
(c) suppresses the release of oxytocin by the hypothalamus.
(d) a, b, and c are correct.

30. During adolescence, the events that interact to promote increased hormone production and sexual maturation result from activity of the
(a) hypothalamus.
(b) anterior pituitary.
(c) ovaries and testicular cells.
(d) a, b, and c are correct.

31. In addition to its role in the nutrition of the fetus, what are the primary endocrine functions of the placenta?

32. Discuss the changes that occur in maternal systems during pregnancy, and indicate the functional significance of each change.

33. During labor, what physiological mechanism ensures that uterine contractions continue until delivery has been completed?

34. During the process of labor, to what does the phrase "having one's water break" refer?

35. For each of the following situations, indicate the inheritance pattern of the trait.
(a) Children who exhibit this trait have at least one parent who exhibits the same trait.
(b) Children exhibit this trait even though neither of the parents exhibits it.
(c) The trait is expressed more frequently in sons than in daughters.
(d) The trait is expressed equally in both daughters and sons.

36. Explain why more men than women are color-blind. Which type of inheritance is involved?

37. Explain the goal and possible benefits of the Human Genome Project.

Level 3 • Critical Thinking and Clinical Applications

38. Hemophilia A, a condition in which blood does not clot properly, is a recessive trait located on the X chromosome (X^h). A woman heterozygous for the trait marries a normal male. What is the probability that this couple will have hemophiliac daughters? What is the probability that this couple will have hemophiliac sons?

39. Explain why the normal heart and respiratory rates of neonates are so much higher than those of adults, even though adults are so much larger.

40. Sally gives birth to a baby with a congenital deformity of the stomach. She believes that it is the result of a viral infection she suffered during the third trimester of pregnancy. Is this a possibility? Explain.

Answers to Checkpoint and Review Questions

CHAPTER 1

ANSWERS TO CHECKPOINTS

Page 3

1. Metabolism refers to all the chemical operations under way in the body. Organisms rely on complex chemical reactions to provide the energy required for responsiveness, growth, reproduction, and movement.

Page 4

2. Anatomy and physiology are closely related because all specific functions are performed by specific structures. **3.** Histologists specialize in histology, the study of the structure and properties of tissues and the cells that compose tissues. Because histologists must use microscopes to observe cells, they are specialists in microscopic anatomy.

Page 6

4. The major levels of organization from the simplest to the most complex are the following: chemical (molecular) level → cellular level → tissue level → organ level → organ system level → organism level. **5.** Major organ systems (and some structures of each) are the integumentary system (skin, hair, sweat glands, and nails), skeletal system (bones, cartilages, associated ligaments, and bone marrow), muscular system (skeletal muscles and associated tendons), nervous system (brain, spinal cord, peripheral nerves, and sense organs), endocrine system (pituitary gland, thyroid gland, pancreas, suprarenal glands, gonads, and other endocrine tissues), cardiovascular system (heart, blood, and blood vessels), lymphoid system (spleen, thymus, lymphatic vessels, lymph nodes, and tonsils), respiratory system (nasal cavities, sinuses, larynx, trachea, bronchi, lungs, and alveoli), digestive system (teeth, tongue, pharynx, esophagus, stomach, small intestine, large intestine, liver, gallbladder, and pancreas), urinary system (kidneys, ureters, urinary bladder, and urethra), male reproductive system (testes, epididymides, ductus deferens, seminal glands, prostate gland, penis, and scrotum), and female reproductive system (ovaries, uterine tubes, uterus, vagina, labia, clitoris, and mammary glands).

Page 13

6. Homeostatic regulation is important because it keeps physiological systems within carefully controlled limits, preventing potentially disruptive changes in the body's internal environment.

Page 15

7. Negative feedback systems provide long-term control over the body's internal conditions—that is, they maintain homeostasis—by counteracting the effects of a stimulus. **8.** Positive feedback is useful in processes that must move quickly to completion, such as blood clotting. It is harmful in situations in which a stable condition must be maintained, because it tends to intensify any departure from the desired condition. Positive feedback in the regulation of body temperature, for example, would cause a slight fever to spiral out of control, with fatal results. For this reason, physiological systems are typically regulated by negative feedback, which tends to oppose any departure from the norm. **9.** When homeostasis fails, organ systems function less efficiently or even malfunction. The result is the state we call disease. If the situation is not corrected, death can result.

Page 19

10. The purpose of anatomical terms is to provide a standardized frame of reference for describing the human body. **11.** In the anatomical position, an anterior view displays the body's front, whereas a posterior view displays the back. **12.** The two eyes would be separated by a midsagittal section.

Page 23

13. Body cavities protect internal organs and cushion them from thumps and bumps that occur while walking, running, or jumping. Body cavities also permit the organs within them to change in size and shape without disrupting the activities of nearby organs. **14.** The ventral body cavities include the pleural and pericardial cavities within the thoracic cavity, and the peritoneal, abdominal, and pelvic cavities within the abdominopelvic cavity. **15.** The body cavity inferior to the diaphragm is the *abdominopelvic* (or *peritoneal*) cavity.

ANSWERS TO REVIEW QUESTIONS

Level 1: Reviewing Facts and Terms

1. (a) superior; (b) inferior; (c) posterior or dorsal; (d) anterior or ventral; (e) cranial; (f) caudal; (g) lateral; (h) medial; (i) proximal; (j) distal **2.** g **3.** d **4.** a **5.** j **6.** b **7.** l **8.** n **9.** f **10.** h **11.** e **12.** c **13.** o **14.** k **15.** i **16.** m **17.** a. frontal b. sagittal c. transverse **18.** c **19.** a **20.** d **21.** b **22.** c **23.** b

Level 2: Reviewing Concepts

24. All living things exhibit responsiveness, adaptability, growth, reproduction, movement, metabolism, absorption, respiration, and excretion. **25.** molecule-cell-tissue-organ-organ system-organism **26.** Homeostatic regulation refers to adjustments in physiological systems that are responsible for the preservation of homeostasis. **27.** In negative feedback, a variation outside normal ranges triggers an automatic response that corrects the situation. In positive feedback, the initial stimulus produces a response that exaggerates the stimulus. **28.** The body is erect, the hands are at the sides with the palms facing forward, and the feet are together. **29.** The stomach. (You would cut the pericardium to access the heart.) **30.** (a) ventral cavity (b) thoracic cavity (c) abdominopelvic cavity

Level 3: Critical Thinking and Clinical Applications

31. When calcitonin is released in response to elevated calcium levels, it brings about a decrease in blood calcium levels, thereby decreasing the stimulus for its own release. **32.** To see a complete view of the medial surface of each half of the brain, midsagittal sections are needed.

CHAPTER 2

ANSWERS TO CHECKPOINTS

Page 32

1. An atom is the smallest stable unit of matter. **2.** The two samples could have different weights if they contain different proportions of hydrogen's three isotopes: hydrogen-1, with a mass of 1; hydrogen-2, with a mass of 2; and hydrogen-3, with a mass of 3.

Page 35

3. A chemical bond is an attractive force acting between two atoms that may be strong enough to hold them together in a molecule or compound. The strongest attractive forces result from the gain, loss, or sharing of electrons. Examples of such chemical bonds are ionic bonds and covalent bonds. **4.** Atoms combine with each other such that their outer electron shells are full. Oxygen atoms do not have a full outer electron shell and so readily combine with many other elements to attain this stable arrangement. Neon does not combine with other elements because it has a full outer electron shell. **5.** The atoms in a water molecule are held together by polar covalent bonds. Water molecules are attracted to each other by hydrogen bonds: attractions between a slight negative charge on the oxygen atom of one water molecule and a slight positive charge on a hydrogen atom of another water molecule.

Page 37

6. The molecular formula for glucose, a compound composed of six carbon atoms, 12 hydrogen atoms, and six oxygen atoms, is $C_6H_{12}O_6$. **7.** Three types of chemical reactions important to human physiology are decomposition reactions, synthesis reactions, and exchange reactions. In a decomposition reaction, a chemical reaction breaks a molecule into smaller fragments. A synthesis reaction assembles smaller molecules into larger ones. In an exchange reaction, parts of the reacting molecules are shuffled around to produce new products. **8.** Because this reaction involves a large molecule being broken down into two smaller ones, it is a decomposition reaction. **9.** Removing the product of a reversible reaction would keep its concentration lower than the concentrations of the reactants. As a result, the reaction of the breakdown of product into reactants would slow, producing a shift in the equilibrium toward the product.

Page 38

10. An enzyme is a special molecule that lowers the activation energy of a chemical reaction, which is the amount of energy required to start the reaction. **11.** Without enzymes, chemical reactions could proceed in the body only under conditions that cells cannot tolerate (e.g., high temperatures). By lowering the activation energy, enzymes make it possible for chemical reactions to proceed under conditions compatible with life. **12.** Organic compounds contain carbon, hydrogen, and (in most cases) oxygen. Inorganic compounds generally do not contain carbon and hydrogen atoms as primary structural components.

Page 39

13. Specific chemical properties of water that make life possible include its solubility (its strong polarity enables it to be used as an efficient solvent), its reactivity (it participates in many chemical reactions), and its high heat capacity (it absorbs and releases heat slowly). **14.** Heat is an increase in the random motion of molecules, and temperature is a measure of heat. Liquid water resists changes in temperature because hydrogen bonds between water molecules retard molecular motion and must be broken to increase the temperature. Temperature must be quite high before individual molecules have enough energy to break free of all hydrogen bonds and become water vapor.

Page 40

15. pH is a measure of the concentration of hydrogen ions in solutions, such as body fluids. On the pH scale, 7 represents neutrality, values below 7 indicate acidic solutions, and values above 7 indicate alkaline (basic) solutions. **16.** Fluctuations in pH of body fluids outside the normal range of 7.35 to 7.45 can break chemical bonds, alter the shape of molecules, and affect cell function, thereby harming cells and tissues.

Page 41

17. An acid is a compound whose dissociation in solution releases a hydrogen ion (H^+) and an anion; a base is a compound whose dissociation releases a hydroxide ion (OH^-) or removes a hydrogen ion from the solution; a salt is an inorganic compound consisting of a cation other than H^+ and an anion other than OH^-. **18.** Antacids reduce stomach discomfort because they contain a weak base that neutralizes excessive stomach acidity ("acid indigestion").

Page 43

19. A compound with a C:H:O ratio of 1:2:1 is a carbohydrate. The body uses carbohydrates chiefly as an energy source. **20.** When two monosaccharides undergo a dehydration synthesis reaction, they form a disaccharide.

Page 46

21. Lipids are a diverse group of compounds that include fatty acids, fats (triglycerides), steroids, and phospholipids. They are organic compounds that contain carbon, hydrogen, and oxygen in a ratio that does not approximate 1:2:1. **22.** The most abundant lipid in a sample taken from beneath the skin would be a triglyceride. **23.** Human cell membranes primarily contain phospholipids, plus small amounts of cholesterol.

Page 49

24. Proteins are organic compounds formed from amino acids, which contain a carbon atom, a hydrogen atom, an amino group (—NH_2), a carboxylic acid group (—COOH), and a variable group, known as an R group or side chain. Proteins function in support, movement, transport, buffering, metabolic regulation, coordination and control, and defense. **25.** The heat of boiling breaks bonds that maintain the protein's three-dimensional shape. The resulting structural change, known as denaturation, affects the ability of the protein molecule to perform its normal biological functions.

Page 50

26. A nucleic acid is a large organic molecule made up of nucleotide subunits containing carbon, hydrogen, oxygen, nitrogen, and phosphorus. Nucleic acids regulate protein synthesis and make up the genetic material in cells. **27.** Both DNA (deoxyribonucleic acid) and RNA (ribonucleic acid) contain nitrogenous bases and phosphate groups, but because this nucleic acid contains the sugar ribose, it is RNA.

Page 52

28. Adenosine triphosphate (ATP) is a high-energy compound consisting of adenosine to which three phosphate groups are attached; the third is attached by a high-energy bond. **29.** Hydrolysis is a decomposition reaction involving water. The hydrolysis of ATP (adenosine triphosphate) yields ADP (adenosine diphosphate) and P (a phosphate group). It would also release energy for cellular activities. **30.** The biochemical building blocks that are components of cells include lipids (forming the cell membrane), proteins (acting as enzymes), nucleic acids (directing the synthesis of cellular proteins), and carbohydrates (providing energy for cellular activities).

ANSWERS TO REVIEW QUESTIONS

Level 1: Reviewing Facts and Terms

1. f **2.** c **3.** i **4.** g **5.** a **6.** l **7.** d **8.** k **9.** b **10.** e **11.** h **12.** j
13. a.

Oxygen atom

b. Two more electrons can fit into the outermost electron shell of an oxygen atom.

14. a **15.** d **16.** a **17.** Enzymes are specialized protein catalysts that lower the activation energy of chemical reactions. Enzymes speed up chemical reactions but are not used up or changed in the process. **18.** carbon, hydrogen, oxygen, nitrogen, calcium, phosphorus **19.** carbohydrates, lipids, proteins, nucleic acids **20.** support (structural proteins), movement (contractile proteins), transport (transport proteins), buffering, metabolic regulation, coordination and control, defense **21.** (a) central carbon; (b) amino group; (c) R group; (d) carboxylic acid group

Level 2: Reviewing Concepts

22. b **23.** a **24.** a **25.** Covalent bonds involve equal sharing of electrons, polar covalent bonds involve unequal sharing of electrons, and ionic bonds involve a loss and/or gain of electrons. **26.** A solution with a pH of 7 (such as pure water) is neutral because it contains equal numbers of hydrogen and hydroxyl ions. **27.** A nucleic acid. Carbohydrates and lipids do not contain the element nitrogen. Although both proteins and nucleic acids contain nitrogen, only nucleic acids contain phosphorus.

Level 3: Critical Thinking and Clinical Applications

28. The number of neutrons in an atom is equal to the atomic mass minus the atomic number. For sulfur, this would be $32 - 16 = 16$ neutrons. Since the atomic number of sulfur is 16, a neutral sulfur atom contains 16 protons and 16 electrons. The electrons would be distributed as follows: 2 in the first level, 8 in the second level, and 6 in the third level. To achieve a full eight electrons in the third level, the sulfur atom could accept two electrons in an ionic bond or share two electrons in a covalent bond. Since hydrogen atoms can share one electron in a covalent bond, the sulfur atom would form two covalent bonds, one with each of two hydrogen atoms. **29.** If a person exhales large amounts of CO_2, the equilibrium will shift to the left and the level of H^+ in the blood will decrease. A decrease in the amount of H^+ will cause the pH to rise.

CHAPTER 3

ANSWERS TO CHECKPOINTS

Page 60

1. The basic concepts of the cell theory are (1) cells are the building blocks of all plants and animals; (2) cells are the smallest functioning units of life; (3) cells are produced through the division of preexisting cells; and (4) each cell maintains homeostasis. **2.** The study of cells is called cytology.

Page 64

3. The general functions of the plasma membrane include physical isolation, regulation of exchange with the environment, sensitivity to the environment, and structural support. **4.** The phospholipid bilayer of the plasma membrane forms a physical barrier between the cell's internal and external environments. **5.** Channel proteins allow water and small ions to pass through the plasma membrane.

Page 68

6. A selectively permeable membrane allows the passage of some substances while restricting the passage of others. It falls between two extremes: impermeable, which allows no substance to pass, and freely permeable, which permits the passage of any substance. **7.** Diffusion is the passive molecular movement of a substance from an area of higher concentration to an area of lower concentration; diffusion proceeds until equilibrium is reached. **8.** Diffusion is driven by a concentration gradient. The larger the concentration gradient, the faster the rate of diffusion; the smaller the concentration gradient, the slower the rate of diffusion. If the concentration of oxygen in the lungs were to decrease, the concentration gradient between oxygen in the lungs and oxygen in the blood would decrease (as long as the oxygen level of the blood remained constant). Thus, oxygen would diffuse into the blood more slowly. **9.** Osmosis is the movement of water across a selectively permeable membrane from one solution to another solution containing a higher solute concentration. **10.** Relative to a surrounding hypertonic solution, the contents of a red blood cell is hypotonic; that is, the solute concentration within a RBC is less than that of the solution surrounding it.

Page 72

11. Active transport processes require the expenditure of cellular energy in the form of the high-energy bonds of ATP molecules. Passive transport processes (*diffusion, osmosis, filtration,* and *facilitated diffusion*) result in the movement of ions and molecules across the plasma membrane without any energy expenditure by the cell. **12.** An active transport process must be involved because H^+ must be transported from the cells lining the stomach, where H^+ are less concentrated, to the interior of the stomach, where H^+ are more concentrated—that is, against their concentration gradient. **13.** This process is an example of phagocytosis.

Page 78

14. Cytoplasm is the material between the plasma membrane and the nuclear membrane; cytosol is the fluid portion of the cytoplasm. **15.** The membranous organelles (and their functions) include: (1) endoplasmic reticulum = synthesis of secretory products; intracellular storage and transport; (2) rough ER = modification and packaging of newly synthesized proteins; (3) smooth ER = lipid and carbohydrate synthesis; (4) Golgi apparatus = storage, alteration, and packaging of secretory products and lysosomal enzymes; (5) lysosomes = intracellular removal of damaged organelles or of pathogens; (6) mitochondria = production of 95% of the ATP required by the cell; (7) peroxisomes = neutralization of toxic compounds. **16.** The fingerlike projections on the surface of intestinal cells are microvilli. They increase the cells' surface area so they can absorb nutrients more efficiently. **17.** Cells that lack centrioles are unable to divide. **18.** The SER functions in the synthesis of lipids, including steroids. Cells of the ovaries and testes would be expected to have a great deal of SER because these organs produce large amounts of steroid hormones. **19.** Mitochondria produce energy for the cell in the form of ATP molecules. A large number of mitochondria in a cell would indicate a high demand for energy.

Page 80

20. The nucleus is a cellular organelle that contains DNA, RNA, and proteins. The nuclear envelope is a double membrane that surrounds the nucleus. Nuclear pores allow for chemical communication between the nucleus and the cytosol. **21.** A gene is a portion of a DNA strand that functions as a hereditary unit. Each gene is located at a particular site on a specific chromosome and codes for a specific protein.

Page 82

22. The nucleus controls the cell's activities through DNA, which codes for the production of all of the cell's proteins. Some of these proteins are structural proteins responsible for the cell's shape and other physical characteristics. Other proteins are enzymes that govern cellular metabolism. By ordering or stopping the production of specific enzymes, the nucleus can regulate all of the cell's activities and functions. **23.** A cell lacking RNA polymerase would not be able to transcribe mRNA from DNA. **24.** The deletion of a base from a coding sequence of DNA during transcription would alter the entire mRNA base sequence after the deletion point. This would result in different codons on the messenger RNA that was transcribed from the affected region, and this, in turn, would result in the incorporation of a different series of amino acids into the protein. Almost certainly the protein product would not be functional.

Page 86

25. The biological term for cellular reproduction is *cell division,* and the term for cell death is *apoptosis.* **26.** Interphase is the portion of a cell's life cycle during which the chromosomes are uncoiled and all normal cellular functions except mitosis are under way. The stages of interphase include G_1, S, and G_2. **27.** Mitosis is the essential step in cell division in which a single cell nucleus divides to produce two identical daughter cell nuclei. The four stages of mitosis are prophase, metaphase, anaphase, and telophase. **28.** If spindle fibers failed to form during mitosis, the cell would not be able to separate the chromosomes into two sets. If cytokinesis occurred, the result would be one cell with two sets of chromosomes, and one cell with none. **29.** An illness characterized by mutations that disrupt normal control mechanisms and produce potentially malignant cells is termed cancer. **30.** Metastasis is the spread of cancer cells from one organ to another, leading to the establishment of secondary tumors.

Page 87

31. Differentiation is the specialization process whereby cells lose the ability to produce certain proteins, such that the cells' functional abilities become increasingly restricted.

ANSWERS TO REVIEW QUESTIONS

Level 1: Reviewing Facts and Terms

1. e **2.** d **3.** h **4.** a **5.** f **6.** b **7.** g **8.** c **9.** m **10.** k **11.** q **12.** i **13.** o **14.** j **15.** l **16.** n **17.** p **18.** b **19.** d **20.** a. isotonic b. hypotonic c. hypertonic **21.** c **22.** d **23.** c **24.** a **25.** (a) G_1; (b) S; (c) G_2; (d) M; (e) prophase; (f) metaphase; (g) anaphase; (h) telophase **26.** c **27.** plasma membrane functions: physical isolation, regulation of exchange with the environment, sensitivity, structural support **28.** major transport mechanisms: diffusion, filtration, carrier-mediated transport, vesicular transport **29.** ER functions: synthesis of proteins, carbohydrates, and lipids; storage of absorbed molecules; transport of materials; detoxification of drugs or toxins

Level 2: Reviewing Concepts

30. b **31.** b **32.** c **33.** c
34.

Facilitated diffusion	*Active transport*
utilizes carrier proteins	utilizes carrier proteins
passive process	active process
no ATP expended	ATP expended
follows concentration gradient	against concentration gradient

35. Cytosol has a high concentration of K^+; interstitial fluid has a high concentration of Na^+. Cytosol also contains a high concentration of suspended proteins, small quantities of carbohydrates, and large reserves of amino acids and lipids. Cytosol may also contain insoluble materials known as inclusions. **36.** In transcription, RNA polymerase uses genetic information to assemble a strand of mRNA. In translation, ribosomes use information carried by the mRNA strand to assemble functional proteins. **37.** Prophase: chromatin condenses and chromosomes become visible; centrioles migrate to opposite poles of the cell and spindle fibers develop; nuclear membrane disintegrates. Metaphase: chromatids attach to spindle fibers and line up along the metaphase plate. Anaphase: chromatids separate and migrate toward opposite poles of the cell. Telophase: the nuclear membrane re-forms; chromosomes disappear as chromatin relaxes; nucleoli reappear. **38.** Cytokinesis is the cytoplasmic movement that separates two daughter cells; it completes mitosis.

Level 3: Critical Thinking and Clinical Applications

39. This process is facilitated transport, which requires a carrier molecule but not cellular energy. The energy for the process is provided by the diffusion gradient for the substance being transported. When all of the carriers are actively involved in transport, the rate of transport plateaus and cannot be increased further. **40.** Solution A must have initially had more solutes than solution B. As a result, water moved by osmosis across the semipermeable membrane from side B to side A, increasing the fluid level on side A.

CHAPTER 4

ANSWERS TO CHECKPOINTS

Page 94

1. Histology is the study of tissues. **2.** The four basic types of tissues that form all body structures are epithelial, connective, muscle, and neural tissues.

Page 97

3. Epithelial tissue is characterized by closely bound cells, a free surface, attachment to underlying connective tissue, avascularity, and regeneration. **4.** Epithelial tissue provides physical protection, controls permeability, provides sensation, and produces specialized secretions. **5.** Epithelial intercellular connections include tight (occluding) junctions, gap junctions, and desmosomes. **6.** The presence of microvilli on the free surface of epithelial cells greatly increases the surface area for absorption. Cilia function to move materials over the surface of epithelial cells.

Page 103

7. The three cell shapes characteristic of epithelial cells are squamous (flat), cuboidal (cube-like), and columnar (rectangular). **8.** No. A simple squamous epithelium does not provide enough protection against infection, abrasion, and dehydration. The skin surface has a stratified squamous epithelium. **9.** The two primary types of glandular epithelia are endocrine glands and exocrine glands. **10.** Sebaceous glands exhibit holocrine secretion. **11.** This gland is an endocrine gland.

Page 108

12. Functions of connective tissues include (1) supporting, surrounding, and interconnecting other types of tissue; (2) transporting fluids and dissolved materials; (3) storing energy reserves; and (4) defending the body from invading microorganisms. **13.** The three types of connective tissues are connective tissue proper, fluid connective tissues, and supporting connective tissues. **14.** The connective tissue containing primarily triglycerides is adipose (fat) tissue. **15.** The reduced collagen production resulting from a lack of vitamin C in the diet would cause connective tissue to be weak and prone to damage. **16.** The two connective tissues that contain a fluid matrix are blood and lymph. **17.** The two types of supporting connective tissue are cartilage and bone. **18.** Cartilage heals slowly because it lacks a direct blood supply, so materials needed to repair damaged cartilage must diffuse from the blood to the chondrocytes. Such diffusion takes a long time and slows the healing process.

Page 112

19. The four types of membranes found in the body are the cutaneous membrane, mucous membranes, serous membranes, and synovial membranes. **20.** Plasma (cell) membranes are composed of lipid bilayers. Tissue membranes consist of a layer of epithelial tissue and a layer of connective tissue. **21.** Serous fluid minimizes the friction between the serous membranes that cover the surfaces of organs and the surrounding body cavity. **22.** The lining of the nasal cavity is a mucous membrane.

Page 114

23. The three types of muscle tissue in the body are skeletal muscle, cardiac muscle, and smooth muscle. **24.** Only skeletal muscle tissue is voluntary. **25.** Muscle tissue that lacks striations is smooth muscle; both cardiac and skeletal muscles are striated. **26.** The cells are most likely neurons. **27.** Both skeletal muscle cells and neurons are called fibers because they are relatively long and slender.

Page 115

28. The two phases in the response to tissue injury are inflammation and regeneration. **29.** Redness, warmth, swelling, and pain are the familiar signs and symptoms of inflammation. **30.** Fibrosis is the permanent replacement of normal tissues by fibrous tissue.

Page 116

31. With advancing age, the speed and effectiveness of tissue repair decrease, the rate of energy consumption in general declines, hormonal activity is altered, and other factors contribute to changes in structure and chemical composition.

ANSWERS TO REVIEW QUESTIONS

Level 1: Reviewing Facts and Terms

1. g **2.** d **3.** j **4.** i **5.** a **6.** f **7.** c **8.** e **9.** b **10.** h **11.** l **12.** k
13. (a) simple squamous epithelium; (b) simple cuboidal epithelium; (c) simple columnar epithelium; (d) stratified squamous epithelium; (e) stratified cuboidal epithelium; (f) stratified columnar epithelium.
14. a **15.** c **16.** d **17.** b **18.** d **19.** c **20.** a **21.** b **22.** b **23.** a
24. (a) mucous membrane; (b) serous membrane; (c) cutaneous membrane; (d) synovial membrane **25.** Layering in epithelia is either simple or stratified. **26.** Connective tissue contains specialized cells,

extracellular protein fibers, and fluid ground substance. **27.** fluid connective tissues: blood and lymph; supporting connective tissues: bone and cartilage **28.** Neural tissue consists of neurons, which transmit electrical impulses, and neuroglia, which includes several kinds of supporting cells, some of which play a role in providing nutrients to neurons.

Level 2: Reviewing Concepts

29. a **30.** During holocrine secretion, gland cells become packed with secretory products and then burst, releasing the secretion but killing the cells. The lost gland cells must be replaced by the division of stem cells. **31.** Exocrine secretions are secreted onto a surface or outward through a duct. Endocrine secretions (called hormones) are secreted by ductless glands into surrounding tissues and usually diffuse into the blood for distribution to other parts of the body. **32.** Tight junctions prevent the passage of water or solutes between cells. In the digestive tract, these junctions keep enzymes, acids, and wastes from damaging delicate underlying tissues. **33.** In skin, tight junctions, intercellular cement, and physical interlocking form extensive connections that hold skin cells together, denying the entry of any pathogens present on their free surfaces. If the skin is damaged and the connections are broken, infection can easily occur. **34.** Unlike serous and mucous membranes, cutaneous membranes are thick, relatively waterproof, and usually dry.

Level 3: Critical Thinking and Clinical Applications

35. Animal intestines are specialized for absorption, so you would look for the slide in which a single layer of epithelium lines the cavity. The cells would be cuboidal or columnar and would probably have microvilli (which increase surface area). With the right type of microscope, you could also see tight junctions between the cells. The esophagus receives undigested food, so the slide of it would have a stratified squamous epithelium that protects against mechanical damage. **36.** Step 1: Check for striations. (If striations are present, the tissue is skeletal muscle or cardiac muscle. If striations are absent, the tissue is smooth muscle.) Step 2: Check for the presence of intercalated discs. (If the discs are present, the tissue is cardiac muscle. If they are absent, the tissue is skeletal muscle.)

CHAPTER 5

ANSWERS TO CHECKPOINTS

Page 123

1. The general functions of the integumentary system include protection, temperature maintenance, synthesis and storage of nutrients, sensory reception, and excretion and secretion.

Page 125

2. The five layers of the epidermis are the stratum germinativum, stratum spinosum, stratum granulosum, stratum lucidum, and stratum corneum. **3.** Dandruff consists of cells from the stratum corneum. **4.** Sanding the tips of the fingers will not permanently remove fingerprints. The ridges of fingerprints are formed in skin layers that are constantly regenerated, so these ridges will eventually reappear.

Page 126

5. The two pigments contained in the epidermis are carotene, an orange-yellow pigment, and melanin, a brown, yellow-brown, or black pigment. **6.** When exposed to the ultraviolet radiation in sunlight or tanning lamps, melanocytes in the epidermis (and dermis) synthesize the pigment melanin, darkening the skin. **7.** When skin gets warm, arriving oxygenated blood is diverted to superficial blood vessels to eliminate heat. The oxygenated blood imparts a reddish coloration to the skin.

Page 127

8. In the presence of ultraviolet radiation in sunlight, epidermal cells in the stratum spinosum and stratum germinativum convert a cholesterol-related steroid into vitamin D_3. **9.** The most common skin cancer is basal cell carcinoma. **10.** The dermis (a connective tissue layer) lies immediately deep to the epidermis. **11.** The capillaries that supply the epidermis are located in the papillary layer of the dermis.

Page 128

12. The tissue that connects the dermis to underlying tissues is the hypodermis or subcutaneous layer. **13.** The hypodermis is a layer of loose connective tissue below the dermis. It is not considered a part of the integument, but it is important in stabilizing the position of the skin in relation to underlying tissues.

Page 130

14. A typical hair is a keratinous strand produced by epithelial cells of a hair follicle. **15.** Contraction of the arrector pili muscle pulls the hair follicle erect, depressing the area at the base of the hair and making the surrounding skin appear higher. The result is known as "goose bumps." **16.** Even though hair is a derivative of the epidermis, the follicles are in the dermis. Where the epidermis and deep dermis are destroyed, new hair will not grow.

Page 131

17. Two types of exocrine glands found in the skin are sebaceous (oil) glands and sweat glands. **18.** Sebaceous secretions (called sebum) lubricate and protect the keratin of the hair shaft, lubricate and condition the surrounding skin, and inhibit bacterial growth. **19.** Deodorants are used to mask the odor of apocrine sweat gland secretions, which contain several kinds of organic compounds that have an odor or produce an odor when metabolized by skin bacteria.

Page 132

20. A fingernail is a keratinous structure produced by epithelial cells of the nail root; it protects the fingertip. **21.** Nail growth occurs at the nail root, an epidermal fold that is not visible from the surface.

Page 134

22. The combination of fibrin clots, fibroblasts, and the extensive network of capillaries in healing tissue is called granulation tissue. **23.** Skin can regenerate effectively even after undergoing considerable damage because stem cells persist in both the epithelial and connective tissue components of skin. When injury occurs, cells of the stratum germinativum replace epithelial cells while connective tissue stem cells replace cells lost from the dermis.

Page 135

24. As a person ages, the blood supply to the dermis decreases and merocrine sweat glands become less active. These changes make it more difficult for the elderly to cool themselves in hot weather. **25.** With advancing age, melanocyte activity decreases, leading to gray or white hair. **26.** The integumentary system provides the whole body, and thus all its systems, mechanical protection against environmental hazards. **27.** The skin is important to muscular system activity because absorption of the calcium needed for muscle contraction requires vitamin D_3, which is synthesized by the skin.

ANSWERS TO REVIEW QUESTIONS

Level 1: Reviewing Facts and Terms

1. f **2.** g **3.** i **4.** j **5.** a **6.** e **7.** b **8.** d **9.** c **10.** h **11.** a **12.** (a) epidermis; (b) dermis; (c) papillary layer; (d) reticular layer; (e) hypodermis (subcutaneous layer) **13.** d **14.** b **15.** c **16.** a **17.** a **18.** (a) Hair shaft; (b) Sebaceous gland; (c) Arrector pili muscle; (d) Hair root; (e) Hair papilla **19.** Carotene and melanin are found in the epidermis. **20.** The dermis is composed of the papillary layer (consists of loose connective tissue and contains capillaries and sensory neurons) and the reticular layer (consists of dense irregular connective tissue and bundles of collagen fibers). Both layers contain blood vessels, lymphatic vessels, and nerve fibers. **21.** Apocrine sweat glands and merocrine sweat glands are contained in the integument.

Level 2: Reviewing Concepts

22. a **23.** Fat-soluble drugs are more desirable for transdermal administration because the permeability barrier is composed primarily of lipids surrounding epidermal cells. Water-soluble drugs are lipophobic and have difficulty penetrating the lipid-based barrier. **24.** A tan results from the synthesis of melanin, which helps prevent skin damage by absorbing ultraviolet radiation before it reaches the deep layers of the epidermis and dermis. Melanin accumulates around the nucleus of epidermal cells, absorbing UV light before it can damage nuclear DNA. **25.** The lack of exposure to UV light in sunlight prevents the production of vitamin D_3 from a cholesterol-related steroid in the deepest layers of the epidermis. Thus, vitamin D_3 cannot be modified by the liver and converted into the hormone calcitriol by the kidneys. Calcitriol is essential for the absorption of the calcium and phosphorus needed to form strong bones, so fragile bones result. **26.** Because the subcutaneous layer, or hypodermis, is not highly vascular and lacks major organs, subcutaneous injection reduces the risk of tissue damage. **27.** As a person ages, the dermis becomes thinner and the elastic fiber network decreases in size, weakening the integument and causing loss of resilience.

Level 3: Critical Thinking and Clinical Applications

28. The child probably has a fondness for vegetables high in the yellow-orange pigment carotene, such as sweet potatoes, squash, and carrots. If a child consumes large amounts of carotene, the pigment will be stored in the skin, producing a yellow-orange skin color. **29.** Like most elderly people, Vanessa's grandmother has poor circulation to the skin. As a result, temperature receptors in the skin sense less warmth compared to good circulation. When this sensory information is relayed to the brain, that organ interprets it as coldness, causing Vanessa's grandmother to feel cold.

CHAPTER 6

ANSWERS TO CHECKPOINTS

Page 143

1. The five primary functions of the skeletal system are support, storage of minerals and lipids, blood cell production, protection, and leverage.

Page 146

2. The four general shapes of bones are flat, irregular, long, and short. **3.** If the ratio of collagen to calcium in a bone increased, the bone would be weaker (but more flexible). **4.** This sample most likely came from the shaft

(diaphysis) of a long bone, as concentric layers of bone around a central canal are indicative of osteons, which make up compact bone. The ends (epiphyses) of long bones are primarily cancellous (spongy) bone. **5.** Mature bone cells are known as osteocytes, bone-building cells are called osteoblasts, and osteoclasts are bone-resorbing cells. **6.** When osteoclast activity exceeds osteoblast activity, bone mass decreases, because osteoclasts break down or demineralize bone.

Page 149

7. During intramembranous ossification, fibrous connective tissue is replaced by bone. **8.** An x-ray of the femur (or any long bone) would indicate whether the epiphyseal cartilage, which separates the epiphysis from the diaphysis, is still present. If it is, then growth is still occurring; if not, the bone has reached its full length. **9.** Growth continues throughout childhood. At puberty, a growth spurt occurs and is followed by the closure of the epiphyseal cartilages. The later puberty begins, the taller the child will be when the growth spurt begins, so the taller the individual will be when growth is completed. **10.** Pregnant women need large amounts of calcium to support bone growth in the developing fetus. If an expectant mother does not take in enough calcium in her diet, her body will mobilize the calcium reserves of her own skeleton to provide for the needs of the fetus, resulting in weakened bones and an increased risk of fracture.

Page 151

11. Bone remodeling refers to the continuous process whereby old bone is being destroyed by osteoclasts while new bone is being constructed by osteoblasts. **12.** In response to mechanical stress on the arm bones during weight lifting, the bones grow heavier. The arm bones of joggers are lighter because they experience relatively little stress. **13.** Parathyroid hormone (PTH) and calcitonin work together to increase blood calcium levels, whereas calcitonin decreases blood calcium levels. **14.** A closed (simple) fracture is completely internal; no break in the skin results. An open (compound) fracture projects through the skin and is thus more dangerous because of the possibility of infection or uncontrolled bleeding.

Page 152

15. Osteopenia is inadequate ossification and is common to the aging process. It results from decreasing osteoblast activity accompanied by normal osteoclast activity. **16.** Osteoporosis is more common in older women because after menopause, levels of estrogens—sex hormones that play an important role in moving calcium into bones—decrease dramatically, making it difficult to replace calcium lost from bones due to normal aging. In men, decreases in sex hormone (androgen) levels occur at later ages. **17.** A bone marking (surface feature) is an area on the surface of a bone structured for a specific function, such as joint formation, muscle attachment, or the passage of nerves and blood vessels.

Page 165

18. The mastoid and styloid processes are projections on the temporal bones of the skull. **19.** The sella turcica is located in the sphenoid bone; it contains the pituitary gland. **20.** The occipital bone of the cranium (specifically, the occipital condyles) articulates with the vertebral column. **21.** The bones fractured by the ball are the frontal bone (which forms the superior portion of the orbit) and the maxillary and zygomatic bones (which form the inferior portion of the orbit). **22.** The paranasal sinuses lighten some of the heavier skull bones. They contain a mucous epithelium that releases a mucous secretions into the nasal cavities that warms, moistens, and filters particles out of the incoming air. **23.** A fracture of the coronoid process would make it difficult to close the mouth because such a fracture would hinder the functioning of muscles that attach to the mandible (lower jaw) at the coronoid process. **24.** Because many muscles that move the tongue and the larynx are attached to the hyoid bone, you would expect a person with a fractured hyoid bone to have difficulty moving the tongue, breathing, and swallowing. **25.** The dens is part of the second cervical vertebra, or axis, which is in the neck. **26.** In adults, the five sacral vertebrae fuse to form a single sacrum. **27.** The lumbar vertebrae must support a great deal more weight than do vertebrae that are more superior in the spinal column. The large vertebral bodies allow the weight to be distributed over a larger area. **28.** True ribs are each attached directly to the sternum by their own costal cartilage. False ribs either do not attach to the sternum (the floating ribs) or attach by means of a shared, common costal cartilage. **29.** Improper compression of the chest during CPR could (and frequently does) result in a fracture of the sternum or ribs.

Page 173

30. By attaching the scapula to the sternum, the clavicle restricts the scapula's range of movement. A broken clavicle thus allows the scapula a greater range of movement (and reduces its stability). **31.** The two rounded prominences on either side of the elbow are the lateral and medial epicondyles of the humerus. **32.** The radius is lateral when the forearm is in the anatomical position. **33.** The three bones that make up the hip are the ilium, the ischium, and the pubis. **34.** The fibula is an important site of attachment for many leg muscles, so its fracture prevents proper muscle function, and moving the leg and walking become difficult and painful. The fibula also helps stabilize the ankle joint. **35.** Cesar has most likely fractured his calcaneus (heel bone).

Page 175

36. The three types of joints as classified by their degree of movement are: (1) an immovable joint or synarthrosis; (2) a slightly movable joint or amphiarthrosis; and (3) a freely movable joint or diarthrosis. A synarthrosis can be fibrous or cartilaginous, depending on the nature of the connection, or it can be a bony fusion, which develops over time. An amphiarthrosis is either fibrous or cartilaginous, depending on the nature of the connection, while a diarthrosis joint is a synovial joint that permits the greatest amount of movement. **37.** In a newborn, these are amphiarthrotic (slightly movable) joints—a type of syndesmosis. When the skull bones interlock, they form synarthrotic (immovable) joints—fibrous joints called sutures.

Page 179

38. (a) Moving the humerus away from the body's longitudinal axis is abduction. (b) Turning the palms forward is supination. (c) Bending the elbow is flexion. **39.** Flexion and extension are associated with hinge joints.

Page 183

40. The tennis player is more likely than the jogger to have subscapular bursitis (inflammation of the bursa) because this bursa is located in the shoulder joint. **41.** Daphne has most likely fractured her ulna. **42.** A complete dislocation of the knee is rare because the joint is stabilized by ligaments on its anterior, posterior, medial, and lateral surfaces, as well as by a pair of ligaments within the joint capsule. **43.** Damage to the menisci in the knee joint would decrease the joint's stability, so the individual would have more difficulty locking the knee in place while standing and would have to use muscle contractions to stabilize the joint. Standing for long periods would fatigue the muscles, and the knee would "give out." The individual is also likely to experience pain.

Page 184

44. The skeletal system provides calcium for the normal functioning of the muscular system (muscle contraction), the nervous system (neural function), and the cardiovascular system (contraction of cardiac muscle of the heart).

ANSWERS TO REVIEW QUESTIONS

Level 1: Reviewing Facts and Terms

1. i **2.** h **3.** m **4.** l **5.** j **6.** k **7.** f **8.** c **9.** o **10.** b **11.** g **12.** n **13.** d **14.** a **15.** e **16.** b **17.** a **18.** c **19.** b **20.** (a) occipital bone; (b) parietal bone; (c) frontal bone; (d) temporal bone; (e) sphenoid bone; (f) ethmoid bone; (g) vomer; (h) mandible; (i) lacrimal bone; (j) nasal bone; (k) zygomatic bone; (l) maxilla (or maxillary bone) **21.** d **22.** a **23.** a **24.** a **25.** a **26.** b **27.** c **28.** (a) joint capsule; (b) synovial membrane; (c) articular cartilage; (d) joint cavity **29.** d **30.** b **31.** c **32.** In intramembranous ossification, bone develops from fibrous connective tissue. In endochondral ossification, bone develops from a cartilage model. **33.** The hyoid is the only bone in the body that does not articulate with another bone. **34.** The thoracic cage (1) protects the heart, lungs, thymus, and other structures in the thoracic cavity, and (2) serves as an attachment point for muscles involved with respiration, positioning the vertebral column, and moving the pectoral girdle and upper extremities. **35.** The acromion and coracoid processes are parts of the scapula associated with the shoulder joint.

Level 2: Reviewing Concepts

36. The osteons are parallel to the long axis of the shaft, which does not bend when forces are applied to either end. An impact to the side of the shaft can lead to a fracture. **37.** The chondrocytes of the epiphyseal cartilage enlarge and divide, increasing the thickness of the cartilage. On the shaft side, the chondrocytes become ossified, "chasing" the expanding epiphyseal cartilage away from the shaft. **38.** The lumbar vertebrae have massive bodies and carry a large amount of weight—both causative factors of disc rupture. The cervical vertebrae are more delicate and have small bodies, increasing the possibility of dislocations and fractures compared with other regions of the vertebral column. **39.** The clavicles are small and fragile, so fractures are quite common. Their position also makes them vulnerable to injury and damage. **40.** The pelvic girdle consists of the two coxal bones. The pelvis is a composite structure that includes the coxal bones of the appendicular skeleton and the sacrum and coccyx of the axial skeleton. **41.** Articular cartilages do not have perichondrium, and their matrix contains more water than do other cartilages. **42.** The slight mobility of the pubic symphysis facilitates childbirth by spreading the pelvis to ease movement of the baby through the birth canal.

Level 3: Critical Thinking and Clinical Applications

43. The fracture might have damaged the epiphyseal cartilage in Yasmin's right leg. Even though the bone healed properly, the damaged leg did not produce as much cartilage as the undamaged leg, producing a shorter bone in the injured leg. **44.** The virus could have been inhaled through the nose and passed into the cranium by way of the cribiform plate of the ethmoid bone. **45.** The large bones of a child's cranium are not yet fused, but connected by areas of connective tissue called fontanelles. By examining the bones, the archaeologist could readily see if sutures had formed. By knowing approximately how long it takes for the various fontanelles to close and by determining their sizes, she could could estimate the age of the individual at death. **46.** Frank may have suffered a shoulder dislocation, which is quite a common injury due to the weak nature of the articulation between the scapula and the humerus, or glenohumeral joint. **47.** Ed has a sprained ankle. This condition occurs when ligaments are stretched to the point at which some of the collagen fibers are torn. Stretched ligaments in joints can cause the release of synovial fluid, which results in swelling and pain in the affected area.

CHAPTER 7

ANSWERS TO CHECKPOINTS

Page 195

1. Skeletal muscles produce skeletal movement, maintain body posture and body position, support soft tissues, guard entrances and exits, and maintain body temperature.

Page 196

2. The epimysium is a dense layer of collagen fibers that surrounds the entire muscle; the perimysium divides the skeletal muscle into a series of compartments, each containing a bundle of muscle fibers called a fascicle; and the endomysium surrounds individual skeletal muscles cells (fibers). **3.** Severing the tendon would prevent the muscle from moving the body part because the muscle would no longer be connected to the bone.

Page 200

4. Sarcomeres, the smallest contractile units of a striated muscle cell, are segments of myofibrils. Each sarcomere has dark A bands and light I bands. The A band contains the M line, H band, and the zone of overlap. Each I band contains thin filaments, but not thick filaments. Z lines mark the boundaries between adjacent sarcomeres. **5.** Skeletal muscle appears striated when viewed under the microscope because the arrangement of the myofilaments actin and myosin within myofibrils produces a banded appearance. **6.** You would expect to find the greatest concentration of calcium ions in the terminal cisternae of the sarcoplasmic reticulum of the muscle fiber.

Page 203

7. The neuromuscular junction—the synapse between a motor neuron and a muscle cell—enables communication between the nervous system and a skeletal muscle fiber. **8.** A drug that blocks acetylcholine release would prevent muscle contraction. A lack of ACh prevents the generation of an action potential in the sarcolemma, which is necessary for the release of calcium ions from the sarcoplasmic reticulum, and subsequent cross bridge formation. **9.** If the sarcolemma of a resting skeletal muscle suddenly became permeable to calcium ions, the intracellular concentration of calcium ions would increase, and the muscle would contract. In addition, because the amount of calcium ions in the sarcoplasm must decline for relaxation to occur, the increased permeability of the sarcolemma to calcium ions might prevent the muscle from relaxing completely.

Page 208

10. The amount of tension produced in a skeletal muscle depends on (1) the frequency of muscle fiber stimulation and (2) the number of muscle fibers activated. **11.** A motor unit with 1500 muscle fibers is most likely from a large muscle involved in powerful, gross movements. Muscles that control fine or precise movements (such as those moving the eye or the fingers) have only a few fibers per motor unit, whereas muscles involved in more powerful contractions (such as those moving the leg) have hundreds of fibers per motor unit. **12.** Yes. A skeletal muscle undergoing an isometric contraction does not shorten, even though tension in the muscle increases. By contrast, in an isotonic contraction, tension remains constant and the muscle shortens.

Page 211

13. Muscle cells continuously synthesize ATP by utilizing creatine phosphate (CP) and metabolizing glycogen and fats. Most cells generate ATP through aerobic metabolism in the mitochondria, and through glycolysis in the cytoplasm. **14.** Muscle fatigue is a muscle's reduced ability to contract due to low ATP levels, low pH (lactic acid buildup), or other problems. **15.** Oxygen debt is the amount of oxygen required to restore normal, preexertion conditions in muscle tissue.

Page 212

16. A sprinter would experience muscle fatigue before a marathon runner because the large amounts of energy needed for a relatively short burst of activity require the muscles to switch to anaerobic metabolism, which is relatively inefficient and produces fatigue-inducing waste products. By contrast, a marathon runner primarily relies on aerobic metabolism, which is more efficient and produces fewer waste products. **17.** Lifting weights, a short-term strenuous activity that relies on anaerobic respiration, would be more likely to produce a greater oxygen debt than would swimming laps, which is an aerobic activity. **18.** The leg muscles of individuals who excel at endurance activities contain a higher-than-normal percentage of slow muscle fibers, which are more vascular and fatigue more slowly than fast fibers.

Page 214

19. Intercalated discs enhance cardiac muscle tissue function by tightly binding cardiac muscle fibers, enabling them to "pull together" efficiently. Because intercalated discs also contain gap junctions, ions and small molecules can move directly between cells, resulting in the rapid passage of action potentials from cell to cell and making their contraction simultaneous. **20.** Extracellular calcium ions are important for the contraction of cardiac and smooth muscle. In skeletal muscle, calcium ions come from the sarcoplasmic reticulum. **21.** Smooth muscle cells can contract over a relatively large range of resting lengths because their actin and myosin filaments are not as rigidly organized as in skeletal muscle.

Page 218

22. Skeletal muscles names are based on several factors, including location in the body, origin and insertion, action, muscle fiber orientation, relative position, structural characteristics, muscle shape, number of origins, and size. **23.** The *triceps brachii,* which extends the forearm, is the antagonist of the biceps brachii. **24.** The name *flexor carpi radialis longus* tells you that this muscle is a long muscle (longus) that lies next to the radius (radialis) and flexes (flexor) the wrist (carpus).

Page 223

25. You would likely be chewing; contracting the masseter muscle raises the mandible, whereas relaxing this muscle depresses the mandible. **26.** You would expect the buccinator muscle, which shapes the mouth for blowing, to be well developed in a trumpet player. **27.** Damage to the external intercostal muscles would interfere with the process of breathing.

28. A blow to the rectus abdominis would cause that muscle to contract forcefully, flexing the torso. In other words, you would "double up."

Page 232

29. When you shrug your shoulders, you are contracting your levator scapulae muscles. **30.** The rotator cuff muscles are the supraspinatus, infraspinatus, teres minor, and subscapularis. (The acronym SITS is useful in remembering these four muscles.) **31.** Injury to the flexor carpi ulnaris would impair the ability to flex and adduct the wrist.

Page 235

32. A "pulled hamstring" refers to a muscle strain affecting one or more of the three muscles that collectively flex the knee: the biceps femoris, semimembranosus, and semitendinosus muscles. **33.** A torn calcaneal tendon would make ankle extension (plantar flexion) difficult because this tendon attaches the soleus and gastrocnemius muscles to the calcaneus (heel bone).

Page 236

34. As we age, the number of myofibrils in a muscle fiber decreases. The overall effects of such a change are a reduction in muscle strength and endurance and a tendency to fatigue rapidly.

Page 238

35. Exercise increases heart rate, dilates blood vessels, increases rate and depth of respiration, and increases sweat gland secretion. The physiological effects of exercise are directed and coordinated by the nervous and endocrine systems.

ANSWERS TO REVIEW QUESTIONS

Level 1: Reviewing Facts and Terms

1. f **2.** i **3.** d **4.** p **5.** l **6.** c **7.** h **8.** n **9.** b **10.** k **11.** o **12.** a **13.** m **14.** j **15.** g **16.** e **17.** (a) sarcolemma; (b) sarcoplasm; (c) mitochondria; (d) myofibril; (e) thin filament; (f) thick filament; (g) sarcoplasmic reticulum; (h) T tubules **18.** d **19.** d **20.** (a) supraspinatus muscle; (b) infraspinatus muscle; (c) teres minor muscle **21.** Step 1: active-site exposure. Step 2: cross-bridge formation. Step 3: pivoting of myosin head (power stroke). Step 4: cross-bridge detachment. Step 5: myosin reactivation (cocking) **22.** energy reserves in resting skeletal muscle cells: ATP, creatine phosphate, glycogen **23.** Aerobic metabolism and glycolysis generate ATP from glucose in muscle cells. **24.** The axial musculature positions the head and spinal column and moves the rib cage, assisting in the movements that make breathing possible. The appendicular musculature stabilizes or moves components of the appendicular skeleton.

Level 2: Reviewing Concepts

25. b **26.** Acetylcholine released by the motor neuron at the neuromuscular junction changes the permeability of the cell membrane at the motor end plate. The permeability change allows the influx of positive charges, which in turn trigger an electrical event called an action potential. The action potential spreads across the entire surface of the muscle fiber and into the interior via the T tubules. The cytoplasmic concentration of calcium ions (released from sarcoplasmic reticulum) increases, triggering the start of a contraction. The contraction ends when the ACh has been removed from the synaptic cleft and motor end plate by AChE. **27.** The extra gene copies contained in multiple nuclei speed up the production of enzymes and structural proteins needed to meet the large metabolic requirements of normally contracting skeletal muscle cells. **28.** The spinal column does not need a massive series of flexors because

(1) gravity tends to flex the spine (because body weight largely lies anterior to the spinal column) and (2) contractions of many of the large trunk muscles flex the spine. **29.** Voluntary control of urination and defecation is possible because the urethral and anal sphincter muscles are innervated by nerves under conscious control. Voluntary relaxation of the sphincters, which are normally constricted to prevent the passage of urine and feces, allows the passage of wastes. **30.** Flexion of the leg and extension of the hip are affected when the hamstrings are injured.

Level 3: Critical Thinking and Clinical Applications

31. The most obvious sign of organophosphate poisoning is uncontrolled tetanic contractions of skeletal muscles. Organophosphates block the action of the enzyme acetylcholinesterase, so acetylcholine released into the neuromuscular cleft would not be inactivated, causing a state of persistent contraction (spastic paralysis). If paralysis affected the muscles of respiration (which is likely), Terry would die of suffocation. **32.** After death, the membranes of muscle cells are no longer selectively permeable, so calcium leaks in, triggering contractions that persist (rigor mortis) because the dead cells can no longer make the ATP required for cross-bridge detachment. The stiffness of rigor mortis begins a few hours after death and lasts until 15–25 hours later, when lysosomal enzymes released by autolysis break down the myofilaments. **33.** Makani should do squatting exercises. Placing a barbell on his shoulders as he does squats will produce better results, because the quadriceps muscles will be working against a greater resistance.

CHAPTER 8

ANSWERS TO CHECKPOINTS

Page 248

1. The two anatomical divisions of the nervous system are the central nervous system (CNS), consisting of the brain and spinal cord, and the peripheral nervous system (PNS), consisting of all neural tissue outside the CNS. **2.** The two functional divisions of the peripheral nervous system are the afferent division, which brings sensory information to the CNS from receptors in peripheral tissues and organs, and the efferent division, which carries motor commands from the CNS to effectors, such as muscles and glands. **3.** Damage to the afferent division of the PNS, whose nerves carry sensory information to the brain and spinal cord, would interfere with a person's ability to experience a variety of sensory stimuli.

Page 254

4. Structural components of a typical neuron include a cell body or soma (which contains the nucleus and nucleolus), an axon, dendrites, Nissl bodies, axon hillock, collaterals, and synaptic terminals. **5.** Unipolar neurons are most likely sensory neurons of the PNS. **6.** CNS neuroglia include ependymal cells, astrocytes, oligodendrocytes, and microglia. **7.** Small phagocytic glial cells called microglia are typically found in increased numbers in infected (or damaged) areas of the CNS. **8.** In the PNS, neuron cell bodies (gray matter) are located in ganglia.

Page 259

9. If the voltage-gated sodium channels in a neuron's plasma membrane were blocked, the neuron would not be able to depolarize because sodium ions could not flow into the cell. **10.** If the extracellular potassium concentration were to decrease, more potassium ions would leave the cell, increasing the electrical gradient across the membrane (the membrane potential). This effect is called hyperpolarization. **11.** The steps in the generation of action potentials are: Step 1: depolarization to threshold; Step 2: activation of voltage-gated sodium channels and rapid depolarization; Step 3: inactivation of sodium channels and activation of voltage-gated potassium channels; and Step 4: return to normal permeability. **12.** The axon that carries action potentials at 50 meters per second is myelinated; it propagates action potentials by saltatory propagation at speeds much higher than those by continuous propagation along unmyelinated axons.

Page 262

13. A synapse—the site where a neuron communicates with another cell—is composed of presynaptic and postsynaptic cells whose plasma membranes are separated by a narrow synaptic cleft. **14.** Blocking calcium channels at the presynaptic terminal of a cholinergic synapse would prevent the influx of calcium that triggers the release of acetylcholine, so no communication would occur across the synapse, and the postsynaptic neuron would not be stimulated. **15.** Convergence permits both conscious and subconscious control of the same motor neurons.

Page 263

16. The three meninges surrounding the CNS are the dura mater, arachnoid matter, and pia mater.

Page 267

17. Damage to the ventral root of a spinal nerve, which is composed of visceral and somatic motor fibers, would interfere with motor function. **18.** You would find poliovirus in the anterior gray horns of the spinal cord, because that is where the cell bodies of somatic motor neurons are located. **19.** All spinal nerves are classified as mixed nerves because they contain both sensory and motor fibers.

Page 278

20. The six regions in the brain and their major functions are (1) the *cerebrum:* conscious thought processes; (2) the *diencephalon:* the thalamic portion contains relay and processing centers for sensory information, and the hypothalamic portion contains centers involved with emotions, autonomic function, and hormone production; (3) the *midbrain:* processes visual and auditory information and generates involuntary motor responses; (4) the *pons:* contains tracts and relay centers that connect the brain stem to the cerebellum; (5) the *medulla oblongata:* contains major centers concerned with the regulation of autonomic function, such as heart rate, blood pressure, respiration, and digestive activities; and (6) the *cerebellum:* adjusts voluntary and involuntary motor activities. **21.** The pituitary gland is attached to the hypothalamus, or the floor of the diencephalon. **22.** If diffusion across the arachnoid granulations decreased, reentry of cerebrospinal fluid into the bloodstream would be reduced, so the volume of cerebrospinal fluid in the ventricles would increase. **23.** The primary motor cortex is located in the precentral gyrus of the frontal lobe of the cerebrum. **24.** Damage to the temporal lobes of the cerebrum would interfere with the processing of olfactory (smell) and auditory (sound) sensations. **25.** The thalamus acts as a relay point for all ascending sensory information but olfactory information. **26.** Changes in body temperature stimulate the hypothalamus, a division of the diencephalon. **27.** Damage to the medulla oblongata can have fatal results because, despite its small size, it contains many vital reflex centers, including those that control breathing and regulate the heart and blood pressure.

Page 283

28. The abducens nerve (N VI) controls lateral movements of the eyes through the lateral rectus muscles, so an individuals with damage to this nerve would be unable to move their eyes laterally (to the side).

29. Control of the voluntary muscles of the tongue occurs through the hypoglossal nerve (N XII). **30.** Damage to the cervical plexus—or more specifically to the phrenic nerves, which extend to and innervate the diaphragm—would greatly interfere with the ability to breathe (and might even be fatal).

Page 286

31. A reflex is a rapid, automatic response to a specific stimulus. It is an important mechanism for maintaining homeostasis. **32.** Physicians use stretch reflexes (such as the knee jerk reflex or patellar reflex) to test the general condition of the spinal cord, peripheral nerves, and muscles. **33.** Polysynaptic reflexes can produce more involved responses because they include interneurons (between the sensory and motor neurons) that may control several muscle groups simultaneously. In addition, some interneurons may stimulate a muscle group or groups, whereas others may inhibit other muscle groups. **34.** A positive Babinski reflex is abnormal in adults; it indicates possible damage of descending tracts in the spinal cord.

Page 289

35. A tract within the posterior column of the spinal cord carrying information about touch and pressure from the lower part of the body to the brain is being compressed. **36.** The primary motor cortex of the right cerebral hemisphere controls motor function on the left side of the body. **37.** An injury to the superior portion of the motor cortex would affect the ability to control muscles in the hand, arm, and upper portion of the leg.

Page 293

38. The sympathetic division of the autonomic nervous system is responsible for the physiological changes that occur in response to stress and increased activity. **39.** The parasympathetic division is sometimes referred to as "the anabolic system" because parasympathetic stimulation leads to a general increase in the nutrient content of the blood. Cells throughout the body respond to the increase by absorbing the nutrients and using them to support growth and other anabolic activities. **40.** A decrease in sympathetic stimulation would result in reduced airflow because parasympathetic effects would dominate, decreasing the diameter of respiratory airways. **41.** Anxiety or stress causes increased sympathetic stimulation, so a person who is anxious about an impending root canal might exhibit some or all of the following: a dry mouth, increased heart rate, increased blood pressure, increased rate of breathing, cold sweats, an urge to urinate or defecate, change in motility of the digestive tract ("butterflies" in the stomach), and dilated pupils.

Page 296

42. Age-related reduction in brain size and weight results from a decrease in the volume of the cerebral cortex due to the loss of cortical neurons. **43.** The nervous system controls contraction of the arrector pili muscles and secretion of the sweat glands within the integumentary system. The integumentary system provides the nervous system with the sensations of touch, pressure, pain, vibration, and temperature through sensory receptors. The integumentary system also protects peripheral nerves, and hair provides some protection and insulation for the skull and brain.

ANSWERS TO REVIEW QUESTIONS

Level 1: Reviewing Facts and Terms

1. f **2.** g **3.** p **4.** s **5.** m **6.** a **7.** b **8.** j **9.** h **10.** c **11.** d **12.** o **13.** t **14.** q **15.** l **16.** i **17.** n **18.** e **19.** r **20.** k **21.** (a) dendrite; (b) cell body; (c) nucleus; (d) nucleolus; (e) axon hillock;

(f) axon; (g) synaptic terminals **22.** c **23.** a **24.** a **25.** a. cerebrum; b. diencephalons; c. midbrain; d. pons; e. medulla oblongata; f. cerebellum **26.** d **27.** b **28.** b **29.** a **30.** b **31.** c **32.** a **33.** d **34.** The all-or-none principle of action potentials: The properties of the action potential are independent of the relative strength of the depolarization stimulus. **35.** N I: olfactory; N II: optic; N III: oculomotor; N IV: trochlear; N V: trigeminal; N VI: abducens; N VII: facial; N VIII: vestibulocochlear; N IX: glossopharyngeal; N X: vagus; N XI: accessory; N XII: hypoglossal **36.** Sympathetic preganglionic fibers emerge from the thoracolumbar area (T_1 through L_2) of the spinal cord; parasympathetic fibers emerge from the brain stem and the sacral region of the spinal cord (craniosacral).

Level 2: Reviewing Concepts

37. d **38.** c **39.** Centers in the medulla oblongata are involved in respiratory and cardiac activity. **40.** Response time in a monosynaptic reflex is faster than in a polysynaptic reflex because with only one synapse, synaptic delay is minimized. In a polysynaptic reflex, total delay is proportional to the number of synapses involved.
41.

Property	Sympathetic	Parasympathetic
Mental alertness	increased	decreased
Metabolic rate	increased	decreased
Digestive/urinary function	inhibited	stimulated
Use of energy reserves	stimulated	inhibited
Respiratory rate	increased	decreased
Heart rate/blood pressure	increased	decreased
Sweat glands	stimulated	inhibited

Level 3: Critical Thinking and Clinical Applications

42. Brain tumors do not result from uncontrolled division of neurons, but instead of neuroglial cells, which can divide. In addition, cells of the meningeal membranes can give rise to tumors. **43.** The officer is testing the function of the cerebellum. A person who is under the influence of many drugs, including alcohol, is unable to properly anticipate the range and speed of limb movement because of slow processing and correction by the cerebellum. As a result, an inebriated or intoxicated Bill would have a difficult time performing simple tasks such as walking a straight line or touching his finger to his nose. **44.** Severing the branches of the vagus nerves (N X) help control stress-induced stomach ulcers by eliminating excessive sympathetic stimulation. Chronic sympathetic stimulation causes long-standing vasoconstriction, which shuts off the blood supply to the stomach, causes cell and tissue death (necrosis), and produces the ulcers. **45.** The radial nerve is involved in crutch paralysis. **46.** Ramon damaged the femoral nerve. Because this nerve supplies the sensory innervation of the skin on the anteromedial surface of the thigh and medial surfaces of the leg and foot, Ramon may also experience numbness in these regions.

CHAPTER 9

ANSWERS TO CHECKPOINTS

Page 308

1. Adaptation is a decrease in receptor sensitivity or perception after constant stimulation. **2.** Receptor A provides more precise sensory information because it has a smaller receptive field. **3.** The five special senses are smell (olfaction), taste (gustation), vision, balance (equilibrium), and hearing.

Page 312

4. The four types of general sensory receptors (and the stimuli that excite them) are nociceptors (pain), thermoreceptors (temperature), mechanoreceptors (physical distortion), and chemical receptors (chemical concentration). **5.** The three classes of mechanoreceptors are tactile receptors, baroreceptors, and proprioceptors. **6.** If proprioceptors in your legs could not relay information about limb position and movement to the CNS (especially the cerebellum), your movements would be uncoordinated, and you likely could not walk.

Page 314

7. Olfaction is the sense of smell; it involves olfactory receptors in paired olfactory organs responding to chemical stimuli. **8.** Repeated sniffing increases the perception of faint odors by increasing the flow of air and the number of odorant molecules passing over the olfactory epithelium.

Page 315

9. Gustation is the sense of taste, provided by taste receptors responding to chemical stimuli. **10.** Drying the surface of the tongue prevents the taste buds (taste receptors) from being stimulated, because they are sensitive only to molecules and ions that are in solution.

Page 324

11. The first layer of the eye to be affected by inadequate tear production is the conjunctiva. **12.** When the lens becomes more rounded, you are looking at an object close to you. **13.** Malia will likely be unable to see at all. The fovea contains only cones, which need high-intensity light to be stimulated. The dimly lit room contains light that is too weak to stimulate the cones.

Page 329

14. Individuals born without cone cells would be able to see so long as they had functioning rod cells. Because cones function in color vision, such individuals would see in black and white only. **15.** A vitamin A deficiency would reduce the quantity of retinal the body could produce, thereby interfering with night vision.

Page 339

16. If the round window could not move, the vibration of the stapes at the oval window would not move the perilymph, and there would be little or no perception of sound. **17.** Loss of stereocilia (as a result of constant exposure to loud noises, for instance) would reduce hearing sensitivity and could lead to deafness. **18.** Because individuals over age 50 experience a decline in the number and sensitivity of taste buds, a given food can be too spicy for children and too bland for the elderly. **19.** With age, the lens loses its elasticity and stiffens, resulting in a flatter lens that cannot be rounded to focus the image of a close-up object on the retina. This condition, called presbyopia, may be corrected with a converging lens.

ANSWERS TO REVIEW QUESTIONS

Level 1: Reviewing Facts and Terms

1. k **2.** c **3.** a **4.** e **5.** f **6.** j **7.** i **8.** b **9.** h **10.** m **11.** g **12.** l **13.** n **14.** d **15.** (a) vascular tunic; (b) iris; (c) ciliary body; (d) choroid; (e) neural tunic, or retina; (f) neural part; (g) pigmented part; (h) fibrous tunic; (i) cornea; (j) sclera **16.** b **17.** d **18.** b **19.** d **20.** b **21.** b **22.** d **23.** a **24.** c **25.** b **26.** b **27.** a **28.** (a) auricle; (b) external acoustic meatus; (c) tympanic membrane; (d) auditory ossicles; (e) semicircular canals; (f) vestibule; (g) auditory tube; (h) cochlea; (i) vestibulocochlear nerve, N VIII **29.** d **30.** The three types of mechanoreceptors are tactile receptors, baroreceptors, and proprioceptors.

31. Tactile receptors in skin: (1) free nerve endings: sensitive to touch and pressure; (2) root hair plexuses: monitor distortions and movements across the body surface; (3) tactile discs: detect fine touch and pressure; (4) tactile corpuscles: detect fine touch and pressure; (5) lamellated corpuscles: sensitive to pulsing or vibrating stimuli (deep pressure); and (6) Ruffini corpuscles: sensitive to pressure and distortion of the skin **32.** (a) The fibrous tunic, composed of the sclera and the cornea, (b) provides mechanical support and some degree of physical protection, serves as attachment sites for the extrinsic muscles, and contains structures that assist in focusing. **33.** The vascular tunic consists of the iris, ciliary body, and choroid. **34.** Step 1: Sound waves arrive at the tympanum. Step 2: Movement of the tympanum causes displacement of the auditory ossicles. Step 3: Movement of the stapes at the oval window establishes pressure waves in the perilymph of the vestibular duct. Step 4: The pressure waves distort the basilar membrane on their way to the round window of the tympanic duct. Step 5: Vibration of the basilar membrane causes hair cells to vibrate against the tectorial membrane. Step 6: Information about the region and intensity of stimulation is relayed to the CNS over the cochlear branch of N VIII.

Level 2: Reviewing Concepts

35. c **36.** c **37.** The general senses include somatic and visceral sensation. The special senses are those whose receptors are confined to the head. **38.** The CNS receives any stimulus detected by a sensory receptor in the form of action potentials, regardless of the type of stimulus. **39.** Olfactory sensations are long lasting and linked to our memories and emotions because the olfactory system has extensive limbic system connections. **40.** A visual acuity of 20/15 means that Jane is able to see details that would be clear to a "normal" eye only at a distance of 15 feet. Jane's visual acuity is better than 20/20 vision.

Level 3: Critical Thinking and Clinical Applications

41. As you turn to look at your friend, your medial rectus muscles will contract, directing your gaze more medially. In addition, your pupils will constrict and the lenses will become more spherical. **42.** The loud noises from the fireworks have transferred so much energy to the endolymph in the cochlea that the fluid continues to move for a long while. As long as the endolymph is moving, it will vibrate the tectorial membrane and stimulate the hair cells. This stimulation produces the "ringing" sensation that Millie perceives. She finds it difficult to hear normal conversation because the vibrations associated with it are not strong enough to overcome the currents already moving through the endolymph, so the pattern of vibrations is difficult to discern against the background "noise." **43.** The rapid descent in the elevator causes the maculae in the saccule of the vestibule to slide upward, producing the sensation of downward vertical motion. When the elevator abruptly stops, the maculae do not. It takes a few seconds for them to come to rest in the normal position. As long as the maculae are displaced, the perception of movement will remain.

CHAPTER 10

ANSWERS TO CHECKPOINTS

Page 347

1. Both the endocrine and nervous systems (1) release chemicals that bind to specific receptors on target cells, (2) share chemical messengers, (3) are primarily regulated by negative feedback control mechanisms, and (4) coordinate and regulate the activities of other cells, tissues, organs, and systems to maintain homeostasis.

Page 351

2. A hormone is a chemical messenger that is secreted by one cell and travels through the bloodstream to affect the activities of cells in other parts of the body. **3.** A cell's sensitivity to any hormone is determined by the presence or absence of the receptor molecule specific to that hormone. **4.** A molecule that blocks adenylate cyclase—the enzyme that converts ATP to cAMP—would block the action of any hormone that required cAMP as a second messenger. **5.** Cyclic-AMP is considered a second messenger because it is needed to convert the binding of first messengers—epinephrine, norepinephrine, and peptide hormones, which cannot enter target cells—into some effect on the metabolic activity of the target cell. **6.** The three types of stimuli that control endocrine activity are (1) humoral (changes in the composition of the extracellular fluid), (2) hormonal (changes in the levels of circulating hormones), and (3) neural (the arrival of neurotransmitter at a neuroglandular junction).

Page 356

7. In dehydration, blood osmotic concentration is increased, which would stimulate the posterior pituitary gland to release more ADH. **8.** Elevated growth hormone levels typically accompany elevated somatomedin levels because somatomedins mediate the action of growth hormone. **9.** Elevated circulating levels of cortisol inhibit the cells that control the release of ACTH from the pituitary gland, so ACTH levels would decrease. This is an example of a negative feedback mechanism.

Page 359

10. Hormones of the thyroid gland are thyroxine (T_4), triiodothyronine (T_3), and calcitonin. **11.** Because an individual who lacks dietary iodine is unable to form the hormone thyroxine, you would expect to see signs and symptoms associated with thyroxine deficiency, such as decreased metabolic rate, decreased body temperature, a poor response to physiological stress, and an enlarged thyroid gland (goiter). **12.** Most of the thyroid hormone in the blood is bound to transport proteins, constituting a large reservoir of thyroxine that would not be depleted until days after the thyroid gland had been removed.

Page 361

13. The hormone secreted by the parathyroid glands is parathyroid hormone (PTH). **14.** Removal of the parathyroid glands would result in decreased blood levels of calcium ions. (This decrease could be counteracted by increasing the dietary intake of vitamin D_3 and calcium.)

Page 363

15. The two regions of the suprarenal gland are (1) the cortex, which secretes mineralocorticoids (primarily aldosterone), glucocorticoids (mainly cortisol, hydrocortisone, and corticosterone), and androgens, and (2) the medulla, which secretes epinephrine and norepinephrine. **16.** Elevated cortisol levels would produce elevated blood glucose levels by (1) decreasing the use of glucose by cells and (2) increasing available glucose (by promoting the breakdown of glycogen and converting amino acids to carbohydrates).

Page 364

17. Increased amounts of light inhibit the production of melatonin by the pineal gland, which receives neural input through the optic tracts. **18.** Melatonin inhibits reproductive functions, protects against free radical damage, and sets circadian rhythms.

Page 365

19. Important cells of the pancreatic islets (and their hormones) are alpha cells (glucagon) and beta cells (insulin). **20.** Insulin causes skele-

tal muscle and liver cells to convert glucose to glycogen. **21.** Increased levels of glucagon would lead to decreased reserves of glycogen in the liver because glucagon stimulates the conversion of glycogen to glucose.

Page 368

22. Two hormones secreted by the kidneys are erythropoietin (EPO), which stimulates bone marrow cells to produce more red blood cells (which increases the delivery of oxygen to body tissues), and calcitriol, which stimulates cells lining the digestive tract to absorb calcium and phosphate. **23.** Leptin is a hormone released by adipose tissue. **24.** Once released into the bloodstream, renin functions as an enzyme, catalyzing a chain reaction that ultimately leads to the formation of the hormone angiotensin II.

Page 372

25. The hormonal interaction exemplified by insulin and glucagon is antagonistic, because the two hormones have opposite effects on their target tissues. **26.** The lack of growth hormone, thyroid hormone, parathyroid hormone, or the reproductive hormones would inhibit the normal formation and development of the skeletal system. **27.** The dominant hormones of the resistance phase of the general adaptation syndrome are the glucocorticoids. They increase blood glucose levels by mobilizing lipid and protein reserves, and by stimulating the synthesis and release of glucose by the liver. **28.** The endocrine system affects the functioning of all other body systems by adjusting metabolic rates and substrate utilization, and by regulating growth and development.

ANSWERS TO REVIEW QUESTIONS

Level 1: Reviewing Facts and Terms

1. h **2.** e **3.** g **4.** l **5.** b **6.** k **7.** c **8.** a **9.** j **10.** i **11.** f **12.** d **13.** (a) hypothalamus; (b) pituitary gland; (c) thyroid gland; (d) thymus; (e) suprarenal glands; (f) pineal gland; (g) parathyroid glands; (h) heart; (i) kidney; (j) adipose tissue; (k) digestive tract; (l) pancreatic islets (within pancreas); (m) gonads **14.** d **15.** a **16.** c **17.** d **18.** b **19.** d **20.** c **21.** b **22.** anterior pituitary hormones: (1) thyroid-stimulating hormones (TSH); (2) adrenocorticotropic hormone (ACTH); (3) follicle-stimulating hormone (FSH); (4) luteinizing hormone (LH); (5) prolactin (PRL); (6) growth hormone (GH); and (7) melanocyte-stimulating hormone (MSH) **23.** The overall effect of calcitonin is to decrease the Ca^{2+} concentration in body fluids. The overall effect of parathyroid hormone is to cause an increase in the concentration of Ca^{2+} in body fluids. **24.** (a) The GAS consists of alarm, resistance, and exhaustion phases. (b) Epinephrine is the dominant hormone of the alarm phase. Glucocorticoids are the dominant hormones of the resistance phase.

Level 2: Reviewing Concepts

25. In nervous system communication, the source and destination are quite specific, and the effects are short-lived. In endocrine communication, the effects are slow to appear and often persist for days, and a given hormone can alter the metabolic activities of multiple tissues and organs simultaneously. **26.** Hormones can (1) direct the synthesis of an enzyme (or other protein) that is not already present in the cytoplasm, or (2) turn an existing enzyme "on" or "off" to increase or decrease the rate of synthesis of a particular enzyme or other protein. **27.** The two hormones may (1) have opposing, or antagonistic, effects; (2) have additive or synergistic effects; or (3) produce different but complementary effects in specific tissues and organs. Additionally, (4) one hormone may have a permissive effect on the other; that is, the first hormone is needed for the second to produce its effect.

28. Blocking the activity of phosphodiesterase would prevent the conversion of cAMP to AMP, which would prolong the effects of hormonal stimulation.

Level 3: Critical Thinking and Clinical Applications

29. Extreme thirst and frequent urination are characteristics of both diabetes insipidus and diabetes mellitus. To distinguish between the two, glucose levels in the blood and urine could be measured. A high glucose concentration would indicate diabetes mellitus. **30.** Julie will likely have elevated blood levels of parathyroid hormone. Because her poor diet does not supply enough calcium for her developing fetus, the fetus removes large amounts of calcium from the maternal blood. The resulting lowered maternal blood calcium levels lead to elevated blood parathyroid hormone levels and increased removal of stored calcium from the maternal skeleton.

CHAPTER 11

ANSWERS TO CHECKPOINTS

Page 302

1. The major functions of blood are transportation of dissolved gases, nutrients, hormones, and metabolic wastes; regulation of the pH and ion composition of interstitial fluids; restriction of fluid losses at injury sites; defense against toxins and pathogens; and stabilization of body temperature. **2.** Whole blood is composed of plasma and formed elements. **3.** Venipuncture is a common blood sampling technique because superficial veins are easy to locate, the walls of veins are thinner than those of arteries, and the puncture wound seals quickly because blood pressure in veins is relatively low.

Page 384

4. The three major types of plasma proteins are albumins, globulins, and fibrinogen. **5.** A decrease in the amount of plasma proteins would cause reductions in (1) plasma osmotic pressure, (2) the ability to fight infections, and (3) the transport and binding of some ions, hormones, and other molecules.

Page 390

6. Hemoglobin is a protein composed of four globular subunits, each bound to a heme molecule, which gives RBCs the ability to transport oxygen in the blood. **7.** By lowering total blood volume, dehydration increases the hematocrit—the percentage of total blood volume occupied by the formed elements (mostly red blood cells). **8.** Bilirubin would accumulate in the blood, producing jaundice, because diseases that damage the liver, such as hepatitis or cirrhosis, would impair the liver's ability to excrete bilirubin in the bile. **9.** A decreased oxygen supply to the kidneys triggers increased erythropoietin levels in the blood, which stimulates increased erythropoiesis (RBC production).

Page 393

10. A person with Type AB blood can accept Type A, Type B, Type AB, or Type O blood. **11.** A person with Type A blood cannot safely receive Type B blood because the anti-B antibodies in the plasma of the Type A recipient would bind to B antigens on the donor's RBCs, causing the transfused RBCs to clump or agglutinate, which could block blood flow to various organs and tissues.

Page 396

12. The five types of white blood cells are neutrophils, eosinophils, basophils, monocytes, and lymphocytes. **13.** An infected cut typically contains numerous neutrophils, phagocytic WBCs that are generally the first to arrive at the site of an injury. **14.** The WBCs that produce circulating antibodies are lymphocytes. **15.** During inflammation, basophils release a variety of chemicals, such as histamine and heparin, that enhance inflammation and attract other types of white blood cells.

Page 398

16. Platelets are non-nucleated cellular fragments found in mammalian vertebrates; thrombocytes are nucleated cells found in nonmammalian vertebrates. **17.** Platelet functions include initiating the clotting process and helping to close damaged blood vessels.

Page 401

18. A decreased number of megakaryocytes, which produce platelets, would impair the clotting process. **19.** The faster extrinsic pathway is initiated by the release of a lipoprotein called tissue factor by damaged endothelial cells and damaged tissues. The slower intrinsic pathway is initiated by the activation of clotting protein proenzymes exposed to damaged collagen fibers, and by the release of platelet factor by aggregating platelets. **20.** A vitamin K deficiency would reduce the production of clotting factors necessary for normal blood coagulation.

ANSWERS TO REVIEW QUESTIONS

Level 1: Reviewing Facts and Terms

1. f **2.** k **3.** a **4.** l **5.** c **6.** j **7.** e **8.** h **9.** g **10.** b **11.** d **12.** i **13.** (a) neutrophil; (b) eosinophil; (c) basophil; (d) monocyte; (e) lymphocyte **14.** c **15.** c **16.** a **17.** c **18.** d **19.** a **20.** d **21.** d **22.** b **23.** Albumins maintain the osmotic pressure of plasma and are important in transporting fatty acids. Transport globulins bind small ions, hormones, or compounds that might otherwise be filtered out of the blood at the kidneys or have very low solubility in water, and immunoglobulins attack foreign proteins and pathogens. Fibrinogen functions in blood clotting. **24.** (a) anti-B antibodies; (b) anti-A antibodies; (c) neither anti-A nor anti-B antibodies; (d) both anti-A antibodies and anti-B antibodies **25.** WBCs exhibit: (1) amoeboid movement, a gliding movement that moves the cell; (2) emigration (diapedesis), squeezing between adjacent endothelial cells in the capillary wall; (3) positive chemotaxis, the attraction to specific chemical stimuli; and (4) phagocytosis (engulfing particles for neutrophils, eosinophils, and monocytes). **26.** For the common pathway to begin, either the extrinsic or intrinsic pathway must produce Factor X activator. **27.** An embolus is a drifting blood clot. A thrombus is a blood clot attached to the wall of an intact blood vessel.

Level 2: Reviewing Concepts

28. a **29.** d **30.** c **31.** d **32.** Red blood cells are biconcave discs that lack mitochondria, ribosomes, and nuclei and contain a large amount of the protein hemoglobin.

Level 3: Critical Thinking and Clinical Applications

33. After donating a pint of blood (or after any other blood loss), you would expect to see a substantial increase in the number of reticulocytes. Because there is insufficient time for erythrocytes to mature, the bone marrow releases large numbers of reticulocytes (immature cells) in an effort to restore levels of formed elements. **34.** In many cases of kidney disease, the cells responsible for producing erythropoietin (EPO) are either damaged or destroyed. The reduction in EPO levels leads to reduced erythropoiesis and fewer red blood cells, resulting in anemia. **35.** A major function of the spleen is to destroy old, defective, and worn out red blood cells. As the spleen increases in size, so does its capacity to eliminate red blood cells, and this produces anemia. The decreased number of RBCs decreases the body's ability to deliver oxygen to the tissues, so tissue metabolism slows; this accounts for feeling tired and the lack of energy. Because there are fewer RBCs than normal, blood circulating through the skin is not as red, so the person has a pale or whitish skin coloration.

CHAPTER 12

ANSWERS TO CHECKPOINTS

Page 415

1. Damage to the semilunar valves on the right side of the heart would interfere with blood flow to the pulmonary artery. **2.** The chordae tendineae prevent the AV valves from swinging into the atria. The contracting ventricles force the AV valves to close, tensing the chordae tendineae. The attached papillary muscles respond by contracting, counteracting the force that is pushing the valves upward. **3.** The left ventricle is more muscular than the right ventricle because it must generate enough force to propel blood throughout the body (except the lungs). The right ventricle must generate only enough force to propel blood the few centimeters to the lungs.

Page 419

4. The fact that cardiac muscle cells cannot undergo tetanus—because they have a longer refractory period than skeletal muscle cells—means that they relax long enough so the heart's chambers can refill with blood. **5.** If cells of the SA node were not functioning, cells of the AV node would become the pacemaker cells, so the heart would continue to beat but at a slower rate. **6.** If impulses from the atria were not delayed at the AV node, they would be conducted through the ventricles so quickly by the bundle branches and Purkinje fibers that the ventricles would begin contracting immediately, before the atria had finished contracting. As a result, the ventricles would not be as full of blood as they could be, and the pumping of the heart would not be as efficient, especially during activity. **7.** One possible cause for an increase in the size of the QRS complex, which indicates a larger-than-normal amount of electrical activity during ventricular depolarization, is an enlarged heart. Because more cardiac muscle is depolarizing, the magnitude of the electrical event would be greater.

Page 421

8. The alternate term for heart contraction is systole, and that for heart relaxation is diastole. **9.** No. When pressure in the left ventricle first rises, the heart is contracting but no blood is leaving the heart. During the initial phase of contraction, both the AV and semilunar valves are closed. The increase in pressure results from increased tension as the cardiac muscle contracts. When ventricular pressure exceeds the pressure in the aorta, the aortic semilunar valves are forced open, and blood is rapidly ejected from the ventricle. **10.** "Lubb" is produced by the simultaneous closing of the AV valves and the opening of the semilunar valves; "dupp" is produced when the semilunar valves close.

Page 423

11. Cardiac output is the amount of blood pumped by the left ventricle in one minute. **12.** Damage to the cardioinhibitory center of the medulla oblongata—a part of the parasympathetic division of the ANS—would result in fewer parasympathetic action potentials to the heart and an

increase in heart rate due to sympathetic dominance. **13.** Stimulating the acetylcholine receptors of the heart lowers heart rate. Given that $CO = HR \times SV$, a reduction in heart rate must produce a reduction in cardiac output (assuming no change in the stroke volume). **14.** According to the Frank-Starling principle, the more the heart muscle is stretched by returning blood (venous return), the more forcefully it will contract (to a point), and the more blood it will eject with each beat (stroke volume). Thus if all other factors are constant, increased venous return increases stroke volume. **15.** If the heart beats too rapidly, it has too little time to fill completely between beats. The heart pumps in proportion to the amount of blood that enters: The less blood that enters, the less the heart can pump. If it beats too fast, very little blood will enter the bloodstream; tissues will suffer damage from the lack of blood supply.

ANSWERS TO REVIEW QUESTIONS

Level 1: Reviewing Facts and Terms

1. i **2.** e **3.** g **4.** h **5.** a **6.** b **7.** k **8.** l **9.** d **10.** f **11.** c **12.** j **13.** (a) superior vena cava; (b) auricle of right atrium; (c) right ventricle; (d) left ventricle; (e) aortic arch; (f) left pulmonary artery; (g) pulmonary trunk; (h) auricle of left atrium **14.** c **15.** b **16.** b **17.** a **18.** (a) ascending aorta; (b) opening of coronary sinus; (c) right atrium; (d) cusp of right AV (tricuspid) valve; (e) chordae tendineae; (f) right ventricle; (g) pulmonary valve; (h) left pulmonary veins; (i) left atrium; (j) aortic valve; (k) cusp of left AV (mitral) valve; (l) left ventricle; (m) interventricular septum **19.** a **20.** b **21.** c **22.** During ventricular contraction, tension in the papillary muscles pulls against the chordae tendineae, which keep the cusps of the AV valve from swinging into the atrium. This action prevents the backflow, or regurgitation, of blood into the atrium as the ventricle contracts. **23.** The atrioventricular (AV) valves prevent backflow of blood from the ventricles into the atria. The right AV valve is the tricuspid valve, and the left AV valve is the bicuspid (mitral) valve. The pulmonary and aortic semilunar valves prevent the backflow of blood from the pulmonary trunk and aorta into the right and left ventricles. **24.** SA node → AV node → AV bundle (bundle of His) → right and left bundle branches → Purkinje fibers (into the mass of ventricular muscle tissue) **25.** (a) The cardiac cycle is a complete heartbeat, including a contraction/relaxation period for both atria and ventricles. (b) The cycle begins with atrial systole as the atria contract and push blood into the relaxed ventricles. As the atria relax (atrial diastole), the ventricles contract (ventricular systole), forcing blood through the semilunar valves into the pulmonary trunk and aorta. The ventricles then relax (ventricular diastole). For the rest of the cardiac cycle, both the atria and ventricles are in diastole; passive filling occurs.

Level 2: Reviewing Concepts

26. c **27.** d **28.** a **29.** The right atrium receives blood from the systemic circuit and passes it to the right ventricle, which pumps it into the pulmonary circuit. The left atrium collects blood returning from the lungs and passes it to left ventricle, which ejects it into the systemic circuit. **30.** The first heart sound ("lubb") marks the start of ventricular contraction and is produced as the AV valves close and the semilunar valves open. The second sound ("dupp") occurs when the semilunar valves close, marking the start of ventricular diastole. Listening to the heart sounds (auscultation) is a simple, effective way to identify certain heart abnormalities. **31.** (a) Sympathetic stimulation causes the release of norepinephrine by postganglionic fibers and the secretion of norepinephrine and epinephrine by the suprarenal medullae. These hormones stimulate cardiac muscle cell metabolism and increase the force and degree of cardiac contraction. (b) Parasympathetic stimulation causes the release of ACh at membrane surfaces; the resulting hyperpolarization and inhibition decrease heart rate and the force of contractions.

Level 3: Critical Thinking and Clinical Applications

32. In this patient, only one of every two action potentials generated by the SA node is reaching the ventricles; thus there are two P waves but only one QRS complex and T wave. This condition frequently results either from damage to the internodal pathways of the atria or problems with the AV node. **33.** Using CO = HR × SV, cardiac output for person A is 4500 mL, and for person B 8550 mL. According to the Frank-Starling principle, in a normal heart CO is directly proportional to venous return, so person B has the greater venous return. Ventricular filling increases as HR decreases, so person A has the longer ventricular filling time. **34.** Blocking the calcium channels in myocardial cells would lead to a decrease in the force of cardiac contraction. Given that the force of cardiac contraction is directly proportional to stroke volume, you would expect a reduced stroke volume.

CHAPTER 13

ANSWERS TO CHECKPOINTS

Page 434

1. The five general classes of blood vessels are arteries, arterioles, capillaries, venules, and veins. **2.** These blood vessels are veins. Arteries and arterioles have a large amount of smooth muscle tissue in a thick, well-developed tunica media. **3.** The relaxation of precapillary sphincters would increase blood flow to a tissue. **4.** Because the very low blood pressure in the venous circulation makes the movement of blood against the pull of gravity difficult, blood flow within peripheral veins depends on the contractions of skeletal muscles to propel the blood, and on valves to prevent blood from backing up.

Page 439

5. Factors that contribute to total peripheral resistance are vascular resistance, vessel length, vessel diameter, blood viscosity, and turbulence. **6.** In a healthy individual, blood pressure is greater at the aorta—just leaving the pump (heart)—than at the inferior vena cava. Blood, like other fluids, moves along a pressure gradient from areas of high pressure to areas of low pressure. **7.** When a person stands for a long time, blood pools in the lower extremities, decreasing venous return to the heart. The resulting decline in cardiac output reduces blood flow to the brain, causing lightheadedness and fainting. A hot day adds to this effect: The loss of body water through sweating reduces blood volume (and venous return).

Page 444

8. Vasodilators increase blood flow locally (that is, through their tissue of origin) by promoting dilation of precapillary sphincters. Vasoconstrictors decrease local blood flow by constricting precapillary sphincters. **9.** Slight compression of the common carotid artery would elevate heart rate. The compression decreases blood pressure at the carotid sinus (the location of the carotid baroreceptors), which stimulates the cardioacceleratory center to increase sympathetic stimulation, which raises the heart rate. **10.** Renal artery vasoconstriction would lead to increases in systemic blood pressure and volume. Such vasoconstriction would decrease both blood pressure and flow at the kidney, which would respond

by releasing more renin. Increased renin would lead to an increase in angiotensin II, which would elevate blood pressure and volume.

Page 446

11. Blood pressure increases during exercise because (1) cardiac output increases and (2) resistance in "nonessential" visceral tissues and organs increases. **12.** The immediate problem during hemorrhaging is the maintenance of adequate blood pressure and peripheral blood flow; the long-term problem is the restoration of normal blood volume. **13.** Both aldosterone and ADH promote fluid retention and reabsorption at the kidneys, preventing further reductions in blood volume.

Page 447

14. The two circuits of the cardiovascular system are the pulmonary circuit and the systemic circuit. **15.** Three general functional patterns of blood vessels include (1) nearly identical peripheral distributions of arteries and veins on the body's left and right sides (except near the heart); (2) several names for a single vessel as it crosses specific anatomical boundaries (making accurate anatomical descriptions possible); and (3) the servicing of tissues and organs by several arteries and veins. **16.** The pulmonary arteries enter the lungs carrying deoxygenated blood, and the pulmonary veins leave the lungs carrying oxygenated blood. **17.** Right ventricle → pulmonary trunk → left and right pulmonary arteries → pulmonary arterioles → alveoli → pulmonary venules → pulmonary veins → left atrium

Page 460

18. Blockage of the left subclavian artery would interfere with blood flow to the left arm. **19.** Compression of the common carotid arteries would lead to loss of consciousness (or even death) by cutting off blood flow to the brain. **20.** Rupture of the celiac trunk would most directly affect the stomach, spleen, liver, and pancreas. **21.** Arteries in the neck and limbs are located deep beneath the skin, protected by bones and surrounding soft tissues; veins in these sites follow two courses, one superficial and one deep. This dual venous drainage helps control body temperature: Blood flow through superficial veins promotes heat loss, and blood flow through deep veins conserves body heat.

Page 461

22. Two umbilical arteries supply blood to the placenta, and one umbilical vein returns from the placenta. The umbilical vein drains into the ductus venosus within the fetal liver. **23.** This blood must have come from the umbilical vein, which carries oxygenated, nutrient-rich blood from the placenta to the fetus. **24.** The vital fetal circulatory structures are the placenta, two umbilical arteries, an umbilical vein, the ductus venosus, the foramen ovale, and the ductus arteriosus. In the newborn, the foramen ovale closes and persists as the fossa ovalis, a shallow depression; the ductus arteriosus persists as the ligamentum arteriosum, a fibrous cord; and the umbilical vessels and ductus venosus persist throughout life as fibrous cords. **25.** Components of the cardiovascular system affected by age include the blood, the heart, and blood vessels. **26.** A thrombus is a stationary blood clot within a blood vessel. **27.** An aneurysm is the ballooning out of an inelastic arterial wall resulting from sudden pressure increases.

Page 462

28. The cardiovascular system provides other body systems with oxygen, hormones, nutrients, and white blood cells, while removing carbon dioxide and metabolic wastes; it also transfers heat. **29.** The cardiovascular system is most closely interconnected with the lymphoid system.

The two systems are physically connected (lymphatic vessels drain into veins), and cell populations of the lymphoid system are carried from one part of the body to another within the cardiovascular system. **30.** The skeletal system provides calcium needed for normal cardiac muscle contraction, and it protects blood cells developing in the bone marrow. The cardiovascular system provides calcium and phosphate for bone deposition, delivers erythropoietin to bone marrow, and transports parathyroid hormone and calcitonin to osteoblasts and osteoclasts.

ANSWERS TO REVIEW QUESTIONS

Level 1: Reviewing Facts and Terms

1. d **2.** l **3.** a **4.** j **5.** i **6.** h **7.** k **8.** f **9.** e **10.** c **11.** g **12.** b **13.** (a) brachiocephalic trunk; (b) brachial; (c) radial; (d) external iliac; (e) anterior tibial; (f) right common carotid; (g) left subclavian; (h) common iliac; (i) femoral **14.** d **15.** b **16.** b **17.** a **18.** d **19.** b **20.** c **21.** b **22.** c **23.** (a) external jugular; (b) brachial; (c) median cubital; (d) radial; (e) great saphenous; (f) internal jugular; (g) superior vena cava; (h) left and right common iliac; (i) femoral **24.** b **25.** d **26.** c **27.** b **28.** c **29.** c **30.** (a) Fluid leaves the capillary at the arteriolar end primarily in response to hydrostatic pressure. (b) Fluid moves into the capillary at the venous end primarily in response to osmotic pressure. **31.** When elevated BP triggers the baroreceptor response, cardiac output decreases (due to parasympathetic stimulation and inhibition of sympathetic activity) and widespread peripheral vasodilation occurs (due to the inhibition of excitatory neurons in the vasomotor center). **32.** Chemoreceptors in the carotid and aortic bodies are sensitive to changes in CO_2, O_2, or pH levels in blood and cerebrospinal fluid. **33.** When an infant takes its first breath, the lungs and the pulmonary vessels expand. Smooth muscles in the ductus arteriosus contract, isolating the pulmonary and aortic trunks, and blood begins flowing through the pulmonary circuit. As pressure rises in the left atrium, the valvular flap closes the foramen ovale, completing the circulatory remodeling. **34.** Blood: decreased hematocrit, formation of thrombin, and valvular malfunction; Heart: reduction in maximum cardiac output, changes in the activities of the nodal and conducting fibers, reduction in the elasticity of the fibrous skeleton, progressive atherosclerosis, and replacement of damaged cardiac muscle fibers by scar tissue; Blood vessels: progressive inelasticity in arterial walls, deposition of calcium salts on weakened vascular walls, and formation of thrombi at atherosclerotic plaques

Level 2: Reviewing Concepts

35. d **36.** c **37.** b **38.** The thicker walls of arteries contain more smooth muscle and elastic fibers, enabling them to resist the pressure generated by the heart, and to constrict when not expanded by blood pressure. The walls of veins can be thinner because venous pressures are low. **39.** Unlike arteries and veins, capillaries are only one cell thick, and small gaps between adjacent endothelial cells permit the diffusion of water and small solutes into the surrounding interstitial fluid while retaining blood cells and plasma proteins. (Some capillaries also contain pores that permit very rapid exchange of fluids and solutes between the plasma and the interstitial fluid.) **40.** Blood flow to the brain is relatively constant because anastomoses formed from four arteries within the cranium ensure that interruption in flow in any one vessel will not compromise blood supply to the brain. **41.** The accident victim is suffering from shock and acute circulatory crisis. The hypotension results from the loss of blood volume and decreased cardiac output. Her skin is pale and cool due to pe-

ripheral vasoconstriction; the moisture results from the sympathetic activation of sweat glands. Falling blood pressure to the brain causes confusion and disorientation. Her pulse would be rapid and weak, reflecting the heart's response to reduced blood flow and volume.

Level 3: Critical Thinking and Clinical Applications

42. Three factors contribute to Bob's elevated blood pressure: (1) Water loss from sweating increases blood viscosity—resulting from the same number of RBCs in a lower plasma volume—which increases peripheral resistance and contributes to increased blood pressure. (2) Increased blood flow to the skin (to cool Bob's body) increases venous return, which increases stroke volume and cardiac output (Frank-Starling's law of the heart). Increased cardiac output raises blood pressure. (3) The heat stress Bob is experiencing increases sympathetic stimulation (the reason for the sweating), which by elevating heart rate and stroke volume increases cardiac output and blood pressure. **43.** Antihistamines and decongestants not only counteract the symptoms of allergies, they also have the same effects as stimulating the sympathetic nervous system—increases in heart rate, stroke volume, and peripheral resistance—all of which elevate blood pressure. Thus these drugs will aggravate these individuals' hypertension, with potentially hazardous consequences. **44.** When Gina went from lying to standing, gravity moved her blood away from her heart and into her lower extremities, reducing venous return. Decreased venous return lowered blood volume at the end of diastole, which by decreasing stroke volume and cardiac output reduced blood flow to the brain, producing light-headedness and faintness. Normally this does not occur because a rapid drop in blood pressure immediately triggers baroreceptors in the aortic arch and carotid sinus to initiate the baroreceptor reflex and transmit action potentials to the medulla oblongata, which orchestrates appropriate responses. If the expected increase in peripheral resistance does not compensate enough for the reduced blood pressure, an increase in heart rate and force of contraction would occur. Normally, these responses occur so quickly that no changes in pressure are noticed after body position is changed.

CHAPTER 14

ANSWERS TO CHECKPOINTS

Page 471

1. Pathogens are disease-causing organisms—including viruses, bacteria, fungi, and parasites—that can thrive inside the body. **2.** Nonspecific defenses, which include anatomical barriers and defense mechanisms that slow or prevent the entry of infectious organisms into the body, do not distinguish among a host of potential threats. Specific defenses involve an immune response against each specific type of threat.

Page 479

3. Components of the lymphoid system are lymph, lymphatic vessels, lymphoid tissues, and lymphoid organs. **4.** Blockage of the thoracic duct would impair lymph circulation in all of the body inferior to the diaphragm and in the left side of the body superior to the diaphragm. The result could be the accumulation of fluid (lymphedema) in the involved extremities. **5.** A lack of thymic hormones would result in an absence of T lymphocytes. **6.** During an infection, lymphocytes and phagocytes in lymph nodes in the affected region multiply in response to the infectious agent. This increase in the number of cells in the nodes causes the nodes to become enlarged or swollen.

Page 482

7. The body's nonspecific defenses include physical barriers, phagocytes, immunological surveillance, interferons, the complement system, inflammation, and fever. **8.** A decrease in the number of monocyte-forming cells in the bone marrow would reduce the abundance of macrophages, because all types of macrophages—including microglia of the CNS, Kupffer's cells of the liver, and alveolar macrophages in the lungs—are derived from monocytes. **9.** A rise in interferon levels indicates a viral infection. This nonspecific defense, released from virus-infected cells, "interferes" with the viruses' ability to infect other cells. **10.** Pyrogens stimulate the temperature control area within the hypothalamus to raise body temperature, thereby producing a fever.

Page 484

11. In cell-mediated (cellular) immunity, T cells defend against abnormal cells and pathogens inside cells. In antibody-mediated (humoral) immunity, B cells secrete antibodies that defend against antigens and pathogens in body fluids. **12.** The two forms of active immunity are naturally acquired active immunity and induced active immunity; the two forms of passive immunity are naturally acquired passive immunity and induced passive immunity. **13.** The four general properties of immunity are specificity, versatility, memory, and tolerance.

Page 486

14. The four types of T cells are cytotoxic T cells, helper T cells, memory T cells, and suppressor T cells. **15.** Abnormal peptides within a cell become attached to MHC proteins and displayed on the cell's surface, where the peptides are recognized by T cells, triggering an immune response. **16.** A decrease in the number of cytotoxic T cells would interfere with cell-mediated immunity, the body's response against foreign cells and virus-infected cells. **17.** A lack of helper T cells would retard the antibody-mediated immune response because they promote B cell division, the maturation of plasma cells, and the production of antibodies by plasma cells.

Page 491

18. Sensitization is the process a B cell undergoes to become reactive against a specific antigen. **19.** An antibody is a Y-shaped molecule that consists of two parallel pairs of polypeptide chains: one pair of heavy chains and one pair of light chains. Each chain contains both constant segments and variable segments. **20.** Given a sample of lymph containing an elevated number of plasma cells, we would expect the number of antibodies in the blood to be increasing, because plasma cells secrete antibodies. **21.** The secondary response would be more affected by the lack of memory B cells for a particular antigen. The ability to produce a secondary response depends on the presence of memory B cells (and memory T cells) formed during the primary response but held in reserve against future contact with the same antigen.

Page 494

22. An autoimmune disorder results when the immune system's sensitivity to normal cells and tissues causes the production of autoantibodies. **23.** Increased stress reduces the effectiveness of the immune response by reducing inflammation, reducing the number and activity of phagocytes, and inhibiting interleukin secretion. **24.** The elderly are more susceptible to viral and bacterial infections because as the number of helper T cells declines with age, B cells are less responsive, so antibody levels rise more slowly after antigen exposure. **25.** The increased incidence of cancer among the elderly may reflect the decline of immunological surveillance with age. **26.** The lymphoid system provides defenses against infection, performs immunological surveillance to eliminate cancer cells, and returns tissue fluid to the circulation. **27.** The cardiovascular system aids the body's nonspecific and specific defenses by distributing white blood cells, transporting antibodies, and restricting the spread of pathogens (through the clotting response).

ANSWERS TO REVIEW QUESTIONS

Level 1: Reviewing Facts and Terms

1. h **2.** k **3.** b **4.** g **5.** d **6.** c **7.** j **8.** a **9.** i **10.** l **11.** f **12.** e
13. (a) tonsil; (b) right lymphatic duct; (c) thymus; (d) thoracic duct; (e) appendix; (f) lymphatics of upper limb; (g) axillary lymph nodes; (h) thoracic duct; (i) spleen; (j) lymphoid nodules of intestines **14.** c
15. d **16.** c **17.** c **18.** b **19.** a **20.** c **21.** a **22.** a **23.** d **24.** d
25. c **26.** The thoracic duct collects lymph from the body inferior to the diaphragm and from the left side of the body superior to the diaphragm. The right thoracic duct collects lymph from the right side of the body superior to the diaphragm. **27.** (a) responsible for cell-mediated immunity, which defends against abnormal cells and pathogens inside living cells; (b) stimulate the activation and function of T cells and B cells; (c) inhibit the activation and function of both T cells and B cells; (d) produce and secrete antibodies; (e) recognize and destroy abnormal cells; (f) interfere with viral replication inside cells and stimulate the activities of macrophages and NK cells; (g) provide cell-mediated immunity; (h) provide antibody-mediated immunity, which defends against antigens and pathogenic organisms in the body; (i) enhance nonspecific defenses, increase T cell sensitivity, and stimulate B cell activity

Level 2: Reviewing Concepts

28. c **29.** d **30.** Specificity: Each immune response is triggered by a specific antigen and defends against only that antigen. Versatility: The immune system can differentiate among tens of thousands of antigens it may encounter during an individual's normal lifetime. Memory: The immune response following a second exposure to a given antigen is stronger and lasts longer than the first exposure. Tolerance: Some antigens, such as those on an individual's own normal cells, do not elicit an immune response. **31.** An antigen–antibody complex can eliminate the antigen by neutralization, agglutination, and precipitation; activation of complement; attraction of phagocytes; stimulation of inflammation; or prevention of bacterial or viral adhesion. **32.** Complement system activation destroys target cell plasma membranes, stimulates inflammation, attracts phagocytes, and enhances phagocytosis.

Level 3: Critical Thinking and Clinical Applications

33. Examination of regional lymph nodes for the presence of cancer cells can help the physician determine if the cancer cells have remained localized in the lungs and were discovered at a relatively early stage, or have already spread (or metastasized) through the lymphoid system to establish tumors in other sites of the body. Both the stage of the disease and the sites involved help the physician decide about treatment options. **34.** The presence of an elevated level of IgM antibodies, but very few IgG antibodies, suggests that Ted is in the early stages of a primary response to the measles virus, so he appears to have contracted the disease. The subsequent levels of IgG antibodies will play a crucial role in the eventual control of the disease.

CHAPTER 15

Page 504

1. The five functions of the respiratory system are providing an extensive surface area for gas exchange between blood and air; moving air to and from gas-exchange surfaces; protecting gas-exchange surfaces from dehydration, temperature changes, and pathogens; producing sounds; and detecting olfactory stimuli. **2.** The respiratory mucosa lines the conducting portion of the respiratory system.

Page 509

3. The surfaces of the nasal cavity are swept by mucus (produced by the respiratory mucosa and the paranasal sinuses) and by tears (carried by the nasolacrimal ducts). **4.** The pharynx is a passageway for both air (respiratory system) and food and liquids (digestive system). **5.** Increased tension in the vocal cords raises the pitch of the voice. **6.** The C-shaped tracheal cartilages allow room for the esophagus to expand when food or drink is swallowed.

Page 514

7. Air passing through the glottis flows into the larynx, through the trachea, and into a primary bronchus, which supplies a lung. In the lung, air passes through bronchi, bronchioles, a terminal bronchiole, a respiratory bronchiole, an alveolar duct, an alveolar sac, an alveolus, and ultimately to the respiratory membrane. **8.** Without surfactant, surface tension in the thin layer of water that moistens alveolar surfaces would cause the alveoli to collapse. **9.** The pleural surfaces (serous membranes) secrete pleural fluid, which lubricates the opposing parietal and visceral surfaces to prevent friction during breathing. **10.** External respiration includes all the processes involved in the exchange of oxygen and carbon dioxide between the body's interstitial fluids and the external environment to meet the respiratory demands of cells. Internal respiration is the absorption of oxygen and the release of carbon dioxide by those cells. **11.** The integrated steps involved in external respiration are pulmonary ventilation (breathing), gas diffusion, and transport of oxygen and carbon dioxide.

Page 518

12. Compliance is the ease with which the lungs expand and contract. Factors affecting compliance include the connective-tissue structure of the lungs, the level of surfactant production, and the mobility of the thoracic cage. **13.** Resting tidal volume is the amount of air you move into and out of your lungs during a single respiratory cycle under resting conditions—about 500 mL for both males and females. **14.** When the rib penetrates the chest wall, atmospheric air enters the thoracic cavity, producing pneumothorax. The ensuing disruption of the fluid bond between the pleurae allows contraction of the elastic fibers in the lung. The result is atelectasis, or a collapsed lung. **15.** The vital capacity would decrease, because the fluid in the alveoli takes up space that would normally be occupied by air.

Page 519

16. True. **17.** Air passing through the nasal cavity becomes warmer and its content of water vapor increases. **18.** Alveolar air contains less oxygen and more carbon dioxide than atmospheric air.

Page 523

19. Carbon dioxide is transported in the bloodstream as carbonic acid, bound to hemoglobin within RBCs, or dissolved in the plasma. **20.** Active

skeletal muscles generate more heat and more acidic waste products that lower the pH of the surrounding fluid. The combination of increased temperature and reduced pH during exercise causes the hemoglobin to release more oxygen than it would at rest. **21.** Blockage of the trachea would lower blood pH by interfering with the body's ability to take in oxygen and eliminate carbon dioxide. The resulting excess carbon dioxide in the blood is converted to carbonic acid, which then dissociates into bicarbonate ions and hydrogen ions, lowering blood pH.

Page 527

22. Peripheral chemoreceptors are more sensitive to carbon dioxide levels than to oxygen levels. **23.** Strenuous exercise stimulates the inflation and deflation reflexes, also known as the Hering-Breuer reflexes. In the inflation reflex, the stimulation of stretch receptors in the lungs results in inhibition of the inspiratory center and stimulation of the expiratory center. In contrast, reducing the volume of the lungs initiates the deflation reflex, resulting in inhibition of the expiratory center and stimulation of the inspiratory center. **24.** Johnny's mother shouldn't worry. While Johnny holds his breath, increasing blood carbon dioxide levels lead to increased stimulation of the inspiratory center, which forces him to breathe again. **25.** Two age-related changes that reduce the efficiency of the respiratory system are (1) reduced chest movements resulting from arthritic changes in rib joints and stiffening of the costal cartilages and (2) some degree of emphysema stemming from the gradual destruction of alveolar surfaces. **26.** The respiratory system provides oxygen and eliminates carbon dioxide for all body systems. **27.** The nervous system controls the pace and depth of respiration and monitors the respiratory volume of the lungs and levels of blood gases.

Level 1: Reviewing Facts and Terms

1. h **2.** f **3.** i **4.** c **5.** b **6.** d **7.** j **8.** e **9.** a **10.** l **11.** g **12.** k **13.** (a) nasal cavity; (b) nasopharynx; (c) right lung; (d) nose; (e) larynx; (f) trachea; (g) right bronchus; (h) bronchioles; (i) left lung **14.** (a) alveolar capillary; (b) respiratory membrane; (c) alveolus; (d) interstitial fluid; (e) systemic capillary. The pink arrows indicate the movements of O_2, and the blue arrows those of CO_2. **15.** c **16.** b

Level 2: Reviewing Concepts

17. a **18.** d **19.** Less cartilage and more smooth muscle in the lower respiratory passageways provide the smooth muscles greater control of bronchial diameter, and thus of resistance to air flow. **20.** Breathing through the nasal cavity ensures that inspired air is cleansed, moistened, and warmed. The drier air that enters through the mouth can irritate the trachea, causing throat soreness. **21.** Smooth muscle tissue in both bronchioles and arterioles controls those structures' diameters. Just as vasodilation and vasoconstriction of the arterioles regulate blood flow and distribution, bronchodilation and bronchoconstriction control the amount of resistance to air flow and the distribution of air in the lungs.

Level 3: Critical Thinking and Clinical Applications

22. An increase in ventilation will increase the movement of venous blood back to the heart. (Recall the respiratory pump.) In turn, increased venous return helps increase blood pressure (according to the Frank-Starling law of the heart). **23.** The air you were breathing while sleeping was so dry that it absorbed more than the normal amount of moisture as it passed through the nasal cavity. The nasal epithelia continued to secrete mucus, but the loss of moisture made the mucus quite viscous, so the cilia had difficulty moving it, causing nasal congestion. After the shower and juice, more moisture was transferred to the mucus, loosening it and making it easier to move—and easing the congestion.

CHAPTER 16

ANSWERS TO CHECKPOINTS

Page 538

1. Organs of the digestive system include the oral cavity (mouth), pharynx, esophagus, stomach, small intestine, large intestine, and accessory organs (salivary glands, pancreas, liver, and gallbladder). **2.** The six primary functions of the digestive system are (a) ingestion, the eating of food; (b) mechanical processing, the chewing of foodstuffs to make them more susceptible to enzymatic attack; (c) digestion, the chemical breakdown of food into smaller products for absorption; (d) secretion, the release of water, acids, and other substances by the epithelium of the digestive tract and by glandular organs; (e) absorption, the movement of digested materials across the digestive epithelium and into the interstitial fluid of the digestive tract; and (f) excretion, the removal of waste products from the body. **3.** The mesenteries support and stabilize the positions of organs in the abdominopelvic cavity and provide a route for the blood vessels, nerves, and lymphatic vessels associated with the digestive tract. **4.** The layers of the digestive tract, beginning with the outermost layer, are the serosa, muscularis externa, submucosa, and mucosa. **5.** Peristalsis is more efficient in propelling intestinal contents down the tract. Segmentation is essentially a churning action that mixes intestinal contents with digestive fluids.

Page 542

6. Structures associated with the oral cavity include the tongue, salivary glands, and teeth. **7.** The oral cavity is lined by a stratified squamous epithelium, which is typical for sites that receive a great deal of friction or abrasion. **8.** The digestion of carbohydrates would be affected by damage to the parotid salivary glands, because these glands secrete salivary amylase, the enzyme that digests complex carbohydrates (starches). **9.** Incisors are the type of tooth best suited for chopping off (or cutting or shearing) pieces of raw vegetables (or any relatively rigid food).

Page 543

10. The pharynx is a passageway that receives food or liquids and passes them on to the esophagus as part of the swallowing process. **11.** The esophagus connects the pharynx to the stomach. **12.** The process being described is swallowing (deglutition).

Page 548

13. The four main regions of the stomach are the cardia, fundus, body, and pylorus. **14.** The low pH in the stomach creates an acidic environment that kills most microbes ingested with food, denatures proteins and inactivates most enzymes in food, helps break down plant cell walls and meat connective tissue, and activates pepsin. **15.** Cutting the branches of the vagus nerves supplying the stomach severs parasympathetic motor fibers that can stimulate gastric secretions even when the stomach is empty (the cephalic phase of gastric secretion). The prevention of parasympathetic secretion reduces the likelihood of new ulcer formation.

Page 552

16. The pyloric sphincter is the ring of muscle that regulates the flow of chyme into the small intestine. **17.** The three segments of the small in-testine are the duodenum, jejunum, and ileum. **18.** The small intestine's absorptive capacity is increased by several features that increase its surface area. Its walls contain folds called plicae circulares, each of which is covered by fingerlike projections called villi. The epithelial cells covering the villi have an exposed surface covered by small fingerlike projections (microvilli). The small intestine also has a very rich supply of blood vessels and lymphatic vessels that transport absorbed nutrients.

Page 557

19. A high-fat meal would increase cholecystokinin (CCK) blood levels. **20.** Damage to the exocrine pancreas would most impair the digestion of fats (lipids) because that organ is the primary source of lipases. **21.** A decrease in the amount of bile salts would reduce the effectiveness of fat digestion and absorption.

Page 561

22. The four segments of the colon are the ascending colon, transverse colon, descending colon, and sigmoid colon. **23.** The large intestine is larger in diameter than the small intestine, but its relatively thin wall lacks villi, and it has an abundance of mucous glands. **24.** A narrowing of the ileocecal valve would interfere with the flow of chyme from the small intestine to the large intestine.

Page 565

25. An increase in the fat content of a meal would increase the number of chylomicrons in the lacteals. **26.** Removal of the stomach would interfere with the absorption of vitamin B_{12}, which requires intrinsic factor, a molecule produced by parietal cells in the stomach. **27.** Diarrhea can be life threatening because the loss of fluid and electrolytes faster than they can be replaced can result in potentially fatal dehydration. Constipation, although uncomfortable, does not interfere with any major body process. The few toxic waste products that are normally eliminated by defecation can move into the blood and be eliminated by the kidneys. **28.** General digestive system changes that occur with age include declines in the rates of stem cell divisions (results in ulcers), decreases in smooth muscle tone (causes reduced tract motility), increases in cumulative damage to other structures or organs, increases in cancer rates, and increases in the occurrence of dehydration. **29.** The digestive system absorbs organic substrates, vitamins, ions, and water needed by cells of all the body's systems. **30.** Digestive system functions related to the cardiovascular system include absorption of water to maintain blood volume; absorption of vitamin K produced by intestinal bacteria (vital to blood clotting); excretion of bilirubin (a breakdown product of the heme portion of hemoglobin) by the liver; and synthesis of blood clotting factors by the liver.

ANSWERS TO REVIEW QUESTIONS

Level 1: Reviewing Facts and Terms

1. c **2.** k **3.** g **4.** a **5.** i **6.** h **7.** j **8.** d **9.** f **10.** b **11.** l **12.** e **13.** d **14.** d **15.** b **16.** c **17.** (a) oral cavity, teeth, tongue; (b) liver; (c) gallbladder; (d) pancreas; (e) large intestine; (f) salivary glands; (g) pharynx; (h) esophagus; (i) stomach; (j) small intestine; (k) anus **18.** b **19.** d **20.** d **21.** (a) mucosa; (b) submucosa; (c) muscularis externa; (d) serosa **22.** a **23.** d **24.** d **25.** The primary digestive functions are ingestion, mechanical processing, secretion, digestion, absorption, and excretion. **26.** The folds increase the surface area available for absorption and may permit expansion of the lumen after a large meal. **27.** The innermost layer, the mucosa, is a mucous membrane consisting of epithelia and loose connective tissue (the lamina propria). The submucosa surrounds the mucosa and contains blood vessels, lymphatic vessels, and neural tissue (the submucosal nerve plexus). The muscularis externa is made up of two layers of smooth muscle tissue—longitudinal and circular, whose contractions agitate and propel materials along the digestive tract—and neural tissue (the myenteric nerve plexus). The outermost layer, the serosa, is a serous membrane that protects and supports the digestive tract inside the peritoneal cavity. **28.** The four primary functions of the oral cavity: (1) analysis of material before swallowing; (2) mechanical processing through the actions of the teeth, tongue, and palatal surfaces; (3) lubrication by mixing with mucus and salivary secretions; and (4) limited digestion of carbohydrates and lipids. **29.** Incisors clip or cut; cuspids tear or slash; bicuspids crush, mash, or grind; and molars crush and grind. **30.** The three segments of the small intestine are the duodenum, jejunum, and ileum. **31.** The pancreas produces digestive enzymes as well as buffers that assist in the neutralization of acidic chyme. The liver produces bile—a solution that contains additional buffers and bile salts that facilitate the digestion and absorption of lipids—and the gallbladder stores and concentrates it. The liver is also responsible for metabolic regulation and is the primary organ involved in regulating the composition of the circulating blood. **32.** The three major functions of the large intestine are (1) reabsorption of water and compaction of chyme into feces; (2) absorption of important vitamins generated by bacterial action; and (3) storage of fecal material prior to defecation. **33.** Age-related changes that occur in the digestive system are (1) the rate of epithelial stem cell division declines; (2) smooth muscle tone decreases; (3) the effects of cumulative damage become apparent; (4) cancer rates increase; (5) dehydration is more common; and (6) changes in other systems have direct or indirect effects on the digestive system.

Level 2: Reviewing Concepts

34. d **35.** d **36.** a **37.** Peristalsis consists of waves of muscular contractions that move along the length of the digestive tract. During a peristaltic movement, the circular muscles contract behind the digestive contents. The longitudinal muscles contract next, shortening adjacent segments. A wave of contraction in the circular muscles then forces the contents in the desired direction. Segmentation movements churn and fragment the digestive contents, mixing them with intestinal secretions. Because they do not follow a set pattern, segmentation movements do not produce directional movement of materials along the tract. **38.** The stomach performs four major digestive functions: bulk storage of ingested food, mechanical breakdown of ingested food, disruption of chemical bonds in the food through the actions of acids and enzymes, and production of intrinsic factor. **39.** The cephalic phase begins with the sight or thought of food. Directed by the CNS, this phase prepares the stomach to receive food. The gastric phase, which begins with the arrival of food in the stomach, is initiated by distension of the stomach, an increase in the pH of the gastric contents, and the presence of undigested materials in the stomach. The intestinal phase begins when chyme starts to enter the small intestine. This phase controls the rate of gastric emptying and ensures that the secretory, digestive, and absorptive functions of the small intestine can proceed efficiently.

Level 3: Critical Thinking and Clinical Applications

40. If the gallstones are small enough, they can pass through the common bile duct and block the pancreatic duct, preventing pancreatic enzymes from reaching the small intestine. As the enzymes accumulate in the pancreas, they irritate the duct and ultimately the exocrine pancreas, producing pancreatitis. **41.** The small intestine, especially the jejunum

and ileum, are likely involved. Barb's abdominal pain results from regional inflammation. Because inflamed intestines cannot absorb nutrients, she is deficient in iron and vitamin B_{12}, which are necessary for formation of hemoglobin and red blood cells; this accounts for her anemia. The underabsorption of other nutrients accounts for Barb's weight loss.

CHAPTER 17

ANSWERS TO CHECKPOINTS

Page 577

1. Metabolism is the sum of all the chemical processes under way within the body; it includes anabolism and catabolism. **2.** Catabolism is the breakdown of complex organic molecules into simpler components; it is accompanied by the release of energy. **3.** Anabolism is the synthesis of complex organic compounds from simpler precursor molecules; it requires an input of energy.

Page 582

4. The primary role of the TCA cycle is to transfer electrons from organic substrates to coenzymes for use in the electron transport system, where the electrons provide an energy source for the production of ATP. **5.** The binding of hydrogen cyanide molecules to the final cytochrome of the ETS would prevent the transfer of electrons to oxygen. As a result, cells would be unable to produce ATP in the mitochondria and would die from energy starvation. **6.** Gluconeogenesis is the synthesis of glucose from noncarbohydrate precursor molecules, such as lactic acid, lipids, and proteins.

Page 584

7. Lipolysis is the chemical breakdown of lipids. **8.** Beta-oxidation is fatty acid catabolism that produces molecules of acetyl-CoA. **9.** HDLs are considered beneficial because they reduce the amount of cholesterol in the bloodstream by transporting it to the liver for storage or for excretion in the bile.

Page 586

10. Transamination is a process in amino acid metabolism and protein synthesis in which one amino acid is formed from another. **11.** Deamination is the removal of an amino group from an amino acid. **12.** A vitamin B_6 (pyridoxine) deficiency would interfere with protein metabolism because this vitamin is an important coenzyme in the processes of deamination and transamination, the first steps in the processing of amino acids.

Page 587

13. DNA is never catabolized for energy because the genetic information it contains is essential to the long-term survival of a cell. **14.** Nitrogenous wastes are metabolic waste products, such as urea and uric acid, that contain nitrogen atoms. **15.** Elevated blood uric acid levels could indicate increased breakdown of nucleic acids, because uric acid is produced when the nucleotides adenine and guanine are degraded.

Page 593

16. The two types of vitamins are fat-soluble and water-soluble vitamins. **17.** Foods containing complete proteins contain all the essential amino acids in nutritionally required amounts; foods containing incomplete proteins are deficient in one or more essential amino acids. **18.** A decrease in the amount of bile salts in the bile would reduce vitamin A absorption from food, because bile salts are necessary for the absorption (and digestion) of fats and fat-soluble vitamins, including vitamin A. Eventually, vitamin A deficiency could result.

Page 595

19. A pregnant woman's BMR would be higher than her own BMR when she is not pregnant because (a) her metabolic activity increases to support the fetus, and (b) fetal metabolism adds to her BMR. **20.** Evaporation is ineffective as a cooling mechanism when the relative humidity is high (when the air is holding large amounts of water vapor). **21.** Vasoconstriction of peripheral vessels would cause body temperature to rise because decreased blood flow to the skin reduces the amount of heat the body can lose to the environment.

Page 596

22. Only caloric requirements change with aging. Caloric requirements generally decrease after age 50 because of associated reductions in metabolic rates, body mass, activity levels, and exercise tolerance.

ANSWERS TO REVIEW QUESTIONS

Level 1: Reviewing Facts and Terms

1. a **2.** g **3.** l **4.** i **5.** j **6.** b **7.** k **8.** e **9.** f **10.** d **11.** h **12.** c **13.** d **14.** c **15.** a **16.** b **17.** c **18.** c **19.** (a) fatty acids; (b) glucose; (c) amino acids; (d) small carbon chains; (e) TCA cycle; (f) CO_2; (g) ATP; (h) electron transport system; (i) H_2O **20.** d **21.** c **22.** b **23.** c **24.** b **25.** a **26.** Metabolism is all of the chemical reactions occurring in the cells of the body. Anabolism is the set of chemical reactions that convert simple reactant molecules into complex molecules needed for maintenance/repair, growth, and secretion. Catabolism is the breakdown of complex molecules into their building block molecules, resulting in the release of energy for the synthesis of ATP and related molecules. **27.** Lipoproteins are lipid–protein complexes consisting of large insoluble glycerides and cholesterol coated with phospholipids and proteins. The major groups are (a) chylomicrons (the largest lipoproteins), which are 95 percent triglyceride and carry absorbed lipids from the intestinal tract to the circulation; (b) low-density lipoproteins (LDLs), which are mostly cholesterol and deliver cholesterol to peripheral tissues (because they can be deposited within arteries, LDLs are also known as "bad cholesterol"); and (c) high-density lipoproteins (HDLs, also called "good cholesterol"), which contain equal parts protein and lipid (phospholipids and cholesterol) and transport excess cholesterol to the liver for storage or excretion in the bile. **28.** Most vitamins and all minerals are essential (must be provided in the diet) because the body cannot synthesize these nutrients. **29.** Carbohydrates yield 4.18 Cal/g; lipids yield 9.46 Cal/g; and proteins yield 4.32 Cal/g. **30.** The BMR is the minimum, resting energy expenditures of an awake, alert person. **31.** The processes of heat transfer are (a) radiation: heat loss as infrared waves; (b) conduction: heat loss to surfaces in physical contact; (c) convection: heat loss to the air; and (d) evaporation: heat loss when water evaporates to a gas.

Level 2: Reviewing Concepts

32. d **33.** b **34.** Glycolysis is a series of enzymatic steps that converts glucose to 2 pyruvic acid molecules plus 4 ATP and 2 NADH molecules. Glycolysis requires glucose; specific cytoplasmic enzymes; ATP and ADP; inorganic phosphates; and NAD (nicotinamide adenine dinucleotide), a coenzyme. **35.** A two-carbon acetyl group (carried by acetyl-CoA) enters the cycle by joining to a four-carbon compound, and CO_2, NADH, ATP,

and $FADH_2$ leave it. The TCA reaction sequence is considered a cycle because the four-carbon starting compound is regenerated at the end. **36.** When a triglyceride is hydrolyzed, glycerol and fatty acids are liberated. The glycerol is converted to pyruvic acid and enters the TCA cycle, and beta-oxidation (which occurs inside mitochondria) breaks the fatty acids into two-carbon compounds that also enter the TCA cycle. **37.** The MyPyramid Plan indicates the relative amounts of each of the five basic food groups an individual should consume each day to ensure adequate intake of nutrients and calories. It also is a reminder that daily physical activity is an important aspect of weight control. **38.** The brain region called the hypothalamus acts as the body's "thermostat" by regulating ANS control (through negative feedback) of such homeostatic mechanisms as sweating and shivering thermogenesis. **39.** "Good cholesterol" and "bad cholesterol" refer to HDL and LDL, respectively, which are lipoproteins that transport cholesterol in the blood. HDL transports excess cholesterol to the liver for storage or breakdown, whereas LDL transports cholesterol to peripheral tissues—including, unfortunately, arteries, where the buildup of cholesterol is linked to cardiovascular disease.

Level 3: Critical Thinking and Clinical Applications

40. During starvation, the body must use its fat and protein reserves to supply the energy needed to sustain life. Among the proteins metabolized for energy are antibodies in the blood. The loss of antibodies coupled with a scarcity of amino acids needed to synthesize replacement antibodies, as well as protective molecules such as interferon and complement proteins, renders an individual more susceptible to contracting diseases, and less likely to recover from them. **41.** Based just on the information given, Charlie would appear to be in good health, at least relative to his diet and probable exercise. Problems are associated with elevated levels of LDLs, which carry cholesterol to peripheral tissues and make it available for the formation of atherosclerotic plaques in blood vessels. High levels of HDLs indicate that a considerable amount of cholesterol is being removed from the peripheral tissues and carried to the liver for disposal. You would encourage Charlie not to change, and keep up the good work.

CHAPTER 18

ANSWERS TO CHECKPOINTS

Page 602

1. The primary functions of the urinary system are (a) excretion of organic wastes from body fluids, (b) elimination of body wastes to the exterior, and (c) regulation of homeostasis by maintaining the volume and solute concentration of blood plasma. **2.** The urinary system consists of two kidneys, two ureters, a bladder, and a urethra. **3.** Micturition, or urination, is the elimination of urine from the body.

Page 609

4. Unlike most other organs in the abdominal region, the kidneys lie behind the peritoneal lining (are retroperitoneal). **5.** Plasma proteins do not normally pass into the capsular space because they are too large to pass through the filtration slits between the processes of the podocytes. **6.** Damage to the juxtaglomerular complex would interfere with the hormonal control of blood pressure.

Page 613

7. A decrease in blood pressure would decrease the GFR by reducing blood hydrostatic pressure within the glomerulus. **8.** If nephrons lacked nephron loops—the ascending limb of which pumps Na^+ and Cl^- out of the filtrate, and the descending limb of which is the site of osmotic flow of water from the filtrate—then there could be no concentration gradient in the renal medulla. As a result, less water would be reabsorbed and the production of concentrated urine would not be possible. **9.** Low circulating levels of ADH would result in a larger volume of dilute urine, because little water will be reabsorbed at the DCT and collecting duct.

Page 617

10. The glomerular filtration rate (GFR) depends on the filtration pressure across glomerular capillaries, and is stabilized by interactions among local autoregulation, ANS regulation, and hormonal regulation. **11.** Sympathetic activation produces vasoconstriction of the afferent arterioles, which decreases the GFR. **12.** Increased amounts of aldosterone would increase the K^+ concentration in urine.

Page 620

13. Peristaltic contractions move urine from the kidneys to the urinary bladder. **14.** Obstruction of a ureter would interfere with the passage of urine from the renal pelvis to the urinary bladder. **15.** Control of the micturition reflex requires the ability to control the external urinary sphincter, a ring of skeletal muscle that acts as a valve.

Page 622

16. The three interrelated processes essential to stabilizing body fluid volume are fluid balance, electrolyte balance, and acid-base balance. **17.** The sole component of the ICF is the cytosol; the major components of the ECF are interstitial fluid, plasma, and other body fluids.

Page 624

18. A fluid shift is a rapid movement of water between the ECF and ICF in response to an osmotic gradient. **19.** Eating a meal high in salt would cause a reduction of fluid in the ICF. Because the ingested salt would temporarily increase the osmolarity of the ECF, water would shift from the ICF to the ECF. **20.** Being in the desert without water would cause the osmotic concentration of your plasma (and other body fluids) to increase, due to fluid losses through perspiration, urine formation, and respiration.

Page 628

21. The body's three major buffer systems are protein buffer systems, the carbonic acid-bicarbonate buffer system, and the phosphate buffer system. **22.** A decrease in the pH of body fluids would stimulate the respiratory centers in the medulla oblongata to increase the breathing rate. As a result, more CO_2 is eliminated, and pH rises. **23.** In a prolonged fast, catabolism of fatty acids produces acidic ketone bodies, which lower body pH. The eventual result is called ketoacidosis. **24.** Aging reduces GFR due to a loss of nephrons, cumulative damage to the filtration mechanism within remaining glomeruli, and reduced blood flow to the kidneys. **25.** After age 40, total body water content gradually decreases.

Page 629

26. The body's excretory system is made up of the urinary, integumentary, respiratory, and digestive systems.

ANSWERS TO REVIEW QUESTIONS

Level 1: Reviewing Facts and Terms

1. q **2.** g **3.** n **4.** j **5.** a **6.** m **7.** e **8.** p **9.** d **10.** f **11.** h **12.** k **13.** b **14.** c **15.** l **16.** o **17.** i **18.** (a) renal sinus; (b) nephron loop; (c) proximal convoluted tubule; (d) distal convoluted tubule; (e) collecting duct **19.** c **20.** d **21.** a **22.** d **23.** (a) renal corpuscle; (b) renal pelvis; (c) hilum; (d) renal papilla; (e) ureter; (f) renal cortex; (g) renal medulla; (h) renal pyramid; (i) minor calyx; (j) major calyx; (k) renal lobe; (l) renal columns; (m) fibrous capsule **24.** c **25.** c **26.** b **27.** d **28.** The urinary system performs vital excretory functions and eliminates organic waste products generated by cells throughout the body. **29.** The urinary system includes the kidneys, ureters, urinary bladder, and urethra. **30.** Fluid shifts are water movements between the ECF and ICF that occur in response to increases or decreases in the osmotic concentration (osmolarity) of the ECF. Such water movements dampen extreme shifts in electrolyte balance. Causes of osmolarity changes include water loss (excessive perspiration, dehydration, vomiting, or diarrhea), water gain (ingestion of pure water, administration of hypotonic solutions through an IV), and changes in electrolyte concentrations (such as sodium). **31.** The three major hormones involved in fluid and electrolyte balance are ADH, which stimulates the thirst center and water conservation at the kidneys; aldosterone, which determines the rate of sodium absorption along the DCT and collecting system; and ANP, which reduces thirst and blocks the release of ADH and aldosterone.

Level 2: Reviewing Concepts

32. d **33.** c **34.** a **35.** b **36.** a **37.** The controls that stabilize GFR are autoregulation at the local level, hormonal regulation initiated by the kidneys, and autonomic regulation (by the sympathetic division of the ANS). **38.** The micturition reflex typically begins when the bladder contains about 200 mL of urine, at which time stretch receptors provide adequate stimulation to parasympathetic motor neurons. Efferent impulses in the motor neurons travel over the pelvic nerves and generate action potentials in the smooth muscle in the bladder wall, producing a sustained contraction of the urinary bladder. Voluntary relaxation of the external sphincter muscle also relaxes the involuntary internal sphincter muscle allowing urine to pass through the urethra to the exterior. **39.** Fluid balance is a state in which the amount of water gained each day equals the amount lost to the environment. Electrolyte balance exists when there is neither a net gain nor a net loss of any ion in body fluids. Acid-base balance exists when hydrogen ion (H^+) production precisely offsets H^+ losses. These balances are needed to keep fluids, electrolytes, and pH within their relatively narrow normal ranges, for variations outside these ranges can be life threatening. **40.** "Drink plenty of fluids" is physiologically sound advice, because for every degree body temperature rises above normal, daily water loss increases by 200 mL. **41.** Sweat is usually hypotonic, so loss of a large volume of sweat causes hypertonicity in body fluids. Fluid is lost primarily from the interstitial space, which leads to a reduction in plasma volume and an increase in the hematocrit. Severe dehydration causes blood viscosity to increase substantially, increasing the workload on the heart, and ultimately increasing the probability of heart failure.

Level 3: Critical Thinking and Clinical Applications

42. By resisting the urge to urinate, long-haul truck drivers may not urinate as frequently as they should. The pressure this puts on kidney tissues can lead to tissue death, and ultimately to kidney failure. **43.** The fever and burning sensation suggest that Susan may have a urinary tract infection; her urine may contain blood cells and bacteria. Because in females the urethra is relatively short, and the urethral orifice is close to the anus and opens near the vagina, bacteria in the anus and vagina can easily reach the urethral orifice (often during sexual intercourse). **44.** Drinking a mannitol solution would increase the volume of urine produced. Because this sugar is filtered but not reabsorbed, the osmolarity of the filtrate would increase, and less water would be absorbed (removed) from the filtrate.

CHAPTER 19

ANSWERS TO CHECKPOINTS

Page 639

1. A gamete is a functional male or female reproductive cell. **2.** Basic components of the human reproductive system are gonads (reproductive organs), ducts (which receive and transport gametes), accessory glands (which secrete fluids), and external genitalia (perineal structures). **3.** Gonads are reproductive organs that produce gametes and hormones.

Page 649

4. Male reproductive structures are the scrotum, testes, epididymides, ductus deferens, ejaculatory duct, urethra, seminal glands (seminal vesicles), prostate gland, bulbo-urethral glands, and penis. **5.** On a warm day, the cremaster muscle (as well as the dartos muscle) would be relaxed, so that the scrotal sac could descend away from the body and cool the testes. **6.** When arteries within the penis dilate, the increased blood flow causes the vascular channels to engorge with blood, producing an erection. **7.** Low FSH levels would lead to low levels of testosterone in the seminiferous tubules, reducing both the sperm production rate and sperm count.

Page 660

8. Structures of the female reproductive system are the ovaries, uterine tubes, uterus, vagina, and mammary glands. **9.** Blockage of both uterine tubes would eliminate the ability to conceive, resulting in sterility. **10.** The acidic pH of the vagina helps prevent bacterial, fungal, and parasitic infections within this structure. **11.** The functional layer of the endometrium sloughs off during menstruation. **12.** Blockage of a single lactiferous sinus would have little effect on the delivery of milk to the nipple because each breast usually has 15–20 lactiferous sinuses. **13.** If the LH surge did not occur during an ovarian cycle, ovulation and the subsequent formation of a corpus luteum would not occur. **14.** Blockage of progesterone receptors in the uterus would inhibit the development of the endometrium, leaving the uterus unprepared for pregnancy. **15.** Declines in estrogen and progesterone levels signal the end of the uterine cycle and the beginning of menses.

Page 661

16. The physiological events of sexual intercourse in both sexes are arousal, erection, lubrication, orgasm, and detumescence; emission and ejaculation are additional phases that occur only in males. **17.** An inability to contract the ischiocavernosus and bulbospongiosus muscles would interfere with a male's ability to ejaculate and to experience orgasm. **18.** Parasympathetic stimulation in females during sexual arousal causes engorgement of the erectile tissue of the clitoris, increased secretion of cervical and vaginal glands, increased blood flow to the wall of the vagina, and engorgement of the blood vessels in the nipples.

Page 662

19. Menopause is the time that ovulation and menstruation cease, typically around ages 45–55. **20.** At menopause, declining levels of circulating estrogens—which have inhibitory effects on FSH—result in FSH levels that rise and remain high. **21.** The male climacteric, or andropause, is a period of declining reproductive function in men, typically between ages 50 and 60.

Page 663

22. The integumentary system covers the external genitalia; sensory receptors in the skin detect sensations that stimulate sexual behaviors; and the mammary glands provide nourishment for the infant. The reproductive system produces hormones (primarily, testosterone in males and estrogens in females) that affect secondary sex characteristics such as the distribution of hair and subcutaneous fat deposits. **23.** Pelvic bones protect reproductive organs in females, and portions of the ductus deferens and accessory glands in males; sex hormones stimulate growth and maintenance of bone, and accelerate growth and closure of epiphyseal cartilages at puberty.

ANSWERS TO REVIEW QUESTIONS

Level 1: Reviewing Facts and Terms

1. i **2.** m **3.** a **4.** c **5.** l **6.** e **7.** n **8.** o **9.** h **10.** b **11.** f **12.** j **13.** d **14.** k **15.** g **16.** c **17.** a **18.** c **19.** a **20.** d **21.** a **22.** (a) urethra; (b) ductus deferens; (c) penis; (d) epididymis; (e) testis; (f) scrotum; (g) seminal gland; (h) prostate gland; (i) ejaculatory duct; (j) bulbo-urethral gland **23.** (a) ovary; (b) uterine tube; (c) greater vestibular gland; (d) clitoris; (e) labium minus; (f) labium majus; (g) uterus; (h) fornix; (i) cervix; (j) vagina **24.** c **25.** c **26.** d **27.** b **28.** c **29.** d **30.** The accessory organs and glands in males include the seminal glands, prostate gland, and the bulbo-urethral glands. These structures activate spermatozoa, provide nutrients sperm need for motility, propel sperm and fluids along the reproductive tract, and produce buffers that counteract the acidity of the urethral and vaginal contents. **31.** The epididymis monitors and adjusts the composition of the tubular fluid, acts as a recycling center for damaged spermatozoa, and stores spermatozoa and facilitates their functional maturation. **32.** The ovaries produce female gametes (ova); secrete female sex hormones, including estrogens and progestins; and secrete inhibin, involved in the feedback control of pituitary FSH production. **33.** The vagina serves as passageway for the elimination of menstrual fluids, receives the penis during sexual intercourse, holds spermatozoa prior to their passage into the uterus, and forms the lower portion of the birth canal through which the fetus passes during delivery.

Level 2: Reviewing Concepts

34. The reproductive system is the only organ system that is not required for the survival of the individual. **35.** Meiosis is the two-step nuclear division resulting in the formation of four haploid cells from one diploid cell. In males, four sperm are produced from each diploid cell, whereas in females only one ovum (plus two or three polar bodies) is produced from each diploid cell. **36.** The first phase, menses (days 1–7), is marked by the degeneration and loss of the functional zone of the endometrium; approximately 35–50 mL of blood is lost. In the proliferative phase (end of menses until the beginning of ovulation around day 14), growth and vascularization result in the complete restoration of the functional zone. In the secretory phase (begins at ovulation and persists as long as the corpus luteum remains intact), the combined stimulatory effects of progestins and estrogens from the corpus luteum cause uterine (endometrial) glands to enlarge and secrete more quickly, and arteries to elongate and spiral through the tissues of the functional zone. **37.** The corpus luteum degenerates, and a decline in progesterone and estrogen levels results in endometrial breakdown (menses). Next, rising FSH, LH, and estrogen levels stimulate the repair and regeneration of the functional zone of the endometrium. During the postovulatory phase, the combination of estrogen and progesterone causes enlargement of the uterine (endometrial) glands and an increase in their secretory activity. **38.** In women, menopause—the time when ovulation and menstruation cease—is accompanied by a sharp and sustained rise in GnRH, FSH, and LH production, while concentrations of circulating estrogens and progesterone decline. Reduced estrogen levels lead to reductions in uterus and breast size, accompanied by a thinning of the urethral and vaginal walls. Reduced estrogen concentrations have also been linked to the development of osteoporosis, presumably because bone deposition proceeds more slowly. During the male climacteric, typically between ages 50 and 60, circulating testosterone levels begin to decline while circulating FSH and LH levels increase. Although sperm production continues in older men, a gradual reduction in sexual activity occurs.

Level 3: Critical Thinking and Clinical Applications

39. Women more frequently experience peritonitis stemming from a urinary tract infection because infectious organisms exiting the urethral orifice can readily enter the nearby vagina. From there, they can then proceed to the uterus, into the uterine tubes, and finally into the peritoneal cavity. No such direct path of entry into the abdominopelvic cavity exists in men. **40.** Damage to the sacral region of the spinal cord, which contains parasympathetic centers that control the genitals, would interfere with the ability to achieve an erection by way of parasympathetic stimuli; tactile stimulation of the penis would not generate an erection. However, erection can also occur when visual, auditory, or cerebral stimuli activate sympathetic centers in the lower thoracic region of the spinal cord; the resulting decreased tone in the arteries serving the penis increases blood flow and produces an erection. **41.** These observations suggest that a certain amount of body fat is necessary for menstrual cycles to occur. The nervous system appears to respond to circulating levels of the adipose tissue hormone leptin; when leptin levels fall below a certain set point, menstruation ceases. Because a woman lacking adequate fat reserves might not be able to have a successful pregnancy, the body prevents pregnancy by shutting down the ovarian cycle, and thus the menstrual cycle. Once sufficient energy reserves become available, the cycles begin again.

CHAPTER 20

Page 673

1. Differentiation is the formation of different types of cells during development. **2.** Development begins at fertilization (conception), the union of an oocyte and sperm. **3.** Inheritance refers to the transfer of genetically determined characteristics from one generation to the next.

Page 675

4. Hyaluronidase released from dozens of spermatozoa breaks down the connections between the follicular cells of the corona radiata; another acrosomal enzyme, released after the binding of a single spermatozoon to the zona pellucida, digests a path through the zona pellucida to the oocyte membrane. **5.** A normal zygote contains 46 chromosomes. **6.** Gestation is the period of prenatal development; it consists of three trimesters. **7.** The first trimester is the period of embryological and early fetal development. During the second trimester, organs and organ systems develop, and the fetus takes on a distinctly human appearance. The third trimester is characterized by rapid fetal growth and the deposition of adipose tissue.

Page 682

8. The inner cell mass of the blastocyst eventually develops into the embryo. **9.** Yes, Sue is pregnant. The hCG detected by the test was produced by the developing trophoblast and/or the placenta. **10.** The placenta (1) supplies the developing fetus with a route for gas exchange, nutrient transfer, and waste product elimination and (2) produces hormones that affect maternal systems.

Page 688

11. The major changes that occur in maternal systems during pregnancy include increases in respiratory rate, tidal volume, blood volume, nutrient requirements, glomerular filtration rate, and size of uterus and mammary glands. **12.** A pregnant woman's blood volume increases in response to the release of renin and EPO stimulated by (a) a reduction in her blood volume due to blood flow through the placenta and (b) the presence in the maternal circulation of carbon dioxide produced by the fetus. **13.** Decreased progesterone levels in late pregnancy would remove that hormone's inhibition of uterine contractions, which could stimulate labor. **14.** The uterus increases in size and weight during gestation through enlargement of uterine cells, primarily smooth muscle cells of the myometrium.

Page 690

15. The three stages of labor are the dilation stage, expulsion stage, and placental stage. **16.** Immature delivery is the birth of a fetus weighing at least 500 g (17.6 oz), which is the normal weight near the end of the second trimester. Premature delivery usually refers to birth at 28–36 weeks at a weight over 1 kg (2.2 pounds). **17.** Fraternal twins are dizygotic, and identical twins are monozygotic.

Page 692

18. The postnatal stages of development are the neonatal period, infancy, childhood, adolescence, maturity, and senescence. **19.** Colostrum is produced by the mammary glands from the end of the sixth month of pregnancy until a few days after birth. After that, the glands begin producing breast milk, which contains fewer proteins (including antibodies) and far more fat than colostrum. **20.** Increases in the blood levels of GnRH, FSH, LH, and sex hormones mark the onset of puberty.

Page 697

21. Genotype is a person's genetic makeup; in contrast, phenotype—a person's visible physical characteristics—results from the interaction between the person's genotype and the environment. **22.** A person who is heterozygous for curly hair would have one dominant ("curly hair") gene and one recessive gene. The person's phenotype would be "curly hair." **23.** I'd tell Joe that if his lack of sons is anyone's "fault," it's his. The sex of each of his children depends on the genetic makeup of the sperm cell that fertilizes his wife's oocyte, because only males—being XY—can provide a gamete containing a Y chromosome. **24.** A genome is the full complement of an organism's genetic material (DNA). One Mb is equal to 1 million base pairs, so the 3200 Mb of the human genome represents 3,200,000,000 base pairs.

Level 1: Reviewing Facts and Terms

1. g **2.** a **3.** c **4.** e **5.** d **6.** n **7.** p **8.** b **9.** o **10.** j **11.** f **12.** h **13.** k **14.** l **15.** m **16.** i **17.** a **18.** b **19.** d **20.** (a) umbilical cord; (b) placenta; (c) amniotic cavity; (d) amnion; (e) chorion **21.** d **22.** a **23.** b **24.** d **25.** b **26.** The four extraembryonic membranes are the yolk sac, amnion, allantois, and chorion. **27.** The first stage of labor, the dilation stage, begins with the onset of true labor; the cervix dilates and the fetus begins to slide down the cervical canal. Late in this stage, the amnion usually ruptures. The expulsion stage begins as the cervix dilates completely and continues until the fetus has completely emerged from the vagina (delivery). In the placental stage, the uterus gradually contracts, tearing the connections between the endometrium and the placenta and ejecting the placenta. **28.** During the neonatal period (birth to 1 month), newborns become relatively self-sufficient and begin to breathe, digest, and excrete for themselves. Heart rates and fluid requirements are higher than those of adults. Neonates have little ability to thermoregulate. During infancy (1 month to 2 years), nonreproductive organ systems become fully operational and start to take on the functional characteristics of adult systems. Daily, even hourly, variations in body temperature continue throughout childhood. During childhood (2 years to puberty), children continue to grow, and significant changes in body proportions occur.

Level 2: Reviewing Concepts

29. d **30.** d **31.** The placenta produces human chorionic gonadotropin (HCG), which maintains the integrity of the corpus luteum and promotes the continued secretion of progesterone (keeping the endometrial lining functional); human placental lactogen (HPL) and placental prolactin, which help prepare the mammary glands for milk production; and relaxin, which increases the flexibility of the symphysis pubis, causes dilation of the cervix, and suppresses the release of oxytocin by the hypothalamus, delaying the onset of labor contractions. **32.** The mother's respiratory rate and tidal volume increase, so that her lungs can meet the fetus's oxygen needs and remove the carbon dioxide it generates. Maternal blood volume increases compensate for blood that will be lost during delivery. Nutrient and vitamin requirements climb 10–30 percent in order to nourish the fetus, and glomerular filtration rate increases by about 50 percent, reflecting increased maternal blood volume and the need to excrete fetal metabolic wastes. **33.** Positive feedback ensures that labor contractions continue until delivery is complete. **34.** "Having one's water break" refers to rupture of the amnion, gener-

ally late in the dilation stage of labor. **35.** The trait is (a) dominant (b) recessive (c) X-linked (d) autosomal. **36.** More men are color-blind than women because the gene for this trait is on the X chromosome. Because men have only one X chromosome, whichever allele is on the X chromosome determines whether a man is color blind or has normal vision. Women have two X chromosomes, so they will be color blind only if they are homozygous recessive. This is an example of X-linked inheritance. **37.** The goal of the Human Genome Project was to identify the genetic composition of a "typical" human being. The project will help identify the genes responsible for inherited disorders and their locations on specific chromosomes. Other benefits include gaining an understanding of the genetic basis of diseases such as cancer, and why the effectiveness of drugs varies among individuals.

Level 3: Critical Thinking and Clinical Applications

38. None of the couple's daughters will be hemophiliacs, because each will receive a normal allele from her father. There is a 50 percent chance that a son will be hemophiliac because there is a 50 percent chance of receiving either the mother's normal allele or her recessive allele. **39.** Adults' larger body sizes are precisely why their heart and respiratory rates are lower. Because neonates have a high surface-area-to-volume ratio, they lose heat very quickly; to maintain a constant body temperature in the face of this heat loss, cellular metabolic rates must be high. Because cellular metabolism requires oxygen, high metabolic rates require an elevated respiratory rate. Cardiac output must then increase to move blood between the lungs and peripheral tissues. Because stroke volume cannot change much in neonatal hearts, an increase in cardiac output is achieved by increasing heart rate. **40.** The baby's condition is almost certainly not the result of a viral infection or any other event during the third trimester, because all organ systems are fully formed before the end of the second trimester.

APPENDIX 1   Periodic Table of the Elements

The periodic table presents the known elements in order of their atomic weights. Each horizontal row represents a single electron shell. The number of elements in that row is determined by the maximum number of electrons that can be stored at that energy level. The element at the left end of each row contains a single electron in its outermost electron shell; the element at the right end of the row has a filled outer electron shell. Organizing the elements in this fashion highlights similarities that reflect the composition of the outer electron shell. These similarities are evident when you examine the vertical columns. All the gases of the right-most column—helium, neon, argon, krypton, xenon, and radon—have full elec-tron shells; each is a gas at normal atmospheric temperature and pressure, and none reacts readily with other elements. These elements, highlighted in blue, are known as the *noble,* or *inert, gases*. In contrast, the elements of the left-most column below hydrogen—lithium, sodium, potassium, rubidium, cesium, and fran-cium—are silvery, soft metals that are so highly reactive that pure forms cannot be found in nature. The fourth and fifth electron levels can hold up to 18 elec-trons. Table inserts are used for the so-called *lanthanide and actinide series* to save space, as higher levels can store up to 32 electrons. Elements of particular impor-tance to our discussion of human anatomy and physiology are highlighted in pink.

Atomic number — 1 — Chemical symbol
H
Hydrogen — Element name
Atomic weight — 1.01

1 H Hydrogen 1.01																		2 He Helium 4.00
3 Li Lithium 6.94	4 Be Beryllium 9.01											5 B Boron 10.81	6 C Carbon 12.01	7 N Nitrogen 14.01	8 O Oxygen 16.00	9 F Fluorine 19.00	10 Ne Neon 20.18	
11 Na Sodium 22.99	12 Mg Magnesium 24.31											13 Al Aluminum 26.98	14 Si Silicon 28.09	15 P Phosphorus 30.97	16 S Sulfur 32.07	17 Cl Chlorine 35.45	18 Ar Argon 39.95	
19 K Potassium 39.10	20 Ca Calcium 40.08	21 Sc Scandium 44.96	22 Ti Titanium 47.88	23 V Vanadium 50.94	24 Cr Chromium 52.00	25 Mn Manganese 54.94	26 Fe Iron 55.85	27 Co Cobalt 58.93	28 Ni Nickel 58.69	29 Cu Copper 63.55	30 Zn Zinc 65.39	31 Ga Gallium 69.72	32 Ge Germanium 72.61	33 As Arsenic 74.92	34 Se Selenium 78.96	35 Br Bromine 79.90	36 Kr Krypton 83.80	
37 Rb Rubidium 85.47	38 Sr Strontium 87.62	39 Y Yttrium 88.91	40 Zr Zirconium 91.22	41 Nb Niobium 92.91	42 Mo Molybdenum 95.94	43 Tc Technetium (98)	44 Ru Ruthenium 101.07	45 Rh Rhodium 102.91	46 Pd Palladium 106.42	47 Ag Silver 107.87	48 Cd Cadmium 112.41	49 In Indium 114.82	50 Sn Tin 118.71	51 Sb Antimony 121.76	52 Te Tellurium 127.60	53 I Iodine 126.90	54 Xe Xenon 131.29	
55 Cs Cesium 132.91	56 Ba Barium 137.33	57 La* Lanthanum 138.91	72 Hf Hafnium 178.49	73 Ta Tantalum 180.95	74 W Tungsten 183.85	75 Re Rhenium 186.21	76 Os Osmium 190.2	77 Ir Iridium 192.22	78 Pt Platinum 195.08	79 Au Gold 196.97	80 Hg Mercury 200.59	81 Tl Thallium 204.38	82 Pb Lead 207.2	83 Bi Bismuth 208.98	84 Po Polonium (209)	85 At Astatine (210)	86 Rn Radon (222)	
87 Fr Francium (223)	88 Ra Radium 226.03	89 Ac† Actinium 227.03	104 Rf Rutherfordium (266)	105 Db Dubnium (262)	106 Sg Seaborgium (266)	107 Bh Bohrium (264)	108 Hs Hassium (269)	109 Mt Meitnerium (268)	110 DS Darmstadtium (271)	111 Rg Roentgenium (272)	112 Uub (277)	113 Uut (284)	114 Uuq (285)	115 Uup (288)	116 Uuh (291)		118 Uuo (294)	

57 La 138.91	*Lanthanide series	58 Ce Cerium 140.12	59 Pr Praseo-dymium 140.91	60 Nd Neodymium 144.24	61 Pm Promethium (145)	62 Sm Samarium 150.36	63 Eu Europium 151.96	64 Gd Gadolinium 157.25	65 Tb Terbium 158.93	66 Dy Dysprosium 162.50	67 Ho Holmium 164.93	68 Er Erbium 167.26	69 Tm Thulium 168.93	70 Yb Ytterbium 173.05	71 Lu Lutetium 174.97
89 Ac 227	†Actinide series	90 Th Thorium 232.04	91 Pa Protactinium 232.04	92 U Uranium 238.03	93 Np Neptunium 237	94 Pu Plutonium (244)	95 Am Americium (243)	96 Cm Curium (247)	97 Bk Berkelium (247)	98 Cf Californium (251)	99 Es Einsteinium (252)	100 Fm Fermium (257)	101 Md Mendelevium (258)	102 No Nobelium (259)	103 Lr Lawrencium (262)

APPENDIX 2 Weights and Measures

Accurate descriptions of physical objects would be impossible without a precise method of reporting the pertinent data. Dimensions such as length and width are reported in standardized units of measurement, such as inches or centimeters. These values can be used to calculate the **volume** of an object, a measurement of the amount of space the object fills. Mass is another important physical property. The **mass** of an object is determined by the amount of matter the object contains; on Earth the mass of an object determines the object's weight.

In the United States, length and width are typically described in inches, feet, or yards; volumes in pints, quarts, or gallons; and weights in ounces, pounds, or tons. These are units of the **U.S. system** of measurement. Table 1 summarizes the familiar and unfamiliar terms used in the U.S. system. For reference purposes, this table also includes a definition of the "household units" popular in recipes. The U.S. system can be very difficult to work with, because there is no logical relationship among the various units. For example, there are 12 inches in a foot, 3 feet in a yard, and 1760 yards in a mile. Without a clear pattern of organization, the conversion of feet to inches or miles to feet can be confusing and time consuming. The relationships among ounces, pints, quarts, and gallons are no more logical than those among ounces, pounds, and tons.

In contrast, the **metric system** has a logical organization based on powers of 10, as indicated in Table 2. For example, a **meter (m)** is the basic unit for the measurement of size. For measurements of larger objects, data can be reported in **dekameters** (*deka,* ten), **hectometers** (*hekaton,* hundred), or **kilometers** (**km;** *chilioi,* thousand); for smaller objects, data can be reported in **decimeters** (0.1 m; *decem,* ten), **centimeters** (**cm** = 0.01 m; *centum,* hundred), **millimeters** (**mm** = 0.001 m; *mille,* thousand), and so forth. In the metric system, the same prefixes are used to report weights, based on the **gram (g),** and volumes, based on the **liter (L).** This text reports data in metric units, in most cases with U.S. system equivalents. Use this opportunity to become familiar with the metric system, because most technical sources report data only in metric units; most of the world outside the United States uses the metric system exclusively. Conversion factors are included in Table 2.

The U.S. and metric systems also differ in their methods of reporting temperatures. In the United States, temperatures are usu-ally reported in degrees Fahrenheit (°F), whereas scientific literature and individuals in most other countries report temperatures in degrees Celsius (°C). The relationship between temperatures in degrees Fahrenheit and those in degrees Celsius is indicated in Table 2.

TABLE 1 The U.S System of Measurement

PHYSICAL PROPERTY	UNIT	RELATIONSHIP TO OTHER U.S. UNITS	RELATIONSHIP TO HOUSEHOLD UNITS
Length	inch (in.)	1 in = 0.083 ft	
	foot (ft)	1 ft = 12 in.	
		= 0.33 yd	
	yard (yd)	1 yd = 36 in.	
		= 3 ft	
	mile (mi)	1 mi = 5280 ft	
		= 1760 yd	
Volume	fluid dram (fl dr) (also fluidram)	1 fl dr = 0.125 fl oz	
	fluid ounce (fl oz)	1 fl oz = 8 fl dr	= 6 teaspoons (tsp)
		= 0.0625 pt	= 2 tablespoons (tbsp)
	pint (pt)	1 pt = 128 fl dr	= 32 tbsp
		= 16 fl oz	= 2 cups (c)
		= 0.5 qt	
	quart (qt)	1 qt = 256 fl dr	= 4 c
		= 32 fl oz	
		= 2 pt	
		= 0.25 gal	
	gallon (gal)	1 gal = 128 fl oz	
		= 8 pt	
		= 4 qt	
Mass	grain (gr)	1 gr = 0.002 oz	
	dram (dr)	1 dr = 27.3 gr	
		= 0.063 oz	
	ounce (oz)	1 oz. = 437.5 gr	
		= 16 dr	
	pound (lb)	1 lb = 7000 gr	
		= 256 dr	
		= 16 oz	
	ton (t)	1 t = 2000 lb	

TABLE 2 The Metric System of Measurement

PHYSICAL PROPERTY	UNIT	RELATIONSHIP TO STANDARD METRIC UNITS	CONVERSION TO U.S. UNITS	
Length	nanometer (nm)	1 nm = 0.000000001 m (10^{-9})	= 3.94×10^{-8} in.	25,400,000 nm = 1 in.
	micrometer (μm)	1 μm = 0.000001 m (10^{-6})	= 3.94×10^{-5} in.	25,400 μm = 1 in.
	millimeter (mm)	1 mm = 0.001 m (10^{-3})	= 0.0394 in.	25.4 mm = 1 in.
	centimeter (cm)	1 cm = 0.01 m (10^{-2})	= 0.394 in.	2.54 cm = 1 in.
	decimeter (dm)	1 dm = 0.1 m (10^{-1})	= 3.94 in.	0.254 dm = 1 in.
	meter (m)	standard unit of length	= 39.4 in.	0.0254 m = 1 in.
			= 3.28 ft	0.3048 m = 1 ft
			= 1.093 yd	0.914 m = 1 yd
	kilometer (km)	1 km = 1000 m	= 3280 ft	
			= 1093 yd	
			= 0.62 mi	1.609 km = 1 mi
Volume	microliter (μL)	1 μL = 0.000001 L (10^{-6}) = 1 cubic millimeter (mm³)		
	milliliter (mL)	1 mL = 0.001 L (10^{-3}) = 1 cubic centimeter (cm³ or cc)	= 0.0338 fl oz	5 mL = 1 tsp
				15 mL = 1 tbsp
				30 mL = 1 fl oz
	centiliter (cL)	1 cL = 0.01 L (10^{-2})	= 0.338 fl oz	2.95 cL = 1 fl oz
	deciliter (dL)	1 dL = 0.1 L (10^{-1})	= 3.38 fl oz	0.295 dL = 1 fl oz
	liter (L)	standard unit of volume	= 33.8 fl oz	0.0295 L = 1 fl oz
			= 2.11 pt	0.473 L = 1 pt
			= 1.06 qt	0.946 L = 1 qt
Mass	picogram (pg)	1 pg = 0.000000000001 g (10^{-12})		
	nanogram (ng)	1 ng = 0 .000000001 g (10^{-9})	= 0.000000015 gr	66,666,666 ng = 1 gr
	microgram (μg)	1 μg = 0.000001 g (10^{-6})	= 0.000015 gr	66,666 μg = 1 gr
	milligram (mg)	1 mg = 0 .001 g (10^{-3})	= 0.015 gr	66.7 mg = 1 gr
	centigram (cg)	1 cg = 0.01 g (10^{-2})	= 0.15 gr	6.67 cg = 1 gr
	decigram (dg)	1 dg = 0.1 g (10^{-1})	= 1.5 gr	0.667 cg = 1 gr
	gram (g)	standard unit of mass	= 0.035 oz	28.4 g = 1 oz
			= 0.0022 lb	454 g = 1 lb
	dekagram (dag)	1 dag = 10 g		
	hectogram (hg)	1 hg = 100 g		
	kilogram (kg)	1 kg = 1000 g	= 2.2 lb	0.454 kg = 1 lb
	metric ton (MT)	1 MT = 1000 kg	= 1.1 t	
			= 2205 lb	0.907 MT = 1 t

TEMPERATURE	CELSIUS	FAHRENHEIT	
Freezing point of pure water	0°	32°	
Normal body temperature	36.8°	98.6°	
Boiling point of pure water	100°	212°	
Conversion	°C → °F: °F = (1.8 × °C) + 32	°F → °C: °C = (°F − 32) × 0.56	

The following illustration spans the entire range of measurements that we consider in this book. Gross anatomy traditionally deals with structural organization as seen with the unaided eye or with a simple hand lens. A microscope can provide higher levels of magnification and can reveal finer details. Before the 1950s, most information was provided by *light microscopy*. A photograph taken through a *light microscope* is called a **light micrograph (LM).** Light microscopy can magnify cellular structures up to about 1000 times and can show details as fine as 0.25 μm. The symbol **μm** stands for **micrometer;** 1 μm = 0.001 mm, or 0.00004 inches. With a light microscope, we can identify cell types, such as muscle fibers or neurons, and can see large structures within a cell. Because individual cells are relatively transparent, thin sections cut through a cell are treated with dyes that stain specific structures to make them easier to see.

Although special staining techniques can show the general distribution of proteins, lipids, carbohydrates, and nucleic acids in the cell, many fine details of intracellular structure remained a mystery until investigators began using *electron microscopy.* This technique uses a focused beam of electrons, rather than a beam of light, to examine cell structure. In *transmission electron microscopy,* electrons pass through an ultrathin section to strike a photographic plate. The result is a **transmission electron micrograph (TEM).** Transmission electron microscopy shows the fine structure of plasma membranes and intracellular structures. In *scanning electron microscopy,* electrons bouncing off exposed surfaces create a **scanning electron micrograph (SEM).** Although it cannot achieve as much magnification as transmission microscopy, scanning microscopy provides a three-dimensional perspective of cell structure.

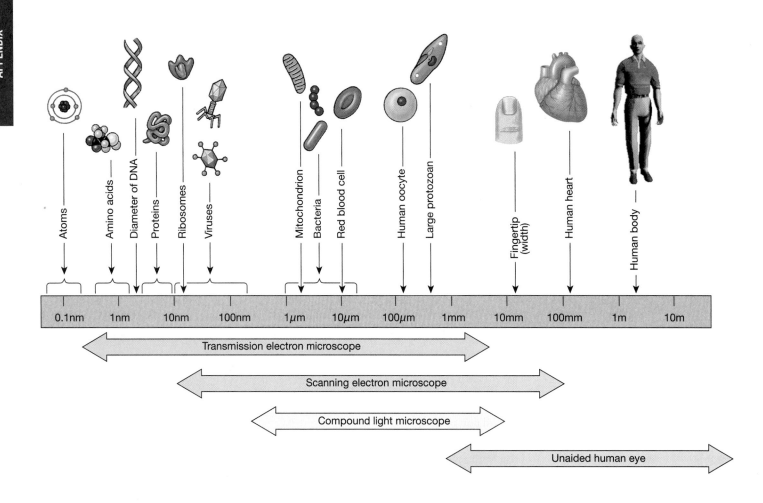

APPENDIX 3 Normal Physiological Values

Tables 3 and 4 present normal averages or ranges for the chemical composition of body fluids. These values are approximations rather than absolute values, because test results vary from laboratory to laboratory owing to differences in procedures, equipment, normal solutions, and so forth. Blanks in the tabular data appear where data are not available; sources used in the preparation of these tables follow. The following locations in the text contain additional information about body fluid analysis:

Table 11-3 (p. 397) presents data on the cellular composition of whole blood.

Table 18-2 (p. 609) compares the average compositions of urine and plasma.

Table 18-3 (p. 613) gives the general characteristics of normal urine.

SOURCES

Braunwauld, Eugene, Kurt J. Isselbacher, Dennis L. Kasper, Jean D. Wilson, Joseph B. Martin, and Anthony S. Fauci, eds. 1998. *Harrison's Principles of Internal Medicine,* 14th ed. New York: McGraw-Hill.

Halsted, James A. 1976. *The Laboratory in Clinical Medicine: Interpretation and Application.* Philadelphia: W.B. Saunders Company.

Lentner, Cornelius, ed. 1981. *Geigy Scientific Tables,* 8th ed. Basel, Switzerland: Ciba–Geigy Limited.

Wintrobe, Maxwell, G. Richard Lee, Dane R. Boggs, Thomas C. Bitnell, John Foerster, John W. Athens, and John N. Lukens. 1981. *Clinical Hematology,* Philadelphia: Lea and Febiger.

TABLE 3 The Composition of Minor Body Fluids

TEST	NORMAL AVERAGES OR RANGES					
	PERILYMPH	ENDOLYMPH	SYNOVIAL FLUID	SWEAT	SALIVA	SEMEN
pH			7.4	4–6.8	6.4*	7.19
SPECIFIC GRAVITY			1.008–1.015	1.001–1.008	1.007	1.028
ELECTROLYTES (mEq/L)						
Potassium	5.5–6.3	140–160	4.0	4.3–14.2	21	31.3
Sodium	143–150	12–16	136.1	0–104	14*	117
Calcium	1.3–1.6	0.05	2.3–4.7	0.2–6	3	12.4
Magnesium	1.7	0.02		0.03–4	0.6	11.5
Bicarbonate	17.8–18.6	20.4–21.4	19.3–30.6		6*	24
Chloride	121.5	107.1	107.1	34.3	17	42.8
PROTEINS (TOTAL) (mg/dL)	200	150	1.72 g/dL	7.7	386†	4.5 g/dL
METABOLITES (mg/dL)						
Amino acids				47.6	40	1.26 g/dL
Glucose	104		70–110	3.0	11	224 (fructose)
Urea				26–122	20	72
Lipids (total)	12		20.9	‡	25–500§	188

*Increases under salivary stimulation.

†Primarily alpha-amylase, with some lysozymes.

‡Not present in eccrine secretions.

§Cholesterol.

TABLE 4 The Chemistry of Blood, Cerebrospinal Fluid, and Urine

TEST	NORMAL AVERAGES OR RANGES		
	BLOOD*	CSF	URINE
pH	S: 7.35–7.45	7.31–7.34	4.5–8.0
OSMOLARITY (mOsm/L)	S: 280–295	292–297	855–1335
ELECTROLYTES		(mEq/L unless noted)	(urinary loss per 24-hour period†)
Bicarbonate	P: 21–28	20–24	
Calcium	S: 4.5–5.5	2.1–3.0	6.5–16.5 mEq
Chloride	S: 97–107	113–122	120–240 mEq
Iron	S: 50–150 μg/L	23–52 μg/L	40–150 μg
Magnesium	S: 1.4–2.1	2–2.5	4.9–16.5 mEq
Phosphorus	S: 1.8–2.9	1.2–2.0	0.8–2 g
Potassium	P: 3.5–5.5	2.7–3.9	35–80 mEq
Sodium	P: 136–145	137–145	120–220 mEq
Sulfate	S: 0.2–1.3		1.07–1.3 g
METABOLITES		(mg/dL unless noted)	(urinary loss per 24-hour period‡)
Amino acids	P/S: 2.3–5.0	10.0–14.7	41–133 mg
Ammonia	P: 20–150 μg/dL	25–80 μg/dL	340–1200 mg
Bilirubin	S: 0.5–1.0	< 0.2 mg/dL	0.02–1.9 mg
Creatinine	P/S: 0.6–1.2	0.5–1.9	1.01–2.5
Glucose	P/S: 70–110	40–70	0
Ketone bodies	S: 0.3–2.0	1.3–1.6	10–100 mg
Lactic acid	WB: 5–20§	10–20	100–600 mg
Lipids (total)	S: 400–1000	0.8–1.7	0–31.8 mg
Cholesterol (total)	S: 150–300	0.2–0.8	1.2–3.8 mg
Triglycerides	S: 40–150	0–0.9	
Urea	P/S: 23–43	12.0	12.6–28.6
Uric acid	S: 2.0–7.0	0.2–1.5	80–976 mg
PROTEINS	(g/dL)	(mg/dL)	(urinary loss per 24-hour period‡)
Total	S: 6.0–7.8	2.0–4.5	47–76.2 mg
Albumin	S: 3.2–4.5	10.6–32.4	10–100 mg
Globulins (total)	S: 2.3–3.5	2.8–15.5	7.3 mg (average)
Immunoglobulins	S: 1.0–2.2	1.1–1.7	3.1 mg (average)
Fibrinogen	P: 0.2–0.4	0.65 (average)	

*S = serum, P = plasma, WB = whole blood.

†Because urinary output averages just over 1 liter per day, these electrolyte values are comparable to mEq/L.

‡Because urinary metabolite and protein data approximate mg/L or g/L, these data must be divided by 10 for comparison with CSF or blood concentrations.

§Venous blood sample.

Glossary/Index

A

A band in sarcomere, 198, 199
Abdomen
  greater omentum, 544, 545
  lesser omentum, 544, 545
  parietal peritoneum, 22, 537, 545
  venous drainage from, 45, 456–458
  visceral peritoneum, 22, 537, 544
Abdominal aorta, 451, 453, 454
Abdominal cavity, 22, 26
Abdominal thrust (Heimlich maneuver), 509
Abdominopelvic cavity: Portion of the ventral body cavity that contains abdominal and pelvic subdivisions, (C1, 7), 21, 22, 26, 223
Abdominopelvic quadrants, 17, 25, 26
Abdominopelvic regions, 17, 25, 26
Abducens nerve, 277, 278, 279, 280, 281
Abduction: Movement away from the midline, (C6, 7), 176, 177, 217
Abnormal hemoglobin, 386
ABO blood types, 391–393
Abortion, 692
Abrasion, 132
Abruptio placentae, 699
Abscess, 482
Absorption: The active or passive uptake of gases, fluids, nutrients, or solutes, (C1, 3, 4, 16), 2, 62, 63, 97, 535
Accessory nerve, 277, 278, 279, 281
Accessory organs of the digestive system, 535, 539–542, 552–557
Accessory structures of the integumentary system, 122, 128–132
Accommodation: Alteration in the curvature of the lens to focus an image on the retina, (C9), 323, 324, 325
Acetabulum (as-e-TAB-ü-lum): fossa on lateral aspect of pelvis that accommodates the head of the femur, (C6), 143, 170
Acetone, 585
Acetyl groups, 578
Acetylcholine (ACh) (as-ē-til-KŌ-lēn): Chemical neurotransmitter in the brain and PNS; dominant neurotransmitter in the PNS, released at neuromuscular junctions and synapses of the parasympathetic division, (C7, 8, 12, 13), 200–202, 260, 261, 291, 422–423
Acetylcholinesterase (AChE): Enzyme found in the synaptic cleft, bound to the postsynaptic membrane, and in tissue fluids; breaks down and inactivates ACh molecules, (C7, 8), 200, 201, 202
Acetyl-CoA: an acetyl group bound to coenzyme A, a participant in the anabolic and catabolic pathways for carbohydrates, lipids, and many amino acids, (C17), 578, 579, 582–583, 584
ACh. *See* **Acetylcholine**
Achalsia, 566
AChE. *See* **Acetylcholinesterase**
Achilles (calcaneal) tendon, 172, 216, 232, 237
Aching pain, 309
Acid: A compound whose dissociation in solution releases a hydrogen ion and an anion; an acidic solution has a pH below 7.0 and contains an excess of hydrogen ions, (C2), 40, 53
Acid-base balance
  acids in the body, 624–625
  buffers and buffer systems, 625–626
  compensatory mechanisms, 626, 627
  disorders of, 627
  homeostasis, 620–622
  maintaining, 626–627
  pH of body fluids, 624

Acidic solutions, 39, 40
Acidosis (as-i-DŌsis): an abnormal physiological state characterized by plasma pH below 7.35, (C18), 624
Acinar cells, 553
Acinus/acini (AS-i-nī): Histological term referring to a blind pocket, pouch, or sac, (C16), 553
Acne, 130, 135
Acoustic (vestibulocochlear) nerve, 277, 278, 279, 280, 281
Acoustic: Pertaining to sound or the sense of hearing, (C9), 307
Acquired immune deficiency syndrome (AIDS), 489, 493, 661
Acquired immunity, 482–483
Acromegaly, 371
Acromial end of the clavicle, 167
Acromion process, 167, 168
Acrosomal cap, 643, 644
ACTH. *See* **Adrenocorticotropic hormone (ACTH)**
Actin: Protein component of microfilaments; form thin filaments in skeletal muscles and produce contractions of all muscles through interaction with thick (myosin) filaments, (C3, 4, 7), 73, 112, 197, 198, 199
Action of muscles, 217
Action potential: A conducted change in the membrane potential of excitable cells, initiated by a change in the membrane permeability to sodium ions, (C7, 8, 9, 12)
  cardiac contractile cells, 415, 416
  explained, 256
  generation of, 249, 256–257
  muscles, 200, 201, 202
  propagation of, 257–258
  sensory information, 307, 308
Activation energy, 37–38
Active immunity, 482–483
Active sites, 48, 49, 198, 199
Active transport: The ATP-dependent absorption or excretion of solutes across a plasma membrane, (C3), 65, 68–71, 72
Acute renal failure, 615
Acute: Sudden in onset, severe in intensity, and brief in duration, (C8), 296
Adaptability in organisms, 2
Adaptation, 308, 312
Addison disease, 371, 373, 493
Adduction: Movement toward the axis or midline of the body as viewed in the anatomical position, (C6, 7), 176, 177, 217
Adductor brevis muscle, 232, 233, 234
Adductor longus muscle, 215, 232, 233, 234, 235
Adductor magnus muscle, 216, 232, 233, 234, 235
Adenine: One of the nitrogenous bases in the nucleic acids RNA and DNA, (C2, 3), 49, 50, 79, 80, 81, 82
Adenosine: A nucleoside consisting of adenine and a five-carbon sugar, (C2), 51
Adenosine diphosphate (ADP): A high-energy compound composed of adenosine monophosphate and one phosphate group, (C2), 51
Adenosine monophosphate (AMP): A high-energy compound composed of adenosine and one phosphate group, (C2, 10), 51, 348
Adenosine triphosphate (ATP): A high-energy compound composed of adenosine monophosphate and two phosphate groups, (C2, 3, 7, 17)
  active transport, carrier-mediated, 69–70
  cellular metabolism, 575, 576, 577
  cellular use, 51, 52
  endocytosis, 70
  generation of, 209–210
  glycolysis, 577, 578, 580, 582
  lipid catabolism, 582

muscle contractions, 208–211
protein catabolism, 584–585
Adenylate cyclase: an enzyme bound to the inner surfaces of cell membranes that can convert ATP to cyclic-AMP; also called adenyl cyclase or adenylyl cyclase, (C10), 348, 350
Adhesion belt, 95
Adhesions, 116
Adipocytes (AD-i-pō-sīts): Fat cells, (C4), 104, 105, 106
Adipose tissue: Loose connective tissue dominated by adipocytes, (C4, 8, 10)
  autonomic nervous system, 295
  body tissues, 106, 107
  endocrine functions, 367–368
  endocrine system overview, 348
Adolescence, 690, 692
ADP. *See* **Adenosine diphosphate (ADP)**
Adrenal cortex: Superficial portion of the suprarenal (adrenal) gland that produces steroid hormones, also called the suprarenal cortex, (C10), 348, 353, 354, 361–362, 363
Adrenal gland: Small endocrine gland secreting hormones, located superior to each kidney, also called the suprarenal gland, (C1, 8, 10), 9, 295, 347, 348, 361–363
Adrenal medulla: Core of the suprarenal (adrenal) gland; a modified sympathetic ganglion that secretes hormones into the blood following sympathetic activation; also called the suprarenal medulla, (C8, 10), 291, 292, 348, 361, 362–363
Adrenergic (ad-ren-ER-jik): A synaptic terminal that releases norepinephrine when stimulated, (C8)
  adrenergic neurons, 291
  adrenergic synapses, 261
Adrenocortical steroids, 361
Adrenocorticotropic hormone (ACTH): Hormone that stimulates the production and secretion of glucocorticoids by the suprarenal (adrenal) cortex; released by the anterior pituitary, (C10, 14)
  endocrine system, 353, 354, 356, 357, 361
  immune response and stress, 493
Adult teeth, 541, 542
Adventitia (ad-ven-TISH-ē-uh): superficial layer of connective tissue surrounding an internal organ; fibers are continuous with those of surrounding tissues, providing support and stabilization, (C16), 537–538
Aer: Air, (C7), 195
Aero-: Air, (C3), 59
Aerobic endurance, 212
Aerobic metabolism: The complete breakdown of organic substrates into carbon dioxide and water; a process that yields large amounts of ATP but requires mitochondria and oxygen, (C3, 7, 17), 77, 209–210, 577
Afferent arteriole: An arteriole that carries blood to the glomerulus of a kidney, (C18), 604, 605, 606
Afferent division of the PNS, 247
Afferent fiber: Axons carrying sensory information to the CNS, (C8, 9), 287, 307, 308, 310, 311, 315, 337
Afferent lymphatics, 476
Afferent vessels. *See* **Veins**
Afterbirth, 689
Agglutination (a-gloo-ti-NĀ-shun): Aggregation of red blood cells due to interactions between surface agglutinogens and plasma agglutinins, (C11, 14), 392, 488
Agglutinins, 381, 392
Agglutinogens, 392
Aging
  calorie and nutrient needs, 595–596
  cardiovascular system, 461

Anterior white commissure, 265, 266

Antibiotic: Chemical agent that selectively kills pathogenic microorganisms, (C14, 18, 19), 489, 491, 619, 645, 646, 653

Antibody (AN-tī-bod-ē): A globular protein produced by plasma cells that will bind to specific antigens and promote their destruction or removal from the body, (C2, 4, 11, 14)
  antibody-producing cells, 104, 106
  B cells, 474
  blood transporting, 381
  classes of, 488
  functions of, 488–489
  plasma proteins, 384
  proteins, 46
  specific defenses, 486–491
  structure of, 486, 487, 488

Antibody-mediated immunity: Immunity resulting from the presence of circulating antibodies produced by plasma cells; also called humoral immunity, (C14), 474, 482, 486

Anticoagulant: Compound that slows or prevents clot formation by interfering with the clotting system, (C11), 400

Anticodon: Triplet of nitrogenous bases on a tRNA molecule that interacts with an appropriate codon on a strand of mRNA, (C3), 81

Antidiuretic hormone (ADH) (an-tī-dī-ū-RET-ik): Hormone synthesized in the hypothalamus and secreted at the posterior pituitary; causes water retention at the kidneys and an elevation of blood pressure, (C8, 10, 13, 18)
  age-related changes, 628
  angiotensin II, 616, 617
  cardiovascular regulation, 443, 444
  hypothalamus, 277
  hypothalamus synthesis, 351
  peptide hormone, 347
  posterior pituitary gland, 355, 356, 357
  reabsorption of water, 612

Antigen: A substance capable of inducing the production of antibodies, (C11, 14), 391, 474, 484–485, 489–490

Antigen binding sites, 486, 487, 488

Antigen recognition, 483

Antigen-antibody complex: The combination of an antigen and a specific antibody, (C14), 474, 487, 488

Antigenic determinant site: A portion of an antigen that can interact with an antibody molecule, (C14), 487, 488

Antigen-presenting cell (APC): A cell that processes antigens and displays them, bound to MHC proteins; essential to the initiation of a normal immune response, (C14), 485

Antihistamines, 494

Anti-inflammatory effects of glucocorticoids, 361

Antioxidant activity, 363

Antipyretic drugs, 596

Antiviral proteins, 481

Antrum (AN-trum): A chamber or pocket, (C19), 651, 652

Anus: External opening of the anorectal canal, (C16, 19), 558, 559, 650, 655, 656

Anvil (incus), 329, 330

Aorta: Large, elastic artery that carries blood away from the left ventricle and into the systemic circuit, (C12, 13)
  abdominal, 451, 453, 454
  ascending, 408, 412, 414, 448, 449, 450, 451
  baroreceptor, 311
  descending, 448, 449, 450, 451, 453–454
  heart anatomy, 411
  thoracic, 411, 451, 453

Aortic arch, arteries of, 448, 449, 450–451

Aortic baroreceptors, 311, 441, 524–525

Aortic bodies, 312, 442

Aortic reflex: Baroreceptor reflex triggered by increased aortic pressures; leads to a reduction in cardiac output and a fall in systemic pressure, (C13), 441

Aortic semilunar valve, 411, 412, 413

Aortic sinus, 311, 441

Apex of the heart, 408–409

Apex of the lungs, 513

Apex of the sacrum, 164

Apgar rating, 699

Aphasia: Inability to speak, (C8), 272, 296

Apical surface of epithelial cells, 96

Apnea, 528

Apocrine secretion (AP-ō-krin): Mode of secretion in which the glandular cell sheds portions of its cytoplasm, (C4), 101–102, 103

Apocrine sweat glands, 130–131

Aponeurosis/aponeuroses (ap-ō-nū-RŌ-sēz): A broad tendinous sheet that may serve as the origin or insertion of a skeletal muscle, (C7), 196, 219, 220, 221, 223, 235

Apoptosis, 84, 485

Appendicitis, 476, 495, 558

Appendicular articulations, 179, 181–184

Appendicular muscles
  functions, 8
  naming, 217
  pelvis and lower limbs, 215–216, 232–235, 236, 237, 238
  shoulders and upper limbs, 215–216, 226–232

Appendicular skeleton
  functions, 7
  lower limb, 155, 171–173
  overview of, 152, 155
  pectoral girdle, 155, 165, 167–168
  pelvic girdle, 155, 169–171
  upper limb, 155, 168–169, 170

Appendix: A blind tube connected to the cecum of the large intestine, (C14, 16), 476, 558, 559

Appositional growth: Enlargement of a bone by the addition of cartilage or bony matrix at its surface, (C6), 148, 149

Aqueduct of midbrain, (mesencephalic aqueduct or cerebral aqueduct): Passageway that connects the third ventricle (diencephalon) with the fourth ventricle (metencephalon), (C8), 269

Aqueous humor: Fluid similar to perilymph or CSF that fills the anterior chamber of the eye, (C9, 18), 317, 319, 322, 621

Aqueous solution, 39

Arachidonic acid, 347

Arachnoid (a-RAK-noyd): The middle meninges that encloses CSF and protects the central nervous system, (C8), 262–263

Arachnoid granulations, 269, 270

Arcuate (AR-kū-āt): Curving, (C18), 605

Arcuate arteries, 604, 605

Arcuate veins, 604, 605

Areola (a-RĒ-ō-la): Pigmented area that surrounds the nipple of a breast, (C19), 656

Areolar: Containing minute spaces, as in areolar connective tissue, (C4), 106

Areolar tissue, 106

Arginine, 585

Arms
  bones of, 155, 168–169
  muscles of, 215–216, 226, 227, 228
  venous drainage from, 455, 456, 457, 458

Arousal, sexual, 660, 661

Arrector pili (a-REK-tor PI-lē): Smooth muscles whose contractions cause erection of hairs, (C5, 8), 129, 295

Arrhythmias (a-RITH-mē-az): Abnormal patterns of cardiac contractions, (C12, 17), 418, 424, 585

Arterial anastomosis, 433

Arterial pressure, 434, 435–436, 438. See also Blood pressure

Arterial puncture, 382

Arteries: Blood vessels that carry blood away from the heart and toward a peripheral capillary, (C1, 4, 12, 13, 18, 19). See also specific arteries
  arteriosclerosis, 432
  cardiovascular system, 406

functions, 9
kidneys, 604–605
Marfan syndrome, 105
ovarian, 649, 650
overview of, 429
pulmonary circuit, 447, 448
size, structure, and function, 429–430, 431
systemic circuit, 448–454
umbilical, 460, 681, 682

Arteriole (ar-TĒR-e-ōl): A small arterial branch that delivers blood to a capillary network, (C13), 429, 430, 431

Arteriosclerosis, 295, 432, 461, 462

Arteriovenous anastomosis, 433

Arthritis (ar-THRĪ-tis): Inflammation of a joint, (C6), 175, 185

Arthroscopic surgery, 185

Articular: Pertaining to a joint, (C6), 144, 173, 174

Articular capsule, 174–175

Articular cartilage: Cartilage pad that covers the surface of a bone inside a joint cavity, (C6), 144, 145, 148, 174, 175

Articular facets, 162, 163

Articular processes of the vertebrae, 162, 163

Articulations. See also Joints
  elbow, 182
  functional and structural classifications of, 173, 174
  hip, 182–183
  intervertebral, 179, 180, 181
  knee, 183–184
  shoulder, 181–182
  synovial membrane lining, 111, 112

Artificial respiration, 516

Arytenoid cartilage, 506, 507

Ascending (sensory) pathways, 253, 254

Ascending aorta, 408, 412, 414, 448, 449, 450, 451

Ascending colon, 558, 559

Ascending limb of the nephron loop, 606, 608

Ascending tract: A tract carrying information from the spinal cord to the brain, (C8), 265

Ascites, 538, 566

Aspiration, 509

Assisted reproductive technologies, 660

Association areas: Cortical areas of the cerebrum responsible for integration of sensory inputs and/or motor commands, (C8), 271

Association neurons (interneurons), 250

Asthma (AZ-muh): Reversible constriction of smooth muscles around respiratory passageways, frequently caused by an allergic response, (5, 15), 126, 509, 528

Astigmatism: Visual disturbance due to an irregularity in the shape of the cornea, (C9), 325

Astrocyte (AS-trō-sīt): One of the glial cells in the CNS; responsible for the blood-brain barrier, (C8), 250, 251

Ataxia, 278, 296

Atelectasis, 528

Atherosclerosis (ath-er-ō-skle-RŌ-sis): Formation of fatty plaques in the walls of arteries, leading to circulatory impairment, (C13, 17, 19), 432, 461, 462, 583, 591, 662, 670

Athletic performance, 368

Atlas (C$_1$), 163, 164

Atmospheric air *versus* alveolar air, 518, 519

Atom: The smallest, stable unit of matter, (C2), 4, 5, 30

Atomic number: The number of protons in an atom, (C2), 30, 32, 34

Atomic structure, 30–31

Atomic weight: The average mass of an element's atoms, (C2), 31

ATP. See **Adenosine triphosphate (ATP)**

ATP synthase, 579, 580

Atria: Thin-walled chambers of the heart that receive venous blood from the pulmonary or systemic circuit, (C12), 406

Atrial baroreceptors, 442

Atrial diastole, 420, 421

Blastocyst: (BLAS-tō-sist): An early stage in the developing embryo, consisting of an outer trophoblast and an inner cell mass, (C20), 676–677

Blastomeres, 676

Bleaching of visual pigments, 327

Blind spot, visual, 320–321, 322

Blindness, 327

Blinking eyes, 316

Blood

    ABO blood types, 391–393

    aging, effects of, 461

    collection and analysis, 382, 383

    composition of, 382, 383

    fluid connective tissue, 103, 104, 106

    functions, 9, 381–382

    hemostasis, 398–401

    plasma, 382, 383, 384

    platelets, 389, 397, 398

    red blood cells, 384–391, 397

    regulation of by liver, 556

    white blood cells, 389, 393–396, 397

Blood-brain barrier: Isolation of the CNS from the general circulation; primarily the result of astrocyte regulation of capillary permeabilities, (C8), 250

Blood clot: A network of fibrin fibers and trapped blood cells, (C11)

    clot retraction and removal, 400–401

    coagulation phase of hemostasis, 398

    process of, 398–400

    structure of, 399

Blood compatibility, 392, 393

Blood doping, 391

Blood flow

    autoregulation of, 433

    factors affecting, 434–435

Blood pressure: A force exerted against the vascular walls by the blood, as the result of the push exerted by cardiac contraction and the elasticity of the vessel walls; usually measured along one of the muscular arteries, with systolic pressure measured during ventricular systole, and diastolic pressure during ventricular diastole, (C3, 4, 9, 10, 12, 13, 18)

    checking, 438

    circulatory pressure, 434, 435–436, 438

    fluid and electrolyte balance, 622–624

    glomerular filtration, 610

    hemorrhage, 445

    hydrostatic pressure, 68

    kidney function, 614

    regulation of, by urinary system, 602

Blood types, 391–393

Blood vessels. *See also* Blood vessels and circulation; **Thermoregulation**

    aging, effects of, 461

    autonomic nervous system, 295

    functional patterns, 446–447

    functions, 9

    kidneys, blood vessels in, 604–605

    muscles, 196

    placental, 681–682

    walls, structure of, 429, 430

Blood vessels and circulation, 428–469. *See also* Blood vessels; Cardiovascular system

    aging, effect of, 461

    arterial (blood) pressure, 435–436, 438

    arteries, 429–430, 431

    blood flow, factors affecting, 434–435

    blood vessel size, structure, and function, 429–434

    blood vessels, functional patterns of, 446–447

    capillaries, 430–433

    capillary pressures and exchange, 436–437

    cardiovascular regulation, 439–444

    exercise, 444–445

    fetal and maternal circulation, 460–461

    hemorrhage, 443, 445–446

    introduction to, 429

    other systems, relationship with, 462, 468

    physiological stress, adaptation to, 443, 444–446

    professional profile, 469

    pulmonary circuit, 447–448

    systemic circuit, 448–460

    veins, 430, 431, 433–434

    venous pressure, 434, 436, 437, 439

Blood volume

    capillary dynamics, 437

    hemorrhage, 445–446

    maternal, during pregnancy, 686

    regulation of, by urinary system, 602

Blood volume reflexes, 421–422

Blue cones, 325, 327

Body (shaft) of the penis, 646, 647

Body cavities, 20–22, 26

Body fluid compartments, 621

Body fluids, normal pH range of, 40, 41

Body of the scapula, 167

Body of the sternum, 165, 166

Body of the stomach, 544, 545

Body of the uterus, 653–654

Body position, sense of, 311–312

Body stalk, 680, 681

Body temperature

    blood, stabilization by, 382

    ovulation, 660

    systemic veins, 454

    variations in, 594

Bolus: A compact mass; usually refers to compacted ingested material on its way to the stomach, (C16), 542, 543

Bone marrow

    blood cell production, 143, 388

    functions, 7

    marrow cavity in bone, 144

    transplantation, 401, 495

Bone(s). *See also* Skeletal system

    auditory ossicles, 329–330

    described, 143–144

    extracellular fluid, 621

    fractures, repair of, 150–151

    functions, 7

    growth of and body proportions, 148–149

    macroscopic features, 144–145

    microscopic features, 145–146

    normal growth, requirements for, 149

    remodeling, 149–150

    skeleton as a calcium reserve, 150

    supporting connective tissue, 104, 106, 108, 110

    surface markings, 152, 153

Bony labyrinth of the inner ear, 330, 331, 332

Bony palate, 158, 159

Botulism, 200, 239

Bowel: The intestinal tract, (C16), 558

Bowman capsule (renal corpuscle), 603, 605, 606–608

Brachial: Pertaining to the arm, 17

Brachial artery, 438, 449, 450, 451

Brachial plexus: Network formed by branches of spinal nerves C_5—T_1 en route to innervating the upper limb, (C8), 282, 283, 284

Brachial region, 17

Brachial vein, 455, 456, 457, 458

Brachialis muscle, 215, 226, 230, 231

Brachiocephalic trunk, 448, 449, 450, 451

Brachiocephalic vein (innominate vein), 455, 456, 457, 458

Brachioradialis muscle, 215, 216, 226, 230, 231

Brachium: The arm, 16, 17, 168

Bradycardia, 418, 424

Brain

    age, effect of, 295–296

    blood supply to, 448, 449, 450–451, 452

    cerebellum, 267, 268, 277, 278

    cerebrum, 267, 268, 269–276

    CNS, division of, 247

    diencephalon, 267, 268, 276–277

    ependymal cells, 251, 252

    functions, 7

    major regions, 267, 268

    medulla oblongata, 267, 268, 277, 278

    meninges, 262–263

    midbrain, 267, 268, 277

    pons, 267, 268, 277, 278

    respiratory control, 523–524

    size, 267

    venous return from, 454, 455, 456, 457, 458

    ventricles, 252, 267, 269, 270

Brain stem: The midbrain, pons, and medulla oblongata (excludes the cerebrum, diencephalon, and cerebellum), (C8), 267, 268, 277

Brain waves, 274

Breast cancer, 657

Breathing, modes of, 516, 524

Breech birth, 699

Broad ligament, 649, 650

Broca's area: The speech center of the brain, usually found on the neural cortex of the left cerebral hemisphere, (C8), 272–273

Bronchial tree: The trachea, bronchi, and bronchioles, (C15), 509, 510

Bronchioles, 509–510

Bronchitis (brong-KĪ-tis): Inflammation of the bronchial passageways, (C15), 528

Bronchoconstriction, 509

Bronchodilation: Dilation of the bronchial passages; can be caused by sympathetic stimulation, (C15), 509

Bronchopulmonary carcinoma, 525

Bronchoscope, 528

Bronchus/bronchi: One of the branches of the bronchial tree between the trachea and bronchioles, (C1, 15), 10, 503, 508, 509, 510

Brush border of microvilli, 548

Buccal (BUK-al): Pertaining to the cheeks, 539

Buccal cavity, 539. *See also* Oral cavity

Buccinator muscle, 219, 220

Buffer: A compound that stabilizes the pH by either removing or releasing hydrogen ions, (C2, 18), 41, 46, 625, 627

Buffer systems: Interacting compounds that prevent increases or decreases in the pH of body fluids; includes the carbonic acid-bicarbonate buffer system, the phosphate buffer system, and the protein buffer system, (C18), 625–626, 627

Bulbospongiosus muscle, 224, 225, 661

Bulbo-urethral glands (bul-bō-ū-RĒ-thral): Mucous glands at the base of the penis that secrete into the penile urethra; also called *Cowper glands* (C19), 640, 645, 646

Bulimia, 550

Bundle branches: Specialized conducting cells in the ventricles that carry the contractile stimulus from the AV bundle to the Purkinje fibers, (C12), 416, 417

Bundle of His (hiss): Specialized conducting cells in the interventricular septum that carry the contracting stimulus from the AV node to the bundle branches and thence to the Purkinje fibers; also called the *AV bundle* (C12), 417

Burkitt lymphoma, 698

Burning pain, 309

Burns

    burn specialist, 141

    common classification of, 134

    skin repair following injury, 134

Bursa: A small sac filled with synovial fluid that cushions adjacent structures and reduces friction, (C6), 175

Bursitis, 182, 185

C

C cells (parafollicular cells), 358–359, 360

Calcaneal tendon: Large tendon that inserts on the calcaneus; tension on this tendon produces plantar flexion of the foot; also called *Achilles tendon* (C6, 7), 172, 216, 232, 237

Calcaneus (kal-KĀ-nē-us): The heelbone, the largest of the tarsal bones, (C6, 7), 16, 172, 173

CAT (computed axial tomography) scans, 24, 25
Catabolic pathways, 586
Catabolism (kah-TAB-ō-lizm): The breakdown of complex organic molecules into simpler components, accompanied by the release of energy, (C2, 17)
  alternate pathways, 580–581
  amino acids, 585, 586
  cellular metabolism, 575, 576
  defined, 36
  lipids, 581, 582
  nucleic acids, 587
Catalyst (KAT-uh-list): A substance that accelerates a specific chemical reaction but is not altered by the reaction, (C2), 37–38
Cataracts, 323, 339, 340
Cathartics, 561
Cation (KAT-ī-on): An ion that bears a positive charge, (C2), 33
Cauda equina, 264, 265
Cauda/caudally: Closest to or toward the tail (coccyx), (C1), 18, 19
Caudate lobe of the liver, 554
Caudate nucleus, 275
Caverous hemangioma, 135
Connective tissue proper, 103, 104–106, 107
Cecum (SĒ-kum): An expanded pouch at the start of the large intestine, (C16), 548, 558, 559
Celiac trunk, 453, 454
Cell: The smallest living unit in the human body, (C1, 2)
  abnormal cell growth and division, 86
  anatomy, 60, 61
  biochemical building blocks, 52
  carrier-mediated and vesicular transport across membranes, 68–72
  components of, 62
  differentiation, 86–87
  diffusion and filtration across the membrane, 64–68, 72
  diversity of, 60
  DNA and RNA, 80–83
  explained, 3, 25
  high-energy compound, 51, 52, 53
  life cycle of, 83–86
  nucleus, 78–80
  organelles within the cytoplasm, 72–78
  plasma membrane, 60–64
  structure and function, 58–91
  study of, 59
Cell adhesion molecules, 95
Cell body, 114
Cell division, 83–86
Cell junctions, 95–96
Cell membrane. *See* Plasma membrane
Cell physiology, 3, 25
Cell-mediated immunity: resistance to disease through the activities of sensitized T cells that destroy antigen-bearing cells by direct contact or through the release of lymphotoxins; also called *cellular immunity,* (C14), 473, 482, 486
Cellular immunity, 473, 482, 486
Cellular level of organization, 4, 5
Cellular maintenance and repair, 575–576
Cellular metabolism, 575–577
Cellular respiration, 77, 577, 580
Cellular trophoblast, 677
Cellulose, 42
Cementum of teeth, 540, 541
Center of CNS neuron cell bodies, 253, 254
Central canal of spinal cord, 264, 265
Central canal of the spinal cord, 252
Central canals of compact bone, 145, 146
Central nervous system (CNS): The brain and spinal cord, (C1, 8)
  brain, 267–278
  functions, 8
  meninges, 262–263
  nervous system anatomical division, 247, 248

neuroglia in, 250–252
neuron organization of the nervous system, 254
PNS connecting with body's external and internal environments, 248, 278–283, 284
spinal cord, 264–267
Central sulcus: Groove in the surface of a cerebral hemisphere, between the primary sensory and primary motor areas of the cortex, (C8), 268, 270, 271
Central vein of the liver, 554, 555
Central white matter of the cerebrum, 269
Centriole: A cylindrical intracellular organelle composed of nine groups of microtubules, three in each group; functions in mitosis or meiosis by organizing the microtubules of the spindle arraratus, (C3, 8), 61, 62, 74
Centromere (SEN-trō-mēr): Localized region where two chromatids remain connected following chromosome replication; site of spindle fiber attachment, (C3), 84, 85
Cephalic direction, 18, 19
Cephalic phase of regulation of gastric secretions, 546
Cephalic region, 17
Cephalic vein, 455, 456, 457, 458
Cerebellar cortex, 278
Cerebellar peduncles, 277, 278
Cerebellum (ser-e-BEL-um): Region of the brain posterior to the pons, containing the cerebellar hemispheres; adjusts voluntary and involuntary motor activities, (C8), 267, 268, 277, 278
Cerebral (basal) nuclei, 269, 275
Cerebral aqueduct, 269
Cerebral arterial circle (circle of Willis), 451, 452
Cerebral cortex: An extensive area of neural cortex covering the surfaces of the cerebral hemispheres, (C8), 270, 274
Cerebral hemispheres: Expanded portions of the cerebrum covered in neural cortex, (C8)
  hemispheric lateralization, 272, 273
  major region of the brain, 267, 268
  structure of, 268, 270, 271
Cerebral meningitis, 264, 297
Cerebral palsy, 289
Cerebral peduncles, 277
Cerebral processing centers
  general interpretive area, 272
  prefrontal cortex, 272, 273
  speech center, 272–273
Cerebrospinal fluid (CSF): Fluid bathing the internal and external surfaces of the CNS; secreted by the choroid plexus, (C8)
  brain, 269, 270
  chemoreceptors, 442
  extracellular fluid, 621
  subarachnoid space, 263
Cerebrovascular accident (CVA), 296
Cerebrum (SER-e-brum): The largest portion of the brain, composed of the cerebral hemispheres; includes the cerebral cortex, the cerebral nuclei, and the white matter, (C8). *See also* **Cerebral hemispheres**
  association areas, 271
  basal nuclei, 269, 275
  cerebral hemisphere structures, 268, 270, 271
  cortical connections, 269, 271
  electroencephalograms, 273–274
  general interpretive area, 272
  hemispheric lateralization, 272, 273
  limbic system, 275–276
  major region of the brain, 267, 268
  memory, 274–275
  overview of, 269
  prefrontal cortex, 272, 273
  sensory and motor areas, 270–271
  speech center, 272–273
Ceruminous glands, 131, 329
Cervical cancer, 666
Cervical cap, 664
Cervical curve, 162

Cervical enlargement of spinal cord, 264
Cervical plexus, 282, 283, 284
Cervical region, 17
Cervical region of the vertebral column, 161
Cervical vertebrae, 161, 162–163, 164
Cervix: the lower part of the uterus, (C19), 654
Cesarean section, 689
Channel proteins, 64
Cheekbone (zygomatic arch), 156, 157, 158
Cheeks, 539
Chemical bonds
  covalent bonds, 33–34
  hydrogen bonds, 35
  ionic bonds, 32–33
Chemical level of organization, 4, 5, 29–57
  acids, bases, and salts, 40–41, 53
  atoms, 30–32
  ATP, 51, 52, 53
  body fluid pH, 39–40
  carbohydrates, 41–43, 52, 53
  chemical bonds, 32–35
  chemical reactions, 35–37
  enzymes, 37–38
  lipids, 43–46, 52, 53
  nucleic acids, 49–50, 52, 53
  organic and inorganic compounds, 38, 52, 53
  proteins, 46–49, 52, 53
  water in physiological systems, 38–39, 53
Chemical notation, rules of, 35
Chemical reactions
  basic energy concepts, 36
  cells, importance for, 35
  decomposition reactions, 36
  exchange reactions, 37
  reversible reactions, 37
  synthesis reactions, 36
Chemiosmosis, 579
Chemistry, explained, 30
Chemoreception: Detection of alterations in the concentrations of dissolved compounds or gases, (C9, 13, 15, 16), 312
Chemoreceptor reflexes, 442–443, 525–526
Chemoreceptors, 308, 312
Chemotaxis (kē-mō-TAK-sis): the attraction of phagocytic cells to the source of abnormal chemicals in tissue fluids, (C11, 14), 480
Chemotherapy, 116
Chest
  movement, effect of age on, 526
  venous return from, 455, 456, 457, 458
Chief cells of the parathyroid gland, 360
Chief cells of the stomach, 544, 545
Childhood, 687, 691–692
Children, skulls of, 160–161
Chlamydia, 653, 661
Chloride
  dietary guidelines, 589, 590
  regulation of, by urinary system, 602
Chloride shift, 522
Chlorine, 31
Cholecystitis, 566
Cholecystokinin (CCK) (kō-lē-sis-tō-KĪ-nin): Duodenal hormone that stimulates the contraction of the gallbladder and the secretion of enzymes by the exocrine pancreas, (C16), 546, 547, 550–551, 552, 557
Cholelithiasis, 566
Cholera, 561
Cholesterol (ko-LES-ter-ol): A steroid component of cell membranes and a substrate for the synthesis of steroid hormones and bile salts, (C2), 43, 45, 53
  dietary fats, 583
Cholinergic synapse (kō-lin-ER-jik): Synapse where the presynaptic membrane releases ACh on stimulation, (C8), 260, 261
Cholinesterase (kō-li-NES-te-rās): Enzyme that breaks down and inactivates ACh, (C7, 8), 200, 201, 202

Connective tissue: One of the four primary tissue types; provides a structural framework for the body that stabilizes the relative positions of the other tissue types; includes connective tissue proper, cartilage, bone, and blood; always has cells, cell products, and ground substance, (C4)
  cardiac skeleton, 409, 414
  components of, 103, 104–105
  connective tissue proper, 103, 104–106, 107
  extracellular fluid, 621
  fluid connective tissues, 103, 104, 106
  functions of, 93, 103
  heart, 409
  membranes, 110–112
  skeletal muscle, 196
  supporting connective tissues, 104, 106, 108–110
  types of, 103–104
Connexons, 96
Constant segments of antibody chains, 486, 487
Constipation, 561
Contact dermatitis, 135
Continuous propagation of an action potential, 258
Contractile cells, 415–416
Contractile proteins, 46
Contractility: the ability to contract, possessed by skeletal, smooth, and cardiac muscle cells, (C6, 7, 12), 205–208. *See also* **Muscles;** Muscular system
Contraction cycle of skeletal muscles, 202–204
Contraction phase in muscle fiber contraction, 205
Control center, and homeostatic regulation, 6, 13, 26
Control segment of DNA, 79
Convection and heat transfer, 594
Convergence: In the nervous system, the term indicates that the axons from several neurons innervate a single neuron; most common along motor pathways, (C8), 261, 262
Convoluted tubules of the kidney, 603, 605, 606, 607, 608
Copper, dietary guidelines for, 590
Copulation, 660
Coracobrachialis muscle, 227, 228, 229
Coracoid process (KOR-uh-koyd): A hook-shaped process of the scapula that projects above the anterior surface of the capsule of the shoulder joint, (C6), 167, 168
Cornea (KOR-nē-uh): Transparent portion of the fibrous tunic of the anterior surface of the eye, (C9), 316, 317, 318, 319, 325
Corneal epithelium, 316
Corniculate cartilage, 506, 507
Cornification: the production of keratin by a stratified squamous epithelium; also called keratinization, (C5), 124–125, 684
Cornified cells, 124–125
Corona radiata (ko-RŌ-nuh rā-dē-A-tuh): A layer of follicle cells surrounding a secondary oocyte at ovulation, (C19, 20), 652, 674
Coronal plane, 19, 20, 26
Coronal suture, 156, 157
Coronary angiogram, 424
Coronary arteries
  ascending aorta, 448
  origin of, 412, 414
Coronary arteriography, 424
Coronary artery bypass graft (CABG), 424, 455
Coronary artery disease (CAD), 424, 432
Coronary circulation, 414–415
Coronary ischemia, 424
Coronary sinus, 409, 411, 414
Coronary sulcus, 408
Coronary thrombosis, 424
Coronoid (KOR-uh-noyd): Hooked or curved, 168
Coronoid fossa of the humerus, 168
Coronoid process of the mandible, 156, 160
Coronoid process of the ulna, 169
Corpora cavernosa, 646, 647
Corpus callosum: Bundle of axons linking centers in the left and right cerebral hemispheres, (C8), 268, 271, 273

Corpus luteum (LOO-tē-um): Progestin-secreting mass of follicle cells that develops in the ovary after ovulation, (C10, 19, 20), 367, 368, 653
Corpus spongiosum, 646, 647
Corpus striatum, 275
Corpus/corpora: Body
Cortex: Outer layer or portion of an organ, 128, 129
Cortical nephrons, 604, 605
Cortical radiate arteries, 604, 605
Cortical radiate veins, 604, 605
Corticospinal pathway (pyramidal system), 287, 288, 289
Corticospinal tracts: Descending tracts that carry motor commands from the cerebral cortex to the anterior gray horns of the spinal cord, (C8), 288
Corticosteroid: A steroid hormone produced by the suprarenal (adrenal) cortex, (C10)
  androgens, 361
  glucocorticoids, 361
  mineralocorticoids, 361
Corticosterone, 361
Corticotropin-releasing hormone (CRH), 353, 354
Cortisol (KOR-ti-sol): One of the corticosteroids secreted by the suprarenal (adrenal) cortex; a glucocorticoid, (C10), 361
Costa/costae: A rib, (C6). *See* Ribs
Costal bones (ribs), 155, 165, 166
Costal cartilages, 165, 166
Costal facets of the thoracic vertebrae, 163
Costal surface of the lung, 512, 513
Cotransport: Membrane transport of a nutrient, such as glucose, in company with the movement of an ion, usually sodium; transport requires a carrier protein but does not involve direct ATP expenditure and can occur regardless of the concentration gradient for the nutrient, (C3, 16), 68
Coughing reflex, 507
Countertransport, 68
Covalent bond (kō-VĀ-lent): A chemical bond between atoms that involves the sharing of electrons, (C2), 33–34
Cowper (bulbo-urethral) glands, 640, 645, 646
Coxal bone: Hip; formed by the fusion of the ilium, ischium, and pubis, (C6), 155, 169, 170
Cranial, use of term, 18, 19
Cranial cavity, 156
Cranial direction, 18, 19
Cranial meninges, 262–263
Cranial nerves: the twelve peripheral nerves originating at the brain, (C8)
  abducens nerve (CN VI), 277, 278, 279, 280, 281
  accessory nerve (CN XI), 277, 278, 279, 281
  distribution and function of, 279–281
  facial nerve (VII), 277, 278, 279, 280, 281, 293, 315
  glossopharyngeal nerve (CN IX), 277, 278, 279, 280, 281, 293, 312, 315
  hypoglossal nerve (CN XII), 277, 278, 279, 281
  oculomotor nerve (CN III), 277, 279, 280, 281, 293
  olfactory nerve (CN I), 279–280, 281
  optic nerve (CN II), 279, 280, 281, 328
  PNS axons, 253
  trigeminal nerve (CN V), 277, 278, 279, 280, 281, 315
  trochlear nerve (CN IV), 277, 279, 280, 281
  vagus nerve (CN X), 277, 278, 279, 280–281, 293, 312, 315, 422
  vestibulocochlear nerve (CN VIII), 277, 278, 279, 280, 281, 334, 337
Cranium: The braincase; the skull bones that surround the brain, (C1, 6)
  bones of, 155, 156–158, 159
  ethmoid bone, 156, 157, 158, 159
  frontal bone, 156, 157
  occipital bone, 156, 157, 159
  parietal bones, 156, 157, 159
  sphenoid bone, 156, 157, 158, 159
  temporal bones, 156, 157, 158, 159
Creatine phosphate (CP): A high-energy compound present in muscle cells; during muscular activity,

the phosphate group is donated to ADP, regenerating ATP, (C7, 18), 208–209
Creatine phosphokinase (CPK or CK), 209
Creatinine: A breakdown product of creatine metabo. (C7, 18)
  ATP energy transfers, 208–209
  urinary excretion of, 609
Cremaster muscle, 641
Crenation: Cellular shrinkage due to an osmotic movement of water out of the cell, (C3), 68
Cretinism, 371, 373
Crib death, 527
Cribiform plate: Portion of the ethmoid bone of the skull that contains the foramina used by the axons of olfactory receptors en route to the olfactory bulbs of the cerebrum, (C6, 9), 158, 159
Cricoid cartilage (KRĪ-koyd): Ring-shaped cartilage forming the inferior margin of the larynx, (C15), 505, 506, 507
Crista, 332, 333
Crista galli, 158, 159
Crista/cristae: A ridge-shaped collection of hair cells in the ampulla of a semicircular canal; the crista and cupula form a receptor complex sensitive to movement along the plane of the canal, (C9), 332, 333
Cristae of mitochondrial membranes, 77
Cross sections, 19
Cross-bridges: Myosin head that projects from the surface of a thick filament and that can bind to an active site of a thin filament in the presence of calcium ions, (C7), 199–200
Crossing-over, 642
Cross-match test for blood, 393
Cross-reactions in transfusions, 392–393
Crown of the tooth, 540, 541
Cruciate, origin of term, 183, 184
Crude touch and pressure receptors, 309
Crural region, 17
Cryptorchidism, 640, 666
CT (computed tomography) scans, 24, 25, 26
Cuboid bone, 172, 173
Cuboidal epithelium, 97, 98, 99, 100
Cuneiform cartilage, 506, 507
Cupula (KŪ-pū-luh): A gelatinous mass in the ampulla of a semicircular canal in the inner ear, whose movement stimulates the hair cells of the crista, (C9), 332, 333
Cushing's disease, 371, 373
Cuspids (canines), 541
Cusps of heart valves, 411
Cutaneous membrane: The epidermis and papillary layer of the dermis, (C1, 4, 5), 7, 111, 122. *See also* Integumentary system; Skin
Cuticle: Layer of dead, cornified cells surrounding the shaft of a hair or surface of nails, (C5)
  hair, 128
  nails, 132
Cyanosis (sī-uh-NŌ-sis): Bluish discoloration of the skin due to the presence of deoxygenated blood in the vessels near the body surface, (C5), 126, 135
Cycles per second of sound, 335
Cyclic-AMP (cAMP), 348, 350, 352
Cyclic-GMP, 348
Cystic duct: A duct that carries bile between the gallbladder and the common bile duct, (C16), 555, 557
Cystic fibrosis, 506, 528
Cystic vein, 459
Cystitis, 619, 629
Cytochromes, 579
Cytokines
  cytotoxic T cells, 485
  described, 347
  helper T cells, 490
  interferon nonspecific defense, 481
Cytokinesis (sī-tō-ki-NĒ-sis): The cytoplasmic movement that separates two daughter cells at the completion of mitosis, (C3), 83, 85–86

characteristic mode of formation for skeletal elements other than the bones of the cranium, the clavicles, and sesamoid bones, (C6), 147–148

Endocrine cells, 347

Endocrine disorders, 371

Endocrine gland: A gland that secretes hormones into the blood, (C10)

Endocrine pancreas, 364–366

Endocrine placenta, 682

Endocrine secretions, 94, 101

Endocrine system, 345–379
  adipose tissue, 367–368
  cardiovascular regulation, 439, 440, 443–444
  cardiovascular system, functional relationship with, 468
  digestive system, functional relationship with, 572
  disorders of, 371
  endocrine pancreas, 364–366
  exercise, effect on, 238
  gonads, 367, 368
  heart, 367
  homeostasis, maintaining, 247
  hormones, interaction of, 368–372
  hormones, overview of, 347, 348
  hormones and receptors, 347–351
  integumentary system, functional relationship with, 140
  intercellular communication, 346–347
  intestines, 366
  kidneys, 366–367
  lymphoid system, functional relationship with, 494, 500
  muscular system, functional relationship with, 244
  nervous system, functional relationship with, 304
  organs/components and primary functions, 9, 26
  other body systems, integration with, 372, 378
  parathyroid glands, 360–361
  pineal gland, 363–364
  pituitary gland, 352–357
  prenatal and early postnatal development, overview of, 685
  professional profile, 379
  reproductive system, functional relationship with, 670
  respiratory system, functional relationship with, 532
  skeletal system, functional relationship with, 192
  suprarenal (adrenal) glands, 354, 361–363
  thymus, 367
  thyroid gland, 350, 357–360
  urinary system, functional relationship with, 636

Endocrine tissues of other organ systems, 366–368

Endocrinology, 373

Endocytosis (en-dō-sī-TŌ-sis): The movement of relatively large volumes of extracellular material into the cytoplasm by the formation of a membranous vesicle at the cell surface; includes pinocytosis and phagocytosis, (C3), 70–71, 72

Endoderm: One of the three germ layers; the layer on the undersurface of the embryonic disc that gives rise to the epithelia and glands of the digestive system, the respiratory system, and portions of the urinary system, (C20), 678, 679

Endogenous: Produced within the body

Endolymph (EN-dō-limf): Fluid contents of the membranous labyrinth (the saccule, utricle, semicircular canals, and cochlear duct) of the inner ear, (C9, 18), 331, 621

Endometrial glands, 654

Endometriosis, 666

Endometrium (en-dō-MĒ-trē-um): The mucous membrane lining the uterus, (C19), 654

Endomysium (en-dō-MIZ-ē-um): A delicate network of connective tissue fibers that surrounds individual muscle cells, (C7), 196

Endoplasmic reticulum (en-dō-PLAZ-mik re-TIK-ū-lum): A network of membranous channels in the cytoplasm of a cell that function in intracellular transport, synthesis, storage, packaging, and secretion, (C3), 61, 62, 74–75

Endosteum, 144, 145

Endothelium (en-dō-THĒ-lē-um): The simple squamous epithelium that lines blood and lymphatic vessels, (11, 13, 14, 15), 398

Endurance of muscle performance, 211

Energy
  basic concepts and types of, 36
  food, energy content of, 593
  lipid catabolism, 582
  metabolic rate, 593
  skeletal storage, 184
  thermoregulation, 593–595
  units of, 593
  use by the body, 593–595

Enterogastric reflex, 546, 547

Enzyme: A protein that catalyzes a specific biochemical reaction, (C2). *See also* specific enzymes
  biochemical reactions, 37–38
  cell membrane proteins, 64
  ejaculate, in, 646
  proteins, 46, 48–49

Eosinophil (ē-ō-SIN-ō-fil): A granulocyte (WBC) with a lobed nucleus and red-staining granules; participates in the immune response and is especially important during allergic reactions, (C11, 14), 393, 394, 395, 397, 479, 480, 489, 490, 491

Ependyma (ep-EN-di-muh): Layer of cells lining the ventricles and central canal of the CNS, (C8), 252

Ependymal cells, 251, 252

Epicardium: Serous membrane covering the outer surface of the heart; also called *visceral pericardium*, (C1, 4, 12), 407, 409, 410

Epicondyles, 168, 171, 172

Epicranial aponeurosis, 219, 221

Epicranium muscle, 221

Epidermal ridges, 122, 124

Epidermis: The epithelium covering the surface of the skin, (C5)
  described, 122
  functions, 7
  intermediate strata, 123, 124
  layers and functions of, 123–125
  skin cancer, 126
  skin color, 124, 125–126
  stratum corneum, 123, 124–125
  stratum germinatum, 122, 123, 124
  vitamin D$_3$, 126, 127

Epididymis (ep-i-DID-i-mus): Coiled duct that connects the rete testis to the ductus deferens; site of functional maturation of sermatozoa, (C1, 19), 12, 640, 644

Epidural block, 262, 297

Epidural hemorrhage, 263

Epidural space: Space between the spinal dura mater and the walls of the vertebral foramen; contains blood vessels and adipose tissue; a frequent site of injection for regional anesthesia, (C8), 262, 263

Epiglottis (ep-i-GLOT-is): Blade-shaped flap of tissue, reinforced by cartilage, that is attached to the dorsal and superior surface of the thyroid cartilage; it folds over the entrance to the larynx during swallowing, (C15, 16), 108, 505, 506, 507

Epilepsies, 275

Epimysium (ep-i-MIZ-ē-um): A dense layer of collagen fibers that surrounds a skeletal muscle and is continuous with the tendons/aponeuroses of the muscle and with the perimysium, (C7), 196

Epinephrine
  alarm phase of general adaptation syndrome, 369, 370
  amino acid derivative, 347
  angiotensin II, 616
  heart, effect on, 422–423
  suprarenal glands, 291, 293
  suprarenal medulla, 362–363

Epiphyseal cartilage (ep-i-FIZ-sē-al): Cartilaginous region between the epiphysis and diaphysis of a growing bone, (C6, 20), 148, 168

Epiphyseal closure, 148

Epiphyseal line, 148

Epiphyseal plates, 148

Epiphysis (ē-PIF-i-sis): The head of a long bone, (C6), 144, 145

Episiotomy, 689

Epistaxis, 528

Epithalamus, 267, 268, 276, 277

Epithelial tissue
  basement membrane, 94, 96, 97
  cell layers, 97–100
  cell shapes, 97–101
  characteristics of, 94
  classification, 98–101
  columnar, 97, 98, 99, 100, 101
  cuboidal, 97, 98, 99, 101
  epithelial surface, 96
  functions of, 94
  glandular epithelia, 101–103
  intercellular connections, 94–96
  physical barrier for nonspecific defense, 479, 480
  psuedostratified columnar, 100, 101
  renewal and repair, 97
  simple columnar, 98, 99
  simple cuboidal, 98, 99
  simple epithelium, 97, 98, 99
  simple squamous, 98, 99
  squamous, 97, 98, 99, 100
  stratified columnar, 98, 101
  stratified cuboidal, 98, 101
  stratified epithelium, 97, 98, 100, 101
  stratified squamous, 98, 100
  tissue level of organization, 93, 94–103
  transitional, 100, 101

Epithelium (ep-i-THĒ-lē-um): One of the four primary tissue types; a layer of cells that forms a superficial covering or an internal lining of a body cavity or vessel, (C4), 94

Eponychium (cuticle), 132

Eponyms, 15

Epstein-Barr virus, 495

Equilibrium, sense of
  explained, 308
  gravity and linear acceleration, 333, 334
  osmosis, 66, 68
  pathways for, 334
  semicircular ducts, 331, 332, 333
  types of, 332

Equilibrium, state of, 37

Erectile tissue of the penis, 646, 647

Erector spinae muscle, 221, 222, 223

Eruption of secondary teeth, 542

Erythroblastosis fetalis, 394

Erythroblasts, 388, 389

Erythrocytes (e-RITH-rō-sīts): A red blood cell; an anucleate red blood cell containing large quantities of hemoglobin, (C4, 11, 15), 382. *See also* Red blood cells (RBCs)

Erythrocytosis, 401

Erythropoiesis (e-rith-rō-poy-Ē-sis): The formation of red blood cells, (C11), 388, 390

Erythropoiesis-stimulating hormone, 390. *See also* **Erythropoietin (EPO)**

Erythropoietin (EPO) (e-rith-rō-poy-Ē-tin): Hormone released by kidney tissues exposed to low oxygen concentrations; stimulates erythropoiesis in bone marrow, (C10, 11, 13, 18), 366, 390, 443, 444

Escherichia coli, 619

Esophageal hiatus of the diaphragm, 542

Esophageal phase of swallowing, 543

Esophageal reflux, 543

Esophagitis, 543, 566

Esophagus: A muscular tube that connects the pharynx to the stomach, (C1, 15, 16), 11, 536, 542, 543

Gene: A portion of a DNA nucleotide chain that functions as a hereditary unit, and is found at a particular location on a specific chromosome, and codes for a specific protein, (C3, 20), 79, 692–698

General adaptation syndrome (GAS), 369–370, 372, 373

General and special senses, 306–344
 aging, effect of, 339
 chemical receptors, 312
 equilibrium and hearing, 329–339
 eye structures, 315–324, 325
 general sensory receptors, stimuli for, 308–312
 gustation, 314–315
 olfaction, 312–314
 pain receptors, 307, 308–309
 photoreceptors, 324–329
 sensory receptor connection to nervous system, 307–308
 temperature receptor, 309
 touch, pressure, and position receptors, 309–312

General interpretive area, 272

Genetic code, 79

Genetic engineering, 87

Genetic stutter, 698

Genetics: The study of mechanisms of heredity, (C20). *See also* Development and inheritance
 chromosomal abnormalities and genetic analysis, 698
 defined, 673
 genetic disorders, 695, 696, 697, 698
 genotype, 692–693
 Human Genome Project, 696–697
 inheritance, patterns of, 693–696

Genitalia
 female, external, 655, 656
 male, external, 640, 646–647

Genome, 696

Genotype (JĒN-ō-tīp): The genetic complement of a particular individual, (C20), 692–693

Gentamicin, 338

Geriatrics, 699

Germ layers
 developmental contributions to the body, 680
 formation of, 678

Germinal centers: Pale regions in the interior of lymphoid tissues or nodules, where cell divisions are occurring, (C14), 475, 476

Germinative cells, 97, 124

Gestation (jes-TĀ-shun): The period of intrauterine development, (C20). *See* Pregnancy

Gigantism, 185, 369

Gingivae, 539, 541

Gingivitis, 565

Gland: Cells that produce exocrine or endocrine secretions, (C4), 94. *See also* specific types of glands

Gland cells, 94

Glandular epithelia, 101–103

Glandular epithelium, 94

Glans of the clitoris, 655, 656

Glans penis: Expanded tip of the penis that surrounds the urethral opening; continuous with the corpus spongiosum, (C19), 646, 647

Glaucoma: eye disorder characterized by rising intraocular pressures due to inadequate drainage of aqueous humor at the canal of Schlemm, (C9), 322, 340

Glenoid cavity (fossa), 167

Glenoid fossa: A rounded depression that forms the articular surface of the scapula at the shoulder joint, (C6), 167

Glial cells (GLĒ-al): Supporting cells in the neural tissue of the CNS and PNS, (C8), 248. *See also* **Neuroglia**

Gliding joints, 179, 180

Gliding movement, 176

Global aphasia, 272

Globular proteins: Proteins whose tertiary structure makes them rounded and compact, (C2), 47, 48

Globulins, 383, 384

Globus pallidus, 275

Glomerular (Bowman) capsule, 605, 606, 607

Glomerular filtration rate (GFR): The rate of filtrate formation at the glomerulus, (C18, 20)
 age-related changes, 628
 angiotensin II, 616
 explained, 610
 kidney function, normal, 613–617
 maternal, during pregnancy, 686

Glomerulonephritis, 629

Glomerulus (glo-MER-ū-lus): A ball or knot; in the kidneys, a knot of capillaries that projects into the enlarged, proximal end of a nephron; the site of filtration, the first step in the production of urine, (C18), 605, 606, 607, 610

Glossopharyngeal nerve (glos-ō-fah-RIN-jē-al): Cranial nerve IX, (C8, 9, 12, 15), 277, 278, 279, 280, 281, 293, 312, 315, 525

Glottis (GLOT-is): The passage from the pharynx to the larynx, (C15), 505, 506, 507

Glucagon (GLOO-ka-gon): Hormone secreted by the alpha cells of the pancreatic islets; elevates blood glucose concentrations, (C10, 12, 16), 364–365, 423, 552, 572

Glucocorticoids (GCs): Hormones secreted by the suprarenal (adrenal) cortex to modify glucose metabolism; cortisol, cortisone, and corticosterone are important examples, (C10, 14)
 ACTH, 353, 354
 Cushing disease, 371
 mineralocorticoid, 354, 361, 363
 resistance phase of general adaptation syndrome, 370

Gluconeogenesis (gloo-kō-nē-ō-JEN-e-sis): The synthesis of glucose from protein or lipid precursors, (C17), 581–582

Glucose (GLOO-kōs): A six-carbon sugar, $C_6H_{12}O_6$, the preferred energy source for most cells and the only energy source for neurons under normal conditions, (C2, 3), 41, 43, 361, 364–365

Glucose-sparing effect, 355, 361

Gluteal muscles, 215, 216, 232, 233, 234, 235

Gluteal nerve, 284

Gluteal region, 17

Gluteus maximus muscle, 216, 232, 233, 234, 235

Gluteus medius muscle, 215, 216, 233, 234, 235

Gluteus minimus muscle, 233, 234

Glycerides: Lipids composed of glycerol bound to 1 to 3 fatty acids, (C2, 16, 17). *See* **Triglycerides**

Glycerol, 44, 52

Glycogen (GLĪ-kō-jen): A polysaccharide that represents an important energy reserve: a polymer consisting of a long chain of glucose molecules, (C2, 17), 42, 43, 581, 582

Glycolipids, 64

Glycolysis (glī-KOL-i-sis): The anaerobic cytoplasmic breakdown of glucose by way of pyruvic acid, with a net gain of two ATP, (C3, 17)
 ATP generation, 209, 210
 carbohydrate metabolism, 577, 578, 582
 cytosol, taking place in, 77
 energy yield, 580

Glycoproteins, 64

Glycosuria, 366, 373, 629

Goblet cell. *See* **Mucous cell**

Goiter, 358, 371, 373

Golgi apparatus (GŌL-jē): Cellular organelle consisting of a series of membranous plates that gives rise to lysosomes and secretory vesicles, (C3), 61, 62, 75–76

Golgi tendon organs, 311

Gomphosis, 174

Gonadal arteries, 453, 454

Gonadal veins, 455, 458

Gonadotropic hormones: FSH and LH, hormones that stimulate gamete development and sex hormone secretion, (C10), 353

Gonadotropin-releasing hormone (GnRH) (gō-nad-ō-TRŌ-pin): Hypothalamic releasing hormone that causes the secretion of FSH and LH by the anterior pituitary gland, (C10, 19, 20), 353, 354
 female reproductive cycle, 657, 658
 leptin, 368
 male reproductive function, 647, 648
 puberty, 692
 source, regulation of, and primary effects, 663

Gonadotropins, 353, 357

Gonads (GŌ-nadz) (testes): Organs that produce gametes and hormones, (C1, 10, 19), 9, 348, 353, 367, 368, 639

Gonorrhea, 619, 653

Gout, 596, 598

Graafian follicle, 651, 657

Gracilis muscle, 215, 216, 232, 233, 234, 235

Graded potentials, 256

Graft-*versus*-host disease, 495

Grains, dietary guidelines for, 587, 588

Granulation tissue, 133, 134, 135

Granulocytes (GRAN-ū-lō-sīts): White blood cells containing granules visible with the light microscope; includes eosinophils, basophils, and neutrophils; also called *granular leukocytes*, (C11), 393

Graves disease, 493

Gravity, 333, 334

Gray commissures, 265, 266

Gray matter: Areas in the CNS dominated by neuron bodies, glial cells, and unmyelinated axons, (C8)
 CNS, 253, 254
 color, source of, 249
 neuron cell bodies, 251, 252
 PNS, 253
 spinal cord, 265, 266

Great cardiac vein, 414

Great saphenous vein, 455, 457

Great vessels, fetal, 460, 461

Greater curvature of the stomach, 544, 545

Greater omentum: A large fold of the dorsal mesentery of the stomach that hangs in front of the intestines, (C16), 544, 545

Greater trochanter, 171, 172

Greater tubercle of the humerus, 168

Greater vestibular glands, 656

Green cones, 325, 327

Groin: The inguinal region, (C1), 16, 17, 130, 218, 232

Gross (macroscopic) anatomy: The study of the structural features of the human body without the aid of a microscope, (C1), 3, 25

Ground substance of connective tissue, 103, 105

Growth
 cellular metabolism, 576
 function of living things, 2
 hormones, 369

Growth hormone (GH): Anterior pituitary hormone that stimulates tissue growth and anabolism when nutrients are abundant and restricts tissue glucose dependence when nutrients are in short supply, (C6, 10, 11, 20), 347, 354–355, 356, 357, 369, 371

Growth hormone-inhibiting hormone (GH-IH), 354, 355

Growth hormone-releasing hormone (GH-RH), 354, 355

GTP (guanosine triphosphate), 348, 579

Guanine: One of the nitrogenous bases found in nucleic acids, (C2, 3, 17), 49, 50

Guanosine triphosphate (GTP), 348, 579

Guillain-Barré syndrome, 253

Gustation (GUS-tā-shun): The sense of taste, (C9), 308, 314–315. *See also* Taste

Gustatory cells, 314

Gustatory cortex of the frontal lobe, 271

Gustatory receptors, 314

Gynecology, 666

Gyrus (JĪ-rus): A prominent fold or ridge of neural cortex on the surfaces of the cerebral hemispheres, (C8), 270

Inert gas, 32
Infancy, 691–692
Infants, skulls of, 160–161
Infarct: An area of dead cells resulting from an interruption of circulation, (C12), 415
Infection: Invasion and colonization of body tissues by pathogenic organisms, (C4, 10), 115
Inferior, use of term, 18, 19
Inferior articular process, 162
Inferior colliculus of the midbrain, 277, 337, 338
Inferior lobe of the left lung, 512, 513
Inferior lobe of the right lung, 512, 513
Inferior mesenteric artery, 453, 454
Inferior mesenteric vein, 459
Inferior nasal conchae, 157, 158, 159, 160
Inferior oblique muscle, 316, 317
Inferior rectus muscle, 316, 317
Inferior vena cava: The vein that carries blood from the parts of the body below the heart to the right auricle, (C10, 12, 13, 14, 16), 409, 411, 455, 456–458, 459
Infertility: Inability to conceive, (C19, 20), 640, 653, 660, 699
Inflammation: A nonspecific defense mechanism that operates at the tissue level, characterized by swelling, redness, warmth, and pain, (C4, 5, 11, 13, 14)
   antibody function, 489
   events during process of, 480, 481–482
   nonspecific defense, 480, 481–482
   purposes of, 481
   skin repair following injuries, 132–134
   tissue injury, response to, 115
Inflammatory bowel disease, 566
Inflation reflex: A reflex mediated by the vagus nerve that prevents overexpansion of the lungs, (C15), 524
Influenza, 528
Infraorbital foramen, 156, 157
Infraspinatus muscle, 168, 216, 226, 227, 229
Infraspinous fossa, 167, 168
Infundibulum (in-fun-DIB-ū-lum): A tapering, funnel-shaped structure; in the nervous system, the connection between the pituitary gland and the hypothalamus; in the uterine tube, the entrance bounded by fimbriae that receives the oocytes at ovulation, (C10, 19), 352, 653, 654
Ingestion: The introduction of materials into the digestive tract by the mouth, (C16), 535
Inguinal canal: A passage through the abdominal wall that marks the path of testicular descent and that contains the testicular arteries, veins, and ductus deferens, (C7, 19), 222, 644
Inguinal hernias, 222
Inguinal region: The area near the junction of the trunk and the thighs that contains the external genitalia; the groin, (C1), 17
Inheritance. See also Development and inheritance; Genetics
   defined, 673
   genetics, 692–698
   inherited disorders, 694–695
   patterns of, 693–696
   polygenic, 694–695
   predicting, 693–695
   sex-linked, 694, 695–696
   simple, 694, 695
Inhibin (in-HIB-in): A hormone produced by the nurse (sustentacular) cells of the testes and the follicular cells of the ovaries that inhibits the pituitary secretion of FSH, (C10, 19)
   female reproductive cycle, 657, 659
   follicle cells of the ovaries, 367, 368
   FSH and GnRH, 353, 354, 356
   nurse (sustentacular) cells of the testes, 367, 368
   nurse cells, 643
   ovaries, 649
   source, regulation of, and primary effects, 663
Inhibiting hormones, 351, 352
Inhibitory neurotransmitters, 261

Injection: Forcing of fluid into a body part or organ, (C1, 5, 7), 24, 128, 234, 239
Innate immunity, 482, 483
Inner cell mass: Cells of the blastocyst that will form the body of the embryo, (C20), 676, 677
Inner ear, 312, 329, 330, 331–332
Inner segment of a photoreceptor, 326
Innervation: The distribution of sensory and motor nerves to a specific region or organ, (C8). See Nervous system
Innominate vein (brachiocephalic vein), 455, 456, 457, 458
Inorganic compounds
   acids, bases, and salts, 40–41, 53
   carbon dioxide, 38, 53
   defined, 38
   oxygen, 38, 53
   water, 38–39, 53
Insensible perspiration, 594
Insertion: Point of attachment of a muscle; the end that is most movable, (C7), 217
Inspiration, 514
Inspiratory center, 523–524
Inspiratory reserve volume (IRV): The maximum amount of air that can be drawn into the lungs over and above the normal tidal volume, (C15), 517
Insula, 270, 271
Insulin (IN-su-lin): Hormone secreted by the beta cells of the pancreatic islets; causes a reduction in plasma glucose concentrations, (C10, 16), 364–365, 369. See also Diabetes mellitus
Insulin-dependent diabetes mellitus (IDDM), 373, 492
Insulin-like growth factors (ILGFs), 354–355, 356
Integration center and homeostatic regulation, 6
Integrative effect of hormones, 369
Integument (in-TEG-ū-ment): The skin, (C5). See Integumentary system; skin
Integumentary system, 121–141
   aging, effects of, 134–135
   autonomic nervous system, 295
   cardiovascular system, functional relationship with, 468
   circulation and blood supply, 126
   dermis, 122, 123, 127
   digestive system, functional relationship with, 572
   endocrine system, functional relationship with, 378
   epidermis, layers of, 123–125
   exercise, effect on, 238
   functional relationships with other systems, 140
   functions, 123
   general structure, 122–123
   hair, 128–130
   hypodermis, 122, 127–128
   lymphoid system, functional relationship with, 500
   muscular system, functional relationship with, 244
   nails, 131–132
   nervous system, functional relationship with, 304
   organs/components and primary functions, 7, 26
   prenatal and early postnatal development, overview of, 684
   professional profile, 141
   protection for other body systems, 135
   repair of, following injuries, 132–134
   reproductive system, functional relationship with, 670
   respiratory system, functional relationship with, 532
   sebaceous and sweat glands, 130–131
   skeletal system, functional relationship with, 192
   skin color, 124, 125–126
   sunlight, 125–126, 126–127
   urinary system, functional relationship with, 628, 636
Intensity (volume) of sound, 334, 335
Interatrial septum, 409, 411
Intercalated discs (in-TER-ka-lā-ted): Region where adjacent cardiocytes interlock and where gap junctions permit the movement of ions and action potentials between the cells, (C4, 7, 12), 112, 113, 213, 409, 410

Intercellular cement: A combination of protein and carbohydrate molecules, especially hyaluronic acid, between adjacent epithelial cells, (C4), 95
Interferons (in-ter-FĒR-onz): Peptides released by virus-infected cells, especially lymphocytes, that make other cells more resistant to viral infection and slow viral replication, (C14), 480, 481, 490, 491
Interleukin-1, 493
Interleukin-2, 494
Interleukins (in-ter-LOO-kinz): Peptides released by activated monocytes and lymphocytes that assist in the coordination of the cellular and humoral immune response, (C14), 490, 491
Interlobar arteries, 604, 605
Interlobar veins, 604, 605
Intermediate filaments, 73–74
Internal anal sphincter, 558, 559
Internal callus, 151
Internal carotid arteries, 441, 450, 451, 452
Internal ear: the membranous labyrinth that contains the organs of hearing and equilibrium, (C9)
Internal iliac arteries, 449, 453, 454
Internal iliac veins, 455, 457, 458
Internal intercostal muscle, 223, 224, 227
Internal jugular veins, 454, 455, 456, 457, 458
Internal nares: The entrance to the nasopharynx from the nasal cavity, (C15), 505, 506
Internal oblique muscle, 223, 224
Internal os (internal orifice), 654
Internal receptors: Sensory receptors monitoring the functions and status of internal organs and systems, (C8), 250
Internal respiration, 514
Internal thoracic artery, 450, 451
Internal urethral sphincter, 618
Interneurons: An association neuron; neurons inside the CNS that are interposed between sensory and motor neurons, (C8), 250
Internodes, 251, 252
Interphase: Stage in the life of a cell during which the chromosomes are uncoiled and all normal cellular functions are being performed, (C3), 83–84
Interstitial cells of the testes, 367, 368, 641, 642
Interstitial cell-stimulating hormone, 353, 648
Interstitial fluid (in-ter-STISH-ul): Fluid in the tissues that fills the spaces between cells, (C3, 8, 11, 13, 14, 15, 18), 60, 106, 621
Interstitial growth: Form of cartilage growth through the growth, mitosis, and secretion of chondrocytes inside the matrix.
Intertubercular groove, 168
Interventricular foramen, 267, 269
Interventricular septum, 409, 411
Intervertebral articulations, 179, 181
Intervertebral disc: Fibrocartilage pad between the bodies of successive vertebrae that acts as a shock absorber, (C6), 162, 174, 179, 181
Intervertebral foramen, 265
Intervertebral foramina, 162
Intestinal gas (flatus), 560
Intestinal glands, 549
Intestinal hormones, 550–551, 552
Intestinal juice, 549, 550
Intestinal movements
   large intestine, 560
   small intestine, 538, 549–550
Intestinal phase, of gastric secretion, 546, 547
Intestinal wall, small intestine, 548–549
Intestines
   endocrine functions, 366
   vitamin production, 590
Intracellular fluid (ICF): The cytosol, (C3, 8, 18), 72, 620–622, 622–623
Intracellular receptors, hormone interaction with, 349, 350
Intramembranous ossification (in-tra-MEM-bra-nus): The formation of bone within a connective tissue without the prior development of a cartilaginous model, (C6), 147
Intramural ganglia, 290

Intramuscular (IM) injection, 234, 239
Intrauterine device (IUD), 653, 664
Intrinsic eye muscles, 319
Intrinsic factor: A compound secreted by the parietal cells of the stomach that facilitates the intestinal absorption of vitamin B_{12}, (C16, 17), 390, 544, 565
Intrinsic muscles, 217, 232
Intrinsic pathway: A pathway of the clotting system within the bloodstream that begins with the activation of platelets and ends with the activation of Factor X, forming prothrombinase, (C11), 399–400
Introns, 81
Intubation, 509
Invasion by tumors, 86
Invasive ductal carcinomas, 657
Invasive lobular carcinomas, 657
Inversion: A turning inward, (C6, 7), 176, 178
Iodine, 31, 357, 358
Ion: An atom or molecule bearing a positive or negative charge due to the loss or gain of an electron, (C2, 18), 33, 381, 621, 622
Ion pumps, 69–70
Ionic bond (ī-ON-ik): Molecular bond created by the attraction between ions with opposite charges, (C2), 32–33
Ionic bonding, 33
Ionization (ī-on-i-ZA-shun): Dissociation; the breakdown of a molecule in solution to form ions, (C2), 39
Iris: A contractile structure made up of smooth muscle that forms the colored portion of the eye, (C9), 318, 319–320
Iron
dietary guidelines, 590
reserves, gender differences in, 388
significance in the human body, 31
Iron deficiency anemia, 388
Irregular bones, 144
Irritability of organisms, 2
Irritable bowel syndrome, 566
Ischemia (is-KĒ-mē-uh); Inadequate blood supply to a region of the body, (C7, 12), 239
Ischial tuberosity, 170
Ischiocavernosus muscle, 224, 225, 661
Ischium (IS-kē-um): One of the three bones whose fusion forms a coxal bone, (C6), 169, 170
Islets of Langerhans (pancreatic islets), 364
Isoleucine, 585
Isometric contraction: A muscular contraction characterized by rising tension production but no change in length, (C7), 207–208
Isotonic: A solution having an osmotic concentration that does not result in water movement across plasma membranes; of the same contractive strength, (C3), 67, 68
Isotonic contraction: A muscular contraction during which tension climbs and then remains stable as the muscle shortens, (C7), 207–208
Isotonic solution, 67–68
Isotopes: Forms of an element whose atoms contain the same number of protons but different numbers of neutrons (and thus differ in atomic weight), (C2), 31
Isthmus of the thyroid, 357, 358
Isthmus of the uterus, 654

J

Jaundice, 388, 401
Jejunum (je-JOO-num): The middle portion of the small intestine, (C16), 548
Joint: An area where adjacent bones interact; an articulation, (C1, 6). *See also* specific joints
classification of, 173–174
freely movable, 174–175
functions, 7
immovable, 174
mobility and strength, 179
slightly movable, 174

Joint capsule: Dense collagen fiber sleeve that surrounds a joint and provides protection and stabilization; also called *articular capsule,* (C6), 145, 174–175
Jugular notch, 165, 166
Jugular veins, 454, 455, 456, 457, 458
Jugular venuous pulse, 456
Juvenile-onset diabetes, 366, 373
Juxtaglomerular complex: The macula densa and the juxtaglomerular cells; a complex responsible for the release of renin and erythropoietin, (C18), 607, 608
Juxtaglomerular cells, 607, 608
Juxtamedullary nephrons, 604, 605

K

Karyotype, 693
Karyotyping (KAR-ē-ō-tī-ping): The determination of the chromosomal characteristics of an individual or cell, (C20), 693, 696
Keloids, 134, 135
Keratin (KER-a-tin): Tough, fibrous protein component of nails, hair, calluses, and the general integumentary surface, (C5), 47, 48, 124
Keratinization (ker-ah-tin-i-ZA-shun): The production of keratin by epithelial cells; also called *cornification,* (C5), 128, 684
Keratinized cells (ker-A-tin-īzed): Flattened, dead, densely packed epithelial cells, filled with keratin, (C5), 124–125
Keto acid, 585
Ketoacidosis, 585, 596
Ketone bodies: Organic acids produced during the catabolism of lipids and certain amino acids; acetone is one example, (C17, 18), 582, 585, 624–625
Ketonemia, 596
Ketonuria, 596
Ketosis, 585, 596
Kidney: A component of the urinary system; an organ functioning in the regulation of plasma composition, including the excretion of wastes and the maintenance of normal fluid and electrolyte balance, (C1, 18)
autonomic nervous system, 295
blood supply to, 604–605
endocrine functions, 366–367
endocrine system overview, 348
failure, treatment of, 615
functions, 9, 11
glomerular filtration rate, 613–617
hormonal control, 615–617
local regulation of, 614
location of, 602–603
nephron, 603, 605–608
summary of, 613, 614
superficial and sectional anatomy, 602, 603
sympathetic division of the ANS, 615
urinary system component, 601
Kidney stones, 617
Kidney transplant, 615
Killer T cells, 485
Kilocalorie (KIL-ō-kal-o-rē): The amount of heat required to raise the temperature of a kilogram of water 1°C, (C17), 593
Kinase enzymes, 348
Kinesiologists, 217
Kinetic energy, 36
Klinefelter syndrome, 698
Knee jerk (patellar) reflex, 284, 285
Knee joint, 183–184
Korotkoff sounds, 438
Krebs cycle (citric acid cycle), 209, 578–579
Kupffer cells (KOOP-fer): Phagocytic cells of the liver sinusoids, (C14, 16), 480, 485, 554, 555
Kwashiorkor, 586
Kyphosis, 162, 185

L

Labia (LA-bē-uh): Lips; labia majora and minora are components of the female external genitalia, (C1, 16, 19)
functions, 12
Labia majora, 655, 656
Labia minora, 655, 656
Labia of oral cavity (lips), 539
Labor
contractions, 688
goal of, 688
initiating and sustaining, 688
multiple births, 690
premature, 690
stages of, 688–690
Labyrinth: A maze of passageways; usually refers to the structures of the inner ear, (C9), 330, 331–332, 334
Lacrimal apparatus, 316
Lacrimal bones, 156, 157, 160
Lacrimal canals, 316
Lacrimal caruncle, 315–316
Lacrimal gland (LAK-ri-mal): Tear gland on the dorsolateral surface of the eye, (C9), 316
Lactase, 562, 563
Lactate ion, 210
Lactation (lak-TĀ-shun): The production of milk by the mammary glands, (C19, 20), 656, 691
Lacteal (LAK-tē-al): A terminal lymphatic within an intestinal villus, (C16), 549
Lactic acid: Compound produced from pyruvic acid under anaerobic conditions, (C2, 7, 18), 210, 614
Lactic acid recycling, 210–211
Lactiferous duct (lak-TIF-e-rus): Duct draining one lobe of the mammary gland, (C19), 656–657
Lactiferous sinus: An expanded portion of a lactiferous duct adjacent to the nipple of a breast, (C19), 656, 657
Lactose intolerance, 564
Lacuna (la-KOO-na): A small pit or cavity, (C4, 6), 108, 145, 146, 677
Lamboid suture (lam-BOYD): Synarthrotic articulation between the parietal and occipital bones of the cranium, (C6), 156, 157
Lamellae (lah-MEL-lē): concentric layers of bone within an osteon, (C6), 143, 145
Lamellated corpuscles, 310
Lamina (LAM-i-na): A thin sheet or layer, 162, 163
Lamina propria (LAM-i-na PRŌ-prē-uh): Loose connective tissue that underlies a mucous epithelium and forms part of a mucous membrane, (C4, 15, 16), 110, 504, 505, 536, 537
Laparoscopy, 566
Large bowel, 558–561
Large intestine: The terminal portions of the intestinal tract, consisting of the colon, the rectum and the anorectal canal, (C1, 16)
absorption in, 559–560
cecum, 558, 559
colon, 558, 559
defecation, 560–561
digestive system component, 536
functions, 11, 558–561
movements of, 560
rectum, 558, 559
sections of, 558, 559
Large veins, 431, 433
Laryngopharynx (la-rin-gō-FAR-inks): Division of the pharynx inferior to the epiglottis and superior to the esophagus, (C15, 16), 505, 506
Larynx (LAR-inks): A complex cartilaginous structure that surrounds and protects the glottis and vocal cords; the superior margin is bound to the hyoid bone, and the inferior margin is bound to the trachea, (C1, 6, 15), 10, 160, 505, 506–508
Latent period: The time between the stimulation of a muscle and the start of the contraction phase, (C7), 205
Lateral, use of term, 18, 19

MRI (magnetic resonance imaging), 24, 25, 26
Mucins, 101, 540
Mucosa (mū-KŌ-sa): A mucous membrane; the epithelium plus the lamina propria, (C4, 16), 110–111, 536–537
Mucous (adjective): Indicating the presence or production of mucus, 102
Mucous cell: A goblet-shaped, mucus-producing, unicellular gland in certain epithelia of the digestive and respiratory tracts; also called *goblet cells*, (C4, 15), 101, 504, 505
Mucous epithelium of the stomach, 544, 545
Mucous glands, 102, 103
Mucous membranes (mucosae), 110–111, 536
Mucus (noun): A lubricating fluid that is composed of water and mucins and is produced by unicellular and multicellular glands along the digestive, respiratory, urinary, and reproductive tracts, (C14, 15), 101
Multiple births, 690
Multiple sclerosis, 253, 297, 492
Multipolar neuron: A neuron with many dendrites and a single axon; the typical form of a motor neuron, (C8), 249, 250
Mumps, 540
Muscle: A contractile organ composed of muscle tissue, blood vessels, nerves, connective tissues, and lymphatics, (C7). *See* specific muscles
Muscle fibers
    elongation following contraction, 208
    frequency of stimulations, 205–206
    number of fibers activated, 206–207
Muscle spindles
    proprioceptors, 311
    stretch reflex, 284
Muscle tissue: A tissue characterized by the presence of cells capable of contraction; includes skeletal, cardiac, and smooth muscle tissues, (C4)
    body tissue type, 93
    cardiac, 112, 113
    skeletal, 112, 113
    smooth, 112, 113, 114
Muscles
    arteries, in, 430, 431
    cardiac muscle cells, 409, 410
    detrusor, 618
    eye, extrinsic, 316, 317
    intrinsic eye (pupillary), 319
    male genitalia, 640–641
    male reproductive system, 661
    muscle cramps, 239
    muscle fatigue, 210
    muscle tone, 207
    papillary, of heart valves, 411
    primary actions, 217
    stapedius muscle, 330
    tensor tympani muscle, 330
    trachealis, 508
    venous return, 434, 439
Muscular dystrophies, 199, 239
Muscular system, 194–245
    age, effect of, 235–236
    appendicular muscles, 215–216, 226–235, 236, 237, 238
    axial muscles, 215–216, 218–225
    cardiac and smooth muscle, 212–214
    cardiovascular system, functional relationship with, 468
    chapter review, 239–242
    digestive system, functional relationship with, 572
    endocrine system, functional relationship with, 378
    energy source for muscular activity, 208–211
    exercise, effect of, 236, 238
    functional relationships to other systems, 244
    integumentary system, functional relationship with, 140
    lymphoid system, functional relationship with, 500
    muscle contractions, 205–208
    muscle performance capabilities, 211–212
    nervous system, functional relationship with, 304

organs/components and primary functions, 8, 26
prenatal and early postnatal development, overview of, 684
professional profile, 245
related clinical terms, 239
reproductive system, functional relationship with, 670
respiratory system, functional relationship with, 532
review questions, 242–243
skeletal muscle, components of, 195–196
skeletal muscle, functions of, 195
skeletal muscle descriptive terms, 214–218
skeletal muscle fibers, 197–200
skeletal muscles and nervous system, communication with, 200–204
skeletal system, functional relationship with, 192
urinary system, functional relationship with, 636
Muscularis externa (mus-kū-LAR-is): Concentric layers of smooth muscle responsible for peristalsis, (C16), 537
Muscularis mucosae: Layer of smooth muscle beneath the lamina propria; responsible for moving the mucosal surface, (C16), 537
Musculocutaneous nerve, 284
Mutations, 81
Myalgia, 239
Myasthenia gravis, 200, 239, 493
Mycobacterium tuberculosis, 514
Myelin (MĪ-e-lin): Insulating sheath around an axon consisting of multiple layers of glial plasma membrane; significantly increases conduction rate along the axon, (C8, 14), 251, 252, 253, 258, 308–309
Myelination: The formation of myelin, (C8), 252, 298
Myelography, 297
Myeloid leukemia, 401
Myeloid stem cells, 382, 388
Myeloid tissue, 388
Myenteric plexus (mī-en-TER-ik): Parasympathetic motor neurons and sympathetic postganglionic fibers located between the circular and longitudinal layers of the muscularis externa, (C16), 537
Mylohyoid muscle, 220, 221
Myocardial infarction, 415, 424
Myocardium: The cardiac muscle tissue of the heart, (C12), 409, 410
Myofibril: Organized collections of myofilaments in skeletal and cardiac muscle cells, (C7), 197, 198
Myofilament: Protein filament consisting of the proteins actin and myosin; bundles of myofilaments from myofibrils, (C7), 197, 198
Myoglobin (MĪ-ō-glō-bin): An oxygen-binding pigment especially common in slow skeletal and cardiac muscle fibers, (C2), 47, 48, 211–212
Myogram: A recording of the tension produced by muscle fibers on stimulation, (C7), 205
Myoma, 239
Myometrium (mī-ō-MĒ-trē-um): The thick layer of smooth muscle in the wall of the uterus, (C19, 20), 654
Myopia, 325, 340
Myosin: Protein component of the thick myofilaments, (C3, 4, 7), 73, 112, 197, 198, 199
Myositis, 239
MyPyramid Plan, 587, 588
Myxedema, 373

N

NAD (nicotinamide adenine dinucleotide), 577, 578, 579
NADH, 579
Nails: Keratinous structure produced by epithelial cells of the nail root, (C1, 5)
    bed, 132
    body, 131–132
    cuticle, 132
    functions, 7
    lunula, 132
    root, 132

Nanometers, 30
Narcolepsy, 493
Nares, external (NĀ-rēz): The entrance from the exterior to the nasal cavity, (C15), 505, 532
Nares, internal: The entrance from the nasal cavity to the nasopharynx, (C15), 505, 506
Nasal bones, 156, 157, 159, 160
Nasal cavity: A chamber in the skull bounded by the internal and external nares, (C1, 9, 15, 16), 10, 504, 505
Nasal complex, 156, 157, 159, 160
Nasal conchae, 157, 158, 159, 160, 505, 506
Nasal septum, 157, 158, 160, 505–506
Nasal vestibule, 505
Nasolacrimal duct: Passageway that transports tears from the nasolacrimal sac to the nasal cavity, (C9, 15), 316
Nasolacrimal sac: Chamber that receives tears from the lacrimal ducts, 316
Nasopharynx (nā-zō-FAR-ingks): Region posterior to the internal nares, superior to the soft palate, and ending at the oropharynx, (C9, 15, 16), 329, 330, 505, 506
Naturally acquired active immunity, 482–483
Naturally acquired passive immunity, 483
Navicular bone, 172, 173
Near point of vision, 339
Nearsightedness (myopia), 325, 340
Neck
    arteries, 450–451, 452
    muscles of, 215–216, 219–221
    venous return from, 454, 455, 456, 457, 458
Neck of a spermatozoon, 643, 644
Neck of the gastric pit, 544, 545
Neck of the tooth, 540, 541
Neck of the urinary bladder, 618
Necrosis, 116, 482
Negative Babinski reflex, 286
Negative feedback: Corrective mechanism that opposes or reverses a variation for normal limits and restores homeostasis, (C1, 8, 10), 13–14, 26, 284, 353, 354
Neomycin, 338
Neonatal period, 690–691
Neonate: A newborn infant, (C20), 690
Neoplasm: A tumor, or mass of abnormal tissue, (C3), 86
Nephritis, 629
Nephrolithiasis, 617
Nephrology, 629
Nephron (NEF-ron): Basic functional unit of the kidney, (C18)
    age-related changes, 628
    collecting system, 605, 606, 608
    distal convoluted tubule, 603, 605, 607, 608
    functions of, 605–606
    location in renal cortex, 603
    loop, 605, 606, 608, 611
    overview of, 603, 605, 606
    proximal convoluted tubule, 605, 606, 608
    renal corpuscle, 603, 605, 606–608
Nerve deafness, 338, 340
Nerve fibers, 114
Nerve impulse: An action potential in a neuron cell membrane, (C7, 8, 12), 256
Nerve plexuses, 282, 283, 284
Nerves. *See also* specific nerves
    muscles, 196
    PNS axons, 253
Nervous system, 246–305
    aging, effect of, 195–196
    anatomical and functional divisions, 247–248
    autonomic nervous system, 289–295
    blood pressure and blood flow, control of, 439, 440–443
    brain, 267–278
    cardiovascular system, functional relationship with, 468
    digestive system, functional relationship with, 572
    endocrine system, differences from, 346

of a tube such as the digestive tract, the ureters, or the ductus deferens, (C16, 19), 538

Peritoneal cavity, 22, 26

Peritoneal fluid, 538, 621

Peritoneum (per-i-tō-NĒ-um): The serous membrane that lines the peritoneal (abdominopelvic) cavity, (C1, 4, 18), 22, 26, 111

Peritonitis, 116, 566

Peritubular capillaries: A network of capillaries that surrounds the proximal and distal convoluted tubules of the kidneys, (C18), 604, 605

Permanent dentition, 541, 542

Permeability: Ease with which dissolved materials can cross a membrane; if freely permeable, any molecule can cross the membrane; if impermeable, nothing can cross. Most biological membranes are selectively permeable, and some materials can cross, (C3), 64–65, 254, 255, 256, 257

Permissive effect of hormones, 369

Pernicious anemia, 390, 493

Peroneus (fibularis) muscles, 215, 233, 237, 238

Peroxisomes, 61, 62, 76

Perpendicular plate of the ethmoid bone, 157, 158

Perspiration, 39, 131

PET (positron emission tomography) scans, 25

Peyer patches, 475–476

pH: The negative exponent of the hydrogen ion concentration, expressed in moles per liter; solutions may be acidic (7), neutral (7), or basic (7), (C2)
blood, in, 312, 382, 602
blood, regulation by, 381
body fluids, 39, 41, 624
oxygen release by hemoglobin, 520–521
saliva, 540
tissues, in, and muscle fatigue, 210
urine, in, 613

Phagocyte: A cell that performs phagocytosis, (C3, 4, 8, 11, 14), 479–480, 489

Phagocytic regulators, 490, 491

Phagocytize, use of term, 104

Phagocytosis (fag-ō-sī-TŌ-sis): The engulfing of extracellular materials or pathogens; movement of extracellular materials into the cytoplasm by enclosure in a membranous vesicle, (C3, 11), 71, 395, 489

Phalanx/phalanges (fa-LAN-jēz): A bone of the fingers or toes, (C6)
fingers, 155, 169, 170
toes, 155, 172, 173

Pharmacology: The study of drugs, their physiological effects, and their clinical uses.

Pharyngeal phase of swallowing, 542, 543

Pharyngeal tonsil, 475, 476, 505, 506

Pharyngotympanic tube: A passageway that connects the nasopharynx with the middle ear cavity; also called *Eustachian tube* or *auditory tube*, (C9, 15), 329, 330. *See also* Auditory (Eustachian) tube

Pharynx: The throat; a muscular passageway shared by the digestive and respiratory tracts, (C1, 15, 16)
digestive system, 536, 542, 543
functions, 10, 11
respiratory system, 505, 506
respiratory system contamination, 504

Phenotype (FĒN-ō-tīp): Physical characteristics that are genetically determined, (C20), 693

Phenotypic characters, 693

Phenylalanine, 585

Phenylketonuria (PKU), 53, 586, 596

Phlebitis, 462

Phlebotomy, 401

Phosphate, requirements for, 149

Phosphate buffer system, 625–626, 627

Phosphate group: PO_4^{3-}, (C2, 3), 45, 49, 50, 51, 52, 63

Phosphate ions, 143

Phosphodiesterase, 348

Phospholipid (FOS-fō-lip-id): An important membrane lipid whose structure includes hydrophilic and hydrophobic regions, (C2, 3, 17), 43, 45, 63, 583, 584

Phospholipid bilayer, 63

Phosphorus
dietary guidelines, 590
significance in the human body, 31

Phosphorylation (fos-for-i-LĀ-shun): The addition of a high-energy phosphate group to a molecule, (C10), 348

Photons, 324

Photoreception: Sensitivity to light, (C9), 327

Photoreceptors
light characteristics, 324
photoreception, 327
rods and cones, 325–326
structure of, 326–327
visual pathway, 327–329

Photorefractive keratectomy (PRK), 325

Phrenic arteries, 451, 453, 454

Phrenic nerve, 284

Phrenic veins, 455, 458

Physical activity in MyPyramid Plan, 587, 588

Physical barriers as nonspecific defense, 479, 480

Physical conditioning, and muscle performance, 212

Physical therapist, 245

Physician assistant, 469

Physiology (fiz-ē-OL-o-jē): Literally the study of the function; considers the ways living organisms perform vital activities, (C1)
defined, 3, 25
science of, 3–4

Pia mater: The innermost layer of the meninges that surrounds the CNS, (C8), 263

Pigmentation of skin, 124, 125–126

Pigmented part of the retina, 318, 320, 321

Pineal gland (PIN-ē-al): Neural tissue in the posterior portion of the roof of the diencephalon, responsible for the secretion of melatonin, (C1, 8, 9, 10), 9, 267, 268, 276, 277, 348, 363–364

Pinna (auricle), 329, 330. *See also* Auricle (ear)

Pinocytosis (pi-nō-sī-TŌ-sis): The introduction of fluids into the cytoplasm by enclosing them in membranous vesicles at the cell surface, (C3), 71

Pisiform bone, 169, 170

Pitch of sound, 334, 335

Pituitary dwarfism, 369

Pituitary gland: Endocrine organ situated in the sella turcica of the sphenoid bone and connected to the hypothalamus by the infundibulum; includes the posterior pituitary and the anterior pituitary glands, (C1, 6, 8, 10)
anterior pituitary, 352–355, 357
endocrine system overview, 348
functions, 9
hypothalamus, 267
location, 352
posterior pituitary, 353, 355–356, 357

Pivot joints, 179, 180

PKU (phenylketonuria), 53, 586, 596

Placenta (pla-SEN-tuh): A complex structure in the uterine wall that permits diffusion between the fetal and maternal circulatory systems; also called *afterbirth*, (C13, 20)
blood supply, 460
circulation, 681–682
as endocrine organ, 367
endocrine organ, as, 682
formation of, 679, 680, 681–682
hormones of, affecting mammary glands, 656

Placenta previa, 699

Placental prolactin, 682

Placental stage of labor, 689–690

Placentation, 679, 680, 681–682

Planes of section, 19, 20

Plantar arch, 449, 454

Plantar flexion, 176, 178

Plantar: Referring to the sole of the foot, 16, 17

Plantar reflex, 286

Plantar region, 16, 17

Plantar veins, 457

Plantar venous arch, 455, 457

Plaque, arterial, 424, 432

Plasma (PLAZ-muh): The fluid ground substance of whole blood; what remains after the cells have been removed from a sample of whole blood, (C4, 11, 18)
blood, element of, 382, 383
carbon dioxide transport, 521
composition of, 382, 383, 384
extracellular fluid, 621
fluid connective tissue, 106
proteins in, 383, 384
solute concentrations, 609

Plasma cells: Activated B cells that secrete antibodies, (C4, 11, 14), 384, 474, 486, 487

Plasma membrane: A cell membrane, (C3)
active transport across, 68–71, 72
cell anatomy and components, 61, 62
cell anatomy overview, 60
cholesterol, 45
diffusion across, 65–66
functions, 60–61, 62
hormonal action at, 347–348, 350
membrane carbohydrates, 64
membrane lipids, 63
membrane proteins, 63–64
osmosis across, 67
passive transport across, 64–68, 72
structure of, 62, 63

Plasmin, 401

Plasminogen, 401

Plateau period after cardiac muscle cell depolarization, 415, 416

Platelet factor, 399–400

Platelet phase of hemostasis, 398

Platelet plugs, 398

Platelets (PLĀT-lets): Small packets of cytoplasm that contain enzymes important in the clotting response; manufactured in the bone marrow by cells called megakaryocytes, (C4, 11), 106, 382, 383, 389, 397, 398
origins and differentiation of, 389

Platys: Flat, (C7), 195

Platysma, 219, 221

Pleura (PLOO-ra): The serous membrane lining the pleural cavities, (C1, 4, 15), 22, 111, 512, 513

Pleural cavities: Subdivisions of the thoracic cavity that contain the lungs, (C1, 15), 22, 26, 512–513

Pleural effusion, 116

Pleural fluid, 513, 621

Pleurisy, 528

Pleuritis, 116

Plexus: A network or braid. *See* specific plexuses

Plica circulares (PLĪ-ka): A permanent transverse fold in the wall of the small intestine, (C16), 548, 549

Pluripotent stem cells, 388

Pneumocystis carinii, 512

Pneumon: Lung, (C15), 503

Pneumonia, 512, 528

Pneumotachometer, 517

Pneumothorax, 513, 528

PNS. *See* Peripheral nervous system (PNS)

Podocyte (PŌ-do-sīt): A cell whose processes surround the glomerular capillaries and assist in filtration, (C18), 606, 607

Point mutation, 81

Polar body: A nonfunctional packet of cytoplasm containing chromosomes eliminated from an oocyte durig meiosis, (C19, 20), 649, 651

Polar covalent bond: A form of covalent bond in which there is an unequal sharing of electrons, (C2), 34

Polar molecules, 34

Polarized plasma membranes, 254

Polio, 239

Pollex: The thumb, (C6), 169

Polycythemia, 401

Polydipsia, 355

Polygenic inheritance, 694–695

Polymer: A large molecule consisting of a long chain of subunits.

Polypeptide: A chain of amino acids strung together by peptide bonds; those containing over 100 peptides are called proteins, (C2), 46, 47, 48

Polyps, 566

Polysaccharide (pol-ē-SAK-uh-rīd): A complex sugar, such as glycogen or starch, (C2), 42, 43, 52

Polyspermy, 675

Polysynaptic reflex: A reflex with interneurons interposed between the sensory fiber and the motor neuron(s), (C8), 285

Polyunsaturated fats: Fatty acids containing carbon atoms linked by double bonds, (C2), 44

Polyuria, 355, 366, 373

Pons: The portion of the brain anterior to the cerebellum, (C8), 267, 268, 277, 278, 523, 525, 526

Popliteal (pop-LIT-ē-al): Pertaining to the back of the knee, 16, 454, 457

Popliteal artery, 438, 449, 454

Popliteal vein, 455, 457

Popliteus muscle, 232, 235, 236

Portal area (hepatic triad), 554, 555

Portal system, hepatic, 458

Portal system of anterior pituitary gland, 352, 353

Portal vessels, hepatic, 458

Portal vessels of anterior pituitary gland, 352, 353

Positive Babinski reflex, 286

Positive chemotaxis
  white blood cells, 395

Positive feedback: Mechanism that increases a deviation from normal limits following an initial stimulus, (C1), 14–15, 26

Positive feedback loop, 14–15

Positron emission tomography (PET) scans, 25

Postcentral gyrus of the parietal lobe, 271

Post-coital contraception, 664

Posterior, use of term, 18, 19

Posterior cavity of the eye, 316–317, 318, 322

Posterior chamber of the anterior cavity of the eye, 317, 318, 322

Posterior column pathway, 287, 288

Posterior cruciate ligament, 183, 184

Posterior gray horns, 265, 266

Posterior interventricular (descending) branch, coronary arteries, 414

Posterior interventricular sulcus, 408

Posterior median sulcus of spinal cord, 264, 265

Posterior pituitary gland, 353, 355–356, 357

Posterior semicircular ducts, 331, 332

Posterior tibial artery, 438, 449, 454

Posterior tibial vein, 455, 457

Posterior: Toward the back, dorsal, (C1), 18, 19

Posterior white column, 265, 266

Postganglionic fiber: The axon of a ganglionic neuron, (C8), 290, 291

Postnatal development
  adolescence, 690, 692
  childhood, 687, 690, 691–692
  continuous process, 673
  early, overview of, 684–685
  infancy, 690, 691–692
  neonatal, 690–691

Postovulatory phase: The secretory phase of the menstrual cycle, (C19), 658

Postsynaptic neuron, 259

Potassium
  aldosterone, 361
  dietary guidelines, 589, 590
  electrolyte balance, 623–624
  exhaustion phase of general adaptation syndrome, 372
  membrane potential, 254–255
  regulation of, by urinary system, 602
  significance in the human body, 31

Potential difference: The separation of opposite charges; requires a barrier that prevents ion migration, (C8), 254

Potential energy, 36

Pott's fracture, 150

Precapillary sphincter, 432, 433

Precentral gyrus: The primary motor cortex of a cerebral hemisphere, anterior to the central sulcus, (C8), 270–271

Precipitation, 488

Precocious puberty, 372

Pre-embryo, 653

Prefrontal cortex, 272, 273

Prefrontal lobotomy, 272

Preganglionic fibers, 290, 291

Preganglionic neuron: Visceral motor neuron inside the CNS whose output controls one or more ganglionic motor neurons in the PNS, (C8)
  autonomic nervous system, 290
  parasympathetic division of the ANS, 293, 294
  sympathetic division of the ANS, 291, 292

Pregnancy
  described, 675
  ectopic, 676, 699
  first trimester, 675, 676–682
  labor and delivery, 688–690
  maternal changes during, 686–687
  maternal systems, effects on, 686–687
  mortality rate in U.S., 665
  multiple births, 690
  premature labor, 690
  second trimester, 675, 682–683, 686–688
  third trimester, 675, 682–683, 686–688
  trimesters in, 675

Premature delivery, 690

Premature labor, 690

Premature menopause, 662

Premolars: Bicuspids; teeth with flattened surfaces located anterior to the molar teeth, (C16), 541

Premotor cortex, 271

Prenatal development, 673, 684–685

Preovulatory phase: A portion of the menstrual cycle; period of estrogen-induced repair of the functional zone of the endometrium through the growth and proliferation of epithelial cells in the glands not lost during menses, (C19), 652, 657–658, 659

Prepuce (PRĒ-pūs): Loose fold of skin that surrounds the glans penis in males or the clitoris in females, (C19)
  clitoris, 655, 656
  glans penis, 646, 647

Preputial glands, 646, 647

Presbycusis, 339

Presbyopia, 325, 339, 340

Pressure
  blood flow, affecting, 434, 435
  lungs, airflow to, 514–516

Pressure gradient, 434, 515

Pressure points, 438

Presynaptic membrane: The synaptic surface where neurotransmitter release occurs, (C8), 259, 260

Presynaptic neuron, 259

Prickling pain, 308–309

Primary amenorrhea, 655

Primary follicles, 651, 652

Primary germ layers, 678, 679

Primary memories, 274

Primary motor cortex, 271

Primary oocytes, 649, 651

Primary response to antigen exposure, 489–490

Primary sensory cortex, 271

Primary spinal curves, 161–162

Primary teeth, 541, 542

Primary tumors (primary neoplasms), 86, 87

Prime mover: A muscle that performs a specific action, (C7), 217

Primitive streak of the inner cell mass, 678

Primordial follicles, 649, 652

Process: A projection or bump of the skeleton, (C6). *See* specific processes

Product of an enzymatic reaction, 48

Products of chemical reactions, 35

Proenzymes, 398, 553

Professional profiles
  burn center specialist, 141
  dental assistant, 573
  health educator, 637
  mammographer, 671
  nurse practitioner, 501
  physical therapist, 245
  respiratory therapist, 533
  sports trainer, 193
  X-ray technologist, 305

Progesterone (prō-JES-ter-ōn): The most important progestin secreted by the corpus luteum following ovulation, (C10, 19, 20)
  corpus luteum, 367
  female reproductive cycle, 658, 659
  LH, 353, 356
  placental hormone, 682
  progesterone-only contraceptives, 664
  source, regulation of, and primary effects, 663
  uterine cycle, 658–660
  uterus, effect on, during pregnancy, 687–688

Progestins (prō-JES-tinz): Steroid hormones structurally related to cholesterol, (C10, 19)
  corpus luteum, 367, 368
  female reproductive cycle, 658
  LH, 353, 354
  ovaries, 649
  source, regulation of, and primary effects, 663

Prolactin (prō-LAK-tin) (PRL): Hormone that stimulates functional development of the mammary gland in females; a secretion of the anterior pituitary gland, (C10, 20), 347, 354, 356, 357

Prolactin-inhibiting hormone, 354

Prolactin-releasing factor, 354

Proliferative phase of the uterine cycle, 655

Promoter region of DNA, 79

Pronation (prō-NĀ-shun): Rotation of the forearm that makes the palm face posteriorly, (C6, 7), 169, 176, 178

Pronator muscle, 215, 230, 231

Prone, use of term, 16, 26

Pronucleus: Enlarged egg or sperm nucleus that forms after fertilization but before amphimixis, (C20), 674, 675

Prophase (PRŌ-fāz): The initial phase of mitosis, characterized by the appearance of chromosomes, breakdown of the nuclear membrane, and formation of the spindle apparatus, (C3), 83, 84, 85

Prophylactic (condom), 653, 664

Proprioception (prō-prē-ō-SEP-shun): Awareness of the positions of bones, joints, and muscles, (C8, 9), 308

Proprioceptors, 250, 311–312

Prostaglandin (pros-tuh-GLAN-din): A fatty acid secreted by one cell that alters the metabolic activities or sensitivities of adjacent cells; also called *local hormones*, (C10, 17, 19, 20)
  lipid derivative hormones, 347
  local hormone (cytokine), 347
  uterus, effect on, during pregnancy, 688

Prostate cancer, 666

Prostate gland (PROS-tāt): Accessory gland of the male reproductive tract, contributing roughly one-third of the volume of semen, (C1, 18, 19), 12, 640, 645–646

Prostatectomy, 666

Prostatic fluid, 645

Prostatitis (prostatic inflammation), 646

Proteases, 553, 562, 563

Proteasomes, 61, 62, 74

Protein: A large polypeptide with a complex structure, (C2)
  amino acids, 46–48, 52, 53
  catabolic and anabolic pathways, 586
  cell membrane, 63–64
  digestion and absorption, 562, 563, 564
  elderly people, 596
  enzymes, 46, 48–49
  functions, 46, 53

plasma, in, 383, 384
structure, 46–48, 52, 53
Protein buffer systems, 625
Protein deficiency diseases, 585–586, 596
Protein metabolism
amino acid catabolism, 585, 586
amino acids and protein synthesis, 585–586
ATP yield, 584–585
Protein synthesis, 80–83
Proteinuria, 629
Proteolytic enzymes, 544
Prothrombin: Circulating proenzyme of the common pathway of the clotting system; converted to thrombin by the enzyme prothrombinase, (C11, 16)
common pathway in clotting process, 399, 400
vitamin K, 560
Proton: A subatomic particle bearing a positive charge, (C2), 30, 31
Protraction: To move anteriorly in the horizontal plane, (C6, 7), 176, 178
Proximal, use of term, 18, 19
Proximal convoluted tubule, 605, 606, 608, 611
Proximal: Toward the attached base of an organ or structure, (C1), 18, 19
Pruritis, 135
Pseudopodia (soo-dō-PŌ-dē-ah): Temporary cytoplasmic extensions typical of mobile or phagocytic cells, (C3), 71
Pseudostratified epithelium: An epithelium containing several layers of nuclei but whose cells are all in contact with the underlying basement membrane, (C4), 100, 101
Psoas major muscle, 223, 232, 233, 234, 235
Psoriasis, 135, 493
Pterygoid muscle, 219, 220
Puberty: Period of rapid growth, sexual maturation, and the appearance of secondary characteristics, usually occurs at age 10–15, (C5, 6, 10)
adolescence beginning at, 692
descent of the testes, 640
precocious, 372
Pubic angle, 171
Pubic region, 17
Pubic symphysis: Fibrocartilaginous amphiarthrosis between the pubic bones of the ossa coxae, (C6, 19), 170
Pubis (PŪ-bis): The anterior, inferior component of the os coxae, (C1, 6), 169, 170
Pudendum, 656
Pulled groin, 232
Pulled hamstring, 232
Pulmonary arteries, 447, 448
Pulmonary circuit: Blood vessels between the pulmonary semilunar valve of the right ventricle and the entrance to the left atrium; the blood circulation through the lungs, (C12)
cardiovascular system, 406
described, 447–448
functional patterns, 446–447
partial pressures of oxygen and carbon dioxide, 519, 520
respiratory membrane of the alveoli, 512
Pulmonary embolism, 400, 461, 462, 512, 528
Pulmonary function tests, 517
Pulmonary semilunar valve, 411
Pulmonary trunk, 411, 447, 448
Pulmonary valve, 41
Pulmonary veins, 447, 448
Pulmonary ventilation: Movement of air into and out of the lungs, (C15), 514–518
Pulp cavity: Internal chamber in a tooth, containing blood vessels, lymphatics, nerves, and the cells that maintain the dentin, (C16), 540, 541
Pulse
checking, 438
described, 435
Pulse pressure, 435–436
Punnett square, 694, 695–696

Pupil: The opening in the center of the iris through which light enters the eye, (C9), 318, 319
Pupillary muscles, 318
Purkinje cell (pur-KIN-jē): Large, branching neuron of the cerebellar cortex, (C12), 418
Purkinje fibers: Specialized conducting cardiocytes in the ventricles, (C12), 416, 417–418
Pus: An accumulation of debris, fluid, dead and dying cells, and necrotic tissue, (C14), 482
Putamen, 275
Pyelitis, 619
Pyelogram, 629
Pyelonephritis, 619, 629
Pyloric sphincter (pī-LOR-ik): Sphincter of smooth muscle that regulates the passage of chyme from the stomach to the duodenum, (C16), 544
Pylorus (pī-LOR-us): Gastric region between the body of the stomach and the duodenum; includes the pyloric sphincter, (C16), 544, 545
Pyramidal cells of the cerebral cortex, 288
Pyramidal system (corticospinal pathway), 287, 288, 289
Pyrexia, 596
Pyrogens, 482
Pyruvic acid (pī-RŪ-vik): A three-carbon compound produced by glycolysis, (C3, 7, 17)
acids in the body, 624
aerobic metabolism, 209, 210–211
glycolysis, 77
glycolysis, 577, 578, 582

Q

QRS complex of the EKG, 418, 419
Quadrate lobe of the liver, 554
Quadratus lumborum muscle, 222, 223
Quadriceps femoris muscles, 171, 172, 232
Quadriplegia, 265, 297
Quality of nutrients, 589
Quantity of nutrients, 589
Quiet breathing, 516, 524

R

Radial artery, 438, 449, 450, 451
Radial fossa, 168
Radial nerve, 284
Radial notch of the ulna, 169
Radial tuberosity, 169
Radial vein, 455, 456, 457, 458
Radiation of heat, 594
Radiodensity: Relative resistance to the passage of x-rays, (C1), 23
Radioisotopes, 31, 53
Radiological procedures, 23–24, 26
Radiologists, 23, 25
Radiology, 25
Radiopharmaceuticals, 53
Radius, 155, 168–169
Ramus: A branch, (C6), 160
Rapid depolarization of cardiac contractile cells, 415, 416
Reabsorption, in urine formation, 609–610, 611–612
Reactants, 35
Reaction times, 296
Receptive field, 307, 308
Receptor proteins, 64
Receptor site for facilitated diffusion, 69
Receptor-mediated endocytosis, 70–71, 72
Receptors
homeostatic regulation, 6, 13, 26
sensory information, 247
Recessive allele, 693–695
Recessive gene: An allele that will affect the phenotype only when the individual is homozygous for that trait, (C20)
Reciprocal inhibition, 286
Recognition proteins, 64
Recombinant DNA, 87
Recovery period of muscle contractions, 210–211

Recruitment of motor units of muscle fibers, 207
Rectum (REK-tum): The last 15 cm (6 in.) of the digestive tract, (C16, 18, 19), 558, 559
Rectus abdominis muscle, 223, 224
Rectus femoris muscle, 215, 232, 233, 235, 236
Rectus: Straight, 217
Red blood cells (RBCs) (erythrocytes)
blood, in, 382, 383
blood as fluid connective tissue, 106
erythropoietin, 366
formation of, 388–391
hemoglobin structure and function, 385–386
hemolytic disease of the newborn, 394
life span and circulation, 386–388
maturation of, 388–389
numbers of, 384–385, 391
origins and differentiation of, 389
overview of, 397
red blood cell count, 384, 391
skeletal system, production in, 143
structure, 385
tests for, 390, 391
Red bone marrow, 143, 388
Red cones, 325, 327
Red muscles, 212
Red pulp of the spleen, 478
Referred pain, 309
Reflex: A rapid, automatic response to a stimulus, (C8), 283. *See also* specific reflexes
Reflex arc: The receptor, sensory neuron, motor neuron, and effector involved in a particular reflex; may include interneurons, (C8), 284, 285
Reflex centers, 278
Reflexes
complex, 285–286
defined, 283
respiration, control of, 524–526
simple, 284–285
spinal, integration and control of, 286
Reflux, 543
Refraction of light, 323–324
Refraction: The bending of light rays as they pass from one medium to another, (C9), 323–324
Refractory period: Period between the initiation of an action potential and the restoration of the normal resting potential; during this period, the membrane will not respond normally to stimulation, (C8, 12), 256–257, 415–416
Regeneration
inflammation, 481
spinal cord, 265
tissue, 115, 116
Regional anatomy, 3, 25
Regions of the human body, 17
Regulatory hormones, 351
Regulatory T cells, 473
Regurgitation of blood through valves, 412
Relaxation phase: The period, following a contraction, when the tension in the muscle fiber returns to resting levels, (C7), 205
Relaxin: Hormone that loosens the pubic symphysis; a hormone secreted by the placenta, (C20), 682
Releasing hormones, 351, 352
Remission, 116
Remodeling of bone, 149–150
Renal arteries, 453–454, 604–605
Renal columns, 603
Renal compensation for acid-base disorders, 627
Renal corpuscle: The initial portion of the nephron, consisting of an expanded chamber that encloses the glomerulus, (C18), 603, 605, 606–608
Renal cortex, 603
Renal failure, 615, 629
Renal medulla, 603
Renal papilla, 603
Renal pelvis, 603, 618
Renal: Pertaining to the kidneys, 603
Renal pyramids, 603
Renal sinus, 603

ossification and appositional growth, 147–149
osteopenia, 152
prenatal and early postnatal development, overview of, 684
professional profile, 193
reproductive system, functional relationship with, 670
respiratory system, functional relationship with, 532
skeletal divisions, 152, 154, 155
skeleton, 154, 155
surface features, 152, 153
synovial joints, 176–179, 180
urinary system, functional relationship with, 636
Skill memories, 274
Skin. *See also* Integumentary system
autonomic nervous system, 295
cancer, 125–126, 126–127
color, 125–126, 693–695
Skleros: Hard, (C9, C13), 307, 429
Skull(s)
axial skeleton, 152, 155
bones of, 152, 155–161
flat bone, 144
infants and children, 160–161
intramembranous ossification, 147
surface markings, 153
Sliding filament theory: The concept that a sarcomere shortens as the thick and thin filaments slide past one another, (C7), 199
Slightly movable joints (amphiarthroses), 173, 174
Slipped disc, 181
Slow pain, 309
Slow skeletal muscle fibers, 211–212
Small intestine: The duodenum, jejunum, and ilieum; the digestive tract between the stomach and large intestine, (C1, 16)
digestion in, 551
digestive system component, 536
functions, 11
hormones, 550–551, 552
intestinal movements, 538, 549–550
intestinal wall, 548–549
secretions, 550
segments of, 548
Small saphenous vein, 455, 457
Smegma, 646
Smell
aging, effect of, 339
olfactory pathways, 313–314
organs of, 312–313
special sense, 308
Smoking, 525
Smooth endoplasmic reticulum (SER): Membranous organelle where lipid and carbohydrate synthesis and storage occur, (C3), 61, 62, 75
Smooth muscle
skeletal and cardiac muscle, comparison of, 214
structure and function, 212, 213, 214
Smooth muscle tissue: Contractile tissue found in the walls of many visceral organs; characterized as nonstriated involuntary muscle, (C4), 112, 113, 114
Sodium
aldosterone, 361
dietary guidelines, 589, 590
electrolyte balance, 623
membrane potential, 254–255
regulation of, by urinary system, 602
significance in the human body, 31
Sodium bicarbonate, 553
Sodium chloride, 33
Sodium-potassium exchange pump, 69–70, 255
Soft keratin, 128
Soft palate: Fleshy posterior extension of the hard palate, separating the nasopharynx from the oral cavity, (C15, 16), 505, 506, 539
Sole: The inferior surface of the foot, (C6), 16, 17
Soleus muscle, 215, 216, 232, 237, 238
Solute: Materials dissolved in a solution, (C2), 39, 66–67

Solvent: The fluid component of a solution, (C2), 39
Somatic (nonreproductive) cell division, 642
Somatic (sō-MAT-ik): Pertaining to the body, 83, 86
Somatic cells, 83, 673
Somatic motor association area, 271
Somatic motor neurons, 250
Somatic nervous system
autonomic nervous system, 290
motor pathways, 288
PNS, division of, 248
Somatic sensory association area, 271
Somatic sensory receptors, 250
Somatomedins: Compounds stimulating tissue growth, released by the liver following GH secretion, (C10), 354–355, 356
Somatotropin, 354
Sound
hearing, 334–338, 339
production by vocal cords, 507–508
sounds of Korotkoff, 438
Sour taste, 314, 315
Special physiology, 3, 25
Special senses
age, effect of, 339
hearing and equilibrium, 329–339
prenatal and early postnatal development, 684
smell, 312–314, 339
taste, 314–315, 339
vision, 315–329, 339
Specific defenses
lymphoid system, 471, 479, 482–484
white blood cells, 395
Specific gravity of urine, 613
Specific resistance, 479
Specificity, and immunity, 483
Specificity of enzymatic reactions, 49
Speech center, 272–273
Sperm count, 646
Sperm duct, 12
Spermatic cord: Spermatic vessels, nerves, lymphatics, and the ductus deferens, extending between the testes and the proximal end of the inguinal canal, (C19), 644
Spermatids (SPER-ma-tidz): The product of meiosis in the male, cells that differentiate into spermatozoa, (C19), 641, 642, 643
Spermatocyte (sper-MA-to-sīt): Cells of the seminiferous tubules that are engaged in meiosis, (C19), 641, 642
Spermatogenesis (sper-ma-to-JEN-e-sis): Sperm production, (C19), 641, 642–643, 647–648
Spermatogonia (sper-ma-to-GŌ-nē-uh): Stem cells whose mitotic divisions give rise to other stem cells and spermatocytes, (C19), 641, 642
Spermatozoa/spermatozoon (sper-ma-to-ZŌ-a): Sperm cells, 639, 641, 642, 643–644, 646
Spermicidal jelly and cream, 664
Spermiogenesis: The process of spermatid differentiation that leads to the formation of physically mature spermatozoa, (C19), 642, 643
Sphenoid bone, 156, 157, 158, 159
Sphenoidal sinuses, 158, 159, 160, 506
Sphincter (SFINK-ter): Muscular ring that contracts to close the entrance or exit of an internal passageway, 213. *See also* specific sphincters
Sphygmomanometer, 438, 462
Spina bifida, 185
Spinal accessory nerves, 277, 278, 279, 281
Spinal cord
central canal, ependymal cells in, 252
CNS, division of, 247
functions, 8
gross anatomy, 264–265
injuries, 265, 620
meninges, 262–263
overview of, 267
sectional anatomy, 265–266
Spinal curvature, 161–162
Spinal meninges, 262–263
Spinal meningitis, 264, 297

Spinal nerve: One of 31 pairs of peripheral nerves that originate on the spinal cord from anterior and posterior roots, (C6, 8), 253, 265, 282, 283
Spinal reflexes, 264, 286
Spinal shock, 297
Spinal tap, 269
Spinalis muscle, 221, 222
Spindle apparatus, 74
Spindle fibers, 84, 85
Spine, muscles of, 215–216, 219, 221–222
Spinocerebellar pathway, 287
Spinothalamic pathway, 287
Spinous process: Prominent posterior projection of a vertebra, formed by the fusion of two laminae, (C6), 162, 163
Spiral fractures, 150
Spiral ganglion, 335, 337
Spirometer, 517
Splanchnic nerves, 291, 292
Spleen: Lymphoid organ important for red blood cell phagocytosis, immune response, and lymphocyte production, (C1), 11, 14
anatomy and physiology, 477–478
functions, 10
injuries, 477
lymphopoiesis, 396
phagocytosis, 387, 478
prenatal hemopoiesis, 388
Splenectomy, 477
Splenic vein, 459
Splenius capitis muscle, 221, 222
Splenomegaly, 495
Spongy bone, 144, 145, 146
Spontaneous abortion, 692
Sports trainer, 193
Spot desmosomes, 96
Sprain, 185
Squamous (SKWĀ-mus): Flattened, 93, 97
Squamous cell carcinoma, 126, 135
Squamous epithelium: An epithelium whose superficial cells are flattened and platelike, (C4), 97, 98, 99, 100
Squamous suture, 156
Stapedius (sta-PĒ-dē-us): A muscle of the middle ear whose contraction tenses the auditory ossicles and reduces the forces transmitted to the oval window, (C9), 330
Stapes (STĀ-pēz): The auditory ossicle attached to the tympanum, (C9), 329, 330, 336
Starches, 42
Static equilibrium, 332
Stem cells (germinative cells)
connective tissue, 104, 105
epidermis, 124
epithelial renewal and repair, 97
interphase periods, 83
neural, 249
skin repair following injuries, 132
spinal cord injuries, 265
Stereocilia: Elongate microvilli characteristic of the epithelium of portions of the male reproductive tract (epididymis) and inner ear, (C4, 9), 331, 332
Sterilization, surgical, 664–665
Sternal end of the clavicle, 167
Sternohyoid muscle, 220, 221
Sternocleidomastoid muscle, 215, 216, 219, 220, 221
Sternothyroid muscle, 220, 221
Sternum, 152, 155, 165, 166
Steroid hormones, 347
Steroid: Large lipid molecules composed of four connected rings of carbon atoms, (C2), 43, 45
Stethoscopes, 421
Stimulus: An environmental alteration that produces a change in cellular activities; often used to refer to events that alter the membrane potentials of excitable cells, (C8), 6
Stomach
anatomy, 544, 545
digestion in, 547

cardiovascular system, 406
descending aorta, 449, 451, 453–454
functional patterns, 446–447
hepatic portal system, 458–459
inferior vena cava, 455, 456–458, 459
partial pressures of oxygen and carbon dioxide, 519, 520
superior vena cava, 454, 455, 456, 457, 458
veins, 454–459
Systemic lupus erythematosus, 493, 495
Systemic physiology, 3–4, 25
Systemic veins
hepatic portal system, 458–459
inferior vena cava, 455, 456–458, 459
superior vena cava, 454, 455, 456, 457, 458
Systole (SIS-to-lē): The period of cardiac contraction, (C12, 13), 419–420
Systolic pressure: Peak arterial pressures measured during ventricular systole, (C13), 435, 438

T

T cells: Lymphocytes responsible for cellular immunity and for the coordination and regulation of the immune response; includes regulatory T cells (helpers and suppressors) and cytotoxic (killer) T cells, (C11, 14)
activation of, 485–486
antigen presentation, 484–485
hormones of the immune system, 490–491
immune response, manipulating, 494
lymph nodes, 476–477
lymphocytes, 396, 473, 474, 475
specific defenses, 482–484
spleen, 478
types of, 485–486
T tubules: Transverse, tubular extensions of the sarcolemma that extend deep into the sarcoplasm to contact terminal cisternae of the sarcoplasmic reticulum, (C7), 197, 198, 202, 204
T wave: Deflection of the ECG corresponding to ventricular repolarization, (C12), 418, 419
T_3 (triiodothyronine), 357, 360
T_4 (thyroxine, tetraiodothyronine), 357, 360
Tachycardia, 418, 424
Tactile corpuscles (Meissner corpuscles), 310
Tactile discs (Merkel discs), 310
Tactile: Pertaining to the sense of touch, 309
Tactile receptors, 309–311
Taenia coli (TE-nē-ē KŌ-lē): Three longitudinal bands of smooth muscle in the muscularis externa of the colon, (C16), 558, 559
Tail fold, 680, 682
Tail of a spermatozoon, 643, 644
Tailbone (coccyx), 161
Talus, 172, 173
Target cell receptors, 347, 349
Target cells, 346, 347, 349
Tarsal bones, 144, 155, 172, 173
Tarsal glands, 315
Tarsus: The ankle, (C6). See Ankle
Taste. See also **Gustation**
aging, effect of, 339
taste buds, 314
taste pathways, 315
taste receptors, 314
taste sensations, 314–315
TCA (tricarboxylic acid) cycle: Aerobic reaction sequence occurring in the mitochondrial matrix; in the process, organic molecules are broken down, carbon dioxide molecules are released, and hydrogen molecules are transferred to coenzymes that deliver them to the electron transport system; also called *citric acid cycle* or *Krebs cycle*, (C7, 17), 209, 578–579, 580
Tears: Fluid secretion of the lacrimal glands that bathes the anterior surfaces of the eyes, (C9, 15), 295, 316

Tectorial membrane (tek-TŌR-ē-al): Gelatinous membrane suspended over the hair cells of the organ of Corti, (C9), 334, 335, 337
Teeth
dental succession, 541–542
digestive system component, 536
structure of, 540, 541
types of, 541
Telophase (TEL-ō-fāz): The final stage of mitosis, characterized by the disappearance of the spindle apparatus, the reappearance of the nuclear membrane, the disappearance of the chromosomes, and the completion of cytokinesis, (C3, 19), 83, 85
Temperature
blood, of, 382
cardiac output, 423
oxygen release by hemoglobin, 520–521
Temperature receptors, 309
Temporal artery, 438
Temporal bones, 156, 157, 158, 159, 330
Temporal lobe, 268, 270, 271
Temporalis muscle, 160, 215, 219, 220
Tendinitis, 239
Tendon: A collagenous band that connects a skeletal muscle to an element of the skeleton, (C1, 4, 6, 7), 8, 106, 107, 144, 196
Tendon sheaths, 232
Tension, 205
Tensor fasciae latae muscle, 215, 216, 233, 234, 235
Tensor tympani muscle, 330
Teratogens, 699
Teres major muscle, 216, 226, 227, 228, 229
Teres minor muscle, 216, 226, 227, 229
Terminal bronchioles, 509, 510
Terminal cisternae, 197, 198
Tertiary bronchi, 509, 510
Tertiary follicle: A mature ovarian follicle, containing a large, fluid-filled chamber, (C19), 651, 652, 657
Testes (TES-tēz): The male gonads, sites of gamete production and hormone secretion, (C1, 10, 19), 9, 11, 367, 368, 639, 640–644
Testicular arteries, 453
Testicular cancer, 640
Testicular torsion, 666
Testosterone (tes-TOS-ter-ōn): The principal androgen produced by the interstitial cells of the testes, (C2, 3, 10, 19)
androgen, 639
athletic performance, 368
cholesterol, 45
interstitial cells of the testes, 367, 642
luteinizing hormone, 353, 356, 357, 648
source, regulation of, and primary effects, 663
Tetanus (disease): A tetanic contraction; also used to refer to a disease state resulting from the stimulation of muscle cells by bacterial toxins, (C7), 206, 239
Tetany: A tetanic contraction; also used to refer to abnormally prolonged contractions resulting from disturbances in electrolyte balance, 213, 416
Tetrad (TET-rad): Paired, duplicated chromosomes visible at the start of meiosis, (C1, 19), 642
Tetraiodothyronine (tet-ra-ī-ō-dō-THĪ-rō-nēn): T_4, or thyroxine, a thyroid hormone, (C10), 357, 360
Tetrodotoxin, 256, 297
Thalamus: The walls of the diencephalon, (C8), 267, 268, 276, 277
Thalassemia, 386, 401
Therapeutic abortion, 692
Thermoreception: Sensitivity to temperature changes, (C9)
Thermoreceptors, 309
Thermoregulation: Homeostatic maintenance of body temperature, (C1, 5, 11, 13, 17), 13–14, 593–595
Thermostat, 13
Thick filament: A myosin filament in a skeletal or cardiac muscle cell, (C3, 7), 73, 197, 198, 199–200
Thick skin, 123
Thigh, muscles of, 215–216, 232, 233, 234

Thighbone (femur), 144, 153, 155, 171, 172
Thin filament: An actin filament in a skeletal or cardiac muscle cell, (C7), 197, 198, 199–200
Thin skin, 123
Third cuneiform bone, 172, 173
Third heart sound, 421, 435
Third molars, 541, 542
Third trimester of pregnancy, 675, 683, 684–685, 686–687
Third ventricle, 267, 269
Third-degree burns, 134
Thoracentesis, 513
Thoracic aorta, 451, 453, 454
Thoracic cage (rib cage), 152, 155, 161–163, 165, 166
Thoracic cavity, 21, 22, 407
Thoracic duct, 473, 474
Thoracic region, 17
Thoracic region of the vertebral column, 161
Thoracic curve, 161–162
Thoracic vertebrae, 161, 163
Thorax: The chest, (C1), 16, 17
Threonine, 585
Threshold: The membrane potential at which an action potential begins, (C8), 256
Thrombin (THROM-bin): Enzyme that converts fibrinogen to fibrin, (C11), 399, 400
Thrombocyte (THROM-bō-sīt), 398. See also **Platelets**
Thrombocytopenia, 398
Thrombocytosis, 398
Thrombus: A blood clot, (C11, 12, 13), 400, 401, 461, 462
Thymine: A nitrogenous compound found in DNA, (C2, 3), 49, 50
Thymosins (THĪ-mō-sinz): Hormones of the thymus essential to the development and differentiation of T cells, (C10, 11, 14), 367, 475, 477
Thymus: Lymphoid organ, site of T cell formation, (C1, 10, 11, 14), 10, 348, 367, 475, 477
Thyrocervical trunk, 450, 451
Thyroid cartilage, 357, 358, 505, 506, 507
Thyroid gland: Endocrine gland whose lobes sit lateral to the thyroid cartilage of the larynx, (C1, 10)
C cells, 358–359, 360
endocrine system overview, 348
functions, 9
thyroid follicles, 357–358, 360
thyroid follicles and hormones, 350, 357–358, 360
Thyroid hormones: Thyroxine (T4) and triiodothyronine (T3); hormones of the thyroid gland that stimulate tissue metabolism, energy utilization, and growth, (C6, 10, 12, 14, 20)
amino acid derivative, 347
goiter and congenital hypothyroidism, 371
growth, effect on, 369
immune response, 494
Thyroid-stimulating hormone (TSH) (thyrotropin): Anterior pituitary hormone that triggers the secretion of thyroid hormones by the thyroid gland, (C10, 14), 353, 354, 356, 357
Thyrotoxicosis, 373
Thyrotropin-releasing hormone (TRH), 353, 354
Thyroxine (TX) (thī-ROKS-ēn): A thyroid hormone (T_4), (C10, 11, 17), 357, 360
Tibia (shinbone), 155, 171–172
Tibial tuberosity, 171, 172
Tibialis anterior muscle, 215, 233, 237, 238
Tibialis muscles, 215, 233, 237, 238
Tibialis posterior muscle, 237
Tidal volume: The volume of air moved in and out of the lungs during a normal quiet respiratory cycle, (C15, 20), 516, 686
Tight junctions, 95–96
Tissue: A collection of specialized cells and cell products that perform a specific function, (C1, 3, 4), 3, 25. See also Tissue level of organization; specific tissues
Tissue factor, 399
Tissue level of organization, 92–120
age, effect of, 115–116
age and cancer incidence, 116

...me whose presence
...aleness; two X
... female, (C20),

...tension of

Illustration Credits

FM-01 Kathleen Welch **FM-02** Zahourek Systems **FM-03** Frederic H. Martini **FM-04** Anita Impagliazzo **FM-05** Anita Impagliazzo

Chapter 1 **Chapter Opener** Jens Lucking/Getty Images **01-07a,b,c** Custom Medical Stock Photo, Inc. **01-11a,b left** Science Source/Photo Researchers **01-11b right** Custom Medical Stock Photo, Inc. **01-12b** CNRI/Photo Researchers **01-12c** Photo Researchers Inc. **01-12d** Ben Edwards/Getty Images

Chapter 2 **Chapter Opener** Tom & Dee Ann McCarthy/CORBIS

Chapter 3 **Chapter Opener** Harry Bartlett/Getty Images **03-07a,b,c** David M. Phillips/Visuals Unlimited **03-14b** Dr.A. Hufnagel, Ultrastructral Aspects of Chemoreception in Ciliated Protists (Ciliophora), Journal of Electron Microscopy Technique, 1919./Photomicrograph by Jurgen Bohmer and Linda Hufnagel, University of Rhode Island. **03-15a** CNRI/Photo Researchers, Inc. **03-16** Don W, Fawcett, M.D., Harvard Medical School

Chapter 4 **Chapter Opener** David Buffington/Getty Images **04-03b** Custom Medical Stock Photo, Inc. **04-04a** Ward's Natural Science Establishment, Inc. **04-04b** Pearson Education/PH College **04-04c** Frederic H. Martini **04-05a,b,c** Frederic H. Martini **04-06a** Caroline Biological Supply Company/Phototake **04-09a** Science Source/Photo Researchers **04-09b** Frederic H. Martini **04-09c** John D. Cunningham/Visuals Unlimited **04-11a** Frederic H. Martini **04-13a** G.W. Willis/ MD/Visuals Unlimited **04-13b** Phototake NYC **04-13c** Pearson Benjamin Cummings

Chapter 5 **Chapter Opener** Lawrence D. Migdale/Mira **05-02** Dr. Richard Kessel and Dr. Randy H. Kardon/Visuals Unlimited **05-04a** Courtesy Elizabeth A. Abel, M.D., from the Leonard C. Winograd Memorial Slide Collection, Stanford University School of Medicine **05-04b** Courtesy Elizabeth A. Abel, M.D., from the Leonard C. Winograd Memorial Slide Collection, Stanford University School of Medicine **05-05a** Manfred Kage/Peter Arnold, Inc. **05-06c** Frederic H. Martini **PP** Pearson Education/PH College

Chapter 6 **Chapter Opener** Paul Mcguire/Alamy **06-03b** Visuals Unlimited/R. G. Kessel and R. H. Kardon, "Tissues and Organs: A Text-Atlas of Scanning Electron Microscopy," W. H. Freeman & Co., 1979. All Rights Reserved. **06-04** Ralph T. Hutchings **06-08a, b** Ralph T. Hutchings **06-17a-c** Ralph T. Hutchings **06-19a,b** Ralph T. Hutchings **06-20a** Ralph T. Hutchings **06-21** Ralph T. Hutchings **06-22a** Ralph T. Hutchings **06-23a,b** Ralph T. Hutchings **06-24a** Ralph T. Hutchings **06-25** Ralph T. Hutchings **06-26c** Ralph T. Hutchings **06-28** Ralph T. Hutchings **06-29** Ralph T. Hutchings **06-30a** Ralph T. Hutchings **06-32c,d** Ralph T. Hutchings **06-34** Ralph T. Hutchings **PP** USSA Coaches Education Program

Chapter 7 **Chapter Opener** Patrik Giardino/CORBIS **07-01** Anita Impagliazzo **07-03** Don W. Fawcett/Photo Researchers, Inc. **07-04a** Don W. Fawcett/Science Source/Photo Researchers, Inc. **07-10a** G.W. Willis/Biological Photo Service **07-10b** Frederic H. Martini **PP** Ashley Knipe

Chapter 8 **Chapter Opener** AJPhoto/Photo Researchers, Inc. **08-02** Ward's Natural Science Establishment **08-05a** Biophoto Associates/Photo Researchers, Inc. **08-05b** Photo Researchers, Inc. **08-10** David Scott/Phototake NYC **08-15** Michael J. Timmons **08-16a,b,c** Ralph T. Hutchings **08-21** Larry Mulvehill/Photo Reasearchers, Inc **PP** David Young-Wolff/Photo Edit

Chapter 9 **Chapter Opener** Creatas Images/Jupiter Images **09-07b** Pearson Education/PH College **09-08a** Ralph T. Hutchings **09-11 left** Diane Hirsch/Fundamental Photographs **09-11 right** Diane Schiamo/Fundamenta[l]

Photographs **09-12a** Ed Reschke/Peter Arnold, Inc. **09-12c** Custom Medical Stock Photo, Inc. **09-18** Richmond Products, Inc. **09-26** Ward's Natural Science Establishment, Inc.

Chapter 10 **Chapter Opener** Elea Dumas/NonStock/Jupiter Images **10-05b** Peter Arnold, Inc. **10-09** Frederic H. Martini **10-12a** Anita Impagliazzo **10-12c** Ward's Natural Science Establishment, Inc. **10-13a** Anita Impagliazzo **10-13b** Ward's Natural Science Establishment, Inc. **10-16a** Project Masters, Inc./The Bergman Collection **10-16b** John Paul Kay/Peter Arnold, Inc. **10-16c** Project Masters, Inc./The Bergman Collection **10-16d** Custom Medical Stock Photo, Inc. **10-16e** Biophoto Associates/Science Source/Photo Researchers, Inc. **PP** Romilly Lockyer/Getty Images

Chapter 11 **Chapter Opener** Karen Moskowitz/Getty Images **11-01a** Martin M. Rotker **11-02a** David Scharf/Peter Arnold, Inc. **11-02b** Dennis Kunkel/CNRI/Phototake NYC **11-03a** Stanley Flegler, Visuals Unlimited **11-03b** Stanley Flegler, Visuals Unlimited **11-08a-e** Ed Reschke/Peter Arnold, Inc. **11-09** Custom Medical Stock Photo, Inc.

Chapter 12 **Chapter Opener** Lois Adamski Peek/Getty Images **12-03a** T. Hutchings **12-04c** Ed Reschke/Peter Arnold, Inc. **12-10a** Larry Mulvehill/Photo Researchers, Inc.

Chapter 13 **Chapter Opener** Stockbyte/agefotostock **13-01** ustom ᵇ, Inc. Timmons **13-03a** William Ober/Visuals Unlimited **13-03b** B-22 Anita Medical Stock Photo, Inc. **13-04b** Biophoto Associates/Pho **13-08b** Creatas Images/Jupiter Images **13-19a** Anita Im Impagliazzo **PP** Romilly Lockyer/Getty Images ᵇ Frederic H.
liazzo **14-08c** Frederic

Chapter 14 **Chapter Opener** Image 100/agfot Martini **14-07c** Frederic H. Martini **14-08b** H. Martini **PP** Hop Americain/Photo Rese v/agefotostock
P. Gehr from Bloom & Fawcett

Chapter 15 **Chapter Opener** Andre **PP** Dana White/Photo Edit **15-04e** Phototake NYC **15-07b** Mic "Textbook of Histology," W. B. Saud/CORBIS **16-13b** Frederic H. Martini a Anita Impagliazzo **PP** Romilly

Chapter 16 **Chapter Open **16-15c** © Michael J. Timm Lockyer/Getty Images ner Mark Leibowitz/Masterfile

Chapter 17 Cha pener Purestock/Getty Images **18-03b** Ralph T. Hutchings **Chapter 18** lips/Visuals Unlimited **16-6a** Anita Impagliazzo **PP** John **18-06c** David Lambertso **Chapter Opener** Chris Rout/Alamy **19-02b** Don W. Fawcett, Chap vard Medical School **19-05b** Visuals Unlimited/©R.G. Kessel and R.H. M. , "Tissues and Organs: A Text Atlas of Scanning Electron Microscopy," W. H. man & Co., 1979. All Rights Reserved. **19-10a-d** Frederic H. Martini **19-10f** G.W. Willis, M.D./Biological Photo Service **19-10e** C. Edelmann/La Villete/Photo Researchers, Inc. **PP** Jose Luis Pelaez, Inc./CORBIS

Chapter 20 **Chapter Opener** James Hardy PhotoAlto/Getty Images **20-01a** Francis Leroy/Photo Researchers, Inc. **20-07a** Dr. Arnold Ramarin **20-07b** Lennart Nilsson/Albert Bonniers Forlag AB **20-07c** Lennart Nilsson/Albert Bonniers Forlag AB **20-07d** Lennart Nilsson/Albert Bonniers Forlag AB **20-08b** Photo Researchers, **20-08a** Lennart Nilsson/Albert Bonniers Forlag AB Inc. **20-13** Science Photo Library/Photo Researchers, Inc.

DE p. 5 David Toase/Photodisc, p. 22 David Buffington/Photodisc